Advanced Algebra

with Transformations and Applications

ZALMAN P. USISKIN
Associate Professor of Education
University of Chicago
Chicago, Illinois

ACKNOWLEDGEMENTS

The author wishes to acknowledge and give thanks to the following teachers who taught preliminary versions of this text, participated in the field-test research, and contributed ideas to help improve the text.

Pamela Bailey
Gonzales Union High School
Gonzales, California

Thomas H. Duffy
Wauwatosa East High School
Wauwatosa, Wisconsin

Sam Ewing
Adrian Senior High School
Adrian, Michigan

Donald W. Field
Niles Township High School West
Skokie, Illinois

Thomas Fitzpatrick
Wauwatosa West High School
Wauwatosa, Wisconsin

S. D. Hoffman
Fennville High School
Fennville, Michigan

Robert E. Murphy, Jr.
Niles Township High School West
Skokie, Illinois

The author also wishes to acknowledge the following schools in which preliminary versions of this text were used. The many helpful suggestions from teachers and students are sincerely appreciated.

Bloomfield Hills, Andover High School
Bloomfield Hills, Michigan

Central YMCA High School
Chicago, Illinois

Elk Grove High School
Elk Grove Village, Illinois

Homewood-Flossmoor High School
Flossmoor, Illinois

La Salle College High School
Philadelphia, Pennsylvania

Longmeadow High School
Longmeadow, Massachusetts

Marquette University High School
Milwaukee, Wisconsin

McCluer High School
Florissant, Missouri

Pittsfield High School
Pittsfield, Massachusetts

Prospect High School
Mount Prospect, Illinois

Redmond Senior High School
Redmond, Washington

Rolling Meadows High School
Rolling Meadows, Illinois

Rutland Senior High School
Rutland, Vermont

St. Benedict High School
Chicago, Illinois

Taconic High School
Pittsfield, Massachusetts

University Liggett School
Grosse Pointe Woods, Michigan

Weston High School
Weston, Massachusetts

Winifred High School
Winifred, Montana

Photograph Credits:

PAGE	
8	A. Devaney, Inc., N.Y.
11	United Press International
25	Monkmeyer Press Photo Service
34	Larry Trone
43	Photri/J. Novak
46	Reprinted from *The Wonderful World of J. Wesley Smith* by Burr Shafer by permission of the publisher, Vanguard Press, Inc. Copyright © 1961 by Burr Shafer.
54	Courtesy AMF Incorporated
55	Courtesy Reliance Electric Company, Toledo Scale Division.
86	Alan Pitcairn from Grant Heilman
107	Courtesy Charles Eames
120	Courtesy Cooper-Hewitt Museum of Decorative Arts & Design, Smithsonian Institution
125	*Left:* Owen Franken, Stock, Boston *Right:* Donald Dietz, Stock, Boston
128	*Left:* Grant Heilman *Right:* Cary Wolinsky, Stock, Boston
135	Bedford Photographic Service
148	H. Armstrong Roberts
150	United Press International
168	Courtesy San Francisco Convention & Visitors Bureau
181	Fujihira from Monkmeyer
198	Photri
204	Wide World Photos
225	H. Armstrong Roberts
228	Courtesy Armstrong Resilient Flooring
255	A. Devaney, Inc., N.Y.
265	H. Armstrong Roberts
275	Grant Heilman
289	Courtesy Boeing Aircraft
291	Courtesy Southern California Edison Company
297	Dr. Harold E. Edgerton, MIT, Cambridge, Mass.
317	Ray Cottingham
325	Photri/G. Turk
389	Compix
406	A. Devaney, Inc., N.Y.
416	A. Devaney, Inc., N.Y.
438	A. Devaney, Inc., N.Y.
446	Courtesy Gibson, Inc.
447	Grant Heilman
449	A. Devaney, Inc., N.Y.
455	Courtesy Simpson, Elgin, Ill.
457	Grant Heilman
459	Courtesy Lick Observatory
502	Courtesy Amtrak
509	*Top:* Courtesy Lick Observatory *Bottom:* Courtesy NASA
515	Jerry Schwartz, Editorial Photo Color Archives
519	*Top:* H. Armstrong Roberts *Bottom:* Compix
521	H. Armstrong Roberts
537	Courtesy United States Postal Service
570	The Bettmann Archive
595	Howard Feldman
596	Courtesy Hirshhorn Museum and Sculpture Garden, Smithsonian Institution

EDITORIAL STAFF

Project Director: Eugene M. Malecki

Staff Editors: G. T. Bravos, Gene S. Kuechmann, Max V. Lyles, Jeffrey Wells

Production Associate: Janet B. Feldman

Art Director: Gloria Muczynski

ILLUSTRATORS

Cover and Title Pages: Robert Borja

Text: Joann Daley, John D. Firestone & Associates, Paul Hazelrigg

ISBN 0-8445-**1960**-X

A Division of Doubleday & Company, Inc.

Printed in the United States of America
1 2 3 4 5 6 7 8 9 10 11 12 13 14 15 4 3 2 1 0 9 8 7 6 5

Contents

Chapter 1 Addition and Multiplication of Real Numbers 1

1.1 Sentences and Solutions 1
1.2 Equations Involving Only Addition 5
1.3 Equations Involving Only Multiplication 8
1.4 The Group Properties 11
1.5 Order of Operations 15
1.6 Repeated Addition and the Distributive Property 17
1.7 Repeated Multiplication and the Power Property 21
1.8 Halves and Square Roots 26
1.9 What Is a Real Number? 29
Chapter Summary 32
Chapter Review 33

Chapter 2 Further Properties of Real Numbers 34

2.1 Order and Inequality 34
2.2 Linear Sentences 37
2.3 Solving Linear Sentences 40
2.4 Sentence-Solving Involving Two or More Variables 44
2.5 The FOIL Theorem 47
2.6 Real Number Lines and One-to-one Correspondences 50
2.7 Real Numbers and Successive Approximations 55
Chapter Summary 58
Chapter Review 59

Chapter 3 Applications and Modeling 60

3.1 Why Are Addition and Multiplication Important? 60
3.2 Mathematical Models for Real Situations 65
3.3 Modeling Distance on a Line 69
3.4 Modeling Estimation 73
3.5 Modeling Distance in a Plane 77
3.6 Translating into Mathematics 82
Chapter Summary 84
Chapter Review 85

Chapter 4 Transformations 86

4.1 Reflections ... 87
4.2 Notation for Transformations ... 91
4.3 Translations ... 96
4.4 Rotations ... 99
4.5 Composites of Transformations ... 102
4.6 Composites of Reflections ... 107
4.7 Congruence ... 111
4.8 Size Transformations and Similarity ... 114
4.9 Symmetry ... 119
Chapter Summary ... 122
Chapter Review ... 123

Chapter 5 Matrices 125

5.1 Introduction ... 125
5.2 Matrix Multiplication ... 128
5.3 Applying Matrix Multiplication to Transformations ... 131
5.4 Matrices for Certain Reflections ... 135
5.5 2×2 Matrices for Transformations ... 138
5.6 Matrices for Certain Rotations ... 143
5.7 Which Transformations Have 2×2 Matrices? ... 145
Chapter Summary ... 148
Chapter Review ... 149

Chapter 6 Lines and Circles 150

6.1 Vocabulary and Notation ... 150
6.2 Equations for Certain Lines ... 154
6.3 Equations for All Circles ... 157
6.4 The Graph Translation Theorem ... 161
6.5 Equations for All Lines ... 165
6.6 Equations for Lines Satisfying Given Conditions ... 169
6.7 Midpoints ... 174
6.8 Inequalities Related to Lines and Circles ... 177
Chapter Summary ... 179
Chapter Review ... 180

Chapter 7 Systems 181

7.1 Compound Sentences 182
7.2 What Is a System? 186
7.3 Strategies for Solving Systems of Equations 190
7.4 Systems Larger Than 2 × 2 193
7.5 History and Applications of System Solving 197
Chapter Summary 202
Chapter Review 203

Chapter 8 Rotations, Sines, and Cosines 204

8.1 Rotations About the Origin 204
8.2 Using Tables of Sines and Cosines 209
8.3 Obtaining Values of Sines and Cosines 211
8.4 The Rotation Matrix 214
8.5 Formulas for $\cos(x + y)$ and $\sin(x + y)$ 217
8.6 Polar Coordinates 219
8.7 Different Names for the Same Point 223
Chapter Summary 226
Chapter Review 227

Chapter 9 Mid-Course Review— Corresponding Group Properties 228

9.1 What Is a Group? 229
9.2 Another Look at Equation Solving 232
9.3 More Work with Real Number Properties 234
9.4 More Work with Matrices 238
9.5 Another Look at System Solving 243
9.6 Further Work with Transformations 246
9.7 Another Look at Sines and Cosines 250
9.8 Another Look at Lines, Circles, etc. 253
9.9 More Work with Applications 256
Chapter Summary 259
Chapter Review 260

Cumulative Review: Chapters 1–9 261

Chapter 10 The Complex Numbers 265

10.1 The Complex Number Plane ... 266
10.2 Addition of Complex Numbers ... 269
10.3 Multiplication of Complex Numbers ... 272
10.4 Relating Addition to Multiplication ... 276
10.5 Special Complex Numbers ... 278
10.6 The $a + bi$ Notation ... 281
10.7 Manipulations in $a + bi$ Notation ... 283
10.8 Are There Positive or Negative Complex Numbers? ... 287
10.9 Physical Applications of Complex Numbers ... 288
10.10 Classification of Complex Numbers ... 292
Chapter Summary ... 295
Chapter Review ... 296

Chapter 11 Quadratic Sentences 297

11.1 A Mathematical Application of Complex Numbers ... 297
11.2 Manipulations Involving Radicals ... 301
11.3 Equations Involving Radicals ... 304
11.4 Completing the Square ... 307
11.5 The Quadratic Formula ... 309
11.6 A Typical Application of Quadratic Sentences ... 313
11.7 Equations for Some Parabolas ... 317
11.8 Quadratic Inequalities ... 320
Chapter Summary ... 323
Chapter Review ... 324

Chapter 12 Quadratic Relations 325

12.1 The Conic Sections ... 326
12.2 Ellipses and Hyperbolas ... 329
12.3 Equations for Some Ellipses ... 333
12.4 Equations for Some Hyperbolas ... 337
12.5 Scale Transformations ... 340
12.6 More Equations for Hyperbolas ... 346
12.7 More Equations for Parabolas ... 350
12.8 Reflection Images of Graphs of Relations ... 354
12.9 Translation Images of Conics ... 357
12.10 Quadratic Systems ... 361
Chapter Summary ... 365
Chapter Review ... 366

Chapter 13 Functions—A Unifying Concept 367

13.1 Function—A Special Type of Relation ... 367
13.2 Function—A Special Type of Correspondence ... 371
13.3 Transformation—A Special Type of Function ... 376
13.4 Composites of Functions ... 379
13.5 Terminology Associated with Functions ... 384
13.6 Functions of Variation ... 387
13.7 Functions with Several Defining Sentences ... 392
13.8 Functions with Disconnected Graphs ... 396
13.9 Approximating Functions by Linear Functions ... 400
Chapter Summary ... 404
Chapter Review ... 405

Chapter 14 Exponential Functions 406

14.1 *N*th Roots ... 407
14.2 Growth Functions—A Need for More Exponents ... 410
14.3 Rational Numbers as Exponents ... 412
14.4 Real Numbers as Exponents ... 417
14.5 Corresponding Sentences with Multiples and Powers ... 420
14.6 Common Logarithms ... 425
14.7 What Number Has a Given Common Logarithm? ... 429
14.8 Applications to Arithmetic ... 431
14.9 Further Applications of Logarithms ... 435
14.10 Logarithms to Bases Other Than 10 ... 439
14.11 Graphs of Exponential and Logarithmic Functions ... 444
Chapter Summary ... 447
Chapter Review ... 448

Chapter 15 Trigonometry and Circular Functions 449

15.1 Radian Measure ... 449
15.2 The Sine and Cosine Functions ... 452
15.3 Symmetries of Sine Waves ... 458
15.4 Trigonometry—The Law of Cosines ... 462
15.5 Trigonometry—The Law of Sines ... 465
15.6 The Secant and Cosecant Functions ... 471
15.7 The Tangent and Cotangent Functions ... 473
15.8 Trigonometry—The Right Triangle ... 477
15.9 Applications of Right Triangle Trigonometry ... 480
Chapter Summary ... 483
Chapter Review ... 484

Chapter 16 Advanced Manipulative Techniques 485

16.1 Factoring ... 485
16.2 Solving Polynomial Equations ... 490
16.3 Division of Polynomials ... 494
16.4 Fractional Expressions ... 498
16.5 Operations with Fractional Expressions ... 503
16.6 Sentences Involving Fractional Expressions ... 506
16.7 Puzzle Problems Involving Rates ... 510
16.8 More Puzzle Problems ... 517
16.9 Mathematical Problems ... 521
Chapter Summary ... 526
Chapter Review ... 527

Chapter 17 Sequences, Sums, and Statistics 528

17.1 Examples of Sequences ... 528
17.2 Linear (Arithmetic) Sequences ... 534
17.3 Exponential (Geometric) Sequences ... 538
17.4 Sums of Finite Sequences ... 542
17.5 Notation for Sums ... 546
17.6 Sums of Infinite Sequences ... 548
17.7 Simple Statistics ... 553
17.8 Pascal's Triangle ... 556
17.9 The Binomial Theorem ... 561
17.10 Counting Subsets ... 564
17.11 Probability ... 566
17.12 Binomial and Normal Density ... 569
Chapter Summary ... 573
Chapter Review ... 573

Cumulative Review: Chapters 10–17 ... 575

Chapter 18 Summary—The Many Facets of Mathematics 580

18.1 Mathematics as a Language ... 581
18.2 Mathematics as a Language (continued) ... 584
18.3 Mathematics as a Study of Relationships ... 586
18.4 Mathematics as a Study of Commonalities ... 590
18.5 Mathematics as an Aid in Applications ... 594
Chapter Summary ... 598
Chapter Review ... 598

Symbols and Postulates ... 599
Named Theorems ... 600
Tables ... 601
Index ... 605
Answers to Selected Exercises ... A1

Chapter 1 Addition and Multiplication of Real Numbers

SENTENCES AND SOLUTIONS 1.1

English sentences normally contain verbs. In place of verbs, *mathematical sentences* have one or more of the symbols $=$, $<$, $>$, $\geq$, $\leq$, $\neq$, $\cong$, $\sim$, and so on. For example, the English sentence

A number increased by five is less than eight

can be translated into the mathematical sentence

$$x + 5 < 8.$$

Finding every number which makes a sentence true is called **solving the sentence.** The numbers that work are called **solutions.**

Since these numbers work, each is a solution to $x + 5 < 8$. Can you find others?

$$\left.\begin{matrix} 2 \\ -400 \\ \frac{3}{2} \end{matrix}\right\} x + 5 < 8 \left\{\begin{matrix} 2 + 5 < 8 & \text{True} \\ -400 + 5 < 8 & \text{True} \\ \frac{3}{2} + 5 < 8 & \text{True} \end{matrix}\right.$$

If two sentences have exactly the same solutions, they are called **equivalent.** There are many sentences equivalent to $x + 5 < 8$. Some look simple. Some are complicated. Here are three of them.

$$x + 4 < 7$$
$$x < 3$$
$$3 > x$$

Solutions to sentences are usually described in one of three ways. Your teacher may prefer one of these ways over the others.

1. Writing a simplified equivalent sentence
2. Listing all solutions
3. Giving the *solution set* (also called the *truth set*)

Example 1: Three ways of describing solutions to $401 = 4y + 1$

1. Write a simplified equivalent sentence: $y = 100$.
2. List the solutions (there is only one solution here): 100.
3. Write the solution set: $\{100\}$.

Example 2: Describing solutions to $A - 3 > 2$

1. Write a simplified equivalent sentence: $A > 5$.
2. When the solution set is infinite, as it is here, listing is impossible.
3. Write the solution set: $\{A: A > 5\}$.

The symbol $\{A: \quad\}$ should be read "the set of numbers A satisfying . . . ." The conditions that A satisfies are listed after the colon. So $\{A: A > 5\}$ is the set of all numbers greater than 5.

Example 3: Describing the solutions to $x + 9 = x$

1. Since no number is 9 more than itself, $x + 9$ never equals x. So no number works, and you should write "no solution."
2. Listing does not apply.
3. The solution set is the null set or empty set. Write $\{ \quad \}$ or $\emptyset$.

Caution The symbol { } clearly stands for a set with no elements. If *anything* is in the braces, the set has elements and is not the null set. Thus, $\{\emptyset\}$ does *not* stand for the null set.

Sometimes solutions are difficult to describe, and at other times exact solutions are not needed. In these cases, we may want to estimate solutions. Consider $x^4 = 100$. Try substituting some numbers for x.

$1^4 = 1 \cdot 1 \cdot 1 \cdot 1 = 1$
$2^4 = 2 \cdot 2 \cdot 2 \cdot 2 = 16$
$3^4 = 81$
$4^4 = 256$

A solution lies between 3 and 4, perhaps closer to 3. Maybe 3.1 is a good estimate.

$(3.1)^4 = 92.3521$ ▶ Too small; try 3.2.
$(3.2)^4 = 104.8576$ ▶ Too large

This indicates that a solution lies between 3.1 and 3.2. For some problems, this answer may be good enough. We write

$3.1 < x < 3.2$ **which means** x is between 3.1 and 3.2

In this book you are often asked to approximate or estimate answers. This may surprise you if you think mathematics deals only with exact things. In fact, much mathematics has been written about estimates.

The exercises in this book are of three kinds. (Answers to selected exercises are given at the back of the book.)

Exercises in this set	Will help you to
Ⓐ	Summarize and see the ideas of the section. (You should do these to test your understanding after reading the section.)
Ⓑ	Apply the ideas of the section to a variety of problems.
Ⓒ	Consider more unusual situations, uncommon applications, or harder problems.

EXERCISES 1.1

Ⓐ **1.** Which is *not* a mathematical sentence?

a. $2x > 5 > x$ **b.** $t = 5 + t$

c. $15b < a + b$ **d.** $x + 3 - 2y$

2. When are two sentences equivalent?

3–5. Which of the four given sentences is not equivalent to the others?

3. $x = 3$	$6 = 2x$	$5 + x = 2$	$2 + x = 5$
4. $A + 1 = 9$	$A + 8 = 15$	$3 - A = -4$	$A = 7$
5. $t > 4$	$8 > 2t$	$2t > 8$	$4 < t$

6. Give the truth set for the sentence $2 = y$.

7. Is there any difference between *truth set* and *solution set*?

8. The solution set for a sentence is $\{0\}$. The sentence is not $x = 0$ or $0 = x$. Give a possible sentence.

9. Write two different symbols for the null set.

10–12. Name a sentence equivalent to the given sentence.

10. $14 + x = 19$ **11.** $d = 8.6 + 42$ **12.** $4000 < A - 3$

13–15. Name at least three solutions to each sentence.

13. $x \leq -2.5$ **14.** $3 < y < 3.1$ **15.** $18 > 100y$

16. What is the meaning of the symbol $\neq$?

Ⓑ **17–18.** Translate the English sentence into a mathematical sentence.

17. The sum of six and a given number is greater than eight.

18. The sum of six and a given number is less than twice the given number.

19. Give a sentence which uses the symbol $<$ and which has no solution.

20–23. Describe the solutions in as many of the three ways mentioned in this section as possible.

20. $9000 = 100A$ **21.** $9000 = 100 + B$

22. $9000 < 100 + C$ **23.** $y = 2 + y$

24–26. Between what two consecutive whole numbers does a solution to the given sentence lie?

24. $x^2 = 20$ **25.** $E^3 = 100$ **26.** $11 = F^{11}$

27. Give a sentence whose solution set is $\{6, -6\}$.

28. Give a sentence whose solution set is $\{V: V > 1000\}$.

29. The set $\{T: T < 0\}$ might also be described as which of the following?

a. the set of negative numbers b. the set of nonnegative numbers

c. the set of positive numbers d. the null set

30. Why is $3.1 < x < 3.2$ *not* equivalent to $x^4 = 100$?

© 31. When the cube of a positive number is added to 3 times the number, the sum is 1. Estimate the number between consecutive tenths.

EQUATIONS INVOLVING ONLY ADDITION

A sentence with the symbol = for equality is called an **equation.** You can solve some equations, like $x + 2 = 3$, very easily. Others, like $-2.8 = y + 11.3$, are not so easy to solve. For these, a strategy is needed.

$$-2.8 = y + 11.3$$

$$-2.8 + (-11.3) = (y + 11.3) + (-11.3)$$ Add the **additive inverse** or **opposite** of 11.3 to each side.

$$-2.8 + (-11.3) = y + [11.3 + (-11.3)]$$

$$-14.1 = y + 0$$ But 0 is the **additive identity.** (Adding 0 to any number x keeps the *identity* of x.)

$$-14.1 = y$$ This simplified sentence is equivalent to $-2.8 = y + 11.3$. Its solution set is $\{-14.1\}$.

Example 1: Solve: $-3 + x = -12$

Add 3: $3 + (-3) + x = 3 + (-12)$

$0 + x = -9$

$x = -9$ The solution checks, for $-3 + (-9) = -12$.

You might not have to write down all of these steps, but many students make errors if they don't. Check all answers. To solve these equations, you must be able to find opposites. This is easy. Call $-x$ the *opposite of x* or the *additive inverse of x*.

x	$-x$	$x + (-x)$
2	-2	0
-5	5	0
0.75	-0.75	0
$-\frac{1}{6}$	$\frac{1}{6}$	0

NOTE: When x is negative, $-x$ is positive. Be careful not to think of $-x$ as a negative number—you may be wrong.

If an equation involves $-z$, you may solve for $-z$ first.

Example 2: Solve:

$$12 + (-z) = 15$$
$$-12 + 12 + (-z) = -12 + 15$$
$$0 + (-z) = 3$$
$$-z = 3 \quad \blacktriangleleft \text{Not yet solved}$$

Take the opposite of each side: $z = -3$

No examples using subtraction have been given. This is because subtraction can be changed to addition by using the following definition.

Definition

To **subtract** b from a, add the opposite of b to a.

$$a - b = a + (-b)$$

So a person does not have to learn how to subtract real numbers, only how to add them. For example, $10 - 12$ becomes $10 + (-12)$. In either case, the answer is -2.

Example 3: Solve:

$$-14 = -3 - x$$

By the definition above: $-14 = -3 + (-x)$

Now solve as usual: $3 + (-14) = 3 + (-3) + (-x)$

$$-11 = 0 + (-x)$$
$$-11 = -x$$

Take opposites: $11 = x$

Why can the same number be added to each side of an equation? The answer is quite simple.

$x = y$ ▶ means x and y stand for exactly the same number.

So $3 + x = 3 + y$ ▶ because we are adding the same number.

addition property of equations

In general, $x = y$ and $a + x = a + y$ are equivalent equations.

EXERCISES 1.2

Ⓐ **1–4.** Name:

1. the additive inverse of 10.

2. the additive identity.

3. the opposite of $-\frac{2}{3}$.

4. the opposite of $-x$.

5–7. Give the opposite of each number.

5. 1.3 **6.** -5 **7.** 0

8. What is the addition property of equations?

9–14. Add the given numbers.

9. 4, -8 **10.** -2, -9 **11.** $\frac{1}{2}$, $\frac{2}{3}$

12. 1.7, -1.8 **13.** 462, -811.4 **14.** -7, 1

15. Any subtraction problem can be converted to a(n) ____ problem.

16–19. Change all subtractions to additions.

16. $x - y$ **17.** $-3 - (-2) + 6$

18. $4a - 4b - 4c = 5$ **19.** $2 - x = -2$

20–25. Subtract the second number from the first in Exercises **9–14.**

26. If $x + 3 = 0$, then $x =$ ____. **27.** If $-y = \frac{1}{2}$, then $y =$ ____.

Ⓑ **28–37.** **(a)** Add a real number to each side of the given equation to make the solution easier. **(b)** Solve and write the solution set. **(c)** Check.

28. $x + (-11) = -100$ **29.** $1.4 = 3.1 + y$

30. $-9 + a + 0.4 = 7$ **31.** $-G + (-\frac{3}{4}) = -\frac{1}{9}$

32. $6 = 6 - N$ **33.** $10 = 19 - M + 42$

34. $-19 - W = -4$ **35.** $210.3 - Q = -1.5$

36. $\sqrt{2} - x = \sqrt{3}$ **37.** $y + \sqrt{10} = -5$

38. If two numbers add to 1000 and one of them is x, the other is ____.

39. If two numbers add to -6 and one of them is v, the other is ____.

40. Solve for b: $P = a + b + c$. **41.** Solve for d: $\frac{1}{2}e - d - 6 = a - 15$.

42. Solve for y: $x + y = 180$. **43.** Solve for a: $x + y + a = 0$.

44–46. Give the opposite of each expression. (HINT: What would you add to make the sum zero?)

44. $x + y$ **45.** $14 - b + d$ **46.** $x - y$

47. What might Exercise **42** have to do with supplementary angles?

48–50. Simplify.

48. $-(x + y)$ **49.** $-(-y + 3 - z)$ **50.** $-(W - 0.2)$

© **51–54.** Translate each statement into an equation. Give the meaning of each letter used.

51. If the temperature were 5° C warmer, it would be at the freezing point of water.

52. Eight years ago she was y years old. Now she is x years old.

53. His golf score exceeded his bowling average by 6.

54. *Banking.* A person had \$32.24 in a checking account and mistakenly wrote a check for \$39.41. By how much is the account overdrawn?

55. *Construction trades.* The sides of a triangular lot have lengths of 47, 70, and x yards. If 171 yards of fencing are available, how much more fencing is needed to fence the lot?

56–59. Follow the instructions for Exercises **28–37.**

56. $-y + 142 - y = 261 - y$ **57.** $-(x + 3) = 4 - x$

58. $n + \pi + n = n + 3$ **59.** $-(t + 1) = -t + \frac{1}{2} + t$

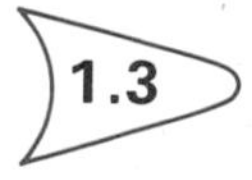

1.3 EQUATIONS INVOLVING ONLY MULTIPLICATION

Some equations involve only multiplication. Again, some of these may not be easy to solve. A useful strategy for multiplication is very similar to that for addition.

$-3x = 2.4$ Remember that $-3x$ means -3 times x or $-3 \cdot x$.

$-\frac{1}{3} \cdot (-3x) = -\frac{1}{3} \cdot 2.4$ Multiply each side by the **multiplicative inverse** or **reciprocal** of -3.

$1 \cdot x = -0.8$ But 1 is the **multiplicative identity.** (Multiplying any number x by 1 keeps the identity of x.)

$x = -0.8$ The solution checks, for $-3 \cdot (-0.8) = 2.4$.

To solve sentences involving multiplication, you must be able to find reciprocals of numbers. This is easy if you remember that the product of a number and its reciprocal is 1. That is, $x \cdot \frac{1}{x} = 1$.

x	$\frac{1}{x}$	$x \cdot \frac{1}{x}$
2	$\frac{1}{2}$	1
-5	$-\frac{1}{5}$	1
0.75	$\frac{1}{0.75}$ or $\frac{4}{3}$	1
$-\frac{2}{3}$	$-\frac{3}{2}$	1

There is a multiplication property of equations similar to the addition property of equations, and true for the same reasons (see page 6). It enables both sides of an equation to be multiplied by the same *nonzero* number without changing the solution set. (Multiplication by zero does change the solution set, as will be seen in Section 1.5.)

multiplication property of equations

If $a \neq 0$, then $x = y$ and $ax = ay$ are equivalent equations.

Example 1: Two methods for solving $0.6P = 21$

$0.6P = 21$	or, converting to fractions ▶	$\frac{6}{10}P = 21$
$\frac{1}{0.6}(0.6P) = \frac{1}{0.6} \cdot 21$	◀ Multiply by the reciprocal. ▶	$\frac{10}{6} \cdot \frac{6}{10}P = \frac{10}{6} \cdot 21$
$1 \cdot P = \frac{21}{0.6}$		$1 \cdot P = \frac{210}{6}$
$P = \frac{210}{6} = 35$		$P = 35$

Example 2: Three methods for solving $\frac{11}{x} = \frac{2}{3}$

I The equation is a **proportion.**
2 and x are the **means.**
3 and 11 are the **extremes.**

$$2x = 33 \quad \text{Product of means = product of extremes}$$
$$\frac{1}{2} \cdot 2x = \frac{1}{2} \cdot 33 \quad \text{Multiply both sides by } \tfrac{1}{2}.$$
$$x = \frac{33}{2}$$

II Multiply both sides by any number which will result in an equation without fractions.

$$3x \cdot \frac{11}{x} = 3x \cdot \frac{2}{3} \quad \text{Note that } x \neq 0.$$
$$33 = 2x \quad \text{Proceed now as in method I.}$$

III First solve for $\frac{1}{x}$.

$$11 \cdot \frac{1}{x} = \frac{2}{3}$$
$$\frac{1}{11} \cdot 11 \cdot \frac{1}{x} = \frac{1}{11} \cdot \frac{2}{3} \quad \text{Multiply by } \tfrac{1}{11}.$$
$$\frac{1}{x} = \frac{2}{33}$$

If the reciprocal of x is $\frac{2}{33}$, then $x = \frac{33}{2}$.

No special strategy is needed for division. You know that

$\frac{3}{4} \div \frac{5}{6}$ **is the same as** $\frac{3}{4} \cdot \frac{6}{5}$. (Either way the result is $\frac{18}{20}$ or $\frac{9}{10}$.)

Every division problem can likewise be changed into a multiplication problem by using the following definition of *division*. (Compare this definition with that for *subtraction*.)

Definition

To **divide** b into a, multiply the reciprocal of b by a.

$$a \div b = a \cdot \frac{1}{b}$$

EXERCISES 1.3

Ⓐ 1. What is the multiplicative identity?

2. What is the multiplicative inverse of 10?

3. What is the meaning of the word *reciprocal*?

4–7. Give the reciprocal of each number.

4. $\frac{2}{3}$ 5. -5 6. -1 7. 1.3

8–12. Multiply the given numbers.

8. 1.2, -2.5 9. -4, -2 10. -11, 11

11. $-\frac{1}{3}$, $-\frac{2}{5}$ 12. $-\frac{8}{3}$, $-\frac{4}{3}$

13. Any division problem can be changed to a(n) ____ problem.

14–17. Change all divisions to multiplications.

14. $\frac{a}{b}$ 15. $12 \div \frac{2}{3}$ 16. $\frac{3}{x} = 5$ 17. $\frac{y}{-6} = -7$

18–22. Divide the first number by the second in Exercises 8–12.

23. What is the multiplication property of equations?

24. If $-\frac{2}{5}x = 1$, then $x =$ ____. 25. If $\frac{2}{3} = \frac{1}{F}$, then $F =$ ____.

Ⓑ **26–33.** **(a)** Multiply each side of the equation by a real number to make the solution easier. **(b)** Solve and write the solution set. **(c)** Check.

26. $-4M = 2$ 27. $N \cdot 3 = 468$ 28. $\frac{3}{2}T = \frac{4}{3}$ 29. $100 = 2 \cdot r$

30. $-4.1 = \frac{x}{5}$ 31. $\frac{8}{y} = \frac{20}{7}$ 32. $\frac{\sqrt{7}}{t} = -3$ 33. $18 = 4 \cdot z \cdot 6$

34. Solve for a: $F = ma$.

35. Solve for b: $\frac{a}{b} = \frac{c}{d}$.

36–37. Translate the given statement into an equation. Give the meaning of each letter used in your equation. Then solve.

36. 36 is 4 percent of what number?

37. What is the rate of a plane which flies m kilometres in h hours?

38–42. Many real problems can be solved using proportions (see Example 2, page 9). For each problem below, set up a proportion, then solve.

38. *Shopping.* If 6 cans of juice cost 99¢, how much do 7 cans cost?

© **39.** *Sports.* On the average, how fast must a person run each 100 metres to equal the women's 1500-metre world record of 4 minutes, 1.4 seconds? (Ludmila Bragina, U.S.S.R., set the record in 1972.)

40. *Labor.* A day worker paid by the hour received $110 for 38 hours' work. How much would be paid for 30 hours' work at the same rate?

41. *Geometry.* If the area of circle P at the right is 40π square centimetres, what is the area of the shaded portion?

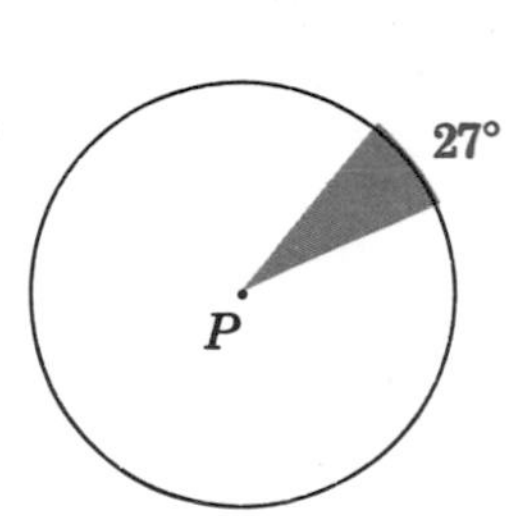

42. *Housekeeping.* If it costs $125 to carpet a $9' \times 12'$ room, what would it cost to carpet a $10' \times 15'$ room at the same price per square yard?

THE GROUP PROPERTIES 1.4

All of mathematics can be arranged to proceed as a logical system, beginning with **undefined terms** (not everything can be defined) and **postulates** (not everything can be proved).

Remember from geometry that the words *point, line,* and *plane* were undefined. In this course, the basic undefined terms are:

real number ● *addition* ● *multiplication*

From these words, such ideas as *subtraction* and *division* have already been defined, and others will be.

Postulates are assumed true, and they serve two major purposes. First, they indicate relationships among undefined terms—otherwise (theoretically) we would not know how to interpret the undefined terms. Second, they are used to prove other relationships.

There are nine postulates in this book. The first two state the properties which are needed to solve the simplest equations involving addition and multiplication. These properties are called the **group** properties (for reasons which are explained in Chapter 9).

POSTULATE 1: GROUP PROPERTIES OF REAL NUMBER ADDITION

There is a set of real numbers and an operation addition $(+)$ so that the following properties hold for any real numbers a, b, and c.

closure	$a + b$ is a real number.
associativity	$(a + b) + c = a + (b + c)$
identity	There is a unique real number 0 such that for any a, $a + 0 = 0 + a = a$.
inverses	For each a, there is a unique real number $-a$ such that $(-a) + a = a + (-a) = 0$.

As Corollary 1.6.2 (page 18) indicates, zero must be excluded if the corresponding group properties are to hold for multiplication.

POSTULATE 2:
GROUP PROPERTIES OF NONZERO REAL NUMBER MULTIPLICATION

There is a set of real numbers and an operation multiplication $(\cdot)$ so that the following properties hold for any nonzero real numbers a, b, and c.

closure	ab is a real number.
associativity	$(ab)c = a(bc)$
identity	There is a unique real number 1 such that for any a, $a \cdot 1 = 1 \cdot a = a$.
inverses	For each a, there is a unique real number $\frac{1}{a}$ such that $\frac{1}{a} \cdot a = a \cdot \frac{1}{a} = 1$.

Notice from the proofs of the following two theorems that *all* the group properties are needed to solve the simplest equations. (Recall that statements which can be proved from postulates are *theorems*.)

Theorem 1.4.1

If a and b are any real numbers, then $a + x = b$ has exactly one solution, $-a + b$.

Theorem 1.4.2

If a and b are any nonzero real numbers, then $ax = b$ has exactly one solution, $\frac{1}{a} \cdot b$.

PROOF (Thm. 1.4.1):		PROOF (Thm. 1.4.2):
$a + x = b$	Given	$ax = b$ and $a \neq 0$
a has an opposite $-a$.	Inverses	a has a reciprocal $\frac{1}{a}$.
$-a + (a + x) = -a + b$	Properties of equations	$\frac{1}{a}(ax) = \frac{1}{a} \cdot b$
$(-a + a) + x = -a + b$	Associativity	$\left(\frac{1}{a} \cdot a\right) x = \frac{1}{a} \cdot b$
$0 + x = -a + b$	Inverses	$1 \cdot x = \frac{1}{a} \cdot b$
$x = -a + b$	Identity	$x = \frac{1}{a} \cdot b$
$-a + b$ is a real number.	Closure	$\frac{1}{a} \cdot b$ is a real number.

The proofs above did not use another well-known property of addition and multiplication—commutativity.

POSTULATE 3: COMMUTATIVITY

If a and b are any real numbers, $a + b = b + a$ and $ab = ba$.

Using commutativity and the definitions of subtraction and division, Theorems 1.4.1 and 1.4.2 can be restated.

Theorem 1.4.1

If a and b are real numbers, then $a + x = b$ and $x = b - a$ are equivalent.

Theorem 1.4.2

If a and b are nonzero real numbers, then $ax = b$ and $x = \frac{b}{a}$ are equivalent.

EXERCISES 1.4

Ⓐ **1–5.** Explain why each equation is equivalent to the one preceding it.

Given: $T - 4 = 3$ **1.** $T + (-4) = 3$ **2.** $[T + (-4)] + 4 = 3 + 4$

3. $T + (-4 + 4) = 3 + 4$ **4.** $T + 0 = 7$ **5.** $T = 7$

6. Name the four group properties of addition of real numbers.

7. If $x + 478 = 932$, then $x + 479 =$ ____.

8. Which set is not closed (does not have closure) under addition?

a. $\{0\}$ **b.** $\{0, 1\}$ **c.** the set of integers **d.** the set of reals

9. If $x = b - a$, then $a + x =$ ____.

10. If $ax = b$, then $x =$ ____.

11. Name the group properties of multiplication of nonzero real numbers.

12. Which set is not closed under multiplication?

   a. the set of negative reals

   b. the set of integers

   c. the set of positive reals

   d. $1, \frac{1}{2}, \frac{1}{3}, \frac{1}{4}, \frac{1}{5}, \frac{1}{6}, \cdots$

13. Which set in Exercise **12** is not closed under addition?

14. Name three terms undefined in this course.

15. Name the two major purposes of postulates.

16. For all real numbers n, $(10 + n)4 = 4(n + 10)$. Why?

Ⓑ **17–21.** Name the postulate(s) or theorem(s) which support(s) each process.

17. checking a division problem by multiplication

18. adding a column of 20 numbers by adding the first 10 numbers, then the second 10, then the two sums

19. adding a column of numbers from top to bottom, then checking by adding from bottom to top

20. checking the subtraction problem $8 - (-10) = 18$ by adding $18 + (-10) = 8$

21. instead of multiplying $\begin{array}{r} 666 \\ \times\ 89 \\ \hline \end{array}$, multiplying $\begin{array}{r} 89 \\ \times\ 666 \\ \hline \end{array}$

22–27. Given the numbers 3, 5, and 8, you can make four true equations which have only one operation: $3 + 5 = 8$, $5 + 3 = 8$, $8 - 5 = 3$, and $8 - 3 = 5$. Do the same with the three given numbers.

22. $8, -4, -2$

23. $-9, -12, -3$

24. $x, y, x + y$

25. ab, a, b

26. $\frac{1}{3}, \frac{1}{2}, \frac{1}{6}$

27. $\frac{3}{4}, \frac{3}{2}, 2$

Ⓒ 28. $\left(\frac{1}{a} \cdot \frac{1}{b}\right)$ and $\frac{1}{ab}$ are both reciprocals of the same number. What is this number? Why is it then true that $\frac{1}{a} \cdot \frac{1}{b} = \frac{1}{ab}$?

29–39. The process used to multiply fractions can be deduced from the postulates in this section and the property in Exercise **28**. The fact that $(b - a)$ and $(a - b)$ are opposites can also be deduced from the postulates in this section. Give reasons for each step of the following proofs.

THEOREM: $\frac{a}{b} \cdot \frac{c}{d} = \frac{ac}{bd}$

PROOF:

29. $\frac{a}{b} \cdot \frac{c}{d} = \left(a \cdot \frac{1}{b}\right) \cdot \left(c \cdot \frac{1}{d}\right)$

30. $= a \cdot \left(\frac{1}{b} \cdot c\right) \cdot \frac{1}{d}$

31. $= a \cdot \left(c \cdot \frac{1}{b}\right) \cdot \frac{1}{d}$

32. $= (a \cdot c) \cdot \left(\frac{1}{b} \cdot \frac{1}{d}\right)$

33. $= ac \cdot \frac{1}{bd}$

34. $= \frac{ac}{bd}$

THEOREM: $(b - a) + (a - b) = 0$

PROOF:

$(b - a) + (a - b)$

35. $= [b + (-a)] + [a + (-b)]$

36. $= b + (-a + a) + (-b)$

37. $= b + 0 + (-b)$

38. $= b + (-b)$

39. $= 0$

40. Prove: $\frac{b}{a}$ and $\frac{a}{b}$ are reciprocals. (Use Exercises **35–39** as a guide.)

41. Prove: $-a + (-b)$ and $-(a + b)$ are opposites of the same number. (Use Exercise **28** as a guide.)

42. Prove: $(a - b) + (c - d) = (a + c) - (b + d)$. (Use Exercises **29–34** as a guide.)

43. The term *commutative* was first used in 1814 by the French mathematician Servois; *associative* was first used in 1835 by the British mathematician W. R. Hamilton. Since people had added and multiplied for centuries, why do you think it took so long for these properties to be recognized and named?

ORDER OF OPERATIONS 1.5

Expressions involving both addition and multiplication are used in the next section. When several operations appear in one expression, there must be rules for deciding which operations to perform first. Otherwise, $2 \cdot 3 + 4$ may equal 14 or 10, depending on whether you add or multiply first. There is worldwide agreement on the following order.

first	Operations inside parentheses (in the order given by the next three rules)
second	Powers
third	Multiplication and division from left to right
fourth	Addition and subtraction from left to right

Examples:

1. $-3x^2$ ◀ Find x^2 before multiplying by -3.
   If $x = 2$, $-3x^2 = -3 \cdot 4 = -12$.

2. $(-3x)^2$ ◀ Multiply by -3 before squaring.
   If $x = 2$, $(-3x)^2 = (-3 \cdot 2)^2 = (-6)^2 = 36$.

3. $9 - 8 - 5$ ◀ Work from left to right.
   $9 - 8 - 5 = 1 - 5 = -4$

4. $7 - 3m$ ◀ Multiply before subtracting.
   If $m = 2$, $7 - 3m = 7 - 6 = 1$. In general, $7 - 3m \neq 4m$.

5. $5(2^3 - 4)$ ◀ Work inside parentheses before multiplying.
   $5(2^3 - 4) = 5(8 - 4) = 5 \cdot 4 = 20$

The rules of order of operations are rules about the written language, not about the concepts. This is why they are not postulates. But the rules are so widely known that they are used in the most common computer languages (see Exercises **25–30**).

Fractions, roots, and equations have "unwritten parentheses."

$\frac{a+3}{a-2}$ means $\frac{(a+3)}{(a-2)}$ ◁ Work with numerator and denominator separately before dividing.

$\sqrt{x^2 + y^2}$ means $\sqrt{(x^2 + y^2)}$ ◁ Work under the radical sign before taking roots; in general, $\sqrt{x^2 + y^2} \neq x + y$.

$x = \frac{1}{2} + y$ means $(x) = (\frac{1}{2} + y)$ ◁ Add to or multiply entire sides of equations; for example, $3x = 3(\frac{1}{2} + y)$.

Be careful to write clearly. The expressions below look similar but mean *different* things. If you are careless, you may confuse them.

$2x$ (means $x + x$) x^2 (means $x \cdot x$) x_2 (means the second x-value)

EXERCISES 1.5

Ⓐ 1. What are the rules for the order of operations?

2. Show by example that rules for an order of operations are needed.

3–6. Calculate.

3. $-10 - 10 - 10$
4. $10 \cdot 9 + 2 \cdot 11$
5. $-3^2 + (-5)^2$
6. $\sqrt{5^2 + 12^2}$

7–10. Place parentheses where they belong but are not usually written.

7. $\frac{100 + 10}{100 + 5}$ **8.** $\frac{x^2 + 4}{x + 2}$ **9.** $\sqrt{6^2 + 8^2}$ **10.** $\frac{3}{2} + x = \frac{1}{4}$

Ⓑ **11–19.** Given $x = 2$, $y = -1$, $a = 4$, and $b = \frac{1}{2}$, evaluate:

11. $-a^2$ **12.** $2 - ab$ **13.** $\sqrt{x^2 + y^2}$

14. xy^2 **15.** $3b + 4y$ **16.** $(x - 1)(x + 2) + 5$

17. $3a^2 - 4a - 32$ **18.** $\frac{b - \frac{1}{2}}{b + \frac{1}{2}}$ **19.** $\frac{2x - y}{x + 2y}$

20–24. Use numbers to show that the statement is *not* always true.

20. $(2V)^2 = 2V^2$ **21.** $\sqrt{m^2 + 4} = m + 2$ **22.** $\frac{2a + 3}{a + 3} = 2$

23. $(x + a)^2 = x^2 + a^2$ **24.** $-x - x = 0$

Ⓒ **25–30.** In the computer language BASIC, x^a is written as $X \uparrow A$, and bc is written as $B * C$. A fraction like $\frac{1}{2}$ is written as 1/2. Parentheses, +, and − are used in the usual way, and the order of operations is the same. Simplify each BASIC expression below.

25. $3 * 2 \uparrow 5 - 8$ **26.** $-1 - 8 * 2 \uparrow 4$ **27.** $1/2 \uparrow 2 * 2 \uparrow 3$

28. $6 - (9 - 1/3) * 12$ **29.** $6 - 2 \uparrow X * 3 + 5$ if $X = 2$

30. $[A * B \uparrow C + (D - E)] \uparrow F$ if $A = 1, B = 2, C = 3, D = 4, E = 5, F = 6$

31–32. Place +, −, ·, ÷, and parentheses so a true sentence results.

31. $9 \quad -3 \quad 2 \quad -1 = 11$ **32.** $8 \quad 4 \quad 16 \quad 1 = -33$

REPEATED ADDITION AND THE DISTRIBUTIVE PROPERTY

You may have met multiplication first as repeated addition.

$$x + x = 2x$$
$$x + x + x = 3x$$
$$\vdots$$
$$\underbrace{x + x + \cdots + x}_{m \text{ terms}} = mx$$

multiples of x

2, 3, · · · , m are **coefficients** of x.

When two multiples are added, $2x + 3x$

$$(x + x) + (x + x + x) = x + x + x + x + x$$

a third multiple is the sum. $= 5x$

The set of multiples of a number is closed under addition. This generalizes even if the coefficients are not whole numbers. This famous generalization was given the name *distributive property* by the French mathematician Servois in 1814.

POSTULATE 4:

DISTRIBUTIVE PROPERTY—CLOSURE OF MULTIPLES UNDER ADDITION

For all real numbers a, b, and x, $(a + b)x = ax + bx$.

By commutativity, the postulate can also be written

$$x(a + b) = xa + xb.$$

We can now consider multiplication by zero.

$$\text{If } a = 1 \text{ and } b = 0, \quad (1 + 0)x = 1 \cdot x + 0 \cdot x$$
$$x = x + 0 \cdot x$$

Adding $-x$ to each side of this equation, we find that the zero multiple of any number is zero.

Theorem 1.6.1

Zero multiple property: For any real number x, $0 \cdot x = 0$.

A **corollary** is a theorem which immediately follows from a preceding theorem.

Corollary 1.6.2

There is no solution to $0 \cdot x = 1$.

Corollary 1.6.2 says that zero has no reciprocal. This is why the group properties hold only for *nonzero* real numbers and multiplication. Since zero has no reciprocal, there can be no division by zero. Also, because of the special properties of multiplication by zero, equations of the three forms shown below must be treated carefully.

1. $0 \cdot x = 0$ — Any real number works, by Theorem 1.6.1.

2. $0 \cdot x = b, b \neq 0$ — No real number works, by Theorem 1.6.1.

3. $a \cdot x = 0, a \neq 0$ — Multiply both sides by $\frac{1}{a}$; then $x = \frac{1}{a} \cdot 0 = 0$.

Forms **1** and **3** are combined in the next theorem.

Theorem 1.6.3

Zero product theorem: If $ax = 0$, then either $a = 0$ or $x = 0$.

Example: If $(y - 3) \cdot (y + 5) = 0$,

then $y - 3 = 0$ or $y + 5 = 0$.

So $y = 3$ or $y = -5$.

By the zero product theorem, if the product of two numbers is 0, then one of the numbers is 0.

The proof of the next theorem also uses the distributive postulate.

Theorem 1.6.4

For any real numbers m and x, $m \cdot x$ and $-m \cdot x$ are opposites.

PROOF: $m \cdot x + (-m \cdot x) = [m + (-m)]x$ Distributive property

$= 0 \cdot x$ Inverses

$= 0$ Zero product theorem

Since $m \cdot x$ and $-m \cdot x$ add to zero, they are opposites.

As a special case, if $m = 1$, then x and $-1 \cdot x$ are opposites; so we can find the opposite of a number by multiplying by -1.

Examples: Using opposites

1. $-(3M + 2)$
$= -1(3M + 2)$
$= -1 \cdot 3M + (-1) \cdot 2$
$= -3M - 2$

2. $5x - (6 - 2x) = 5x + (-1)(6 - 2x)$
$= 5x + (-6) + 2x$
$= 7x + (-6)$
$= 7x - 6$

EXERCISES 1.6

Ⓐ **1.** What is the distributive property and who named it?

2. According to the distributive property, $3(x - 4) = 3x +$ ____.

3. According to distributivity, $9B - 21 = 3($____$)$.

4–9. Give the solution set.

4. $y \cdot 0 = 5$ **5.** $N + 0 = 6$ **6.** $0 = 10m$

7. $0 = 0 \cdot x$ **8.** $5x - 5x = 0$ **9.** $6y + 3y = 0$

10. If $(m + 2)(m - 8) = 0$, then $m =$ ____ or $m =$ ____.

11. If $(x + 2)(9 + y) = 0$, then $x =$ ____ or y ____.

12. $5a - 9a - 2a =$ ____

13. $-z + 8z =$ ____

14. $-x - x =$ ____

15. $-4A - A =$ ____

16–27. Solve each problem in your head.

16. $19 \cdot 7 + 19 \cdot 3 =$ ____

17. $53 \cdot 6 - 3 \cdot 6 =$ ____

18. $4 \cdot 712 +$ ____ $= 14 \cdot 712$

19. $(\frac{1}{4}) \cdot 812 + (\frac{3}{4}) \cdot 812 =$ ____

20. $12 +$ ____ $= 101 \cdot 12$

21. $-21 \cdot 43 + 20 \cdot 43 =$ ____

22. $57 \cdot 14 + 43 \cdot 14 =$ ____

23. $51 \cdot 112 +$ ____ $\cdot 112 = 11{,}200$

24. $81.61 - 37.12 + 141.79 = 141.79 + 81.61 +$ ____

25. $(\frac{1}{5}) \cdot 62 + (\frac{1}{5}) \cdot 62 + (\frac{1}{5}) \cdot 62 + (\frac{1}{5}) \cdot 62 + (\frac{1}{5}) \cdot 62 =$ ____

26. $10 \cdot 9 \cdot 8 \cdot 7 \cdot 6 \cdot 5 \cdot 4 \cdot 3 \cdot 2 \cdot 1 \cdot 0 =$ ____

27. If $3 \cdot 5 \cdot x \cdot (-2) \cdot (-4) = 0$, then $x =$ ____.

Ⓑ **28–38.** Use distributivity to simplify.

28. $\frac{1}{2}B + \frac{2}{3}B$

29. $\frac{D}{2} + \frac{2D}{3}$

30. $V - (4 - V)$

31. $(2W - 8) + 4(9 - 3W)$

32. $3E - 8E + 5E - 2E - E$

33. $x + [2 - 3(1 - x)]$

34. $7(a + 2b) - 3a$

35. $y - [2 - 3(1 - y)]$

36. $z + 3 - 12(z + 8)$

37. $t - 1.53t$

38. $a - (2 - 4b + a) + (3a + b - 8) - 5(9 - 2b)$

39. How can you check your answer to a problem like Exercise **38**?

40. How is the distributive property related to multiples?

41–43. Fill in the blanks with real numbers to make the equations true.

41. $-10m -$ ____$m = 0$

42. $5(2x +$ ____$y) =$ ____$x + 15y$

43. $30x + 12y = 6($____$x +$ ____$y)$

Ⓒ 44. Explain how distributivity is used in adding $\frac{2}{3}$ and $\frac{5}{3}$.

45. The average of two numbers is their sum divided by 2. Show that it is possible to obtain the average of two numbers by halving each number, then adding the halves.

46. Modify Exercise **45** to consider the average of 3 numbers.

47. Where is distributivity used in this multiplication?

```
  312
×  46
-----
 1872
1248
-----
14352
```

48. How can this rectangle be used to show distributivity?

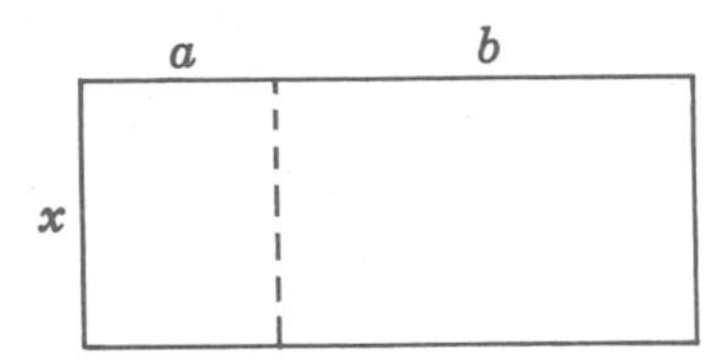

49. Pick a number. Multiply it by 12. Add 30 to the product. Now divide the number you have by 3. Now divide the last number by 4. Use properties we have had to show that the final answer is 2.5 larger than the original number chosen.

50. *Banking*. An amount of x dollars is placed in a bank at 5.10% interest per year. How much money is in the account at the end of one year? Write this amount as the product of two numbers.

REPEATED MULTIPLICATION AND THE POWER PROPERTY

Your first experience with "taking a power" may have been as a result of repeated multiplication.

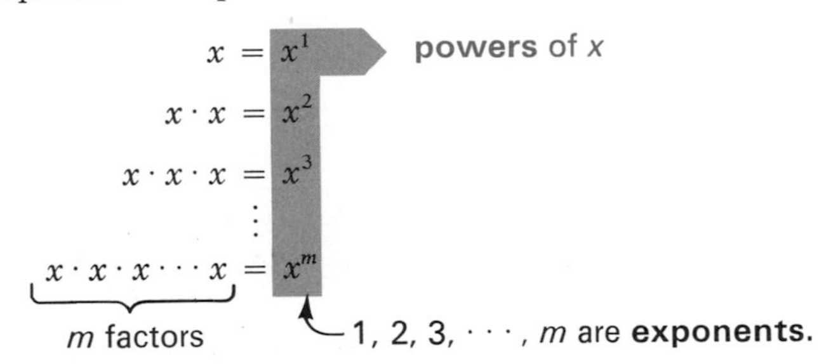

When two powers are multiplied,

$$x^2 \cdot x^3$$

$$(x \cdot x) \cdot (x \cdot x \cdot x) = x \cdot x \cdot x \cdot x \cdot x$$

a third power is the product.

$$= x^5$$

The set of powers of a number is closed under multiplication. This generalizes if the exponents are any numbers in the set $\{\cdots, -4, -3, -2, -1, 0, 1, 2, 3, 4, \cdots\}$. (As is usual with properties of multiplication, 0 must be treated carefully, so $x \neq 0$.)

POSTULATE 5:

POWER PROPERTY—CLOSURE OF POWERS UNDER MULTIPLICATION

For all integers a and b and nonzero real numbers x,

$$x^a \cdot x^b = x^{a+b}.$$

Examples:

1. $2^8 \cdot 2^{10} = 2^{18}$ 2. $5x^4 \cdot x^3 = 5 \cdot x^7$

Postulate 5 uses repeated multiplication just like Postulate 4 uses repeated addition. These postulates ensure that every property of multiples has a corresponding property of powers. (Were it not for Servois, who named it in 1814, the *distributive property* might be known as the *multiple property*.)

You have dealt both with multiples which represent repeated addition, like $4x$, and with multiples which do not represent repeated addition, like $-4x$ and $0x$. Some powers, like x^4, arise from repeated multiplication. Now we consider powers, like x^0, which do *not* arise from repeated multiplication.

In Postulate 5, if $a = 1$ and $b = 0$, $x^1 \cdot x^0 = x^{1+0}$

$$x \cdot x^0 = x$$

Multiplying both sides by $\frac{1}{x}$, we find that the zero power of any nonzero real number is 1.

Theorem 1.7.1

Zero power theorem: For any nonzero real number x, $x^0 = 1$.

Compare the zero coefficient and the zero exponent.

$0 \cdot x = 0$	$x^0 = 1$
the additive identity	the multiplicative identity

What about negative exponents? Here are some powers of 2.

exponent	power
4	$2^4 = 16$
3	$2^3 = 8$
2	$2^2 = 4$
1	$2^1 = 2$
0	$2^0 = 1$
-1	$2^{-1} = \frac{1}{2}$
-2	$2^{-2} = \frac{1}{4}$
-3	$2^{-3} = \frac{1}{8}$

Notice that each power is $\frac{1}{2}$ the power above it.

This pattern continues for negative exponents.

That is, $2^{-n} = \frac{1}{2^n}$.

Theorem 1.7.2

For any nonzero x, x^m and x^{-m} are reciprocals.

PROOF: $x^m \cdot x^{-m} = x^{m+(-m)} = x^0 = 1$

Since x^m and x^{-m} multiply to 1, they are reciprocals.

Notice that multiples and powers possess similar properties.

	mx and $-mx$ are opposites.	x^m and x^{-m} are reciprocals.
When $m = 1$:	$1 \cdot x$ and $-1 \cdot x$ are opposites.	x^1 and x^{-1} are reciprocals.

Examples:

1. $3^4 = 3 \cdot 3 \cdot 3 \cdot 3 = 81$

2. $3^{-4} = \frac{1}{3^4} = \frac{1}{81}$

3. $(d^2)^3 = d^2 \cdot d^2 \cdot d^2 = d^6$

4. $\left(\frac{5}{6}\right)^{-2} = \frac{1}{(\frac{5}{6})^2} = \frac{1}{\frac{25}{36}} = \frac{36}{25}$

5. $\frac{v^{-3}x}{y^2m^{-2}} = v^{-3} \cdot x \cdot \frac{1}{y^2} \cdot \frac{1}{m^{-2}} = \frac{1}{v^3} \cdot x \cdot \frac{1}{y^2} \cdot m^2 = \frac{xm^2}{v^3y^2}$

EXERCISES 1.7

Ⓐ **1.** $q + q + q + q =$ ____ **2.** $r \cdot r \cdot r \cdot r \cdot r =$ ____

3–7. Evaluate.

3. -4^2 **4.** 2^5 **5.** $(-2)^5$ **6.** $(-2)^4$ **7.** -5^3

8–13. Write as the power of a single number.

8. $x^2 \cdot x^9$ **9.** $y \cdot y^{14}$ **10.** $z^{-3} \cdot z^{-2}$

11. $a^0 \cdot a^2$ **12.** $b^4 \cdot b^4 \cdot b^4$ **13.** $c^{-1} \cdot c^0 \cdot c^1$

14–15. Which number is *not* positive?

14. a. 2^3 **b.** 2^0 **c.** 2^{-3} **d.** All are positive.

15. a. $(-4)^2$ **b.** -4^2 **c.** 4^{-2} **d.** All are positive.

16. x^m and x^{-m} are ____. **17.** For any $x \neq 0$, $x^0 =$ ____.

18–21. Evaluate x^3, x^2, x^1, x^0, x^{-1}, x^{-2}, and x^{-3} for each value of x.

18. $x = 3$ **19.** $x = -4$ **20.** $x = 1$ **21.** $x = \frac{2}{3}$

22. Name the exponent and the coefficient of m^3 in $-4m^3$.

23. Name the exponent and the coefficient of x^{-4} in $2x^{-4} + 3x^5$.

24–28. Express each number without negative or zero exponents.

24. 2^0 **25.** $\left(-\frac{1}{2}\right)^0$ **26.** $\left(\frac{2}{3}\right)^{-2}$ **27.** $\left(\frac{7}{16}\right)^{-1}$ **28.** $3\left(\frac{1}{3}\right)^{-3}$

29–31. Evaluate.

29. 10^{-3} **30.** $4.6 \cdot 10^{-3}$ **31.** $2 \cdot 10^4 + 2 \cdot 10^{-4}$

32. What is the power property?

Ⓑ **33–38.** Given the numbers 9, 18, and 2, you can make four *true* equations which have only one operation: $9 \cdot 2 = 18$, $2 \cdot 9 = 18$, $\frac{18}{9} = 2$, and $\frac{18}{2} = 9$. Do the same with the given three numbers.

33. h^5, h^8, h^3 **34.** $x^5, x^{-5}, 1$ **35.** $\frac{1}{v}, v^5, v^4$

36. w^0, w^{-3}, w^{-3} **37.** z^2, z^4, z^6 **38.** y^2, y^{-4}, y^{-6}

39–48. Simplify or write without negative or zero exponents.

39. $-2m^3 \cdot 3m^{-5}$ **40.** $(6a^2)(2a^0)(3a^5)$ **41.** $2V^2 + V^2 + V^2$

42. $W^2 \cdot W^2 \cdot W^2 \cdot W^2$ **43.** $3(M^3)^2$ **44.** $3(9m)^0 + 4(2m)^0$

45. $\frac{x}{y^{-2}}$ **46.** $a^{-3}b$ **47.** $\frac{3x^{-1}y^2}{4m^3}$ **48.** $\frac{6v^{-2}u^{-2}}{wr^{-1}}$

49–56. True or False?

49. $2^{100} < 2^{101}$ **50.** $2^{-100} < 2^{-101}$ **51.** $10^{-3} < 0.006 < 10^{-2}$

52. $(\frac{4}{3})^0 > (\frac{4}{3})^{-1}$ **53.** $(-\frac{1}{2})^{98} < (-\frac{1}{2})^{97}$ **54.** $-2^{-3} = -3^{-2}$

55. $3^{-2} < (3.1)^{-2}$ **56.** If $x > 0$, then $x^{-n} > 0$.

57–62. Evaluate when $x = 2$, $y = 3$, $a = 4$, $b = -2$.

57. $a^{-x} + y^0$ **58.** $-xy^{-1}$ **59.** $(xy)^{-a} \cdot (xy)^a + 10$

60. $b^{-1} + x^{-5}$ **61.** $\frac{b}{a^{x+b}}$ **62.** $\left(\frac{y}{a}\right)^{-y}$

63. One micron $= 10^{-4}$ cm. Then a micron is what part of a centimetre?
a. one fortieth **b.** one thousandth **c.** one ten-thousandth

64. To the nearest tenth, estimate π^{-1}.

65–67. Express each number as a decimal.

65. $6.23 \cdot 10^{-5}$ **66.** $-1.2 \cdot 10^0$ **67.** $78.306 \cdot 10^{-5}$

68. The gravitational attraction between two gram masses one cm apart is approximately $6.670 \cdot 10^{-8}$ dynes (a unit of force). Write this number as a decimal.

© **69–75.** Every positive real number can be written as a product of a power of 10 and a number between 1 and 10. For example,

$$7800 = 7.8 \cdot 10^3 \qquad 0.0132 = 1.32 \cdot 10^{-2}$$

This way of writing numbers is called *scientific notation.* Rewrite each number in scientific notation.

69. 4 million **70.** 0.0025 **71.** 70,000,000,000

72. 0.000006 **73.** 0.4 **74.** 69.2

75. (0.000006)(0.0000000002) (HINT: Write each number in scientific notation before multiplying.)

76. Show how the number $-4x$ can be obtained from x by "repeated subtraction." Obtain x^{-4} from x by a similar kind of process.

77–78. If $3x = x + x + x$ corresponds to $x^3 = x \cdot x \cdot x$, what equation involving repeated multiplication corresponds to each of the following?

77. $3x + 11x = 14x$ **78.** $9x - 15x = -6x$

79–80. About $1 \cdot 10^6$ tons of carbon dioxide are released into the earth's atmosphere in one year by volcanoes and hot springs, and about $6 \cdot 10^9$ tons are released by burning fuels of all types. Give your answers to the following questions in scientific notation.

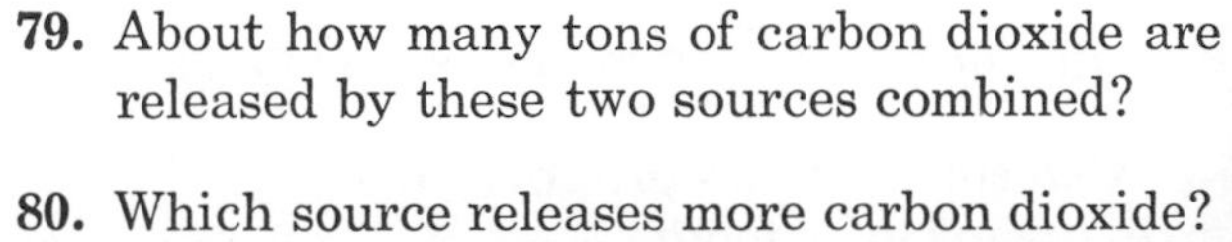

79. About how many tons of carbon dioxide are released by these two sources combined?

80. Which source releases more carbon dioxide? How many tons more?

1.8 HALVES AND SQUARE ROOTS

We have shown that addition and multiplication of real numbers have many corresponding properties. Some of these properties involve halves and square roots.

Definition

Let a be a real number. Any solution of the equation $x^2 = a$ is called a **square root** of a.

If *half a number* is *added* to itself, the sum is the number.	If a *square root of a number* is *multiplied* by itself, the product is the number.
Half of 109 is a solution to $2x = 109$.	A square root of 109 is a solution to $x^2 = 109$.

For now, we are interested in square roots of positive numbers.

When $a > 0$, a has two square roots. $\sqrt{a}$ is positive. $-\sqrt{a}$ is negative.

Note that the symbol $\sqrt{\ }$ stands for only one square root of a number. The two square roots of 3 are $\sqrt{3}$ and $-\sqrt{3}$, or approximately 1.732 and -1.732. Now consider two corresponding equations and their solutions.

$2x = a + b$	◀ equation ▶	$x^2 = ab$
$x = \frac{a+b}{2}$	◀ solution ▶	$x = \sqrt{ab}$ or $x = -\sqrt{ab}$

Definitions

$\frac{a+b}{2}$ is the **average**, or **arithmetic mean**, of a and b.

$\sqrt{ab}$ and $-\sqrt{ab}$ are the **mean proportionals**, or **geometric means**, of a and b.

Just as $\frac{a+b}{2}$ can be calculated by adding $\frac{a}{2}$ and $\frac{b}{2}$, the mean proportional $\sqrt{ab}$ can be calculated by multiplying $\sqrt{a}$ and $\sqrt{b}$.

Theorem 1.8.1

Square-root multiplication: If a and b are positive,

$$\sqrt{ab} = \sqrt{a} \cdot \sqrt{b}.$$

PROOF: Each side of the equation $\sqrt{ab} = \sqrt{a} \cdot \sqrt{b}$ is a positive number which, multiplied by itself, yields ab. There is only one such positive square root of ab, so $\sqrt{a} \cdot \sqrt{b}$ and $\sqrt{ab}$ are identical.

The tables of square roots on page 601 of this book go only from 1 to 100. Theorem 1.8.1 can be used to approximate square roots of numbers not in the table, as shown in the following example.

Example: $\sqrt{432} = \sqrt{9 \cdot 4 \cdot 4 \cdot 3}$ ◀ Find perfect-square factors of 432.

$= \sqrt{9} \cdot \sqrt{4} \cdot \sqrt{4} \cdot \sqrt{3}$ ◀ Apply Theorem 1.8.1.

$= 3 \cdot 2 \cdot 2 \cdot \sqrt{3}$

$= 12\sqrt{3}$

$\doteq 12(1.732) \doteq 20.78$

$\doteq$ means *is approximately equal to.*

You can check that $(20.78)(20.78) \doteq 432$.

The property $\sqrt{ab} = \sqrt{a}\sqrt{b}$ is natural because square roots arise from multiplication. No simple property relates square roots and addition. (Students make *errors* like $\sqrt{3^2 + 2^2} = 3 + 2$, but $\sqrt{13} \neq 5$.) However, there is a property which connects square roots and division.

Theorem 1.8.2

Square-root division: If x and y are positive, $\sqrt{\frac{x}{y}} = \frac{\sqrt{x}}{\sqrt{y}}$.

PROOF: $\sqrt{\frac{x}{y}}$ is a positive number whose square is $\frac{x}{y}$. So is $\frac{\sqrt{x}}{\sqrt{y}}$. A number has only one positive square root, so these are equal.

Examples: Square roots and division

1. $\sqrt{\frac{2}{3}} = \frac{\sqrt{2}}{\sqrt{3}} = \frac{\sqrt{2} \cdot \sqrt{3}}{\sqrt{3} \cdot \sqrt{3}} = \frac{\sqrt{6}}{3}$ (From a table, $\sqrt{6} \doteq 2.449$. So $\frac{\sqrt{6}}{3} \doteq 0.816$.)

2. FIRST METHOD:

$$\frac{\sqrt{50}}{\sqrt{2}} = \sqrt{\frac{50}{2}} = \sqrt{25} = 5$$

SECOND METHOD:

$$\frac{\sqrt{50}}{\sqrt{2}} = \frac{\sqrt{25 \cdot 2}}{\sqrt{2}} = \frac{\sqrt{25} \cdot \sqrt{2}}{\sqrt{2}} = \sqrt{25} = 5$$

EXERCISES 1.8

Ⓐ **1.** What is a square root of a number?

2. Why is the phrase *square root of x* not equivalent to the symbol $\sqrt{x}$?

3–6. Calculate the following for 2 and 5.

3. the average

4. the geometric mean

5. the mean proportional

6. the arithmetic mean

7. The square of the geometric mean of two numbers is their ____.

8. Twice the arithmetic mean of two numbers is their ____.

9–16. Square each number.

9. $\sqrt{a} \cdot \sqrt{b}$ 10. $\sqrt{11.2}$ 11. $\sqrt{ab}$ 12. -6

13. $\sqrt{7}$ 14. $\sqrt{\frac{a}{3}}$ 15. $\frac{\sqrt{a}}{\sqrt{3}}$ 16. $\sqrt{\frac{1}{2}}$

17–33. True or False?

17. $\sqrt{2} + \sqrt{3} = \sqrt{5}$ 18. $\sqrt{2} \cdot \sqrt{3} = \sqrt{6}$ 19. $\sqrt{x}$ may be negative.

20. $\sqrt{20} = \sqrt{4} \cdot \sqrt{5}$ 21. $\sqrt{20} = 2\sqrt{5}$ 22. $\sqrt{300} = 10\sqrt{3}$

23. $\sqrt{2} \cdot \sqrt{2} \cdot \sqrt{3} \cdot \sqrt{3} \cdot \sqrt{4} \cdot \sqrt{4} \cdot \sqrt{5} \cdot \sqrt{5} \cdot \sqrt{6} \cdot \sqrt{6}$ is an integer.

24. $\frac{\sqrt{100}}{\sqrt{25}} = 4$ 25. $-1 = \sqrt{1}$ 26. $\sqrt{\frac{64}{81}} = \frac{8}{9}$

27. $\sqrt{\frac{9}{12}} = \frac{3}{4}$ 28. $\sqrt{6} \cdot \sqrt{6} = 36$ 29. $\sqrt{\frac{1}{2}} \cdot \sqrt{\frac{1}{2}} = \frac{1}{2}$

30. $\sqrt{3} \cdot \sqrt{27}$ is an integer. 31. $\sqrt{8} \div \sqrt{2} = 4$

32. $(-\sqrt{2})(-\sqrt{3}) = -\sqrt{6}$ 33. $-2\sqrt{2} + 3\sqrt{2} = \sqrt{2}$

Ⓑ **34–49.** **(a)** Rewrite each number in the form $x\sqrt{y}$ where y is an integer between 1 and 100. **(b)** Approximate correct to 1 decimal place, using tables if necessary.

34. $\sqrt{500}$ 35. $\sqrt{450}$ 36. $\sqrt{24}$ 37. $\sqrt{10^7}$

38. $\sqrt{98}$ 39. $\sqrt{22 \cdot 33}$ 40. $\sqrt{0.24}$ 41. $\sqrt{6300}$

42. $3\sqrt{2} + \sqrt{32} - 4\sqrt{8}$ 43. $-(\sqrt{2} \cdot \sqrt{128} - 4\sqrt{3} \cdot \sqrt{108})$

44. $\sqrt{0.0016} - \sqrt{0.000784}$ 45. $\sqrt{6^2 + 5^2}$

46. $\sqrt{\frac{1}{2}}$ 47. $\sqrt{\frac{1}{3}}$ 48. $\sqrt{2} \cdot \sqrt{\frac{3}{2}}$ 49. $\sqrt{\frac{4}{5}}$

50–53. Estimate to the nearest tenth, using tables as seldom as possible.

50. $3\sqrt{7}(5 + \sqrt{28})$ 51. $10\sqrt{2}(3\sqrt{2} + \sqrt{18})$

52. $\frac{\sqrt{2}}{2} \cdot \frac{2}{\sqrt{3}}$ 53. $\frac{-1 - \sqrt{5}}{2}$

54. Use the decimal approximations given in your tables to show that the product of $\sqrt{2}$ and $\sqrt{3}$ seems to be $\sqrt{6}$.

55. Without using tables, check that 20.78 is a good approximation to $\sqrt{432}$.

© **56–57.** Which is larger?

56. $(\sqrt{350} + \sqrt{150})$ or $(\sqrt{450} + \sqrt{50})$ **57.** $(\sqrt{1001} - \sqrt{1000})$ or $(\sqrt{1501} - \sqrt{1500})$

58–61. The term *geometric mean* receives its name from its many applications in geometry. Apply the given theorem to find as many indicated lengths in the drawings as possible.

58. Theorem: In a right triangle, the altitude is the mean proportional between the segments of the hypotenuse.

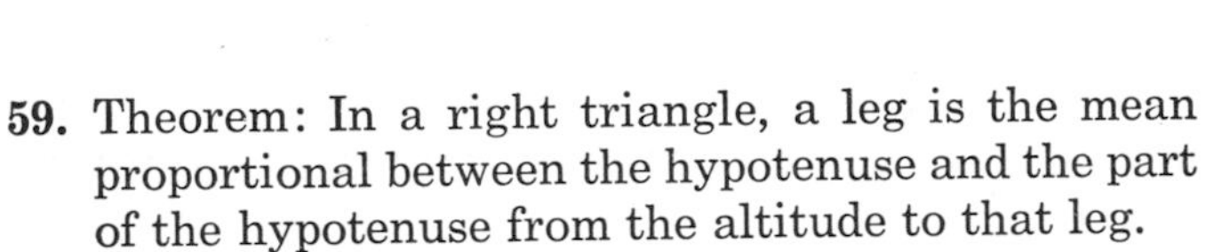

59. Theorem: In a right triangle, a leg is the mean proportional between the hypotenuse and the part of the hypotenuse from the altitude to that leg.

60. Theorem: In a circle, a tangent from a point is the mean proportional between a secant from that point and its external segment.

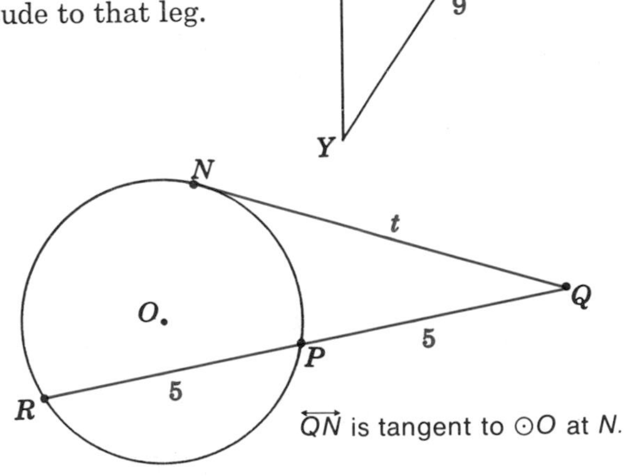

$\overleftrightarrow{QN}$ is tangent to $\odot O$ at N.

61. What does the phrase *square root* have to do with squares as found in geometry?

WHAT IS A REAL NUMBER? 1.9

In a logical system, undefined terms are needed because it is impossible to define all words. In early mathematics courses, other terms are undefined because their definitions might be difficult to understand. Also, common English words and terms from logic (such as *set*, *not*, *and*, *or*, and *if*) will not be defined here.

You have already learned that in this book, *real number*, *addition*, and *multiplication* are undefined. This may surprise you. After all, you have known properties and examples of real numbers for years.

If *real number* is undefined, the big question is: What is a real number? An answer is given in the postulates you have already studied. They are repeated here. Asterisks (*) indicate the six assumed properties that tell *what numbers are real numbers.*

POSTULATES 1–5

There is a set of real numbers and two operations, addition (+) and multiplication (·), so that if a, b, and c are real numbers, then:

1. *A. $a + b$ is a real number.
   B. $(a + b) + c = a + (b + c)$.
   *C. There is a unique real number 0 so that $a + 0 = a$.
   *D. For each a, there is a unique real number $-a$ so that $a + (-a) = 0$.

2. *A. ab is a real number.
   B. $(ab)c = a(bc)$.
   *C. There is a unique real number 1 so that $a \cdot 1 = a$.
   *D. For each nonzero a, there is a unique real number $\frac{1}{a}$ so that $a \cdot \frac{1}{a} = 1$.

3. A. $a + b = b + a$.
   B. $ab = ba$.

4. $a(b + c) = ab + ac$.

5. $a^b \cdot a^c = a^{b+c}$ (b, c integers).

These are **real numbers**	Because of this property:
1	Multiplicative identity (2C)
$1 + 1 = 2, 2 + 1 = 3, 3 + 1 = 4, \cdots$	Closure of addition (1A)
$-1, -2, -3, \cdots$	Additive inverse (1D)
0	Additive identity (1C)
$\cdots, -5, -4, -3, -2, -1, 0, 1, 2, 3, 4, 5, \cdots$	These are the **integers**, used in counting and indexing.
$\cdots, -\frac{1}{5}, -\frac{1}{4}, -\frac{1}{3}, -\frac{1}{2}, \frac{1}{2}, \frac{1}{3}, \frac{1}{4}, \frac{1}{5}, \cdots$	Multiplicative inverse (2D)
all sums and products of the above numbers	Closure (1A and 2A)

These are the **rational numbers**, used in computation and approximation.

There are other real numbers we will work with—numbers like $\sqrt{2}$ and π and $-4.869238914\cdots$—but for these another postulate is needed.

Even though we are not finished stating postulates, we do have enough assumptions to prove many theorems, like the next one, which you have known for years. First we define the terms used in the theorem.

Definitions

The real number $1 + 1$ is called **2**.
Also, $2 + 1 =$ **3**, $3 + 1 =$ **4**, $4 + 1 =$ **5**, $\cdots$

THEOREM: $4 = 2 + 2$

PROOF:	$4 = 3 + 1$	Definition of 4
	$= (2 + 1) + 1$	Definition of 3
	$= 2 + (1 + 1)$	Associativity of addition
	$= 2 + 2$	Definition of 2

Since you know arithmetic by now, we will not prove any other "theorems of arithmetic." There are many other needed properties and only enough space to prove the most important. But we want to give enough postulates so you could (if you wanted to) deduce any property needed in this book. So in the next chapter, we give three more postulates. These indicate:

- how real numbers may be compared (Section 2.1),
- how real numbers may be graphed (Section 2.6), and
- that all decimals are real numbers (Section 2.7).

EXERCISES 1.9

Ⓐ **1.** What is a postulate?

2. Name one statement which is a postulate in this book.

3. What is a theorem?

4. Name one statement not in this section which is a theorem in this book.

5. Why are undefined terms needed in any mathematical system?

6. Name two terms which are normally undefined in geometry.

7. Name two terms which are undefined in this book.

8. Name three postulates which help to tell which numbers may be called real numbers.

Ⓑ **9–12.** Given the postulates, why is each number a real number? (These exercises are related.)

9. 2 **10.** 3 **11.** $\frac{1}{2}$ **12.** $\frac{3}{2}$

13–14. Using the proof that $4 = 2 + 2$ as an example, prove:

13. $5 = 2 + 3$. **14.** $6 = 2 + 4$. (First give a definition for 6.)

Ⓒ **15.** The common words *positive*, *negative*, *rational*, and *real* are used to describe numbers. For each word, give **(a)** a nonmathematical meaning and **(b)** its mathematical meaning.

1

CHAPTER SUMMARY

The major idea of this chapter is that addition of real numbers and multiplication of nonzero real numbers have corresponding (not always identical) properties. First we have the simplest sentences—equations with one operation.

$a + x = b$	$ax = b$
has a unique real solution. To solve it, apply the *associative, closure, identity,* and *inverse* properties, called	has a unique nonzero real solution. To solve it, apply the *associative, closure, identity,* and *inverse* properties, called
the group properties of addition of real numbers.	*the group properties of multiplication of nonzero real numbers.*
An equivalent sentence, $x = b + (-a) = b - a,$ helps to define *subtraction.*	An equivalent sentence, $x = b \cdot \frac{1}{a} = \frac{b}{a},$ helps to define *division.*

Corresponding equations for multiplication and for powers lead to certain corresponding properties and definitions.

Repeated addition leads to the *distributive postulate.*	Repeated multiplication leads to the *power postulate.*
multiples of x ▶ $ax + bx = (a + b)x$	powers of x ▶ $x^a \cdot x^b = x^{a+b}$
0 multiple ▶ $0x = 0$ ◀ additive identity	0 power ▶ $x^0 = 1$ ◀ multiplicative identity
−1 multiple ▶ $-1x = -x$ ◀ additive inverse	−1 power ▶ $x^{-1} = \frac{1}{x}$ ◀ multiplicative inverse
In general, $ax + (-ax) = 0.$	In general, $x^a \cdot x^{-a} = 1.$

	$2x = a$	equation	$x^2 = a$	
halves ▶	$x = \frac{a}{2}$	solution	$x = \sqrt{a}$ or $-\sqrt{a}$	◀ square roots
	$2x = a + b$	equation	$x^2 = ab$	
arithmetic mean ▶	$x = \frac{a + b}{2}$	solution	$x = \sqrt{ab}$ or $-\sqrt{ab}$	◀ geometric means

Halves are added to yield arithmetic means.	Square roots are multiplied to yield geometric means.
$\frac{a}{2} + \frac{b}{2} = \frac{a + b}{2}$	$\sqrt{a} \cdot \sqrt{b} = \sqrt{ab}$
Similarly, $\frac{a}{2} - \frac{b}{2} = \frac{a - b}{2}.$	Similarly, $\frac{\sqrt{a}}{\sqrt{b}} = \sqrt{\frac{a}{b}}.$

Some of these properties are assumed true as *postulates*. These postulates relate the undefined terms *real number*, *addition*, and *multiplication*. Thus a *real number* is any number which satisfies all of the postulates in the chapter (and a few more mentioned in Chapter 2).

From the undefined terms, *definitions* are made. From the postulates and definitions, *theorems* are proved. All of mathematics can be built up in this way. The properties of real numbers you have used (such as $2 + 2 = 4$ or $0 \cdot a = 0$) are all postulates, definitions, or theorems.

CHAPTER REVIEW

1

1. An assumption about the properties of real numbers is a (*definition*, *postulate*, *theorem*).

2. The term (*set*, *real number*, *division*) is not undefined in this book.

3–8. Let $m = -2$, $n = \frac{1}{2}$, and $p = \frac{9}{2}$. Find each of the following.

3. opposite of m
4. arithmetic mean of n and p
5. reciprocal of n
6. geometric means of p and n
7. n^m
8. multiplicative inverse of p

9–20. Name the property illustrated by each statement.

9. $3(a + 2) = 3a + 6$
10. $\sqrt{2} \cdot \sqrt{3} = \sqrt{6}$
11. $2\sqrt{3} = \sqrt{3} \cdot 2$
12. $\frac{1}{4}(\frac{1}{3})$ is a real number.
13. $\frac{1}{3} \cdot 1 = \frac{1}{3}$
14. $3 + (-3) = 0$
15. $5 + (1 + 2) = 5 + (2 + 1)$
16. $2(4a) = 8a$
17. $a^2 \cdot a^n = a^{2+n}$
18. $3 + (4 + 1) = 7 + 1$
19. $0 + 5 = 5$
20. $-\frac{1}{7} \cdot (-7) = 1$

21–23. Approximate to the nearest tenth. (Do not use tables.)

21. $\sqrt{3^2 + 5^2}$
22. $-\sqrt{2700}$
23. $(\frac{3}{5})^{-3}$

24–29. Solve.

24. $0.25 = \frac{1}{x}$
25. $0.06a = 0.3$
26. $\frac{21}{n} = \frac{3}{7}$
27. $0b = 5$
28. $5 - y = 10$
29. $3(x - 5) = 0$

30. When are two sentences equivalent?

31–32. Simplify.

31. $5 \cdot 10^1 + 2 \cdot 10^0$
32. $14 + 3(2^2 + 1) - 6 \cdot 3 + 1$

Chapter 2 Further Properties of Real Numbers

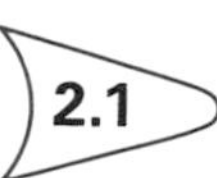

2.1 ORDER AND INEQUALITY

The symbol $<$, meaning "is less than" in English, is taken as undefined in this book. Other symbols, however, are defined using $<$.

Definitions

$\boldsymbol{a \leq b}$	means	$a < b$ or $a = b$.
$\boldsymbol{a > b}$	means	$b < a$.
$\boldsymbol{a \geq b}$	means	$a > b$ or $a = b$.

Given two different real numbers, one is always less than the other. In fact, exactly one of the following holds:

$$a < b \qquad a = b \qquad a > b$$

This property is called the *trichotomy property* (from the Greek, meaning "split into three"). This probably comes from the fact that when $b = 0$, the real numbers are split into three sets: the negative real numbers, zero, and the positive real numbers.

Another order property of real numbers is the *transitive property*.

$$\text{If } a < b \text{ and } b < c, \text{ then } a < c.$$

Transitivity allows you to write $a < b < c$. With trichotomy, it allows you to place the real numbers in an order. In the first row below, several real numbers are ordered from smallest to largest. You could write the symbol < between any two of these numerals.

	-100	0	10^{-3}	1	π	$3\frac{1}{2}$
Adding 10 to each number in row 1 ➡	-90	10	10.001	11	$10 + \pi$	$13\frac{1}{2}$
Adding −25 to each number in row 2 ➡	-115	-15	-14.999	-14	$\pi - 15$	$-11\frac{1}{2}$

In the second and third rows, the numbers still read from smallest to largest. So we say that addition preserves order. Turning to multiplication, we look at the original list and *multiply* each number by 10.

$$-1000 \qquad 0 \qquad 10^{-2} \qquad 10 \qquad 10\pi \qquad 35$$

The order remains the same. (Check it.) But see the results when we multiply each number in the last list by -2.

$$2000 \qquad 0 \qquad -0.02 \qquad -20 \qquad -20\pi \qquad -70$$

The numbers at the left are larger. Multiplication by a negative number *reverses* the order of the list.

We assume the preceding properties. They relate the undefined symbol < to the other undefined terms.

POSTULATE 6: ORDER PROPERTIES

Let a, b, and c be real numbers. Then

trichotomy	Either $a < b$ or $a = b$ or $a > b$, but only one of these.
transitivity	If $a < b$ and $b < c$, then $a < c$.
addition property of order	$a < b$ and $a + c < b + c$ are equivalent sentences.
multiplication properties of order	If c is positive, $a < b$ and $ac < bc$ are equivalent sentences.
	If c is negative, $a < b$ and $ac > bc$ are equivalent sentences.

The order properties can be used to solve inequalities.

Examples:

1. $5 - x < 12$

$-x < 7$ ◀ Add -5.

$x > -7$ ◀ Multiply by -1.

Check: Try -6.

$5 - (-6) < 12$

$11 < 12$ OK

2. $6.09 > 0.03N$

$\frac{1}{0.03}(6.09) > N$ ◀ Multiply by $\frac{1}{0.03}$.

$203 > N$

Check: Try 200.

$6.09 > 0.03(200)$

$6.09 > 6$ OK

In Example **2**, 300 cannot be a solution. If you try 300, you have $6.09 > 0.03(300)$ or $6.09 > 9$, which is a false sentence.

3. The properties of equality and order allow sentences with $\leq$ and $\geq$ to be solved.

$\frac{2t}{3} \geq -1$

$t \geq -\frac{3}{2}$ Multiply by $\frac{3}{2}$.

4. It is even possible to solve two inequalities at once.

$-4 < -8n < 1$

$\frac{1}{2} > n > -\frac{1}{8}$ Multiply by $-\frac{1}{8}$.

This says that any number between $-\frac{1}{8}$ and $\frac{1}{2}$ satisfies the given inequality.

EXERCISES 2.1

Ⓐ **1.** If $x < 4$ and $y > 4$, what property enables you to conclude $x < y$?

2. Choose the correct sentence: $\frac{2}{3} = 0.666$; $\frac{2}{3} < 0.666$; $\frac{2}{3} > 0.666$.

3. What property assures that only one sentence is true in Exercise **2**?

4–12. Which symbol, $<$, $>$, or $=$, should replace each blank?

4. $-4 - 5$ ___ 0 **5.** 2^{-2} ___ 0 **6.** 0.333 ___ $\frac{1}{3}$

7. -0.333 ___ $-\frac{1}{3}$ **8.** $(-\frac{1}{2})(-\frac{2}{3})$ ___ 0 **9.** $(38)(2.4)$ ___ $(38)(2.5)$

10. 8^{-3} ___ 8^{-4} **11.** $(\frac{1}{2})^5$ ___ 1 **12.** If $x > 10$, then $-2x$ ___ -20.

13. What is wrong with this statement? If $x < y$, then $ax < ay$.

14. What does the statement "Addition preserves order" mean?

15. $a > b > c$ is equivalent to $c <$ ___ $<$ ___.

Ⓑ **16.** What is the shorthand for $3 > x$ and $y < x$?

17–25. Solve each sentence. Check your answer in some way.

17. $2z \geq 14$ **18.** $-9t \leq \frac{1}{3}$ **19.** $-x > 0$

20. $\frac{p}{3} < -1$ **21.** $-\frac{4}{3} < \frac{m}{6}$ **22.** $-12 < 2m$

23. $5 \leq x + 7.2$ **24.** $7.2 - y > 5$ **25.** $-m - 4 \leq -3$

26. If $3 < n + 1 < 3.1$, then ___ $< n <$ ___.

27. If $3v$ is between -10 and -20, then v is between ___ and ___.

28. If $15 > x > 8$, then $11 <$ ___ < 18.

Ⓒ **29–34.** Solve.

29. $2.99 < 2x < 3.01$ **30.** $-8 \geq y - 1.2 \geq -40$

31. $100 \leq 9 - W < 61$ **32.** $-\frac{5}{7} \leq \frac{2}{3} + t \leq -\frac{4}{11}$

33. $3 + x < 47 < 8 + x$ **34.** $x - 4 > 2 > x - 5$

35–38. Which symbol, $<$, $>$, or $=$, should replace each blank?

35. $\frac{41}{29}$ ___ $\sqrt{2}$ **36.** $\sqrt{3}$ ___ $\frac{26}{15}$ **37.** 3.14 ___ π **38.** $3\frac{1}{7}$ ___ π

LINEAR SENTENCES

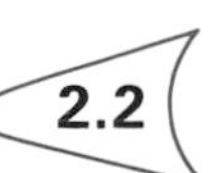

Until now, each sentence we have discussed has involved only one operation. But it is common for more than one operation to be used. As simple a sentence as

$$2 - 3y = 5$$

uses both subtraction and multiplication. (y is multiplied by 3, the product is subtracted from 2, and the difference is 5.) Often problems in real situations lead to such sentences.

Examples:

1. A certain phone company charges \$8.60 a month for the first 80 calls and $4\frac{3}{4}$ cents each for the next 120 calls. If a person's phone bill is \$11.12, how many calls were made?

   Translation: Let n be the number of calls *above 80* used.

   In pennies: $860 + 4.75n = 1112$

   - 860 ↑ cost for 80 calls
   - $4.75n$ ↑ cost for n calls over 80
   - 1112 ↑ total cost

2. A newspaper reports that 48% of people surveyed prefer candidate A. The rest prefer candidate B. Is it possible that *only one* more person prefers B than A?

   Translation: Let x be the total number of people surveyed. Then $0.48x$ prefer A, $0.52x$ prefer B. We are asking: Does this sentence have a solution which is an integer?

$$\underbrace{0.52x}_{\text{number who prefer B}} - \underbrace{0.48x}_{\text{number who prefer A}} = 1$$

Notice that numbers used in real situations are not always so simple. But the processes used in earlier problems still apply to these problems. Also notice that (as in Example **2**) sometimes we do not care about finding all solutions. We only want to know if there is a solution.

Sometimes more than one unknown is needed. Sometimes we are only interested in particular solutions. Sometimes inequalities are needed. Each of these is in the next situation.

3. In a sale, all pairs of shoes are reduced to \$4.99, all skirts to \$8.99, and blouses to \$2.49. How many combinations of these could be bought for \$20.00 or less?

   Translation: Let s be the number of pairs of shoes bought.
   Let k be the number of skirts bought.
   Let b be the number of blouses bought.

   We want to know how many solutions this inequality has. s, k, and b must be nonnegative integers.

$$\underset{\substack{\uparrow \\ \text{cost of } s \\ \text{pairs of shoes}}}{4.99s} + \underset{\substack{\uparrow \\ \text{cost of } k \\ \text{skirts}}}{8.99k} + \underset{\substack{\uparrow \\ \text{cost of } b \\ \text{blouses}}}{2.49b} \leq 20.00$$

All three situations involve unknowns which are raised only to the first power. Such expressions are called *linear expressions*.

$$3x + 5 \qquad 9x - 4y + 2 \qquad \frac{x}{2} - 8.3z \qquad 8y$$

When linear expressions only are used in sentences, the sentences are called *linear sentences*.

$$3x + 5 \geq 9x - 4y + 2 \qquad \frac{x}{2} - 8.3z = 0.5 \qquad 2x = 4$$

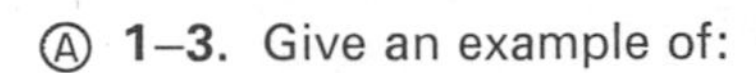

EXERCISES 2.2

Ⓐ **1–3.** Give an example of:

1. a linear expression.

2. a linear sentence.

3. a sentence that is not linear.

4–7. True or False?

4. Occasionally you may not be interested in solving a linear sentence, but only in determining whether or not there is a solution.

5. Every linear sentence has exactly one solution.

6. A linear sentence may have more than one unknown.

7. The multiplicative identity is a solution to $\frac{3 - x}{2} = 5x - 4$.

8–11. Each sentence has a solution which is an integer between -2 and 4, inclusive. By trial and error find this solution.

8. $7m - 8 = \frac{39}{m}$

9. $7 - P = 3P + 15$

10. $q^{14} = 2q^{11}$

11. $3^R = \frac{-R}{18}$

12–13. x and y both stand for integers between -9 and -11, inclusive. By trial and error solve for x and y.

12. $x - 2 = y$

13. $xy = 99$

Ⓑ **14.** If one pencil costs 5¢, what is the cost of p pencils?

15. The cost of one shirt is x dollars and of one belt is y dollars. What is the cost of 10 shirts and 3 belts?

16. A school contains b boys and g girls. 80% of the boys plan to go to college; 75% of the girls plan to go to college. Write a mathematical expression for the number of students who plan to go to college.

17–20. Pick the larger of the two numbers.

17. $3x + 100$; $3x + 99$

18. $4y - 100$; $4y - 99$

19. $100 - 8x$; $80 - 8x$

20. $-3x + 5$; $-3x - 2$

21–26. Solve each linear sentence in your head.

21. $3F + 5 = 30005$	**22.** $6000 = 6(V - 3)$
23. $378T = 377T + 14$	**24.** $79m - 472 = 138m - 472$
25. $410 - x = 10 - x$	**26.** $4y - 3 = -(3 - 4y)$

27–30. Substitute a number for each unknown to give a solution for each linear inequality.

27. $3x + 2y \leq -1$	**28.** $-6 > 5z - w$
29. $a + 4b < 3a$	**30.** $0 < 3u - 4v < 1$

© **31.** A survey indicates that 4% of 28 people polled favor product M over product N. If the survey rounds the percentage to the nearest integer, how many people polled preferred product M?

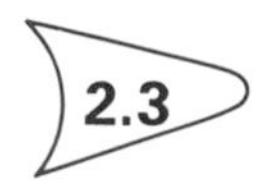

SOLVING LINEAR SENTENCES

A linear expression such as $-4 + 3x$ can be obtained as shown at the left below. Once you have $-4 + 3x$, you can use inverses and the same operations in reverse order to obtain x again.

	x	Reverse process:	$-4 + 3x$
Multiply by 3:	$3x$	Add 4:	$3x$
Add -4:	$-4 + 3x$	Multiply by $\frac{1}{3}$:	x

The process at the right above can be used in equations and inequalities. It converts sentences involving the expression $-4 + 3x$ into equivalent sentences which involve x.

Example: Two different but similarly solved sentences

a.		**b.**
$-4 + 3x = 7$		$17 \leq -4 + 3Q$
$3x = 11$	Add 4 to each side.	$21 \leq 3Q$
$x = \frac{11}{3}$	Multiply each side by $\frac{1}{3}$.	$7 \leq Q$

Check: Try $\frac{11}{3}$.

$-4 + 3 \cdot \frac{11}{3} = -4 + 11 = 7$ OK

Check: Try numbers 7 or larger.

$17 \leq -4 + 3 \cdot 7 = 17$ OK

$17 \leq -4 + 3 \cdot 82 = 242$ OK

In some sentences, the unknown appears on both sides of the equation. An appropriate addition can be made to simplify.

Example: Solve: $2 - 4y = 17 + 3y$

Add $4y$: $2 - 4y + 4y = 17 + 3y + 4y$

$2 = 17 + 7y$

This equation is of the earlier form and can easily be solved.

Add -17: $-15 = 7y$

Multiply by $\frac{1}{7}$: $\frac{-15}{7} = y$

Would the process have changed if the $=$ sign were replaced by $<$? The answer is "No," for at no time were both sides multiplied by a *negative* number.

Here is an example which does have a change in order.

Example: Solve: $4z + 9 < 6z - 14$

Add $-6z$: $-2z + 9 < -14$

Add -9: $-2z < -23$

Multiply by $-\frac{1}{2}$: $z > \frac{23}{2}$ (Notice the inequality is switched.)

You can check any number larger than $\frac{23}{2}$ in the original sentence.

Sentences should be solved one line at a time. So you should concentrate on how to convert a sentence into a simpler equivalent sentence. If you can do this well enough, sentence solving will be automatic.

Examples: Obtaining simpler equivalent sentences

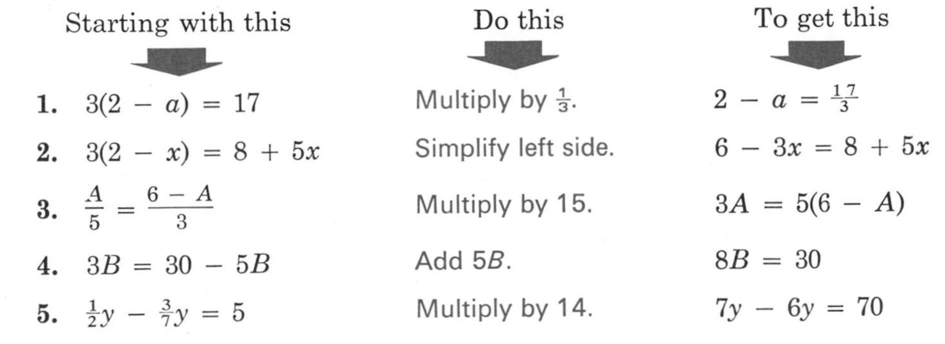

	Starting with this	Do this	To get this
1.	$3(2 - a) = 17$	Multiply by $\frac{1}{3}$.	$2 - a = \frac{17}{3}$
2.	$3(2 - x) = 8 + 5x$	Simplify left side.	$6 - 3x = 8 + 5x$
3.	$\frac{A}{5} = \frac{6 - A}{3}$	Multiply by 15.	$3A = 5(6 - A)$
4.	$3B = 30 - 5B$	Add $5B$.	$8B = 30$
5.	$\frac{1}{2}y - \frac{3}{7}y = 5$	Multiply by 14.	$7y - 6y = 70$

Finally, note two special situations.

6. $-3(4 - 2x) = 6x + 2$

$-12 + 6x = 6x + 2$

$-12 = 2$ (never true)

So *no number* works.

7. $2A \leq 2A + 1$

$0 \leq 1$ (always true)

So *any number* works.

EXERCISES 2.3

Ⓐ **1.** What can be done to both sides of a sentence which will give an equivalent sentence?

2. In solving a sentence, when do you have to change $<$ to $>$?

3–6. A girl solved $9y - 8 \leq 3 - 10y$. What did she do in each step?

3. $19y - 8 \leq 3$

4. $19y \leq 11$

5. $y \leq \frac{11}{19}$

6. $19 \cdot 0 - 8 = -8 \leq 3$

7–10. A sentence and a direction are given. Tell what sentence results.

7. $M \leq 3M$; add $-M$.

8. $\frac{x}{2} - 9 = 3$; multiply by 2.

9. $3(2y + 9) < 7y - 2$; apply distributivity.

10. $-v \geq -4$; multiply by -1.

11–30. In each sentence, tell what might be done to find a simpler equivalent sentence. Give the simpler equivalent sentence.

11. $4t + 10 = -2$

12. $9 - 2x = -8$

13. $v - 3 = v + 10$

14. $19 - 3m < 19 - 4m$

15. $2(x + 1) \geq 3(1 - 4x)$

16. $y - 10 = 4 + 3y$

17. $9(z - 2) + 3z < 400$

18. $y - 10 < 4 + 3y$

19. $\frac{3}{2}t + \frac{2}{5}t = 17$

20. $-(z + 2) + 3z \geq 2z$

21. $\frac{d}{9} \leq 3(d - 5) + 6$

22. $-4x - 8 - 3x = 14x - 16$

23. $A^2 + 3A - \pi \leq A^2$

24. $17(B - 5) = \frac{B}{2} + 3$

25. $\frac{3c - 3}{2} = \frac{c + 4}{5}$

26. $-1 \geq 4E + \sqrt{2}$

27. $1 - \frac{2F - 1}{3} > F$

28. $3.7 - \frac{G + 6}{2} = -1.7$

29. $\frac{v + 2}{3} < \frac{2 - 4v}{6}$

30. $\frac{w}{9} = \frac{w}{3} + 2$

Ⓑ **31–50.** Solve the sentences of Exercises **11–30**. Check all answers.

51–58. Solve and check.

51. $H \le 5H$

52. $-2x = -3x$

53. $-1 - x > -(2 + x)$

54. $0.03t - 5 = 103$

55. $2.19w + 6 = 2.21w - 9$

56. $\frac{2v - 8}{3} = \frac{5 - 4v}{-6} + 158629$

57. $\frac{7}{9} - \frac{3K}{2} \le \frac{5K}{6}$

58. $-L - 8L = 3(2L - 5)$

59–62. The solution of each equation may help you with the next. Solve.

59. $13x = -156$

60. $13(y - 217) = -156$

61. $13\left(\frac{z}{8} - 217\right) = -156$

62. $13\left(\frac{w + 61}{8} - 217\right) = -156$

Ⓒ **63–66.** Solve and check.

63. $\frac{a + 2}{3} - \frac{4 - 3a}{6} \ge \frac{2(4 - a)}{7}$

64. $B - \frac{B - 1}{2} = \frac{2B - 6}{3}$

65. $9 \le \frac{2B - 3}{2} + 6 \le 13$

66. $-a > -(-a)$

67–69. Copy and complete each sentence. Then prove the sentence.

67. If $3(T - 1) + 10 = 14 + 6T$, then $9T + 21 =$ ____.

68. If $2x + 4 < -10 < 2x + 9$, then x is between ____ and ____.

69. If $\frac{a}{b} \cdot \frac{c}{d} = -1$, then $ac + bd =$ ____.

70. Paula and her brother have \$100 in a savings account, and they plan to deposit \$25 each week. In how many weeks will they have enough to buy a motorcycle that costs \$800? How much will they save in w weeks?

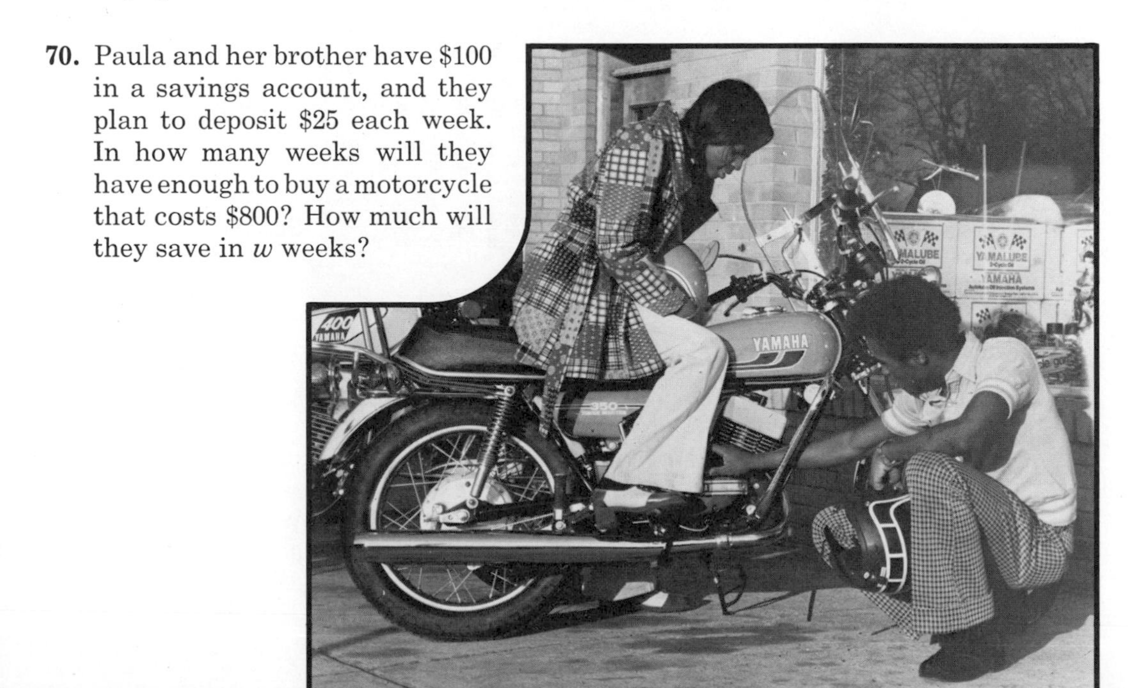

2.4 SENTENCE–SOLVING INVOLVING TWO OR MORE VARIABLES

Let us consider the equation

$$4(m + 2) + \frac{m + 2}{5} = 8 + 5(m + 2).$$

This equation can be simplified by substituting x for $m + 2$.

$$4x + \frac{x}{5} = 8 + 5x$$

Solving (you should fill in the details), we find

$$x = -10.$$

But it is m we want to find. So, substituting back $m + 2$ for x,

$$m + 2 = -10$$
$$m = -12.$$

Check: $\quad 4(-12 + 2) + \frac{-12 + 2}{5} = 8 + 5(-12 + 2)$

$$-40 + (-2) = 8 + (-50) \qquad \text{OK}$$

You could have solved the equation above without a substitution, but it might have been harder for you. Here is another sentence which you might find difficult to solve.

$$\frac{5}{3x - 9} - 3 = \frac{11}{3x - 9}$$

Now we let $y = \frac{1}{3x - 9}$. Then

$$5y - 3 = 11y.$$

This is a linear sentence, and it is easy to solve.

$$-\frac{1}{2} = y$$

$$-\frac{1}{2} = \frac{1}{3x - 9} \qquad \text{Substituting back}$$

$$-2 = 3x - 9$$

$$7 = 3x$$

$$\frac{7}{3} = x$$

If a variable in a sentence *always* appears in the same expression, a substitution for that expression *may* make it easier to solve the sentence.

So sometimes it is easier to introduce a second variable into a problem rather than to solve the problem with only one variable. Here is a third example.

1. Given: $(A + 9)^2 = 11$

2. We let $B = A + 9$: $B^2 = 11$

3. This is easy to solve: $B = \sqrt{11}$ or $B = -\sqrt{11}$

4. Substituting back: $A + 9 = \sqrt{11}$ or $A + 9 = -\sqrt{11}$

5. This is also easy: $A = -9 + \sqrt{11}$ or $A = -9 - \sqrt{11}$

You may not need to substitute to solve the above problem. You can go from Step 1 to Step 4 in your head. This is fine as long as you know what you are doing.

Some sentences contain two or more variables to begin with, and you must solve for one of them.

Solve for a: $a + b + c = 180$

Adding $-c$ and $-b$: $a = 180 + (-c) + (-b)$

$a = 180 - c - b$

We say that we have found *a in terms of b and c.*

Examples: Solving for one variable in terms of others

1. Solve for x in terms of y:

$$8x - 7y < 15$$

$$8x < 15 + 7y$$

$$x < \frac{15 + 7y}{8}$$

2. Solve for y in terms of x:

$$8x - 7y < 15$$

$$-7y < 15 - 8x$$

$$y > \frac{15 - 8x}{-7}$$

3. Solve for t: $d = rt$

$$\frac{d}{r} = t$$

4. Solve for h: $A = \frac{1}{2}hb$

$$2A = hb$$

$$\frac{2A}{b} = h$$

Examples **3** and **4** use formulas. Many formulas have more than one variable and can be treated by the same methods used in this and other sections.

EXERCISES 2.4

Ⓐ **1–4.** What substitution might aid in solving each sentence?

1. $3(x - 5) - 4 \geq 9(x - 5)$

2. $\frac{3}{y} = 7 - \frac{2}{y}$

3. $(3m + 8)^2 = 4$

4. $4P - 2 = \frac{4P - 2}{3}$

5. In the sentence $A = \frac{s^2\sqrt{3}}{4}$, ___ is solved in terms of ___.

6. In the formula $c = \pi d$, ___ is solved in terms of ___.

7. Solve for d: $c = \pi d$.

8. Solve for b: $V = abc$.

9–10. Tell what sentence results from the given substitution.

9. $\frac{4}{t + 3} - 8 = \frac{6}{3 + t}$ Substitute x for $\frac{1}{t + 3}$.

10. $98 = 2(\frac{3}{2} - v)^2$ Substitute m for $\frac{3}{2} - v$.

Ⓑ **11–18.** Solve each sentence for the given variable.

11. $3x - y \geq 2$ for y

12. $0 \geq 9v - 3w + 6$ for v

13. $\frac{1}{2}(e + f) = g$ for f

14. $4m - 2p = 2(3m - p)$ for m

15. $\frac{9}{A} - \frac{2}{3} = \frac{5}{3A}$ for A

16. $(q - 5)^2 = 2$ for q

17. $(8 + 3x)^2 = 9$ for x

18. $az + bz = c$ for z

19–20. Solve the sentences of Exercises **9–10**.

21–24. Solve the sentences of Exercises **1–4**.

"I think, Mr. Fahrenheit, that most people know when it's hot or cold enough to take off their coat or light a fire."

25–27. The formula $C = \frac{5}{9}(F - 32)$ relates Celsius (centigrade) and Fahrenheit temperatures. (The U.S. is one of the few countries using Fahrenheit temperatures.)

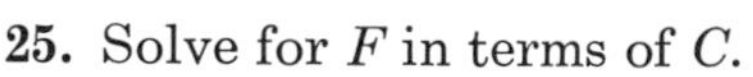

25. Solve for F in terms of C.

26. (Use Exercise **25**.) Give the Fahrenheit equivalents.

a. $-70°$ C **b.** $-40°$ C **c.** $0°$ C **d.** $30°$ C **e.** $40°$ C

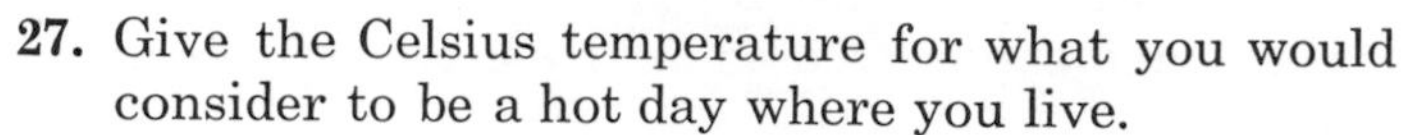

27. Give the Celsius temperature for what you would consider to be a hot day where you live.

28. In a trapezoid, $A = \frac{1}{2}(b_1 + b_2)h$. Interpret the letters and solve for b_2 in terms of the other variables.

29–30. Let S be the sum of the measures of the interior angles of an n-gon. Then $S = 180(n - 2)$.

29. Solve for n in terms of S.

30. (Use Exercise **29.**) How many sides has a polygon if $S = 1440$?

© **31–36.** Let t be the time (in seconds) that it takes a car to travel one mile and r be the speed of the car (in mph). Then $tr = 3600$.

31. Solve for r in terms of t.

32. Solve for t in terms of r.

33. How long does it take a car to travel one mile at 50 mph? 45 mph? 65 mph?

34. How long does it take a car to travel k miles at 50 mph?

35. A car travels a measured mile in 55 seconds. What is the average speed of the car?

36. A car travels a measured mile in t seconds. What is the average speed of the car?

37. A person presently has x record albums and buys at most 3 albums a month. In m months, at most how many albums will the person own? Let y be the number of albums owned at the end of m months. What sentence is satisfied by x, m, and y?

38. Solve for x: $\frac{9}{(3x + 1)^2} = 2 + \frac{1}{(3x + 1)^2}$.

39. How can you check your answer to a problem like that in Exercise **13, 14,** or **18**?

THE FOIL THEOREM 2.5

Some substitutions can change simple sentences into more complicated ones. One such substitution in the distributive property yields a very important theorem concerning the multiplication of sums.

We know $(a + b)x = ax + bx$.

What happens if $c + d$ is substituted for x?

$$\begin{aligned}(a + b)(c + d) &= a(c + d) + b(c + d) \\ &= ac + ad + bc + bd\end{aligned}$$

The name of this theorem should help you remember it.

Theorem 2.5.1

FOIL theorem: The product of $a + b$ and $c + d$ is the sum of

ac (First terms)
ad (Outside terms)
bc (Inside terms)
and bd (Last terms)

That is, $(a + b)(c + d) = ac + ad + bc + bd$.

Examples: Applying the FOIL theorem

1. $(x + 4)(x + 3) = x^2 + 3x + 4x + 12 = x^2 + 7x + 12$
2. $(2 - 4a)(3b + 5) = 6b + 10 - 12ab - 20a$
3. $(2y - 9)(4y + 18) = 8y^2 + 36y - 36y - 162 = 8y^2 - 162$

A nice geometric interpretation of the FOIL theorem is with areas of rectangles.

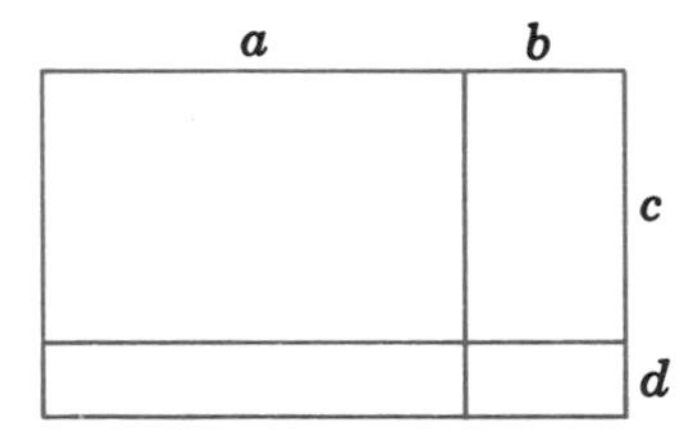

The large rectangle has dimensions $a + b$ by $c + d$, so its area is:

$$(a + b)(c + d).$$

But the four smaller rectangles have areas ac, ad, bc, and bd. Adding these gives the area of the larger rectangle.

An expression, like $3x - 146$, which is the sum (or difference) of two terms is called a **binomial.** Thus the FOIL theorem and the examples show how two binomials may be multiplied.

If the binomials to be multiplied are the same, then multiplication is really the same as squaring the one binomial.

Corollary 2.5.2

$$(x + y)^2 = x^2 + 2xy + y^2$$

PROOF: $(x + y)^2 = (x + y)(x + y) = x^2 + xy + yx + y^2$
$= x^2 + 2xy + y^2$

Examples: Squaring binomials

1. $(x - 3)^2 = x^2 - 6x + 9$ 2. $(2a + 3b)^2 = 4a^2 + 12ab + 9b^2$

Notice that $(x + y)^2$ does *not* simplify to $x^2 + y^2$.

An expression which is the sum of three terms is called a **trinomial.** The distributive property can be generalized to cover these expressions. Each term of one trinomial must be multiplied by every term of the other, and the products added.

$$(a + b + c)(x + y + z) =$$
$$ax + ay + az + bx + by + bz + cx + cy + cz$$

The same idea applies to sums of even more terms. These sums, as well as binomials and trinomials, are called **polynomials.**

Examples: Multiplying polynomials

1. $(2x - 3y + 5)(x + y) = 2x^2 + 2xy - 3yx - 3y^2 + 5x + 5y$
$= 2x^2 - xy - 3y^2 + 5x + 5y$

2. $4(9a - b + c - 10) = 36a - 4b + 4c - 40$

EXERCISES 2.5

Ⓐ **1–3.** Give an example of a:

1. binomial. **2.** trinomial.

3. polynomial which is neither a binomial nor a trinomial.

4. What property is basic in proving the FOIL theorem?

5. Describe the FOIL theorem. Explain how this theorem gets its name.

Ⓑ **6–14.** Express the product as a single polynomial.

6. $(x - 4)(x + 5)$ **7.** $(3a + 1)(3a + 2)$ **8.** $(3 + c)(2c - 4)$

9. $(4 - y)(2 - y)$ **10.** $(\frac{1}{2} - z)(z + \frac{1}{2})$ **11.** $(2x + 1)(2x - 1)$

12. $(x - y)(x + y)$ **13.** $(3a + 4b)(a - 2)$ **14.** $(10 - 8)(17 - 14)$

15–17. Square each binomial.

15. $x + y$ **16.** $2y - 3$ **17.** $a - b$

18–20. Write as a polynomial.

18. $(3 + 3a)^2$ **19.** $(10t + u)^2$ **20.** $(x - 2y)^2$

21. Verify the FOIL theorem with the binomials $50 + 8$ and $60 + 7$. Check your work by multiplying by more usual methods.

22–28. Let $A = 3x - 2y$, $B = x + y$, $C = x - y$. Calculate.

22. AB **23.** BA **24.** BC **25.** $(AB)C$

26. $A(BC)$ **27.** $AB + AC$ **28.** $A(B + C)$

29. How can you check your work in problems such as Exercises **6–20**?

30. Applying the FOIL theorem: $(x + 4)(x + 3) = x^2 + 7x + 12$. Find 5 values of x for which this sentence is true.

31–32. What binomial must be squared to obtain each given trinomial?

31. $x^2 + 2x + 1$ **32.** $4y^2 - 12y + 9$

33. Show that it is not always true that $(x + 2)^2 = x^2 + 4$ by finding a value of x for which the statement is not true.

34. Solve for x: $x^2 + 4 = (x + 2)^2$.

35. True or False? $(-3 - x)^2 = (x + 3)^2$ for *all* values of x.

© **36.** What should m be if $x^2 + mx + 9$ is to be the square of a binomial?

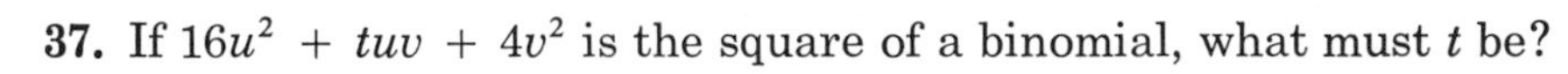

1 x

x

5

37. If $16u^2 + tuv + 4v^2$ is the square of a binomial, what must t be?

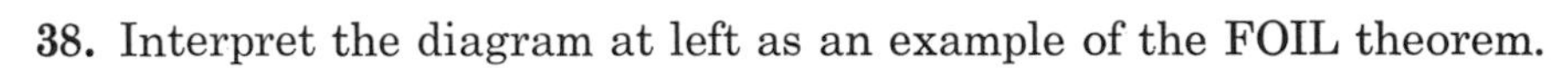

38. Interpret the diagram at left as an example of the FOIL theorem.

39. Make a rectangle diagram to give a picture of Corollary 2.5.2.

40. Multiply $3a - 4b + c$ by $2a + 6c - 11$.

41. Multiply $a + b + c + d$ by $a - b + c - d$.

42. Write as a single polynomial: $(4y + x)(2x - y)(3x + 5y)$.

43. Solve for a in terms of x: $(x + 3)(a + 1) = 2x$.

44. Solve for x in terms of a: $(x + 3)(a + 1) = 2x$.

45. Solve for y: $(2 - y)(3 - 6y) \leq (2y + 5)(3y - 4)$.

46. Use a dictionary, if necessary, to interpret the following statement: The acronym FOIL is a mnemonic device.

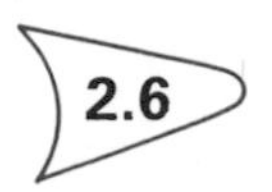

2.6 REAL NUMBER LINES AND ONE–TO–ONE CORRESPONDENCES

The postulates of real numbers stated in previous sections have all involved relationships between numbers and operations. We now turn to a postulate of a different type—a postulate which enables us to picture or graph real numbers.

POSTULATE 7: RULER POSTULATE

There is a one-to-one (abbreviated 1–1) correspondence between the points of any line and the real numbers.

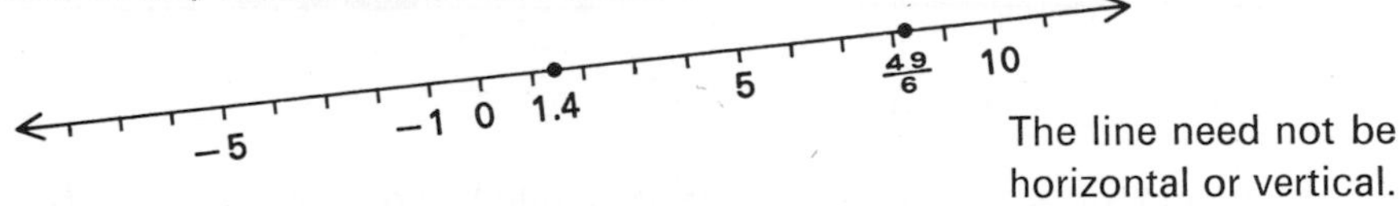

The line need not be horizontal or vertical.

When the corresponding real numbers are identified with points on the line, the line is *coordinatized*, and the real numbers are called *coordinates*. The line is called a *real number line*. There are many ways to coordinatize lines. In fact,

(1) *any* point may be given coordinate 0, and

(2) *any* other point may be given coordinate 1.

But lines are *always* coordinatized so that

(3) if $a < b < c$, then the point for b is between the points for a and c.

And *usually* (but not always) lines are coordinatized so that

(4) the scale does not vary.

Solution sets to sentences are often pictured on number lines. Here are examples:

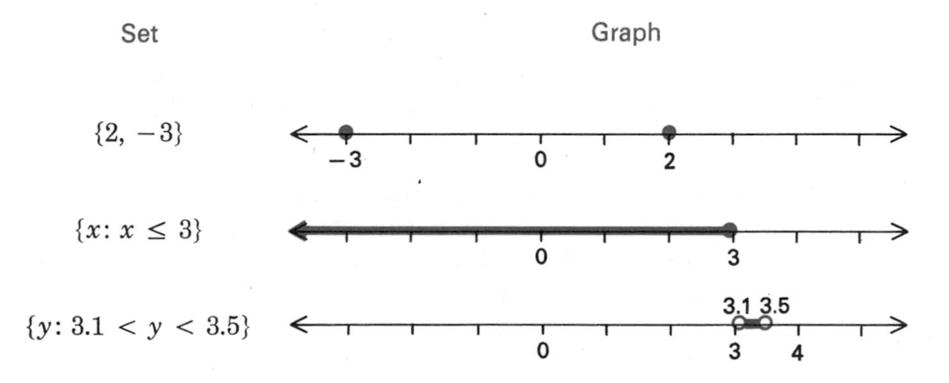

The solution set to $\{y: 3.1 < y < 3.5\}$ is one example of an *interval*. Intervals are important in applications which involve estimates.

Definition

An **interval** is the set of numbers between two given numbers a and b, perhaps including a or b.

We call a and b the *endpoints* of the interval whether or not they are included.

Here are graphs of two intervals. The small circle indicates that an endpoint is *not* included.

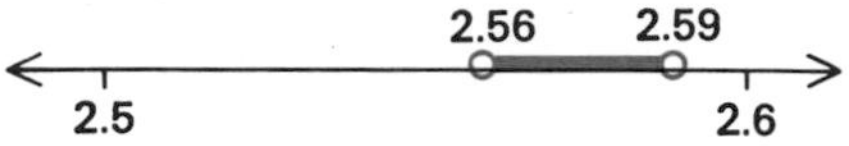

2.56 2.59
2.5 2.6

$\{x: 2.56 < x < 2.59\}$

m n

$\{y: m \leq y \leq n\}$

Elements of sets are often corresponded. For sets A and B, the arrows indicate a 1–1 correspondence between their elements.

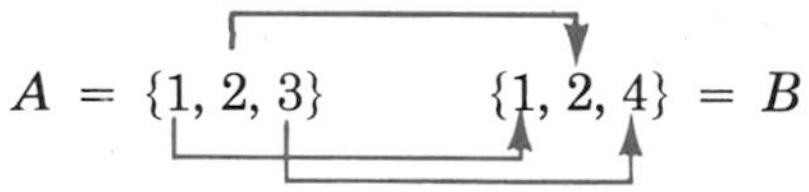

$$A = \{1, 2, 3\} \qquad \{1, 2, 4\} = B$$

The correspondence between sets A and B can also be written in table form as follows.

column form

A	B
1	1
2	2
3	4

row form

A	1	2	3
B	1	2	4

The sets A and B can be put into 1–1 correspondence in a *different* way.

A	1	2	3
B	2	4	1

There can be many 1–1 correspondences between two sets. For example, there are many 1–1 correspondences between all points of a line and all real numbers.

There also can be 1–1 correspondences between infinite sets. Here is a 1–1 correspondence between set P, the set of positive integers, and set E, the set of even positive integers. This 1–1 correspondence may surprise you because E is a subset of P.

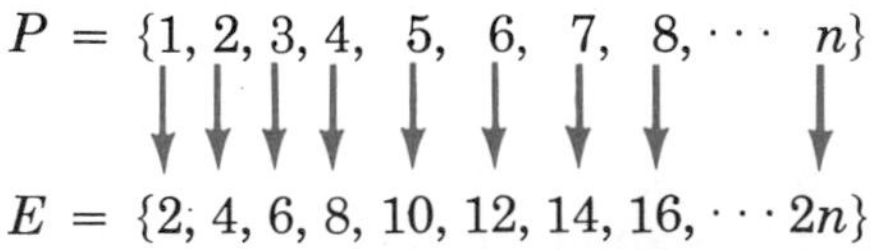

$$P = \{1, 2, 3, 4, 5, 6, 7, 8, \cdots n\}$$
$$\downarrow \quad \downarrow \quad \downarrow \quad \downarrow \quad \downarrow \quad \downarrow \quad \downarrow \quad \downarrow \qquad \downarrow$$
$$E = \{2, 4, 6, 8, 10, 12, 14, 16, \cdots 2n\}$$

The arrows connecting n and $2n$ indicate the *rule of correspondence.* That is, the number n in P corresponds to twice the number, or $2n$, in E.

Here are two examples of 1–1 correspondences between the set of real numbers and itself. The rules $x \rightarrow x + 1$ and $x \rightarrow -x$ indicate what elements correspond. Under the rules are given examples of corresponding elements.

Example 1:

The "adding one" correspondence

x	$\rightarrow$	$x + 1$
2		3
$3.14\cdots$		$4.14\cdots$
-7		-6
0		1
$\vdots$		$\vdots$

Example 2:

The "oppositing" correspondence

x	$\rightarrow$	$-x$
2		-2
-95.5		95.5
0		0
$-\frac{1}{2}$		$\frac{1}{2}$
$\vdots$		$\vdots$

EXERCISES 2.6

Ⓐ **1.** There is a one-to-one correspondence between the points of a line and _____.

2. When is a line called a "real number line"?

3. Which sentence's solution set is pictured here?

a. $-200 < p < 17$ **b.** $-200 < p \leq 17$

c. $-200 \leq p \leq 17$ **d.** $-200 \leq p < 17$

4. What is an interval?

5–7. Graph the solution set to each sentence.

5. $x > 3$ **6.** $-9 < y < -\frac{1}{2}$ **7.** $z \leq 5$

8–9. Graph each set.

8. $\{x: x^2 = 4\}$ **9.** $\{m: -3.01 > m > -3.02\}$

10. Write the correspondence between sets S and T in column form.

$$S = \{1, 2, 3, 4, \cdots\} \qquad T = \{1, 3, 5, 7, \cdots\}$$

11. Which of these might be the rule of correspondence for the 1–1 correspondence between sets S and T of Exercise **10**?

a. $n \rightarrow 2n$ **b.** $n \rightarrow 2n - 1$ **c.** $n \rightarrow 2n + 1$ **d.** $n \rightarrow n + 2$

12. Give a rule for a 1–1 correspondence between the set of integers and the set of even integers.

13. Suppose there is a 1–1 correspondence between sets A and B. If A has 10 elements, must B also have 10 elements?

Ⓑ 14. A thermometer has an accuracy of 0.2 degrees. If the thermometer shows 98.7, in what interval is the actual temperature t?

15. A caliper measures widths with an accuracy of 0.0005 cm. A rod is shown to have width 3.2461 cm. If w is the actual width of the rod, what sentence must w satisfy?

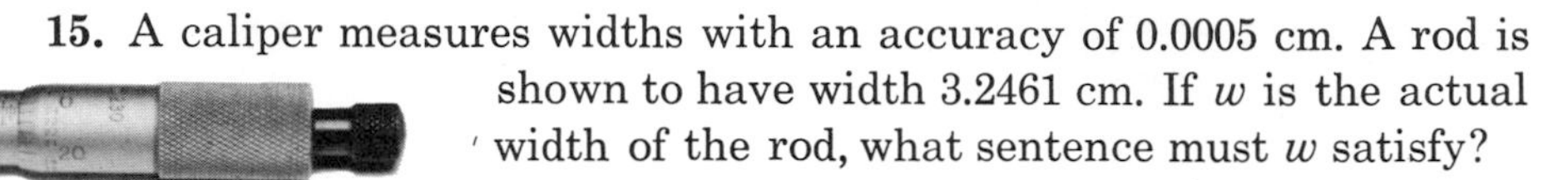

16. A town census is said to have accuracy to within 10%. If the census indicates a population of 23,812 for the town, and p is the true population of the town, what sentence must p satisfy?

17. Suppose that the U.S. Census is accurate to within 3% (not an unreasonable guess). If the U.S. population is estimated as 215 million, by how much might the actual population differ from the U.S. Census estimate?

18–21. Find a rule for a 1–1 correspondence between the two given sets. (Remember that elements do not have to correspond in the order given.) There are many possible answers to each question.

18. $\{1, 2, 3, 4, 5\}$, $\{-5, -4, -3, -1, -2\}$

19. $\{70, 80, 100\}$, $\{9, 39, 29\}$

20. $\{6, 4, 11, 12\}$, $\{1.2, 0.4, 0.6, 1.1\}$

21. $\{2, 5, 6\}$, $\{10, 30, 25\}$

22–37. Solve each sentence and graph the solution set.

22. $\frac{x + 2}{3} > 1$

23. $0.4 \le 2(5 + y)$

24. $9z - 9 \le 9$

25. $3A - 5A \le 1$

26. $3 + 4x \ge 2x - 7$

27. $y - 19 < 23 + y$

28. $4(2 - z) + 3z < 4$

29. $371 \ge 14m - 3(m - 10)$

30. $-(5 - 6t) < 1$

31. $-1.7 \le u - (2 + u)$

32. $0 < 9(W - 3)$

33. $86 > 10V + 6 > 87$

Ⓒ 34. $10 < 9 - 10A < 12$

35. $0.001 \le 100B \le 0.0013$

36. $\frac{6}{7} \ge \frac{-C}{40} > 10$

37. $\frac{1}{2} \le -\frac{B + 1}{4} < \frac{3}{2}$

38. Two sets each have three elements. How many different 1–1 correspondences exist between their elements?

39. Repeat Exercise 38 for two sets with four elements each.

40. Physical models of parts of number lines are found on rulers and thermometers. Give a third place where physical models of parts of number lines may be found.

41. True or False? The intersection of two intervals is an interval. Explain your answer.

REAL NUMBERS AND SUCCESSIVE APPROXIMATIONS

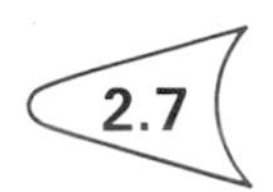

Suppose you have a scale for measuring weights and it is calibrated (marked off) in pounds. You have a small rock that you want to weigh. When you put it on the scale, it shows that the weight of the rock is between 5 and 6 pounds.

Maybe this is not good enough, so you find a more accurate scale—perhaps one of the new food-store scales—which shows that the weight of the rock is between 5.42 and 5.43 pounds.

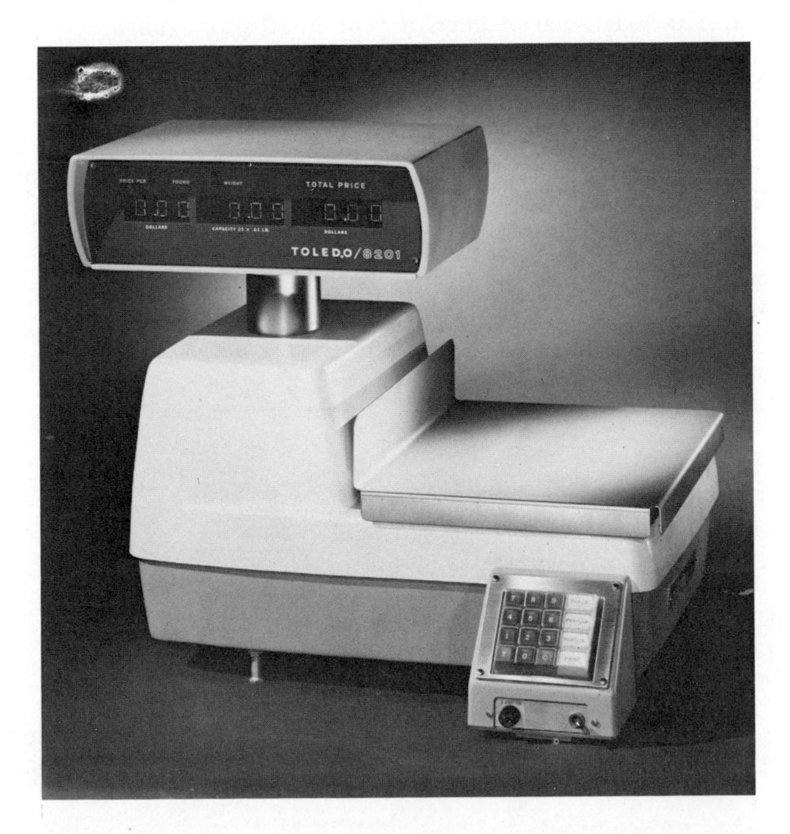

So what is the weight of the rock? This is not an easy question. No matter how accurate a scale is, it does not measure exactly. The weight always lies in some interval whose size depends on the accuracy of the scale. For the previous example, the intervals are

Interval 1: $5 < \text{weight} < 6$

Interval 2: $5.42 < \text{weight} < 5.43$

Because the second interval lies inside the first, we call it *nested* in the first interval. A still more accurate scale might give a third interval which is nested in the first two.

Interval 3: $5.42 < \text{weight} < 5.423$

When intervals are listed in an order, with each interval nested in the previous ones, a *sequence of nested intervals* is said to be formed. In successive approximation by better and better measuring devices, such a sequence can always be formed.

For convenience, we want a real number to stand for *the* weight of the rock. The existence of such a real number is guaranteed by the following postulate.

POSTULATE 8: NESTED INTERVAL PROPERTY

Common to any sequence of nested intervals is at least one real number.

The nested interval property can be used to show that $\sqrt{2}$ is a real number. Suppose you let x be the positive number whose square is 2, that is, $x^2 = 2$.

Squaring some numbers

$$1.3^2 = 1.69$$
$$1.4^2 = 1.96$$
$$1.5^2 = 2.25$$

$1.4 < x < 1.5$

Squaring some numbers between 1.4 and 1.5

$$1.40^2 = 1.9600$$
$$1.41^2 = 1.9811$$
$$1.42^2 = 2.0164$$

$1.41 < x < 1.42$

Choosing some numbers between 1.41 and 1.42, we get smaller intervals.

$1.414 < x < 1.415$

$1.4142 < x < 1.4143$

etc.

By the nested interval property, there is at least one real number that lies in all these intervals. Since $\sqrt{2}$ is the only such number, $\sqrt{2}$ must be real.

An infinite decimal like $-12.3456789101112\cdots$ also lies in a sequence of smaller and smaller intervals. If x stands for the given decimal, then

$$-13 < x < -12$$
$$-12.4 < x < -12.3$$
$$-12.35 < x < -12.34$$
$$\vdots$$
$$-12.3456789101113 < x < -12.3456789101112$$
$$\vdots$$

These intervals can be graphed on the number line. (However, you may need to enlarge the scale to show the smaller intervals.) From the nested interval property, you know x is a real number.

Because it can be used to show that infinite decimals are real numbers, the nested interval property finishes the job of identifying the real numbers begun in Chapter 1. For this reason, some books call it the *property of completeness.*

EXERCISES 2.7

Ⓐ **1–3.** These exercises are review from Section 1.9.

1. What properties of real numbers guarantee that 468 is a real number?

2. What additional property of real numbers guarantees that -468 is a real number?

3. What additional properties of real numbers show that $-\frac{468}{3}$ is a real number?

4. What property of real numbers indicates that $\sqrt{7}$ is a real number?

5. What is an interval?

6. When is one interval nested in a second interval?

7–10. Determine whether or not the second interval is nested in the first.

7. $-2 < a < -1,\quad -3 < a < 1$

8. $5 < x < 5.2,\quad 5.01 < x < 5.13$

9. $6.1 < x < 6.2,\quad 6.1 < x < 6.199$

10. $-1 < x < 0,\quad 0 < x < 1$

11. What is a sequence of nested intervals?

12–19. Give three intervals of a sequence of nested intervals which contains the given number.

12. 0 13. $\frac{3}{2}$ 14. $-1.686868\cdots$ 15. 14.3

Ⓑ 16. π 17. $\pi + 10$ 18. $\sqrt{3}$ 19. $\sqrt{5}$

20. Four intervals are given for $\sqrt{2}$ in this section. Graph these intervals. You may need to use more than one number line.

21. Repeat Exercise **20** for $-12.34567891011121\cdots$.

22–23. Find an interval which is nested in:

22. $\{x: \sqrt{2} < x < \sqrt{3}\}$ 23. $\{y: 2.001 < y < 2.002\}$

24. If a scale measures to the nearest kilogram and shows that an object has a mass of 217 kg, in what interval does the mass belong?

25. If a person tells you that her temperature was 99.8° F yesterday, in what interval did the temperature probably lie?

Ⓒ 26. The interval $1.4142 < x < 1.4143$ contains $\sqrt{2}$. Find a still smaller interval containing $\sqrt{2}$.

27. Suppose you wished to accurately measure the length of this page. How does the nested interval property guarantee that, given a certain unit, the length will be a real number?

28. Give an example which shows that if "real" is replaced by "rational" in the nested interval property, then the property does not hold.

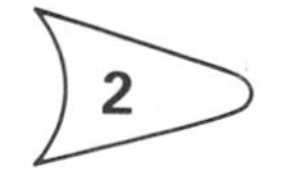

CHAPTER SUMMARY

Three more postulates about real numbers were introduced in this chapter. They deal with order, the real number line, and nested intervals.

Of the four order properties, trichotomy asserts that given two real numbers, one is less than, equal to, or greater than the other. Transitivity indicates that if $a < b$ and $b < c$, then $a < c$. These two properties imply that the real numbers can be placed in an order. This order is unaffected by adding or by positive multiplication, but multiplication by a negative number reverses the order. These are the addition and multiplication properties of order.

The order properties, together with the earlier properties of addition and multiplication, enable any linear sentence to be solved. Many formulas are linear sentences with more than one variable and can be solved by the same procedures. Strategic substitutions can simplify a complicated sentence into one which is easy to solve.

A substitution in the distributive property results in the FOIL theorem: $(a + b)(c + d) = ac + ad + bc + bd$. This theorem tells how to multiply binomials. A generalization allows any polynomials to be multiplied.

The ruler postulate assumes that there is a 1–1 correspondence between the points of any line and the real numbers. This allows solution sets to sentences to be graphed. The graph of the solution set to $a < x < b$ is an interval.

Finally, the nested interval property states that within any sequence of nested intervals there is a real number. This property finds applications in estimation and successive approximation.

Together, the postulates of this and the first chapter sufficiently describe the real numbers.

CHAPTER REVIEW

2

1–2. Solve.

1. $2x + 4 = 5x - 3$

2. $\frac{2}{m + 5} = 3$

3–4. Graph the solution set to each sentence.

3. $x < -x$

4. $-\frac{2}{3}B > \frac{1}{6}$

5. If shirts are $6.99 apiece and slacks are $18.99, and a person buys h shirts and k slacks, how much has he spent?

6. A formula for the surface area of a cylinder is $A = 2\pi r^2 + 2\pi rh$. Solve for h.

7. Square the binomial $2x - 3$.

8. Express the product as a single polynomial: $(a - 2)(5a + 7)$.

9. There is a one-to-one correspondence between the points on a line and the elements in the set of ___.

10. Give an example of a sentence whose solution set is an interval.

11. Name an interval which is nested in $\{t: 13 < t < 13.1\}$.

12. What is the nested interval property?

13. The speedometer of a car registers 90 km/h but may be off by as much as 10%. Graph the set of values which indicate the possible speeds of the car.

Chapter 3 Applications and Modeling

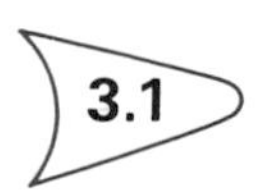

3.1 WHY ARE ADDITION AND MULTIPLICATION IMPORTANT?

The importance of addition lies in its many real-world applications. Here are some common examples you have probably seen before.

addition: counting application

x elements in one set

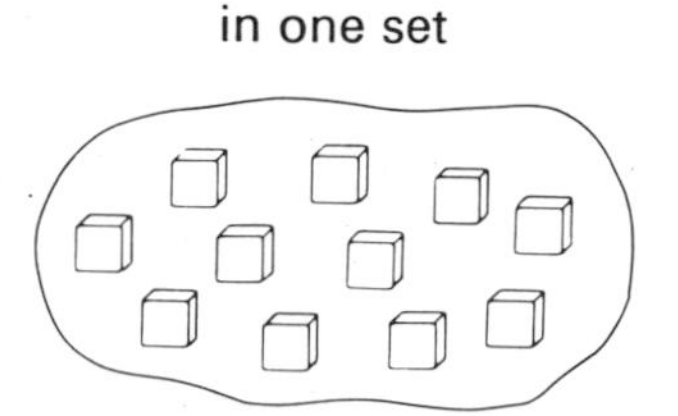

y different elements in another set

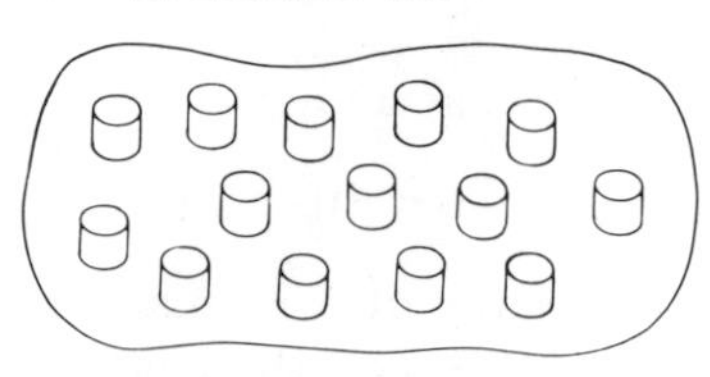

$x + y$ elements in all

If $\overline{AB}$ and $\overline{BC}$ are laid end-to-end along the same line as below, the length of $\overline{AC}$ is the sum of the lengths of $\overline{AB}$ and $\overline{BC}$.

addition: joining application

$AB + BC$ is the total length.

As another example, areas may be joined.

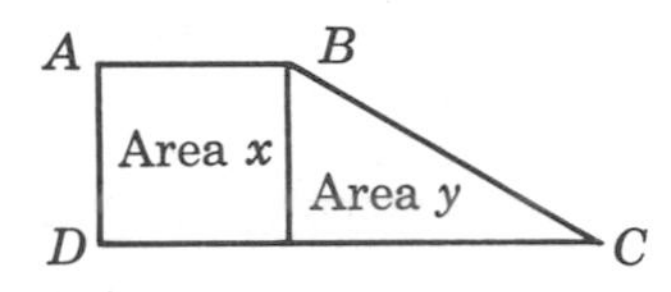

The area of $ABCD$ is $x + y$.

If a slide of length x is followed by a slide of length y (along the same line), the result is the same as a slide of length $x + y$.

addition: slide application

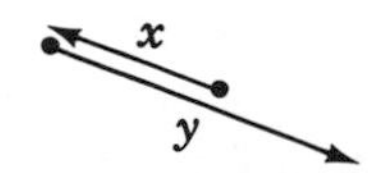

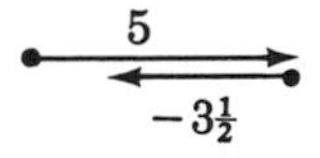

A gain of 5 yards in football followed by a loss of $3\frac{1}{2}$ yards gives a result found by adding 5 and $-3\frac{1}{2}$.

Many real-world situations use multiplication.

multiplication: counting application

x elements in one set

y elements in another set

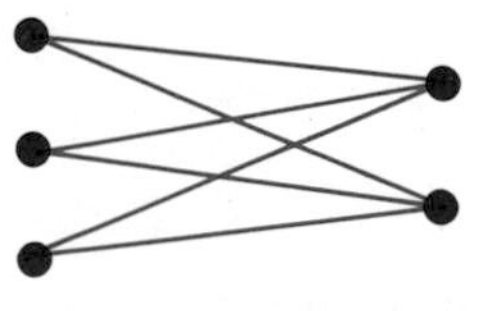

$x \cdot y$ ways of connecting the elements

There are $3 \cdot 2 = 6$ ways of connecting 3 objects to 2 objects. For example, 6 outfits are possible with 3 sweaters and 2 pairs of slacks.

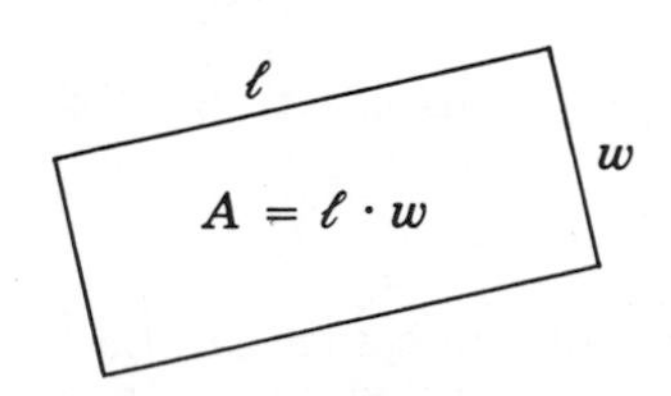

The area of a rectangle is the product of the lengths of two adjacent sides.

multiplication: area application

You are given a segment of length L and asked to find the length of a segment that is $2\frac{1}{2}$ times bigger. (Even the terminology tells you what to do.) Multiplying, you find the second segment has length $2\frac{1}{2} \cdot L$.

multiplication: size-change application

The size-change application has a very common use in percentage. If you want 3% of 150, you multiply:

$$3\% \cdot 150 = 0.03 \cdot 150$$
$$= 4.5.$$

You can think of this process as "shrinking" 150 because you have multiplied by a positive number less than 1. Two hundred percent of 150 is 2 · 150, so 150 is being "expanded." This is why the application is called a *size change*. (Later, the application is extended to explain multiplying by a negative number.)

A well-known application that was used in Chapter 1 relates multiplication and addition.

multiplication: repeated addition application

$$\underbrace{x + x + x + \cdots + x}_{} = mx$$

Using x as a term m times, the result is

When you buy 6 items at $2.49 each, you probably multiply to get the total cost. Thinking of a cash register ringing $2.49 up 6 times shows that this multiplication is a shortcut for repeated addition..

The operations of subtraction and division, which are very closely related to addition and multiplication, also have many applications. When there are real situations which can be treated mathematically and a certain operation will be used very often, the operation is given a name and perhaps a special symbol. The operation of "taking the square root" (known since ancient times) and the symbol $\sqrt{}$ (introduced in 1525 by Christoff Rudolff) developed in this way.

EXERCISES 3.1

Ⓐ **1–7.** Describe a real situation in which the given type of application can be used.

1. addition—counting
2. multiplication—counting
3. addition—joining
4. multiplication—area
5. addition—slide
6. multiplication—size change
7. multiplication—repeated addition

8–14. For each given situation, make up a question that can be answered with $x + y$ or xy. Answer your question, and identify the type of application by using one of the terms in Exercises **1–7**.

8. There are x people who own y cars each.

9. It takes x seconds to react and step on the brake pedal. It takes y seconds for the car to stop, once the brakes are applied.

10. There are x ways of getting from home to school and y ways of getting from school to the football game.

11. There are x boys and y girls at the dance.

12. I bought x records for y dollars each.

13. I drove for x hours at y miles per hour.

14. Bob earns x times as much as Mary does, and Mary earns y dollars per hour.

Ⓑ **15–18.** State which operation—subtraction or division—should be used.

15. Distances are given from A to B and from A to C. You want the distance from B to C.

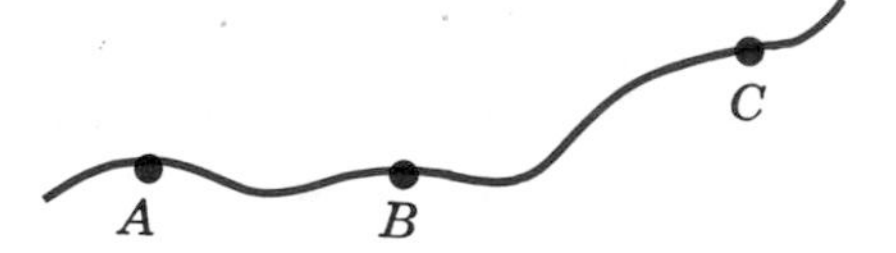

16. It took x hours to drive y kilometres. What was the average speed?

17. Seventy-five litres of milk cost d dollars. How much does one litre cost?

18. How much older than Laura is Miguel if Miguel was born in year a and Laura in year b?

19–22. What is the distance traveled by:

19. a plane flying at 560 kilometres per hour for 7 hours?

20. a sound traveling at r metres per second for 11.5 seconds?

21. a car going r mph for t hours?

22. a car going 35 mph for h_1 hours and 40 mph for h_2 hours?

23–26. A solution contains x grams; 20% is water; the rest is alcohol.

23. How many grams of water are in the solution?

24. How many grams of alcohol are in the solution?

25. If y grams of *water* are added, how much *water* will be in the resulting solution?

26. If y grams of *water* are added, how much *alcohol* will be in the resulting solution?

27. If a gram of medicine costs \$3, what is the cost of x grams of the medicine?

28. What is the total value of 10 litres of \$2.29-a-litre paint and p litres of \$2.49-a-litre paint?

29. A store sells x items at 13¢ each and y items at 17¢ each. How much does the store receive in sales?

30. A student bought m pencils at 9¢ each and half as many erasers for a penny less each. What algebraic expression stands for the total amount spent?

31. A woman invests P dollars at 8% interest per year. How much money does she collect in interest at the end of a year? What is the total amount that she has at the end of a year?

32–37. A man's age now is n years. Give his age:

32. 20 years from now.

33. 4 years ago.

34. next year.

35. last year.

36. in the year 2000.

37. $3\frac{1}{2}$ years from now.

38–41. In the year t, a woman is 32 years old. Give the year in which she:

38. was born

39. was 16 years old.

40. will be 48 years old.

41. will be twice as old as she was in the year t.

42. The difference of the ages of two people is m. What will be the difference in their ages 10 years from now?

43–44. A jet plane flies at r mph in still air. What is its speed if there is:

43. a tail wind of t mph?

44. a head wind of h mph?

45. There are T students in the school, and g of them are girls. How many are boys?

46. There are T students in the school, and 70% of them are boys. How many are girls?

© By using the terms in Exercises **1–7**, name the type(s) of application(s) found in **each** exercise in the given set of exercises.

47. Exercises 19–25

48. Exercises 26–32

49. Exercises 33–39

50. Exercises 40–46

MATHEMATICAL MODELS FOR REAL SITUATIONS

Various applications of addition and multiplication were summarized in the last section. Another way of viewing these applications is to think of addition and multiplication as *models* for real situations. Here are some examples.

Real situation	Possible mathematical model
Wealth of a person	Count the person's assets and add them.
How much material is in that tabletop?	Measure the dimensions; multiply to find the volume.
Is that girl a good bowler?	Add her scores; divide by number of games to find average; compare with some standard.

Definition

A **mathematical model** is a mathematical representation of a situation.

The mathematics used in a mathematical model may include numbers, variables (as in formulas), sets of points (as in geometry), or many other ideas (some of which you will study in the next chapter).

A mathematical model is very often simpler than the real situation it represents. A person's wealth is usually thought to involve more than material assets. When we measure a tabletop, we usually ignore slight defects in the surface and small errors in measurement.

The process of using a mathematical model to analyze a situation is called **modeling**. Here is an example.

> Amy has $5 to buy phonograph records. How many can she buy?

This problem is not clear enough. More information is needed. Is Amy interested in long-playing records only? In 45-rpm records only? What is the cost of each type of record?

To clarify the problem, even Amy herself would add restrictions. She might decide to buy only 45-rpm records. She might do some shopping and find that the best price for these records is 87¢ each. So the problem is changed to

> Amy has $5 to buy 45-rpm records that cost 87¢ each. How many can she buy?

We can make up a mathematical model. Let n = number of records Amy can buy. Then $0.87n$ = cost of the records. So, we would like the largest integer that is a solution for

$$0.87n \leq 5.00.$$

This sentence is equivalent to

$$n \leq \frac{500}{87},$$

and since $\frac{500}{87} \doteq 5.747$, the largest integral solution is 5.

Maybe there is a store that gives a special price on 5 or more records. If there is such a store, perhaps Amy can buy 6 records for \$5 or less. In fact, she may even have enough money to buy 6 records at 87¢ each. (She may have rounded in stating that \$5 is available.) Perhaps Amy wants at most 4 records.

If one of these possibilities exists, Amy may decide that the solution is not acceptable, and she may reject it. Thus, the real problem is not always solved when a mathematical solution has been found.

Amy's simple problem illustrates the process of solving *any* real problem by using mathematics. There are at least 6 steps.

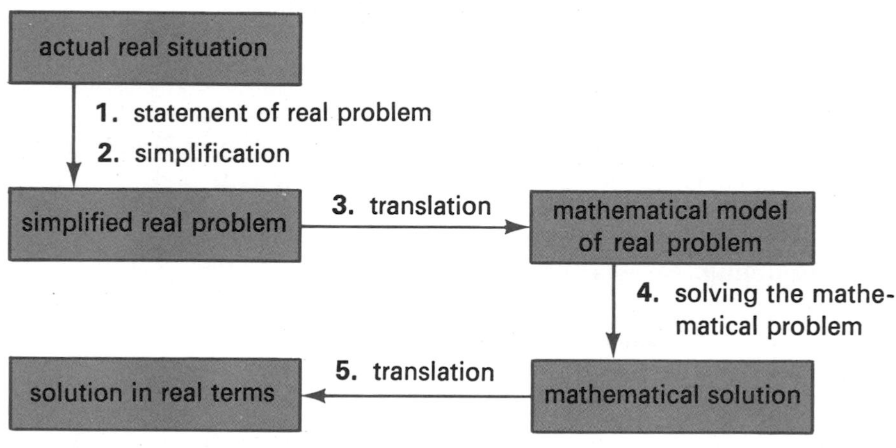

Much of this book is concerned with making Step 4, solving the mathematical model, automatic. This step should become automatic for anyone who wants to apply mathematics.

In the last section, using mainly addition and multiplication, we briefly considered Step 3, forming a mathematical model for a simplified real problem. Step 5, translating a solution back into real terms, is usually (but not always) easy.

It is important to realize that only Step 4 can be automatic. Let the real problem (Step 1) be

Should TV show X be canceled?

Then the simplified real problem (Step 2) might be

Is show X watched by fewer people
than each other show in its time slot?

There are many ways of translating this simplified problem into mathematics (Step 3). Once a solution has been given (Step 4), the translation back into real terms (Step 5) may not be easy. (Suppose show X is watched by fewer people than the other shows but is doing better against them than any previous show. Suppose show X is being watched by more teen-agers than the other shows—maybe its sponsors want this.)

Selecting the problem and deciding whether the solution is acceptable are important but require little knowledge of mathematics. However, simplifying the real problem and translating back and forth from mathematics to reality often require a great deal of mathematical know-how. Here, mathematics is far from an exact science. But the assumptions and decisions which must be made again and again are exactly what cause many people to be interested in mathematics.

EXERCISES 3.2

Ⓐ **1.** What is a mathematical model? **2.** What is modeling?

3. Give an example of a real situation and a possible mathematical model for it.

4. Name six steps involved in the modeling process.

Ⓑ **5–10.** A real situation and a possible mathematical model are given. Name one advantage and one disadvantage of the mathematical model as in the example.

Example:

GIVEN: *Real situation:* How warm is it?

Possible mathematical model: Measure the temperature.

ANSWER: *An advantage:* You can easily compare the warmth this day to other days.

A disadvantage: Temperature does not always tell how warm a person feels. Wind and humidity also affect warmth.

	Real situation	Possible mathematical model
5.	How rich is that person?	Count the person's assets and add them.
6.	How large is that home?	Count the number of rooms.
7.	How mature is that person?	Determine the person's age.
8.	How intelligent is that person?	Determine the person's score on an IQ test.
9.	How much paper is on this page?	Measure; use formula $A = \ell w$.
10.	How good is that baseball player?	Divide the number of hits by the number of at-bats to obtain a batting average.

11. Everyone grows older continuously. Yet the usual mathematical model for a person's age does not include all the real numbers, only the integers. For example, a person's age is 16 for a year; then it becomes 17. A person's age is rarely given as 16.3. Discuss the advantages and disadvantages of using only integers for ages.

12–17. In your school or local library, find a technical book about the given subject. Then very briefly identify one application which uses mathematics. (You do not have to understand the mathematics.)

12. economics **13.** business management **14.** physiology

15. archaeology **16.** experimental psychology **17.** botany

Ⓒ **18–20.** Recent applications of mathematics include the fine arts. Very briefly tell how mathematics is related to the work of:

18. Irene Rice Pereira (painter).

19. Maurits Escher (artist).

20. Karlheinz Stockhausen (composer).

21. Lillian R. Lieber (author).

Oblique Progression
by Irene Rice Pereira

1948, Collection of the Whitney Museum of American Art, New York

MODELING DISTANCE ON A LINE

3.3

Number lines (or coordinatized lines) are used in models of many real situations. You know about most of the following.

- thermometers
- weight scales
- rulers and tape measures
- scales used in scoring tests
- time lines

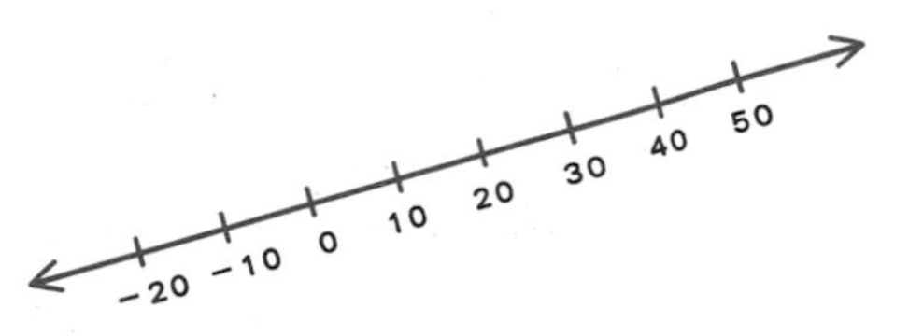

There are other applications to graphing numerical results in such areas as population, business, and sports. In these applications, we often want to know how much one result differs from another. How much better or worse is it? How much change has there been?

In the mathematical model, these questions are answered by locating two points on the number line and finding the length of the interval between them. For some intervals, the length—the distance between the endpoints—can be found by counting unit segments.

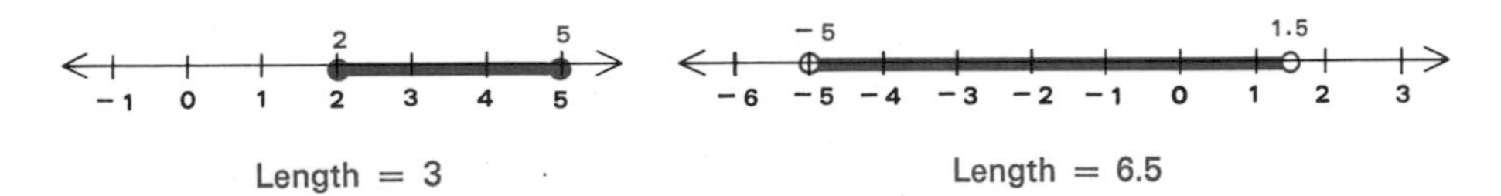

An interval may contain its endpoints (see left, above) or it may not (see right, above). In either case, the length is not affected. In general, the length of an interval is found by subtracting the coordinates of its endpoints—the smaller from the larger. That is,

Definition

The **length** of $\{x: a \leq x \leq b\}$ is $b - a$.

Examples: Lengths of intervals

1. The length of $\{x: 5 \leq x \leq 5.01\}$ is $5.01 - 5 = 0.01$.

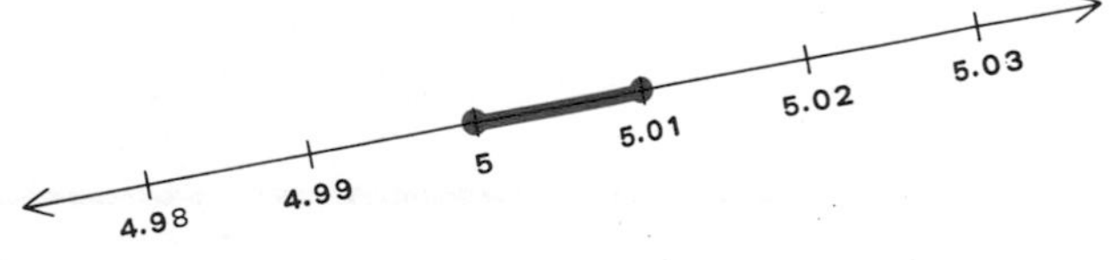

2. What is the length of the interval with endpoints $\frac{2}{3}$ and $\frac{5}{7}$? Since it is not easy to tell which number is larger, let's subtract both ways.

$$\left.\begin{array}{l} \frac{2}{3} - \frac{5}{7} = \frac{14}{21} - \frac{15}{21} = -\frac{1}{21} \\ \frac{5}{7} - \frac{2}{3} = \frac{15}{21} - \frac{14}{21} = \frac{1}{21} \end{array}\right\}$$ The length is $\frac{1}{21}$.

3. The distance between -4 and 0 is 4.

4. The interval $\{n: 0 \leq n \leq 42\}$ has length 42.

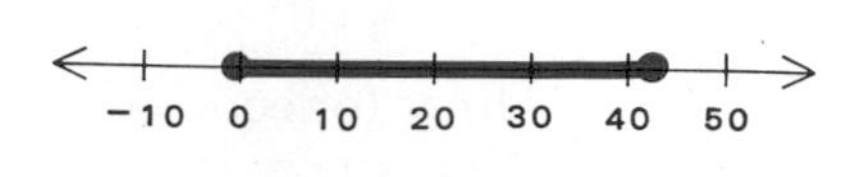

Distance between points is quite important and very often used in mathematics and its applications. So a special term and symbol are used to denote the distance between a point and 0.

Definition

The **absolute value** of a real number x is the distance (or length of interval) between x and 0, and it is denoted as $|x|$.

It is easy to find the absolute value of any number.

Theorem 3.3.1

a. If x is negative, $|x| = -x$.

b. If x is positive (or zero), $|x| = x$.

PROOF: We agreed in the definition of *length* to subtract smaller from larger. So,

a. when x is negative:

b. when x is positive:

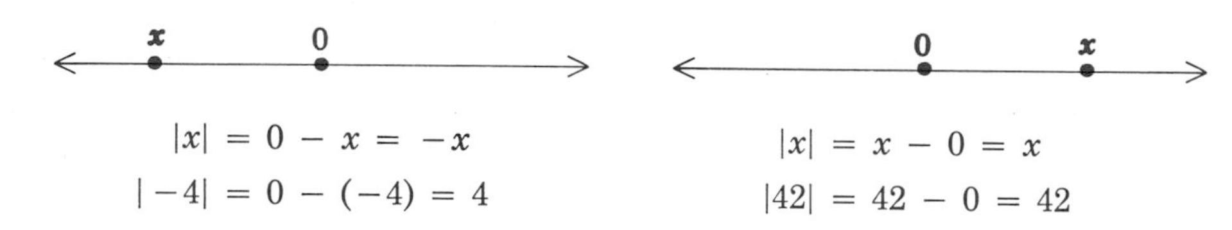

$|x| = 0 - x = -x$

$|-4| = 0 - (-4) = 4$

$|x| = x - 0 = x$

$|42| = 42 - 0 = 42$

Theorem 3.3.1 shows that $|x|$ is never negative. In part **a**, x is negative, so $-x$ is positive. There are only two possibilities for $|x|$ in any case—either $|x| = x$ or $|x| = -x$. For each case, squaring gives $|x|^2 = x^2$. Since $|x|$ is not negative, taking the square roots yields $|x| = \sqrt{x^2}$. These are all useful properties of absolute value.

Theorem 3.3.2

For any real number x,

a. $|x|$ is never negative.

b. $|x|^2 = x^2$.

c. $|x| = \sqrt{x^2}$.

Using absolute values, we can find the distance between points even if we do not know which point has the larger coordinate.

Theorem 3.3.3

The distance between points with coordinates a and b is $|b - a|$, or restated, the length of an interval with endpoints a and b is $|b - a|$.

PROOF: If $a < b$, then the interval is $\{x: a \leq x \leq b\}$, and its length is $b - a$. Since $a < b$, we also know that $b - a$ is positive. So, $|b - a| = b - a$.

If $b < a$, then the interval is $\{x: b \leq x \leq a\}$, and its length is $a - b$. Since $b < a$, we also know that $b - a$ is negative. So, $|b - a| = -(b - a) = a - b$.

In either case, $|b - a|$ is the length of the interval.

Examples: Using Theorem 3.3.3

1. The length of the interval with endpoints $\frac{14}{9}$ and $\frac{7}{4}$ is

   $|\frac{7}{4} - \frac{14}{9}| = |\frac{63}{36} - \frac{56}{36}| = |\frac{7}{36}| = \frac{7}{36}$.

   You can also subtract in the other order:

   $|\frac{14}{9} - \frac{7}{4}| = |\frac{56}{36} - \frac{63}{36}| = |-\frac{7}{36}| = \frac{7}{36}$.

   Absolute value guarantees that, either way, the same answer results.

2. The distance between points with coordinates x and 2 is $|x - 2|$. This cannot be simplified unless you know that x is definitely larger or definitely smaller than 2.

EXERCISES 3.3

Ⓐ **1–8.** Give the absolute value of each number.

1. 10 **2.** -46.2 **3.** 0 **4.** $\sqrt{8}$

5. x when x is positive **6.** y when $y = -12$

7. z when z is negative **8.** $6 - 13$

9. What is the distance between points with coordinates 0 and x?

10. One item costs d dollars; another costs f dollars. What is the difference between their costs?

11–16. Two points on a number line have the given coordinates. Find the distance between them.

11. 3, 100 **12.** -1, 1 **13.** 706, -122

14. -11, -29 **15.** 0, 46 **16.** -46, 0

17–19. Find the length of the interval:

17. $\{x: -3 < x < -2\}$.

18. $\{a: -462 \leq a < 1\}$.

19. with endpoints 6 and -10.

20–29. True or False?

20. $|422| = |-422|$

21. $|422| = -|422|$

22. $|x| = -|x|$

23. $|x| = |-x|$

24. $|x| \geq 0$

25. $|-x| \geq 0$

26. $|-7| < 0$

27. $|-4| = \sqrt{16}$

28. Sometimes $|x| = -x$.

29. Sometimes $|x|$ stands for a negative number.

Ⓑ **30–33.** Refer to the diagram of an Interstate Highway route from Chicago to Philadelphia with numbers indicating mileage and direction from Cleveland. Using a theorem of this section, find the distance between:

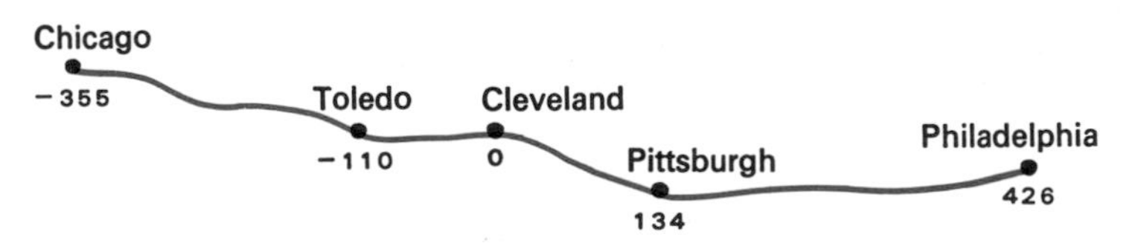

30. Chicago and Toledo.

31. Toledo and Pittsburgh.

32. Pittsburgh and Toledo.

33. Chicago and Philadelphia.

34–35. Find the length of the interval with endpoints:

34. -2.003 and -0.001.

35. $\frac{63}{100}$ and $\frac{7}{11}$.

36. If the average score on a test is m and you score 50, by how much does your score differ from the average?

37. True or False? If one interval is nested inside another, the length of the "inside" interval is less than that of the other interval.

38. The highest natural temperature ever recorded on earth was 136.4° F (Azizia, Libya, 1922) and the lowest was $-126.9°$ F (Vostok, Antarctica, 1960). Find the range of earth's recorded temperatures.

39. When does $-x$ stand for a positive number?

40–45. Find all solutions to each sentence.

40. $|x| = 8$

41. $|y| = -2$

42. $|z| = 0$

Ⓒ **43.** $2 = -|-a|$

44. $6|b| - 3 = 10$

45. $19 = 4 + 8|c|$

46. Find an interval with length 0.006 which contains $\sqrt{3}$. (HINT: Do not try to estimate $\sqrt{3}$.)

47. Find two numbers x and y which satisfy $|x - y| = 0.002$.

Except for counting in small numbers, measurements tend to contain errors. You are familiar with errors in measurements of length. But errors also occur in other types of measurement, such as opinion polls, temperatures, test scores, and TV ratings. Here is an example.

> An opinion poll says that 58% of U. S. voters favor a certain law and that its poll is accurate to within 3% almost all the time. What percentage of voters favor the issue?

From the information, we can see that 55% to 61% of voters seem to favor the law.

We can describe this interval as follows. If p is the actual percentage of voters favoring the law, then

$$0.55 \leq p \leq 0.61.$$

But this description may not be the most convenient. It has two $\leq$ signs and does not use either of the given numbers 58% and 3%. Using absolute value, we can give a second description.

We know that p is within 3% of 58%.

That is, the distance from p to 58% is less than or equal to 3%.

Or, the distance from p to $0.58 \leq 0.03$.

Using the absolute value description of distance (Theorem 3.3.3), we get

$$|p - 0.58| \leq 0.03.$$

This number (0.58) is the coordinate of the midpoint of the interval.

This number (0.03) is the accuracy of the measurement.

The only numbers which satisfy this sentence are those in the interval. Notice that two numbers used in the sentence are the coordinate of the midpoint of the interval and the *accuracy* of the measurement.

Generalizing, we now state a theorem which describes an interval by its midpoint and length. (In measurements, the length of an interval is twice the accuracy of the measurement.)

Theorem 3.4.1

The interval with midpoint m and length d can be described as

$$|x - m| < \frac{d}{2}.$$

Suppose we want to construct intervals which include various estimates of π.

$|x - \pi| < 0.01$ **means** The distance from x to π is less than 0.01.

That is, x is quite near to π. The sentence $|x - \pi| < 0.005$ means that x is even closer to π. With this description, it is very easy to construct nested intervals.

$|x - \pi| < 0.01$ (3.13 ..., 3.14 ..., 3.15 ...; $\pi - 0.01$, π, $\pi + 0.01$)

$|x - \pi| < 0.005$ ($\pi - 0.005$, π, $\pi + 0.005$)

$|x - \pi| < 0.002$ ($\pi - 0.002$, π, $\pi + 0.002$)

Some absolute-value sentences can be solved quickly by applying Theorem 3.4.1.

Examples:

1. To solve $|x - 1| < 5$, we think "The distance from x to 1 is less than 5." So x must lie in the interval with midpoint 1. The endpoints are 5 units away. So $-4 < x < 6$.

   $|x - 1| < 5$ (−4, 1, 6)

   The next two sentences are related, and they are solved in a similar way.

2. $|x - 1| = 5$

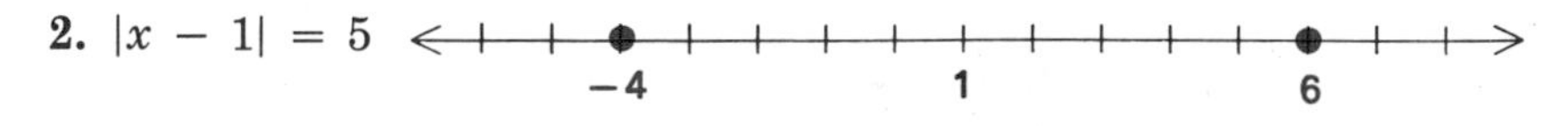

3. $|x - 1| > 5$

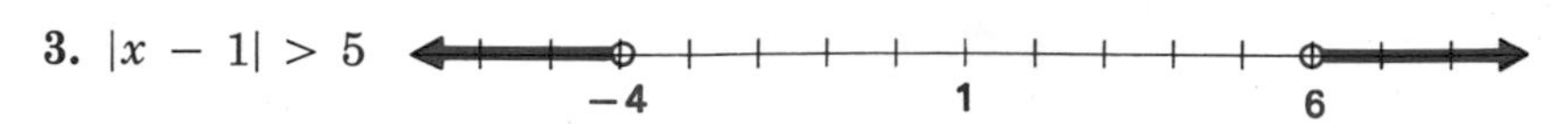

In all the examples above, the midpoint of the interval was given. If the midpoint is not given, it is usually easy to find.

Theorem 3.4.2

The midpoint of the interval $\{x: a \leq x \leq b\}$ has coordinate $\frac{a+b}{2}$.

PROOF: Let m be the coordinate of the midpoint.

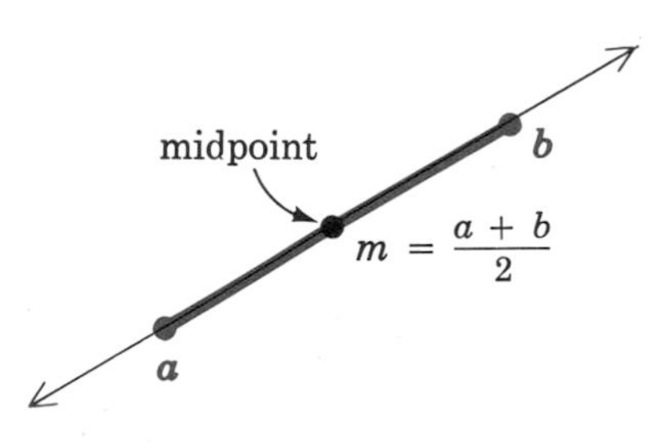

1. The length of $\{x: a \leq x \leq m\}$ is $m - a$.
2. The length of $\{x: m \leq x \leq b\}$ is $b - m$.
3. Since m is the midpoint, $m - a = b - m$
4. So, $2m = b + a$
5. $m = \frac{b+a}{2}$

So the coordinate of the midpoint is the *average* of the coordinates of the endpoints. (This makes sense since the average of two numbers is *midway* between them.) For example,

the interval  $-50 \leq y \leq -40$

has midpoint ➡ $\frac{-50 + (-40)}{2} = -45$

EXERCISES 3.4

Ⓐ **1–3.** Which points are at a distance:

1. of 7 from the point at 0?

2. of 7 from the point at 2?

3. of $2\frac{1}{2}$ from the point at -4?

4–7. Solve.

4. $|y| = 7$ **5.** $|t - 2| = 7$ **6.** $|v - (-4)| = 2.5$ **7.** $|v + 4| = 2.5$

8. The solution set to $|1 + A| = 10$ is:

a. $\{9, -9\}$. **b.** $\{9, 11\}$. **c.** $\{9, -11\}$. **d.** $\{-9, -11\}$.

9. $|L - 26|$ may be interpreted as the distance from ____ to ____.

10. Interpret $|L - 26| < 5$ using ideas of distance.

11. The graph of $|L - 26| < 5$ is a(n) ____.

12. A sentence equivalent to $|L - 26| < 5$ is:

a. $21 < L < 31$. **b.** $16 < L < 36$. **c.** $-21 < L < 21$.

13. A sentence equivalent to $|x - 2| < 0.003$ is:

a. $1.97 < x < 2.03$. **b.** $1.997 < x < 2.003$. **c.** $-2.003 < x < 2.003$.

14. Name four solutions to $|x - 2| < 0.003$.

15–20. Give the midpoint of the interval with endpoints at:

15. 10 and 20. **16.** -10 and -20. **17.** -17 and 17.

18. a and b. **19.** 3.01 and 3.02. **20.** x and $-x$.

21–23. Use this diagram:

21. What is the midpoint of the interval?

22. What is a sentence for the interval?

23. What is a sentence satisfied by all numbers *not* in the interval?

24. Name two solutions to $|y - 132| < 1$.

Ⓑ **25–30.** Graph the solution set.

25. $|w| > 3$ **26.** $|z| < 0.2$ **27.** $|a - 4| > 6$

28. $|B + 10| \geq 11$ **29.** $2 \geq |x - 9|$ **30.** $|y + 3| < 8\frac{1}{2}$

31–35. Write a sentence of the form $|x - a| \leq b$ that is a model for the given situation.

31. W is the actual weight of a person who weighs 132 lb on a scale that is at most 3 lb off.

32. D is the diameter of a ball bearing that is advertised as being $\frac{3}{8}$ cm in diameter with a possible leeway of 0.001 cm.

33. L is an approximation to $\sqrt{2}$ that is correct within 10^{-4}.

34. P is the percentage of voters who prefer candidate Smith, when a poll that is accurate to 3.5% shows Smith is preferred by 52% of the voters.

35. Estimated production P is within 1% of 30,000 units.

Ⓒ **36.** The actual temperature is T. The weather bureau gives the temperature as 68°. In what interval might T lie?

37. *Social issues.* The 1970 census indicated there were 22,580,289 blacks in the United States. The census is generally believed to be accurate within 3%. However, some critics felt the census figure was low by as much as 25%. **(a)** Give reasons for possible inaccuracies in the census. **(b)** Graph the intervals which include the black population according to the Census Bureau and according to the critics. **(c)** Why is accuracy important in the census?

38–41. Give a sentence of the form $|x - a| < b$ for each interval.

38. $5 < y < 7$

39. $-100 < y < -90$

40. $-0.006 < s < 0.006$

41. $199.5 < v < 200.5$

42–43. Find at least two solutions to each sentence.

42. $|x^2 - 3| < 0.01$

43. $|4 - \sqrt{y}| < 3 \cdot 10^{-3}$

MODELING DISTANCE IN A PLANE

We often want to locate points and to find distances between them. On the earth's surface, the latitude-longitude system is used for locations. On a line, coordinates are used. In this section, we want to locate points in a *plane*. Here is the most common method. (A second method is given in Chapter 8.)

1. Two intersecting lines x and y are coordinatized so that the point of intersection has coordinate 0 on each line. This point is called the **origin**. The lines x and y are called **axes**.

2. An **ordered pair** (a, b) of real numbers is assigned to each point P in the plane as follows: Lines are drawn through P parallel to x and y. Where these lines intersect the axes determines (a, b) as at the right. The numbers a and b are called the **coordinates** of point P.

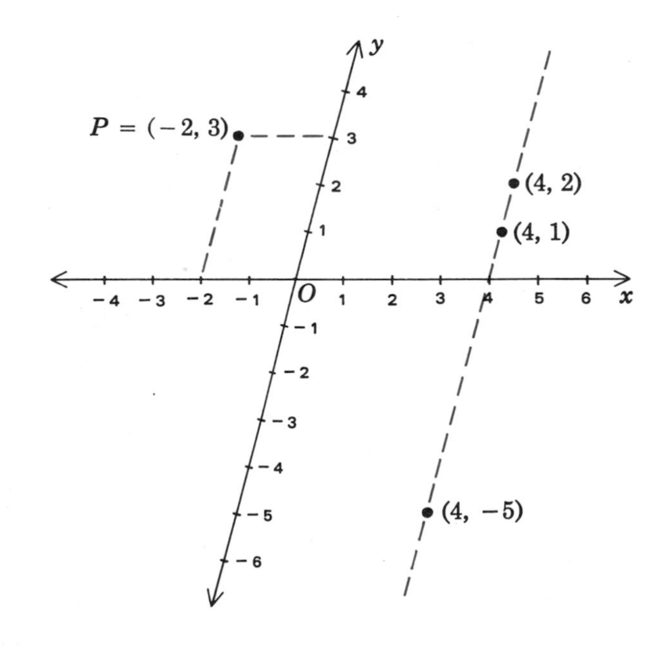

The x and y axes are usually chosen to be perpendicular. Then, when lines parallel to the axes are drawn, a rectangle is formed as in the next diagram. This method of assigning ordered pairs of real numbers to points is consequently called the *rectangular coordinate system.* (It is also called the *Cartesian coordinate system*, after the French mathematician and philosopher Descartes, 1596–1650, who was one of the first to show how useful this system could be.)

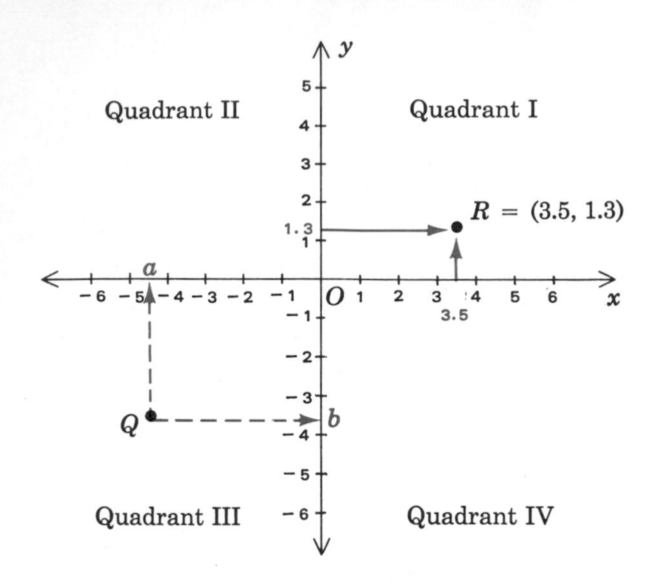

The axes divide the plane into four **quadrants,** which are numbered as at the left. Points on the axes are not considered to be in any quadrant.

Given a point Q, there is exactly one ordered pair (a, b) for it. This is so because there is exactly one line through Q perpendicular to either axis. (See diagram.) Conversely, given an ordered pair (3.5, 1.3), there is exactly one point R for it. This is so because there is exactly one perpendicular to the x-axis at 3.5 and exactly one to the y-axis at 1.3. So, we conclude the following theorem.

Theorem 3.5.1

There is a 1–1 correspondence between points of the plane and ordered pairs of real numbers.

The distance between two points on the coordinatized plane can be found by using the Pythagorean theorem (which is proved in most geometry books).

Theorem 3.5.2

Pythagorean theorem: Let a, b, and c be the lengths of the sides of $\triangle ABC$ with the longest side (c) opposite $\angle C$. Then,

$$m\angle C = 90° \text{ if and only if } c = \sqrt{a^2 + b^2}.$$

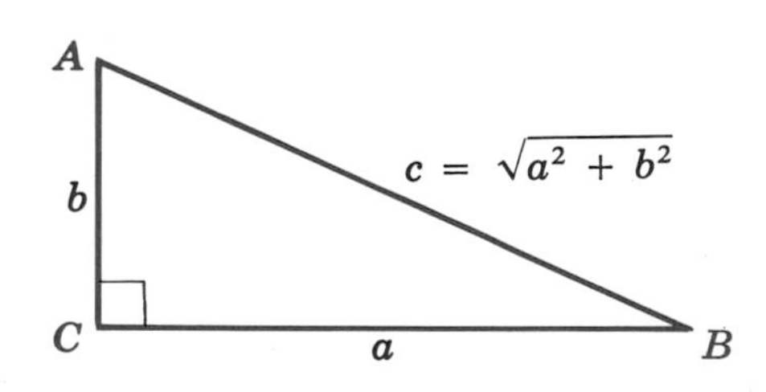

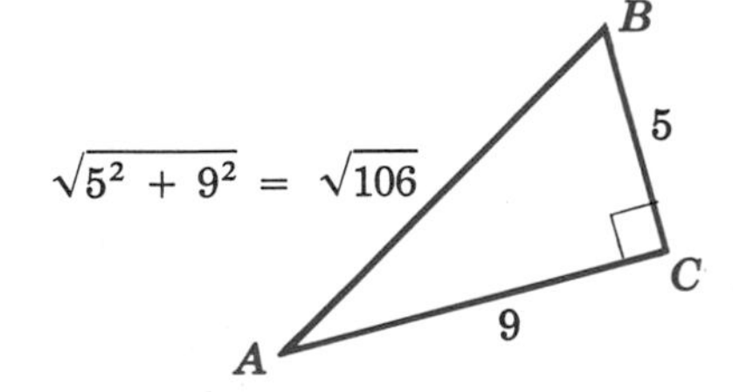

Examples: Applying the Pythagorean theorem

1. If the hypotenuse of a right triangle with legs 5 and 9 has length c, then

$$c^2 = 5^2 + 9^2 = 106$$
$$c = \sqrt{5^2 + 9^2} = \sqrt{106}$$

2. The numbers 1, 2, and $\sqrt{3}$ can be lengths of the sides of a right triangle because $1^2 + (\sqrt{3})^2 = 2^2$.

3. To find the distance d between $(2, -1)$ and $(3, 4)$, use a right triangle as at the right.

$$d^2 = 1^2 + 5^2$$
$$= 26$$
$$d = \sqrt{26}$$

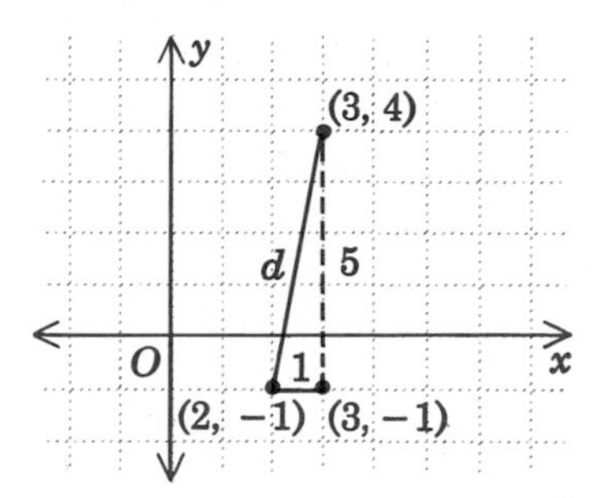

You can always draw a triangle and use it to find the distance between points (a, b) and (c, d). But this is not necessary.

Theorem 3.5.3

Distance formula theorem: The distance between (a, b) and (c, d) is

$$\sqrt{(a - c)^2 + (b - d)^2}.$$

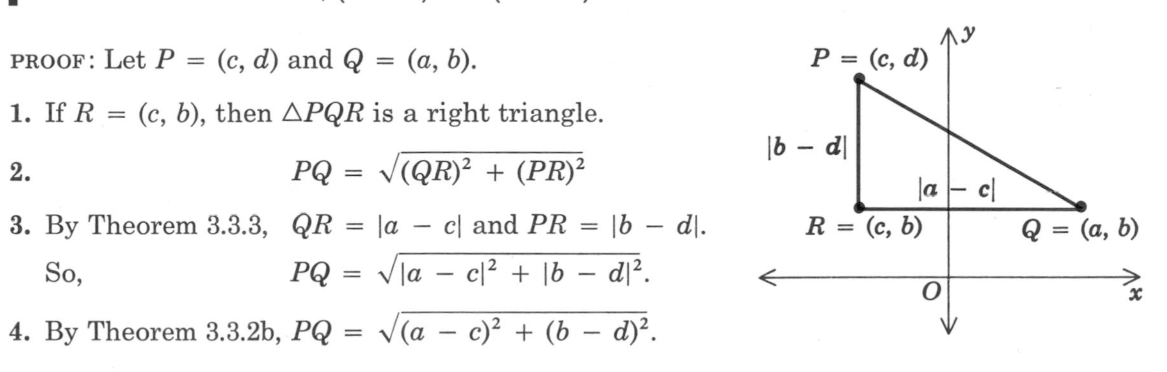

PROOF: Let $P = (c, d)$ and $Q = (a, b)$.

1. If $R = (c, b)$, then $\triangle PQR$ is a right triangle.

2. $$PQ = \sqrt{(QR)^2 + (PR)^2}$$

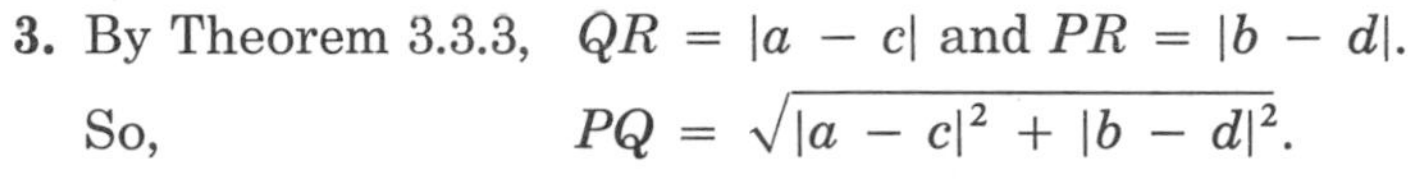

3. By Theorem 3.3.3, $QR = |a - c|$ and $PR = |b - d|$.

   So, $PQ = \sqrt{|a - c|^2 + |b - d|^2}$.

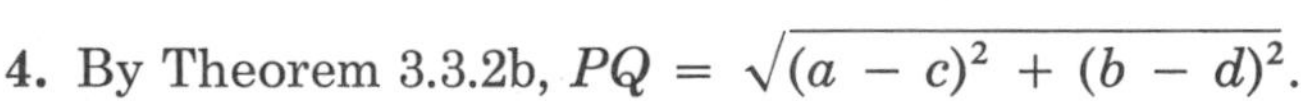

4. By Theorem 3.3.2b, $PQ = \sqrt{(a - c)^2 + (b - d)^2}$.

Examples: Using the distance formula

1. Distance between $(6, -5)$ and $(2, 1)$ $= \sqrt{(6 - 2)^2 + (-5 - 1)^2}$
   $= \sqrt{16 + 36} = \sqrt{52}$.

2. Distance between $(-2, 5)$ and $(6, -1)$ $= \sqrt{(-2 - 6)^2 + (5 + 1)^2}$
   $= \sqrt{64 + 36} = 10$.

3. Distance between $(0, 0)$ and (x, y) $= \sqrt{(0 - x)^2 + (0 - y)^2}$
   $= \sqrt{x^2 + y^2}$.

EXERCISES 3.5

Ⓐ **1–4.** Graph each set on a coordinatized plane.

1. $(2, 5), (2, 3), (2, 1), (2, 0), (2, -1\frac{1}{2})$

2. $(-1, -2), (-3, -4), (-5, -6)$

3. $(0, 4), (0, 5), (0, 6), (0, 7), (0, 8)$

4. $(1, -5), (-1, 5)$

5–9. Give the coordinates of one point that is:

5. in quadrant I.

6. in the second quadrant.

7. in quadrant III.

8. in the fourth quadrant.

9. not in any quadrant.

10. Name and graph three points whose y-coordinates are 5 less than their x-coordinates.

11. There is a 1–1 correspondence between ____ and ordered pairs of real numbers.

12–14. Find the distance between each pair of points without using any theorem of this section. (Graphing may help.)

12. $(2, 9), (-4, 9)$ **13.** $(0, 7), (0, 17)$ **14.** $(6, -2), (6, -6)$

15–20. The lengths of the legs of a right triangle are given. Find the length of the hypotenuse.

15. 3; 4 **16.** 6; 8 **17.** 30; 40

18. 1; 2 **19.** 1; 1 **20.** 9; 8

21–23. Estimate to nearest integer.

21. $\sqrt{61}$ **22.** $\sqrt{6^2 + 5^2}$ **23.** $\sqrt{(-3)^2 + (-4)^2}$

24. True or False? $\sqrt{17^2 + 10^2} = 27$

25–32. Find the distance between each pair of points.

25. $(4, 6), (-1, 10)$ **26.** $(104, 106), (99, 110)$ **27.** $(-6, -3), (1, -4)$

28. $(5, 5), (6, 6)$ **29.** $(-7, 10), (10, -7)$ **30.** $(\sqrt{225}, \sqrt{144}), (15, 12)$

Ⓑ **31.** $(a, b), (0, 1)$ **32.** $(x, y), (-x, -y)$

33. In the proof of the distance formula theorem (page 79), the Pythagorean theorem is used in going from Step ____ to Step ____.

34. What earlier postulate is most like Theorem 3.5.1?

35. To the nearest 0.1 inch, approximate the length of the longest line segment that can be drawn on a sheet of $8\frac{1}{2} \times 11$ inch paper.

36–38. The lengths of the hypotenuse and one leg of a right triangle are given. Find the length of the other leg.

36. 15; 12 **37.** 7; 6 **38.** $h; \ell$

39. Before solving this problem, guess at an answer. City X is 100 miles due west of city Y. A house is located 102 miles from city Y and due north of city X. How far is the house from city X?

40–41. Let $A = (x, y)$, $B = (-x, -y)$, $C = (x, -y)$, $D = (-x, y)$, and $E = (0, 0)$.

40. Graph a possible set of positions for A, B, C, D, and E, given that x is negative.

41. True or False?

a. $AB = CD$ **b.** $AC = BD$ **c.** $CE = DE$

42–47. Tell whether the three given numbers could be lengths of sides of a right triangle.

42. 0.3; 0.5; 0.4 **43.** 20; 21; 29 **44.** 20; 21; 28

45. $\sqrt{2}$; $\sqrt{3}$; $\sqrt{5}$ **46.** 100; 40; 60 **47.** 26; 10; 24

48. *Testing.* Betty gets 90 on an English test and 83 on a physics test. Takeo gets 96 and 82, while Juanita gets 93 and 88. Graph (90, 83), (96, 82), and (93, 88). Use the distance formula to find out which two of these students are most alike in their knowledge of the subjects tested. (A variation of this idea is commonly used to determine how different two groups might be on tests or in health.)

49–51. *Distances on earth.* For small regions the earth can be thought of as a plane. Many cities and towns are laid out in rectangular grids. Part of such a town is shown below, where the distance between consecutive streets is 200 metres for N–S streets and 100 metres for E–W streets.

49. As the crow flies, what is the distance from 1st and Elm to 3rd and Bell?

50. What is the shortest street-distance from 1st and Elm to 3rd and Bell?

51. If a walkway is built directly from 3rd and Ash to 4th and Coe, how much walking distance would be saved?

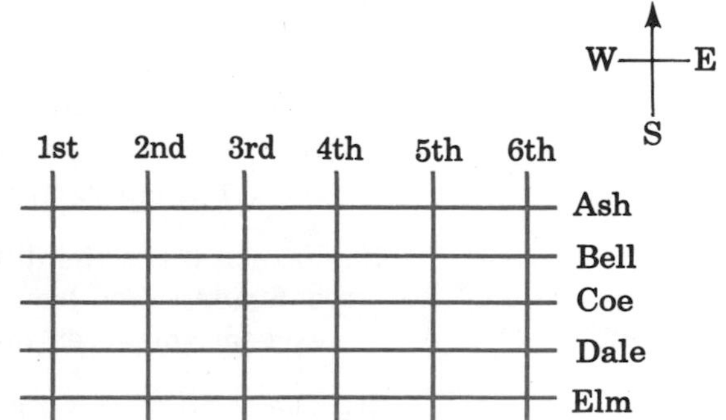

© **52.** For this exercise, call points A and B *very close* to each other if $AB < 0.02$. Name 10 points that are very close to (1, 1).

53. Use any references you can for these questions. (**a**) Who were the Pythagoreans? (**b**) What work did they do with music? (**c**) Were they aware of Theorem 3.5.2?

TRANSLATING INTO MATHEMATICS

Step 3 of the modeling process (page 66) is translating into mathematics. As with a foreign language, translating requires practice. Given here are exercises of a variety of types to help you practice.

EXERCISES 3.6

Ⓐ **1–24.** *Mathematical language.* These exercises review terminology you have met before. Translate each phrase or sentence into mathematics.

1. the product of two numbers

2. the sum of two numbers

3. a number is decreased by 3

4. 10 greater than a number

5. twice a given number

6. 6 percent of an amount

7. a number is divided by 30

8. a number is added to -13

9. One number exceeds another number.

10. One number exceeds another number by 42.

11. one number less 68

12. A number is less than 68.

13. six and one fifth is subtracted from twice a number

14. a given number is added to 6 and the result quadrupled

15. two thirds of a given number is subtracted from three

16. The sum of three numbers is less than twice one of them.

17. One number is divided into 6; the quotient is a third of a second number.

18. When one number is doubled, it equals a second number increased by 56.

19. Fifteen times the difference of 6 subtracted from a number exceeds the given number.

20. One quantity is more than 10 times larger than a second quantity.

21. The ratio of one number to 17 is 5:3.

22. Two numbers are in the ratio 3:1.

23. One number is within 0.01 of 212.

24. Two numbers are within 1000 of each other.

Ⓑ **25–32.** *Business.* Both large and small businesses today use mathematical models of many types. Here are some that involve linear expressions. Suppose that a company has orders for three types of items—A, B, and C. (Actual applications may involve hundreds of types.) Refer to the table to answer these questions.

	Type A	Type B	Type C
Number of items of each type on order	x	y	z
Amount of steel needed to make one item	3 lb	1.5 lb	0 lb
Time needed to make one item	7 hr	3 hr	30 min
Cost to make one item	$320	$100	$53
Selling price of one item	$400	$150	$75

25. How many total items does the company have orders for?

26. How much steel will be needed to fill these orders?

27. How much time will be needed to make these items?

28. How much will it cost the company to make these items?

29. How much will the company receive from selling these items?

30. How much profit will the company make (before taxes)?

31. If a cancellation of 30 items of type A had come in, what would be the answer to the question in Exercise **26**?

32. If a new order for 60 items of type A had come in, what would be the answer to the question in Exercise **26**?

33. If 1.1% of births results in twins, about how many sets of twins would be expected in a year with b births? (If your business makes double strollers, you might want to know.)

34. A racetrack expects to take 5% of the amount bet on each race. If f dollars are bet on the first race, g dollars on the second, and h dollars on the third, how much should the track expect to take?

35. If you must pay p percent in income tax on an income of $10,000, how much must be paid?

36. An item sells for x dollars. How much would the item cost at a "20% off" sale?

37. Suppose the unemployment rate is 4.8% among whites and 10% among nonwhites. If the labor force contains w whites and n nonwhites, how many are unemployed?

38. How many grams of beef are in x kilograms of dog food if this product contains at least 80% meat and at least half the meat is beef?

© **39–40.** *Picturing information.* Graphing in the coordinate plane is often used to picture information. Draw an accurate graph for each exercise, and if there is a pattern, describe it. (HINT: See Exercise **48**, page 81.)

39. Final Standings, National League Baseball, Western Division, 1974

	Won	Lost
Los Angeles	102	60
Cincinnati	98	64
Atlanta	88	74
Houston	81	81
San Francisco	72	90
San Diego	60	102

40. Median Heights and Weights for 17-Year-Olds (U. S. Public Health Service)

	Height (in)	Weight (lb)
Shortest 5% boys	65.2	106.5
All boys	69.8	139.8
Tallest 5% boys	74.4	174.0
Shortest 5% girls	60.1	97.9
All girls	64.2	125.8
Tallest 5% girls	68.3	153.7

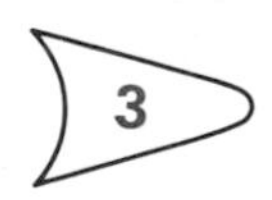

CHAPTER SUMMARY

A *mathematical model* is a mathematical representation of a situation. The importance of mathematics is due primarily to the great variety of real situations which can be modeled.

Some of the mathematics used in models is very simple. Addition is used in models for problems involving counting, joining, and slides. Multiplication is used in models for other situations involving counting, for area, and for size changes, as well as being a shortcut for repeated addition.

The *absolute value* of x, indicated as $|x|$, is defined as the distance between x and 0. If points on a line have coordinates a and b, then the distance between them is $|b - a|$. Thus, subtraction and absolute value are used to model distance on a line.

In a plane, *ordered pairs* (x, y) of real numbers locate points. Using the Pythagorean theorem, the distance between the points (a, b) and (c, d) is proved to be $\sqrt{(a - c)^2 + (b - d)^2}$.

Distance can be used to model closeness of measurement. The interval with midpoint m and length d is the solution set of $|x - m| < \frac{d}{2}$. The midpoint of an interval with endpoints a and b is $\frac{a + b}{2}$. Thus, division and inequality are also used in simple models.

The *modeling process* has at least six steps:

1. statement of real problem;
2. simplification of real problem so that it can be handled mathematically;
3. translation into mathematics;
4. solution of mathematical problem;
5. translation back into real situation;
6. deciding whether solution is acceptable for the real situation.

You have had much experience with Step 4. The first and last sections of this chapter gave you some practice with Step 3.

CHAPTER REVIEW

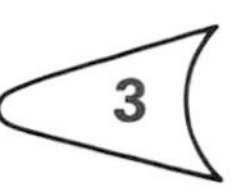

1–4. Describe a real situation in which the given type of application can be used.

1. addition—counting

2. multiplication—area

3. addition—slide

4. multiplication—size change

5. If a litre of paint costs $2.99, how much will ℓ litres cost?

6. A person bought j shirts at $12 each and k ties at $5 each. What expression stands for the total amount spent?

7. A boat cruises at s km/h in still water. What is its speed if it cruises:

a. with a current of c km/h? **b.** against a current of c km/h?

8. What are six steps involved in using mathematics to solve a real problem?

9. Give an example of a real situation and a possible mathematical model for it.

10–12. Find all solutions to each sentence.

10. $|x| = 7$

11. $|y| = -4$

12. $|n| = 0$

13–14. An interval has endpoints -100 and -500. Give:

13. its length.

14. the coordinate of its midpoint.

15–17. Graph the solution set.

15. $|m| < 0.4$

16. $|y| > 2$

17. $|x - 3| < 0.2$

18. Write a sentence of the form $|x - a| \leq b$ that is a model for: The speedometer of a car registers 50 mph but may be as much as 5% off.

19. Give the distance between points (x, y) and (h, k).

20. Are the points $(1, -1)$, $(5, 4)$, and $(-4, 3)$ vertices of an isosceles triangle? Of an equilateral triangle?

21. At 5%, how much sales tax should be paid on sales of s dollars?

Translate each phrase or sentence into mathematics.

22. a number increased by 7

23. $2\frac{1}{2}$ less than a number

24. the product of x and the sum of 5 and y

25. $2\frac{1}{2}$ is less than a number.

Chapter 4 Transformations

You may already have studied transformations in either elementary-school or high-school geometry. Transformations are a fundamental concept in geometry and algebra, and the ideas in this chapter are applied throughout the remainder of this book. One type of transformation is a *reflection*.

The mathematical idea known as a reflection is a model for real situations involving mirrors and images in mirrors. If you stand near a calm lake, you might see an image like that in the photo on page 86.

Notice that for each point P of the mountain, there is a corresponding point P' of the image, so located that the reflecting surface appears to bisect $\overline{PP'}$.

Each diagram below shows a point P and a point P' which could be found by folding along line m. In each case P' is the *reflection image* of P.

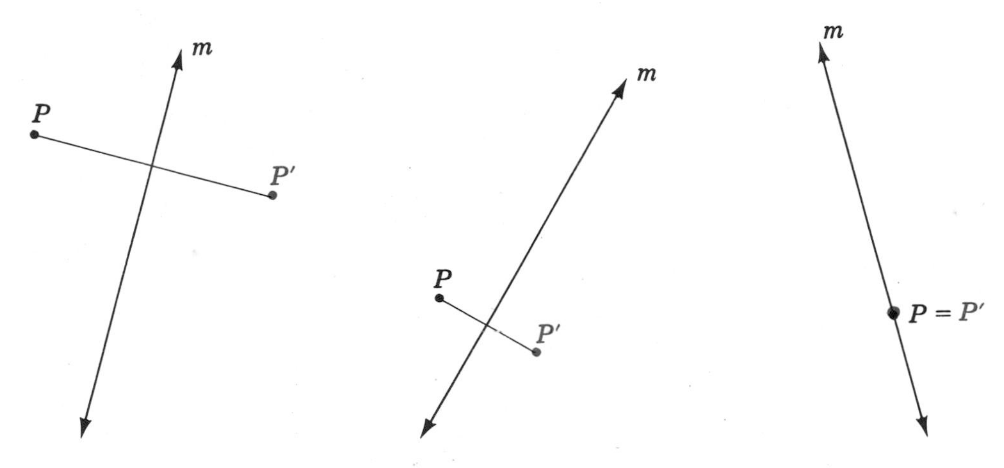

Definition

If point P is not on line m, the **reflection image** of P over line m is the point P' if and only if m is the perpendicular bisector of $\overline{PP'}$.

If P is on line m, the **reflection image** of P is P itself.

The line m is called the *reflecting line*, or *line of reflection*. When P' is the reflection image of P, the original point P is called the *preimage* of P'. Reflections have several important properties.

(1) If points are collinear, their reflection images are collinear.

From this property, we can deduce that the reflection image of a line is a line, of a segment is a segment, and of an angle is an angle.

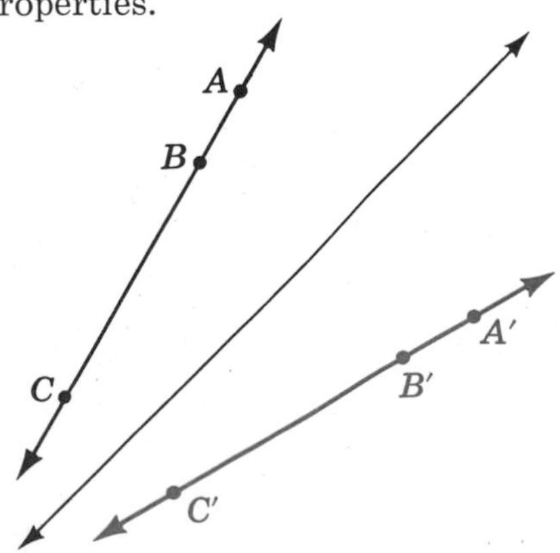

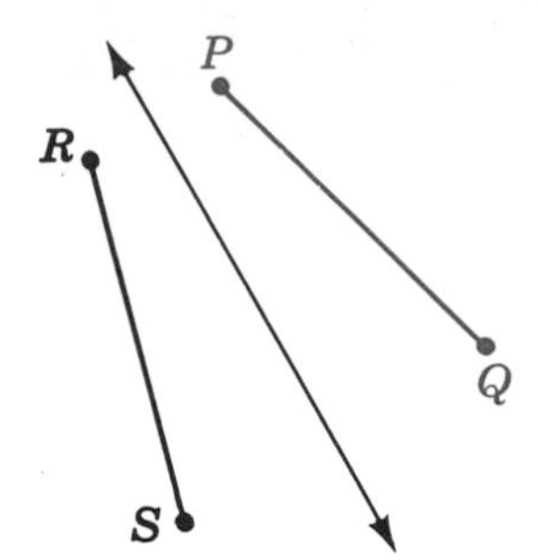

P is the image of R.
Q is the image of S.
$\overline{PQ}$ is the image of $\overline{RS}$.

$$PQ = RS$$

(2) Reflections preserve distance.

This property implies that the distance between two points equals the distance between their reflection images. So, *the reflection image of a segment is a segment of the same length.*

A third property of reflections deals with angles. A mirror can be used to illustrate a reflection. At the left, $\angle PQR$ is the reflection image of $\angle STU$ over line t.

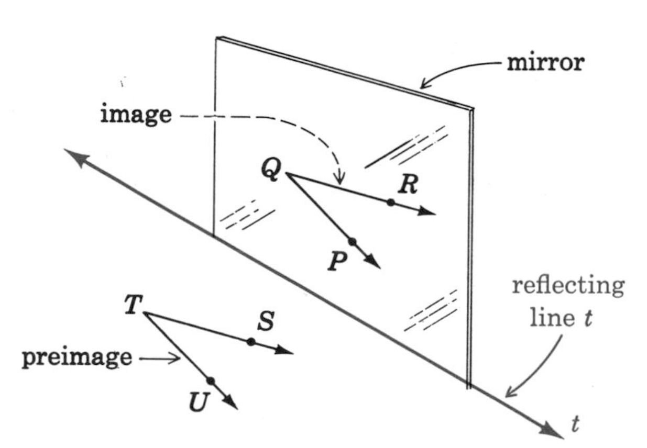

Notice that the angles have the same measure.

(3) Reflections preserve angle measure.

The fourth property of reflections is most obvious. From a drawing it is often impossible to tell which figure is the image and which is the preimage, except for coloring. In fact, for *any figures* α and β,

(4) If α is the reflection image of β over a line m, then β is the reflection image of α over that line.

The next property is in some ways the most interesting. Trace the path from A to B to C to D, below. You have traced *clockwise*, in the same direction as the hands of a clock.

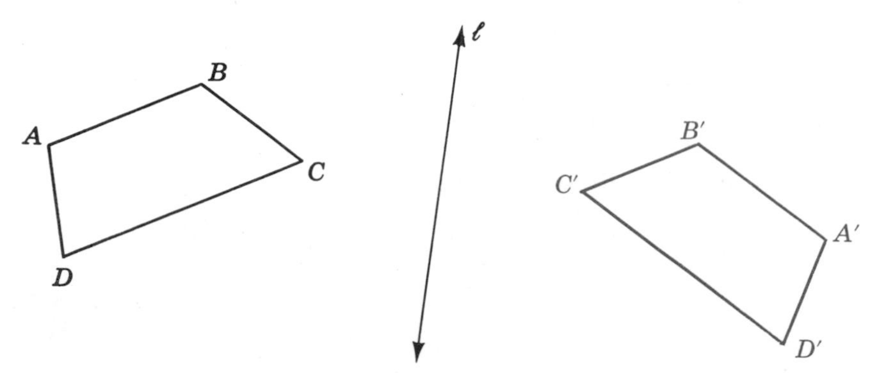

Now trace the reflection image from A' to B' to C' to D'. You have traced *counterclockwise* (opposite the direction of the hands of a clock).

Every convex polygon can be traced either clockwise or counterclockwise. We say that each polygon has clockwise or counterclockwise *orientation*. When a tracing is clockwise, the tracing of the image points (in corresponding order) will be counterclockwise, and vice versa.

(5) A reflection switches the orientation of convex polygons.

It is the reversal of orientation which causes reflection images of certain letters to look "backwards," as with the letter *R* below.

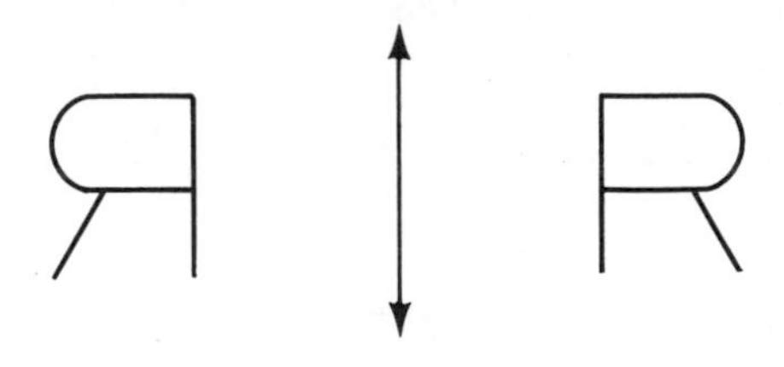

EXERCISES 4.1

Ⓐ **1.** Mathematical reflections model what real-world situation?

2–3. How can you find the reflection image of a point *F* over a line *m*:

2. if *F* is on *m*? **3.** if *F* is not on *m*?

4–13. *Given:*

P is the reflection image of *A* over line *n*.

B is the reflection image of *T* over line *n*.

What property or definition justifies each statement below?

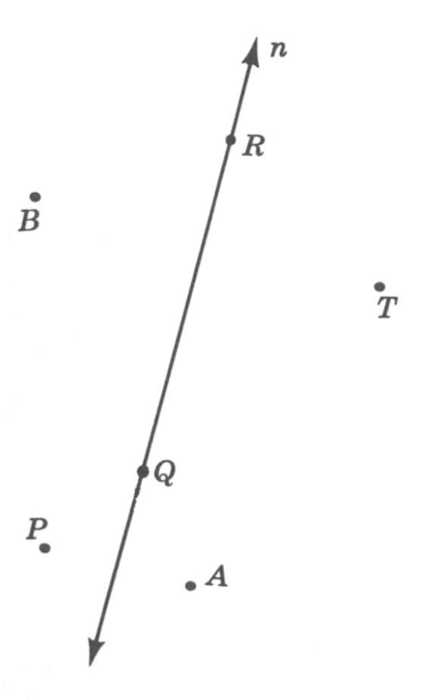

4. The image of *Q* is *Q*. **5.** $PB = AT$

6. $m\angle PBQ = m\angle ATQ$ **7.** $\overleftrightarrow{BT} \perp n$

8. n is the perpendicular bisector of $\overline{PA}$.

9. $m\angle BQR = m\angle TQR$ **10.** $QT = QB$

11. The reflection image of *P* over line *n* is *A*.

12. If *P*, *Q*, and *T* are collinear, then *A*, *Q*, and *B* are collinear.

13. The image of $\overleftrightarrow{PQ}$ is a line.

14–19. In the figure, if you traced from point to point in the order given, would the path be clockwise or counterclockwise oriented?

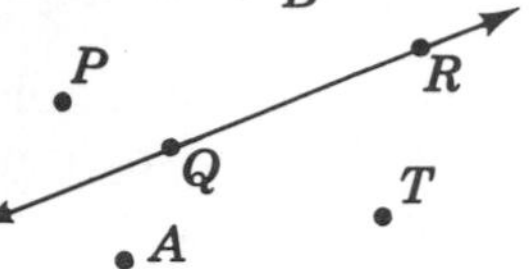

14. P, Q, B **15.** A, P, B, T **16.** R, B, T

17. R, T, B **18.** B, Q, T, R **19.** R, B, Q, T

20. What does the statement "Reflections preserve distance" mean?

21. What property of convex polygons is not preserved by reflections?

Ⓑ **22–29.** Trace each figure onto your paper before doing the drawing.

22. Draw the reflection image of $\overline{PQ}$ over line t.

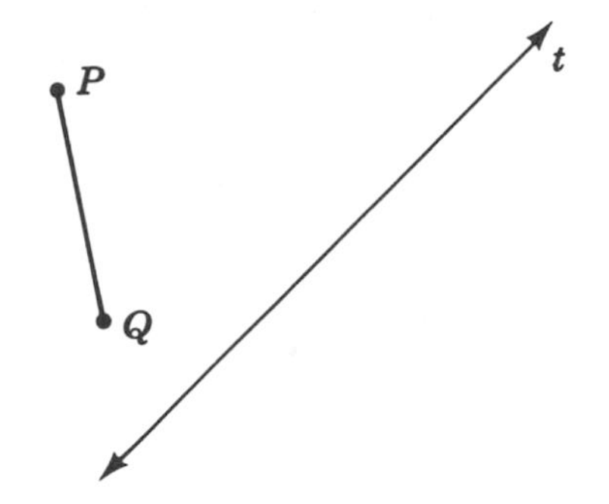

23. Draw the reflection image of $\overline{NT}$ over line $\overleftrightarrow{AB}$.

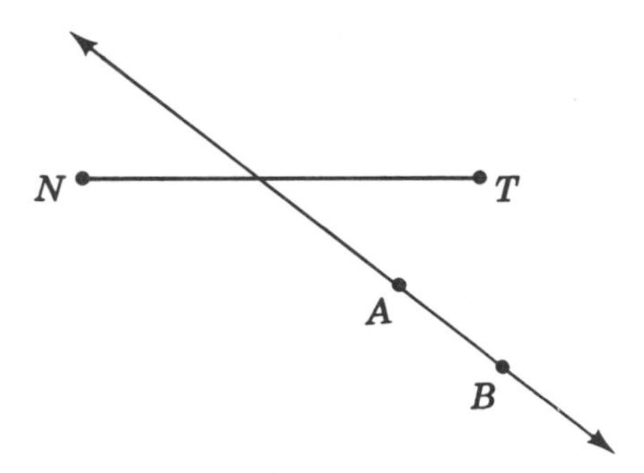

24. Draw the reflection image of $\angle MNO$ over line ℓ.

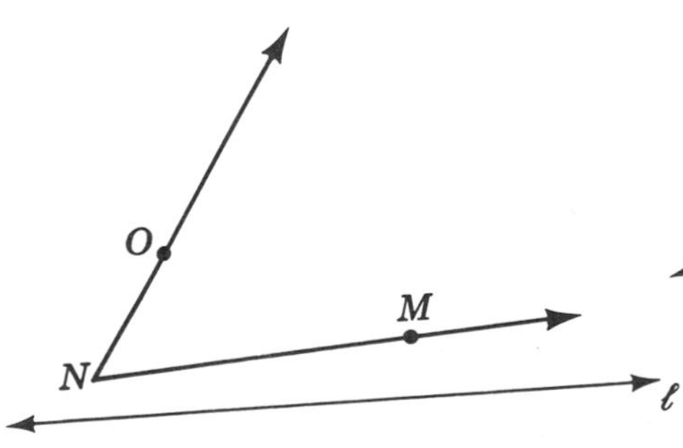

25. Draw the reflection image of $\angle W$ over line m.

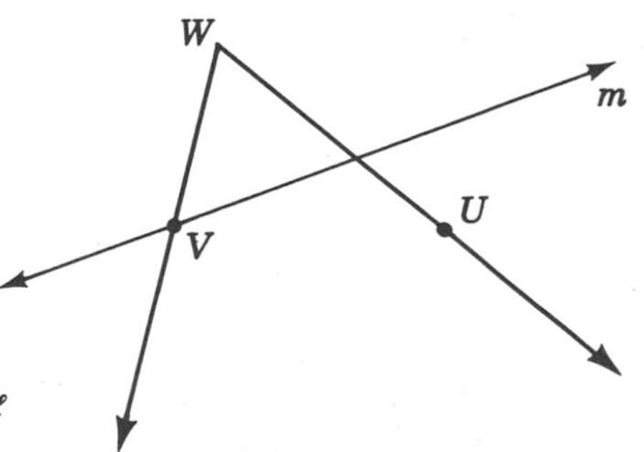

26. Draw the reflection image of $\triangle ABC$ over line d.

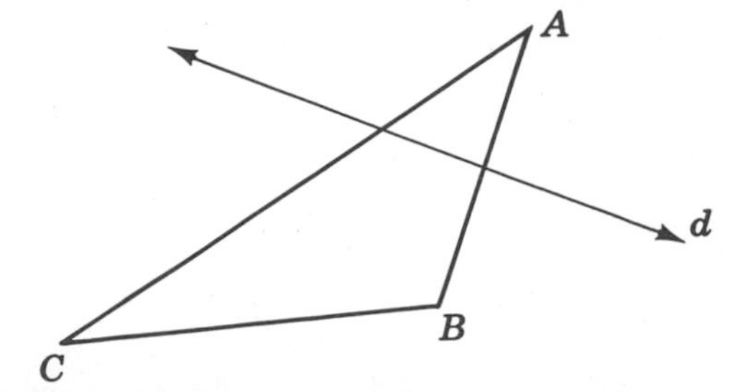

27. Draw the reflection image of $GHJKL$ over line f.

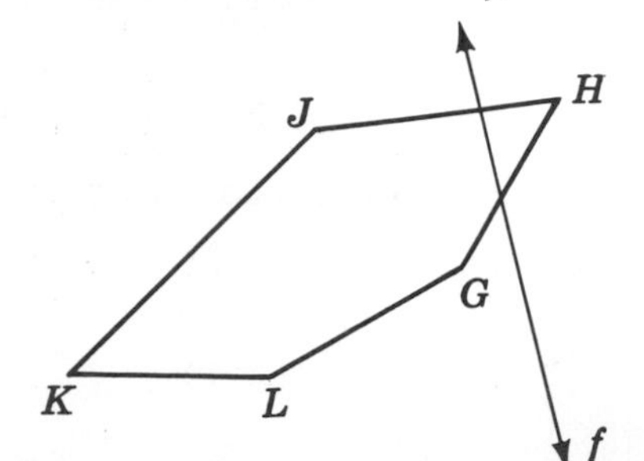

28. Draw the reflection image of circle M over line k.

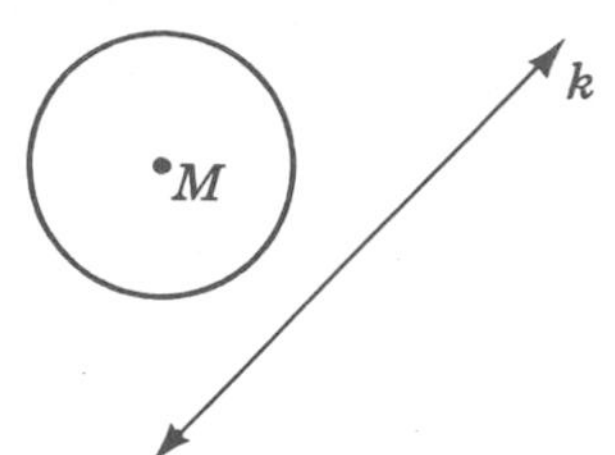

29. The reflection image of A is B. Draw the reflecting line. Then find the image of C when reflected over this line.

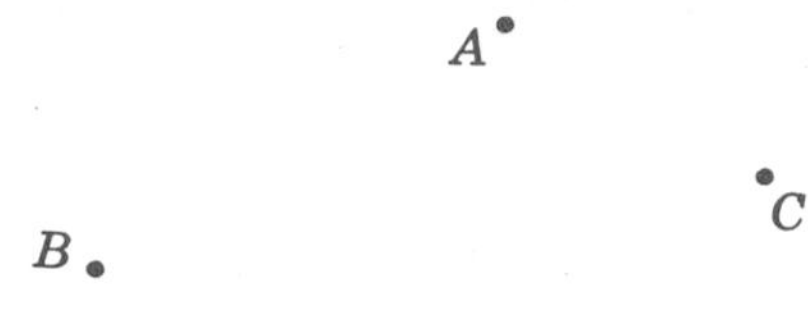

30. Find the images of (2, 4), (0, 5), (−3, −2), and (2, −6) when reflected over the x-axis. Connect the preimages to form a polygon. Do the same for the images. What can you say about the sides and angles of these polygons?

31. Repeat Exercise **30**, but with the y-axis as the reflecting line.

© **32.** Trace the drawing below. Reflect $\triangle ABC$ over line m, calling the image $\triangle A'B'C'$. Then reflect $\triangle A'B'C'$ over line n, calling the image $\triangle A''B''C''$. Use the properties of reflections to prove $AB = A''B''$.

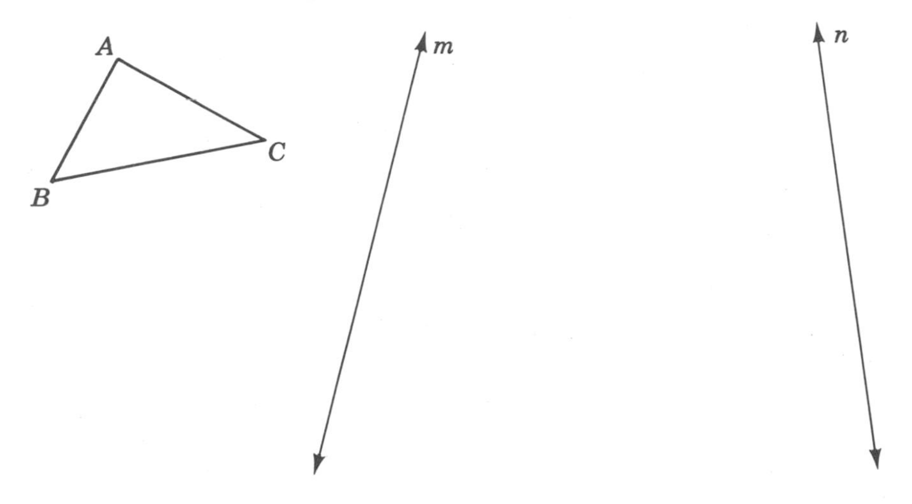

33. Reflect (7, 2) and (−1, −4) over the y-axis. Verify that, for these two points and this line, reflections preserve distance.

NOTATION FOR TRANSFORMATIONS

The terms *reflection*, *reflection image*, and *reflecting line* are long and will be used often. Therefore, as is the custom in mathematics, we introduce abbreviations.

The letter r refers to a reflection. The symbol r_m refers to a reflection over a specific line m.

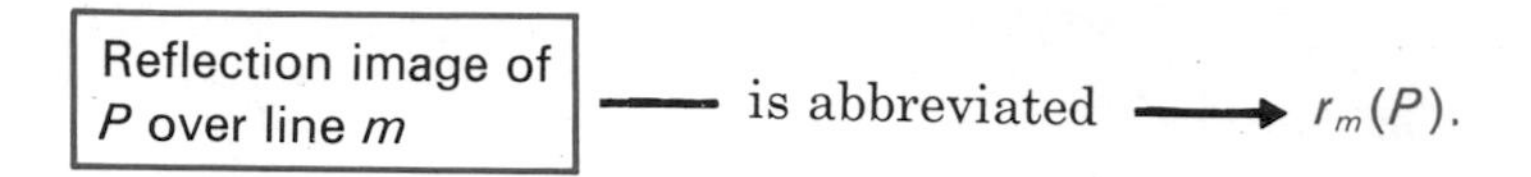

If the reflecting line is not named, we write simply $r(P)$ for the reflection image of a point P.

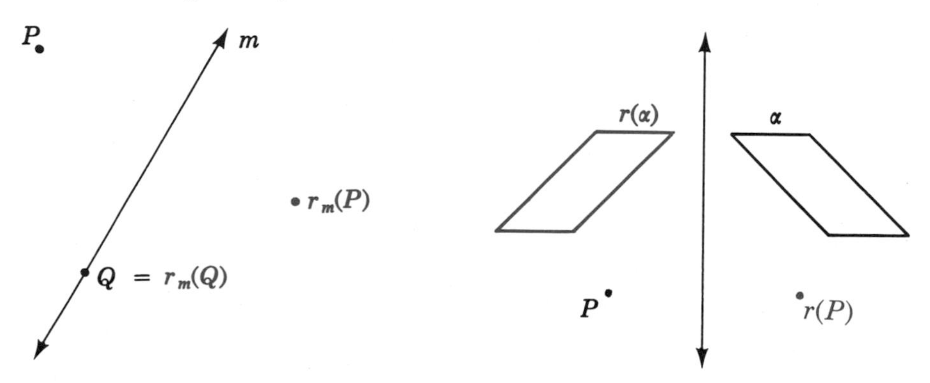

The abbreviations allow shortened statements of many properties of reflections. For example, statement (4) on page 88 can be written:

$$\text{If } r_m(\alpha) = \beta, \text{ then } r_m(\beta) = \alpha.$$

A special form of this notation is used for images of polygons. The order of vertices in the preimage determines the order of vertices in the image.

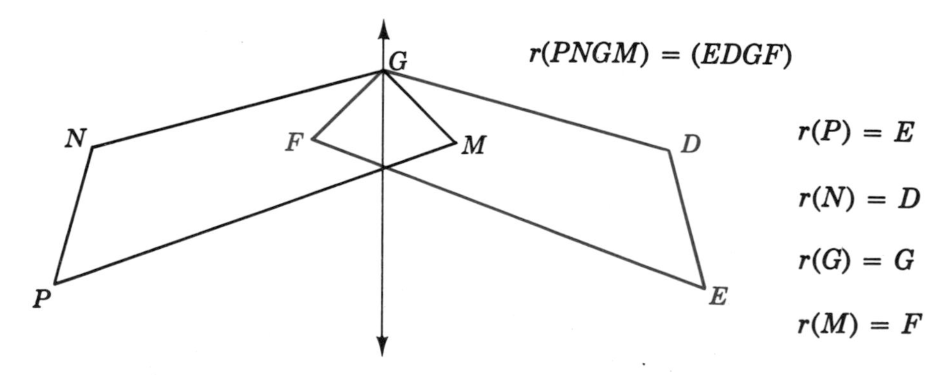

Over each reflecting line in a plane,

(1) each point in the plane has exactly one image.

(2) each point in the plane is the image of exactly one point.

Thus, there is a 1–1 correspondence between preimages and images. The general term for such 1–1 correspondences is *transformation.*

Definition

A **transformation** is a 1–1 correspondence between two sets of points or between a set of points and itself.

In this book, the sets of points chosen for a transformation will be either the entire plane or some figures in the plane. A reflection is one type of transformation. There are many other types. The following rule describes a transformation of a second type.

RULE: If the point is:
(1) above the x-axis, its image is 2 units to the right,
(2) on the x-axis, it coincides with its image,
(3) below the x-axis, its image is 2 units to the left.

Here is $\triangle ABC$ and its image under the transformation described by the rule.

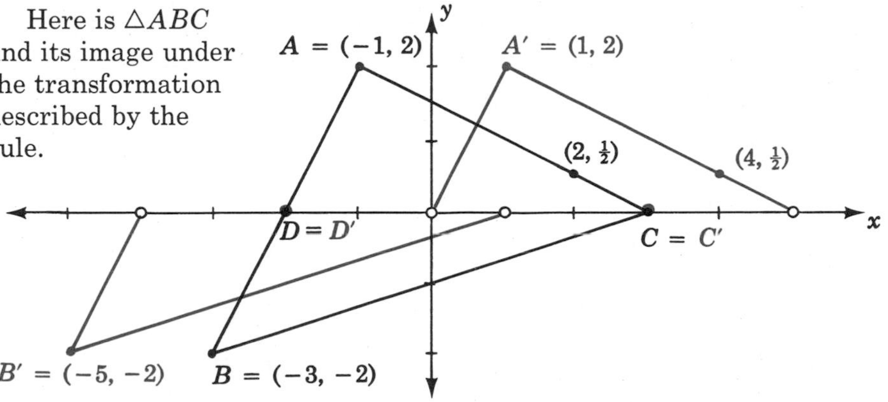

$A = (-1, 2)$ $A' = (1, 2)$ $(2, \frac{1}{2})$ $(4, \frac{1}{2})$ $D = D'$ $C = C'$ $B' = (-5, -2)$ $B = (-3, -2)$ x y

Notice that each point has exactly one image and that every point is the image of exactly one point. So the given rule does describe a 1–1 correspondence between points of the plane—it is a rule for a transformation. This transformation splits the plane, shoving the top half one way, the bottom half the other way, and keeping the x-axis where it is. We can also describe this transformation with coordinates, as in the following restatement of the rule.

RULE:
(1) If $y > 0$, the image of (x, y) is $(x + 2, y)$.
(2) If $y = 0$, the image of (x, y) is (x, y).
(3) If $y < 0$, the image of (x, y) is $(x - 2, y)$.

Just as $r(A)$ stands for the image of A under a reflection r, we use the notation $T(A)$ to stand for the image of A under a transformation T. Calling the above transformation T, we can again shorten the rule.

RULE:
(1) If $y > 0$, $T(x, y) = (x + 2, y)$.
(2) If $y = 0$, $T(x, y) = (x, y)$.
(3) If $y < 0$, $T(x, y) = (x - 2, y)$.

In maps of the earth, there is (theoretically) a 1–1 correspondence between points on the surface of the earth and points on the map. For this reason, the word *map* is often used when transformations are discussed. We say that a transformation *maps* a preimage onto an image, or that a preimage point is *mapped* by a transformation onto its image.

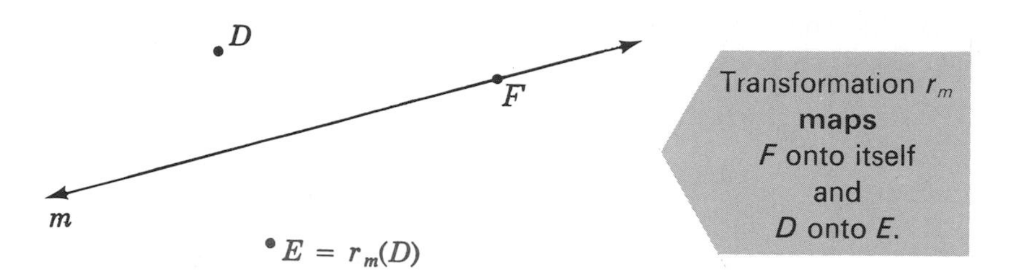

EXERCISES 4.2

Ⓐ **1–3.** Let r be a reflection. Let P and Q be points. Tell the meaning of

1. $r_m(P)$. **2.** $r(Q)$. **3.** $r_t(\overline{PQ})$.

4–7. Given $r(ABCD) = EFGH$, what is

4. $r(\angle ABD)$? **5.** $r(\triangle DAC)$? **6.** $r(B)$? **7.** $r(\overline{BD})$?

8. If $r(\triangle LMO) = \triangle PQR$, then $r(L) =$ ____ and $r(P) =$ ____ .

9. What is a transformation?

10. The symbol ____ stands for the image of point A under a transformation T.

11–13. Given $T(x, y) = (x - 8, y)$, find

11. $T(3, 4)$. **12.** $T(-2, 0.9)$. **13.** $T(0, 0)$.

14–16. Refer to the diagram at the right. Use the language of "maps" to finish each sentence.

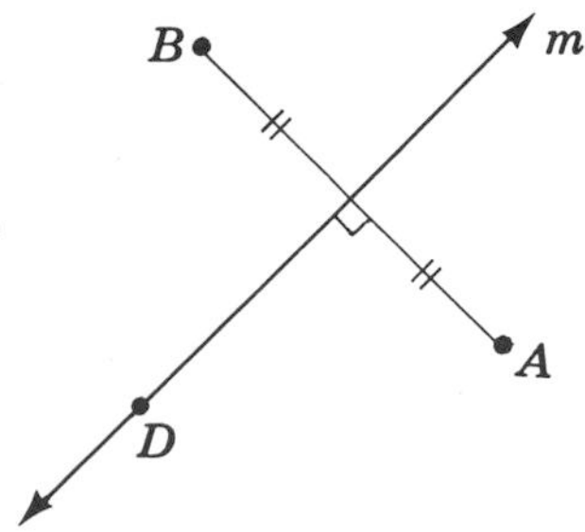

14. r_m ____ B onto A.

15. The point D is ____ onto itself under r_m.

16. The point A is ____ onto B by r_m.

Ⓑ **17–21.** Give the definition or property which supports each statement. (r is a reflection.)

17. If $r(\angle ABC) = \angle XYZ$, then $m\angle ABC = m\angle XYZ$.

18. If $r(E) = F$ and $r(G) = H$, then $EG = FH$.

19. If x is the perpendicular bisector of $\overline{LM}$, then $r_x(M) = L$.

20. If C is on $\overleftrightarrow{AB}$, then $r(C)$ is on the line containing $r(A)$ and $r(B)$.

21. $r(WXYZ)$ and $WXYZ$ have opposite orientation.

22–29. Trace the figure where $r_k(S) = T$ and $r_k(R) = U$. Then draw the following.

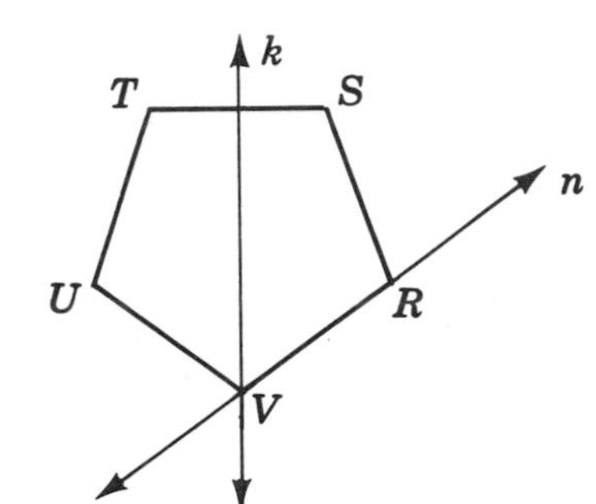

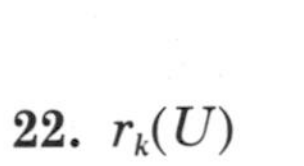

22. $r_k(U)$ **23.** $r_n(U)$

24. $r_n(VRSTU)$ **25.** $r_k(\angle VUT)$

Ⓒ **26.** $r_k(r_n(U))$ **27.** $r_n(r_n(U))$ **28.** $r_k(r_n(S))$ **29.** $r_n(r_k(S))$

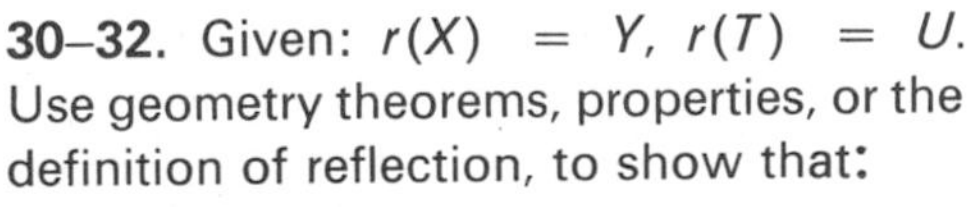

30–32. Given: $r(X) = Y$, $r(T) = U$. Use geometry theorems, properties, or the definition of reflection, to show that:

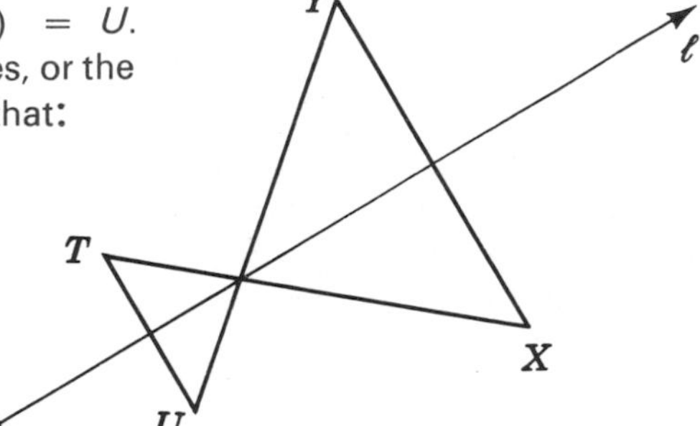

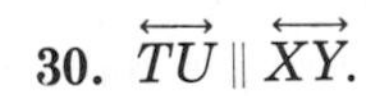

30. $\overleftrightarrow{TU} \parallel \overleftrightarrow{XY}$.

31. $YU = XT$.

32. $m\angle XTU = m\angle YUT$.

33. Show that transformation T on page 93 does *not* preserve distance.

34. Give a rule for the transformation which maps a point on the y-axis onto itself, moves points to the right of the y-axis 2 units up, and moves points to the left of the y-axis 4 units up. Draw the triangle with vertices $(3, 0)$, $(-3, 0)$, and $(0, 4)$ and its image under this transformation.

35–36. Trace the figure of Exercises **22–29**. Draw:

35. $r_k(r_n(VRSTU))$. **36.** $r_n(r_k(VRSTU))$.

4.3 TRANSLATIONS

Transformations which model the physical idea of *sliding* are called *translations.*

A translation t maps a point P onto an image $t(P)$ which is a given distance away in a given direction.

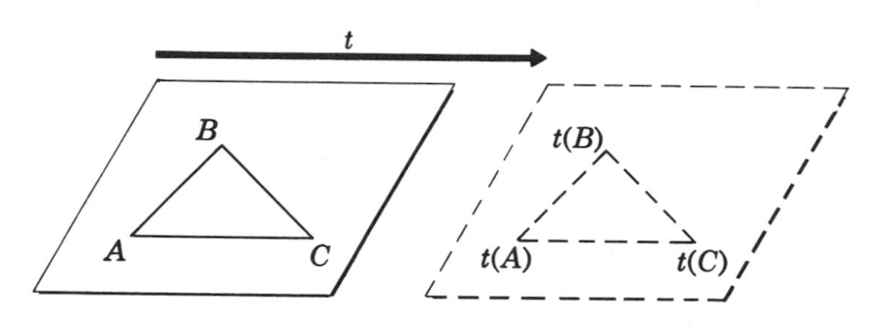

The arrow indicates the *direction* and *distance* for translation t

Notice that the arrow, if moved (but not turned) until its tail is at A, would then have its head at $t(A)$. Similarly, the arrow would connect B to $t(B)$, and C to $t(C)$.

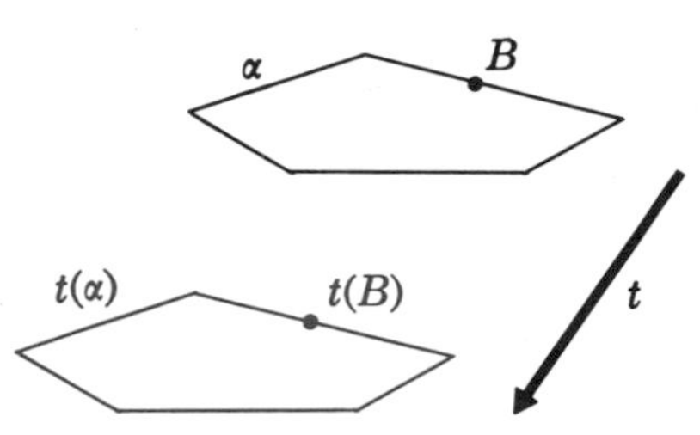

Here is another figure α and a translation image $t(\alpha)$, a point B and its translation image $t(B)$, and the arrow associated with translation t.

Translations are easily described by coordinates. If we add 4 to the first coordinate of each point in a figure, and -2 to the second coordinate, then for each point (x, y) the image is $(x + 4, y - 2)$. Some points of a triangle and their images are given in the table. The entire triangle and its image are graphed at the left.

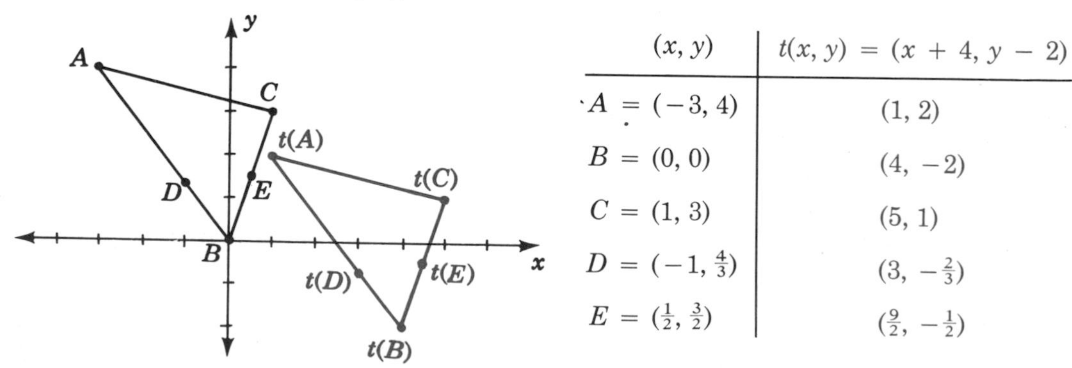

(x, y)	$t(x, y) = (x + 4, y - 2)$
$A = (-3, 4)$	$(1, 2)$
$B = (0, 0)$	$(4, -2)$
$C = (1, 3)$	$(5, 1)$
$D = (-1, \frac{4}{3})$	$(3, -\frac{2}{3})$
$E = (\frac{1}{2}, \frac{3}{2})$	$(\frac{9}{2}, -\frac{1}{2})$

In the graph, notice that adding 4 to the first coordinates has the effect of sliding a figure 4 units to the right. Similarly, adding -2 to second coordinates slides the figure 2 units down. Notice that the combined effect is also a slide (translation).

Of course, adding numbers other than 4 or -2 will produce other translations. In fact, all translations in a plane can be described this way.

Definition

> A **translation** is a transformation which maps (x, y) onto $(x + a, y + b)$, where a and b are given real numbers.

In a translation, the distance between a point and its image is the same for *all points*. This distance (the length of the "arrow") is called the **magnitude** of the translation. For example, the translation on page 96 mapping (x, y) onto $(x + 4, y - 2)$ has *magnitude* $\sqrt{20}$—the distance between any point, say (1, 3), and its image, (5, 1), is $\sqrt{20}$.

EXERCISES 4.3

Ⓐ **1–4.** Let t be a translation such that $t(\triangle ABC) = \triangle MPQ$.

1. What is the magnitude of t?

2. Trace the figure and draw $t(D)$.

3. Trace the figure and draw $t(Q)$.

4. Which of the following statements is an indication that translations preserve distance?

a. $BP = CQ$ **b.** $AC = MQ$ **c.** $AM = BP$

5. Translations are mathematical models of physical actions called ______.

6. Which is the more general term, *translation* or *transformation*?

7–10. A translation maps (x, y) onto $(x - 5, y + \frac{9}{2})$. Find the image of each point.

7. (1, 6) **8.** $(5, \frac{9}{2})$ **9.** $(5, -\frac{9}{2})$ **10.** $(0, -4)$

Ⓑ **11–13.** Translation t has the given arrow. Trace the given figure and draw the following.

11. $t(A)$

12. $t(\angle BDC)$

13. $t(ABCD)$

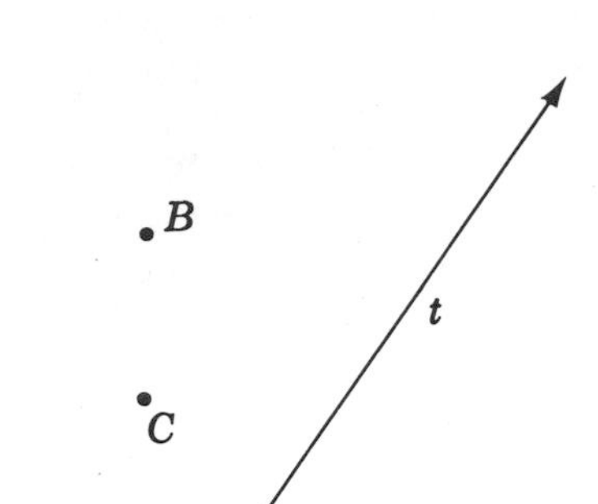

14. A translation t has the rule $t(x, y) = (x + 1000, y - 1)$. Describe the effect this translation has on each point.

15. A translation maps (3, 6) onto (5, 15). Find the image of (x, y).

16. Translation t maps $(2, -9)$ onto $(-1, -8)$. Find $t(4, 0)$.

17. A triangle has vertices (1, 3), (2, −4), and (−3, 8). Graph this triangle and its image under the translation which maps (x, y) onto $(x + 3, y - 1)$.

18. A translation maps Q onto P. Trace the figure and draw the image of $\triangle MNQ$ under this translation.

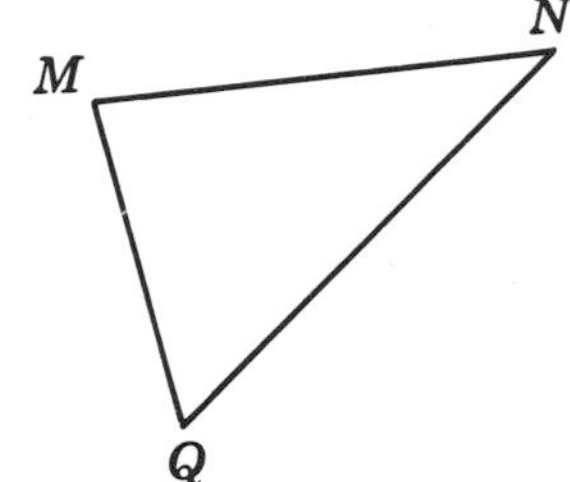

19. Which is not an equation describing a translation t?

a. $t(x, y) = (x - 1, y - 2)$ **b.** $t(x, y) = (1 + x, 2 + y)$

c. $t(x, y) = (x + 1, y + 2)$ **d.** $t(x, y) = (1 - x, 2 - y)$

20. If $t(x, y) = (x - 2, y - 3)$, find the translation image of the square with vertices (0, 1), (1, 0), (0, −1), and (−1, 0). (Use graph paper).

Ⓒ **21.** Let (x_1, y_1) and (x_2, y_2) be any points. Then $(x_1 + a, y_1 + b)$ and $(x_2 + a, y_2 + b)$ are the images of these points under a translation. Use the distance formula to show that these four points are vertices of a parallelogram.

22. How does Exercise **21** show that translations preserve distance?

23. How does Exercise **21** show that, under a given translation, the distance between a point and its image is the same for all points?

If you put a pin through two sheets of paper, then hold one sheet fixed while you *turn* the other, you have performed a physical action whose mathematical model is a *rotation*. Shown below is $\triangle ABC$ and its rotation image, $\triangle A'B'C'$.

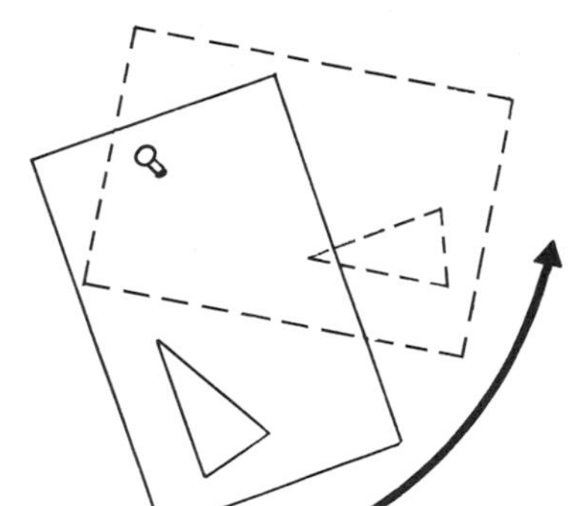

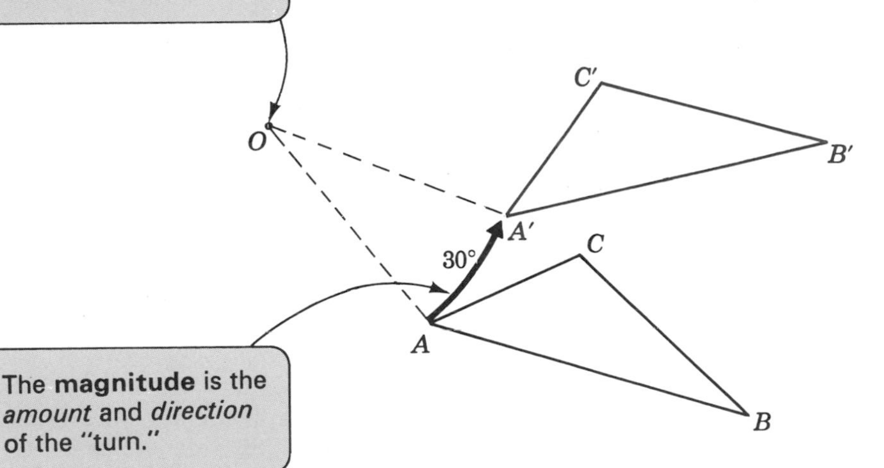

A rotation is determined by its *center* and *magnitude*. For the given rotation, the statements at the right should be true. Check them.

$$m\angle A'OA = 30^\circ \qquad AO = A'O$$
$$m\angle B'OB = 30^\circ \qquad BO = B'O$$
$$m\angle C'OC = 30^\circ \qquad CO = C'O$$

We use positive numbers to refer to counterclockwise rotations and negative numbers to refer to clockwise rotations. So, the rotation above has magnitude 30°. But, if we consider $\triangle ABC$ to be the image of $\triangle A'B'C'$ under a clockwise rotation with center O, then the magnitude is -30°.

Definition

A **rotation** is a transformation which maps

1. a point O (the *center*) onto itself;
2. any other point A onto A' where the arc AA' has center O and its measure is a real number x (the *magnitude*).

Example: Find the image of N under a rotation with magnitude $-50°$ and center C.

- N and its image will be the same distance from C. So, draw the circle passing through N with center C.
- Since the magnitude is $-50°$, the rotation is clockwise. So, measure a $50°$ angle with $\overrightarrow{CN}$ for one of the sides as shown. ($\overrightarrow{CN}$ means "ray CN," the ray with endpoint C and containing N.)
- The other side of the angle intersects the circle at N', the image of N.

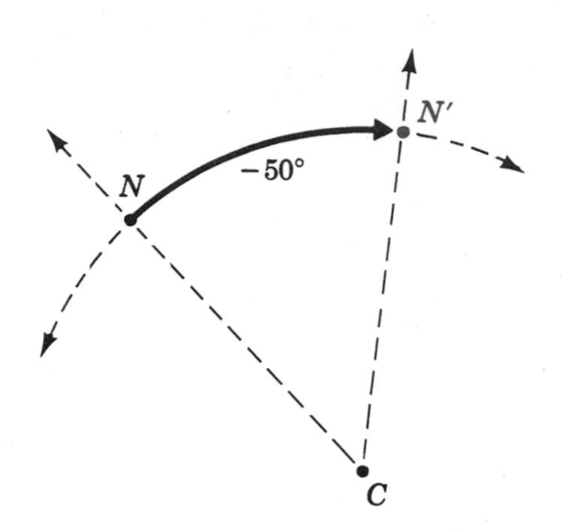

Some of the most important rotations are those of 90°, 180°, and 270° (which is the same as $-90°$). Here is a right triangle and its images under these rotations, given center G.

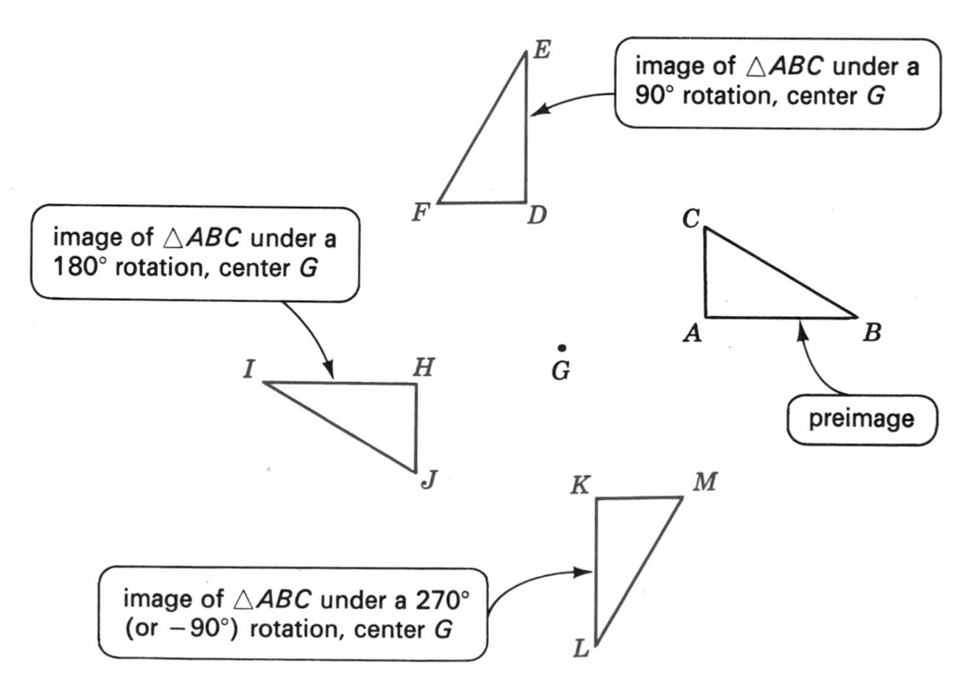

Like reflections, rotations preserve distance. For example, notice that $\overline{DF}$ is the image of $\overline{AC}$ under the 90° rotation and $DF = AC$.

Ⓐ **1.** Rotations are mathematical models of physical actions called ____.

2. What is the definition of *rotation*?

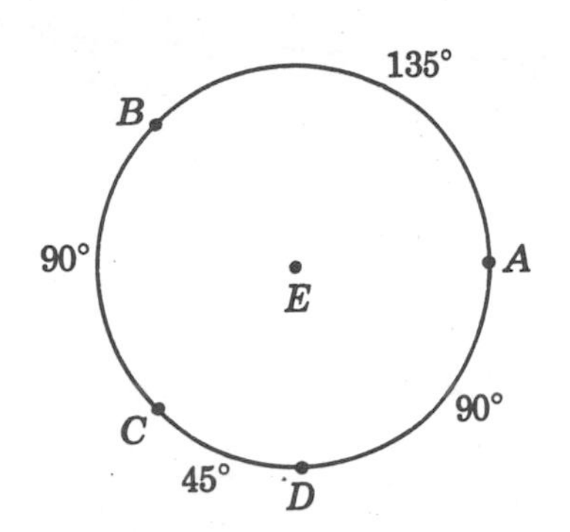

3–8. The circle at the right has center E. Some arc measures are given in degrees. Give the magnitude of the rotation with center E for which:

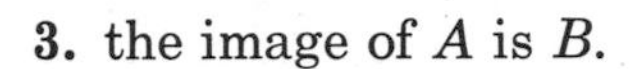

3. the image of A is B.

4. the image of B is A.

5. the image of B is D.

6. the image of C is A.

7. the image of D is B.

8. the image of C is C.

9–11. Let R be a rotation with center Z and $F' = R(F)$.

9. Measure an appropriate angle to estimate the magnitude of R.

10. $R(Z) =$ ____

11. True or False? $FZ = F'Z$

Ⓑ **12–15.** Trace the figure at the right.

12. Rotate W 150° about V.

13. Rotate W $-10°$ about V.

14. Rotate $\overline{AM}$ 95° about W.

15. Rotate $\overline{AM}$ 95° about M.

16–20. Trace the indicated preimage and all key points. (Use a *single* tracing for **18–20.**)

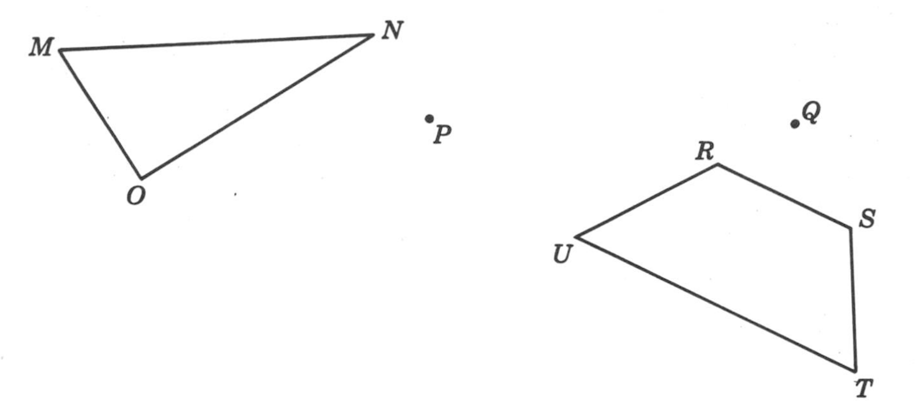

16. Rotate $\triangle MNO$ 60° about N.

17. Rotate $\triangle MNO$ 90° about P. Call the image $\triangle M'N'O'$. How do $\overleftrightarrow{MN}$ and $\overleftrightarrow{M'N'}$ seem to be related?

18. Rotate $RSTU$ $-115°$ about Q. Call the image $R'S'T'U'$.

19. Rotate $RSTU$ $-115°$ about U. Call the image $R''S''T''U''$.

20. Compare the results of Exercises **18–19**. Make a decision: Is $R''S''T''U''$ the image of $R'S'T'U'$ under a translation?

21. Estimate the image of (6, 2) when rotated $-89.5°$ about the origin.

© **22.** A transformation maps (x, y) onto $(-y, x)$. Find the images of a few points. Then describe the transformation.

23. Repeat Exercise **22** for the transformation which maps (x, y) onto $(-x, -y)$.

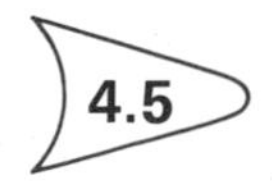

COMPOSITES OF TRANSFORMATIONS

Suppose that a number x is multiplied by 10. Then the result is divided by 5. What is the total effect on the original number?

$x \cdot 10 = 10x$ → $10x \div 5 = 2x$

The effect is to multiply the original number by 2.

We could write

(division by 5) following (multiplication by 10) = multiplication by 2,

or (division by 5) ∘ (multiplication by 10) = multiplication by 2.

The symbol ∘ can be read, "following."

Now, we ask what happens if one transformation follows another.

The drawing at the right shows a rotation of 45° following a rotation of 90°, each with center O.

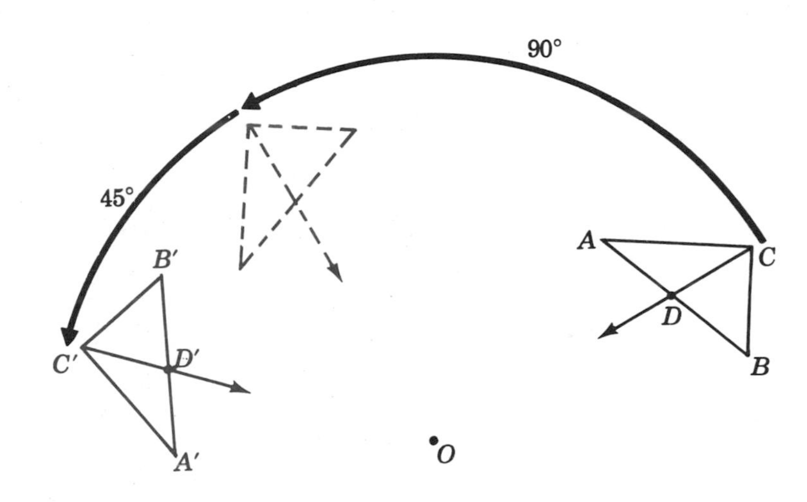

What transformation maps $ABCD$ *directly* onto $A'B'C'D'$? You should see that a rotation of 135° (with point O as center) does this. That is,

(rotation of 45°) following (rotation of 90°) = rotation of 135°.

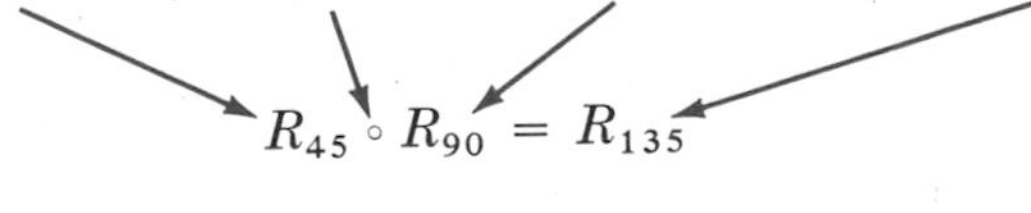

IMPORTANT: This is true only if the rotations have the same center.

From the figure, you can verify that

$$A'B'C'D' = R_{45}(R_{90}(ABCD))$$

because $R_{90}(ABCD)$ is the first image (dashed) and has been rotated 45° to get $A'B'C'D'$.

Theorem 4.5.1

A rotation of magnitude x following a rotation of magnitude y with the same center results in a rotation of magnitude $x + y$ with that center. In short,

$$R_x \circ R_y = R_{x+y}.$$

For each point in the plane, there is exactly one final image as a result of the two rotations, and no point is the final image of two different given points. Thus the result of performing rotation R_{90} followed by rotation R_{45} is a transformation. We call this transformation the *composite* of R_{90} and R_{45}, written $R_{45} \circ R_{90}$.

In the notation $R_{45} \circ R_{90}$, notice that the transformation applied first is on the *right*. The operation indicated by $\circ$ is called *composition*. From Theorem 4.5.1, we can draw the following conclusion.

> The composite of two rotations with the same center is a rotation.

We now define the composite of any two transformations.

Definition

Let T_1 and T_2 be transformations. The transformation which maps a point P onto $T_2(T_1(P))$ is called the **composite** of T_1 and T_2, written $T_2 \circ T_1$.

Now we consider the composite of two translations.

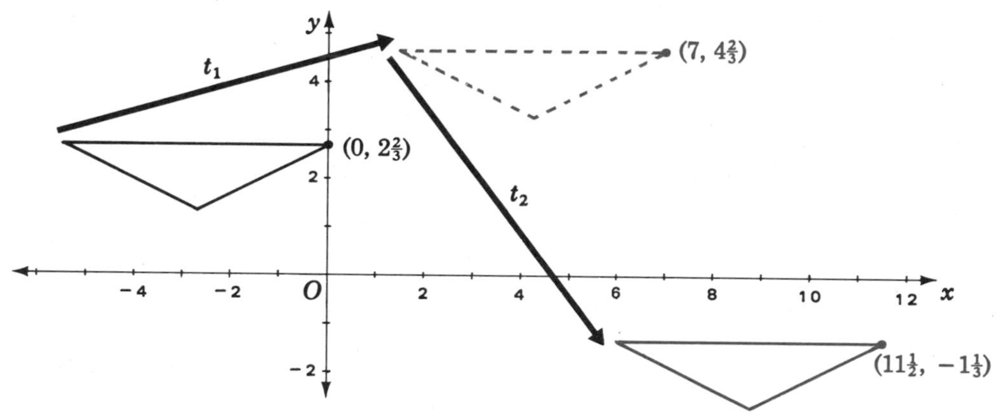

Translation t_1 adds 7 to first coordinates and 2 to second coordinates. Translation t_2 adds $4\frac{1}{2}$ to first coordinates and -6 to second coordinates.

$$t_1(x, y) = (x + 7, y + 2) \qquad t_2(x, y) = (x + 4\tfrac{1}{2}, y - 6)$$

When t_1 is followed by t_2, the result is a composite which adds $11\frac{1}{2}$ to first coordinates and -4 to second coordinates.

$$\begin{aligned} t_2 \circ t_1(x, y) = t_2(t_1(x, y)) &= t_2(x + 7, y + 2) \\ &= (x + 7 + 4\tfrac{1}{2}, y + 2 - 6) \\ &= (x + 11\tfrac{1}{2}, y - 4) \end{aligned}$$

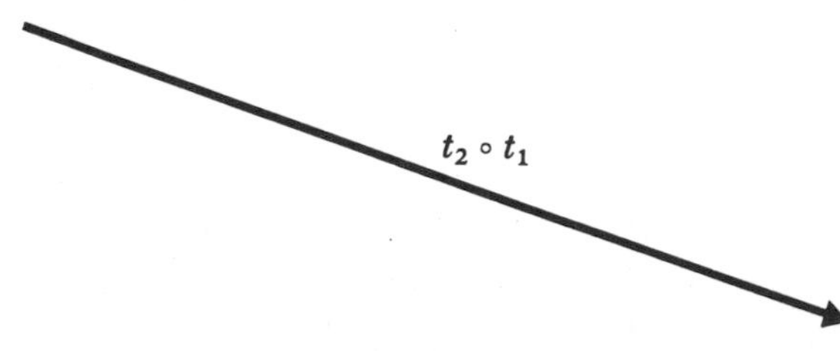

So $t_2 \circ t_1$ is a translation (as you can see from looking at the graph). An arrow for this translation is given at the left. Trace the arrow and place it on the picture above to check that it represents the translation.

These results are generalized in the next theorem.

Theorem 4.5.2

Let t_1 and t_2 be translations.

$$t_1(x, y) = (x + a, y + b) \qquad t_2(x, y) = (x + c, y + d)$$

Then $t_2 \circ t_1$ maps (x, y) onto $(x + a + c, y + b + d)$.

PROOF: $t_2 \circ t_1(x, y) = t_2(t_1(x, y))$ — Def. of composite

$= t_2(x + a, y + b)$ — Given what t_1 does

$= ((x + a) + c, (y + b) + d)$ — Given what t_2 does

$= (x + a + c, y + b + d)$ — Associativity of addition

Theorem 4.5.2 tells how to get a formula for the composite of two translations and also shows that

> The composite of two translations is a translation.

EXERCISES 4.5

Ⓐ 1. When one transformation is followed by another, the result is called the _____ of the transformations.

2. The composite of two rotations with the same center is a _____.

3. If T_1 is applied to a point, then T_2 is applied to the image point, which symbol denotes the composite: $T_1 \circ T_2$ or $T_2 \circ T_1$?

4. The image of Q under a transformation T_1 is Q'. The image of Q' under a transformation T_2 is Q''. Then $Q'' =$

   a. $T_2(Q)$. b. $T_1(Q')$. c. $T_2(T_1(Q))$. d. $T_1(T_2(Q))$.

5–8. R is a rotation of 60°, S is a rotation of 90°, and T is a rotation of −90°, all with the same center. Describe each composite.

5. $R \circ S$ 6. $S \circ R$ 7. $R \circ T$ 8. $S \circ T$

9. The composite of two translations is a _____.

10–15. Let $t(x, y) = (x + 2, y + 3)$ and $h(x, y) = (x - 2, y + 4)$. Calculate:

10. $t(12, 20)$ 11. $h(t(12, 20))$ 12. $h \circ t(12, 20)$

Ⓑ 13. $h \circ t(-3, 8)$ 14. $h(t(x, y))$ 15. a formula for $h \circ t$

16. If t_1 maps (x, y) onto $(x, y - 3)$ and t_2 maps (x, y) onto $(x + 10, y - 1)$, then $t_2 \circ t_1$ maps (x, y) onto ____.

17–26. Each of the small triangles in the drawing is equilateral. R is a rotation of 60° with center O. A translation t maps O onto A. Find each image.

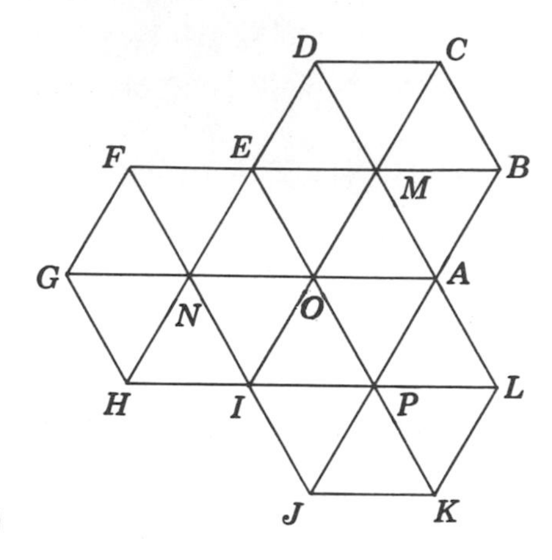

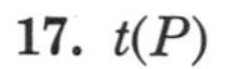

17. $t(P)$ 18. $R(I)$

19. $R(\triangle POI)$ 20. $t(\overline{FI})$

21. $R \circ R(M)$ 22. $t \circ t(E)$

23. $t \circ R(I)$ 24. $R \circ t(I)$

25. $R \circ t(ENIO)$ 26. $R \circ R(\triangle NHG)$

27–31. Trace the given figure for each exercise. R is a rotation of 90° about P. Translations t_1 and t_2 are described by the arrows. Draw the image of $\triangle ABC$ under each composite transformation.

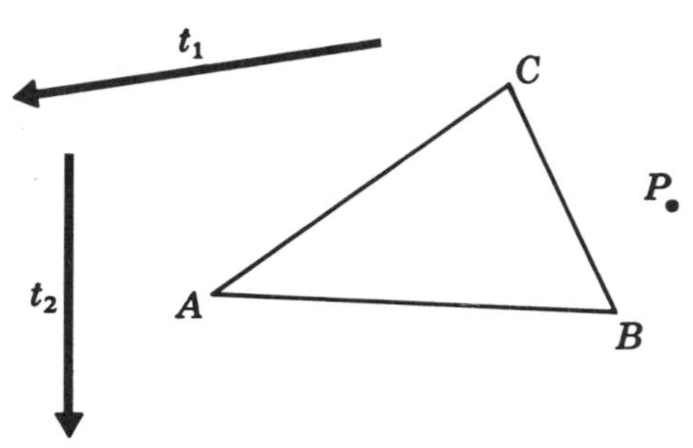

27. $R \circ R$

28. $t_2 \circ t_1$

29. $t_1 \circ t_2$

30. $t_1 \circ R$ 31. $R \circ t_1$

32. The answers to Exercises **30** and **31** are not the same. What does this tell about the operation of composition?

Ⓒ 33. The composite of two rotations *with different centers* can be a translation. Let R_1 be a rotation of 90° about A. Let R_2 be a rotation of 270° about B.

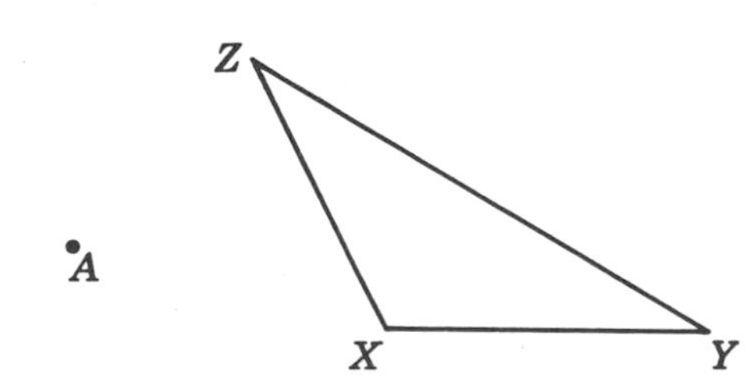

a. Trace the figure and draw $R_2 \circ R_1(\triangle XYZ)$.

b. Draw the arrow which describes $R_2 \circ R_1$.

34–36. Refer to Exercises **17–26**. The transformation $t \circ R \circ R \circ R$ maps E onto L. What composite of the transformations t and R maps

34. K onto A? 35. $\overline{GH}$ onto $\overline{PA}$? 36. O onto H?

COMPOSITES OF REFLECTIONS

It may surprise you that the composite of two reflections is not a reflection. Pictured below is a flag and its image under the composite $r_\ell \circ r_m$.

The flag was reflected over m. Then the image was reflected over ℓ.

The lines ℓ and m have been selected parallel.

The composite is the transformation which maps the preimage onto the image. You can see that the composite seems to be the translation associated with the arrow drawn at the right.

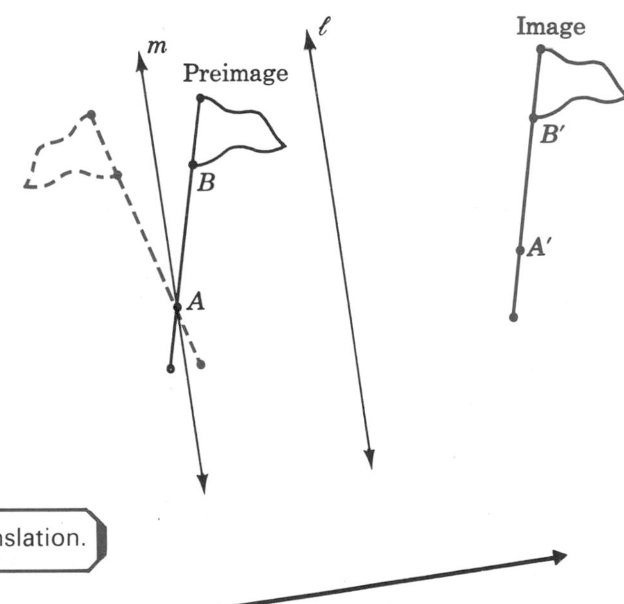

> Whenever $\ell \parallel m$, $r_\ell \circ r_m$ is a translation.

In fact,

> (1) the direction of the translation is perpendicular to the reflecting lines.
>
> (2) the magnitude of the translation is twice the distance between the reflecting lines.

It is natural now to consider composites of reflections where the reflecting lines intersect.

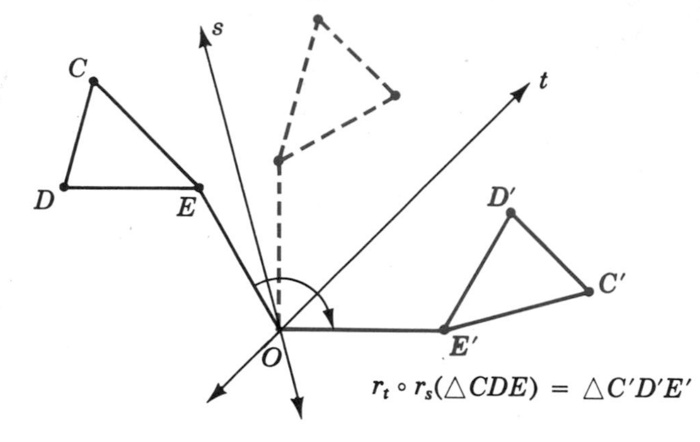

The drawing indicates that such a composite seems to be a *rotation* about the point of intersection of the reflecting lines.

The reflecting lines determine the rotation. Check the drawing to see that

> (1) the center of the rotation is the intersection of the reflecting lines.
>
> (2) the magnitude of a rotation is twice the measure of the angle formed by the reflecting lines.

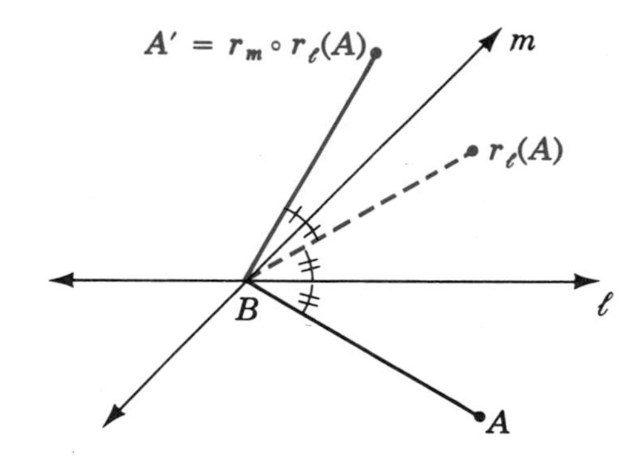

This last property can be illustrated by the given diagram.

$r_m \circ r_\ell$ is a *composite rotation.*

B is the *center.*

$m\angle A'BA$ is the *magnitude.*

And, $m\angle A'BA$ = twice the measure of an angle formed by ℓ and m.

From the properties of reflections, it is possible to prove the following theorem. Because the proof is long and involved, we omit it.

Theorem 4.6.1

Let ℓ and m be lines. Let r_ℓ and r_m be reflections.

a. If $\ell \parallel m$, $r_\ell \circ r_m$ is a translation.

b. If ℓ intersects m, $r_\ell \circ r_m$ is a rotation.

Any composite of reflections is called an **isometry**. Thus, reflections, rotations, and translations are types of isometries. We now have three ways to describe translations and two ways to describe rotations.

DESCRIPTIONS	Translations	Rotations
Geometric	an arrow with a given direction and length	a given center and magnitude C −30°
Algebraic	maps (x, y) onto $(x + a, y + b)$	will be discussed in Chapter 8
Isometric (Composites of reflections)	composite of two reflections over parallel lines	composite of two reflections over intersecting lines

Each type of description serves a useful purpose. The geometric descriptions show how figures are related to their images. In graphing, the algebraic descriptions are helpful. Finally, isometric descriptions are related to the important idea of congruence in the next section.

EXERCISES 4.6

Ⓐ 1. A composite of two reflections over parallel lines is a ____.

2. A composite of two reflections over intersecting lines is a ____.

3. Lines m and n are parallel. So $r_n \circ r_m$ is a ____.

4. What is the magnitude of $r_n \circ r_m$?

5. What is the direction of $r_n \circ r_m$?

Ex. 3–5

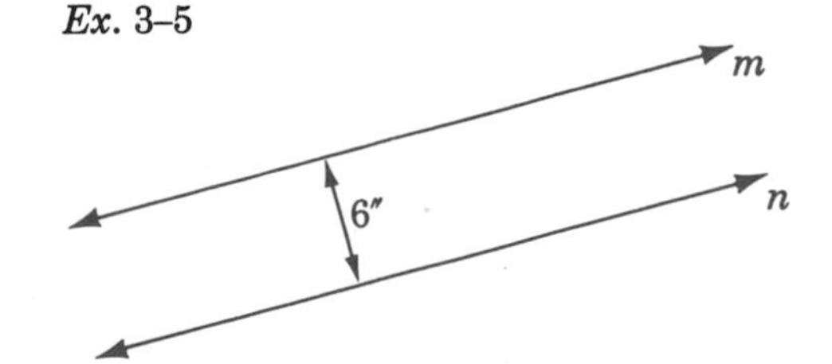

6. What type of transformation is $r_t \circ r_s$?

7. Give the magnitude and center of $r_t \circ r_s$.

8. What is an isometry?

9. Give two ways of describing rotations.

10. Give three ways of describing translations.

Ex. 6–7

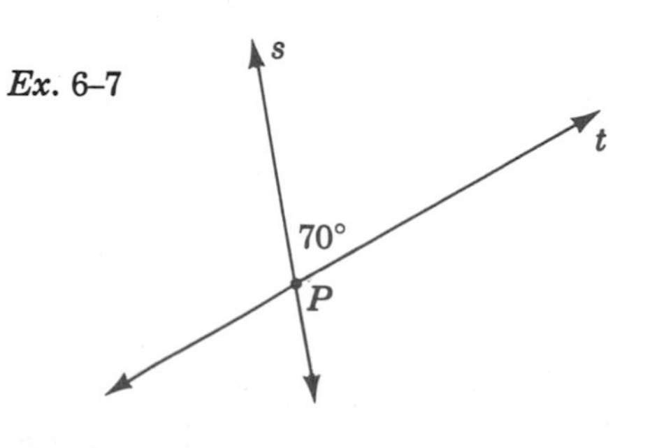

Ⓑ **11–14.** Trace the drawing for each exercise.

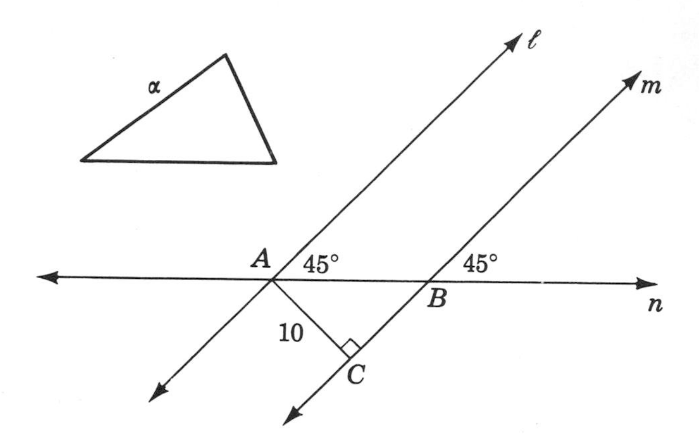

11. Draw $r_m \circ r_\ell(\alpha)$ and describe $r_m \circ r_\ell$.

12. Draw $r_\ell \circ r_n(\alpha)$ and describe $r_\ell \circ r_n$.

13. Draw $r_n \circ r_\ell(\alpha)$ and describe $r_n \circ r_\ell$.

14. Draw $r_m \circ r_m(\alpha)$ and describe $r_m \circ r_m$.

15. If k and m are lines and $k \perp m$, describe $r_k \circ r_m$.

16–19. What theorem, property, or definition can help explain each situation?

16. In a clothing store, mirrors are placed at angles to each other so that a person can see how the clothes look even from the back.

17. If two mirrors are placed parallel and you are between them, you will see many images behind each other in each mirror.

18. In a mirror, the image of your right hand looks like your left hand. (The mirror does *not* switch right and left, as some people think.)

Ⓒ **19.** In a kaleidoscope there are many rotation images.

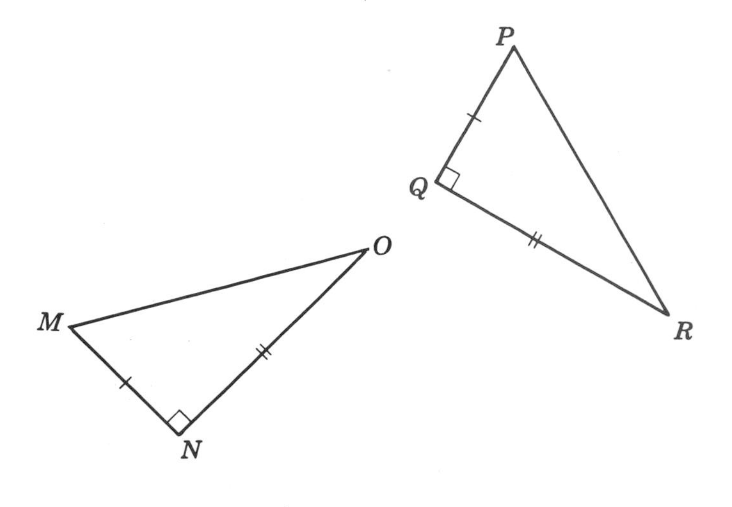

20. Trace the figure. Draw two reflecting lines a and b so that $r_b \circ r_a(\triangle MNO) = \triangle PQR$. (There is more than one correct answer.)

21. Trace the figure. $\triangle PQR$ is the image of $\triangle MNO$ under a rotation. Locate the center of this rotation.

Young children are asked to test whether two figures are congruent by tracing one of the figures, then sliding, turning, or flipping the paper to see if the tracing falls upon the other figure.

Since results of slides, turns, and flips are mathematically described by translations, rotations, and reflections, it is natural to have the following definition of congruence.

Definition

Any two figures α and β are **congruent** if and only if there is a composite of reflections, rotations, or translations which maps α onto β.

As you know, a definition should not be longer than it has to be. The last section indicated that rotations and translations are themselves composites of reflections—isometries. Thus, we can shorten the preceding definition.

Definition (Shortened)

Any two figures α and β are **congruent** if and only if there is an isometry which maps α onto β.

In symbols, we write $\alpha \cong \beta$ which means α is congruent to β.

By the definition, each figure below is congruent to the original figure and to each of the others. Can you see how each is obtained from the others by reflections?

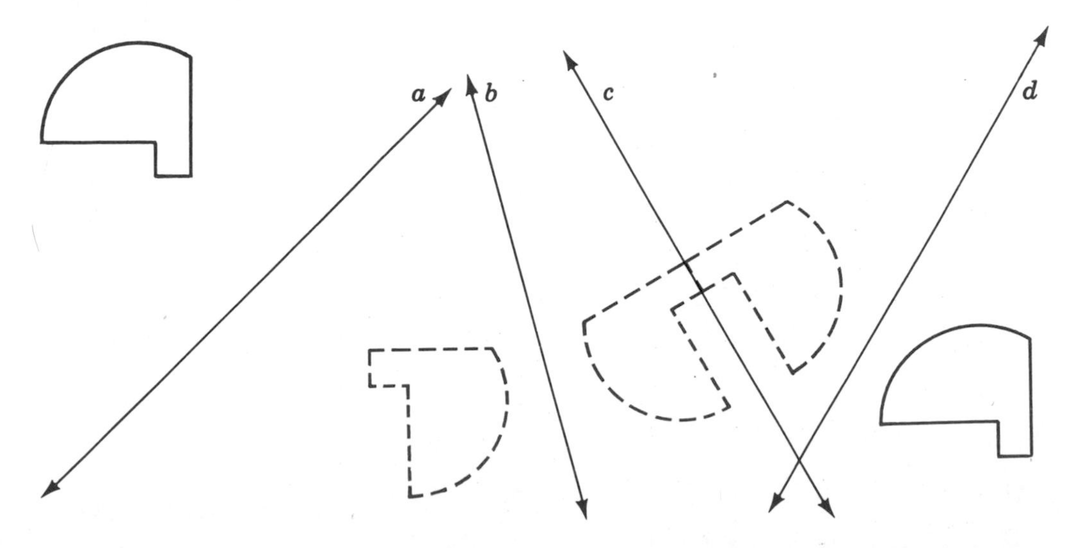

Congruent figures look very much alike. This is because reflections preserve distance and angle measure. So do all composites of reflections. Thus, for any isometry,

(1)	images of collinear points are collinear points.
(2)	distance is preserved.
(3)	the image of a segment is a segment of the same length.
(4)	the image of an angle is an angle of the same measure.

From properties (3) and (4), we can deduce a theorem.

Theorem 4.7.1

In congruent figures, corresponding segments have the same length and corresponding angles have the same measure.

In earlier work in geometry, you have studied many conditions under which figures are congruent. We can use transformations to verify that these conditions guarantee congruence. Below, $\triangle ABC$ and $\triangle XYZ$ have two sides and the included angle of one congruent to two sides and the included angle of the other (*SAS*).

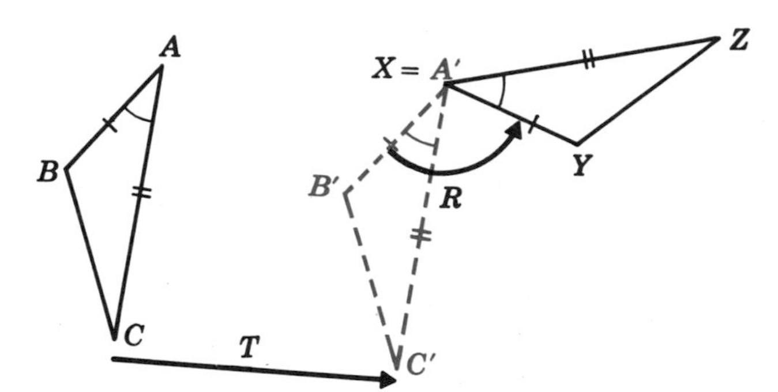

If T is a translation mapping A onto X and $\triangle ABC$ onto $\triangle XB'C'$, and R is a rotation mapping $\triangle XB'C'$ onto $\triangle XYZ$, then

$$R \circ T(\triangle ABC) = \triangle XYZ.$$

So, $\triangle ABC \cong \triangle XYZ$.

Since rotations and translations are composites of reflections, this diagram indicates that $\triangle ABC$ could be mapped onto $\triangle XYZ$ by a composite of *four* reflections (two for the translation, two for the rotation).

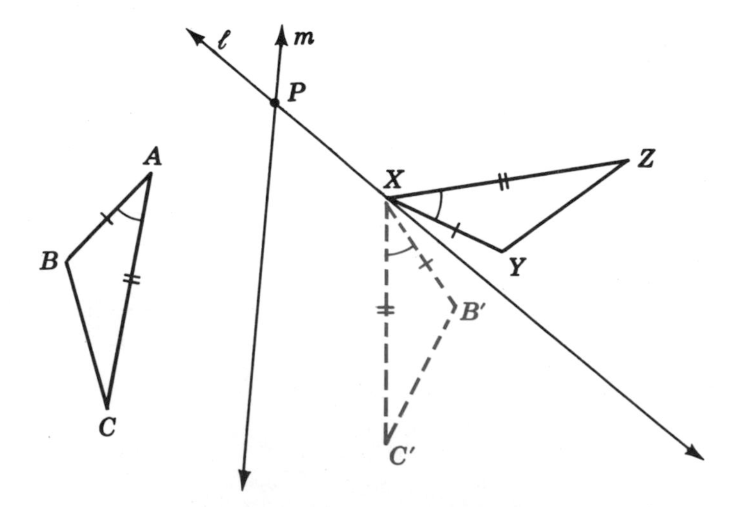

It is possible to map $\triangle ABC$ onto $\triangle XYZ$ by a composite of *two* reflections, as shown at the left.

The reflecting lines intersect, so indeed $\triangle XYZ$ is the image of $\triangle ABC$ under a single rotation!

$$r_\ell \circ r_m(\triangle ABC) = \triangle XYZ$$

Again, $\triangle ABC \cong \triangle XYZ$.

In later chapters, we often talk about congruent graphs. This means that one graph can be mapped onto the other by some isometry.

Pictured below are two congruent intervals. Each can be mapped onto the other by a translation.

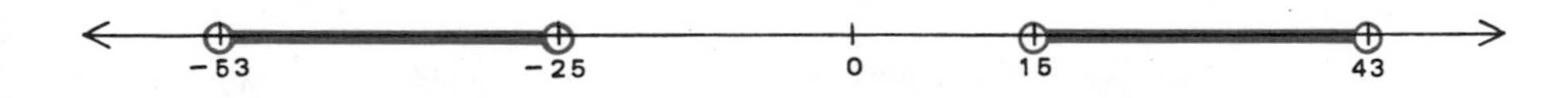

Here are two graphs α and β which are congruent. Can you give two different ways of mapping α onto β?

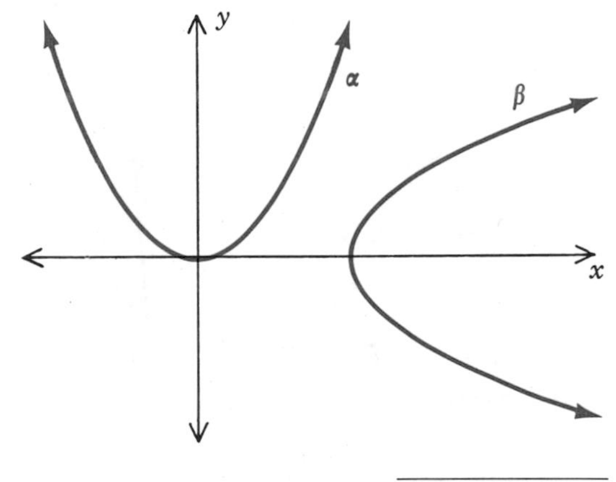

EXERCISES 4.7

Ⓐ **1.** When are two figures congruent, by definition?

2. What are congruent graphs?

3. Name four properties preserved by isometries.

4. Name two properties of congruent figures.

Ⓑ **5–10.** Recall from geometry, or use your intuition, to answer each question. What conditions are sufficient to guarantee that

5. two circles are congruent?

6. two segments are congruent?

7. two angles are congruent?

8. two rectangles are congruent?

9. two triangles are congruent? (Give at least 3 answers.)

10. two right triangles are congruent? (Give at least 4 answers.)

11. Refer to the illustrations on page 112. Explain why it is impossible to map $\triangle ABC$ onto $\triangle XYZ$ by a composite of *three* reflections. (HINT: Consider orientation.)

12. Under what condition(s) would two intervals be congruent?

13. Trace the figure. Given $AB = CD$, show that $\overline{AB}$ can be mapped onto $\overline{CD}$ by a composite of two reflections.

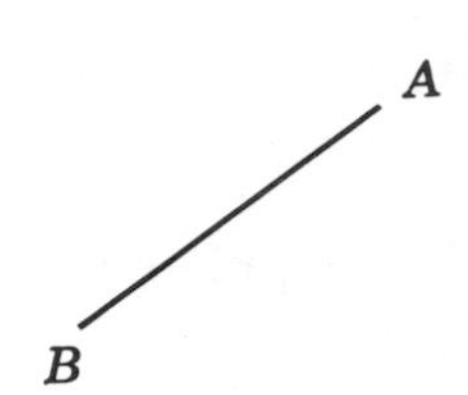

C

D

Ⓒ **14–16.** Trace the figure for each exercise. Given $\triangle GHI \cong \triangle JKL$, show that $\triangle GHI$ can be mapped onto $\triangle JKL$ by a composite of:

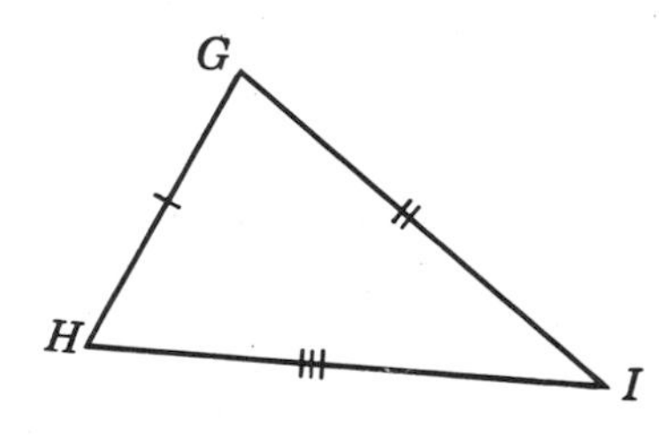

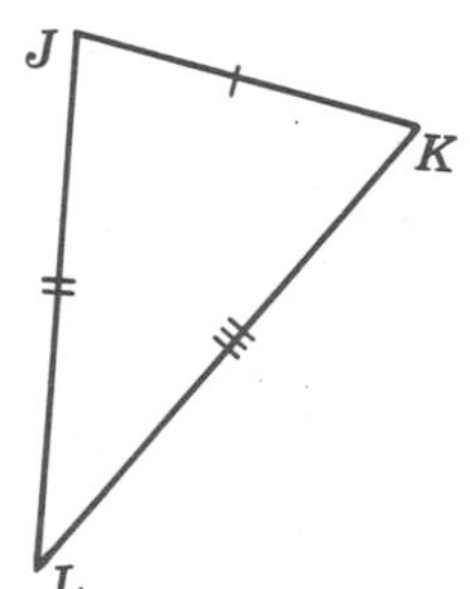

14. a reflection, a rotation, and a translation.

15. a reflection and a rotation.

16. three reflections.

SIZE TRANSFORMATIONS AND SIMILARITY

Distance-preserving transformations, like reflections, rotations, and translations, always yield images which are congruent to the preimages. To study similar figures, we need to introduce a new type of transformation. A **size transformation** is determined by a point called the *center* and a nonzero number called the *magnitude*.

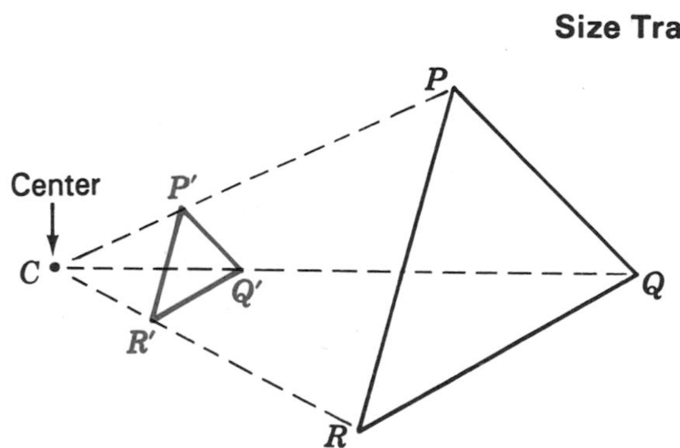

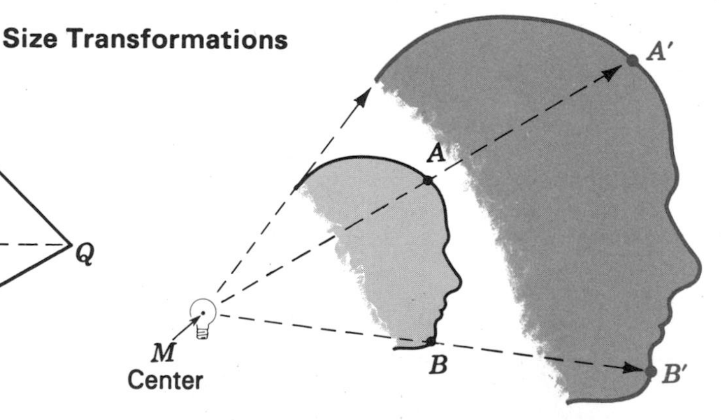

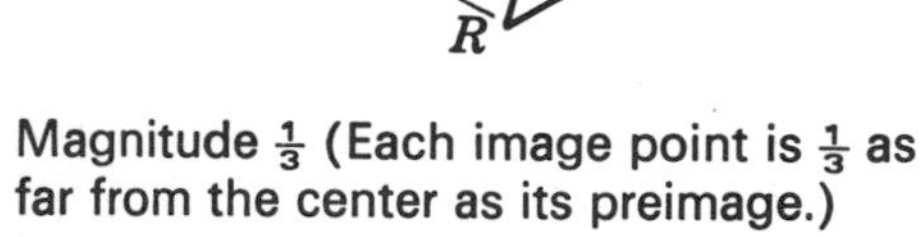

Magnitude $\frac{1}{3}$ (Each image point is $\frac{1}{3}$ as far from the center as its preimage.)

Magnitude 2 (Each image point is 2 times as far from the center as its preimage.)

In the example on the left, the length of $P'Q'$ is $\frac{1}{3}$ the length of PQ. In the example on the right, $A'B'$ is 2 times the length of AB. So size transformations *do not preserve distance*. But notice that $m\angle PQR = m\angle P'Q'R'$. Size transformations *do preserve angle measure*.

Definition

Let C be a point and k be a nonzero real number. The image of P under the **size transformation** *with center C, magnitude k,* is the point P' such that

1. $P'C = |k| \cdot PC$.
2. If $k > 0$, P' is on ray $\overrightarrow{CP}$.
3. If $k < 0$, P' is on the ray opposite ray $\overrightarrow{CP}$.

Here is a figure and its image under a size transformation with a *negative* magnitude, -1.5.

Notice that the center is between each point and its image.

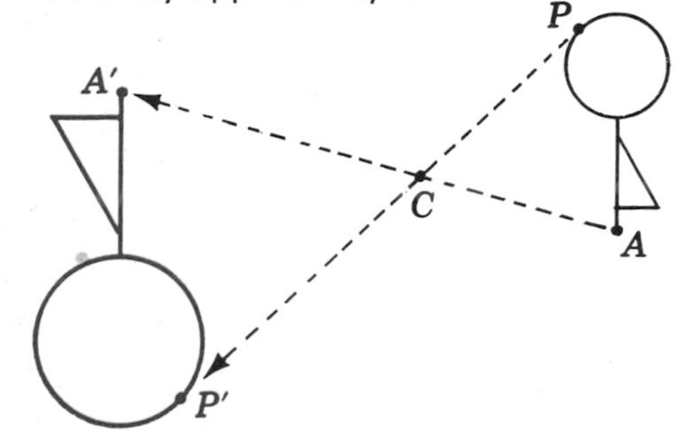

For any size transformation having (0, 0) as center, there is a simple algebraic description.

Theorem 4.8.1

The size transformation with center (0, 0) and magnitude k maps (x, y) onto (kx, ky).

PROOF: The proof involves the distance formula and a figure such as at the right.

The proof is outlined in Exercises **29–33.**

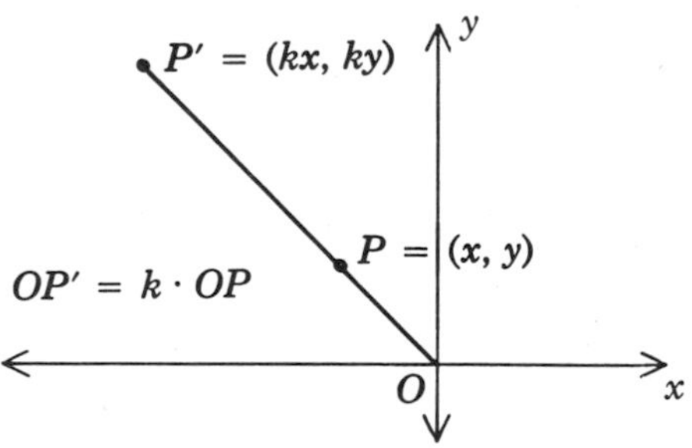

Theorem 4.8.1 is very easy to apply. For example, consider the size transformation with center (0, 0) and magnitude 2.5.

According to the theorem, we simply multiply coordinates of points in the preimage by 2.5 to obtain points in the image.

Notice that $A'C' = 2.5(AC)$.

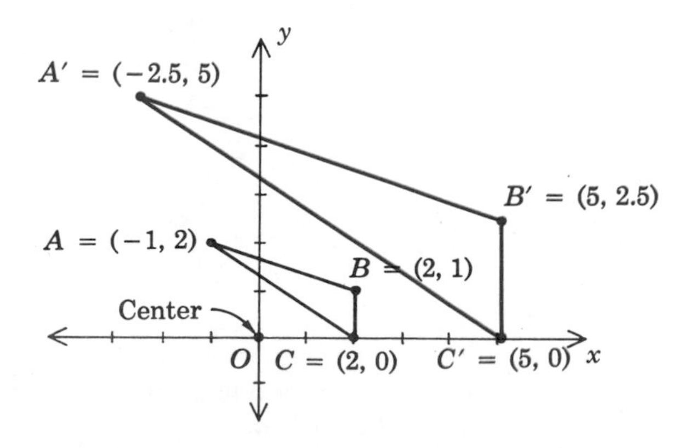

As the examples show, size transformations do *not* always preserve distance. But they affect distance in a definite way.

Theorem 4.8.2

Under a size transformation of magnitude k, the distance between images is k times the distance between the corresponding preimages.

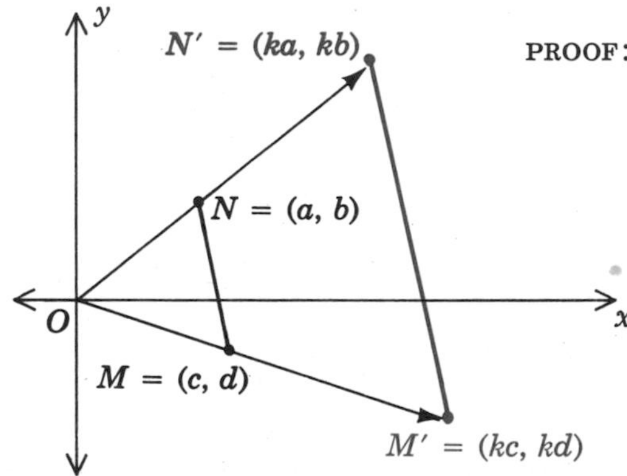

PROOF: Let (a, b) and (c, d) be any two preimages. Then (ka, kb) and (kc, kd) are the images. So by the distance formula:

$$\begin{aligned} M'N' &= \sqrt{(ka - kc)^2 + (kb - kd)^2} \\ &= \sqrt{k^2[(a - c)^2 + (b - d)^2]} \\ &= k\sqrt{(a - c)^2 + (b - d)^2} \\ &= k \cdot MN \end{aligned}$$

Size transformations have numerous properties and applications. One very important application of size transformations is to *similarity*.

Definition

Two figures α and β are **similar** if and only if there is a composite of reflections and/or size transformations which maps α onto β.

In symbols, we write $\alpha \sim \beta$

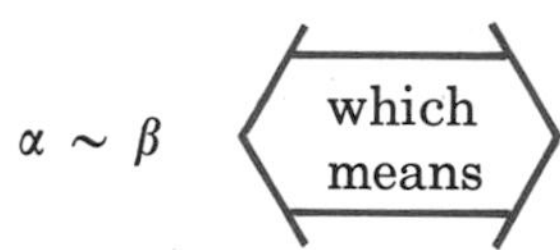

α is similar to β.

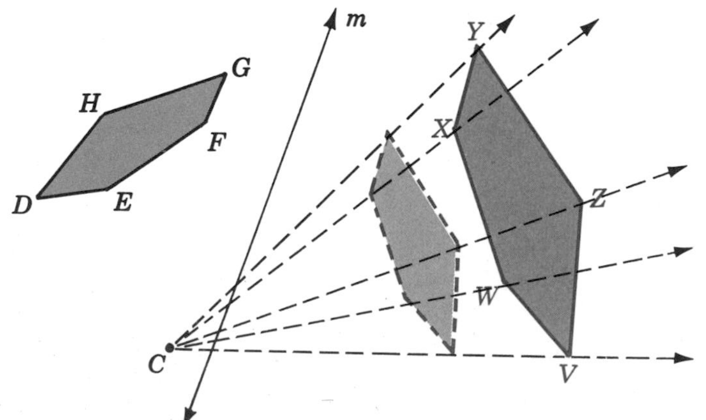

At the left $S \circ r_m(DEFGH) = VWXYZ$.

S is the size transformation with center C and magnitude 1.4. Thus $S \circ r_m$ is a composite of reflections and size transformations mapping $DEFGH$ onto $VWXYZ$.

By the definition of similarity, we can write $DEFGH \sim VWXYZ$.

Definition

A composite of reflections and/or size transformations is a **similarity transformation.**

Similar figures are related by similarity transformations in the same way that congruent figures are related by isometries. The relationships among the transformations we have mentioned are indicated by the diagram below.

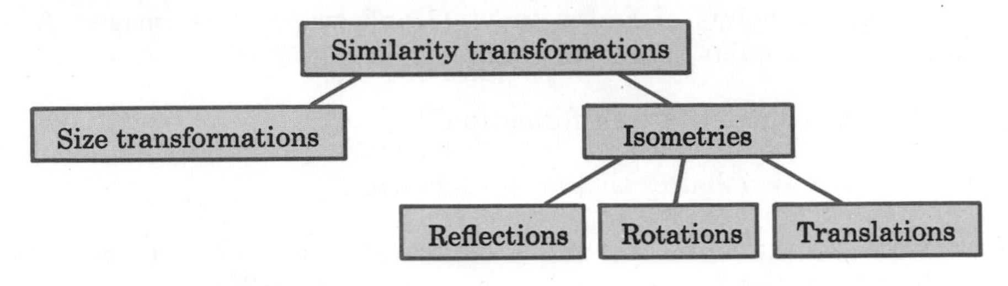

EXERCISES 4.8

Ⓐ 1. A size transformation is determined by a point called its ____ and a number called its ____.

2. How do size transformations affect angle measure?

3. How do size transformations affect distance?

4–8. A size transformation S has center Q and magnitude 3. $S(\triangle MNP) = \triangle M'N'P'$. ($P'$ is not shown.) Find a number to complete each statement.

$\bullet\ M'$

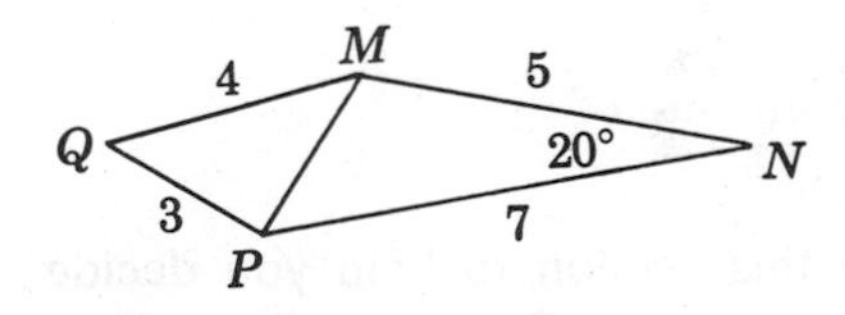

$\bullet\ N'$

4. $m\angle M'N'P'$ = ____
5. QM' = ____
6. $M'N'$ = ____
7. $P'N'$ = ____
8. $\overline{MM'}$ is ____ times as long as $\overline{QM}$.

9–13. T is a size transformation such that $T(ABCD) = EFGH$. Refer to the drawing at the right.

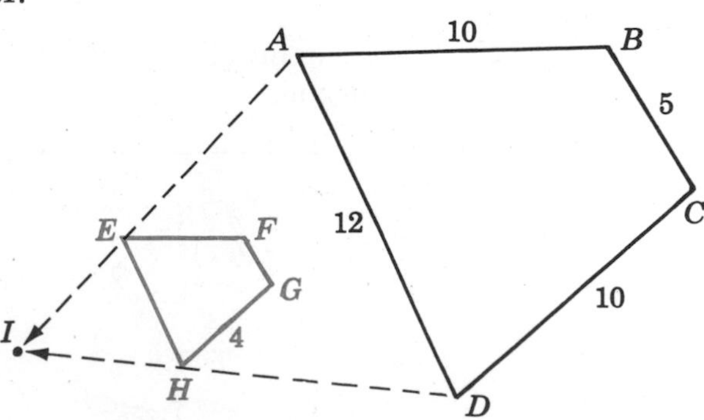

9. What is the center of T?
10. What is the magnitude of T?
11. FG = ____
12. EF = ____ 13. EH = ____

14–17. Find the image of each point under a size transformation with center (0, 0) and magnitude $-\frac{1}{2}$.

14. (2, 8) **15.** (−1, 5) **16.** (0, 0) **17.** (−4, 9)

18. Graph the points of Exercises **14–17** and graph their images. Are there any similar figures determined by the graphs?

19. What is a similarity transformation?

20. When are two figures similar by definition?

21. What is a difference between a size transformation and a similarity transformation?

Ⓑ **22.** Find the images of (2, 9) and (−4, 1) under a size transformation with center (0, 0) and magnitude 2.3. Graph both preimages and images. Use the distance formula to verify that distances between images are 2.3 times the distances between corresponding preimages.

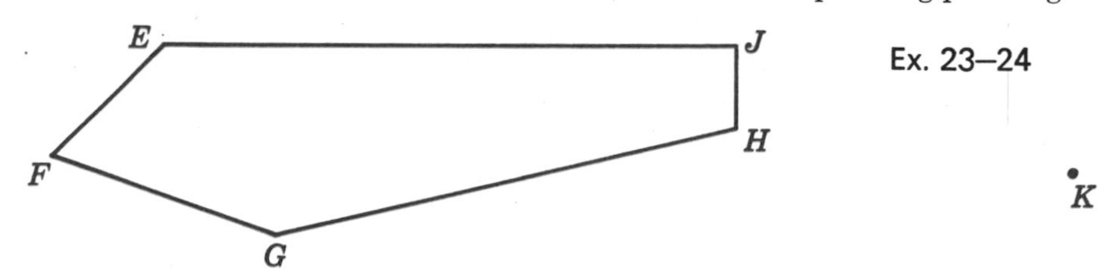

Ex. 23–24

23. Trace polygon $EFGHJ$. Find its image under a size transformation with center K and magnitude $\frac{2}{3}$.

24. Repeat Exercise **23**, except use a magnitude of $-\frac{2}{3}$.

25–28. Look at the illustrations given in this section to help you decide whether each statement below *is* or *is not* a property of *size transformations*.

25. A line is parallel to its image.

26. Collinearity is preserved.

27. The image of a segment is longer than its preimage.

28. If the magnitude is negative, a figure and its image have opposite orientation.

A SIZE TRANSFORMATION?

© **29–33.** Refer to the figure following Theorem 4.8.1. These exercises outline a proof of the theorem. Justify each step. (HINT: Use the distance formula.)

29. $OP' = |k| \cdot OP$

30. If $0 < k \leq 1$, then $OP' + P'P = OP$. This shows that P' lies on ray $\overrightarrow{OP}$.

31. If $k > 1$, then $OP + PP' = OP'$.

32. If $k < 0$, then $P'O + OP = PP'$.

33. How do the statements in Exercises **29–32** imply Theorem 4.8.1?

SYMMETRY

The idea of symmetry is extremely important both in mathematics and in its applications. Artists and architects are interested in symmetry for its beauty and pleasing properties.

Physicists have predicted the existence of atomic particles merely on the basis of symmetry. Mathematicians and chemists have used symmetry to simplify many of the problems they work on.

Definition

Let T be an isometry* and let α be any figure. Then α is **symmetric** if and only if $T(\alpha) = \alpha$.

If T is a reflection and α is mapped onto itself by T, then α is called **reflection-symmetric**. Below, figures **(a)**, **(b)**, and **(c)** are reflection-symmetric. The reflecting *lines of symmetry* are shown in color. (Such lines are not considered to be part of the figure.)

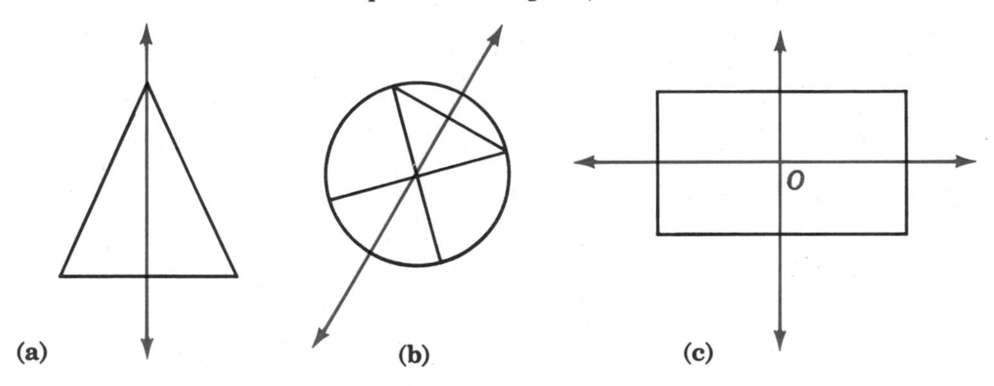

* Exception: T cannot be a rotation of 0° which maps each point (and thus *every* figure) onto itself.

If $T(\alpha) = \alpha$ and T is a rotation with nonzero magnitude, then α is called **rotation-symmetric**. The center of the rotation is called a *center of symmetry* for the figure. Figure **(c)** has rotation-symmetry since a 180° rotation about point O maps figure **(c)** onto itself. Figures **(d)** and **(e)**, below, are rotation-symmetric but not reflection-symmetric. The centers of symmetry are P and Q.

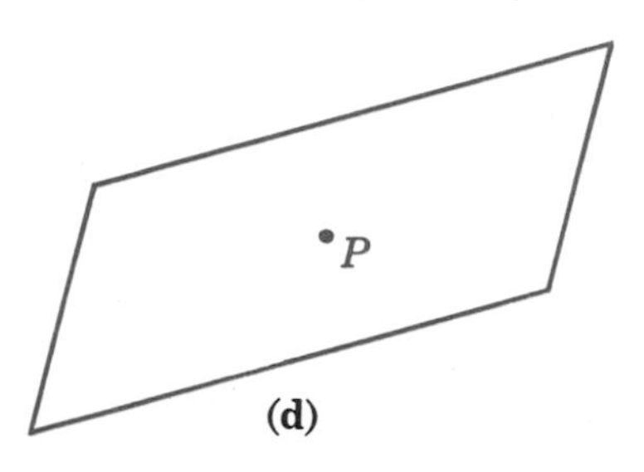

(d)

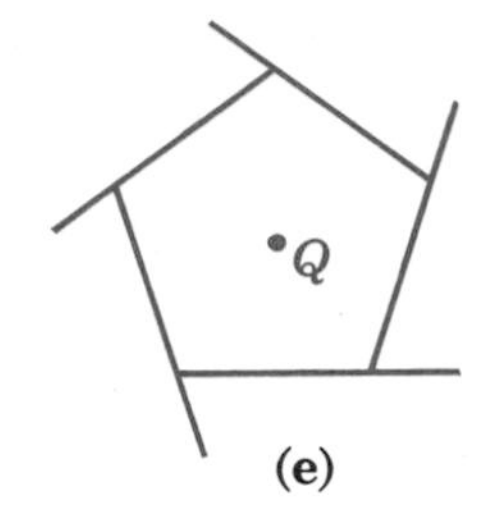

(e)

Many wallpaper and tile patterns exhibit **translation-symmetry** as illustrated below.

The symmetry of a figure can be used to deduce properties of that figure. For example, the isosceles triangles ABC and ADE are both symmetric to ℓ, the bisector of angle A.

Thus $r_\ell(E) = D$
and $r_\ell(B) = C$.

So $BE = DC$, since reflections preserve distance.

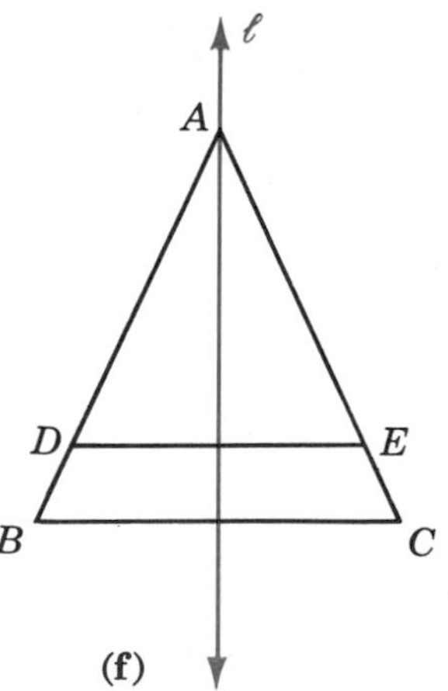

(f)

EXERCISES 4.9

Ⓐ **1.** When is a figure reflection-symmetric?

2. When is a figure rotation-symmetric?

3. When is a figure transformation-symmetric?

4. What is a symmetry line for a figure?

5. What is a center of symmetry for a figure?

Ⓑ **6–13.** Trace each figure and tell whether it is rotation-symmetric or reflection-symmetric. Draw all lines and centers of symmetry. For each center of symmetry, give the magnitudes of appropriate rotations between 0° and 360°.

6. square

7.

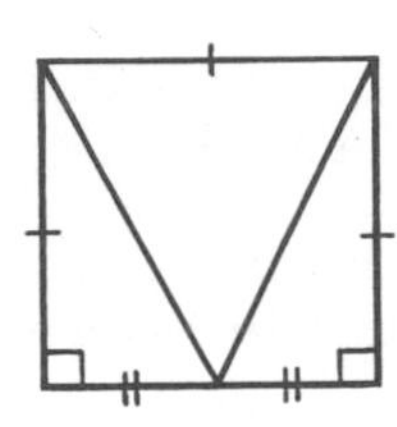

8.

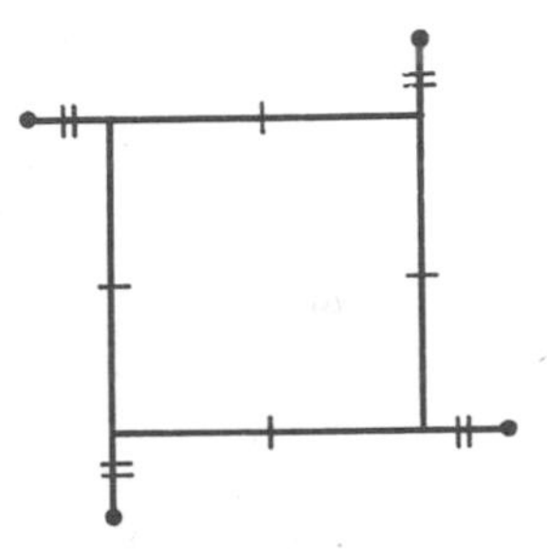

9. parallelogram

10. regular hexagon

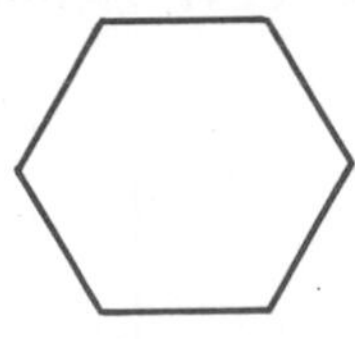

11. rhombus

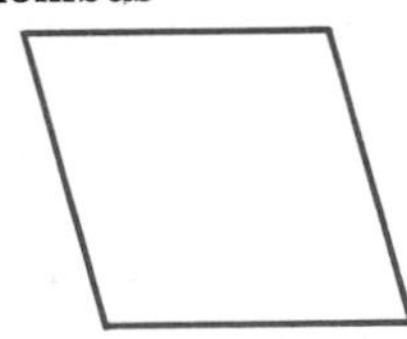

12. intersecting circles

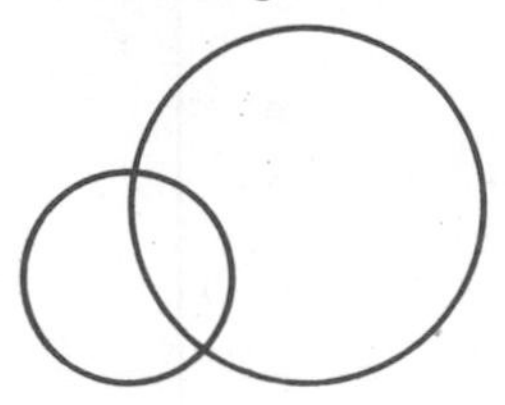

13. concentric circles

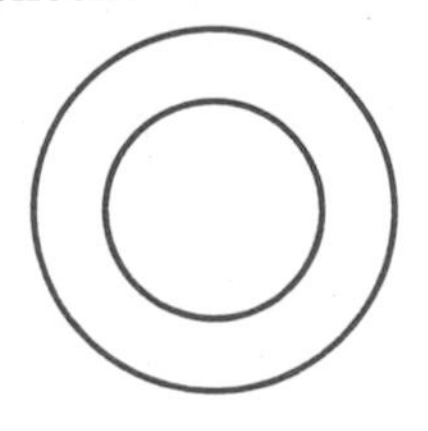

14. Draw a figure which is translation-symmetric but not rotation-symmetric.

15. Draw a figure which can be mapped onto itself by two translations in directions which are perpendicular to each other.

16. $ABCD$ and $BEFH$ are congruent squares with B the midpoint of $\overline{AH}$. Why is this figure *not* translation-symmetric?

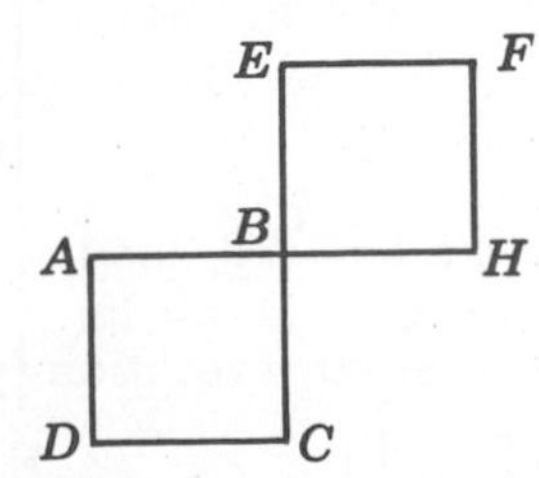

© **17–18.** A figure α is said to be *size-transformation-symmetric* if and only if there is a size transformation T with $T(\alpha) = \alpha$.

17. The set of concentric circles with radii 1, 2, $\frac{1}{2}$, 4, $\frac{1}{4}$, 8, $\frac{1}{8}$, $\cdots$ (the integral powers of 2) is size-transformation-symmetric. Draw a picture to illustrate part of this set.

18. Draw or describe a figure which has both translation-symmetry and size-transformation-symmetry.

19. Almost every crossword puzzle in a newspaper has a particular type of symmetry. Determine this symmetry by looking in newspapers.

20. Use figure **(f)** of this section. Prove: $m\angle BEA = m\angle CDA$ without using any congruent triangles.

21. Prove: If a figure has two lines of symmetry, then it is either rotation-symmetric or translation-symmetric.

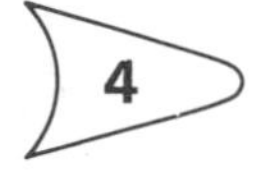

CHAPTER SUMMARY

A *transformation* is a 1–1 correspondence between sets of points. The original point or figure F is called the *preimage*, and the corresponding point or figure under the transformation T is called the *image*, denoted by $T(F)$.

Four basic types of transformations are *reflections*, *rotations*, *translations*, and *size transformations*. These are mathematical ways of describing the physical actions of flips (or folds), turns, slides, and expansions or contractions.

When one transformation t_1 is followed by a second t_2, the resulting correspondence between the first preimage and the final image is called the *composite* $t_2 \circ t_1$ of the two transformations.

From Theorems 4.5.1, 4.5.2, and 4.6.1, we have three important results about composites.

(1) The composite of two rotations with the same center is a rotation.

(2) The composite of two translations is a translation.

(3) The composite of two reflections

(a) over intersecting lines is a rotation, and

(b) over parallel lines is a translation.

Reflections, rotations, translations, and composites of these are *isometries*. Isometries preserve distance, angle measure, and collinearity, so that a figure and its image look very much alike. Thus, the definition of *congruence* is in terms of isometries.

$\alpha \cong \beta$ if and only if there is an isometry (composite of reflections) which maps α onto β.

Size transformations preserve angle measure and collinearity but not distance, which means the image of a figure has the same shape, but not necessarily the same size, as the preimage.

The composite of a size transformation with an isometry is a *similarity transformation. Similarity* is defined in terms of size transformations and isometries.

> $\alpha \sim \beta$ if and only if there is a similarity transformation (composite of reflections and/or size transformations) which maps α onto β.

There are symmetries associated with each of the basic types of transformations. A figure F is *reflection-symmetric* if there is a reflection r with $r(F) = F$. In similar fashion, a figure may be *rotation-symmetric* or *translation-symmetric.*

Thus three important geometric concepts—congruence, similarity, and symmetry—can be described *for any figures* in terms of transformations.

CHAPTER REVIEW

1. Trace the figure at the right. Then draw $r_\ell(\triangle ABC)$.

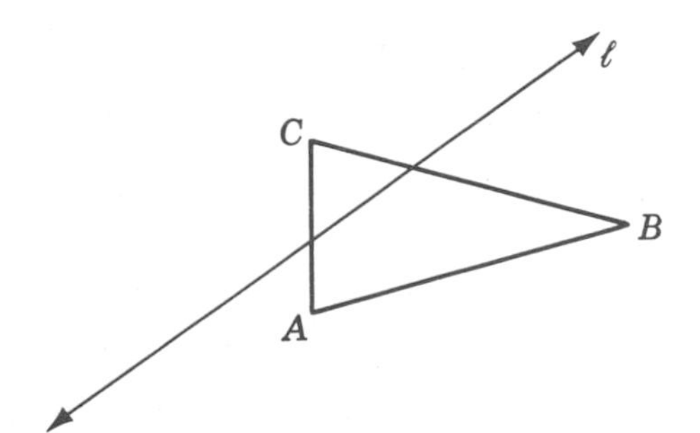

2. Given that $T(x, y) = (x + 2, 2y - 1)$, find $T(3, -2)$.

3. A translation maps (2, 5) onto (5, 8). What is the image of (x, y)?

4. A translation maps A onto B. Trace the figure and draw the image of circle P under this translation.

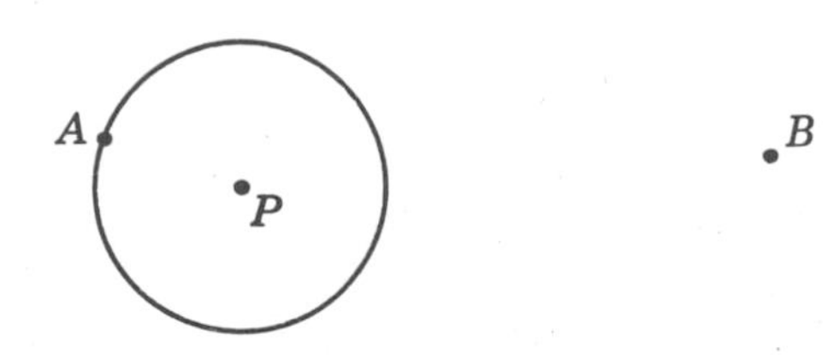

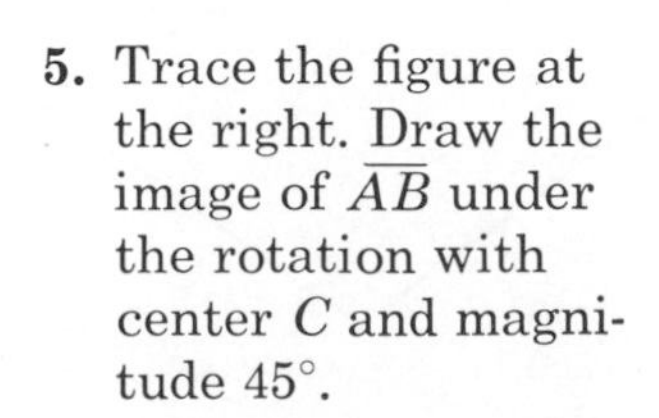

5. Trace the figure at the right. Draw the image of $\overline{AB}$ under the rotation with center C and magnitude 45°.

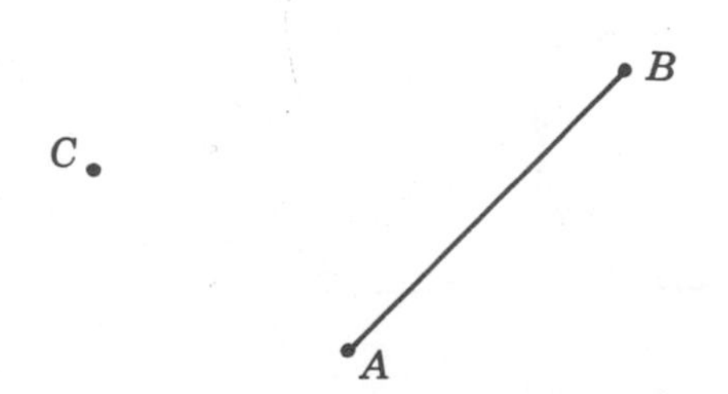

6. R_1 is a rotation of $-30°$ about a point Q and R_2 is a rotation of $57°$ about Q. What is $R_2 \circ R_1$?

7. Let S be the translation which maps (x, y) onto $(x + 2, y - 3)$. Let T be the translation which maps (x, y) onto $(x + 5, y + 3)$. Find $T \circ S(x, y)$.

8. The composite of two reflections r_ℓ and r_m is a ____ if ℓ and m intersect, and a ____ if ℓ and m are parallel.

9. Name a type of transformation which does not preserve distance.

10. Trace the figure at the right. Draw the image of $\triangle MNQ$ under a size transformation with center C and magnitude 2.

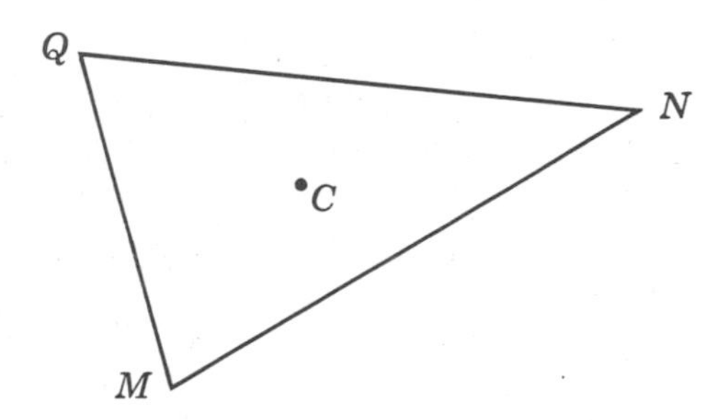

11. For *any* figures α and β:

    a. under what conditions is α congruent to β?

    b. under what conditions is α similar to β?

12. Find the images of (24, 6) and (9, 3) under a size transformation with center (0, 0) and magnitude $\frac{1}{3}$.

13. What does it mean to say a figure is *rotation-symmetric*?

14–16. Trace each figure and tell whether it is rotation-symmetric or reflection-symmetric. Draw all lines of symmetry and all centers of symmetry.

14.

15.

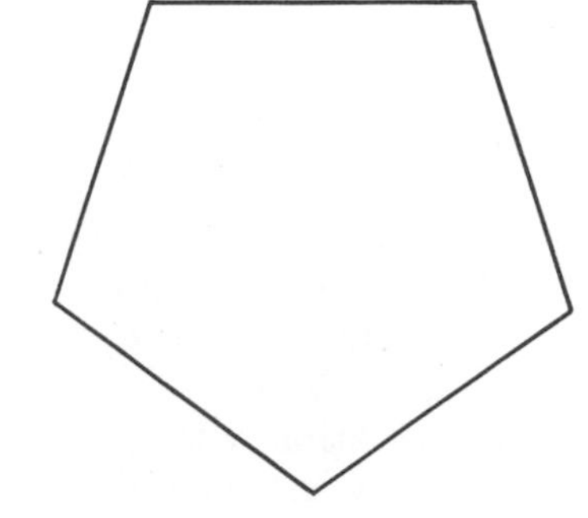

16.

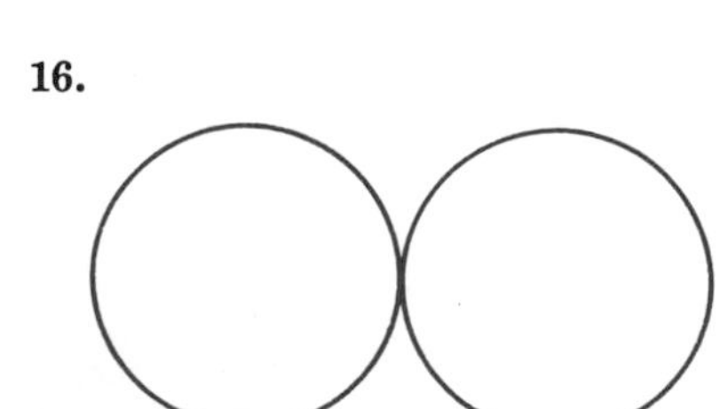

233	3	2.73	2280	100	3600
90	4	4.09	3770	75	5800
140	3	2.92	2600	75	4400
79	4	3.90	3670	67	6000

5	0	1	3	1	0	0	1	0
1	0	0	3	0	0	1	1	2

Chapter 5 Matrices

INTRODUCTION

A **matrix** (plural: **matrices**) is a sequence of elements arranged in rows and columns, as in the two examples above.

The variety of uses of matrices may surprise you. The elements of a matrix might be arrival and departure times, new car specifications, scores in each quarter or inning of a ball game, or the coordinates of a set of points.

The theory of matrices was first developed around 1858 by the British mathematician Arthur Cayley. Matrices are now used extensively in business, science, and social science, as well as mathematics.

A matrix with m rows and n columns is said to have **dimensions** m by n or $m \times n$. (A 2×3 matrix is shown here.) An element of a matrix is identified by giving its row and column.

row 1
row 2

$$\begin{bmatrix} 9 & -8 & 7 \\ -6 & 5 & 10 \end{bmatrix}$$

column 1 column 2 column 3

the element in row 1, column 3

The matrix $\begin{bmatrix} a \\ b \end{bmatrix}$ will generally stand for the point (a, b). Thus, $\begin{bmatrix} 3 \\ -2 \end{bmatrix}$ stands for the point $(3, -2)$.

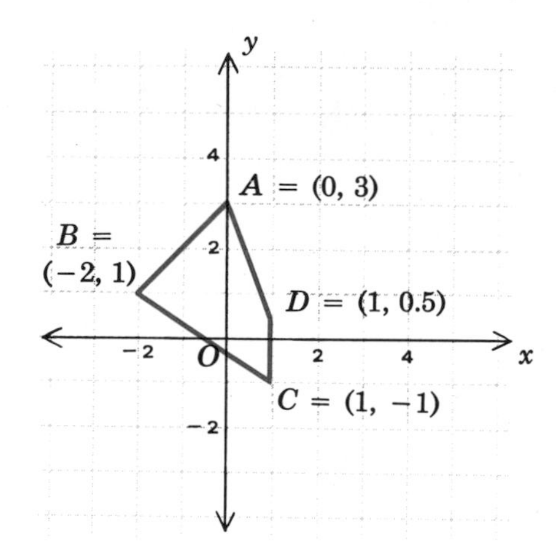

Matrices can also represent polygons. The quadrilateral at the left has vertices.

$$\begin{bmatrix} 0 \\ 3 \end{bmatrix}, \begin{bmatrix} -2 \\ 1 \end{bmatrix}, \begin{bmatrix} 1 \\ -1 \end{bmatrix}, \text{ and } \begin{bmatrix} 1 \\ 0.5 \end{bmatrix}.$$

We can combine these into one 2×4 matrix representing quadrilateral $ABCD$.

$$\begin{bmatrix} 0 & -2 & 1 & 1 \\ 3 & 1 & -1 & 0.5 \end{bmatrix}$$

Similarly, $\begin{bmatrix} 1 & 0 \\ -1 & 3 \end{bmatrix}$ represents diagonal $\overline{CA}$.

Like sets and ordered pairs, two matrices are equal if and only if they are identical. Consequently, equal matrices have the same elements in corresponding positions. So matrices A and B below are equal, but neither of them is equal to $\begin{bmatrix} 9 & -8 & 7 \\ -6 & 5 & 10 \end{bmatrix}$. It is common to let capital letters stand for matrices. We may write $A = B$.

$$A = \begin{bmatrix} -6 & -8 & 7 \\ 9 & 5 & 10 \end{bmatrix} \qquad B = \begin{bmatrix} -2 \cdot 3 & -8 & \frac{7}{2} \cdot 2 \\ 9 & \frac{10}{2} & 5 + 5 \end{bmatrix}$$

EXERCISES 5.1

Ⓐ **1–2.** Give the number of rows, number of columns, and dimensions of each of the matrices shown on page 125.

3. Which matrix represents the point $(6, -4)$?

a. $[6 \quad -4]$ **b.** $[-4 \quad 6]$ **c.** $\begin{bmatrix} 6 \\ -4 \end{bmatrix}$ **d.** $\begin{bmatrix} -4 \\ 6 \end{bmatrix}$

4. $P = (-2, 7)$; $Q = (-3, 8)$. Which matrix represents $\overline{PQ}$?

a. $\begin{bmatrix} -2 & 7 \\ -3 & 8 \end{bmatrix}$ b. $[-2 \quad 7 \quad -3 \quad 8]$ c. $\begin{bmatrix} -2 & -3 \\ 7 & 8 \end{bmatrix}$ d. $\begin{bmatrix} -2 \\ 7 \\ -3 \\ 8 \end{bmatrix}$

5. If $\begin{bmatrix} 4 & 5 \\ y & 3 \end{bmatrix} = \begin{bmatrix} 4 & x \\ 2 & 3 \end{bmatrix}$, then $\begin{bmatrix} x \\ y \end{bmatrix} =$ ______.

6. How many elements are in a 3×5 matrix?

7. How many elements are in a $m \times n$ matrix?

8. Must all elements of a matrix be integers?

9. Who first worked with the mathematics of matrices, and when?

Ⓑ **10–13.** Name the element in the indicated row and column of the matrix at the right.

$$\begin{bmatrix} 2 & 4 & 6 \\ 9 & 12 & 15 \\ -3 & -7 & -11 \end{bmatrix}$$

10. 1st row, 2nd column

11. 3rd row, 2nd column

12. 2nd row, 2nd column

13. 2nd row, 3rd column

14. What are the dimensions of $\begin{bmatrix} 3x + 2y \\ 5x - 4y \end{bmatrix}$?

15. What are the dimensions of a matrix which represents a hexagon?

16. What are the dimensions of a matrix which represents an n-gon?

17. Find the lengths of the sides of the polygon $\begin{bmatrix} 2 & -1 & 6 \\ 5 & 4 & 11 \end{bmatrix}$.

Ⓒ **18–19.** Networks of paths can be described by matrices. Here is a network and its associated matrix. The element in row *m*, column *n*, gives the number of paths *from* point ⓜ directly *to* point ⓝ.

$$\begin{bmatrix} 0 & 1 & 1 & 2 \\ 0 & 0 & 1 & 0 \\ 1 & 2 & 0 & 1 \\ 0 & 0 & 0 & 0 \end{bmatrix}$$

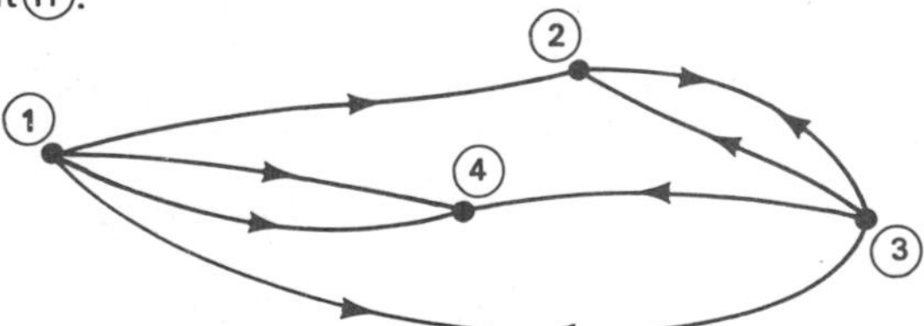

Give a matrix for each network.

18.

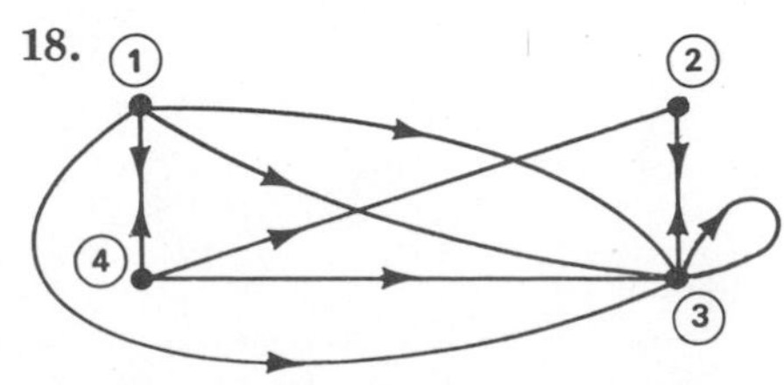

19.

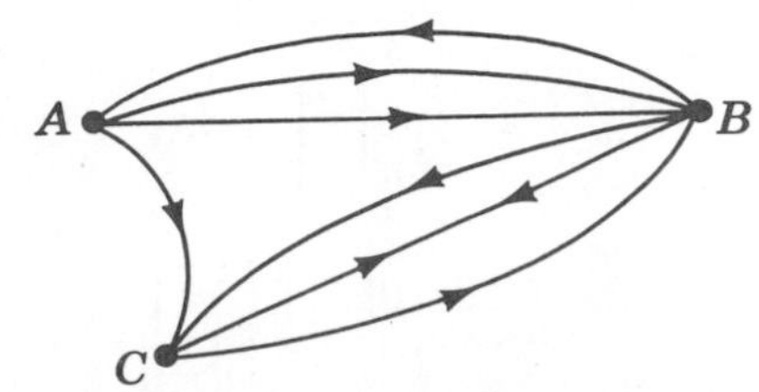

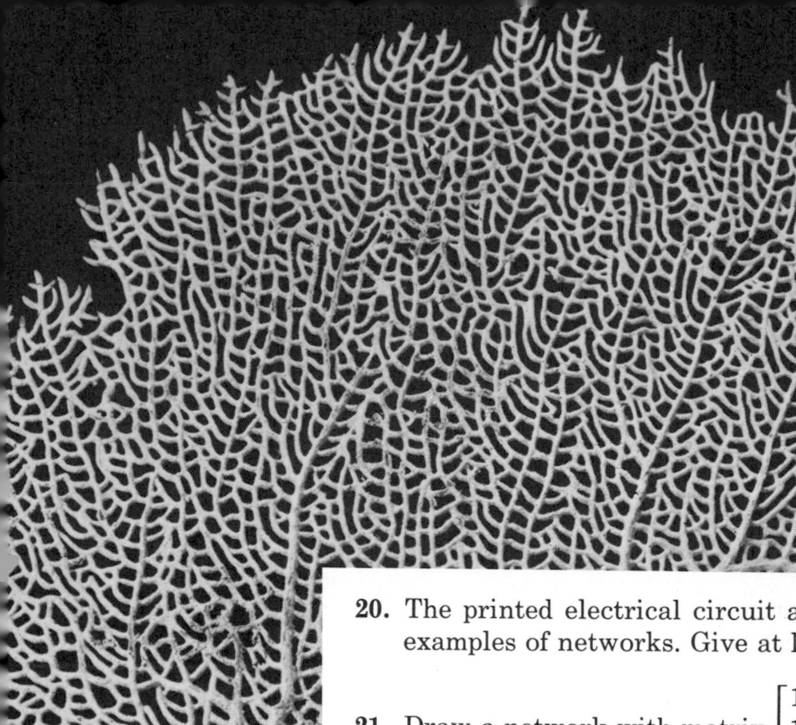

20. The printed electrical circuit and sea-fan skeleton above are both examples of networks. Give at least five more examples.

21. Draw a network with matrix $\begin{bmatrix} 1 & 1 & 1 \\ 1 & 0 & 2 \\ 0 & 2 & 0 \end{bmatrix}$.

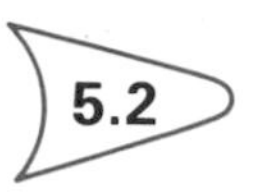

5.2 MATRIX MULTIPLICATION

You are familiar with addition, subtraction, and other operations on numbers. In Chapter 4 an operation on transformations, called composition, was discussed. We now introduce an operation on matrices: **matrix multiplication.** Matrix multiplication is based on *row-by-column* multiplication.

procedure for row-by-column multiplication

To multiply a row by a column, multiply the first element in the row by the first element in the column; then multiply the second elements, then the third elements, and so on. Lastly, add the products.

Examples: Row-by-column multiplication

1. $[9 \quad -2 \quad 4] \cdot \begin{bmatrix} 2 \\ 3 \\ 5 \end{bmatrix} = [9 \cdot 2 + (-2 \cdot 3) + 4 \cdot 5] = [32]$

2. $[3 \quad 2] \cdot \begin{bmatrix} x \\ y \end{bmatrix} = [3x + 2y]$

3. $[-3 \quad 0] \cdot \begin{bmatrix} 2 \\ 8 \end{bmatrix} = [-3 \cdot 2 + 0 \cdot 8] = [-6]$

Notice that the row and the column *must have the same number of elements* in order to be multiplied.

$$[1 \quad 2] \text{ and } \begin{bmatrix} 3 \\ 4 \\ 5 \end{bmatrix} \text{ cannot be multiplied.}$$

Larger matrices can be multiplied. But you must be able to multiply the rows of the left matrix by the columns of the right matrix.

$$\underbrace{\begin{bmatrix} 3 & 4 & 6 \\ 2 & 9 & 1 \end{bmatrix} \cdot \begin{bmatrix} 13 & 0 & 4 \\ 8 & 0 & -2 \\ 1 & 1 & 1 \end{bmatrix}}_{\text{can be multiplied}} \qquad \underbrace{\begin{bmatrix} 3 & 4 & 6 \\ 2 & 9 & 1 \end{bmatrix} \cdot \begin{bmatrix} 13 & 0 & 4 \\ 8 & 0 & -2 \end{bmatrix}}_{\text{cannot be multiplied}}$$

$A \cdot B$, or AB, exists only when the number of columns of A equals the number of rows of B. That is, if A is $m \times n$, then B must be $n \times s$. Rows of the left matrix are used to find corresponding rows of the product; columns of the right matrix are used to find corresponding columns of the product.

Let A and B be matrices, and let AB exist. Then the element in row i, column j, of AB is the product of row i of A and column j of B.

---

procedure for matrix multiplication

Examples: Matrix multiplication

1. 2nd row × 3rd column goes in the 2nd row, 3rd column.

$$\begin{bmatrix} 6 & 0 \\ -1 & 4 \\ 2 & 5 \end{bmatrix} \cdot \begin{bmatrix} 4 & 1 & 3 & 0 \\ 6 & 2 & 8 & 4 \end{bmatrix} = \begin{bmatrix} 24 & 6 & 18 & 0 \\ 20 & 7 & 29 & 16 \\ 38 & 12 & 46 & 20 \end{bmatrix}$$

$3 \times 2 \qquad 2 \times 4 \qquad 3 \times 4$

If these are equal, the product exists.

The product has the same number of rows as the left matrix, and the same number of columns as the right matrix.

2. $$\begin{bmatrix} 1 & 2 \\ 0 & 3 \end{bmatrix} \cdot \begin{bmatrix} -2 & -1 \\ 3 & 6 \end{bmatrix} = \begin{bmatrix} 4 & 11 \\ 9 & 18 \end{bmatrix}$$

$2 \times 2 \qquad 2 \times 2 \qquad 2 \times 2$

3. $$\begin{bmatrix} 4 & 0 \\ 1 & -2 \end{bmatrix} \cdot \begin{bmatrix} 1 & 4 & 1 \\ 3 & -6 & 2 \end{bmatrix} = \begin{bmatrix} 4 & 16 & 4 \\ -5 & 16 & -3 \end{bmatrix}$$

$2 \times 2 \qquad 2 \times 3 \qquad 2 \times 3$

4. $$\begin{bmatrix} 1 \\ 2 \\ 3 \end{bmatrix} \cdot [1 \quad 2 \quad 3] = \begin{bmatrix} 1 & 2 & 3 \\ 2 & 4 & 6 \\ 3 & 6 & 9 \end{bmatrix}$$

$3 \times 1 \qquad 1 \times 3 \qquad 3 \times 3$

5. $$\begin{bmatrix} 4 & 0 & -3 & 1 \\ -2 & 9 & 8 & 6 \end{bmatrix} \cdot \begin{bmatrix} 6 \\ 4 \\ 0 \\ 1 \end{bmatrix} = \begin{bmatrix} 25 \\ 30 \end{bmatrix}$$

$2 \times 4 \qquad 4 \times 1 \qquad 2 \times 1$

The procedures used in the examples are summarized in the following definition.

Definition

Let A be an $m \times n$ matrix and B be an $n \times r$ matrix. Then the **product** $\boldsymbol{AB}$ is the $m \times r$ matrix in which the element in row i and column j is the product of row i of A and column j of B.

CAUTION: $A \cdot B$ is different from $B \cdot A$. In matrix multiplication, *rows* at *left* are multiplied by *columns* at *right*.

EXERCISES 5.2

Ⓐ **1–6.** Multiply the row by the column, if possible.

1. $[4 \quad 1 \quad 2] \cdot \begin{bmatrix} 3 \\ 1 \\ 5 \end{bmatrix}$ **2.** $[2 \quad 2 \quad 2 \quad 2] \cdot \begin{bmatrix} 3 \\ 4 \end{bmatrix}$ **3.** $[0 \quad 1 \quad 2] \cdot \begin{bmatrix} 1 \\ 2 \\ 3 \end{bmatrix}$

4. $[-4 \quad 2] \cdot \begin{bmatrix} -3 \\ 3 \end{bmatrix}$ **5.** $[6 \quad 0 \quad 1 \quad 0] \cdot \begin{bmatrix} 0 \\ -2 \\ 0 \\ 3 \end{bmatrix}$ **6.** $[\frac{1}{2} \quad -\frac{3}{2}] \cdot \begin{bmatrix} 4 \\ 6 \\ 3 \end{bmatrix}$

7–10. Let $M = \begin{bmatrix} 4 & 1 \\ 6 & 3 \end{bmatrix}$ and $N = \begin{bmatrix} 8 & 2 & 6 \\ 1 & 4 & 3 \end{bmatrix}$. For MN, calculate:

7. the dimensions. **8.** the element in row 1, column 1.

9. the element in row 2, column 3.

10. the element in row 2, column 2.

11–16. Give the dimensions of AB.

11. A is 3×2, B is 2×4. **12.** A is 8×2, B is 2×9.

13. A is 8×1, B is 1×9. **14.** A is 2×3, B is 3×2.

15. Give the dimensions of two matrices which cannot be multiplied.

Ⓑ **16.** X has dimensions 3×5, and XY has dimensions 3×2. What are the dimensions of Y?

17–25. Multiply, if possible.

17. $\begin{bmatrix} 1 & 2 \\ 0 & 3 \end{bmatrix} \cdot \begin{bmatrix} -2 & -1 \\ 4 & 6 \end{bmatrix}$ **18.** $\begin{bmatrix} 3 & -5 \\ 6 & 2 \end{bmatrix} \cdot \begin{bmatrix} 0 \\ 7 \end{bmatrix}$ **19.** $\begin{bmatrix} 7 & 0 \\ 0 & 7 \end{bmatrix} \cdot \begin{bmatrix} 1 \\ 4 \\ -1 \end{bmatrix}$

20. $\begin{bmatrix} 1 & 0 \\ 0 & -1 \end{bmatrix} \cdot \begin{bmatrix} 2 & 4 & 0 \\ 6 & 3 & 0 \end{bmatrix}$

21. $\begin{bmatrix} 1 & 0 \\ 0 & -1 \end{bmatrix} \cdot \begin{bmatrix} 0 & 1 \\ 1 & 0 \end{bmatrix}$

22. $\begin{bmatrix} 0 & 1 \\ 1 & 0 \end{bmatrix} \cdot \begin{bmatrix} 0 & 1 \\ 1 & 0 \end{bmatrix}$

23. $\begin{bmatrix} \sqrt{2} & -\sqrt{2} \\ \sqrt{2} & \sqrt{2} \end{bmatrix} \cdot \begin{bmatrix} 0 & 1 & 4 \\ 0 & 0 & -4 \end{bmatrix}$

24. $\begin{bmatrix} 1 \\ 2 \\ 4 \end{bmatrix} \cdot \begin{bmatrix} 3 & 2 & 0 \\ 6 & 8 & 4 \end{bmatrix}$

25. $\begin{bmatrix} 1 & 4 & 7 \end{bmatrix} \cdot \begin{bmatrix} 8 & 0 & 0.3 \\ 1 & 4 & 0.2 \\ 2 & 6 & 0.4 \end{bmatrix}$

26. Solve for x: $\begin{bmatrix} 3 & 1 \\ 0 & 2 \end{bmatrix} \cdot \begin{bmatrix} x \\ 9 \end{bmatrix} = \begin{bmatrix} 10 \\ 18 \end{bmatrix}$.

27. Solve for a and b: $\begin{bmatrix} 2 & a \\ 3 & b \end{bmatrix} \cdot \begin{bmatrix} 5 \\ 6 \end{bmatrix} = \begin{bmatrix} 7 \\ 8 \end{bmatrix}$.

28. Solve for c and d: $\begin{bmatrix} 2 & c \\ 3 & d \end{bmatrix} \cdot \begin{bmatrix} x \\ y \end{bmatrix} = \begin{bmatrix} 2x + y \\ 3x - 4y \end{bmatrix}$.

© **29.** Find two 2×2 matrices A and B for which $A \cdot B = B \cdot A$.

30–31. Multiply.

30. $\begin{bmatrix} 3 & 4 & 6 \\ -1 & 2 & 0 \\ -2 & 4 & 0 \end{bmatrix} \cdot \begin{bmatrix} 0 & -8 & 3 \\ -1 & -1 & -1 \\ 2 & 4 & 3 \end{bmatrix}$

31. $\begin{bmatrix} 1 & 2 & 3 & 4 \\ 5 & 6 & 7 & 8 \\ 9 & 10 & 11 & 12 \\ 13 & 14 & 15 & 16 \end{bmatrix} \cdot \begin{bmatrix} 1 & 0 \\ 0 & 1 \\ 1 & 0 \\ 0 & 1 \end{bmatrix}$

32. As you would expect for square matrices, $M^2 = M \cdot M$. If $M = \begin{bmatrix} 0 & -3 \\ -3 & 0 \end{bmatrix}$, calculate M^2 and M^3.

APPLYING MATRIX MULTIPLICATION TO TRANSFORMATIONS

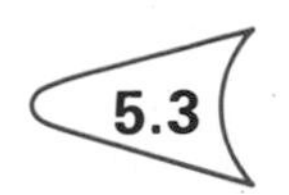

When a point matrix is multiplied by a 2×2 matrix, the result is a point matrix.

$$\begin{bmatrix} 1 & 0 \\ 0 & -1 \end{bmatrix} \cdot \begin{bmatrix} -6 \\ 2 \end{bmatrix} = \begin{bmatrix} -6 \\ -2 \end{bmatrix}$$

2×2 matrix T point matrix A point matrix TA

Multiplying two other points by the 2×2 matrix above, we have:

$$\begin{bmatrix} 1 & 0 \\ 0 & -1 \end{bmatrix} \cdot \begin{bmatrix} 5 \\ 0 \end{bmatrix} = \begin{bmatrix} 5 \\ 0 \end{bmatrix} \qquad \begin{bmatrix} 1 & 0 \\ 0 & -1 \end{bmatrix} \cdot \begin{bmatrix} 2 \\ -3 \end{bmatrix} = \begin{bmatrix} 2 \\ 3 \end{bmatrix}$$

$$T \cdot B = TB \qquad T \cdot C = TC$$

The points A, B, C, TA, TB, and TC are graphed on the next page.

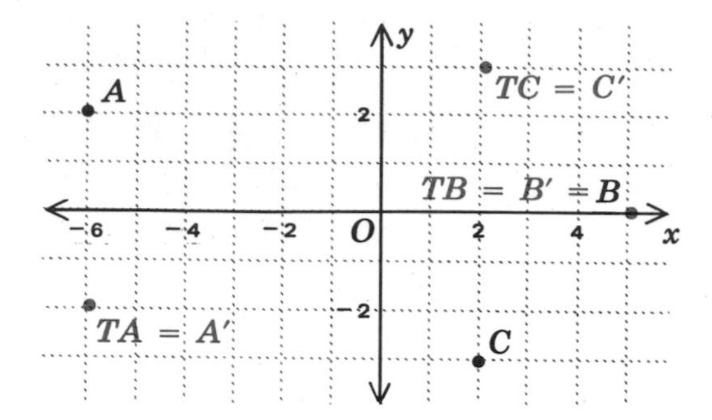

The point matrices A, B, and C are **preimages.** The products $TA = A'$, $TB = B'$, and $TC = C'$ are reflection **images** of A, B, and C. The reflecting line is the x-axis. This can be proved.

We know that the image of (x, y) under $r_{x\text{-axis}}$ is $(x, -y)$. This image can be obtained by matrix multiplication.

$$\begin{bmatrix} 1 & 0 \\ 0 & -1 \end{bmatrix} \cdot \begin{bmatrix} x \\ y \end{bmatrix} = \begin{bmatrix} x \\ -y \end{bmatrix}$$

Definition

Let T be a transformation and let M be a matrix. Then M is the **matrix associated with the transformation** T if and only if, for any point matrix P,

$$T(P) = M \cdot P.$$

Here is another example of the use of $\begin{bmatrix} 1 & 0 \\ 0 & -1 \end{bmatrix}$ to reflect points over the x-axis.

Example 1: Find the image of each point under the transformation $r_{x\text{-axis}}$.

$\begin{bmatrix} 3 \\ 4 \end{bmatrix}$ $\qquad$ $\begin{bmatrix} -1 \\ 2 \end{bmatrix}$ $\qquad$ $\begin{bmatrix} -1 \\ 3 \end{bmatrix}$

SOLUTION:

$$\begin{bmatrix} 1 & 0 \\ 0 & -1 \end{bmatrix} \cdot \begin{bmatrix} 3 \\ 4 \end{bmatrix} = \begin{bmatrix} 3 \\ -4 \end{bmatrix}$$

$$\begin{bmatrix} 1 & 0 \\ 0 & -1 \end{bmatrix} \cdot \begin{bmatrix} -1 \\ 2 \end{bmatrix} = \begin{bmatrix} -1 \\ -2 \end{bmatrix}$$

$$\begin{bmatrix} 1 & 0 \\ 0 & -1 \end{bmatrix} \cdot \begin{bmatrix} -1 \\ 3 \end{bmatrix} = \begin{bmatrix} -1 \\ -3 \end{bmatrix}$$

A simpler way to find the images is to combine the three points into one matrix and multiply by $\begin{bmatrix} 1 & 0 \\ 0 & -1 \end{bmatrix}$. This labor saver always works because of the row-by-column multiplication of matrices.

$$\begin{bmatrix} 1 & 0 \\ 0 & -1 \end{bmatrix} \cdot \begin{bmatrix} 3 & -1 & -1 \\ 4 & 2 & 3 \end{bmatrix} = \begin{bmatrix} 3 & -1 & -1 \\ -4 & -2 & -3 \end{bmatrix}$$

1st point, 2nd point, 3rd point; 1st image point, 2nd image point, 3rd image point

Other 2 × 2 matrices can also represent transformations. The transformation used in Example **2** below has not previously been discussed.

Example 2: Find the image of the square with vertices (1, 1), (−1, 1), (−1, −1), and (1, −1) under the transformation associated with the matrix

$$M = \begin{bmatrix} 2 & 1 \\ -2 & 3 \end{bmatrix}.$$

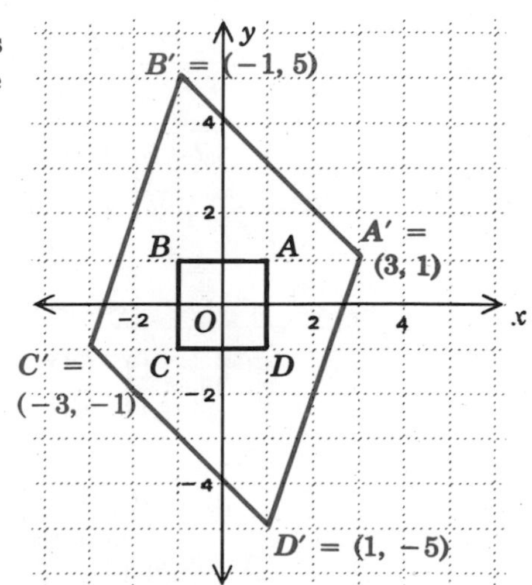

SOLUTION: Represent the square by a single matrix and multiply by M.

$$\begin{bmatrix} 2 & 1 \\ -2 & 3 \end{bmatrix} \cdot \begin{bmatrix} 1 & -1 & -1 & 1 \\ 1 & 1 & -1 & -1 \end{bmatrix}$$

$$= \begin{bmatrix} 3 & -1 & -3 & 1 \\ 1 & 5 & -1 & -5 \end{bmatrix}$$

EXERCISES 5.3

Ⓐ **1–4.** Find the image of the given point under the transformation T if T is represented by the matrix $\begin{bmatrix} 0 & -2 \\ 3 & 0 \end{bmatrix}$

1. $\begin{bmatrix} -3 \\ 2 \end{bmatrix}$ **2.** $\begin{bmatrix} 4 \\ 6 \end{bmatrix}$ **3.** $\begin{bmatrix} 0 \\ 0 \end{bmatrix}$ **4.** $\begin{bmatrix} -7 \\ -2 \end{bmatrix}$

5. Which matrix is associated with $r_{x\text{-axis}}$?

6–9. Give the image of each point under $r_{x\text{-axis}}$.

6. (4, −3) **7.** (100, 70) **8.** $(\frac{1}{2}, -\frac{3}{2})$ **9.** (6, 0)

10. The image of a point under a transformation T can be found by multiplying the corresponding ____ ____ by a ____ associated with the transformation.

11. Let A be a matrix associated with a transformation T. Then, if P is any point, $T(P) =$ ____.

Ⓑ 12–15. Let $A = (2, 4)$, $B = (3, 2)$, $C = (-4, -6)$, and $D = (2, 5)$. Find the image of polygon $ABCD$ under the transformation with the given matrix. Describe the transformation if you can.

12. $\begin{bmatrix} 3 & 0 \\ 0 & 3 \end{bmatrix}$ 13. $\begin{bmatrix} -1 & 0 \\ 0 & 1 \end{bmatrix}$ 14. $\begin{bmatrix} 0 & 1 \\ -1 & 0 \end{bmatrix}$ 15. $\begin{bmatrix} 1 & 2 \\ 0 & 1 \end{bmatrix}$

16. Find the image of triangle ABC under transformation T, where $\triangle ABC = \begin{bmatrix} 2 & 3 & 0 \\ -1 & 2 & 4 \end{bmatrix}$ and T has matrix $\begin{bmatrix} -1 & 0 \\ 0 & 1 \end{bmatrix}$. Describe T.

17–18. Three collinear points and a matrix for a transformation are given.

a. Find the images of the points under the transformation.

b. Does the transformation preserve distance?

c. Are the images collinear?

17. $\begin{bmatrix} 1 \\ 4 \end{bmatrix}, \begin{bmatrix} 0 \\ 2 \end{bmatrix}, \begin{bmatrix} -2 \\ -2 \end{bmatrix}; \begin{bmatrix} 2 & 7 \\ -1 & -4 \end{bmatrix}$ 18. $(3, 0)$, $(5, 0)$, $(8, 0)$; $\begin{bmatrix} -1 & 1 \\ 0 & 2 \end{bmatrix}$

19. The isosceles right triangle with vertices $(0, 1)$, $(0, 0)$, and $(1, 0)$ is mapped onto the nonisosceles triangle with vertices $(3, -4)$, $(0, 0)$, and $(2, -1)$ by a transformation W. Which matrix, from those listed below, could be associated with W?

a. $\begin{bmatrix} -1 & 3 \\ 2 & -4 \end{bmatrix}$ b. $\begin{bmatrix} 2 & 3 \\ -1 & -4 \end{bmatrix}$ c. $\begin{bmatrix} 3 & 2 \\ -1 & -4 \end{bmatrix}$

20. The matrix $\begin{bmatrix} -1 & 0 \\ 0 & -1 \end{bmatrix}$ stands for a transformation which was mentioned in Chapter 4. By choosing preimages and calculating images, determine this transformation.

Ⓒ 21. The matrix $\begin{bmatrix} 2 & -2 \\ 2 & 2 \end{bmatrix}$ stands for the composite of a size transformation and a rotation. Find the center and magnitude of each.

22. Prove or Disprove: The transformation with matrix $\begin{bmatrix} 1 & 1 \\ 0 & 1 \end{bmatrix}$ preserves distance.

23. Find the 2×2 matrix associated with the transformation which maps (x, y) onto $(3x + 2y, -x)$.

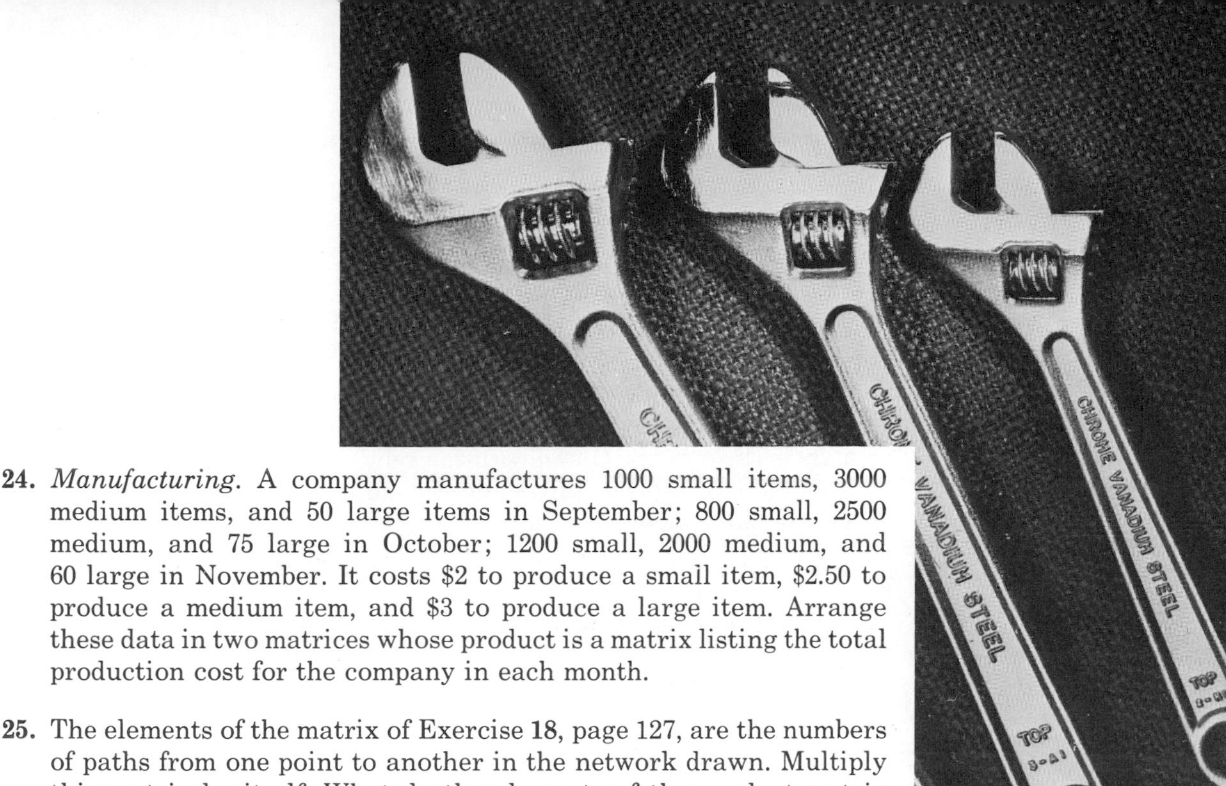

24. *Manufacturing.* A company manufactures 1000 small items, 3000 medium items, and 50 large items in September; 800 small, 2500 medium, and 75 large in October; 1200 small, 2000 medium, and 60 large in November. It costs \$2 to produce a small item, \$2.50 to produce a medium item, and \$3 to produce a large item. Arrange these data in two matrices whose product is a matrix listing the total production cost for the company in each month.

25. The elements of the matrix of Exercise **18**, page 127, are the numbers of paths from one point to another in the network drawn. Multiply this matrix by itself. What do the elements of the product matrix represent?

26. Write the matrix $\begin{bmatrix} ax + by \\ cx + dy \end{bmatrix}$ as the product of a 2×2 and a 2×1 matrix.

MATRICES FOR CERTAIN REFLECTIONS 5.4

In Section 5.3, we proved the following theorem.

Theorem 5.4.1

The matrix associated with $r_{x\text{-axis}}$ is $\begin{bmatrix} 1 & 0 \\ 0 & -1 \end{bmatrix}$.

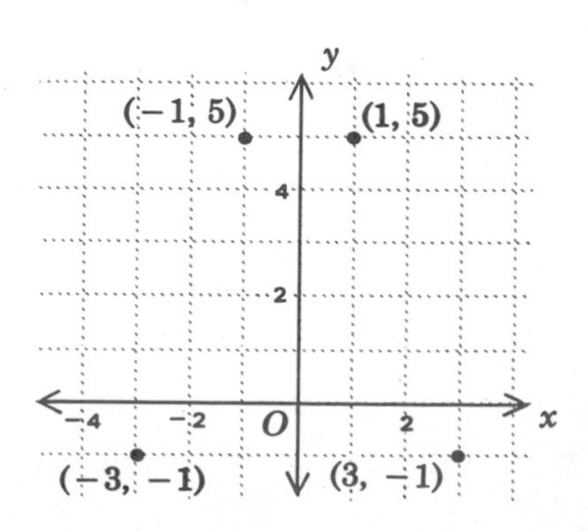

Now let us consider $r_{y\text{-axis}}$. Two points and their images are shown in the diagram. It is clear that $r_{y\text{-axis}}(x, y) = (-x, y)$. Can you fill in the blanks in the matrix?

$$\begin{bmatrix} \_\_ & \_\_ \\ \_\_ & \_\_ \end{bmatrix} \cdot \begin{bmatrix} x \\ y \end{bmatrix} = \begin{bmatrix} -x \\ y \end{bmatrix}$$

Filling in the blanks to make a true sentence proves the next theorem.

Theorem 5.4.2

The matrix associated with $r_{y\text{-axis}}$ is $\begin{bmatrix} -1 & 0 \\ 0 & 1 \end{bmatrix}$.

Example: Reflect $(-1, 5)$ over the y-axis.

SOLUTION: $\begin{bmatrix} -1 & 0 \\ 0 & 1 \end{bmatrix} \cdot \begin{bmatrix} -1 \\ 5 \end{bmatrix} = \begin{bmatrix} 1 \\ 5 \end{bmatrix}$, so the image is $(1, 5)$.

Of course, you do not need matrices to reflect points over the axes. But these matrices will come in handy later. A particularly useful matrix is the one associated with the reflection over the line containing all points with the same first and second coordinates. To describe this line you could write:

x-coordinate equals y-coordinate  $x = y$.

The mathematical shorthand at the right above is the **equation for the line.**

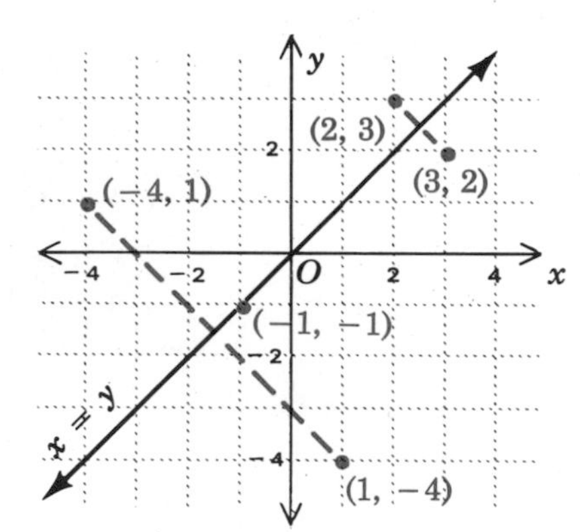

What about reflecting over the line $x = y$? From the diagram, it seems that (a, b) and (b, a) are images of each other when reflected over this line. We can prove this by showing that the line with equation $x = y$ is the perpendicular bisector of the segment joining (a, b) and (b, a). (Recall from geometry that the set of points equidistant from two given points A and B is the perpendicular bisector of $\overline{AB}$.)

Theorem 5.4.3

The image of (a, b) reflected over $x = y$ is (b, a).

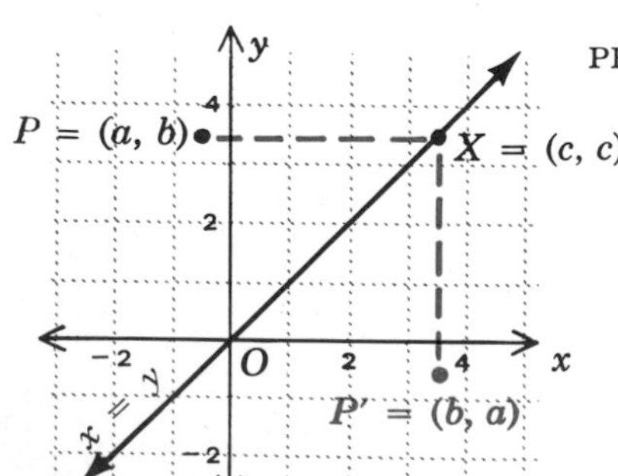

PROOF: Let $X = (c, c)$ be a point on the line $x = y$.

We want to show that $PX = P'X$.

$PX = \sqrt{(c - a)^2 + (c - b)^2}$

$P'X = \sqrt{(c - b)^2 + (c - a)^2}$

Clearly, $PX = P'X$, so each point on the line is equidistant from P and P'. So the line $x = y$ is the perpendicular bisector of $\overline{PP'}$.

Corollary 5.4.4

The matrix for $r_{x=y}$ is $\begin{bmatrix} 0 & 1 \\ 1 & 0 \end{bmatrix}$.

PROOF: Since $\begin{bmatrix} 0 & 1 \\ 1 & 0 \end{bmatrix} \cdot \begin{bmatrix} a \\ b \end{bmatrix} = \begin{bmatrix} b \\ a \end{bmatrix}$, the associated transformation maps (a, b) onto (b, a). That transformation is $r_{x=y}$.

There is also a simple matrix for a reflection over the line n shown at the right. Exercises **14–18** involve finding a matrix for this reflection.

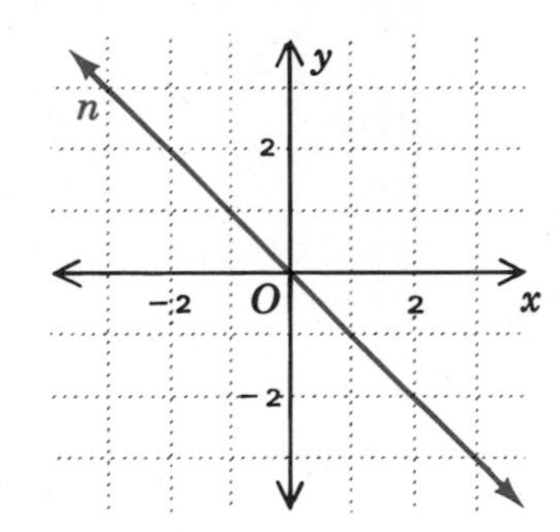

EXERCISES 5.4

Ⓐ **1–3.** Give the matrix for each transformation.

1. $r_{x\text{-axis}}$ **2.** $r_{x=y}$ **3.** $r_{y\text{-axis}}$

4–6. Give the image of $(-7, 2)$ under each transformation.

4. $r_{x\text{-axis}}$ **5.** $r_{x=y}$ **6.** $r_{y\text{-axis}}$

7–9. Repeat Exercises **4–6** for the point (1032, 1033).

10. When it is used to describe a line, $x = y$ is shorthand for ____.

11. To prove that $P = (c, d)$ is the image of $Q = (a, b)$ under a reflection over a line m, you could show that m is the ____ of $\overline{PQ}$.

Ⓑ **12.** Use matrices to find the image of $\begin{bmatrix} 3 & -1 & 0 \\ -2 & 6 & 4 \end{bmatrix}$ under $r_{x=y}$. Graph the preimage and the image.

13. Find the images of (1, 0), (1, 1), and (6, 2) under $r_{y\text{-axis}}$. Graph preimage and image points.

14–18. *An experiment.* Draw the line n which contains $(-4, 4)$ and $(5, -5)$.

14. Choose the correct equation for n.

a. $x = y$ **b.** $x = -y$ **c.** $|x| = y$

15. Using a ruler and protractor, reflect points over n until you see a pattern which enables you to predict what the image will be.

16. What are the images of (100, 43) and $(-17, 21)$ reflected over n?

17. What is the image of (x, y) under r_n? **18.** Find a matrix for r_n.

© **19.** The matrix $\begin{bmatrix} \frac{\sqrt{3}}{2} & \frac{1}{2} \\ \frac{1}{2} & -\frac{\sqrt{3}}{2} \end{bmatrix}$ is associated with a reflection over a line ℓ which contains the origin. What is the measure of the acute angle formed by ℓ and the x-axis? (Experiment using graph paper.)

20. Write the matrices for $r_{x\text{-axis}}$, $r_{x=y}$, and $r_{y\text{-axis}}$. Multiply each matrix by itself. Explain the results.

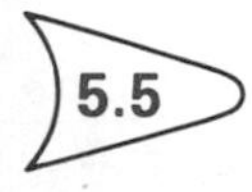

5.5 2 × 2 MATRICES FOR TRANSFORMATIONS

The simplest transformation is the transformation which maps each point onto itself; the image of (x, y) is (x, y). There are different ways of describing this transformation. You may think of it as

1. a rotation of 0°,
2. a size transformation of magnitude 1, with any point as center,
3. the composite of two reflections over the same line, or
4. a translation with magnitude 0.

Definition

The transformation which maps each point onto itself is the **identity transformation**, denoted by the letter I. That is,

$$I(P) = P \text{ for any point } P.$$

The *identity transformation* is so named because under it each preimage keeps its *identity*. Filling in the blanks at the right gets the matrix for I.

$$\begin{bmatrix} \_\_ & \_\_ \\ \_\_ & \_\_ \end{bmatrix} \cdot \begin{bmatrix} x \\ y \end{bmatrix} = \begin{bmatrix} x \\ y \end{bmatrix}$$

Theorem 5.5.1

The matrix for the identity transformation I is $\begin{bmatrix} 1 & 0 \\ 0 & 1 \end{bmatrix}$.

PROOF: You should verify that $\begin{bmatrix} 1 & 0 \\ 0 & 1 \end{bmatrix} \cdot \begin{bmatrix} x \\ y \end{bmatrix} = \begin{bmatrix} x \\ y \end{bmatrix}$.

The matrix for the *identity transformation* is an **identity matrix.**

Theorem 5.5.2

In the set of 2 × 2 matrices, $\begin{bmatrix} 1 & 0 \\ 0 & 1 \end{bmatrix}$ is a multiplicative identity.

PROOF: We need to show that the product, when any matrix A is multiplied by $\begin{bmatrix} 1 & 0 \\ 0 & 1 \end{bmatrix}$, is A. Let $A = \begin{bmatrix} a & b \\ c & d \end{bmatrix}$. There are two possible orders for the matrices.

$$\begin{bmatrix} a & b \\ c & d \end{bmatrix} \cdot \begin{bmatrix} 1 & 0 \\ 0 & 1 \end{bmatrix} = \begin{bmatrix} a & b \\ c & d \end{bmatrix} \qquad \begin{bmatrix} 1 & 0 \\ 0 & 1 \end{bmatrix} \cdot \begin{bmatrix} a & b \\ c & d \end{bmatrix} = \begin{bmatrix} a & b \\ c & d \end{bmatrix}$$

Though the order of the matrices multiplied above did not make any difference, you would be wrong if you thought this is true for all matrices.

Theorem 5.5.3

Multiplication of 2×2 matrices is not commutative.

PROOF: Only one example is needed to show that something is not always so.

Let $A = \begin{bmatrix} 2 & 1 \\ 1 & 2 \end{bmatrix}$ and $B = \begin{bmatrix} 1 & 0 \\ 3 & -2 \end{bmatrix}$.

Then $AB = \begin{bmatrix} 5 & -2 \\ 7 & -4 \end{bmatrix}$ and $BA = \begin{bmatrix} 2 & 1 \\ 4 & -1 \end{bmatrix}$.

So $AB \neq BA$, proving the theorem.

Now let $C = \begin{bmatrix} 4 & 1 \\ 5 & 3 \end{bmatrix}$. To find $A \cdot B \cdot C$, should we multiply $A \cdot B$ or $B \cdot C$ first?

$$AB = \begin{bmatrix} 5 & -2 \\ 7 & -4 \end{bmatrix}$$

$$(AB)C = \begin{bmatrix} 5 & -2 \\ 7 & -4 \end{bmatrix} \cdot \begin{bmatrix} 4 & 1 \\ 5 & 3 \end{bmatrix} = \begin{bmatrix} 10 & -1 \\ 8 & -5 \end{bmatrix}$$

$$BC = \begin{bmatrix} 4 & 1 \\ 2 & -3 \end{bmatrix}$$

$$A(BC) = \begin{bmatrix} 2 & 1 \\ 1 & 2 \end{bmatrix} \cdot \begin{bmatrix} 4 & 1 \\ 2 & -3 \end{bmatrix} = \begin{bmatrix} 10 & -1 \\ 8 & -5 \end{bmatrix}$$

Though matrix multiplication is unusual in some ways, it makes no difference whether AB or BC is done first. That is, $(AB)C = A(BC)$. The general proof of this for any 2×2 matrices is left as an exercise.

Theorem 5.5.4

Multiplication of 2×2 matrices is associative.

Associativity helps to show just how closely transformations and matrices are related.

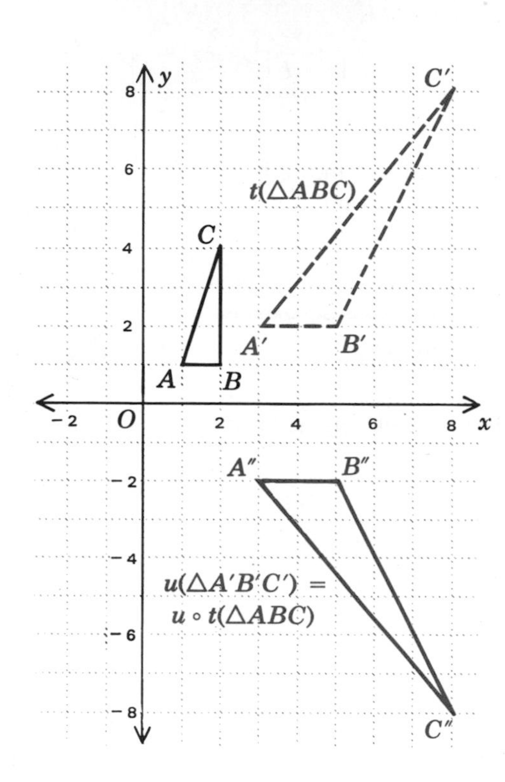

Example:

Suppose $\triangle ABC = \begin{bmatrix} 1 & 2 & 2 \\ 1 & 1 & 4 \end{bmatrix}$ and $\begin{bmatrix} 2 & 1 \\ 0 & 2 \end{bmatrix}$ is the matrix for t. Then $t(\triangle ABC) = \triangle A'B'C'$, as pictured at the left. Now suppose u has matrix $\begin{bmatrix} 1 & 0 \\ 0 & -1 \end{bmatrix}$. Then

$$u(\triangle A'B'C') = \triangle A''B''C''.$$

The transformation which maps $\triangle ABC$ directly onto $\triangle A''B''C''$ is $u \circ t$.

$$u \circ t(\triangle ABC) = \triangle A''B''C''$$

Notice that $u(t(\triangle ABC))$ is found by multiplying three matrices.

$$\begin{bmatrix} 1 & 0 \\ 0 & -1 \end{bmatrix} \cdot \left(\begin{bmatrix} 2 & 1 \\ 0 & 2 \end{bmatrix} \cdot \begin{bmatrix} 1 & 2 & 2 \\ 1 & 1 & 4 \end{bmatrix} \right)$$

Associativity allows regrouping.

$$\left(\begin{bmatrix} 1 & 0 \\ 0 & -1 \end{bmatrix} \cdot \begin{bmatrix} 2 & 1 \\ 0 & 2 \end{bmatrix} \right) \cdot \begin{bmatrix} 1 & 2 & 2 \\ 1 & 1 & 4 \end{bmatrix}$$

So multiplying the matrices for u and t gives the matrix for $u \circ t$.

Theorem 5.5.5

Matrix-transformation isomorphism (MTI) theorem:

If M is the matrix associated with a transformation t, and N is the matrix associated with a transformation u, then $N \cdot M$ is the matrix associated with the transformation $u \circ t$.

PROOF: 1. Let P be any point. From the given,

$$t(P) = M \cdot P.$$

2. $M \cdot P$ is a point matrix. We find its image under u by multiplying by N (the matrix for u).

So $u(t(P)) = N \cdot (M \cdot P)$.

3. Since matrix multiplication is associative,

$$u(t(P)) = (N \cdot M) \cdot P.$$

4. So $N \cdot M$ is the matrix which maps P onto $u(t(P))$.

5. Hence $N \cdot M$ is the matrix for $u \circ t$.

The word *isomorphism* comes from the Greek words for *same* and *structure*. The MTI theorem indicates that multiplying matrices corresponds to (has the same structure as) composing transformations.

Example: Using the MTI theorem

$r_{x\text{-axis}}$ has matrix $\begin{bmatrix} 1 & 0 \\ 0 & -1 \end{bmatrix}$. By the MTI theorem,

$$r_{x\text{-axis}} \circ r_{x\text{-axis}} \text{ has matrix } \begin{bmatrix} 1 & 0 \\ 0 & -1 \end{bmatrix} \cdot \begin{bmatrix} 1 & 0 \\ 0 & -1 \end{bmatrix} = \begin{bmatrix} 1 & 0 \\ 0 & 1 \end{bmatrix}.$$

the identity transformation **the identity matrix**

The MTI theorem enables a matrix to be determined for any composite of transformations for which the matrices are known. Since rotations are composites of reflections, we can find matrices for some of them. This is done in the next section.

EXERCISES 5.5

Ⓐ **1–7.** Match each numbered item with the best lettered choice.

1. transformations

2. composition

3. composites

4. point

5. $r_{x\text{-axis}}$

6. I

7. triangle

a. $\begin{bmatrix} 2 \\ 3 \end{bmatrix}$

b. $\begin{bmatrix} 1 & 0 \\ 0 & 1 \end{bmatrix}$

c. $[2 \quad 3]$

d. $[3 \quad 4 \quad 5]$

e. $\begin{bmatrix} -1 & 0 \\ 0 & 1 \end{bmatrix}$

f. $\begin{bmatrix} 1 & 0 \\ 0 & -1 \end{bmatrix}$

g. products

h. matrices

i. multiplication

j. $\begin{bmatrix} 2 & 0 & 3 \\ 0 & 1 & 2 \end{bmatrix}$

8. What is the identity transformation?

9. True or False? The identity matrix is associated with the identity transformation.

10. An identity for multiplication of 2 × 2 matrices is ____.

11. What is the matrix-transformation isomorphism theorem?

12–19. A is a matrix for transformation t, B is a matrix for transformation u, and C is a matrix for transformation v. Tell what matrix product is associated with the given transformation or what transformation has the given matrix.

12. $t \circ u$ **13.** $u \circ t$ **14.** $t \circ v \circ u$ **15.** $v \circ v$

16. AB **17.** BC **18.** CBA **19.** CA

Ⓑ **20.** If $A = \begin{bmatrix} 10 & 1 \\ 3 & 0 \end{bmatrix}$, find a matrix B so that $AB = BA$.

21. Let $C = \begin{bmatrix} -1 & 2 \\ 0 & 2 \end{bmatrix}$, $D = \begin{bmatrix} 3 & 0 \\ 5 & -4 \end{bmatrix}$, and $P = \begin{bmatrix} 9 \\ -5 \end{bmatrix}$. Calculate CD, DP, $C(DP)$, and $(CD)P$. Which two of the four matrices you have calculated are equal, and why?

22–23. Give an example different from any mentioned in this book to demonstrate that multiplication of 2×2 matrices is:

22. associative. **23.** not commutative.

24–25. Transformation t has matrix $\begin{bmatrix} 3 & 5 \\ 1 & 2 \end{bmatrix}$. Transformation u has matrix $\begin{bmatrix} 6 & 7 \\ -2 & 5 \end{bmatrix}$. If $\triangle ABC = \begin{bmatrix} 8 & 3 & 2 \\ -2 & 0 & -5 \end{bmatrix}$, calculate:

24. $t \circ u\ (\triangle ABC)$. **25.** $u \circ t\ (\triangle ABC)$.

26. Find the image of $\begin{bmatrix} 3.461 & \sqrt{12} & 4.12 \\ 2.196 & \sqrt{93} & -3.80 \end{bmatrix}$ under the identity transformation.

27. Write as one matrix.

$$\begin{bmatrix} -1 & 0 \\ 0 & 1 \end{bmatrix} \cdot \begin{bmatrix} 1 & 0 \\ 0 & 1 \end{bmatrix} \cdot \begin{bmatrix} -1 & 0 \\ 0 & 1 \end{bmatrix} \cdot \begin{bmatrix} 1 & 0 \\ 0 & 1 \end{bmatrix} \cdot \begin{bmatrix} 1 & 0 \\ 0 & -1 \end{bmatrix} \cdot \begin{bmatrix} 1 & 0 \\ 0 & 1 \end{bmatrix}$$

Ⓒ **28.** Prove Theorem 5.5.4.

29. Find a multiplicative identity for the set of 3×3 matrices.

By permission of John Hart, courtesy of Publishers-Hall Syndicate

MATRICES FOR CERTAIN ROTATIONS

Composite $r_{x=y} \circ r_{x\text{-axis}}$ is a rotation because the reflecting lines intersect. Its center is (0, 0) and its magnitude is $2 \cdot 45°$, or $90°$. We call this rotation R_{90}. Because of the MTI theorem, multiplying the matrices for the two reflections gives the matrix for R_{90}.

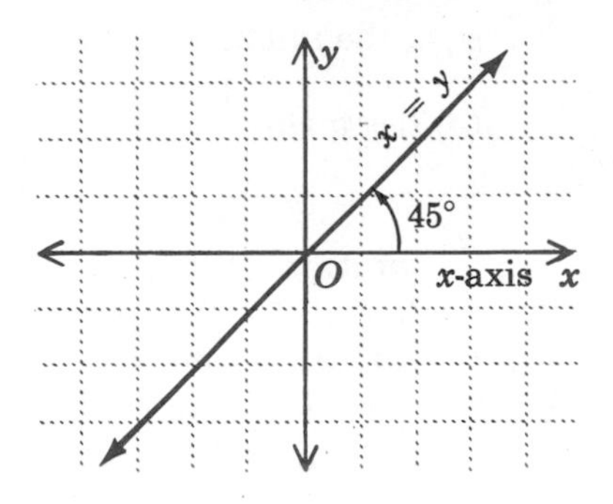

Theorem 5.6.1

R_{90}, the rotation of 90° about the origin,

(**a**) has matrix $\begin{bmatrix} 0 & -1 \\ 1 & 0 \end{bmatrix}$ and (**b**) maps (x, y) onto $(-y, x)$.

PROOF: **a.** $r_{x=y} \circ r_{x\text{-axis}} = R_{90}$

By the MTI theorem,

$$(\text{matrix for } r_{x=y}) \cdot (\text{matrix for } r_{x\text{-axis}}) = \text{matrix for } R_{90}$$

$$\begin{bmatrix} 0 & 1 \\ 1 & 0 \end{bmatrix} \cdot \begin{bmatrix} 1 & 0 \\ 0 & -1 \end{bmatrix} = \begin{bmatrix} 0 & -1 \\ 1 & 0 \end{bmatrix}$$

b. $\begin{bmatrix} 0 & -1 \\ 1 & 0 \end{bmatrix} \cdot \begin{bmatrix} x \\ y \end{bmatrix} = \begin{bmatrix} -y \\ x \end{bmatrix}$

Example: Rotate $\triangle ABC$ 90° about (0, 0).

$$\triangle ABC = \begin{bmatrix} -4 & -3 & 6 \\ -1 & 5 & 2 \end{bmatrix}$$

SOLUTION: $\begin{bmatrix} 0 & -1 \\ 1 & 0 \end{bmatrix} \cdot \begin{bmatrix} -4 & -3 & 6 \\ -1 & 5 & 2 \end{bmatrix} = \begin{bmatrix} 1 & -5 & -2 \\ -4 & -3 & 6 \end{bmatrix}$

Graphing the preimage and image points verifies the theorem. The triangle is rotated 90° about (0, 0).

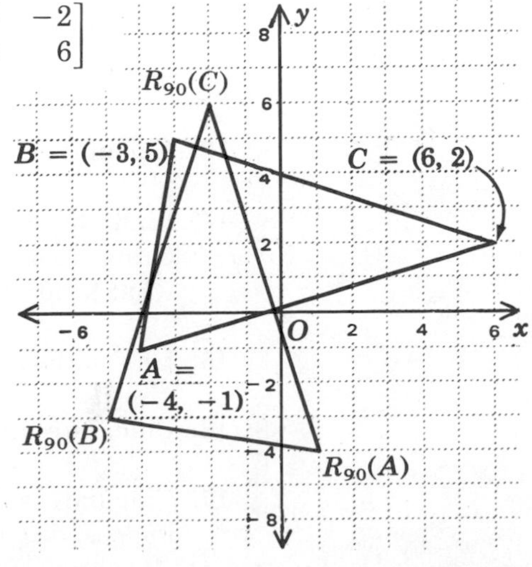

One of the simplest ways to find the matrix for R_{180} is to compose the rotation of 90° with itself.

$$R_{90} \circ R_{90} = R_{180}$$

By the MTI theorem,

$$(\text{matrix for } R_{90}) \cdot (\text{matrix for } R_{90}) = \text{matrix for } R_{180}$$

$$\begin{bmatrix} 0 & -1 \\ 1 & 0 \end{bmatrix} \cdot \begin{bmatrix} 0 & -1 \\ 1 & 0 \end{bmatrix} = \begin{bmatrix} -1 & 0 \\ 0 & -1 \end{bmatrix}$$

Theorem 5.6.2

R_{180}, the rotation of 180° (half-turn) about the origin,

(a) has matrix $\begin{bmatrix} -1 & 0 \\ 0 & -1 \end{bmatrix}$ and (b) maps (a, b) onto $(-a, -b)$.

The rotation of 270° about the origin is denoted by R_{270}. Because $R_{270} = R_{180} \circ R_{90}$, a matrix is easy to obtain. Except for the identity, other rotations do not have matrices with integer elements. Matrices for these other rotations are derived in Section 8.4.

EXERCISES 5.6

Ⓐ **1.** $r_{x=y} \circ r_{x\text{-axis}} =$ ____

2. $R_{270} \circ R_{90} =$ ____

3. How is the matrix-transformation isomorphism theorem applied in this section?

4. Give the matrix for R_{90}.

5. Give the matrix for R_{180}.

6. $R_{90}(-3, 1) =$ ____

7. $R_{180}(8, 10) =$ ____

8. $R_{90}(x, y) =$ ____

9. $R_{180}(a, b) =$ ____

Ⓑ **10–11.** Under what two transformations mentioned in this or previous sections is the statement true?

10. The image of (2, 2) is (2, −2).

11. The image of (5, −5) is (−5, 5).

12. Find the image of $\begin{bmatrix} 0 & 2 & 5 & -1 \\ 0 & 3 & 11 & 6 \end{bmatrix}$ under R_{90}. Graph preimage and image.

13. Calculate a matrix for R_{270}.

14. Find the image of (2, 5) under R_{90}, under R_{180}, and under R_{270}. Graph (2, 5) and the three images. The four points are vertices of what kind of polygon?

15. Use matrices to verify that $R_{180} \circ R_{180} = I$.

16. Calculate a matrix for $r_{x\text{-axis}} \circ r_{x=y}$. Describe this transformation.

17. Calculate a matrix for $R_{180} \circ r_{x=y}$. By choosing points and finding images, describe this transformation.

© **18–19.** A figure which coincides with its image under R_{180} is called *point-symmetric*. Prove each statement.

18. $\begin{bmatrix} 2 & 3 & -2 & -3 \\ -4 & 5 & 4 & -5 \end{bmatrix}$ is point-symmetric.

19. The figure of Exercise **18** is a parallelogram. (HINT: Use distance.)

20. Prove that (x, y), $(0, 0)$, and $(-y, x)$ are vertices of an isosceles right triangle. Guess why this exercise follows this section.

21. In a later section, the matrix for R_{30} is found to be $\begin{bmatrix} \frac{\sqrt{3}}{2} & -\frac{1}{2} \\ \frac{1}{2} & \frac{\sqrt{3}}{2} \end{bmatrix}$. Use this matrix to calculate R_{60} and R_{210}.

WHICH TRANSFORMATIONS HAVE 2 × 2 MATRICES?

Not all transformations can be described by 2 × 2 matrices. In particular, a transformation must map (0, 0) onto (0, 0) in order to have a 2 × 2 matrix, since for any numbers a, b, c, and d,

$$\begin{bmatrix} a & b \\ c & d \end{bmatrix} \cdot \begin{bmatrix} 0 \\ 0 \end{bmatrix} = \begin{bmatrix} 0 \\ 0 \end{bmatrix}.$$

This immediately shows:

Theorem 5.7.1

a. The only reflections which can have 2 × 2 matrices are those over lines containing (0, 0).

b. The only rotations which can have 2 × 2 matrices are those with center (0, 0).

c. There is no 2 × 2 matrix for any translation but the identity.

But which other transformations can be described by 2 × 2 matrices? The general formula $\begin{bmatrix} a & b \\ c & d \end{bmatrix} \cdot \begin{bmatrix} x \\ y \end{bmatrix} = \begin{bmatrix} ax + by \\ cx + dy \end{bmatrix}$ indicates that a transformation which maps (x, y) onto $(ax + by, cx + dy)$ has a 2 × 2 matrix. If $a = k$, $b = 0$, $c = 0$, and $d = k$, then $(ax + by, cx + dy) = (kx, ky)$. This shows that size transformations have 2 × 2 matrices.

Theorem 5.7.2

The size transformation with center (0, 0), magnitude k, has matrix

$$\begin{bmatrix} k & 0 \\ 0 & k \end{bmatrix}.$$

Examples: Matrices for size transformations

1. The size transformation of magnitude -5.3 has matrix

$$\begin{bmatrix} -5.3 & 0 \\ 0 & -5.3 \end{bmatrix}.$$

2. The size transformation of magnitude 1 has matrix $\begin{bmatrix} 1 & 0 \\ 0 & 1 \end{bmatrix}$.

   (This agrees with earlier results that this transformation is the identity.)

You may be wondering how to remember the matrices for particular transformations. Memorizing them is not necessary, due to the following theorem, which is amazing because of its wide applicability and because of the shortness of its proof.

Theorem 5.7.3

Matrix basis theorem: Suppose T is a transformation, $T(1, 0) = (x_1, y_1)$, and $T(0, 1) = (x_2, y_2)$. If T has a 2×2 matrix, the matrix is $\begin{bmatrix} x_1 & x_2 \\ y_1 & y_2 \end{bmatrix}$.

PROOF: Let M be the matrix for T.

Since $T(1, 0) = (x_1, y_1)$ and $T(0, 1) = (x_2, y_2)$, $\quad M \cdot \begin{bmatrix} 1 & 0 \\ 0 & 1 \end{bmatrix} = \begin{bmatrix} x_1 & x_2 \\ y_1 & y_2 \end{bmatrix}$.

But $\begin{bmatrix} 1 & 0 \\ 0 & 1 \end{bmatrix}$ is the multiplicative identity, so $\quad M = \begin{bmatrix} x_1 & x_2 \\ y_1 & y_2 \end{bmatrix}$.

Suppose you have forgotten the matrix for R_{90}. By picturing the rotation in your head, you can determine that $R_{90}(1, 0) = (0, 1)$ and $R_{90}(0, 1) = (-1, 0)$. Applying the matrix basis theorem,

image of (1, 0)

image of (0, 1)

$$\text{matrix for } R_{90} = \begin{bmatrix} 0 & -1 \\ 1 & 0 \end{bmatrix}.$$

The theorem is named the *matrix basis theorem* because the matrix is "based" upon the images of points (1, 0) and (0, 1).

Using matrices, we can deduce properties of transformations which might otherwise be difficult to determine. One such property is given in the next theorem. Others are given in the exercises.

Theorem 5.7.4

The composite of two size transformations with magnitudes j and k and center C is the size transformation with center C and magnitude jk.

PROOF: Coordinatize the plane so that $C = (0, 0)$. Then multiply the matrices for the size transformations.

$$\begin{bmatrix} j & 0 \\ 0 & j \end{bmatrix} \cdot \begin{bmatrix} k & 0 \\ 0 & k \end{bmatrix} = \begin{bmatrix} jk & 0 \\ 0 & jk \end{bmatrix}$$

The product is the matrix for a size transformation of magnitude jk and center (0, 0).

Henceforth, we shall use the symbol S_k to denote the size transformation with center (0, 0), magnitude k. This will shorten many statements. For example, Theorem 5.7.4 becomes

$$S_j \circ S_k = S_{jk}.$$

EXERCISES 5.7

Ⓐ 1. Why is there no 2 × 2 matrix associated with most translations?

2. A transformation T has a 2 × 2 matrix. If $T(1, 0) = (4, 7)$ and $T(0, 1) = (2, 6)$,what is the matrix?

3. What is the matrix for a size transformation of magnitude 2?

4. What is the matrix for S_{-11}?

5. What is the matrix basis theorem?

6–10. For each transformation, give **(a)** the image of (1, 0), **(b)** the image of (0, 1), and **(c)** the 2 × 2 matrix for the transformation.

6. R_{90} 7. $r_{x=y}$ 8. $r_{x\text{-axis}}$ 9. R_{180} 10. $r_{y\text{-axis}}$

11. Can a size transformation have magnitude π?

12. Translate into English: $S_2 \circ S_{-3} = S_{-6}$.

Ⓑ **13–14.** Find the 2 × 2 matrix for T if T maps (x, y) onto:

13. $(3x - y, x + y)$. 14. $(-y, -x)$.

15. Apply S_{-2} to the polygon with vertices (2, 3), (−2, −3), (−2, 1), (2, 4). Apply $S_{\frac{1}{2}}$ to the image. Describe and graph $S_{\frac{1}{2}} \circ S_{-2}$.

16. A machine enlarges a photograph by a factor of 1.5. A second machine magnifies the image 2 times. How does the final result compare to the original photograph?

17. Suppose 90% of a hamburger is meat. If 70% of the meat is beef, what percentage of the hamburger is beef?

18. What theorem of this section is most applicable in Exercises **16–17**?

19–21. Use matrices to prove each property of transformations.

19. R_{180} is a size transformation.

© 20. Composition of size transformations with the same center is commutative.

21. If T is any transformation with a 2×2 matrix and S is any size transformation with center (0, 0), then $S \circ T = T \circ S$.

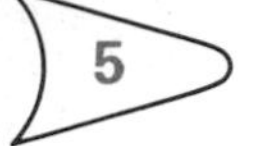

CHAPTER SUMMARY

A matrix with *dimensions* $m \times n$ is an array of objects arranged in m rows and n columns. Matrices have many uses; this chapter concentrated on applying 2×2 matrices to transformations.

Two matrices may be multiplied if the number of columns of the matrix on the left equals the number of rows of the matrix on the right. The element in row i, column j, of the product matrix MN is the product of row i of matrix M and column j of matrix N.

The 2×1 matrix $\begin{bmatrix} x \\ y \end{bmatrix}$ represents point (x, y). A matrix M represents a transformation T if and only if

$$M \cdot \begin{bmatrix} x \\ y \end{bmatrix} = T(x, y).$$

Multiplication of matrices is associative and has an identity, $\begin{bmatrix} 1 & 0 \\ 0 & 1 \end{bmatrix}$, but is not commutative. Properties of matrix multiplication correspond to properties of transformation composition. When matrices for transformations are multiplied, the product matrix stands for the composite of the corresponding transformations, as shown by the *matrix-transformation isomorphism* (MTI) *theorem.*

Since rotations are composites of reflections, the MTI theorem helps in deriving matrices for R_{90}, R_{180}, and R_{270}. You do not have to memorize these matrices because of the *matrix basis theorem* (Theorem 5.7.3): If (a, b) is the image of (1, 0) and (c, d) is the image of (0, 1) under transformation T with matrix M, then $M = \begin{bmatrix} a & c \\ b & d \end{bmatrix}$

Matrices of some transformations are:

$r_{x\text{-axis}}: \begin{bmatrix} 1 & 0 \\ 0 & -1 \end{bmatrix}$ $R_{90}: \begin{bmatrix} 0 & -1 \\ 1 & 0 \end{bmatrix}$

$r_{y\text{-axis}}: \begin{bmatrix} -1 & 0 \\ 0 & 1 \end{bmatrix}$ $R_{180}: \begin{bmatrix} -1 & 0 \\ 0 & -1 \end{bmatrix}$

$r_{x=y}: \begin{bmatrix} 0 & 1 \\ 1 & 0 \end{bmatrix}$ $R_{270}: \begin{bmatrix} 0 & 1 \\ -1 & 0 \end{bmatrix}$

$I: \begin{bmatrix} 1 & 0 \\ 0 & 1 \end{bmatrix}$ $S_k: \begin{bmatrix} k & 0 \\ 0 & k \end{bmatrix}$

Not all transformations have 2 × 2 matrices. Because most translations do not map (0, 0) onto itself, they do not have 2 × 2 matrices. Still, matrices are useful for representing transformations and are applied many times in succeeding chapters.

CHAPTER REVIEW

5

1–2. Multiply.

1. $[3 \quad 5] \cdot \begin{bmatrix} 6 & -2 & 3 & 0 \\ 1 & 4 & 0 & 2 \end{bmatrix} \cdot \begin{bmatrix} 3 \\ 7 \\ 0 \\ 2 \end{bmatrix}$ **2.** $\begin{bmatrix} 2 & 4 & 1 \\ 3 & 6 & 0 \end{bmatrix} \cdot \begin{bmatrix} 1 \\ 2 \\ 3 \end{bmatrix}$

3–6. What 2 × 2 matrix corresponds to each transformation?

3. identity transformation **4.** $r_{y\text{-axis}}$ **5.** R_{180}

6. size transformation of magnitude 6, center (0, 0)

7–8. Find the image of (3, −7) under the given transformation.

7. a rotation of 180° with center (0, 0) **8.** $r_{x=y} \circ r_{y\text{-axis}}$

9. Find a matrix A satisfying $[2 \quad 6 \quad 1] \cdot A = [3 \quad 2]$.

10. Find the image of $\triangle ABC$ under the transformation with matrix M. $\triangle ABC = \begin{bmatrix} 1 & 4 & -3 \\ -2 & 0 & 3 \end{bmatrix}$ $M = \begin{bmatrix} 2 & 6 \\ 3 & 8 \end{bmatrix}$

11. Suppose $T(1, 0) = (2, 3)$ and $T(0, 1) = (4, 5)$. Give the matrix for T. Then calculate $T(2, 5)$.

12–13. Describe a transformation which has the given matrix. **12.** $\begin{bmatrix} 0 & 1 \\ -1 & 0 \end{bmatrix}$ **13.** $\begin{bmatrix} -\frac{1}{2} & 0 \\ 0 & \frac{1}{2} \end{bmatrix}$

14–15. Use matrices to determine whether the statement is true.

14. $r_{x\text{-axis}} \circ R_{90} = R_{90} \circ r_{y\text{-axis}}$ **15.** $r_{x\text{-axis}} \circ r_{x=y} = R_{270} \circ r_{x\text{-axis}}$

16. Give an example of two matrices which cannot be multiplied.

17. State the matrix-transformation isomorphism theorem and give an example of its use.

Lines and Circles

Chapter 6

6.1 VOCABULARY AND NOTATION

Many words and symbols are used in solving sentences. In this section, we try to make their meanings clearer.

A **variable** is a symbol which may stand for any object from a given set of objects. Most commonly, the objects are *numbers*—real numbers, integers, positive numbers, and so on—and the symbol used is a letter, such as a, b, x, y, or z.

If a sentence contains one variable which stands for real numbers, then its solution set may be graphed on the number line.

Sentence	*Solution set*	*Graph of solution set*
$3 \geq 9 - 4x$	$\{x: x \geq \frac{3}{2}\}$	0 $\frac{3}{2}$

Often sentences have more than one variable to begin with.

$$8x - 7y = 15$$

What does it mean to find a solution to such a sentence? We look for a value of x and a value of y which work. For example, substituting 1 for x and -1 for y makes the sentence above true.

$$8 \cdot 1 - 7 \cdot (-1) = 15$$

This solution is usually written as an ordered pair $(1, -1)$. There are other solutions, among them $(2, \frac{1}{7})$, $(\frac{15}{8}, 0)$, and $(8, 7)$. (The value of x is written first only out of tradition—usually the order is alphabetical.)

If a sentence contains exactly two variables, each solution is an ordered pair.

Since ordered pairs of real numbers can be graphed in the plane, we can easily graph solution sets to sentences with two variables.

Sentence	*Solution set*	*Graph of solution set*
$8x - 7y = 15$	$\{(x, y): 8x - 7y = 15\}$	
	Some solutions:	
	$(1, -1)$	
	$(2, \frac{1}{7})$	
	$(\frac{15}{8}, 0)$	
	$(8, 7)$	

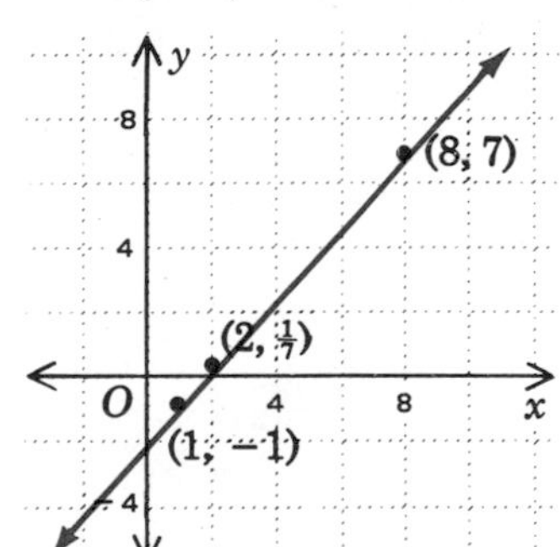

The notation $\{(x, y): \cdots\}$ tells a person that the set contains ordered pairs with the first member of each pair denoted by x, the second by y. Notice:

$\{x: x = 5\}$ is different from $\{(x, y): x = 5\}$.

Graph is:

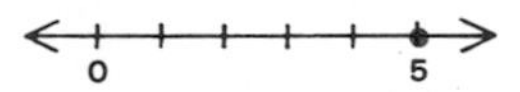

Solution: 5

Graph is:

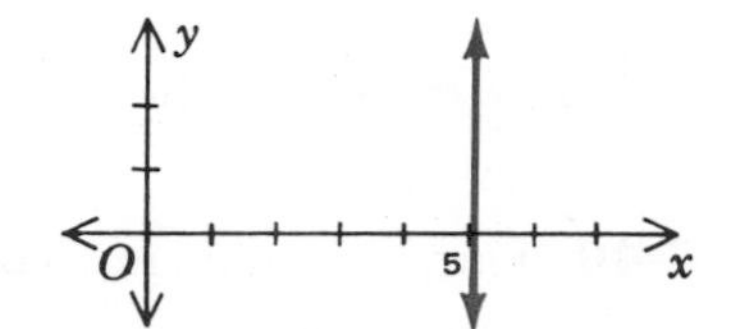

Solutions: $(5, 3)$, $(5, 10)$, $\cdots$

The graphs of $\{x: x = 5\}$ and $\{(x, y): x = 5\}$ are obviously different. But there is no difference in the sentences. Both sentences are $x = 5$. The set notation shows that the second sentence involves two variables. It may help you to write $0 \cdot y + x = 5$ so that you see the two variables.

How many variables has the sentence $y = kx$? This question has no definite answer without further information. Are we solving for x? What is given? Are we solving for (x, y)? And so on. Because x and y are used, it is the custom to assume that

$$\{(x, y): y = kx\}$$

is under discussion. This notation indicates that x and y are variables and k is a *constant*.

A **constant** is a symbol which stands for exactly one object during the course of a problem. Some symbols always stand for constants:

$$\pi, \quad \sqrt{2}, \quad 2, \quad 76.5, \quad \text{etc.}$$

But when a letter is used, you have to examine the situation to decide whether the symbol is a variable or a constant.

The number of variables in a sentence is the **dimension** of a sentence. Because we usually read, write, and draw in two dimensions, most sentences in mathematics are two-dimensional. However, it is possible for a sentence to have any number of dimensions. The solution sets of two-dimensional sentences are called relations—they relate two variables. A **relation** is a set of ordered pairs.

EXERCISES 6.1

Ⓐ **1–4.** Give the meaning of each term.

1. variable **2.** constant **3.** dimension of a sentence

4. relation

5. Each solution to $9x - y = 6$ is a(n)_____ of real numbers.

6. How many dimensions does the graph of a relation have?

7–10. Find one solution to each two-dimensional sentence.

7. $4y - 462z > 8$ **8.** $-1 = c + d$

9. $6 - (e + 2f) = 6$ **10.** $9y = 6x$

11. Find six solutions to $0 \cdot x + y = 9$.

12. Using set notation, denote the solution set to the two-dimensional sentence $3y - 5x > -10$.

13–16. Give the number of variables in each sentence.

13. $3x - 5y = 2$

14. $-9 - x = \pi$

15. $(v_1{}^3) = k(v_2{}^3)$, k a constant

16. $5ax^2 - 6b = 7d + 8ea - 9x$

17–20. From the solution set, determine the dimension of each sentence.

17. $\{(x, y): x + 3y = 2\}$

18. $\{a: a > 5\}$

19. $\{(x, y): y = 5\}$

20. $\{(a, b, c): 3a - 4b + c \leq 8\}$

21. Which sets in Exercises **17–20** are relations?

22. The real number line is _____-dimensional.

23. The coordinate plane is _____-dimensional.

24. A sentence with four variables is at least a _____-dimensional sentence.

25. Explain how the dimensions of $y = 4$ may be more than one.

26–29. From the solution set, determine the number of *letters* which are used as constants.

26. $\{(x, y): wx + zy = v\}$

27. $\{x: ax = b\}$

28. $\{(a, b): ax = 1\}$

29. $\{(x, y, z): x = 2\}$

Ⓑ **30–35.** Find four solutions to each two-dimensional sentence.

30. $10t + u = 10u + t$

31. $5x - 2y = 10$

32. $6 + 3y < y - 4x$

33. $5a - 2b > 9$

34. $-\frac{x}{4} > \frac{y}{2}$

35. $3(p + q) = 12$

36–39. One solution to $51x - 29y = 1600$ is $(49, 31)$. Use this information to find one solution to:

36. $51(x - 5) - 29(y + 3) = 1600.$

37. $51(x + 10) - 29y = 1600.$

38. $51\left(\frac{x}{2}\right) - 29\left(\frac{y}{3}\right) = 1600.$

39. $102x - 290y = 1600.$

© **40–43.** An equation in two or more dimensions is called a Diophantine equation if you are looking only for *integer* solutions. Diophantine equations occupy an important role in the history of mathematics. For each Diophantine equation, find the indicated number of solutions.

40. $x^2 + y^2 = 145$ (5 solutions)

41. $\frac{1}{a} + \frac{1}{b} = \frac{1}{2}$ (2 solutions)

42. Pell's equation: $x^2 - 2y^2 = 1$. (3 solutions)

43. $\frac{1}{p} + \frac{1}{q} = \frac{1}{3}$ (*all* solutions)

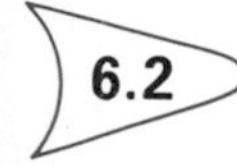

EQUATIONS FOR CERTAIN LINES

You have graphed lines in previous mathematics courses. As a review, let's graph the simple sentences $x = 106$ and $y = -24.2$.

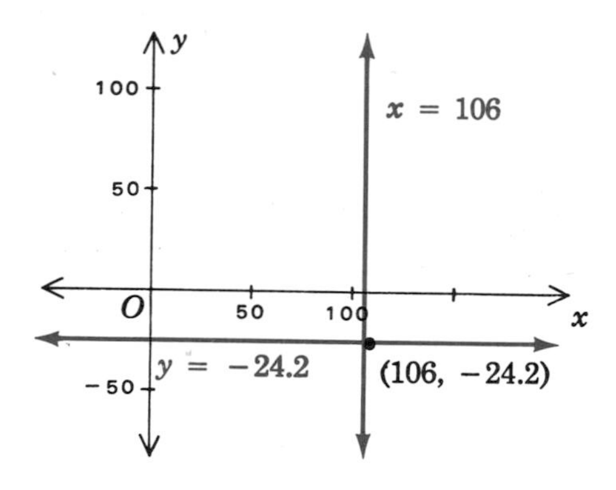

The points whose first (x) coordinate is 106 are the solutions to

$$x = 106 \text{ or}$$
$$x + 0 \cdot y = 106.$$

The points whose second (y) coordinate is -24.2 are the solutions to

$$y = -24.2.$$

As just shown, the graph of $x = 106$ is a vertical line. Any vertical line has a similar equation $x = h$, where h is constant. The graph of $y = -24.2$ is a horizontal line. Every horizontal line has an equation of the form $y = k$, where k is constant.

Theorem 6.2.1

The graph of $\{(x, y) : x = h\}$ is the vertical line containing $(h, 0)$. The graph of $\{(x, y) : y = k\}$ is the horizontal line containing $(0, k)$.

It is also easy to obtain the equation for any *oblique* (not horizontal or vertical) line through the origin. Suppose the line contains (a, b). We would like to know what sentence must be satisfied by any point (x, y) on this line.

1. If (x, y) is not the origin, then (x, y) is the image of (a, b) under a size transformation with center $(0, 0)$ and some magnitude k.

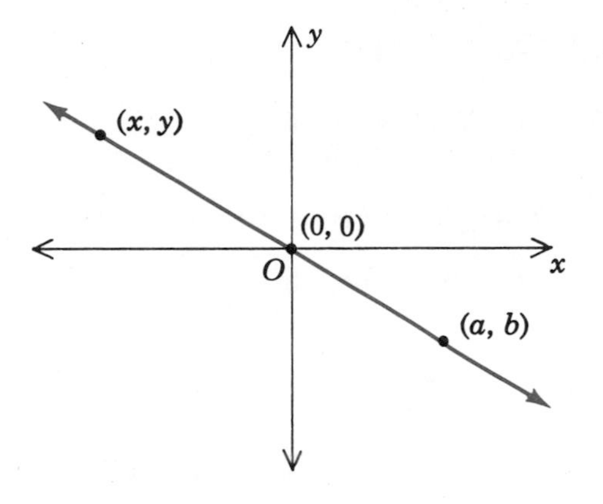

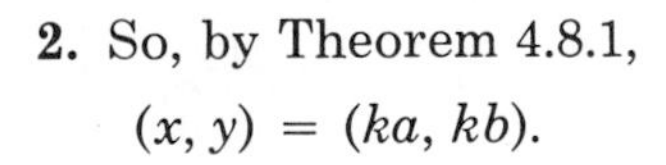

2. So, by Theorem 4.8.1,

   $(x, y) = (ka, kb)$.

3. $x = ka$ and $y = kb$.

4. $\frac{x}{a} = k$ and $\frac{y}{b} = k$.

5. So $\frac{x}{a} = \frac{y}{b}$. Since $(0, 0)$ also satisfies this equation, every point on the line satisfies the equation. So we have **proved**:

Theorem 6.2.2

The oblique line through the origin and (a, b) has equation $\frac{x}{a} = \frac{y}{b}$.

Examples: Equations of lines through the origin

1. If the line contains $(1, 1)$, then $a = 1$ and $b = 1$. So an equation is $\frac{x}{1} = \frac{y}{1}$ or $x = y$. This agrees with your earlier knowledge.

2. If the line contains $(2, -3)$, then $a = 2$ and $b = -3$, so an equation is $\frac{x}{2} = \frac{y}{-3}$ or $3x + 2y = 0$.

Solving the equation of Theorem 6.2.2 for y, we have:

Corollary 6.2.3

The oblique line through the origin and (a, b) has equation $y = mx$, where $m = \frac{b}{a}$.

Here are graphs of lines with equations of the form $y = mx$, for particular values of m.

Notice that if m is positive, the larger m is, the faster the line goes up as you go to the right. If m is negative, the line tilts downward to the right.

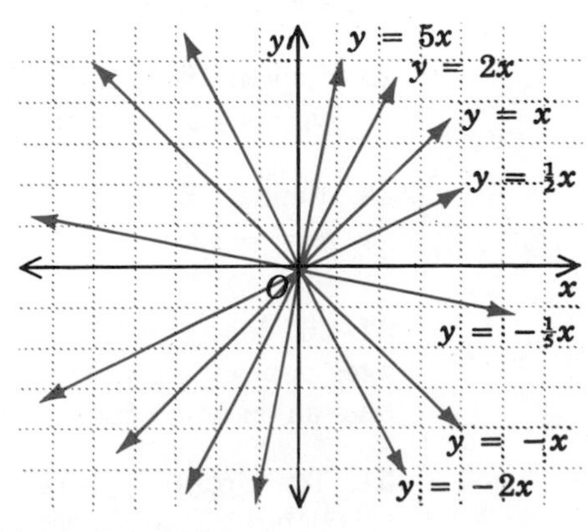

EXERCISES 6.2

Ⓐ **1.** What is an oblique line?

2–4. Give an equation whose graph is:

2. a horizontal line. **3.** a vertical line. **4.** an oblique line.

5. True or False? (0, 0), (−3, −5), and (6, 10) are collinear.

6–8. Give an equation for the line which contains (2, 3) and:

6. is horizontal. **7.** is vertical. **8.** (0, 0).

9–11. Repeat Exercises **6–8** for the line which contains (−1, 4).

12–14. Repeat Exercises **6–8** for the line which contains (a, b).

15–26. Graph the solution set of each sentence. Consider each sentence to have two variables.

15. $x = -4$ **16.** $\sqrt{2} = x$ **17.** $14 - y = 0$

18. $y = 0$ **19.** $x = 0$ **20.** $x + 0y = 4$

21. $4m = n$ **22.** $a = \frac{3}{2}b$ **23.** $2c - 3d = 0$

Ⓑ **24.** $\frac{x}{5} + \frac{y}{3} = 0$ **25.** $\frac{2x}{5} = \frac{y}{3}$ **26.** $9m = 10n$

27. Graph the lines with equations $y = x$, $y = \frac{1}{2}x$, $y = \frac{1}{3}x$, and $y = \frac{1}{4}x$. If you continued the pattern to graph $y = \frac{1}{5}x$, $y = \frac{1}{6}x$, etc., what would you observe about the graphs?

28. Repeat Exercise **27** for the lines $y = x$, $y = 2x$, $y = 3x$, $y = 4x$, $\cdots$.

29. Repeat Exercise **27** for the lines $y = -x$, $y = -2x$, $y = -3x$, $y = -4x$, $\cdots$.

30. Repeat Exercise **27** for the lines $y = -x$, $y = -\frac{1}{2}x$, $y = -\frac{1}{3}x$, $y = -\frac{1}{4}x$, $\cdots$.

31–36. Many real situations are closely approximated by lines. Label the axes appropriately. Then graph ten ordered pairs of the indicated type and give an equation for the line which contains all ten pairs.

31. The ordered pairs (n, c), where n is a number of gallons of milk bought at \$1.75 per gallon and c is the total amount paid for the milk

32. The ordered pairs (t, d), where d is the distance (in kilometres) traveled in a time t (in hours) in an automobile traveling at 80 km/h on an expressway.

33. The ordered pairs (m, y), where y is a length measured in yards and m is the same length measured in metres (One metre $\doteq$ 1.1 yards.)

34. The ordered pairs (n, s), where n is the number of sides of a polygon and s is the sum of the measures of its exterior angles

35. The ordered pairs (n, h), where h is the number of "heads" you would expect in n tosses of a penny (You may allow n to be even only.)

36. The ordered pairs (t, p), where p is the pay you would expect to receive for working t hours at \$3.25 an hour

Ⓒ **37–40.** Graph the solution set to each sentence.

37. $(x + 3y)(x - 3y) = 0$

38. $\left(\frac{m}{2} + \frac{n}{3}\right)(m - 4n) = 0$

39. $\frac{3}{a} + \frac{4}{b} = 0$

40. $\frac{9}{x} = \frac{2}{y}$

EQUATIONS FOR ALL CIRCLES

6.3

Lines are not the only graphs of solution sets. Many curves are graphs of solution sets to sentences. Here is one such sentence.

$$x^2 + y^2 = 25$$

Here are some solutions (check them).

$$(3, 4), (0, 5), (-5, 0), (\sqrt{24}, 1), (4, -3)$$

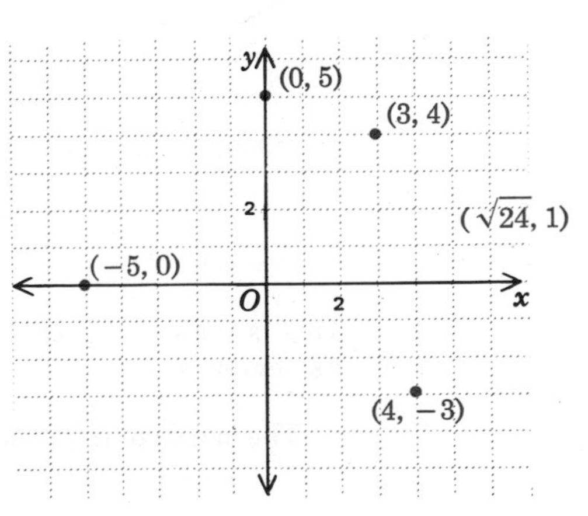

Graphing, you see that the points seem to lie on a *circle*. This guess is shown to be correct in the proof of the next theorem. But first we need to know what a circle is, so we give the familiar definition.

Definition

A **circle** is the set of points at a given distance (the *radius*) from a given point (the *center*).

Suppose we want an equation for the circle with center $(\frac{1}{2}, -4)$, radius 5. We then want a sentence which any point (x, y) on the circle will satisfy. Since the distance from (x, y) to the center $(\frac{1}{2}, -4)$ is 5, we must have

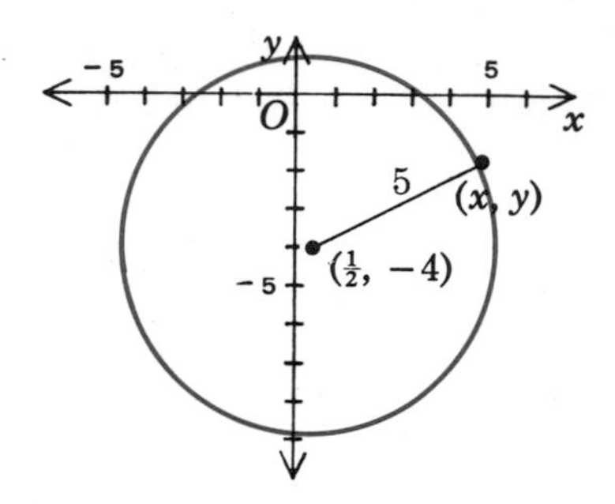

$$\sqrt{(x - \tfrac{1}{2})^2 + (y + 4)^2} = 5.$$

Squaring each side of the equation,

$$(x - \tfrac{1}{2})^2 + (y + 4)^2 = 25.$$

Generalizing gives an easily proved statement.

Theorem 6.3.1

The circle with center (h, k) and radius r is the set of points whose coordinates satisfy

$$(x - h)^2 + (y - k)^2 = r^2.$$

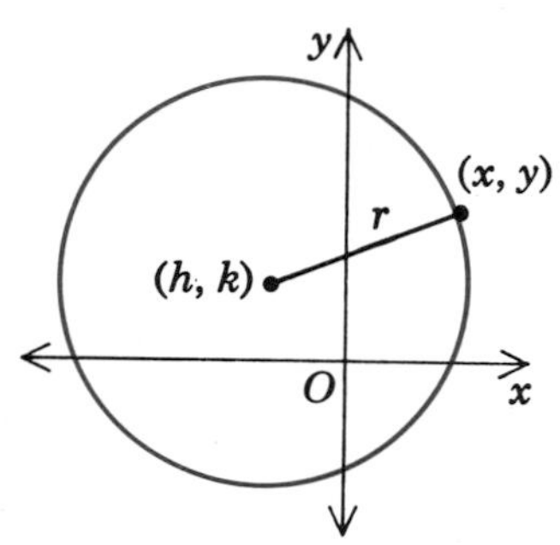

PROOF: If a point (x, y) is on the circle, by the definition of "circle," its distance from (h, k) is r. So

$$\sqrt{(x - h)^2 + (y - k)^2} = r.$$

Squaring both sides of the equation gives the theorem.

$$\{(x, y): (x - h)^2 + (y - k)^2 = r^2\}$$

When $(h, k) = (0, 0)$ and $r = 5$, we have

$$(x - 0)^2 + (y - 0)^2 = 25$$

or more simply $$x^2 + y^2 = 25.$$

This is the circle mentioned at the start of this section. Its radius is 5; its center is $(0, 0)$.

The particular circle with center $(0, 0)$ and radius 1 has equation

$$x^2 + y^2 = 1.$$

This circle is called the **unit circle** and has many applications.

Finding points on a unit circle is easy. Suppose we begin with the unit circle. There are two points P and Q on the circle with first coordinate $\frac{1}{2}$. (See the diagram on the next page.)

To find the second coordinates, substitute in the equation:

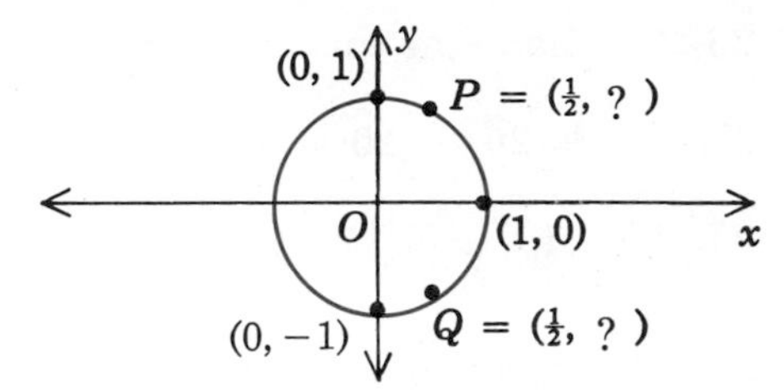

$$(\tfrac{1}{2})^2 + y^2 = 1$$
$$\tfrac{1}{4} + y^2 = 1$$
$$y^2 = \tfrac{3}{4}$$

So $y = \sqrt{\frac{3}{4}} = \frac{\sqrt{3}}{2} \doteq 0.866$ or $y = -\sqrt{\frac{3}{4}} = \frac{-\sqrt{3}}{2} \doteq -0.866$. The two points are $\left(\frac{1}{2}, \frac{\sqrt{3}}{2}\right)$ and $\left(\frac{1}{2}, -\frac{\sqrt{3}}{2}\right)$. In decimals, $P \doteq (0.5, 0.866)$ and $Q \doteq (0.5, -0.866)$. The graph makes these answers seem reasonable.

EXERCISES 6.3

Ⓐ **1–2.** Define:

1. circle. **2.** unit circle.

3–6. Is the given point on the circle with center (0, 0), radius 4?

3. $(0, -4)$ **4.** $(0, 0)$ **5.** $(3, 1)$ **6.** $(2, 2)$

7–10. Give an equation whose graph is the circle with center (0, 0) and the given radius.

7. $\frac{1}{2}$ **8.** 4 **9.** $\sqrt{143.5}$ **10.** r

11–14. Give an equation for the circle with:

11. center (h, k), radius r.

12. center $(-1, -2)$, radius 5.

13. center $(6, 0)$, radius 9.

14. center $(-103, 412)$, radius 10.

15–18. Give the center and radius of each circle.

15. $\{(x, y): (x + 2)^2 + (y + 3)^2 = 4\}$

16. $\{(m, n): m^2 + (n - 2)^2 = 1\}$

17. $\{(a, b): 25 = (a + 7)^2 + b^2\}$

Ⓑ **18.** $\{(x, y): (x - 9)^2 + (y + 8)^2 = \sqrt{11.5}\}$

19–22. Name five elements of each set and accurately describe the graph.

19. $\{(x, y): x^2 + y^2 = 145\}$

20. $\{(a, b): a^2 + b^2 = 1\}$

21. $\{(x, y): y^2 + x^2 = 11\}$

22. $\{(m, n): 12 - 3n^2 = 3m^2\}$

23–26. Graph the solution set to each sentence.

23. $2u^2 + 2v^2 - 20 = 0$

24. $x^2 + y^2 = 0$

25. $16 = (y - 5)^2 + x^2$

26. $(x + 0.3)^2 + (y - 1.5)^2 = 0.04$

27–28. Name four solutions to each sentence.

27. $(x + 8)^2 + (y - 2)^2 = 25$

28. $(a - 10)^2 = 100 - (b - 5)^2$

29–32. Find an equation for a circle which:

29. is tangent to the x-axis and y-axis and has its center in the second quadrant.

30. contains the origin and has its center at (2, 5).

31. contains (5, 11) and has its center at (3, −1).

32. contains (2, 4) and (12, 4).

33–36. One coordinate of a point on the unit circle is given. Find the other coordinate. Check with an accurate graph.

33. first coordinate −0.6

34. second coordinate 0.28

35. first coordinate $\frac{\sqrt{2}}{2}$

36. second coordinate $\frac{12}{13}$

37. Which point is not on the unit circle?

a. $\left(\frac{1}{2}, \frac{\sqrt{3}}{2}\right)$ **b.** $\left(-\frac{\sqrt{3}}{2}, \frac{1}{2}\right)$ **c.** $\left(\frac{1}{2}, \frac{1}{2}\right)$ **d.** All are.

38. One point on the circle $\{(x, y): x^2 + y^2 = 65\}$ is (7, 4). Use the symmetry of the circle to find seven other points with integer coordinates that are on the circle.

Ⓒ **39.** A point is on the circle with center (0, 0), radius 15, and is collinear with (5, 6) and (0, 0). Find the point.

40. Graph $\{(x, y): x = \sqrt{9 - y^2}\}$.

41. Graph $\{(x, y): x^2 + y^2 < 1\}$.

42–45. Find an equation for the image of $\{(x, y) : (x - 5)^2 + (y - 2)^2 = 6\}$ under:

42. $r_{x\text{-axis}}$.

43. $r_{y\text{-axis}}$.

44. R_{90}.

45. R_{180}.

THE GRAPH TRANSLATION THEOREM 6.4

At right are graphed the circles with equations A and B.

A: $x^2 + y^2 = 25$

B: $(x - \frac{15}{2})^2 + (y + 3)^2 = 25$

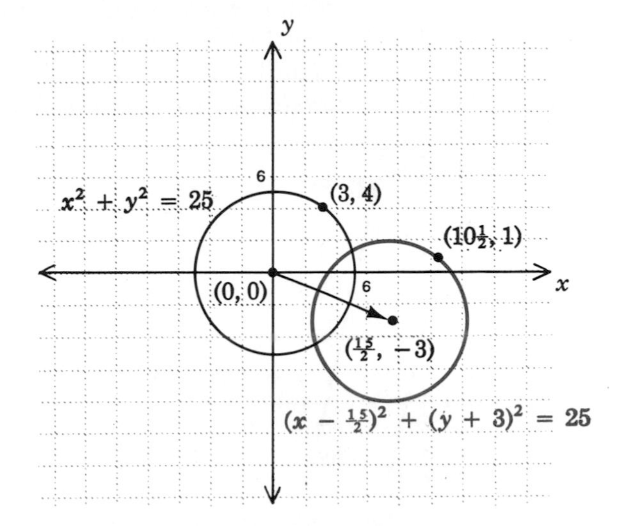

The circles have the same radius, 5. So they are congruent. In fact, one circle can be mapped onto the other by a translation (slide).

This slide maps $(0, 0)$ onto $(\frac{15}{2}, -3)$. So in general, (x, y) is mapped onto $(x + \frac{15}{2}, y - 3)$.

Now examine the equations A and B. Replacing x by $x - \frac{15}{2}$ and y by $y + 3$, you can change equation A into equation B. This causes the graph to be translated $\frac{15}{2}$ units to the *right* and 3 units *down*.

This pattern may be the opposite of what you might expect. But here is another example. Suppose you have found the solution $(6, -23)$ to the sentence

$$30x + 7y = 19$$

$$\text{Then } 30(6) + 7(-23) = 19.$$

Can this help in finding a solution to the following sentence?

$$30(x - 3) + 7(y - 2) = 19$$

Notice that this sentence is like the first above, with $x - 3$ in place of x and $y - 2$ in place of y. Hence, if $x - 3 = 6$ and $y - 2 = -23$, then (x, y) is a solution to the second sentence. The point $(9, -21)$ is such a solution.

Examine this table of solutions to the given sentences. *You should check solutions for accuracy.*

$30x + 7y = 19$ ▶	$(-1, 7)$	$(0, 2\frac{5}{7})$	(a, b)
$30(x - 3) + 7(y - 2) = 19$ ▶	$(2, 9)$	$(3, 4\frac{5}{7})$	$(a + 3, b + 2)$

Notice the pattern. Replacing x by $x - 3$ causes solutions to have x-coordinates which are 3 *greater*; replacing y by $y - 2$ causes solutions to have y-coordinates which are 2 greater.

When we graph the solutions to the previous sentences, those to the second sentence are 3 units to the right and 2 units above the first. (See Figure I.) The solution set to $30(x - 3) + 7(y - 2) = 19$ is thus graphed 3 units to the right and 2 units above that of $30x + 7y = 19$. So it is a *translation image* of the first sentence.

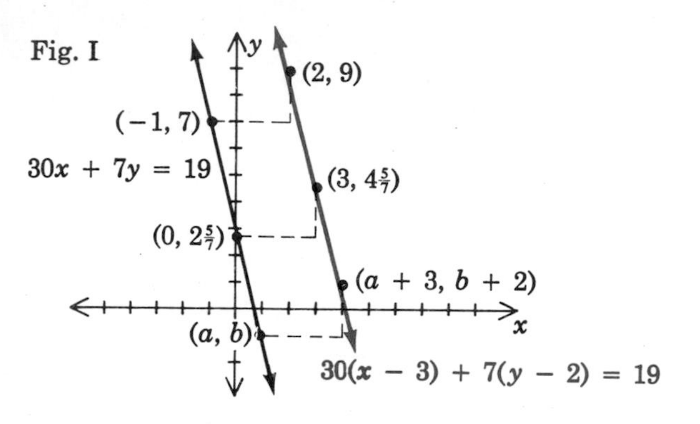

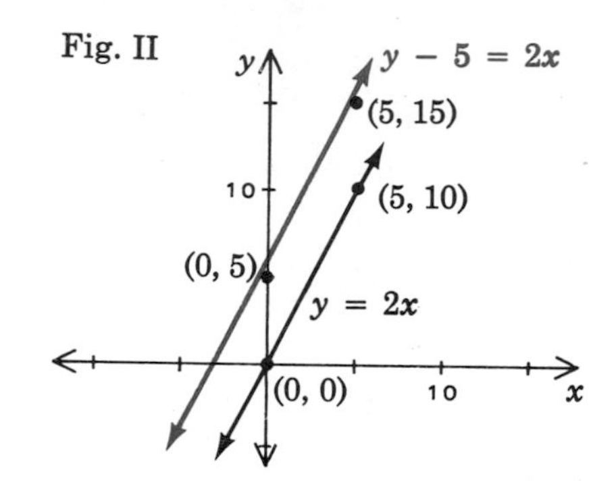

Let's take another example, simpler than the first. (See Figure II.)

$y = 2x$ ▶	(1, 2)	(2, 4)	(100, 200)
$y - 5 = 2x$ ▶	(1, 7)	(2, 9)	(100, 205)

We have only replaced y by $y - 5$. This causes ordered pairs in the second relation (in red) to have y-coordinates which are 5 greater than those of the first relation. So the second relation is graphed 5 units above the first.

These examples illustrate the following *very important* theorem.

Theorem 6.4.1

Graph translation theorem: If in a sentence for a relation, x is replaced by $x - h$ and y by $y - k$, then the graph of the resulting sentence is the image of the graph of the original sentence under the translation which maps (x, y) onto $(x + h, y + k)$.

In other words, to translate a graph h units to the right, replace x by $x - h$ in the sentence; to translate a graph k units up, replace y by $y - k$.

EXERCISES 6.4

Ⓐ **1–4.** A translation maps (x, y) onto $(x + a, y + b)$. Find a and b if the translation:

1. maps (2, 5) onto (3, 5).

2. maps (−1, 4) onto (−3, 12).

3. maps (6, 14) onto (5, 0).

4. maps (0, 0) onto (106, −3.5).

5–6. Find four points which satisfy each sentence.

5. $x^2 + y^2 = 36$

6. $(x - 2)^2 + y^2 = 36$

7. What translation maps $\{(x, y): x^2 + y^2 = 36\}$ onto $\{(x, y): (x - 2)^2 + y^2 = 36\}$?

8–9. Find six points which satisfy each sentence.

8. $a^2 + b^2 = 25$

9. $(a + 2)^2 + (b - 3)^2 = 25$

10. What translation maps $\{(a, b): a^2 + b^2 = 25\}$ onto $\{(a, b): (a + 2)^2 + (b - 3)^2 = 25\}$?

11. What is the graph translation theorem?

12–17. Suppose G is the graph of a relation in which the variables are x and y. In the sentence for the relation, what should you replace x and y with in order to form a new relation whose graph is:

12. 5 units above G?

13. 2 units to the left of G?

14. $\frac{1}{2}$ unit below G?

15. π units to the right of G?

16. 1 unit above and 3 units to the right of G?

17. 2 units to the left and 6 units below G?

18–19. Give the center and radius of the circle.

18. $x^2 + y^2 = 8$

19. $(x - 8)^2 + (y + 2)^2 = 8$

20–21. What translation maps $\{(x, y) : y = 5x\}$ onto:

20. $\{(x, y): y - 8 = 5x\}$?

21. $\{(x, y): y + 2 = 5(x - 3)\}$?

Ⓑ **22.** The point $(-37, 11)$ satisfies $-a - 4b = -7$. Find a point which satisfies $-a - 4(b + 6) = -7$.

23. $(-6, 13)$ is an element of $\{(x, y): 15x + 7y = 1\}$. Find a point which satisfies $15(m + 61) + 7(p - 1) = 1$.

24. How does the graph of $\{(x, y): 2x^3 - 1 = y^3\}$ compare with the graph of $\{(x, y): 2(x + 4)^3 - 1 = (y + 8)^3\}$?

25. Graph 5 points satisfying $3x - 2y = 1$. Graph 5 points satisfying $3x - 2(y + 1) = 1$.

© Ex. 26

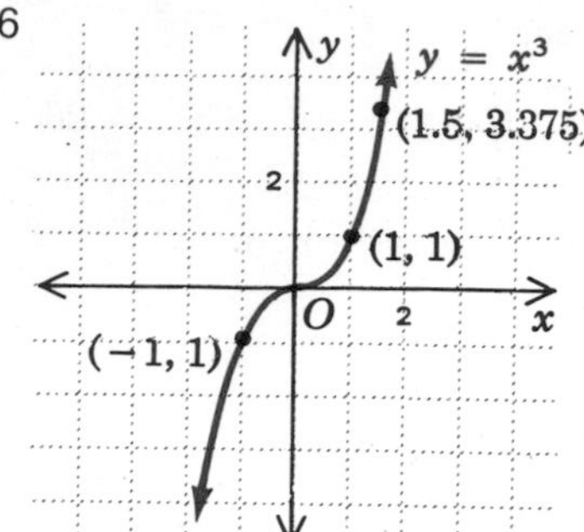

Ex. 27

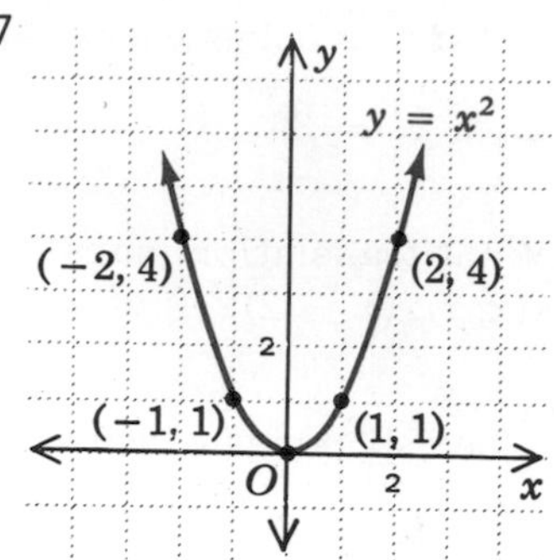

26. Use the graph at the left above and the graph translation theorem to graph $\{(x, y): y - 2 = (x - 3)^3\}$.

27. Use the graph at the right above and the graph translation theorem to graph $\{(x, y): y - 5 = (x + 8)^2\}$.

28. Graph the solution sets to $|x| < 3$ and $|x - 10| < 3$ on the same number line. How does this relate to the graph translation theorem?

29. Solve $t^2 = 4$. Use the solutions and the graph translation theorem to help solve $(t - \sqrt{3})^2 = 4$.

6.5 EQUATIONS FOR ALL LINES

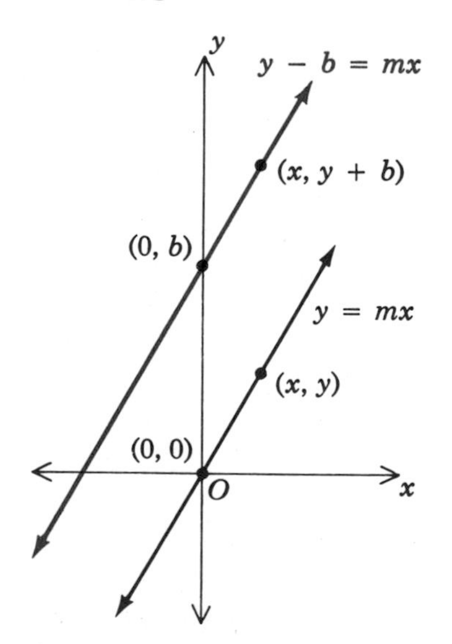

The graph translation theorem (6.4.1) enables sentences to be found for translation images of any given graph. An easy application gets an equation for any line.

Any *nonvertical* line must intersect the y-axis. Let us say the point of intersection is $(0, b)$. This line is parallel to some line $y = mx$. The translation

$$(x, y) \rightarrow (x, y + b)$$

maps the line $y = mx$ onto the given nonvertical line. So we substitute $y - b$ for y to find the desired equation: $y - b = mx$.

Adding b to each side gives a famous theorem.

Theorem 6.5.1

Slope-intercept form: The line that contains $(0, b)$ and is parallel to $y = mx$ has equation $y = mx + b$.

The constant m determines the tilt of the line (refer back to the drawing, page 164) and is called the **slope** of the line. The constant b is called the ***y*-intercept** of the line because the line intersects the y-axis at $(0, b)$. So the equation $y = mx + b$ is called the **equation in slope-intercept form** for the line.

Example: Graph the line with y-intercept -3 and slope 4.

(There are many ways to analyze this problem. Here are two ways.)

SOLUTION 1: If the line has equation $y = mx + b$, then $m = 4$ and $b = -3$. So an equation is $y = 4x - 3$. It is now easy to find points and graph.

SOLUTION 2: From the given, the line is parallel to $y = 4x$ and contains $(0, -3)$. This makes it easy to graph.

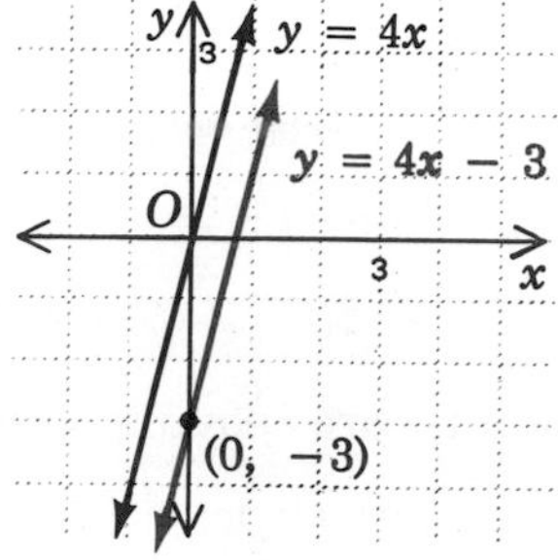

From the earlier arguments, all lines parallel to $y = 9x$ have equations of the form $y = 9x + b$, and so have the same slope. Conversely, all lines with slope m are parallel to $y = mx$, and so are parallel to each other.

Theorem 6.5.2

Parallel nonvertical lines are exactly those lines with the same slope.

Sameness of slope is thus a characteristic of parallel lines. So knowing the slopes of lines (1) aids in graphing and (2) tells whether lines are parallel. In the next section, we show that knowing slope also aids in studying perpendicularity. So it helps to be able to calculate the slope of a line.

Theorem 6.5.3

If $x_1 \neq x_2$, the slope of the line through (x_1, y_1) and (x_2, y_2) is

$$\frac{y_1 - y_2}{x_1 - x_2}.$$

PROOF: The line contains (x_1, y_1) and (x_2, y_2). We translate the line by the translation with rule $(x, y) \to (x - x_2, y - y_2)$. The image of (x_2, y_2) is $(0, 0)$. The image of (x_1, y_1) is $(x_1 - x_2, y_1 - y_2)$. By Corollary 6.2.3, an equation for the image is $y = \frac{y_1 - y_2}{x_1 - x_2}x$. So the image has slope $\frac{y_1 - y_2}{x_1 - x_2}$. But the line and its image are parallel, so they have the same slope.

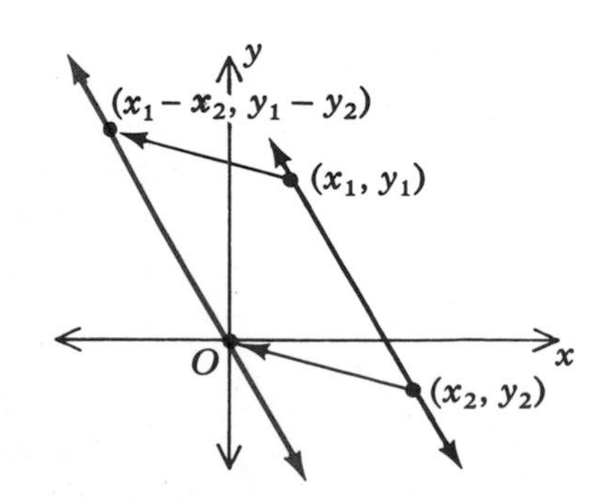

Example: Calculate the slope of the line which is pictured.

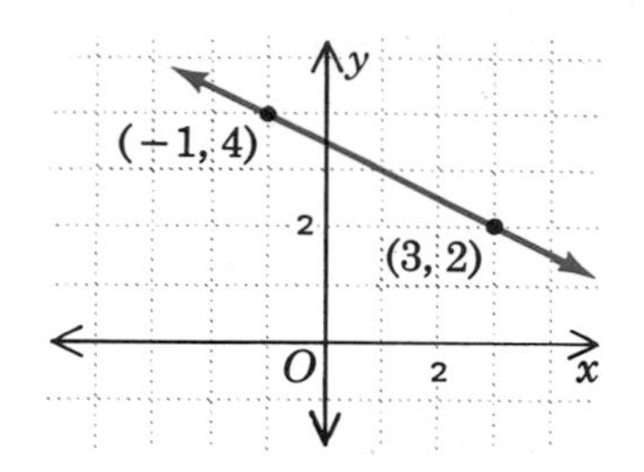

Let $(x_1, y_1) = (-1, 4)$ and $(x_2, y_2) = (3, 2)$. Using Theorem 6.5.3, the slope is

$$\frac{4 - 2}{-1 - 3} = \frac{2}{-4} = -\frac{1}{2}.$$

For vertical lines, all x-coordinates of points are equal. The denominator of $\frac{y_1 - y_2}{x_1 - x_2}$ would be 0. This is impossible. So *slope is not defined for vertical lines.* For horizontal lines, all y-coordinates of points are equal. The slope $\frac{y_1 - y_2}{x_1 - x_2} = \frac{0}{x_1 - x_2} = 0$. *Horizontal lines have zero slope.*

Three forms of equations for lines have been studied.

Type of line	horizontal	vertical	oblique
Equation form	$y = k$	$x = h$	$y = mx + b$

One equation form includes all these. The form is $Ax + By = C$.

Theorem 6.5.4

The graph of a sentence is a line if and only if the sentence is equivalent to $Ax + By = C$, where A, B, and C are constants and A and B are not both 0.

PROOF: 1. If the graph is a line, then it is horizontal, vertical, or oblique. Equations for each of these can be put into the form $Ax + By = C$. Namely,

$y = k$	is equivalent to	$0 \cdot x + 1 \cdot y = k$
$x = h$	is equivalent to	$1 \cdot x + 0 \cdot y = h$
$y = mx + b$	is equivalent to	$-m \cdot x + 1 \cdot y = b$

2. Now suppose $Ax + By = C$ is an equation for a relation. Either $B \neq 0$ or $B = 0$. If $B \neq 0$, the equation is equivalent to $y = \frac{-A}{B}x + \frac{C}{B}$, an equation in $y = mx + b$ form. If $B = 0$, then $A \neq 0$ (given), and so $Ax + By = C$ is equivalent to $x = \frac{C}{A}$, an equation in $x = k$ form. So $Ax + By = C$ is always an equation for a line.

Example: Graph $\{(x, y): 2x + 3y = 2\}$. (We know the graph is a line because of Theorem 6.5.4.)

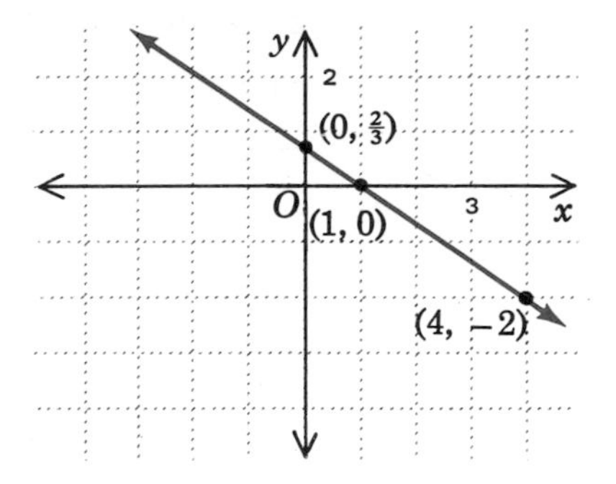

SOLUTION 1: Find two solutions, for example, $(1, 0)$ and $(4, -2)$. Graph these and draw the line containing them. Find a third point, say $(0, \frac{2}{3})$, to check.

SOLUTION 2: Solve for y:

$$\begin{aligned} 2x + 3y &= 2 \\ 3y &= -2x + 2 \\ y &= -\tfrac{2}{3}x + \tfrac{2}{3} \end{aligned}$$

So the line has slope $-\frac{2}{3}$ and y-intercept $\frac{2}{3}$, making graphing easy.

EXERCISES 6.5

Ⓐ **1.** How are the graphs of $\{(x, y): y - 4 = 3x\}$ and $\{(x, y): y = 3x\}$ related?

2–10. Give the slope of each line.

2. $y = 3x + 4$ **3.** $2y = 3x + 5$ **4.** $y - 3x = -4$

5. $y = 4 - 3x$ **6.** $y = -2$ **7.** $-3y = -2x$

8. $-8 = 2x$ **9.** $x = -2y$ **10.** $2a = b + 4$

11. What is the y-intercept of a line?

12–16. Give the y-intercept of each line of Exercises **2–6**.

17. A ____ line has a slope equal to 0.

18. For ____ lines, slope is not defined.

19–22. Give an equation for the line with

19. slope $-\frac{1}{4}$, y-intercept 6. **20.** slope 0, y-intercept $-\frac{2}{3}$.

21. no slope, containing $(-3, 2)$. **22.** slope 1, y-intercept 2.

23–26. Equations for two lines are given. Are the lines parallel?

23. $y = 3x, \quad x = 3y$ **24.** $-2y + 3x = 7, \quad 4y = 3(4 + 2x)$

25. $x - 8 = y, \quad x - 6 = y + 14$ **26.** $w - 2v = 4, \quad \frac{w}{2} - 2 = v$

27–32. Give the slope of the line containing the two given points.

27. $(-6, 4), (2, 9)$ **28.** $(a, b), (c, d)$

29. $(0, 11), (0, 14)$ **30.** $(-2, 1), (-2, -2)$

31. $(-8, -7), (-7, -9)$ **32.** $(-8, 2), (5, -7)$

Ⓑ **33–38.** Graph each solution set.

33. $3x - 4y = 7$ **34.** $5x + 2y = 10$ **35.** $10 = 2(y - 5x)$

36. $0.3x = 0.4(y + 6)$ **37.** $\frac{x - 8}{3} = \frac{y}{9}$

38. $b + 6a = 9a - 4b - 10$

39. A line has slope -86. If $(1, 21)$ is on this line, name a second point on the line.

40. A line has slope $\frac{2}{5}$. If $(-6, 1)$ and $(4, t)$ are on this line, find t.

41–46. Refer to Exercises **31–36**, pages 156–157. In each case, find the slope of the line. What does the slope stand for?

47. Prove or Disprove: The slope of the line through (x_1, y_1) and (x_2, y_2) is the opposite of the slope of the line through (x_2, y_2) and (x_1, y_1).

48. Name four other points on the line containing $(-1, 3)$ and $(4, -5)$.

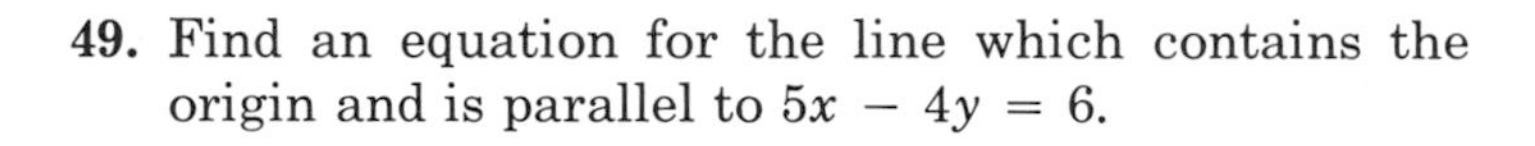

49. Find an equation for the line which contains the origin and is parallel to $5x - 4y = 6$.

50. A highway is 130 feet above sea level at one point and 60 feet above sea level one mile farther. If the road gradually goes downhill from the first point to the second, what is its percent of rise or fall?

Ⓒ **51.** The maximum grade (slope) on certain roads in the U.S. follows: Interstate Highways, 7%; Pikes Peak road, 11%; a San Francisco street, 27%. Which road contains the steepest parts?

52. Use the sentence $4x - 2y = k$. Pick four values of k of your own choosing and graph the four corresponding lines. What do these lines have in common?

53. Repeat Exercise **52** for the sentence $kx + 3y = 6$.

54. Repeat Exercise **52** for the sentence $2kx + ky = 4$.

55–59. A line has slope $\frac{2}{7}$. Find the slope of its image under:

55. $r_{x\text{-axis}}$. **56.** $r_{y\text{-axis}}$. **57.** R_{180}. **58.** R_{90}.

59. the transformation with matrix $\begin{bmatrix} 2 & 1 \\ 1 & 2 \end{bmatrix}$.

60. Look at the standings in a sports league. Graph the pair (wins, losses) for each team in the league. The points should all be on a line or very close to a line. Why is this so?

EQUATIONS FOR LINES SATISFYING GIVEN CONDITIONS

You are familiar with the famous parallel postulate from your study of geometry:

■ *Through a point, there is exactly one line parallel to a given line.* ■

This postulate indicates that a line is determined by knowing (1) a point on it and (2) a line parallel to it.

Now suppose we want an equation for the line parallel to $y = \frac{1}{2}x$ and passing through (1, 6). Because one line is a translation image of the other line, we can find an equation for this line by using the graph translation theorem.

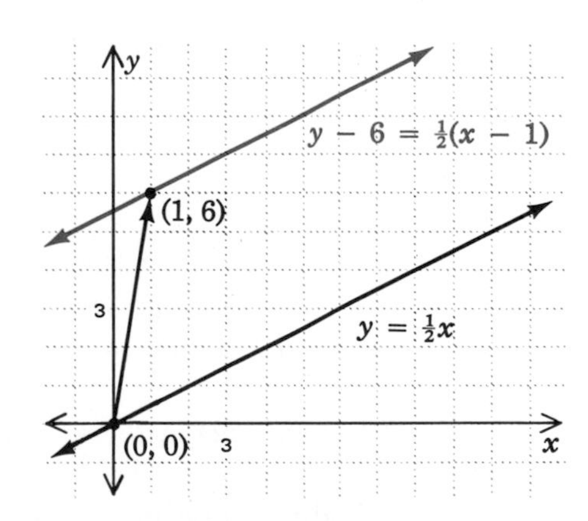

The translation which maps (x, y) onto $(x + 1, y + 6)$ maps $y = \frac{1}{2}x$ onto the desired line. So we substitute $x - 1$ for x, $y - 6$ for y to find the desired equation:

$$y - 6 = \frac{1}{2}(x - 1).$$

This process can be generalized for the following theorem.

Theorem 6.6.1

Point-slope form: The line through (h, k) parallel to $y = mx$ (with slope m) has equation $y - k = m(x - h)$.

We call this the *point-slope form* for an equation of a line.

Example: Find an equation for the line which contains $(4, -7)$ and is parallel to $y = 3x$.

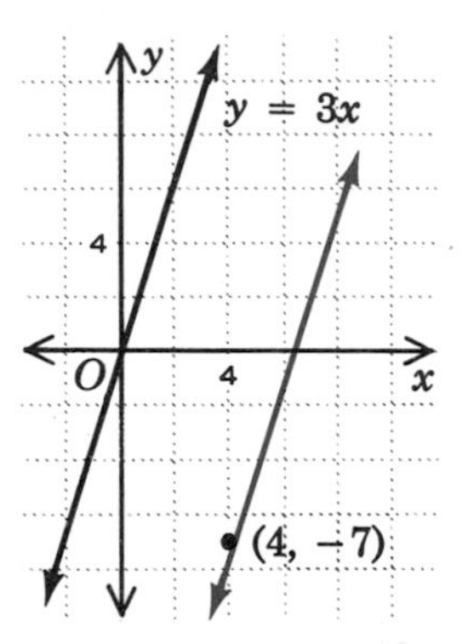

SOLUTION: Here $m = 3$, $(h, k) = (4, -7)$. An equation in point-slope form is

$$y + 7 = 3(x - 4).$$

You might wish to convert to slope-intercept form.

$$y + 7 = 3x - 12$$
$$y = 3x - 19$$

Any of these equations is OK.

Here is another statement which deals with determining a line.

■ *Through two different points, there is exactly one line.* ■

How can an equation for this line be found? The process is quite easy, as shown in the next example.

Example: Find an equation for the line through $(32, 0)$ and $(212, 100)$.

SOLUTION: By Theorem 6.5.3, the slope of this line is $\frac{0 - 100}{32 - 212}$ or $\frac{5}{9}$. Then using the point $(32, 0)$ and the point-slope form, we obtain

$$y - 0 = \tfrac{5}{9}(x - 32)$$
$$y = \tfrac{5}{9}(x - 32)$$

Finally, here is a third statement from geometry which involves determining a line.

■ *Through a point, there is exactly one line perpendicular to a given line.* ■

Finding equations involving perpendicular lines is aided by knowing a relationship involving the slopes of such lines. Notice the use of rotations and translations in the proof of this relationship.

Theorem 6.6.2

If a line has nonzero slope m, any line perpendicular has slope $\frac{-1}{m}$.

PROOF: As in other proofs, we use a translation to the origin to make the proof easier.

1. Given:

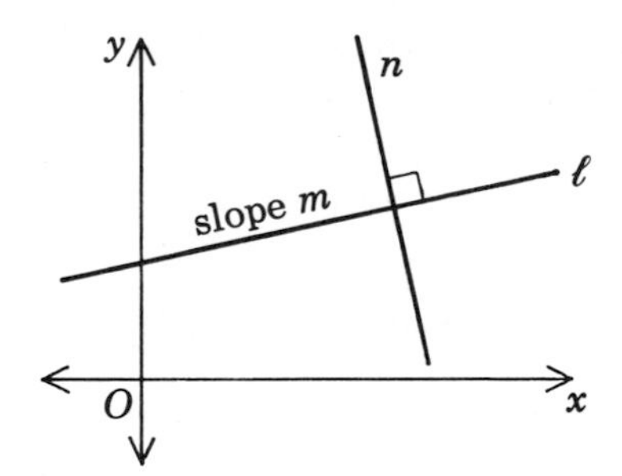

We want to find the slope of n.

2. Translate n and ℓ to the origin.

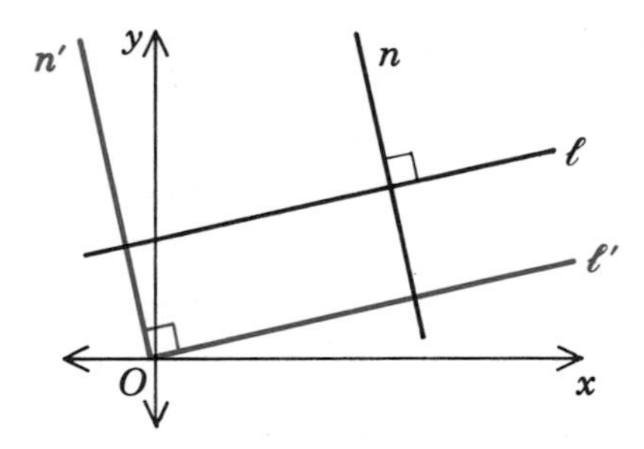

Call the images ℓ' and n'.

3. $\ell' \perp n'$ because translations preserve angle measure. Furthermore, since parallel lines have the same slope, ℓ' has slope m, and n' has the same slope as n. So we want to find the slope of n'.

4. Pick any points A and B on ℓ'. Because $\ell' \perp n'$, $R_{90}(A)$ and $R_{90}(B)$ must be on n'. Recall that $R_{90}(x, y) = (-y, x)$.

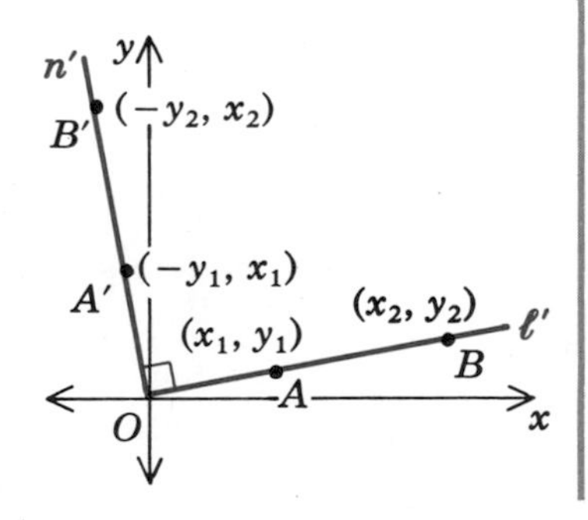

5. Now we can calculate the slopes of ℓ' and n' (which has the same slope as n).

$$m = \text{slope of } \ell' = \frac{y_1 - y_2}{x_1 - x_2}$$

$$\text{slope of } n' = \frac{x_1 - x_2}{-y_1 + y_2} = \frac{x_1 - x_2}{-(y_1 - y_2)}$$

6. So slope of $n' = -\dfrac{1}{\text{slope of } \ell'} = -\dfrac{1}{m}$

Corollary 6.6.3

Two lines with slopes are perpendicular if and only if the product of their slopes is -1.

Examples: Slopes of perpendicular lines

1. If a line has slope $\frac{2}{3}$, any perpendicular line has slope $-\frac{3}{2}$.
2. Lines with slopes 4 and $-\frac{1}{4}$ are perpendicular.
3. The line through $(-6, 7)$ perpendicular to $y = 3x - 5$ must have slope $-\frac{1}{3}$. Since it contains $(-6, 7)$, by the point-slope form, an equation is $y - 7 = -\frac{1}{3}(x + 6)$.

EXERCISES 6.6

Ⓐ **1.** Name the three conditions given in this section which determine exactly one line.

2. What is the point-slope form for an equation of a line?

3–4. Give an equation for the line parallel to the given line through the given point.

3. $y = \frac{1}{2}x$; $(4, -7)$

4. $y = \frac{5}{3}x$; $(\frac{1}{2}, \frac{1}{3})$

5–8. A line has the given slope. What is the slope of a line perpendicular to it?

5. 10

6. -6

7. $\frac{1}{4}$

8. $-\frac{3}{5}$

9. What is the slope of a line perpendicular to $\{(x, y): 2x + y = 9\}$?

10. A line contains $(11, 4)$ and $(-6, -13)$. What is the slope of this line?

Ⓑ **11.** Calculate the slope of the line through $(8, 0)$ and $(-6, 3)$. Now rotate the points $-90°$ about the origin and calculate the slope of the image. What theorem of this section is verified by your calculations?

12. Repeat Exercise **11** for the line through $(2, -9)$ and $(1, 1)$.

13–22. Give an equation for the line which satisfies the given conditions.

13. contains $(3, 180)$ and $(4, 360)$

14. contains $(10, \frac{1}{2})$ and $(-6, -4)$

15. contains $(4, 7)$; is parallel to $-3x = 4y + 2$

16. contains $(-3, 5)$; is parallel to $x = 9$

17. contains $(6, 8)$; is perpendicular to $9x - 8y = 17$

18. is perpendicular to $x - 3y = 6$ at the point $(9, 1)$

19. has y-intercept -2; is parallel to $2x + 3y = 1$

20. has y-intercept $\frac{1}{3}$; is perpendicular to $5y = 8x + 2$

21. has y-intercept 146; contains $(-281, 65)$

22. contains the origin; is perpendicular to $y = 4x$

23. The example preceding Theorem 6.6.2 has something to do with temperature. What is it?

24. What might Exercise **13** have to do with angle measures of polygons?

25. Marla has $500 in the bank, and she adds $40 each month. If interest is not added to the account, give a formula for the amount A in the bank after t months.

26. A line contains (13, 6), (−11, 4), and (8, y). Find y.

27. A line contains (0, 4), (x, 11), and (10, 13). Find x.

28. A line contains (−3, 12) and (−4, 7). Where does the line intersect the x-axis?

29. A line contains (30, 900) and (31, 961). If the line contains (b, 950), find b correct to two decimal places. (This kind of process can be used to approximate square roots.)

30. Use the idea of Exercise **29** and the points (2, 4) and (3, 9) to approximate $\sqrt{8}$. Is your approximation too large or too small?

31. Give an equation for the line tangent to the circle $\{(x, y): x^2 + y^2 = 25\}$ at the point (3, 4). HINT: This line is perpendicular to a radius of the circle.

32–33. Determine whether the points are vertices of the named figure.

32. (1, 4), (6, 7), (−2, 6); a right triangle

33. (2, 9), (5, 12), (−3, 14), (0, 17); a rectangle

© **34–38.** Find an equation for the image of $\{(x, y): 7x - 4y = 5\}$ under:

34. R_{90}. **35.** R_{180}. **36.** $r_{x\text{-axis}}$. **37.** $r_{y\text{-axis}}$.

38. the translation which maps (3, 4) onto (8, 7).

39–43. Repeat Exercises **34–38** for the line with equation $y = 3x + 2$.

44. A taxi charges 40¢ for the first $\frac{2}{5}$ kilometre and 10¢ for each succeeding $\frac{1}{3}$ kilometre. Find a linear sentence which approximates the fare f in terms of the distance d traveled (in kilometres). Why is this sentence only an approximation?

6.7 MIDPOINTS

Theorem 3.4.2 is a formula for the midpoint of a segment with endpoints a and b on a line. Now we prove a corresponding theorem for a segment in a plane. It shows that the coordinates of the midpoint are the averages of the corresponding coordinates of the endpoints.

Theorem 6.7.1

Midpoint formula: Let $P = (a, b)$ and $Q = (c, d)$. Then the midpoint of $\overline{PQ}$ is $\left(\frac{a+c}{2}, \frac{b+d}{2}\right)$.

PROOF: There are many ways to prove this theorem. The proof below can be generalized to get any point which divides $\overline{PQ}$ in some other way.

1. Given:

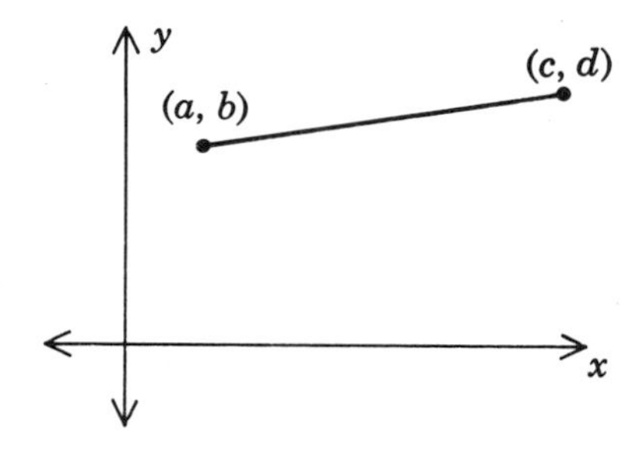

2. Translate given segment to origin: $(x, y) \to (x - a, y - b)$.

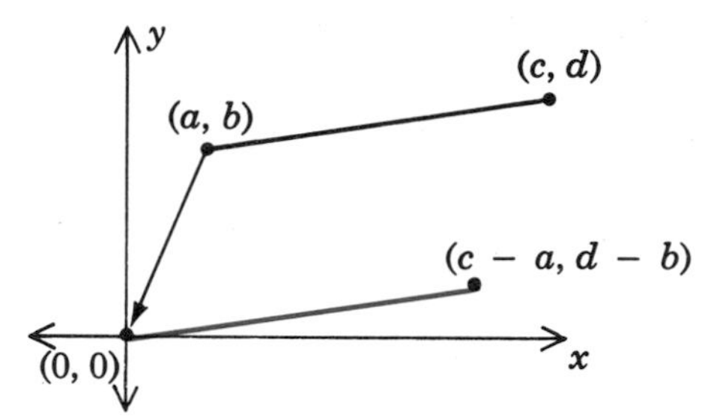

3. Apply size transformation $S_{\frac{1}{2}}$ to get midpoint of image segment.

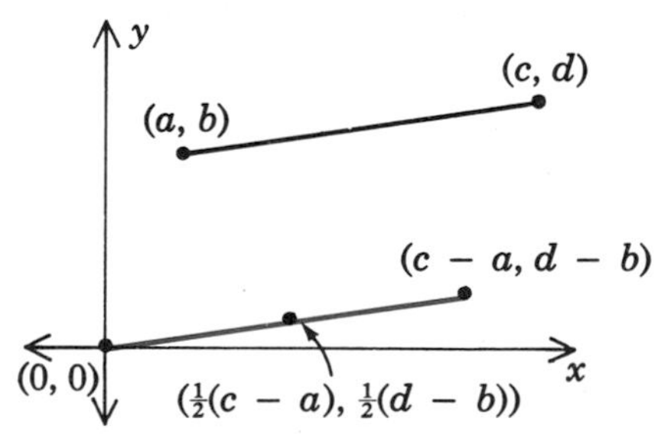

4. Translate back, $(x, y) \to (x + a, y + b)$.

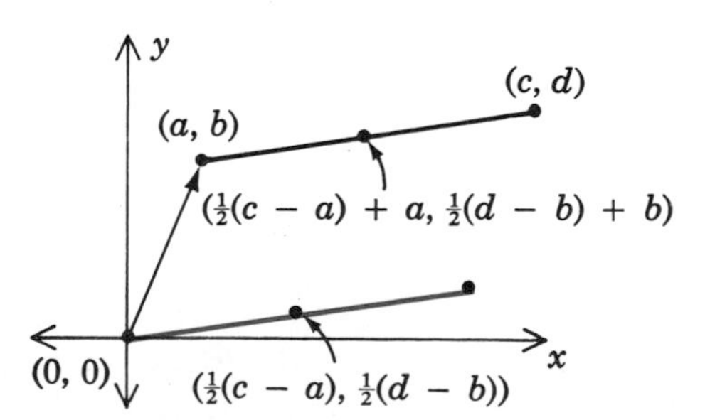

5. Since $\frac{1}{2}(c - a) + a$ simplifies to $\frac{a+c}{2}$ and $\frac{1}{2}(d - b) + b$ simplifies to $\frac{d+b}{2}$, the theorem is proved.

Examples: Using the midpoint formula

1. If $P = (2, 5)$ and $Q = (-2, -7)$, then the midpoint of $\overline{PQ}$ is $\left(\frac{2 + (-2)}{2}, \frac{5 + (-7)}{2}\right)$ or $(0, -1)$.

2. Find an equation for a circle if the endpoints of a diameter are $(-2, 6)$ and $(8, -4)$.

SOLUTION: The center of the circle is $(3, 1)$, the midpoint of the given diameter. The radius is $\sqrt{50}$, the distance from $(3, 1)$ to either endpoint. So an equation is

$$(x - 3)^2 + (y - 1)^2 = 50.$$

Check by noting that $(-2, 6)$ and $(8, -4)$ satisfy the equation.

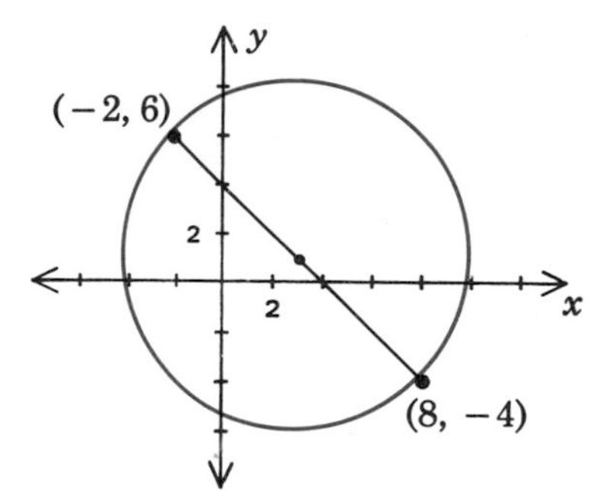

The midpoint formula has surprising uses, as Example **2** shows. The exercises point out further applications.

EXERCISES 6.7

Ⓐ **1.** What is the geometric definition of *midpoint of a segment*?

2–7. Find the midpoint of the segment with the given endpoints.

2. (a, b) and (c, d)

3. $(3, 14)$ and $(3, 16)$

4. $(-1, 4)$ and $(11, 6)$

5. $(2, -3)$ and $(-9, -7)$

6. $(0, 0)$ and $(-1000, -1000)$

7. (x_1, y_1) and (x_2, y_2)

Ⓑ **8.** One endpoint of a segment is $(3, 15)$. The midpoint is $(-1, 7)$. Find the other endpoint.

9. True or False? $(\sqrt{8}, \sqrt{12})$ is the midpoint of the segment with endpoints $(\sqrt{2}, \sqrt{3})$ and $(\sqrt{18}, \sqrt{27})$.

10. Give the endpoints of two segments with the same midpoint, $(2, 3)$.

11. The endpoints of a diameter of a circle are $(9, 1)$ and $(-6, 3)$. Find an equation for the circle.

12. Find an equation for the perpendicular bisector of the segment joining $(6, 8)$ and $(12, 0)$.

13. Find an equation for reflecting line ℓ if $r_\ell(-2, 5) = (-8, 95)$.

14. Find the image of $(7, 9)$ under a size transformation of magnitude $\frac{1}{2}$, center $(2, 1)$.

15. Verify the simplifications in Step 5 of the proof of Theorem 6.7.1.

© **16–17.** Let M be the midpoint of $\overline{PQ}$ as in Theorem 6.7.1.

16. Use distance to verify that $PM = MQ$.

17. Use slope to verify that M is on $\overleftrightarrow{PQ}$.

18. Find the two points of trisection of the segment with endpoints (9, 1) and (18, 2).

19. Generalize Exercise **18** for any endpoints (a, b) and (c, d). HINT: Follow the proof of Theorem 6.7.1 but use a different size transformation.

20. Any trapezoid is congruent to a trapezoid with vertices (0, 0), $(a, 0)$, (b, c), and (d, c) where a, b, c, and d are positive. Prove that if the midpoints of the diagonals of this trapezoid are P and Q, then $\overleftrightarrow{PQ}$ is horizontal and PQ is $\frac{1}{2}$ the difference of the lengths of the parallel sides of the trapezoid.

21. Using coordinates, prove Varignon's theorem: The midpoints of the sides of *any* quadrilateral are the vertices of a parallelogram.

22. One team has 14 wins, 9 losses. A second team has 10 wins, 11 losses. Put this data into ordered pairs and find the midpoint. If a third team has the record indicated by the midpoint, where is the third team in the standings?

23. A bowler scores 157, 149, 153, 170, 130, and 152. Find her average score by (1) subtracting 150 from each of the scores—this gives "image" scores, (2) averaging the 6 image scores, and (3) adding 150 to the average you found.

INEQUALITIES RELATED TO LINES AND CIRCLES

6.8

Both the line and the circle separate the plane into two regions. For the line, these regions are the *half-planes* determined by the line; for the circle, they are called its *interior* and its *exterior*.

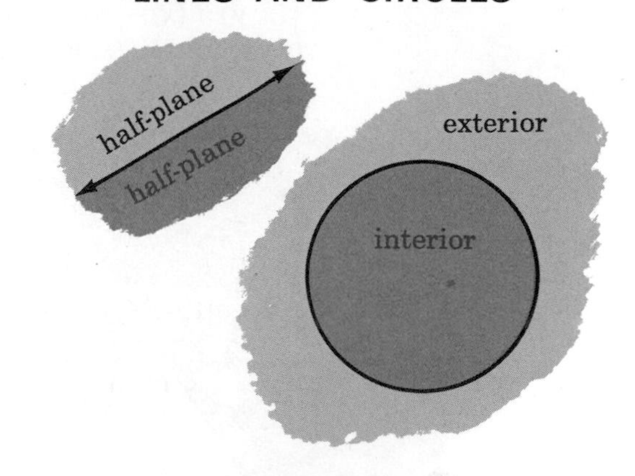

The regions of the plane are the graphs of sentences which look much like the sentences for the lines and the circles themselves. Here are two examples.

1. *A sentence for a half-plane.* $\{(x, y): y > 2\}$ contains those points whose second coordinates are greater than 2. Hence its graph consists of all points *above* the line $y = 2$. This set of points is a half-plane, indicated by dashing its edge and shading the region.

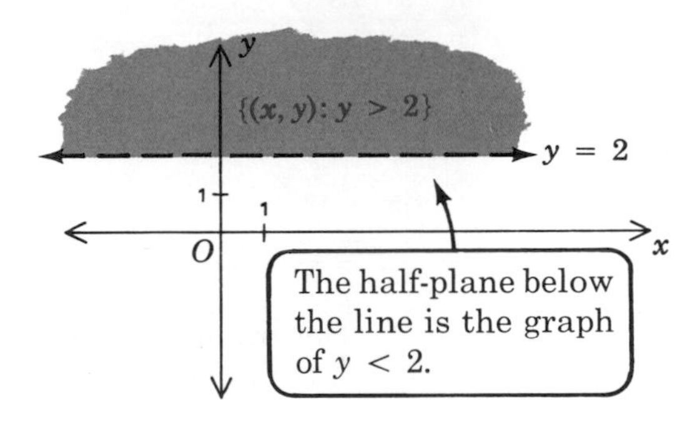

2. *A sentence for the interior of a circle.* If the distance from (x, y) to $(0, 0)$ is less than 5, then (x, y) lies in the interior of the circle with center $(0, 0)$, radius 5. We then have

$$\sqrt{(x - 0)^2 + (y - 0)^2} < 5.$$

Squaring (which doesn't change the inequality because both numbers are positive),

$$x^2 + y^2 < 25.$$

The solution set is graphed at the right. A sentence for the circle is

$$x^2 + y^2 = 25.$$

A sentence for the exterior of the circle is

$$x^2 + y^2 > 25.$$

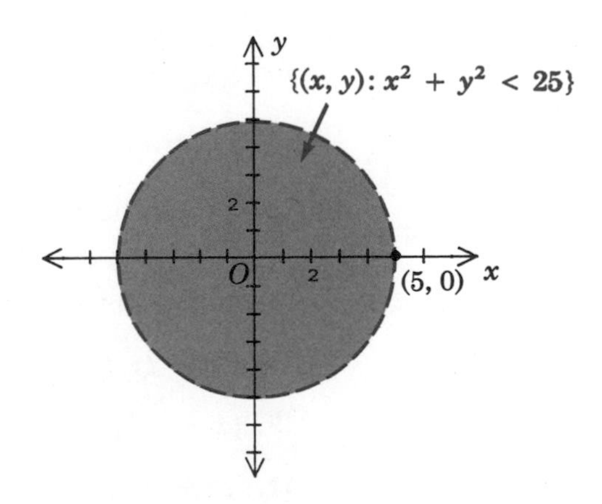

Theorem 6.8.1

The graphs of $\{(x, y) : Ax + By < C\}$ and $\{(x, y) : Ax + By > C\}$ are the half-planes of the line $\{(x, y) : Ax + By = C\}$.

Theorem 6.8.2

The graphs of $\{(x, y) : (x - h)^2 + (y - k)^2 < r^2\}$ and $\{(x, y) : (x - h)^2 + (y - k)^2 > r^2\}$ are the interior and exterior of the circle $\{(x, y) : (x - h)^2 + (y - k)^2 = r^2\}$.

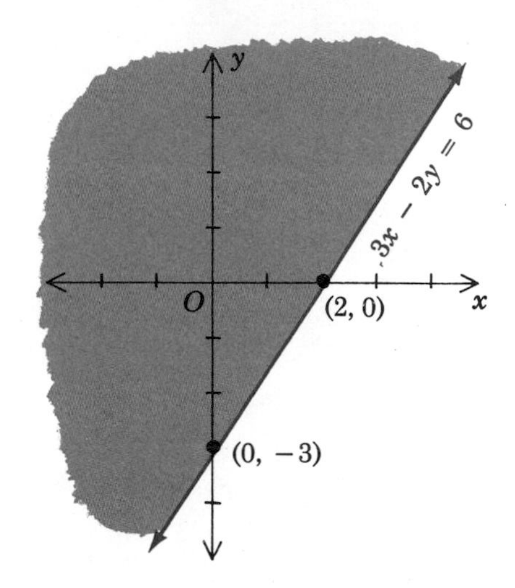

Example: Graph $\{(x, y): 3x - 2y \leq 6\}$.

SOLUTION: From Theorem 6.8.1, we know that the graph is the union of a half-plane and its edge $\{(x, y): 3x - 2y = 6\}$. We graph this line. The only question is, Which half-plane? We see that (0, 0) is a solution to $3x - 2y \leq 6$. Hence (0, 0) must be in the desired half-plane. This is enough information to draw the graph.

EXERCISES 6.8

Ⓐ **1.** The graph of $\{(x, y): x < -1\}$ is a ____ and lies to the (left, right) of the line $x = -1$.

2. The graph of $\{(x, y): y > 5\}$ is (above, below) the line $y = 5$.

3. Describe the graph of $\{(x, y): Ax + By \geq C\}$.

4. Give a sentence whose graph is the interior of $\{(x, y): x^2 + y^2 = r^2\}$.

5. Describe $\{(x, y): (x + 4)^2 + (y - 3)^2 > 16\}$.

Ⓑ **6.** Graph the set of Exercise **5**.

7–16. Graph the solution set to each two-dimensional sentence.

7. $3x + 2y > 5$

8. $2x - 3 \geq y$

9. $(x - 3)^2 - 6 \leq -(y + 4)^2$

10. $3x^2 + 3(y - 2)^2 > 1$

11. $x^2 + y^2 > 0$

12. $x^2 + y^2 = 0$

13. $3y - 5 > 6$

14. $9 = 8x - 2$

15. $k - 3 = 4(j + 2)$

16. $A^2 > 9 - B^2$

© **17.** Let $A = (6, 2)$, $B = (1, 4)$, $C = (-1, -2)$. The interior of $\angle ABC$ is the intersection of the graphs of what two sentences?

18. Is the point (20, 6.6) above or below the line containing (3, 7) and (41, 6)?

19–22. Graph the solution set to each sentence.

19. $y + 6 \leq \sqrt{9 - (x - 1)^2}$

20. $2x > \sqrt{8 - 4y^2}$

21. $4 < x^2 + y^2 < 9$

22. $17 \geq x + y$ or $x + y \geq 19$

CHAPTER SUMMARY

6

A *relation* is a set of ordered pairs. This chapter examined those relations whose graphs are lines or circles. The method used was to find equations for conveniently placed lines or circles, then use translations to find equations for all others.

Conveniently placed *lines* with their equations are:

vertical through $(h, 0)$	$x = h$
horizontal through $(0, k)$	$y = k$
through the origin with slope m	$y = mx.$

The *graph translation theorem* tells how to find an equation for a translation image of a graph. Replacing x by $x - h$ and y by $y - k$ translates the graph under the translation which maps (x, y) onto $(x + h, y + k)$. Applying this theorem to the equations above, we get the following equations.

line through $(0, b)$ with slope m:

$$y = mx + b$$

line through (h, k) with slope m:

$$y - k = m(x - h).$$

All these lines have equations of the general form $Ax + By = C$.

The *slope* of a line is a measure of the tilt of the line. Thus slope is a property preserved under translations, and parallel lines have the same slope. Horizontal lines have slope 0; vertical lines have no slope. In general, the slope of the oblique line through (x_1, y_1) and (x_2, y_2) is

$$\frac{y_1 - y_2}{x_1 - x_2}.$$

Using slope, we can get the equation of a line through two given points or of a line through a given point and parallel or perpendicular to a given line.

Translations to the origin were used to prove two theorems: (1) When perpendicular lines have slopes, the product of the slopes is -1; (2) The midpoint of the segment with endpoints (a, b) and (c, d) is $\left(\frac{a + c}{2}, \frac{b + d}{2}\right)$.

A conveniently placed *circle* has center (0, 0). If its radius is r, an equation is

$$x^2 + y^2 = r^2.$$

The distance formula or the graph translation theorem implies that the congruent circle with center (h, k) has equation

$$(x - h)^2 + (y - k)^2 = r^2.$$

Replacing the $=$ sign in any of the preceding equations with $<$ or $>$ gives a sentence for a *half-plane* of a line or the *interior* or *exterior* of a circle.

6

CHAPTER REVIEW

1–3. A circle C has center $(-4, 2)$ and contains $(5, 1)$.

1. What is the radius of C?

2. Give an equation for C.

3. Give an equation for the circle which is congruent to C but has center at the origin.

4. Give the slope of the line containing the origin and $(-6, -7)$.

5. A segment has endpoints $(3, 5)$ and $(-2, 7)$. What is its midpoint?

6. Name one point which is on the unit circle but not on either the x-axis or y-axis.

7. Give an equation for the line with slope -11 and containing $(6, 7)$.

8. Find an equation for the line that has y-intercept -6 and is parallel to $2y - x = 3$.

9–12. Graph the solution set to each two-dimensional sentence.

9. $x = 2$

10. $a + b > 10$

11. $x^2 + (y + 2)^2 = 4$

12. $t - 3r = 1$

13. Find an equation for the line which contains $(1, 4)$ and $(3, -2)$.

14. If 4 is a solution to $x^4 - 3x^3 - 32 = 2x^2$, then find a solution to $(x + 3)^4 - 3(x + 3)^3 - 32 = 2(x + 3)^2$.

15–17. A line n has slope -2.5. Find the slope of:

15. the line perpendicular to n containing $(3, 2)$.

16. the reflection image of n over the x-axis.

17. the image of n under the translation which maps (x, y) onto $(x + 3, y - 2)$.

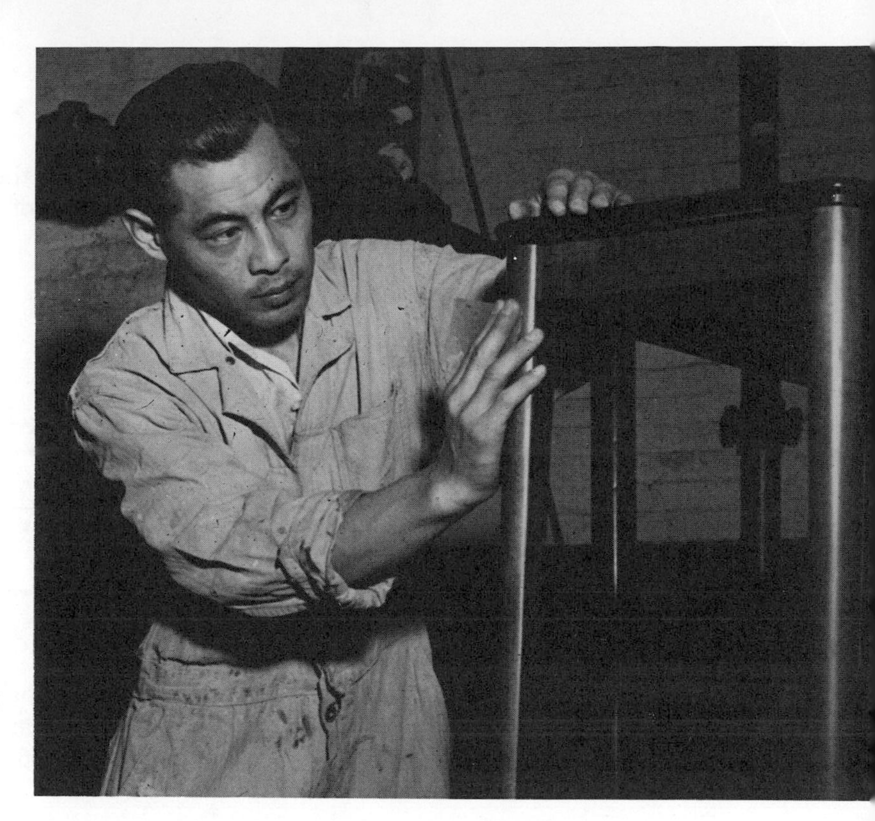

Chapter

7 Systems

Many realistic problems, such as the one below, are difficult to translate into a single mathematical sentence but can be translated into two or more sentences rather easily.

A company makes four types of wood furniture. Carpenters and finishers work on each item. The company wants to know how many items of each type to make in order to get the maximum profit, assuming everything made can be sold. Here are the times required to make each item and the profit per item.

	Table	Desk	Chair	Dresser	Total hours available
Hours in carpentry	4	9	7	10	6000
Hours in finishing	1	1	3	20	4000
Profit	\$12	\$20	\$18	\$40	

This chapter considers first the mathematics needed to solve such problems. Then some problems are given.

7.1 COMPOUND SENTENCES

Even though they are very simple, the words *and* and *or* can cause confusion. Here are two common uses of these words.

$3 < x < 5$

means

$3 < x$ **and** $x < 5$

$3 < x$

$x < 5$

$3 < x < 5$

The word *and* is associated with the **intersection** of sets. The solution set to $3 < x < 5$ is the *intersection* of the solution sets to $3 < x$ and $x < 5$.

$y \leq 14$

means

$y < 14$ **or** $y = 14$

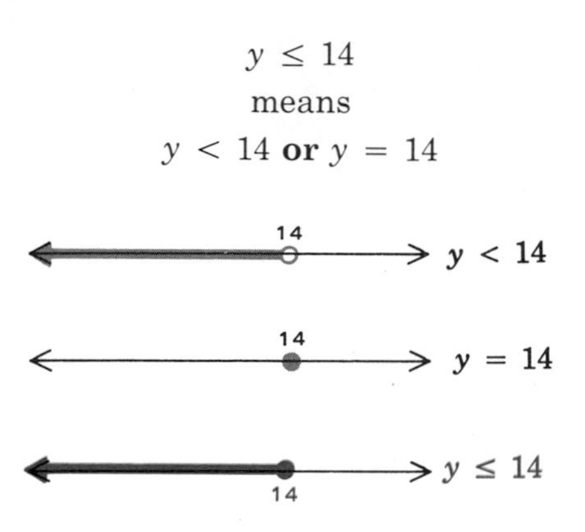

The word *or* is associated with the **union** of sets. The solution set to $y \leq 14$ is the *union* of the solution sets to $y < 14$ and $y = 14$.

Two individual sentences connected by the word *and* or the word *or* make up one **compound sentence.** Graphs of compound sentences in two variables are given below. Remember: *and* denotes intersection; *or* denotes union.

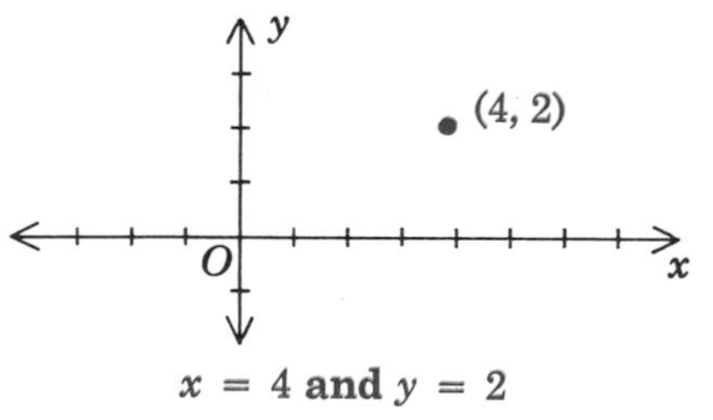

$x = 4$ **and** $y = 2$

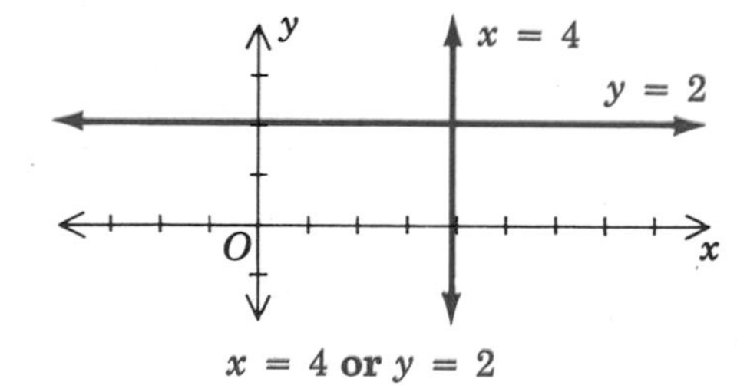

$x = 4$ **or** $y = 2$

Here are two common errors:

1. In solving the sentence $x^2 = 4$, a student writes "$x = 2$ and $x = -2$." But no number can equal both 2 and -2. The student should write "$x = 2$ or $x = -2$."

2. In solving $|b - 2| > 3$, it is correct to write "$5 < b$ or $b < -1$" but incorrect to combine as "$5 < b < -1$." The last sentence means "$5 < b$ **and** $b < -1$," which is impossible.

Usually a sentence involving absolute value can be rewritten as a compound sentence.

Examples: Rewriting absolute-value sentences as compound sentences

	Absolute-value sentence		Compound sentence	Shorthand form
1.	$\lvert x\rvert \leq 4$	means	$-4 \leq x$ **and** $x \leq 4$	$-4 \leq x \leq 4$
2.	$\lvert t\rvert > 5$	means	$t > 5$ **or** $t < -5$	none

Other types of sentences can be rewritten as compound sentences.

Examples: Rewriting individual sentences as compound sentences

1. $(y + 2)(2y - 5) = 0$	means	$y = -2$ **or** $y = \frac{5}{2}$
2. $m^2 = 14$	means	$m = \sqrt{14}$ **or** $m = -\sqrt{14}$
3. $x^2 + y^2 = 0$	means	$x = 0$ **and** $y = 0$
4. $(x - 4)^2 + (y + 7)^2 = 0$	means	$x = 4$ **and** $y = -7$
5. $x^2 < 9$	means	$x < 3$ **and** $x > -3$

There is no rule that tells when to use *and* and when to use *or*. However, a graph will help.

An absolute-value sentence that cannot be solved easily by using the length of an interval, as in Section 3.4, can often be solved by rewriting it as a compound sentence. The following theorem is then useful.

Theorem 7.1.1

When a is not negative,

a. $\lvert x\rvert < a$ if and only if $x > -a$ and $x < a$.
b. $\lvert x\rvert > a$ if and only if $x < -a$ or $x > a$.
c. $\lvert x\rvert = a$ if and only if $x = -a$ or $x = a$.

PROOF: **1.** By definition, $\lvert x\rvert$ is the distance from x to 0.

2. The distance from x to 0 is less than a if and only if x is between $-a$ and a.

3. So, $\lvert x\rvert < a$ if and only if $x < a$ and $x > -a$.

4. $\lvert x\rvert > a$ at all other times, except when $\lvert x\rvert = a$.

Graphs illustrate this theorem very well.

$\{x\colon \lvert x\rvert < a\}$

$\{x\colon \lvert x\rvert > a\}$

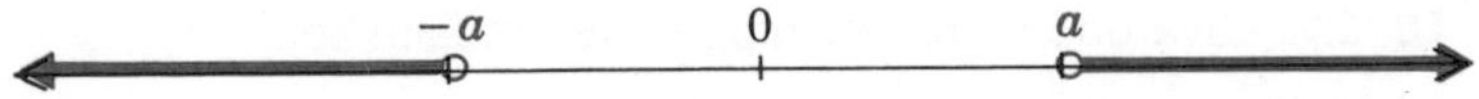

$\{x\colon \lvert x\rvert = a\}$

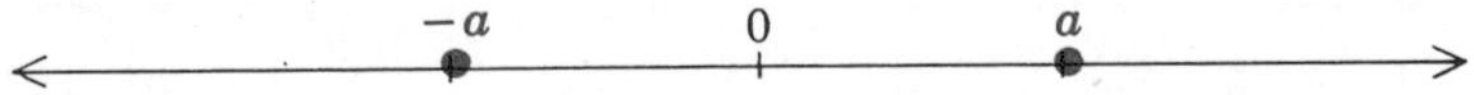

Example: Solve: $|3x + 5| < 6$

Use Theorem 7.1.1: $3x + 5 > -6$ and $3x + 5 < 6$

$3x > -11$ and $3x < 1$

$x > -\frac{11}{3}$ and $x < \frac{1}{3}$

Check some values in this interval.

EXERCISES 7.1

Ⓐ **1.** What is a compound sentence?

2. $y \geq 6$ means ____ or ____.

3. $-2.02 < a < -2.01$ means ____ and ____.

4. The word *and* is associated with ____ of sets.

5. The word *or* is associated with ____ of sets.

6–10. Copy. Fill each blank with $<$, $\leq$, $>$, $\geq$, $=$, *and*, or *or*.

6. $|x| > 3$ means x ____ 3 ____ x ____ -3.

7. $|3 - t| \leq 5$ means $3 - t$ ____ 5 ____ $3 - t$ ____ -5.

8. $16 - m^2 = 0$ means m ____ 4 ____ m ____ -4.

9. $a^2 + (b - 3)^2 = 0$ means a ____ 0 ____ $b - 3$ ____ 0.

10. $a(b - 3) = 0$ means a ____ 0 ____ $b - 3$ ____ 0.

11. Which sentence is *not* equivalent to the others?

a. $x^2 = 100$

b. $|x| = 10$

c. $x = 10$ or $x = -10$

d. $x = 10$ and $x = -10$

12–15. Graph the solution set to each compound sentence.

12. $x > 3$ and $x < 5$

13. $100 < m$ and $97 < m$

14. $z < -1$ or $z > -2$

15. $v < 1$ and $v > 9$

16–17. Why does each sentence have no solution?

16. $x = 11$ and $x = 9$

17. $5 < d < -1$

18–21. Give one number which is *not* in each set.

18. $\{v: v < 99 \text{ and } v > 80\}$

19. $\{a: a > 3 \text{ or } a < 2\}$

Ⓑ **20.** $\{x: |x - 2| > 0.01\}$

21. $\{w: 0.01 \leq (w + 3)^2\}$

22–27. Write as one sentence.

22. $x = 9$ or $x = 3$

23. $y = -6$ or $y = 0$

24. $z = 3$ or $z = -3$

25. $w = 5$ and $x = 2$

26. $x = 5$ or $y = -2$ or $z = 1$

27. $x = 5$ and $y = -2$ and $z = 1$

28–36. Solve. Also graph the solution set if it is infinite.

28. $|x| > 0$

29. $0 = |v|$

30. $0 > |v|$

31. $|q| = -6$

32. $|w| = w$

33. $|y| = -y$

34. $|3f| = 14$

35. It is estimated that between 20 and 30 percent of the juniors in a certain high school smoke. Let S be the number of smokers. There are 1900 students in the school, and $\frac{1}{4}$ of the students are juniors. Give an absolute-value sentence which is satisfied by S.

36. A scale is accurate to within 0.3 pound. What sentence is satisfied by the actual weight w of a coin if the scale indicates that 800 of the coins weigh 125.1 pounds?

37–39. Write an equivalent compound sentence without absolute-value signs. Then solve.

37. $|x - 3| \leq 4$

38. $|x - 3| > 4$

39. $|x - 3| = 4$

© **40–44.** Solve by any means. Graph the solution set.

40. $|x - 2| = x - 2$

41. $|6 - 3m| < 10$

42. $|2a + 7| = 6$

43. $5 - z = |z - 5|$

44. $|y - 3| \leq 3y$

45. When x is near 70, $3x - 10$ is near 200. How close must x be to 70 in order for $3x - 10$ to be within 5 of 200?

46. If $4x - 3y = 12$, how close must y be to 8 in order for x to satisfy $|9 - x| < 0.01$?

47. What is the allowable interval for the radius of a circle if the circumference is to be 1 metre, give or take a millimetre?

48. A circular test track is to be 440 yards in inner circumference, with accuracy to an inch. What is the allowable interval for the inner radius?

49. True or False? After a number is multiplied by k, the absolute value of the resulting product is k times the absolute value of the given number.

50. Write as a single sentence: $x = 2y$ or $x = -2y$.

51. Find all points on the line $x = 4$ whose distance from $(4, 11)$ is twice their distance from $(4, -3)$.

52. $A = (3, 0)$, $B = (9, 0)$, and P is on the x-axis. If $PA = \frac{3}{4}PB$, find all possible points P.

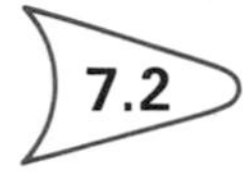

7.2 WHAT IS A SYSTEM?

The sentence	$\lvert 9 - x\rvert = 5$	$\lvert x - 1\rvert = 3$
has solution set	$\{14, 4\}$	$\{4, -2\}$

The two sentences have a common solution, 4, which is the only element in the intersection of the solution sets:

$$\{14, 4\} \cap \{4, -2\} = \{4\}.$$

↖ set intersection symbol

When we want to find all *common* solutions to two or more sentences, the set of sentences is called a **system.** The solution set for a system is the *intersection* of the solution sets of the individual sentences.

Example 1: A number is negative. Its absolute value is 7. What is the number?

SOLUTION: Translate each condition into mathematical language.

Let n be the number.

A number is negative. ➡ $n < 0$

Its absolute value is 7. ➡ $|n| = 7$

The solution set of $n < 0$ includes all negative real numbers. The solution set of $|n| = 7$ is $\{7, -7\}$. So, only -7 is in both solution sets, and only -7 satisfies both sentences.

Example 2: The sum of two numbers is 10. Their product is 11. Find the numbers.

SOLUTION: Translating, let x and y be the numbers. We want x and y to satisfy the system at the right.

$x + y = 10$
and ← Understood but usually omitted
$xy = 11$

Many ordered pairs satisfy the first sentence, for example, $(0, 10)$, $(2, 8)$, $(-1, 11)$. Likewise, many pairs satisfy the second sentence: $(1, 11)$, $(2, 5\frac{1}{2})$, $(-\frac{1}{2}, -22)$. Finding a pair which satisfies both may be difficult.

A system is a special type of compound sentence, made up of individual sentences joined by the word *and.* Just like sentences, systems are **equivalent** if and only if they have the same solutions. These three systems are equivalent, each having solution set $\{(-1, 4)\}$.

$$\begin{cases} 3a + 2b = 5 \\ 7a + 4b = 9 \end{cases} \qquad \begin{cases} a + b \leq 10 \\ -14a - 3b = 2 \\ 2a - b = -6 \end{cases} \qquad \begin{cases} a = -1 \\ b = 4 \end{cases}$$

A single brace is often used to denote a system.

This is the simplest of the three equivalent systems.

The three ways of describing solutions to individual sentences also apply to systems.

Example: Ways of describing solutions to the system $\begin{cases} 4x - y = 10 \\ y + 3x = 11 \end{cases}$

1. List the solutions: (3, 2).
2. Write the solution set: $\{(3, 2)\}$.
3. Write a simplified equivalent system: $\begin{cases} x = 3 \\ y = 2. \end{cases}$

Graphing the solution set of each equation in the original system above, we get:

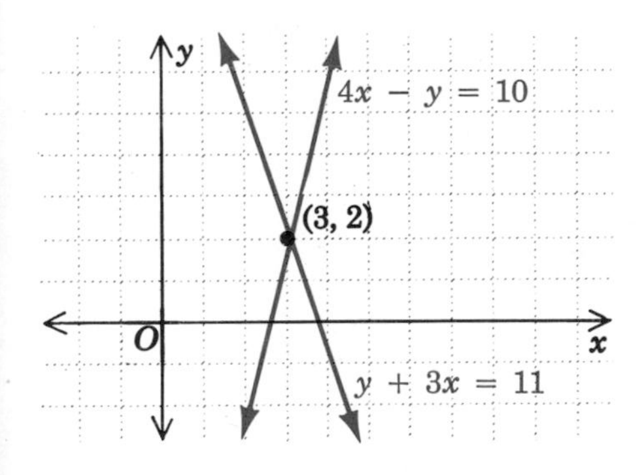

Graphing the solution set of each equation in the simplified system above, we get:

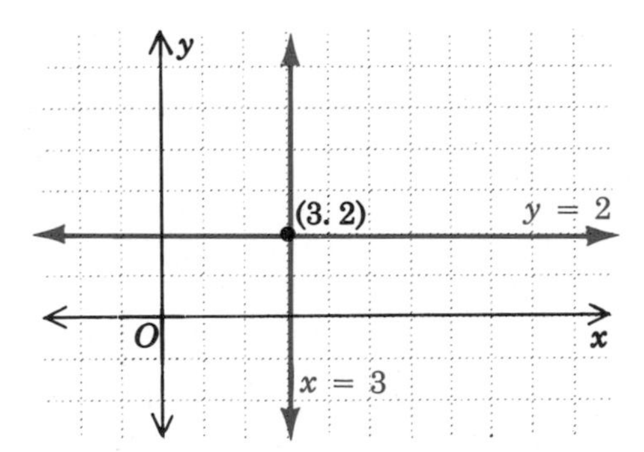

The intersection of the solution sets is (3, 2) in each case. This shows that the systems are equivalent. Using set notation, we can write

$$\begin{aligned} &\{(x, y): 4x - y = 10\} \cap \{(x, y): y + 3x = 11\} \\ &= \{(x, y): x = 3\} \cap \{(x, y): y = 2\} \\ &= \{(3, 2)\}. \end{aligned}$$

In general, the graphing method enables us to determine the number of solutions to a system and to estimate the solutions.

Example: Estimate all solutions to the system $\begin{cases} w^2 + (z - 1)^2 = 4 \\ 3z - w = 2. \end{cases}$

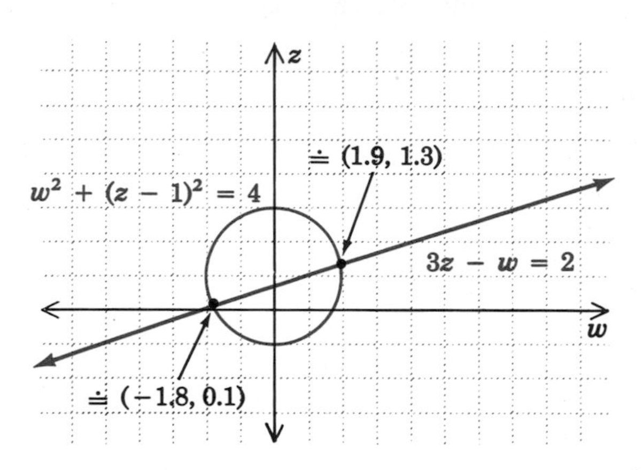

SOLUTION: Graph each sentence as at the left. The graphs intersect at two points, so there are two solutions. One is near $(-1.8, 0.1)$. The other is near $(1.9, 1.3)$.

Check: Substitute $(-1.8, 0.1)$ in *each* sentence.

$$(-1.8)^2 + (0.1 - 1)^2 = 3.24 + 0.81$$
$$= 4.05 \doteq 4$$

$$3(0.1) - (-1.8) = 0.3 + 1.8$$
$$= 2.1 \doteq 2$$

The other estimate can be checked similarly.

EXERCISES 7.2

Ⓐ **1.** What is meant by "solving a system of sentences"?

2–7. Find at least one solution to each system.

2. $x + 1 \geq 0$
$|x| = 9$

3. $y^2 = 17$
$y < 0$

4. $b = 3$
$a + b < 0$

5. $10 = 3r + t$
$r = 9$

6. $2x - 9 = 0$
$3y + 2 = 1$

7. $2x - 3y \geq 6$
$y < x + 2$

8. How can graphs help in solving systems?

9. Name four points in the solution set of $x = 3y - 1$.

10. Name four points in the solution set of $y = 1 - |w|$.

Ⓑ **11.** Name four elements of $\{(x, y): x = 9\}$.

12. True or False? $\{(a, b): b = -7\} \cap \{(a, b): a = 3\} = \{(3, -7)\}$

13. Name three elements of $\{(x, y\}: y - x = y + x\}$.

14. Graph the solution set of: $x > 3$ *or* $x > -1$. How does this differ from the solution set of: $x > 3$ *and* $x > -1$?

15. True or False? $\{(a, b): 9a - 2b = 5\} \cap \{(x, y): x + 2y = 5\}$
$= \{(1, 2)\}$

16–18. Find at least one solution to each system.

16. $x + y \geq 7$
$x - y \leq 0$
$y \geq 14$

17. $a - 3b \leq 1$
$b \leq 2a$
b is *not* an integer.

18. $3p + 4q < 100$
$3p + 4q > 50$
$2p + q > 75$

19–27. Give the number of solutions and the solution set of each system. (Graphing may help. In each case, the number of dimensions of the graph is the number of variables.)

19. $u \geq 3$
$u \geq 4$

20. $x < 2$
$x > 9$

21. $z < 2$
$z > -2$

22. $|x - 1| = 7$
$|2 - x| > 7$

23. $a^2 = 9$
$8 > |3a - 2|$

24. $y^{-1} = 14$
$3x = \frac{12}{y}$

25. $|2x + 3| \leq 1$
$|x - 9| > 3$
$|x| = 6$

26. $a = 3b$
$b = 4c$
$c = 8$

27. $v - 3z + 6 = y$
$2z - 11 = 14$
$z + y = 3$

28. Simplify: $\{(x, y): \frac{y}{6} = 0\} \cap \{(x, y): 100 = 25(x + y)\}$.

29–35. Graph the solution sets of each sentence to *estimate* one solution to each system. Give estimates to the nearest integer. Check.

29. $y = x - 10$
$y = 4x + 1$

30. $A + 2B = 6$
$3A - B = 6$

31. $-6 = m$
$p - m = 3$

32. $-x + 2y = 100.2$
$x - 8y = 61.3$

33. $w - 9.001y = 180.013$
$2w + y = -6.5$

34. $c^2 + d^2 = 9$
$(c - 2)^2 + (d - 3)^2 = 16$

35. $x^2 + y^2 = 1$
$y = 5x + 6$

© **36.** Find the solution set to the system $|2x + 3| \leq 1$, $|x - 9| > 3$, $|x| > 6$.

37. Find every point on the x-axis whose distance from $(-8, 0)$ is less than 5 and which is closer to $(-6, 0)$ than to $(-4, 0)$.

38–40. Graph the solution set to each system.

38. $x^2 + y^2 = 9$
$3y - x < 4$

39. $(a - 4)^2 + b^2 \leq 16$
$a^2 + (b + 3)^2 \leq 1$

40. $D - C > 4(D + C)$
$C^2 = 6 - D^2$

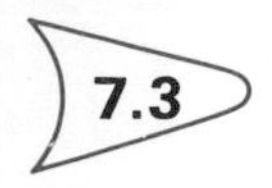

7.3 STRATEGIES FOR SOLVING SYSTEMS OF EQUATIONS

As you have seen in earlier work, three properties of equality are very important in solving equations:

1. substitution
2. addition property of equations
3. multiplication property of equations

We will now use these properties in solving systems.

Examples: Solving systems by substitution

1. Given: $\begin{cases} x = 10 \\ 4x - y = 14 \end{cases}$ ← This tells us that x must be 10.

Substitute 10 for x in the second equation:

$$\begin{cases} x = 10 \\ 4 \cdot 10 - y = 14 \end{cases}$$

Simplify: $\begin{cases} x = 10 \\ y = 26 \end{cases}$

All three systems above are equivalent. The last one has the obvious single solution $(x, y) = (10, 26)$.

2. Given: $\begin{cases} 4A - 3F = 5 \\ A = F + 2 \end{cases}$

The second equation lets us substitute $F + 2$ for A in the first equation:

$$\begin{cases} 4(F + 2) - 3F = 5 \\ A = F + 2 \end{cases}$$

Solve the first equation for F:

$$\begin{cases} F = -3 \\ A = F + 2 \end{cases}$$

Substitute -3 for F in the second equation:

$$\begin{cases} F = -3 \\ A = -3 + 2 = -1 \end{cases}$$

So, $(A, F) = (-1, 3)$.

The last example illustrates a strategy for solving systems.

> To solve a system, find an equivalent system in which some of the sentences contain fewer variables than in the given system.

Besides using substitution to apply this strategy, we can use the *addition property of equations*:

If $a = b$ and $c = d$, then $a + c = b + d$.

Example: Solving a system by using the addition property

$$\text{Given: } \begin{cases} 5x - 4y = 6 \\ x + 4y = 18 \end{cases}$$

Adding the two equations gives an equation in one variable.

$$6x \quad = 24$$

Thus, $$x = 4$$

The last equation and *any* one of the original equations gives an equivalent system, which can be solved by substitution as follows.

$$\begin{cases} 5x - 4y = 6 \\ x = 4 \end{cases} \Rightarrow \begin{cases} 20 - 4y = 6 \\ x = 4 \end{cases} \Rightarrow \begin{cases} y = \frac{7}{2} \\ x = 4 \end{cases}$$

The solution $(4, \frac{7}{2})$ should satisfy the original system. Does it?

$$\text{Check: } \begin{cases} 5 \cdot 4 - 4 \cdot \frac{7}{2} = 6 \\ 4 + 4 \cdot \frac{7}{2} = 18 \end{cases} \Rightarrow \begin{cases} 6 = 6 \\ 18 = 18 \end{cases} \quad \text{OK}$$

The addition property is helpful when the resulting equation has one less variable than the original equations. The multiplication property—if $a = b$, then $ca = cb$—can be used to prepare a system for addition.

Examples: Solving systems by using the multiplication property

1. Given: $\begin{cases} 8c = d + 6 \\ 4c - 3 = 3d \end{cases}$

First, change the form to get the variables on the same side:

$$\begin{cases} 8c - d = 6 \\ 4c - 3d = 3 \end{cases}$$

Multiply first equation by -3:

$$\begin{cases} -24c + 3d = -18 \\ 4c - 3d = 3 \end{cases}$$

Now add and form a new system as in the Example above:

$$\begin{cases} -20c = -15 \\ 4c - 3d = 3 \end{cases} \Rightarrow \begin{cases} c = \frac{3}{4} \\ 4c - 3d = 3 \end{cases} \Rightarrow \begin{cases} c = \frac{3}{4} \\ d = 0 \end{cases}$$

Check $(\frac{3}{4}, 0)$ in the original system. The solution is $(\frac{3}{4}, 0)$.

2. Given: $\begin{cases} 4x + 5y = 6 \\ 7x + 8y = 9 \end{cases}$

Here two multiplications are needed. A good choice is to multiply the first equation by 7 and the second equation by -4.

$$\begin{cases} 28x + 35y = 42 \\ -28x - 32y = -36 \end{cases}$$

Now add to get $3y = 6$ and choose one of the given sentences to get an equivalent system.

$$\begin{cases} 3y = 6 \\ 4x + 5y = 6 \end{cases}$$ Solve and check as before.

EXERCISES 7.3

Ⓐ **1–3.** Give the solution to each system.

1. $3M - 4N = 2$, $M = 1$

2. $8 = 4P + Q$, $6Q = 0$

3. $3 - x = 0$, $10z + 1 - x = 0$

4–6. Give the equation which results from addition.

4. $y + 3x = 1$, $y - 2x = 5$

5. $a^2 - 3b = 4a + 2$, $b - a^2 = 3 - 4a$

6. $5w - 4z = 1$, $6w + 4z = 21$

7. The ordered pair $(6, -4)$ satisfies $5x + 4y = 14$ and $y = x - 10$. If we add the equations, must the ordered pair satisfy the sum?

8. The ordered pair $(1, \pi)$ satisfies $y = \pi x^2$ and $\pi x = y$. If we add the equations, must the ordered pair satisfy the sum?

9–16. Let A be the equation $3x + 2y = 10$ and B be the equation $x - 5y = 1$. Add or multiply as indicated.

9. 5A

10. 2B

11. 5A + 2B

12. -3B

13. A + (-3B)

14. A + (-10B)

15. Which two equations of those that you found in Exercises **9–14** are most helpful in solving the given system?

16. Verify that $(\frac{52}{17}, \frac{7}{17})$ satisfies each answer to Exercises **9–14**.

17–19. Write an equivalent system in which, if you added the equations, an equation with only one variable would result.

17. $-x - 5y = 17$, $5x + 2y = 3$

18. $4x - 3y = 0$, $x + 4y = 2$

19. $6a = b - 2$, $2a = 4b + 2$

Ⓑ **20–22.** Solve each system of Exercises **17–19.**

23–25. Solve by substitution.

23. $3A + B = 7$
$B = 9A + 5$

24. $y = 100x + 7$
$y = 98x + 20$

25. $a + b = 6$
$a - b = -6$

26–31. Solve using any method.

26. $4m - 3n + 2 = 6$
$-8m + 4 = 7n - 3$

27. $9(10t + u) = 6(u + 10t)$
$u = 2t$

28. $0.03x - 0.04y = 75$
$x + y = 4000$

29. $\dfrac{f + s}{2} = 60; \quad \dfrac{f - s}{2} = 30$

30. $5 = a - 3(b + 2)$
$100b + 200 = 400a$

31. $a - 3b - 2\sqrt{2} = 0$
$4a + b + \sqrt{3} = 0$

32–33. First, estimate a solution to each system by graphing. Then see how good your estimate was by solving the system algebraically.

32. $3x - y = 10$
$x + 4y = 3$

33. $E - 2F = 6$
$3E + F = -2$

Ⓒ **34–37.** Solve each system for (x, y).

34. $x + 3y = 4b$
$2x - 2y = 3a$

35. $ax + by = 1$
$cx + dy = 0$

36. $ax - by = a$
$bx + ay = b$

37. $d^2x + c^2y = 2cd$
$dx + cy = c + d$

SYSTEMS LARGER THAN 2 × 2

$$\begin{cases} 2x + 3y = 5 \\ x - 4y = -3 \end{cases}$$

The system above, with two sentences, can be rewritten as a single sentence by using matrix multiplication.

$$\underbrace{\begin{bmatrix} 2 & 3 \\ 1 & -4 \end{bmatrix}}_{\text{This is called the coefficient matrix.}} \cdot \begin{bmatrix} x \\ y \end{bmatrix} = \begin{bmatrix} 5 \\ -3 \end{bmatrix}$$

Check that this is equivalent to the first system.

This is called the **coefficient matrix.**

Because the coefficient matrix above has dimensions 2 × 2, the original system is called a **2 × 2 system.**

At the left, below, is a 3×2 system. It has 3 sentences and 2 variables. Its coefficient matrix, shown at the right, is 3×2.

$$\begin{cases} x + 4y = 8 \\ 3x - 2y = 6 \\ 5x + y = -9 \end{cases} \qquad \begin{bmatrix} 1 & 4 \\ 3 & -2 \\ 5 & 1 \end{bmatrix} \cdot \begin{bmatrix} x \\ y \end{bmatrix} = \begin{bmatrix} 8 \\ 6 \\ -9 \end{bmatrix}$$

3×2 coefficient matrix

To solve a 3×2 system, first use the methods of Section 7.3 to find all solutions to the system composed of *any two* of the equations. Then test the solutions in the third equation. In this case, $(\frac{20}{7}, \frac{9}{7})$ is the solution to $x + 4y = 8$ and $3x - 2y = 6$. This solution does not work in $5x + y = -9$, so there is no solution to the system.

Methods used in the previous section can be applied to any small-dimensioned system. Here is a 3×3 system in which the equations are labeled A, B, and C for easy reference.

A: $x - 2y + z = 9$
B: $4x + 3y - z = 10$
C: $5x - y + 2z = -6$

$$\begin{bmatrix} 1 & -2 & 1 \\ 4 & 3 & -1 \\ 5 & -1 & 2 \end{bmatrix} \cdot \begin{bmatrix} x \\ y \\ z \end{bmatrix} = \begin{bmatrix} 9 \\ 10 \\ -6 \end{bmatrix}$$

3×3 coefficient matrix

Multiply and add to obtain equations with only two variables. (The letters A, B, and C in red indicate what was done.)

A + B: $5x + y = 19$
2B + C: $13x + 5y = 14$

Solving as before, $x = \frac{27}{4}$ and $y = -\frac{59}{4}$. Substituting in any of the original equations, $z = -\frac{109}{4}$. The solution to this system is written as the ordered triple $(\frac{27}{4}, -\frac{59}{4}, -\frac{109}{4})$. You should check this solution in equations A, B, and C.

The single sentence $3x - 4y = 2$ can be rewritten as a 1×2 system:

$$\underset{1 \times 2}{[3 \quad -4]} \cdot \begin{bmatrix} x \\ y \end{bmatrix} = [2].$$

This sentence has many solutions, each an ordered pair. Solving $3x - 4y = 2$ for y results in $y = \frac{3x - 2}{4}$.

Therefore, $(x, y) = \left(x, \frac{3x - 2}{4}\right)$.

Ordered pairs of this form are solutions to $3x - 4y = 2$. Picking the value 5 for x gives $\left(x, \frac{3x - 2}{4}\right) = \left(5, \frac{13}{4}\right)$. The pair $\left(5, \frac{13}{4}\right)$ satisfies $3x - 4y = 2$. Other values of x give other solutions.

The same idea can be used with other systems that have more variables than equations.

eq 1: $a - 4b + c = 2$
eq 2: $3a + b - c = 0$

$$\begin{bmatrix} 1 & -4 & 1 \\ 3 & 1 & -1 \end{bmatrix} \cdot \begin{bmatrix} a \\ b \\ c \end{bmatrix} = \begin{bmatrix} 2 \\ 0 \end{bmatrix}$$

2 × 3

A system of dimensions 2 × 3 usually does not have a unique solution. But its solutions can sometimes be given in terms of one of the variables. Adding the equations:

(eq 1) + (eq 2): $4a - 3b = 2$

$$b = \frac{4a - 2}{3}$$

Substituting in either equation and solving for c results in

$$c = \frac{13a - 2}{3}.$$

Now b and c have been expressed in terms of a. Each solution is an ordered triple of the form

$$(a, b, c) = \left(a, \frac{4a - 2}{3}, \frac{13a - 2}{3}\right).$$

Let $a = 2$. Then $(a, b, c) = (2, 2, 8)$.

Let $a = 1$. Then $(a, b, c) = (1, \frac{2}{3}, \frac{11}{3})$.

In this way, any number of solutions can be found.

In general,

A system with more variables than equations is likely to have many solutions.	A system with more equations than variables is likely to have no solutions.

EXERCISES 7.4

Ⓐ **1.** By what procedure can this system be solved?

$$\begin{cases} x - 8m = 3 \\ 2x - 6m = 7 \\ x + 2m = 10 \end{cases}$$

2–4. Give the coefficient matrix and the dimensions of each system. Then tell how many solutions each system is likely to have.

2. $x - 3y = 2$
$4x + y = 6$
$5x - 2y = 8$

3. $x + 4y - 3z = 6$
$2y + z = 9$
$z = 8$

4. $3a - b + c = 9$
$a + 2b - 3c = 6$

Ⓑ **5.** Find one solution to the system: $\begin{cases} 2m - 4p + 5q = 3m + 2p \\ m - q = p + 1. \end{cases}$

6–16. Find all solutions to each system.

6. $\begin{aligned} x + y - z &= 6 \\ -2x - 4z &= 10 \\ 3y + 2z &= 1 \end{aligned}$

7. $\begin{aligned} 3a + b - 4c &= 3 \\ 6a - 3b + 2c &= -4 \\ -3a + b + 6c &= 4 \end{aligned}$

8. $\begin{aligned} 4m &= 2a + 6b \\ 7a &= b + 1 \\ 8m &= a + 2 \end{aligned}$

9. $\begin{aligned} 6 &= 4w - 10 + z \\ w &= 3z - 8 \\ 3z + 6w &= 9 \end{aligned}$

10. $\begin{aligned} 8(m + p) &= 20 \\ 6(m - p) &= 18 \\ 5m &= 4p - \tfrac{1}{2} \end{aligned}$

11. the system of Exercise **2**

12. the system of Exercise **3**

Ⓒ **13.** $\begin{aligned} 8x - 3y + z &= 14 \\ -6x + 2y - 3z &= 8 \end{aligned}$

14. $\begin{aligned} A - 4B + 7 &= C \\ C + 2B - 3A &= 6 \end{aligned}$

15. $\begin{aligned} a + b + c + d &= 5 \\ 3a - 2b - c - d &= 0 \\ -a + 6b - 4c + d &= 7 \\ a - b - c - d &= -3 \end{aligned}$

16. $\begin{aligned} m + n + p + q &= 1 \\ 8m + 4n + 2p + q &= 6 \\ 27m + 9n + 3p + q &= 14 \\ 64m + 16n + 4p + q &= 29 \end{aligned}$

17. Find a 3×3 system in which the solution set consists of all ordered triples of the form $(a, 4a - 3, 3a + 2)$.

18. Repeat Exercise **17** for solutions of the form $(3y, y, 4y + 1)$.

19. Solve this 6×6 system.
HINT: Look for an easy way.

$$\begin{cases} a + b + c + d + e = -2 \\ b + c + d + e + f = 0 \\ c + d + e + f + a = 5 \\ d + e + f + a + b = 9 \\ e + f + a + b + c = -1 \\ f + a + b + c + d = 7 \end{cases}$$

20. Carmen has some dollar bills, quarters, and dimes. She has one third as many dollar bills as quarters and fifteen times as many dimes as quarters. If the total value of the money is \$50, find how many dollar bills, dimes, and quarters she has.

21. A bicycle, three tricycles, and a unicycle cost \$187. Seven bicycles and a tricycle cost \$302. Five unicycles, two bicycles, and seven tricycles cost \$586. What is the cost of one bicycle? (Assume that all bicycles are the same price, all tricycles are the same price, and all unicycles are the same price.)

HISTORY AND APPLICATIONS OF SYSTEM SOLVING

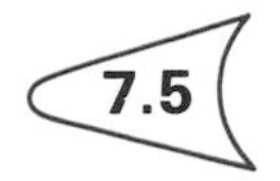

A good procedure for solving systems of linear *equations* was first developed by the German mathematician Karl Friedrich Gauss in 1819. In 1821, the French mathematician Fourier considered ways of solving systems of linear *inequalities*. The procedure of Gauss is still used today. Fourier's methods have been modified in recent years.

In the 1800's, mathematicians tried to find better ways of solving systems because applications were involving systems of larger dimensions. Out of this type of work Cayley invented matrices around 1858. (The geometric applications of matrices studied in Chapter 5 were discovered later. In Chapter 9, matrices are used to solve systems.)

Today's applications may involve systems of dimensions as large as $5{,}000 \times 10{,}000$. Faster methods than those developed in the 19th century are needed. The mathematics behind these methods was developed in this century, the most important procedure being the *simplex algorithm* invented in 1947 by the econometrician Leonid Hurwicz and mathematicians George Dantzig and T. C. Koopmans, all from the United States.

In 1939, the Russian mathematician L. V. Kantorovich was the first to announce that large systems might have applications in production planning in industry. (His work went largely unnoticed for 20 years.) In 1945, George Stigler (then at Columbia University, now at the University of Chicago) was looking for the cheapest diet that would provide a person's daily needs of calories, proteins, calcium, iron, vitamin A, thiamine, riboflavin, niacin, and ascorbic acid.

He considered 70 possible foods and found that the lowest-cost diet was a combination of wheat flour, cabbage, and hog liver. By mixing amounts of these, a person could live in good health for $59.88 a year (then). Costs today are higher, so it might now cost about $150 a year.

Stigler could not consider a much greater number of possible foods nor add variables to make the diet more appetizing because computers were not available in 1945. Today, we could consider hundreds of possible foods and many more daily needs than he did.

Problems which lead to large systems solved by the simplex algorithm are called *linear programming* problems. (The word *programming* does not refer to a computer; it means that the solution gives a "program" to follow for best results.) Linear programming is used often in industries in which all competitors make the same product, so that efficiency determines the amount of profit. These industries include the paper, oil, milk, steel, and other raw-material processing industries.

Two examples of linear programming problems follow. The first is of the diet type considered by Stigler, and the second is of the production type considered by Kantorovich. Both are simplified from real situations in which hundreds or thousands of variables might be used.

Example 1: *A diet problem.* Parents shopping for their family want to know how much steak and potatoes to buy. From a food-value table they find:

	Units of carbohydrates	Units of vitamins	Units of proteins
Minimum daily requirement (per person)	8	19	7
1 unit of steak has	1	3	3
1 unit of potatoes has	3	4	1

Furthermore, 1 unit of potatoes costs \$0.40, and 1 unit of steak costs \$1.10. If the parents want to be most economical yet meet minimum requirements, how much should they buy for each member of the family?

SOLUTION:

1. *Identify the variables.*

   Let p = no. of units of potatoes to buy;
   s = no. of units of steak to buy.

   Note that $p \geq 0$;
   $s \geq 0$.

2. *Identify the requirement for each resource in terms of the variables.*

   Carbohydrates: $3p + s \geq 8$
   Vitamins: $4p + 3s \geq 19$
   Proteins: $p + 3s \geq 7$

3. *Graph the system of 5 inequalities.* This is shown below in stages. The shaded area contains points which satisfy the inequalities considered until that time.

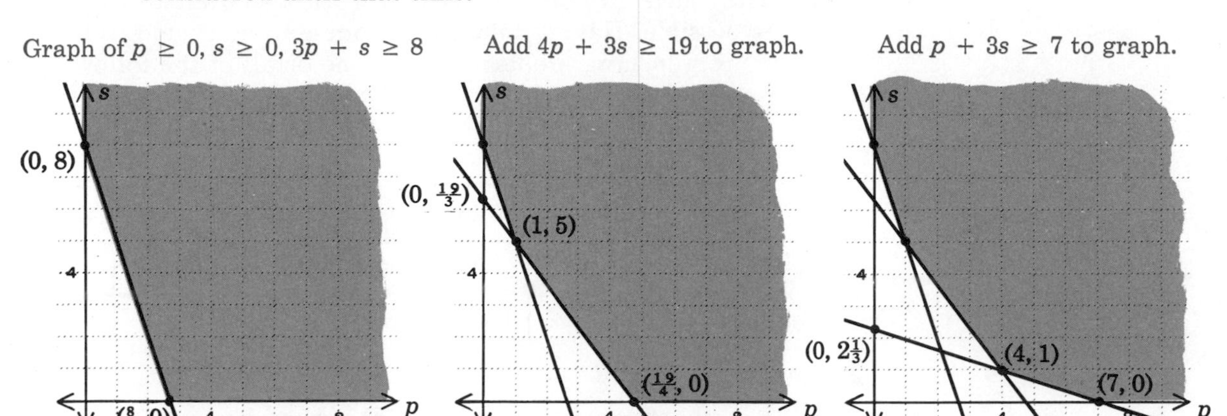

The final shaded region is called the **feasible region.** In this region, the graph shows that there are infinitely many ways to meet the minimum daily requirements. We want the cheapest way.

4. *Identify the expression which is to be made smallest* (*or, in other problems, largest*). This is the expression for the cost.

$$0.04p + 1.10s$$

By substituting in this expression, we can find the cost for any solution to the system. For example, (8, 3) is in the feasible region. It corresponds to buying 8 units of potatoes, 3 of steak. Substituting determines a cost of 0.40(8) + 1.10(3), or \$6.50.

5. *Apply the following theorem* (first proved by Fourier in 1826).

> A solution to a linear programming problem is always one of the vertices of the feasible region.

So even though there may be infinitely many points in the feasible region, only some need to be tried. In this case, the region has 4 vertices: (0, 8), (1, 5), (4, 1), and (7, 0).

Cost for (0, 8) ▶	$0.40(0) + 1.10(8) = 8.80$	
(1, 5) ▶	$0.40(1) + 1.10(5) = 5.90$	
(4, 1) ▶	$0.40(4) + 1.10(1) = 2.70$	◀ Cheapest
(7, 0) ▶	$0.40(7) + 1.10(0) = 2.80$	

6. *Interpret the results.* Since (4, 1) is cheapest, the parents should buy 4 units of potatoes and 1 of steak for each person.

Example 2: *A production problem.* Some students make earrings and bracelets in their spare time and know they can sell all they make. They have 15 hours a week to work and want to earn as much as possible. Having taken this course, they decide to form a linear programming problem using some or all of the following data.

	Time to make	Metal used	Cost of material	Selling price	Profit
Earrings (pair)	20 min.	120 grams	\$0.60	\$3.50	\$2.90
Bracelet (each)	10 min.	200 grams	\$1.00	\$2.00	\$1.00
Total available	900 min.	15 kilograms			

SOLUTION:

1. Let e = no. of pairs of earrings made per week;
   b = no. of bracelets made per week.

2. Time: $20e + 10b \le 900$
   Metal: $120e + 200b \le 15000$ Also: $b \ge 0, e \ge 0$

3. Graph.

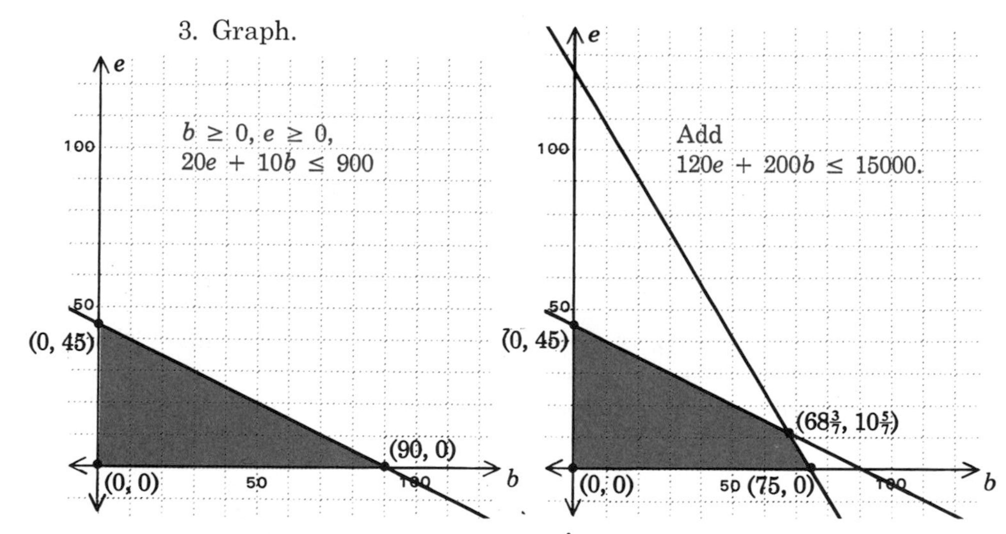

4. The students want to maximize their profit. The expression for the profit is $1.00b + 2.90e$.

5. The feasible region has 4 vertices: (0, 0), (0, 45), (75, 0), and $(68\frac{3}{7}, 10\frac{5}{7})$. Use (69, 11) as an estimate of the last vertex.

Profit for			
(0, 0) ▶	$1.00(0) + 2.90(0) =$	0.00	
(0, 45) ▶	$1.00(0) + 2.90(45) =$	130.50	◀ Maximum
(75, 0) ▶	$1.00(75) + 2.90(0) =$	75.00	
(69, 11) ▶	$1.00(69) + 2.90(11) =$	100.90	

6. They should make earrings only. They have time to make 45 pairs and would make a profit of \$130.50. Also, they would have 9600 grams of metal left.

Is this solution acceptable? It may not be. The students may feel that their displays should have both earrings and bracelets to look nice enough that all the work is sold. So, they might reject this solution, add new restrictions on b and e, and solve again. (This would not be unusual. Remember that deciding whether a solution is acceptable is part of the modeling process.)

EXERCISES 7.5

Ⓐ **1–4.** Give the nationality, century, and work related to linear programming for each person.

1. Kantorovich **2.** Dantzig **3.** Stigler **4.** Fourier

5. How large a system might be involved in a real application of linear programming?

6. In the diet problem of this section, what are the parents trying to find?

7. In the production problem, what are the students trying to find?

8. What is the feasible region of a linear programming problem?

9. What is Fourier's theorem for linear programming problems?

Ⓑ **10–14.** Suppose that the shaded area at the right is the feasible region for a problem. Which vertex would maximize profit if the given expression denotes the profit?

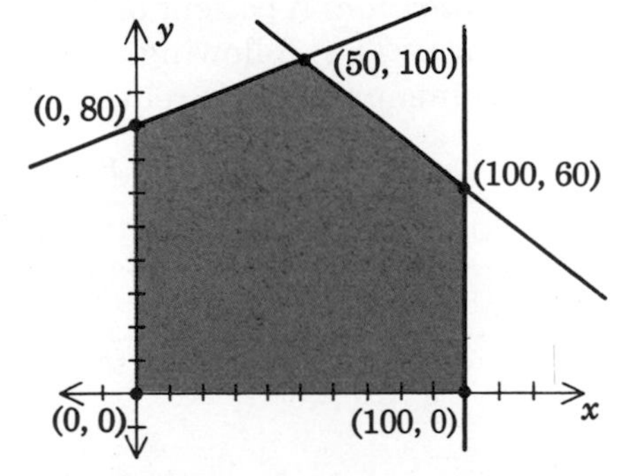

10. $x + 4y$ **11.** $3x - 4y$

12. $5x + 2y$ **13.** $3x - 4y + 250$

14. $4x + 5y$

15–20. Refer to the problem stated on page 181. This problem requires 4 variables, so it cannot be graphed easily. But the system can still be set up. Follow steps as in Example **1** of this section.

15. Identify the variables.

16. Identify the requirement for the carpentry resource.

17. Identify the requirement for the finishing resource.

18. Identify the expression to be made as large as possible.

19. By trial and error find a solution giving a profit over $12,000.

20. Can you find a solution giving a profit over $14,000?

© **21–23.** Refer to Example **2** of this section.

21. What is the best profit the students can make if they decide that 5 bracelets must be made?

22. What is the best profit if exactly 30 pairs of earrings are made?

23. What is the best profit if all the metal available is to be used?

24–25. These problems are from *Linear Optimization* by Spivey and Thrall.

24. *Manufacturing.* The Apex Metal Products Corporation produces waste cans, ashtrays, metal bookshelves and lunch boxes. Labor and raw material requirements are given by the following table. What problem can be solved in order to find the production requirements which would maximize the potential income for Apex?

	Waste can	Ashtray	Bookshelf	Lunch box	Total available
Units of metal	5	1	15	5	100
Units of labor	3	2	7	5	125
Selling price	$2	$1	$10	$4	

25. *Nutrition.* A patient on a special diet is allowed to eat only steak and rice. The following table gives nutritional values, costs, and minimum dietary requirements. Find the cheapest diet.

	Rice	Steak	Minimum requirement
Units of carbohydrates	2	1	3
Units of protein	1	4	4
Unit cost	$0.30	$0.70	

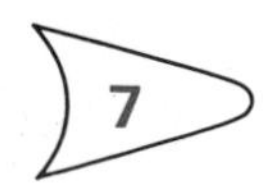

CHAPTER SUMMARY

Two or more individual sentences connected by the word *and* or *or* make up a compound sentence. Sentences with absolute value are often equivalent to compound sentences.

If a is positive,

$|x| < a$ implies $x < a$ and $x > -a$;

$|x| > a$ implies $x > a$ or $x < -a$;

$|x| = a$ implies $x = a$ or $x = -a$.

If the individual sentences are connected by the word *and*, then the solution set to the compound sentence is the *intersection* of the individual solution sets. The word *or* is similarly connected to *union* of sets.

A compound sentence in which the word *and* is used is called a *system.* Most systems in this chapter have two variables, and intersections can be pictured by graphing. Precise solutions usually require use of substitution or the addition and multiplication properties of equations. In solving a system, the idea is to find an equivalent system in which some of the sentences contain fewer variables.

A system can be rewritten as a single sentence by using matrix multiplication. The dimensions of the coefficient matrix that results are the dimensions of the system also.

A system with more variables than equations is likely to have many solutions. A system with more equations than variables is likely to have no solution.

Systems have been used to solve problems since the 1800's. Problems which lead to large systems are called *linear programming* problems. Typical linear programming problems involve minimizing cost or maximizing profit.

CHAPTER REVIEW

7

1–3. On a number line, graph the solution set to each sentence.

1. $x < 4$ or $x > 3$ **2.** $|z| \geq 1$ **3.** $y < 4$ and $y < -2$

4. How many solutions does this system have? $\begin{cases} a = 3d \\ a^2 + d^2 = 1 \end{cases}$

5–6. Find all solutions to each system.

5. $\begin{aligned} -3x + 3y &= 2 \\ -4x - 2y &= 3 \end{aligned}$

6. $\begin{aligned} m &= 4n - 2 \\ 2m &= 6n \end{aligned}$

7–8. Give the coefficient matrix and the dimensions of each system. Also tell how many solutions each system is likely to have.

7. $\begin{aligned} x - y &= 2 \\ 2x + y &= 5 \\ 3x - 4y &= -1 \end{aligned}$

8. $\begin{aligned} x + y + z &= 0 \\ 2x - y + 3z &= 5 \end{aligned}$

9. Solve the system of Exercise **7.**

In a linear programming problem, the feasible region has exactly 4 vertices: (0, 0), (0, 8), (5, 10), and (10, 0). Which vertex would maximize profit if the given expression denotes the profit?

10. $2x + 4y$ **11.** $\frac{1}{2}x + 2y$

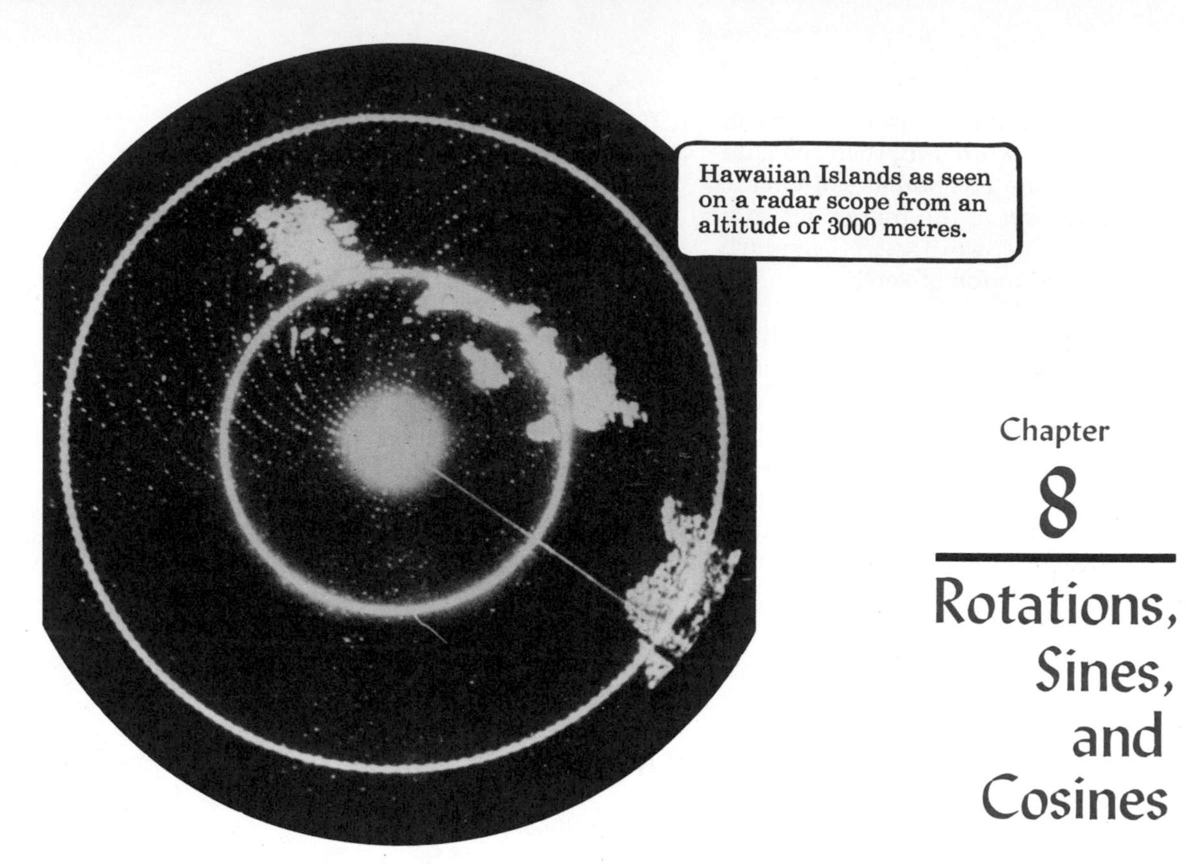

Chapter

8

Rotations, Sines, and Cosines

8.1 ROTATIONS ABOUT THE ORIGIN

Consider the point (1, 0). Under different rotations about the origin, (1, 0) has different images. Yet all these images lie on the *unit circle*. Each such image may be written as $R_t(1, 0)$ for some value of t.

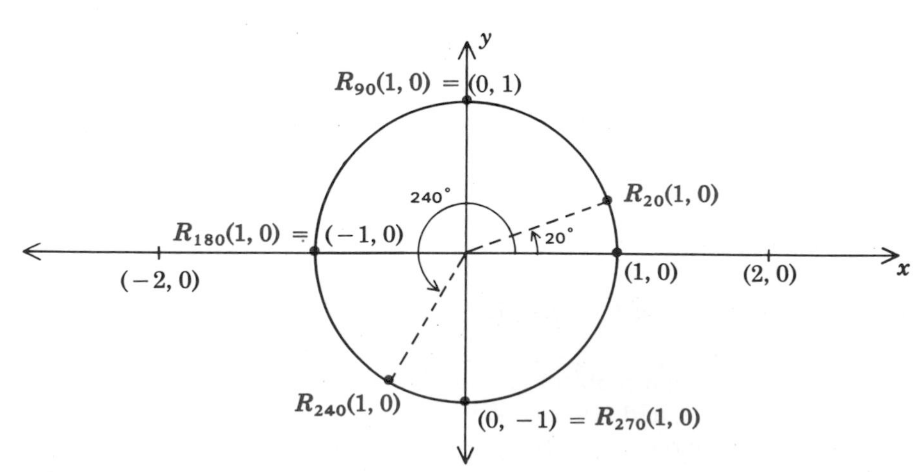

The first and second coordinates of $R_t(1, 0)$ have famous names.

Definition

> Let t be the magnitude of a rotation with center (0, 0). The **cosine of t** (abbreviated **cos t**) and the **sine of t** (abbreviated **sin t**) are the first and second coordinates for the image of (1, 0) under this rotation. That is,
> $$R_t(1, 0) = (\cos t, \sin t).$$

Since you know the coordinates for the image of (1, 0) under rotations with certain magnitudes (such as 90° and −180°), you can already calculate cos t and sin t for certain values of t.

Examples: Calculating cos t and sin t

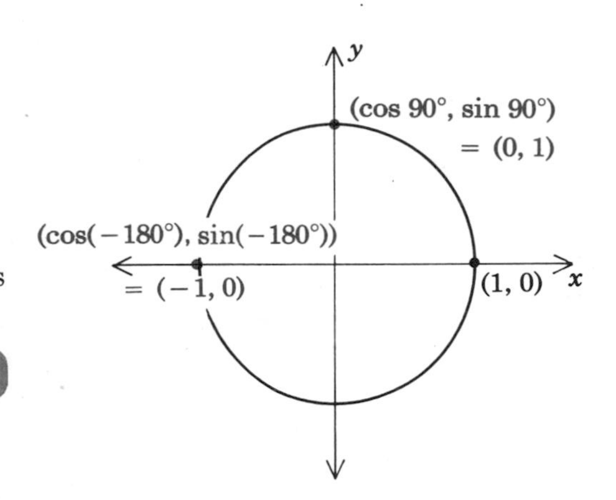

1. Under R_{90}, the image of (1, 0) is (0, 1). Thus,

   $$\cos 90° = 0, \quad \sin 90° = 1.$$

2. Under R_{-180}, the image of (1, 0) is (−1, 0). Hence,

   $$\cos(-180°) = -1, \quad \sin(-180°) = 0.$$

   Note the use of parentheses when the magnitude is negative.

3. To find cos 30° and sin 30°, we rotate (1, 0) 30°.

   Refer to the drawing. Notice that $\cos 30° = OB$ and $\sin 30° = A'B$. These are easy to calculate because $\triangle OA'B$ is a 30-60-90 triangle and $OA' = 1$ (the radius of the circle).

   Recall from geometry that the side opposite the 30° angle in a right triangle is half the hypotenuse. So,

   $$\sin 30° = A'B = \tfrac{1}{2} = 0.500.$$

   By the Pythagorean theorem:

   $$(OB)^2 + (A'B)^2 = 1^2 \quad \Rightarrow \quad (OB)^2 + \tfrac{1}{4} = 1$$
   $$(OB)^2 = \tfrac{3}{4}$$

   So, $$\cos 30° = OB = \sqrt{\tfrac{3}{4}} = \tfrac{\sqrt{3}}{2} \doteq 0.866.$$

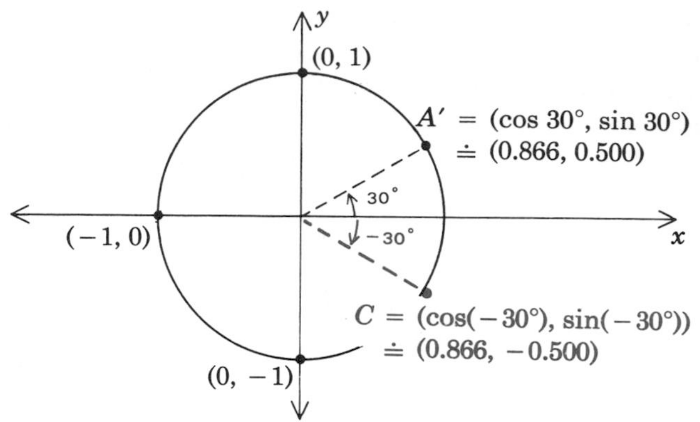

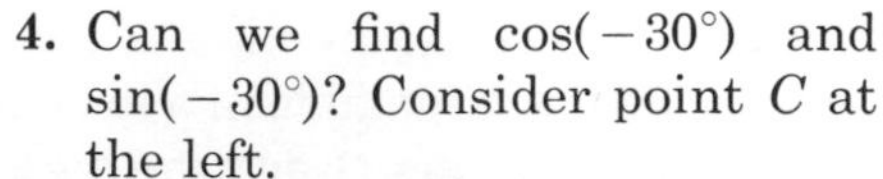

4. Can we find $\cos(-30°)$ and $\sin(-30°)$? Consider point C at the left.

You can see that C is the reflection image of A' over the x-axis. So, from the results of Example **3**,

$$\cos(-30°) \doteq 0.866$$
$$\sin(-30°) = -0.500$$

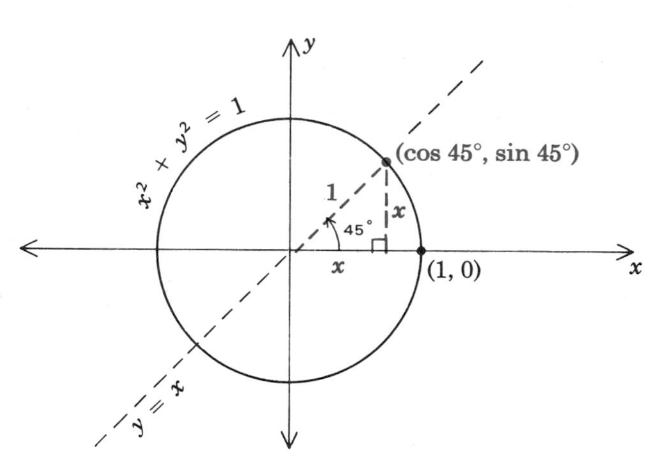

5. When we rotate $(1, 0)$ $45°$, the image is on the line $y = x$ and on the circle $x^2 + y^2 = 1$. To find the coordinates of this point we solve the system

$$\begin{cases} y = x \\ x^2 + y^2 = 1. \end{cases}$$

By substitution,
$$x^2 + x^2 = 1$$
$$2x^2 = 1$$
$$x^2 = \tfrac{1}{2}$$

Since $x > 0$,

$$x = \sqrt{\frac{1}{2}} = \sqrt{\frac{2}{4}} = \frac{\sqrt{2}}{2} \doteq 0.707.$$

Thus,
$$\cos 45° = \frac{\sqrt{2}}{2} \doteq 0.707$$
$$\sin 45° = \frac{\sqrt{2}}{2} \doteq 0.707$$

Notice that images of $(1, 0)$ under rotations with

magnitudes between	are in	quadrant	with	$\cos t$ first coordinate	and	$\sin t$ second coordinate
0° and 90°		I		positive		positive
90° and 180°		II		negative		positive
180° and 270°		III		negative		negative
270° and 360°		IV		positive		negative

EXERCISES 8.1

Ⓐ **1.** If (1, 0) is rotated about the origin, where must its image lie?

2–3. Suppose (1, 0) is rotated magnitude t about the origin.

2. The first coordinate of the image is ____.

3. The second coordinate of the image is ____.

4. A simpler name for the rotation R_{721} is ____.

5. Name the smallest rotation of positive magnitude which is identical to a rotation of magnitude $-30°$.

6. A rotation of 0° is the ____ transformation.

7–16. Which letter most probably stands for each of the following?

7. cos 80° **8.** sin 80°

9. cos 180° **10.** sin 180°

11. cos 280° **12.** sin 280°

13. cos 380° **14.** sin 380°

15. cos(−80°) **16.** sin(−80°)

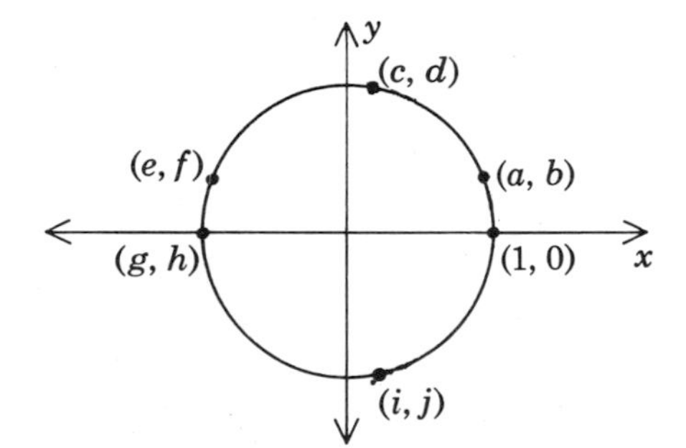

17–22. Find each length. (Refer to the figures below.)

17. AB **18.** BC **19.** DE **20.** EF **21.** GH **22.** HI

Ex. 17–18

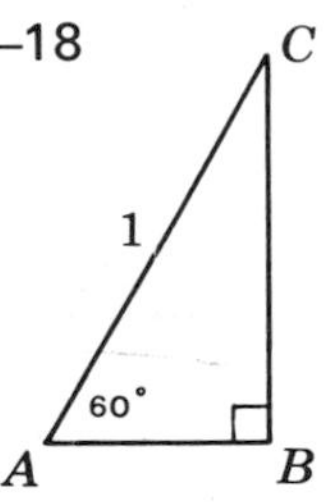

Ex. 19–20

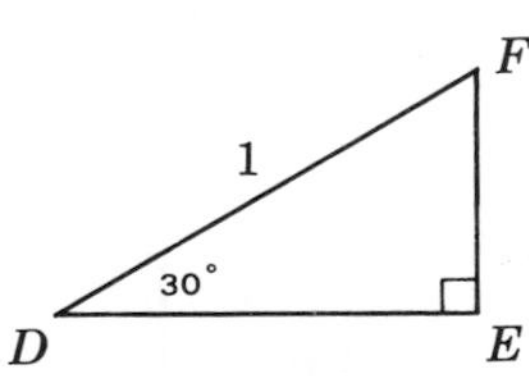

Ex. 21–22

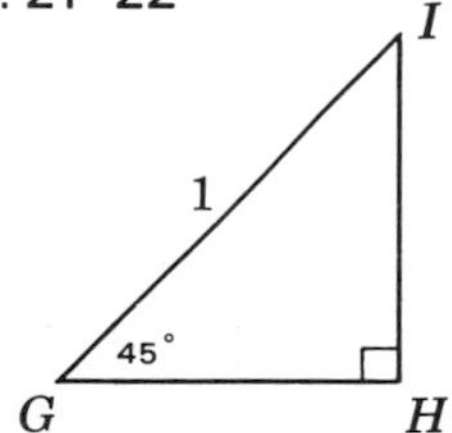

23–26. Find a decimal approximation (to thousandths) for each number.

23. $\sqrt{2}$ **24.** $\frac{\sqrt{2}}{2}$ **25.** $\sqrt{3}$ **26.** $\frac{\sqrt{3}}{2}$

Ⓑ **27.** Let (1, 0) be rotated $-240°$ about the origin. Find the approximate coordinates of the image, to the nearest hundredth.

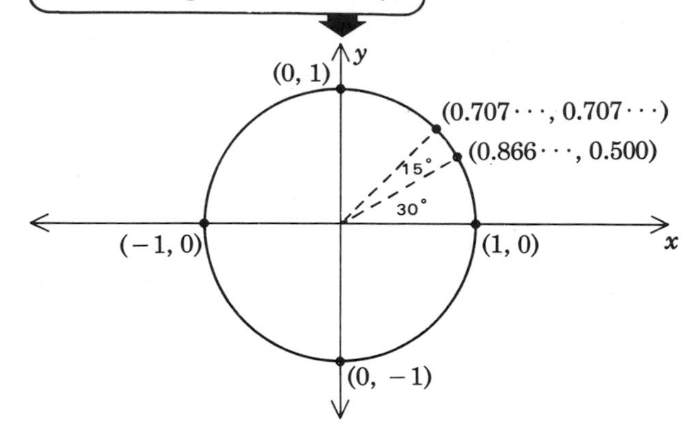

28–43. Express each number as a decimal.

28. $\cos 0°$ **29.** $\sin 0°$

30. $\cos 90°$ **31.** $\sin 90°$

32. $\cos 45°$ **33.** $\sin 45°$

34. $\cos 30°$ **35.** $\sin 30°$

36. $\cos 180°$ **37.** $\sin 180°$

38. $\cos(-90°)$ **39.** $\sin(-90°)$

40. $\cos(-30°)$ **41.** $\sin(-30°)$

42. $\cos 60°$ **43.** $\sin 60°$

44–47. Carefully graph approximate points. Then tell which number in each pair is the greater.

44. $\sin 204°$ or $\sin 207°$ **45.** $\cos 63°$ or $\cos 64°$

46. $\sin 213°$ or $\cos 213°$ **47.** $\cos 94°$ or $\sin 94°$

48. True or False? $\sin 160° = \sin(-160°)$

49. True or False? $\cos 160° = \cos(-160°)$

50–55. For what values of t, between 0° and 360°, will:

50. $\cos t$ be positive? **51.** $\cos t$ be negative?

52. $\sin t$ be positive? **53.** $\sin t$ be zero?

Ⓒ **54.** $\cos t$ be greatest? **55.** $\sin t$ be least?

56. What is the largest possible value of $\cos t$?

57. What is the least possible value of $\sin t$?

A ROTATION ?

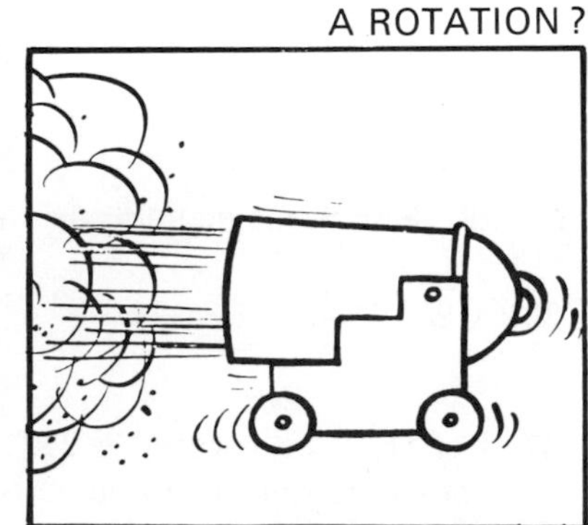

USING TABLES OF SINES AND COSINES

8.2

Here is a portion of a table giving approximations for sines and cosines. A more complete table appears on page 602.

deg	sin	cos	
0°	.000	1.000	90°
1°	.017	1.000	89°
2°	.035	0.999	88°
⋮	⋮	⋮	⋮
18°	.309	.951	72°
⋮	⋮	⋮	⋮
43°	.682	.731	47°
44°	.695	.719	46°
45°	.707	.707	45°
	cos	sin	deg

The table may seem to give values only from 0° to 45°. However, the right column is read *up* and indicates degrees from 45° to 90°.

When reading *up*, the sines and cosines are indicated by labels at the bottom of the table. For example, reading *down*, cos 18° $\doteq$ 0.951. Reading *up*, the same position in the table shows sin 72° $\doteq$ 0.951.

Why are cos 18° and sin 72° equal? A picture will help.

As the picture shows, the arcs $\widehat{AB}$ and $\widehat{A'B}$ are congruent. Thus $r_{x=y}(A) = A'$. But a reflection over the line $x = y$ switches coordinates of points. That is,

$$r_{x=y}(a, b) = (b, a).$$

So, $\cos 18° = \sin 72°$.

And $\sin 18° = \cos 72°$.

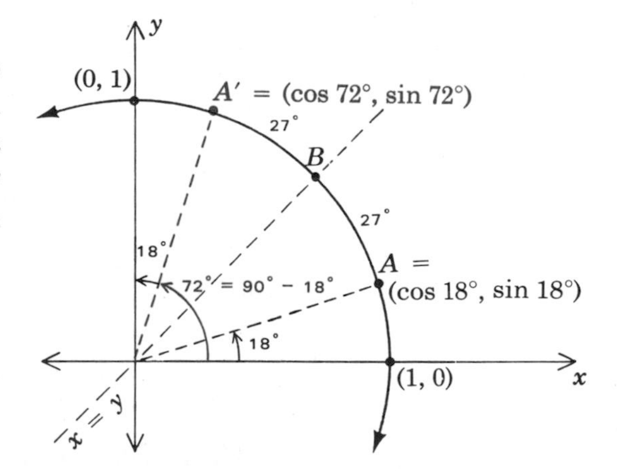

This argument is generalized in the next theorem.

Theorem 8.2.1

For any real number x, $\begin{cases} \textbf{a.}\ \cos x = \sin(90° - x). \\ \textbf{b.}\ \sin x = \cos(90° - x). \end{cases}$

The picture above shows a special case of this theorem for $x = 18°$. The theorem tells us that if two numbers have a sum of 90°, the sine of one number is the cosine of the other. This fact is used to save space when tables (as on page 602) are set up.

There is another surprising relationship between sines and cosines.

Theorem 8.2.2

For any real number x, $(\cos x)^2 + (\sin x)^2 = 1$.

PROOF: An equation for the unit circle is $x^2 + y^2 = 1$. If a point (a, b) is on the circle, then $a^2 + b^2 = 1$. Since $(\cos x, \sin x)$ is always on the circle, the theorem is proved.

Example: Given $\sin x = 0.6$, find $\cos x$.

SOLUTION: For any value of x, $(\cos x)^2 + (\sin x)^2 = 1$

Substituting, $(\cos x)^2 + 0.36 = 1$

$$(\cos x)^2 = 0.64$$

So, $\cos x = +0.8$

or, -0.8

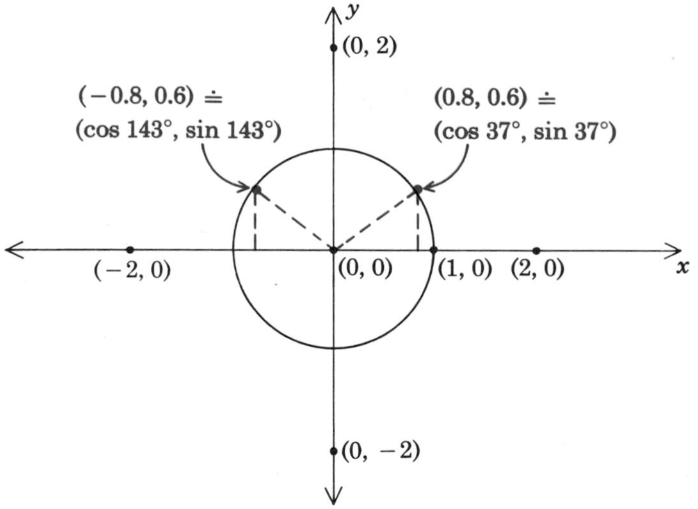

Thus, when $\sin x = 0.6$, there are two possible values of $\cos x$, 0.8 or -0.8. The reason for this can be seen in the picture at the left.

From the table (page 602) we find that x is approximately 37° or 143°.

EXERCISES 8.2

Ⓐ **1–8.** Look in the table (page 602) for approximations to each number.

1. sin 12° **2.** cos 12° **3.** cos 29° **4.** sin 71°

5. cos 70° **6.** sin 20° **7.** cos 45° **8.** sin 88°

9. Why is it possible to set up the table so that we can read *up* for rotations between 45° and 90°?

10–13. Find the expression which best completes each statement.

10. cos 60° = sin ____.

11. sin 8° = cos ____.

12. $\cos(90° - x) =$ ____.

13. $(\cos 15°)^2 + (\sin 15°)^2 =$ ____.

Ⓑ **14.** If $\cos x = 0.28$, find all possible values of $\sin x$. Then graph the appropriate points.

15. If $\sin x = -\frac{5}{13}$, find all possible values of $\cos x$. Then graph the appropriate points.

16. From the table, verify Theorem 8.2.2 for $\cos 57°$ and $\sin 57°$.

17–20. Find x to the nearest degree if $0° < x < 90°$. Use the table.

17. $\sin x = 0.400$

18. $\cos x = 0.2$

19. $\sin x = \frac{2}{3}$

20. $\cos x = \frac{20}{23}$

21. The table lists 0.999 for $\cos 2°$ and $\cos 3°$. Does this mean $\cos 2° = \cos 3°$? Explain your answer.

22–29. Give *exact values* for each number. (These should be memorized.)

22. $\cos 45°$ **23.** $\sin 45°$ **24.** $\sin 0°$ **25.** $\cos 0°$

26. $\cos 30°$ **27.** $\sin 60°$ **28.** $\sin 30°$ **29.** $\cos 60°$

OBTAINING VALUES OF SINES AND COSINES

8.3

For rotations of 30° and 45°, and multiples of these, we can usually find the coordinates for the image of (1, 0) without looking in tables. For other magnitudes, tables are usually used. But tables seldom list sines and cosines of magnitudes less than 0 or greater than 90. Reflections and rotations enable us to obtain other values.

Example 1: (A negative magnitude) Suppose you need to find $\cos(-20°)$ and $\sin(-20°)$.

SOLUTION: A picture helps. Reflect $(\cos 20°, \sin 20°)$ over the x-axis to get the desired point.

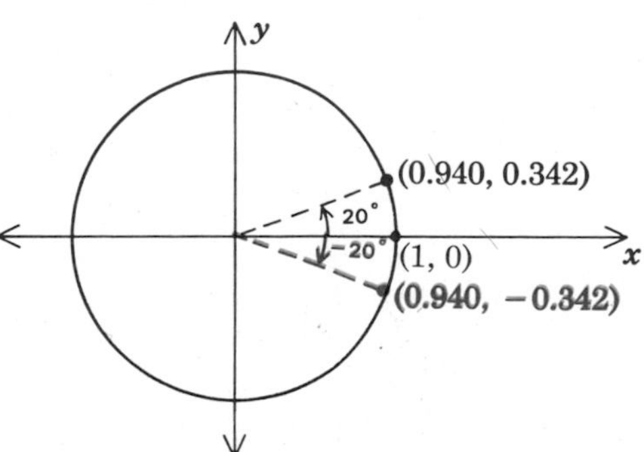

From the table, $\cos 20° \doteq 0.940$, and $\sin 20° \doteq 0.342$. When reflected over the x-axis, the image of point (0.940, 0.342) is (0.940, −0.342). Thus, $\cos(-20°) \doteq 0.940$, $\sin(-20°) \doteq -0.342$.

Since the image of (1, 0) under R_{-20} is in the fourth quadrant, you should expect the first coordinate, $\cos(-20°)$, to be positive, and the second coordinate, $\sin(-20°)$, to be negative. It checks.

Example 2: (Images in the second quadrant) Suppose we want decimal approximations to cos 500° and sin 500°.

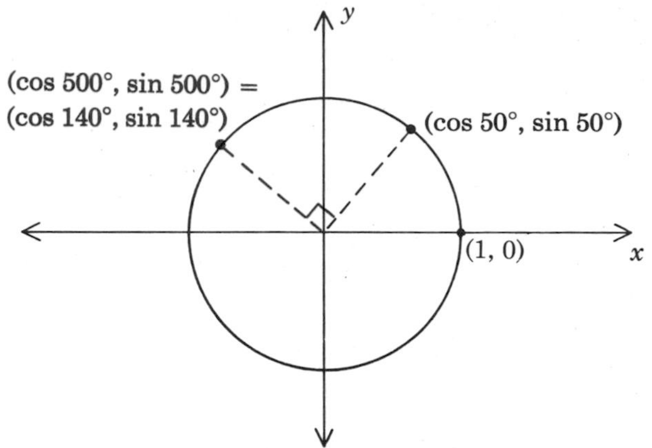

SOLUTION: Again, a drawing is helpful. The desired numbers are the coordinates of the image of (1, 0) under R_{500}. Notice that the image under R_{500} is identical to the image under R_{140}.

Also, (cos 140°, sin 140°) is the image of (cos 50°, sin 50°) under a rotation of 90°. We can find cos 50° and sin 50° in the table, and there is a matrix for a rotation of 90°. The work is summarized as follows.

From the table

$$\begin{bmatrix}\cos 500^\circ\\ \sin 500^\circ\end{bmatrix} = \begin{bmatrix}\cos 140^\circ\\ \sin 140^\circ\end{bmatrix} = \begin{bmatrix}0 & -1\\ 1 & 0\end{bmatrix}\cdot\begin{bmatrix}\cos 50^\circ\\ \sin 50^\circ\end{bmatrix} \doteq \begin{bmatrix}0 & -1\\ 1 & 0\end{bmatrix}\cdot\begin{bmatrix}0.643\\ 0.766\end{bmatrix}$$

Matrix for R_{90}

$$= \begin{bmatrix}-0.766\\ 0.643\end{bmatrix}$$

So, cos 500° $\doteq$ −0.766, sin 500° $\doteq$ 0.643. (The signs check. In the second quadrant, the cosine should be negative, the sine positive.)

Example 3: (Images in the third quadrant) Find values of cos 225° and sin 225°.

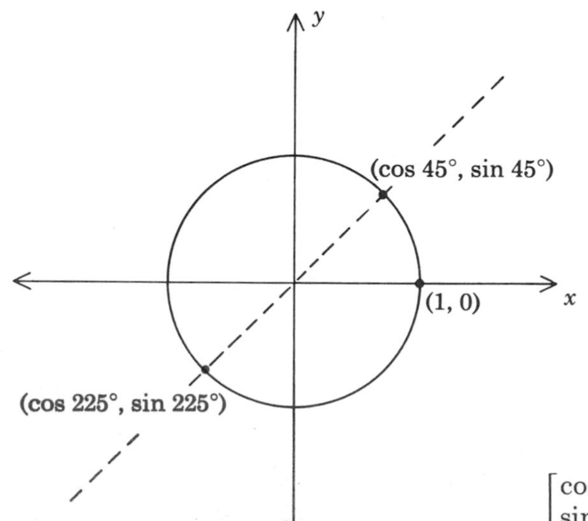

SOLUTION: If the point (cos 45°, sin 45°) is rotated 180°, the image is the point (cos 225°, sin 225°). Thus, in this case we can find exact values, since we know

$$\cos 45^\circ = \frac{\sqrt{2}}{2}$$

$$\sin 45^\circ = \frac{\sqrt{2}}{2}$$

and we know the matrix for a rotation of 180° (a half-turn).

Matrix for R_{180}

$$\begin{bmatrix}\cos 225^\circ\\ \sin 225^\circ\end{bmatrix} = \begin{bmatrix}-1 & 0\\ 0 & -1\end{bmatrix}\cdot\begin{bmatrix}\frac{\sqrt{2}}{2}\\ \frac{\sqrt{2}}{2}\end{bmatrix} = \begin{bmatrix}-\frac{\sqrt{2}}{2}\\ -\frac{\sqrt{2}}{2}\end{bmatrix}$$

In a similar way, you could use the matrix for R_{270} to evaluate sine and cosine in the fourth quadrant. Here are the matrices for rotations of 90°, 180°, and 270°.

$$R_{90}: \begin{bmatrix} 0 & -1 \\ 1 & 0 \end{bmatrix} \qquad R_{180}: \begin{bmatrix} -1 & 0 \\ 0 & -1 \end{bmatrix} \qquad R_{270}: \begin{bmatrix} 0 & 1 \\ -1 & 0 \end{bmatrix}$$

In the next section we develop a formula which gives the matrix corresponding to *any* rotation about the origin.

EXERCISES 8.3

Ⓐ **1.** What is the image of (1, 0) under a rotation of magnitude t about the origin?

2. To obtain the image of (1, 0) under R_{140}, you could find the image of (1, 0) under R_{50}, then rotate this image ____.

3. To obtain the image of (1, 0) under R_{300}, you could find the image of (1, 0) under R_{30}, then rotate this image ____.

4. To obtain the image of (1, 0) under R_{300}, you could find the image of (1, 0) under R_{60}, then reflect over ____.

Ⓑ **5–24.** Find each value correct to three decimal places. You may use the table on page 602.

5. sin 70°	**6.** cos 70°	**7.** sin 160°	**8.** cos 160°
9. sin 20°	**10.** cos 20°	**11.** sin(−20°)	**12.** cos(−20°)
13. sin 200°	**14.** cos 200°	**15.** cos 250°	**16.** sin 250°
17. cos 171°	**18.** sin 171°	**19.** cos 232°	**20.** sin 232°
21. cos 304°	**22.** sin 304°	**23.** cos(−107°)	**24.** sin(−107°)

Ⓒ **25–27.** Name a transformation which maps:

25. $(\cos t, \sin t)$ onto $(\cos(-t), \sin(-t))$.

26. $(\cos t, \sin t)$ onto $(\cos(t + 90), \sin(t + 90))$.

27. $(\cos t, \sin t)$ onto $(\cos(t + 180), \sin(t + 180))$.

28. Prove: $(\cos(-t), \sin(-t)) = (\cos t, -\sin t)$. Use matrices and refer to Exercise **25**. (HINT: Each point will be the image of $(\cos t, \sin t)$ under the same transformation.)

29. Prove: $(\cos(t + 90), \sin(t + 90)) = (-\sin t, \cos t)$. Use matrices and refer to Exercise **26**.

30–35. Find at least one value of t which satisfies each equation.

30. $\cos t = 1$ **31.** $\sin t = 1$ **32.** $\cos t = -1$

33. $\sin t = -\frac{\sqrt{2}}{2}$ **34.** $\sin t = \frac{1}{2}$ **35.** $\cos t = -\frac{\sqrt{3}}{2}$

THE ROTATION MATRIX

Using sines and cosines, a formula can be derived for the matrix of any rotation R_t about (0, 0).

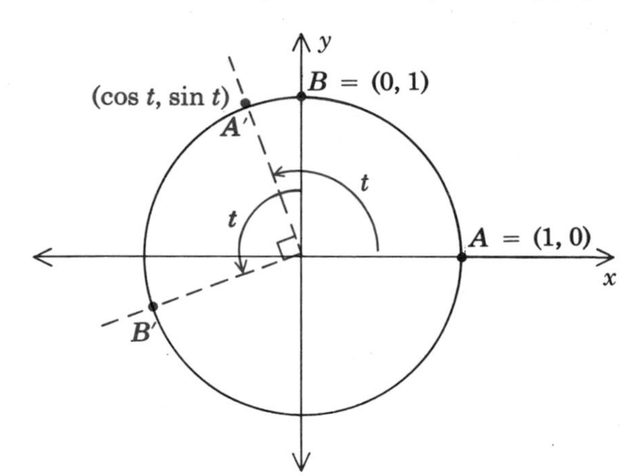

We know that under the transformation R_t, the image of (1, 0) is $(\cos t, \sin t)$—by the definition of $\sin t$ and $\cos t$.

Now, B is 90° clockwise from A. So, if we rotate A' 90°, we obtain B', the image of $\begin{bmatrix} 0 \\ 1 \end{bmatrix}$ under the original rotation of t degrees. We can calculate the coordinates of B' because we already know the matrix for a rotation of 90°.

$$B' = \text{image of} \underset{B}{\begin{bmatrix} 0 \\ 1 \end{bmatrix}} = \underset{R_{90}}{\begin{bmatrix} 0 & -1 \\ 1 & 0 \end{bmatrix}} \cdot \underset{A'}{\begin{bmatrix} \cos t \\ \sin t \end{bmatrix}} = \underset{B'}{\begin{bmatrix} -\sin t \\ \cos t \end{bmatrix}}$$

Hence, $R_t(0, 1) = (-\sin t, \cos t)$.

Since we have the images of (1, 0) and (0, 1), and assuming that there is a matrix for R_t, we can apply Theorem 5.7.3 (the matrix basis theorem) to get the matrix for R_t.

Theorem 8.4.1

Rotation matrix theorem: For any real number t, a matrix for R_t is

$$\begin{bmatrix} \cos t & -\sin t \\ \sin t & \cos t \end{bmatrix}$$

If you check back, you will find that the matrices given earlier for R_{30}, R_{90}, R_{180}, and R_{270} are all special cases of this theorem.

Example: matrix for $R_{30} = \begin{bmatrix} \cos 30^\circ & -\sin 30^\circ \\ \sin 30^\circ & \cos 30^\circ \end{bmatrix} = \begin{bmatrix} \frac{\sqrt{3}}{2} & -\frac{1}{2} \\ \frac{1}{2} & \frac{\sqrt{3}}{2} \end{bmatrix}$

(Remember that we are presently considering only rotations about the origin. Other rotations do not have 2 × 2 matrices.)

The rotation of 0° leaves each point fixed and the image of (1, 0) is (1, 0). So cos 0° = 1 and sin 0° = 0. Substituting these values into the rotation matrix, we get

$$\begin{bmatrix} \cos 0^\circ & -\sin 0^\circ \\ \sin 0^\circ & \cos 0^\circ \end{bmatrix} = \begin{bmatrix} 1 & 0 \\ 0 & 1 \end{bmatrix},$$

the *identity matrix*, which is as expected since the transformation is the identity transformation.

Example: Approximate the image of $\begin{bmatrix} 0 & -2 & 1 \\ 0 & 4 & 5 \end{bmatrix}$ under R_{82}.

SOLUTION: From Theorem 8.4.1, the matrix for R_{82} is

$$\begin{bmatrix} \cos 82^\circ & -\sin 82^\circ \\ \sin 82^\circ & \cos 82^\circ \end{bmatrix}$$

which is approximately

$$\begin{bmatrix} 0.139 & -0.990 \\ 0.990 & 0.139 \end{bmatrix}.$$

$C = (1, 5)$
$B = (-2, 4)$
$C' \doteq (-4.811, 1.685)$
$B' \doteq (-4.238, -1.424)$

By multiplying, we get the image triangle.

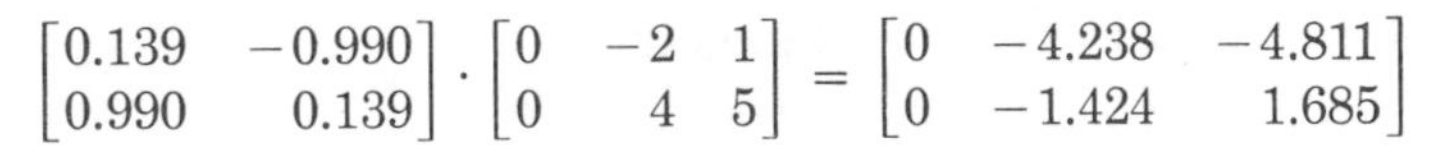

$$\begin{bmatrix} 0.139 & -0.990 \\ 0.990 & 0.139 \end{bmatrix} \cdot \begin{bmatrix} 0 & -2 & 1 \\ 0 & 4 & 5 \end{bmatrix} = \begin{bmatrix} 0 & -4.238 & -4.811 \\ 0 & -1.424 & 1.685 \end{bmatrix}$$

The preimage and the image are shown above.

EXERCISES 8.4

Ⓐ 1. Which rotations can be represented by 2 × 2 matrices?

2. What is the matrix for R_t, the rotation of magnitude t about the origin?

3. Given $\sin 35^\circ \doteq 0.574$, $\cos 35^\circ \doteq 0.819$, what is an approximate matrix for R_{35}?

4. What is the matrix for R_0?

5. What is the matrix for R_{90}?

6. What is the matrix for R_{180}?

7. What is the matrix for R_{-90}?

8. Given $\sin(-10°) \doteq -0.174$ and $\cos(-10°) \doteq 0.985$, what is an approximate matrix for R_{-10}?

Ⓑ 9. Find the image of $\begin{bmatrix} 2 & 4 & 0 \\ 3 & -1 & 6 \end{bmatrix}$ under R_{17}. Graph preimage and image.

10. Find the image of $(5, -10)$ under R_{503}. Graph preimage and image.

11. Rotate (1000, 1000) 100° *clockwise* about the origin. Check your answer by showing that preimage and image are the same distance from the origin.

12–14. Use the table on page 602. Find the matrix for each rotation, with elements correct to three decimal places.

12. R_{33}

13. R_{451}

14. R_{-210}

Ⓒ 15. A regular pentagon is inscribed in the unit circle. If one vertex of this pentagon is (1, 0), determine (correct to thousandths) the coordinates of the other vertices of this pentagon.

16–17. A rotation of magnitude x about any point (a, b) equals $T' \circ R_x \circ T$, where T is the translation mapping (a, b) to the origin, R_x is the rotation of magnitude x about the origin, and T' is the translation mapping the origin back to (a, b).

16. Rotate (7, 3) 212° about point (1, 2). Graph the preimage and the image. Then calculate appropriate distances to check your answer.

17. Find a *formula* for the image of (x, y) under a rotation of 90° about (a, b). (HINT: Let (x', y') be the image.)

A ROTATION ?

FORMULAS FOR COS($x + y$) AND SIN($x + y$)

8.5

The symbol at the right stands for the cosine of a number, the number $x + y$.

$\cos(x + y)$ — The parentheses are only for grouping purposes—no multiplication is intended.

It is *almost never true* that $\cos(x + y)$ is equal to $\cos x + \cos y$.

For example, let $x = 30°$ and $y = 45°$ **then** $\cos(30° + 45°) = \cos 75°$.

But $\begin{cases} \cos 30° \doteq 0.866 \\ \cos 45° \doteq 0.707 \\ \cos 75° \doteq 0.259 \end{cases}$ **and so** $\cos 30° + \cos 45° > \cos 75°$.

Notice the difference.

We now derive a formula for computing $\cos(x + y)$ when the sines and cosines of x and y are known. At the same time, with no additional work, a formula for $\sin(x + y)$ will be found. The next theorem is very important and should be memorized.

Theorem 8.5.1

For any real numbers x and y,

a. $\cos(x + y) = \cos x \cdot \cos y - \sin x \cdot \sin y$.

b. $\sin(x + y) = \sin x \cdot \cos y + \cos x \cdot \sin y$.

PROOF:

1. By definition of sine and cosine $(\cos(x + y), \sin(x + y))$ is the image of $(1, 0)$ under R_{x+y}.

Remember that R_{x+y} is a rotation of magnitude $x + y$ and is the composite of rotations of magnitudes x and y. That is, $R_{x+y} = R_x \circ R_y$.

2. That is, $(\cos(x + y), \sin(x + y)) = R_{x+y}(1, 0)$
3. By Theorem 4.5.1 $= R_x \circ R_y(1, 0)$
4. Using the definition of sine and cosine again $= R_x(\cos y, \sin y)$
5. Now we switch to matrix form, using the matrix for R_x.

$$\begin{bmatrix} \cos(x + y) \\ \sin(x + y) \end{bmatrix} = \begin{bmatrix} \cos x & -\sin x \\ \sin x & \cos x \end{bmatrix} \cdot \begin{bmatrix} \cos y \\ \sin y \end{bmatrix}$$

6. Multiplying,

$$\begin{bmatrix} \cos(x + y) \\ \sin(x + y) \end{bmatrix} = \begin{bmatrix} \cos x \cdot \cos y - \sin x \cdot \sin y \\ \sin x \cdot \cos y + \cos x \cdot \sin y \end{bmatrix}$$

The matrices on the left and right are equal—so *the theorem is proved.*

Example: Letting $x = 30°$, $y = 45°$, we can now find an *exact* value for $\cos 75°$.

$$\cos 75° = \cos(30° + 45°) = (\cos 30°)(\cos 45°) - (\sin 30°)(\sin 45°)$$

$$= \frac{\sqrt{3}}{2} \cdot \frac{\sqrt{2}}{2} - \frac{1}{2} \cdot \frac{\sqrt{2}}{2}$$

$$= \frac{\sqrt{6}}{4} - \frac{\sqrt{2}}{4} \quad \longleftarrow \text{Exact value}$$

Approximating the square roots yields the value found in tables. →

$$\doteq \frac{2.449 - 1.414}{4}$$

$$= \frac{1.035}{4} \doteq 0.259 \longleftarrow \text{Approximate value}$$

Notice that we have also found $\sin 15°$, since $\sin 15° = \cos 75°$.

EXERCISES 8.5

Ⓐ **1–2.** True or False?

1. $\cos(x + y) = \cos x + \cos y$

2. $\sin(x + y) = \sin x + \sin y$

3–4. Give a decimal answer without using tables.

3. $\sin(30° + 60°)$

4. $\cos(120° + 240°)$

5. $\cos(x + y)$ is the ____ coordinate of the image of $(1, 0)$ under a rotation of magnitude ____.

6. $\sin(x + y)$ is the ____ coordinate of the image of $(1, 0)$ under a rotation of magnitude ____.

7. $(\cos(x + y), \sin(x + y))$ is the image of $(\cos x, \sin x)$ under a rotation of magnitude ____.

8–9. According to the theorem in this section:

8. $\sin(x + y) =$ ____.

9. $\cos(x + y) =$ ____.

Ⓑ **10–17.** For these exercises you are expected to calculate sines and cosines of multiples of 30° or 45° (for example, 150°, 135°, and so forth) without using tables. Then use these values and Theorem 8.5.1 to *give an exact value* for each expression.

10. $\cos 75°$ **11.** $\sin 75°$ **12.** $\cos 105°$ **13.** $\sin 105°$

14. $\cos 15°$ **15.** $\cos(-15°)$ **16.** $\cos 195°$ **17.** $\sin(-165°)$

18. Give an exact matrix for R_{165}.

19–20. True or False?

19. $\cos 60° = (\cos 30°)^2 - (\sin 30°)^2$ **20.** $\sin 60° = \sin 30° + \sin 30°$

© **21–22.** Let $x = y$ in the formulas of Theorem 8.5.1. Then prove:

21. $\cos 2x = (\cos x)^2 - (\sin x)^2$. **22.** $\sin 2x = 2 \sin x \cdot \cos x$.

23. Verify the formulas of Exercises **21** and **22** for $x = 45°$.

24. Use tables to verify the formula of Exercise **21** for $x = 20°$.

25. Use tables to verify the formula of Exercise **22** for $x = 53°$.

26. An alternate proof of Theorem 8.5.1 uses the matrix-transformation isomorphism theorem and the relationship $R_{x+y} = R_x \circ R_y$. Using these hints, write the alternate proof.

27–30. Use Theorem 8.5.1 to prove each statement. Interpret the results geometrically.

27. $\cos(x + 360°) = \cos x$ **28.** $\sin(180° + x) = -\sin x$

29. $\cos(x + 90°) = -\sin x$ **30.** $\sin(45° + x) = \frac{\sqrt{2}}{2}(\sin x + \cos x)$

POLAR COORDINATES 8.6

Suppose that you are in a lighthouse and wish to locate a ship at sea, or you are at a weather station and want to tell where a storm is. You would probably be interested in the *distance* and *direction* of the ship (or storm) from you.

The grid at the right might be helpful. The lighthouse (or weather station) is located at the center.

A ship at point A would be 2 miles away NNE (read "north-northeast" or "north by north-east"). A tornado at point B might be 3 miles away in the SW direction.

Abbreviating, we could say A is "2, NNE" and B is "3, SW."

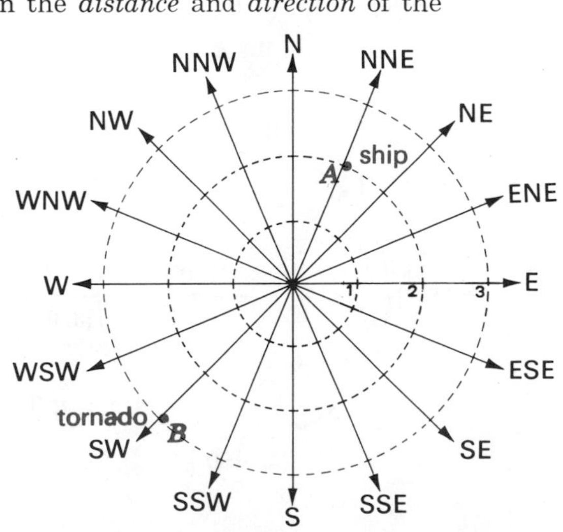

A similar system is used in mathematics. The horizontal ray to the right is used as a base direction, and the point (1, 0) is used as a base point.

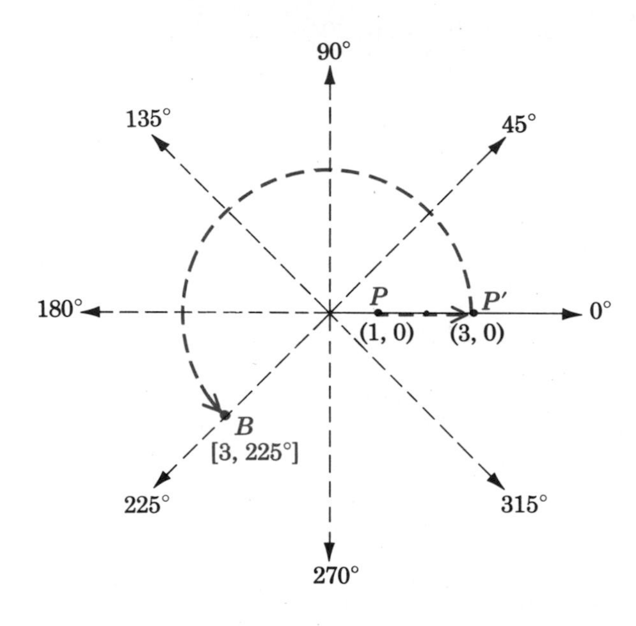

To get the *polar coordinates* of B, we apply a size transformation of magnitude 3 to (1, 0) so that the image P' is the same distance from the origin as B.

Then we rotate P' until its image is B. This rotation has magnitude 225° in the drawing. The two magnitudes give the polar coordinates of B.

We write $B = [3, 225°]$, using brackets [ ] to distinguish these polar coordinates from rectangular coordinates (the degree sign also helps you tell the difference).

Definition

The **polar coordinates** $[r, \theta]$ of a point B are the magnitudes r and θ of the size transformation and rotation, each with (0, 0) as center, whose composite maps (1, 0) onto B.

All points with *first polar coordinate* 3 lie on the circle with center (0, 0), radius 3.

All points with *second polar coordinate* 40° lie on a line.

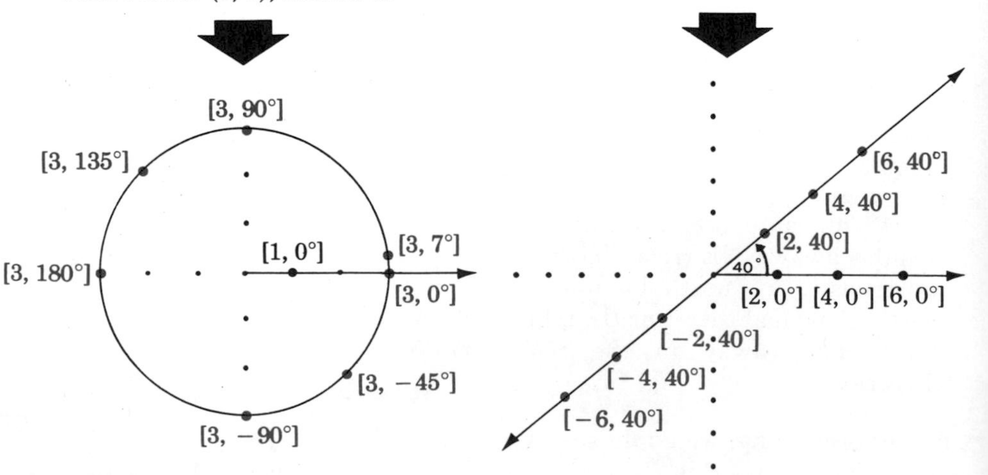

Polar-coordinate graph paper is often used for graphing in polar coordinates.

The point [0, 0°] is at the center.

Some other points and their polar coordinates are shown at the right.

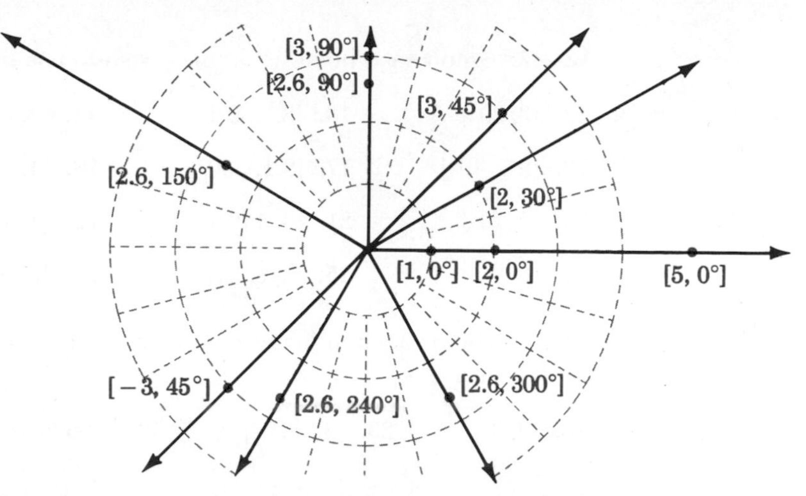

The polar coordinates of the origin cannot be determined from the definition on page 220 because there is no rotation and size transformation with center (0, 0) which can map (1, 0) onto the origin.

But, since the distance from the origin to itself is 0, any pair $[r, \theta]$ with $r = 0$ represents the origin.

Thus, the origin has many pairs of polar coordinates, for example, [0, 90°] and [0, −27.5°]. This is also true of every other point of the plane—each has many different representations in polar coordinates.

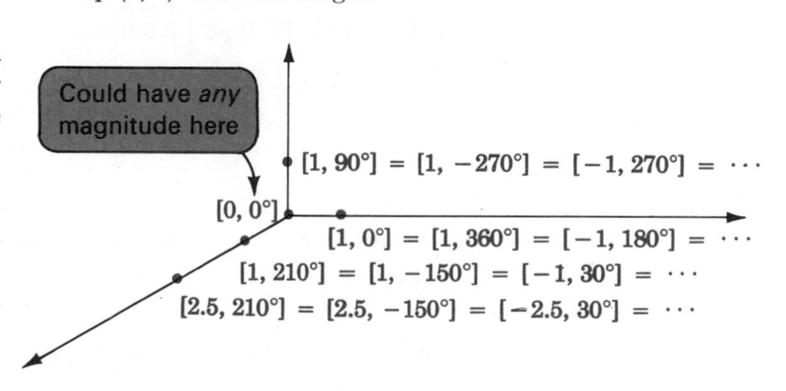

EXERCISES 8.6

Ⓐ **1.** What are the polar coordinates of a point?

2–11. Estimate polar coordinates for each point shown. Use a ruler or protractor if needed.

2. *A*	**3.** *B*
4. *C*	**5.** *D*
6. *E*	**7.** *F*
8. *G*	**9.** *H*
10. *J*	**11.** *K*

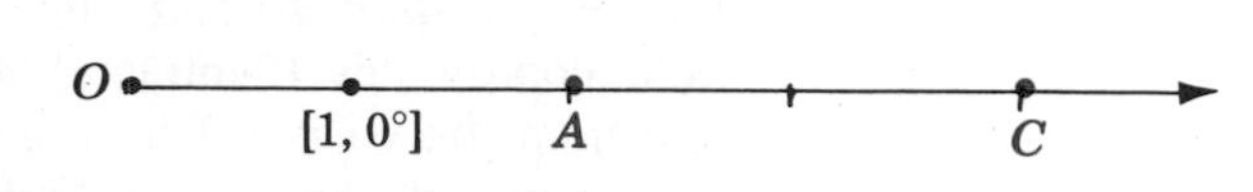

12–27. Graph each point. (You may wish to use polar graph paper.)

12. $[3, 90°]$ **13.** $[3, 180°]$ **14.** $[2, 0°]$ **15.** $[\frac{1}{2}, 270°]$

16. $[2.5, 40°]$ **17.** $[2.1, 300°]$ **18.** $[4, 111°]$ **19.** $[0.1, 12°]$

20. $[0, 70°]$ **21.** $[0, 140°]$ **22.** $[1, 140°]$ **23.** $[-1, 140°]$

24. $[6, -10°]$ **25.** $[-6, 170°]$ **26.** $[6, 530°]$ **27.** $[6, 350°]$

28–31. The polar coordinates of a point are given. Give the exact rectangular coordinates.

28. $[2, 0°]$ **29.** $[4.1, 90°]$ **30.** $[106.3, 180°]$ **31.** $[0.001, 270°]$

32. Another pair of polar coordinates for $[6, 100°]$ is ____.

33. Another pair of polar coordinates for $[-1, 1000°]$ is ____.

34. How far is $[-10, 3°]$ from the origin?

Ⓑ **35.** If a point has first polar coordinate 5, where must this point lie?

36. Suppose a point has the polar coordinates $[-\frac{1}{3}, \theta]$. Where must this point lie?

37. Suppose the second polar coordinate of a point is 100°. Where must this point lie?

38–40. Give five different polar coordinates for each point.

38. $[6, 0°]$ **39.** $[2, 17°]$ **40.** $[-11, 40°]$

41–44. *Meteorology.* The direction north stands for 90° (as pictured on page 219). Give the second polar coordinate corresponding to each direction. (Assume a positive first coordinate.)

41. S **42.** NW **43.** SSE **44.** WSW

Ⓒ **45.** In your own opinion why might the name *polar coordinates* have been chosen?

46–49. *Aviation.* Airport runways are often numbered in a way related to polar coordinates. If you land from the north, you will see a 0 on the runway, and from the west a 9 on the runway. Each additional unit corresponds to 10° counterclockwise, the highest possible being 35. From what direction do you land on a runway with the given number?

46. 18 **47.** 1 **48.** 22 **49.** 8

DIFFERENT NAMES FOR THE SAME POINT

Polar coordinates give a second way of describing points in the plane. The point (1, 1) may now be described as $[\sqrt{2}, 45°]$. So we can write $(1, 1) = [\sqrt{2}, 45°]$. Also, $(1, 1) = [\sqrt{2}, -315°]$.

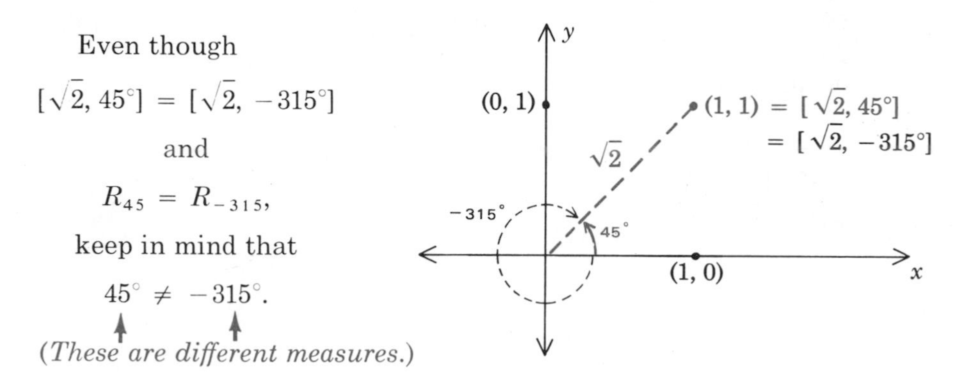

Even though

$[\sqrt{2}, 45°] = [\sqrt{2}, -315°]$

and

$R_{45} = R_{-315}$,

keep in mind that

$45° \neq -315°$.

(These are different measures.)

So we have two languages for points—polar coordinates and rectangular coordinates. We can translate from polar to rectangular as follows.

Theorem 8.7.1

Polar coordinates ➡ $[r, \theta] = (r \cos \theta, r \sin \theta)$ ⬅ Rectangular coordinates

PROOF: The polar coordinates $[r, \theta]$ are obtained by rotating (1, 0) and applying a size transformation.

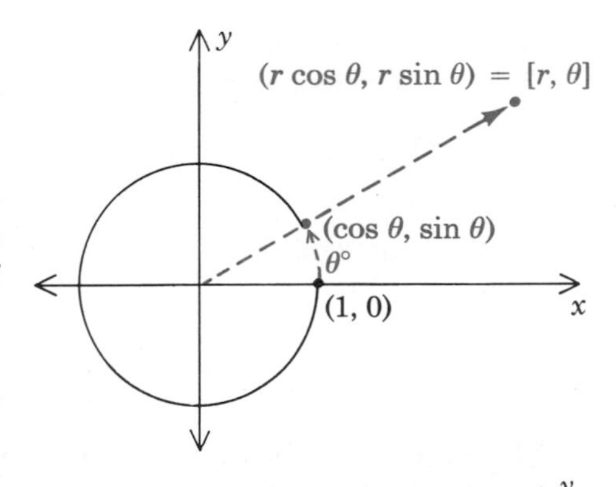

In rectangular coordinates, rotating (1, 0) through $\theta°$ results in the image $(\cos \theta, \sin \theta)$. The image of $(\cos \theta, \sin \theta)$ under a size transformation having magnitude r is the point $(r \cos \theta, r \sin \theta)$. Thus the theorem is proved.

Example 1: Find the rectangular coordinates for $[6, 240°]$.

SOLUTION: By the theorem,

$$[6, 240°] = (6 \cos 240°, 6 \sin 240°).$$

$$= \left(6\left(-\frac{1}{2}\right), 6\left(-\frac{\sqrt{3}}{2}\right)\right)$$

$$= (-3, -3\sqrt{3}) \longleftarrow \text{Exact}$$

$$\doteq (-3, -5.2) \longleftarrow \text{Approximate}$$

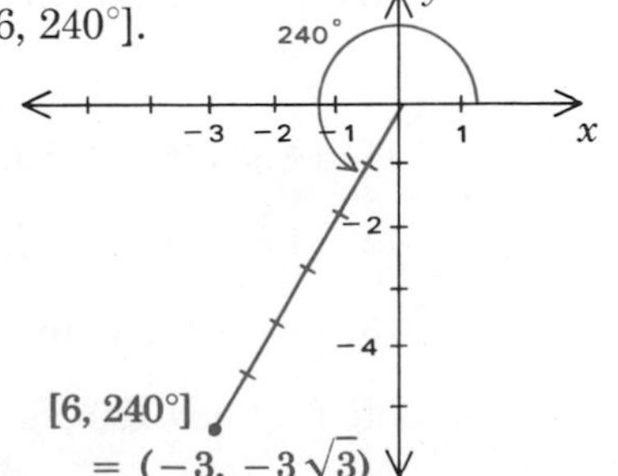

It is possible to translate the other way, from rectangular to polar, but the general formula is difficult and not needed, so we skip it. But, in special cases, where you *know* the amount of rotation, you should be able to convert.

Example 2: Find polar coordinates for (5, −5).

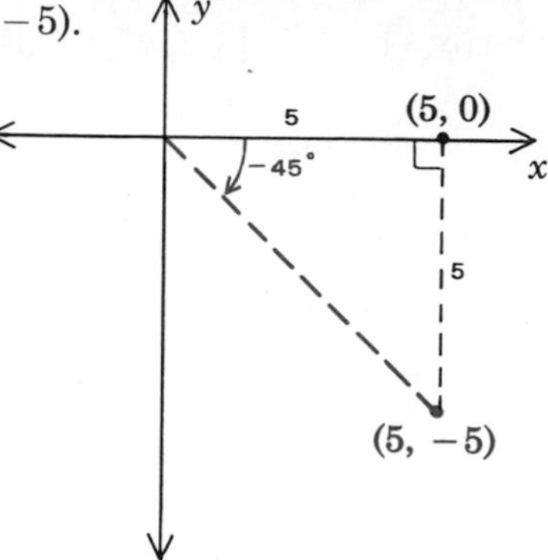

SOLUTION: Drawing a triangle, you can see that the magnitude of rotation is −45°.

By the distance formula, the distance from the origin to (5, −5) is $\sqrt{(5-0)^2 + (5-0)^2} = \sqrt{50} = 5\sqrt{2}$.

So $(5, -5) = [5\sqrt{2}, -45°]$.

EXERCISES 8.7

Ⓐ **1.** When (1, 0) is rotated a magnitude θ about the origin, its image is ____.

2. When the answer to Exercise **1** is size transformed a magnitude r with center (0, 0), its image is ____.

3–6. Translate from polar to rectangular coordinates. Calculation or approximation of sines and cosines is not necessary.

3. $[r, \theta]$ **4.** [10, 39°] **5.** [−2, 45°] **6.** [190, 2°]

Ⓑ **7–10.** Approximate the rectangular coordinates of each point to the nearest tenth as in Example **1**. Graph each point to check your answer.

7. [3, 48°] **8.** [−2, 112°] **9.** [100, 290°] **10.** [1, 199°]

11–14. Each point named in column **I** is identical to a point named in column **II**. Match them. (An item may be used more than once.)

I	II
11. (4 cos 90°, 4 sin 90°)	**a.** (0, 4)
12. (4 cos 180°, 4 sin 180°)	**b.** (4, 0)
13. (4 cos 0°, 4 sin 0°)	**c.** (−4, 0)
14. (−4 cos 180°, −4 sin 180°)	**d.** (0, −4)
	e. (4, 4)

15–20. Without using tables, graph each point.

15. $(\cos 100°, \sin 100°)$

16. $(\cos(-20°), \sin(-20°))$

17. $(3 \cos 12°, 3 \sin 12°)$

18. $(\frac{1}{2} \cos 200°, \frac{1}{2} \sin 200°)$

19. $(-\cos 142°, -\sin 142°)$

20. $(-2 \cos 700°, -2 \sin 700°)$

21–26. Without using tables, translate into polar coordinates. (Graphing may help.)

21. $(-5, 0)$

22. $(-12, -12)$

23. $(0, 1)$

24. $(6, 6)$

Ⓒ **25.** $(1, \sqrt{3})$

26. $(-2, 2\sqrt{3})$

27. A ship in distress is in a position 2 kilometres SE of a lighthouse. A Coast Guard cutter is 10 kilometres NNE of the lighthouse. If the cutter travels 55 kilometres per hour, in how many minutes could it reach the ship in distress?

28. From a point A, a tornado is sighted in the direction SSW. At the same time, from a point B, 10 miles due west of A, the same tornado is in the direction SSE. If the tornado is traveling NNE at 40 mph, in how many minutes will the tornado be at A?

29. Give polar coordinates for 8 points which could be the vertices of a regular octagon. Would it be easier to find rectangular coordinates? Explain.

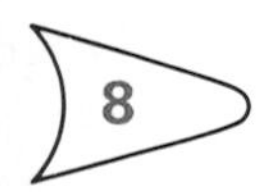

CHAPTER SUMMARY

This chapter is devoted to relationships among sines, cosines, and rotations. These are applied to study polar coordinates.

We defined the sine and cosine of x as the coordinates of certain points.

$$(\cos x, \sin x) = R_x(1, 0)$$

These points all lie on the unit circle. Sines and cosines for multiples of 90° can be remembered by thinking of the graph. Sines and cosines of 30°, 45°, and 60° can be calculated exactly. It will be to your benefit to memorize the sines and cosines given in the following table, for they are needed often in many types of situations.

x	$\cos x$	$\sin x$
0°	1	0
30°	$\frac{\sqrt{3}}{2}$	$\frac{1}{2}$
45°	$\frac{\sqrt{2}}{2}$	$\frac{\sqrt{2}}{2}$
60°	$\frac{1}{2}$	$\frac{\sqrt{3}}{2}$
90°	0	1
180°	−1	0
270°	0	−1

Tables are needed for sines and cosines of other numbers between 0° and 90°. Rotations or reflections can be used to find sines and cosines for points in the 2nd, 3rd, or 4th quadrant. The *rotation matrix* may be used for this purpose.

$$R_x: \quad \begin{bmatrix} \cos x & -\sin x \\ \sin x & \cos x \end{bmatrix}$$

The formulas given below are helpful in obtaining and relating values of sines and cosines.

$$\sin(90° - x) = \cos x$$
$$\cos(90° - x) = \sin x$$

$$\cos(x + y) = \cos x \cdot \cos y - \sin x \cdot \sin y$$
$$\sin(x + y) = \sin x \cdot \cos y + \cos x \cdot \sin y$$

If a size transformation having magnitude r is applied to the point $(\cos \theta, \sin \theta)$, then the resulting image is $(r \cos \theta, r \sin \theta)$. This point has *polar coordinates* $[r, \theta]$. The polar coordinate system gives a second way of locating points of the plane. In this system every point of the plane can be represented by many different pairs of polar coordinates.

CHAPTER REVIEW

1. Give a definition for *sine of t.*

2. Give the exact value of each expression.

a. $\sin 30°$ **b.** $\cos 90°$ **c.** $\sin(87° + 93°)$

d. $\cos(-45°)$ **e.** $\sin(-180°)$ **f.** $\sin 45°$

3. Use the table to find an approximation for each expression.

a. $\sin 20°$ **b.** $\cos 400°$ **c.** $\sin(-80°)$

4–9. Without using tables, graph each point.

4. $(\cos 45°, \sin 45°)$ **5.** $[3, 45°]$ **6.** $(-10 \cos 180°, -10 \sin 180°)$

7. $(\cos(-90°), \sin(-90°))$ **8.** $[-2, 180°]$ **9.** $(\frac{1}{3} \cos 225°, \frac{1}{3} \sin 225°)$

10. For any x, $(\sin x)^2 + (\cos x)^2 =$ ____.

11. Write the matrix for a rotation of 110° about the origin. (Give the elements of the matrix correct to three decimal places.)

12. Give *exact values* for the elements of the matrix for R_{45}.

13. Find the exact image of (1, 4) under R_{45}.

14. Given $\cos x = 0.60$, find $\sin x$.

15. Find coordinates (to the nearest hundredth) for the image of $(10, -10)$ under a rotation of 70° about the origin.

16–18. True or False?

16. $\sin 110° = \sin(50° + 60°)$ **17.** $\cos(140° - 50°) = \cos 90°$

18. $\sin(m + n) = \sin m \cdot \cos n + \cos m \cdot \sin n$

19. Find the image of $\begin{bmatrix} 1 & 2 & 3 \\ 4 & 0 & -1 \end{bmatrix}$ under R_{18}. (Give the coordinates to the nearest hundredth.) Then graph the preimage and the image.

20–22. Translate from polar to rectangular coordinates. Approximations are not necessary.

20. $[5, 40°]$ **21.** $[-4, 75°]$ **22.** $[150, 5°]$

Chapter 9 | Mid-Course Review—Corresponding Group Properties

In Chapter 1, the four group properties—closure, associativity, existence of an identity, existence of inverses—were considered. In this chapter, these group properties are connected to ideas from nearly every other chapter you have studied. Thus this chapter serves as a review of the first half of this book.

WHAT IS A GROUP?

Postulates 1 and 2 gave properties of addition and multiplication which are necessary for solving equations and simplifying expressions. These two postulates are reworded below. (If you do not understand the restatements, you should refer back to the original statements of the postulates on page 12.)

POSTULATE 1

With addition, the set of real numbers

A. is closed;

B. is associative;

C. contains the identity 0;

D. contains an inverse for each element.

POSTULATE 2

With multiplication, the set of nonzero real numbers

A. is closed;

B. is associative;

C. contains the identity 1;

D. contains an inverse for each element.

The similarities between Postulates 1 and 2 are obvious. The only differences between the postulates are the given set (all real numbers and all nonzero real numbers) and the given operation (addition and multiplication). The properties are alike.

Many other sets and operations have these four properties. When a set and an operation satisfy the properties, that set and operation are said to form a **group**.

A definition of the mathematical term *group* follows. Because we want the definition to be general, we use the symbol $*$ to stand for the operation. If $*$ is replaced by $+$, the operation is addition. If $*$ is replaced by $\cdot$, the operation is multiplication, and so on. Two forms of the definition are given, one in words, the other more symbolic.

Definition

A set S and an operation $*$ form a **group** if and only if

In words:	*More symbolic:* If a, b, and c are in S,
A. The set is closed under the operation.	A. $a * b$ is in S.
B. The operation is associative.	B. $(a * b) * c = a * (b * c)$
C. An identity for the operation is in the set.	C. There is an element I in S with $a * I = I * a = a$.
D. Each element in the set has an inverse in the set.	D. For each a there is an a' in S with $a * a' = a' * a = I$.

When a set S and operation $*$ form a group, we identify the group by the symbol $\langle S, *\rangle$. Postulate 1 shows that $\langle$set of real numbers, $+\rangle$ is a group. It is the *additive group of real numbers*. Postulate 2 guarantees that $\langle$set of nonzero real numbers, $\cdot\rangle$ is a group. It is the *multiplicative group of nonzero real numbers*. There are many other additive or multiplicative groups.

Examples:

Additive groups

1. $\langle$set of integers, $+\rangle$

2. $\langle$set of even integers, $+\rangle$

Multiplicative groups

3. $\langle \{1, -1\}, \cdot \rangle$

4. $\langle$set of nonzero rational numbers, $\cdot\rangle$

5. $\langle \{1, 2, \frac{1}{2}, 4, \frac{1}{4}, 8, \frac{1}{8}, \cdots\}, \cdot \rangle$

You should check the four group properties for each example.

The operation is very important to a group. The set of integers and $\cdot$ do *not* form a group because condition D is not satisfied. In particular, $\frac{1}{2}$ is the multiplicative inverse of 2, but $\frac{1}{2}$ is not in the set.

Many sets do not form groups either with addition or multiplication. Consider $\{1, \frac{1}{2}, 2, \frac{1}{3}, 3, \frac{1}{4}, 4, \cdots\}$. Since $3 \cdot \frac{1}{2}$ is not in the set, condition A is not satisfied for a multiplicative group. Since 0 is not in the set, condition C is not satisfied for an additive group.

The idea of a group originated about 1800 and was once thought to have few applications outside of mathematics itself. Then in 1891 the Russian mathematician Fedorov proved a theorem which has applications to the construction of wallpaper designs, mosaics, and repeating patterns of all kinds. Today, group theory is applied to quantum mechanics in physics and the study of crystals in chemistry, as well as being an essential topic in mathematics.

EXERCISES 9.1

Ⓐ **1.** What properties must S and $*$ satisfy to have a group $\langle S, *\rangle$?

2. If R is the set of real numbers, what does $\langle R, +\rangle$ mean?

3. What is an additive group?

4. What is a multiplicative group?

5. Give an example of a multiplicative group.

Ⓑ **6–9.** Indicate why each set and operation do *not* make up a group.

6. $\{1, 2, 4, 8, 16, \cdots\}$, $\cdot$

7. $\{-2, -1, 0, 1, 2\}$, $+$

8. $\{0, 3, 6, 9, 12, \cdots\}$, $+$

9. set of real numbers, $\cdot$

10–14. Consider the four sets below. Tell which sets:

Z = set of integers $\qquad$ P = set of positive integers

E = set of even integers $\qquad$ D = set of odd integers

10. are closed under addition. **11.** contain the additive identity.

12. contain the additive inverse of each element.

13. form groups with addition. **14.** form groups with multiplication.

15. Make a reasonable definition for *finite group*. Under your definition, which groups in Examples **1–5** on page 230 are finite groups?

16. Repeat Exercise **15** for *commutative group*.

17–20. State (**a**) the identity and (**b**) a second element and its inverse.

17. $\langle$set of integral powers of 3, $\cdot\rangle$ **18.** $\langle\{1, -1\}, \cdot\rangle$

19. $\langle$set of integers divisible by 10, $+\rangle$

20. $\langle$set of positive real numbers, $\cdot\rangle$

21–27. Decide whether or not the set and operation make up a group.

21. $\{1, 0, -1\}, +$ **22.** $\{2, 1, \frac{1}{2}\}, \cdot$ **23.** $\{\sqrt{1}, \sqrt{2}, \sqrt{3}, \sqrt{4}, \sqrt{5}, \cdots\}, \cdot$

24. set of integral powers of 1.3, $\cdot$ **25.** set of integral multiples of 7, $+$

26. set of integral multiples of any given number, $+$

27. set of integral powers of any given number, $\cdot$

© **28.** Suppose B is a subset of real numbers and 3 is an element of B. If $\langle B, +\rangle$ is a group, but B is not the set of integers, give a possible set B. Find a second possible set.

29. Let # be defined as follows: $a \# b = 5ab$. Does # form a group with the positive real numbers?

30. Find a group $\langle S, \cdot\rangle$, where S contains $\sqrt{2}$ and π but does not contain all positive real numbers.

31–34. (Use any references you can.) What role did each mathematician play in the development of the study of groups?

31. Niels Henrik Abel (1802–1829) **32.** Evariste Galois (1811–1832)

33. Sophus Lie (1842–1899) **34.** Felix Klein (1849–1925)

9.2 ANOTHER LOOK AT EQUATION SOLVING

In the second grade, you only knew about positive integers. You could answer $3 + ? = 4$, but you could not answer $4 + ? = 3$. When you learned how to add negative integers, you could solve $4 + ? = 3$. Recall that the set of positive integers does not form an additive group. But the set of all integers does.

In an additive group, $a + x = b$ can always be solved for x.

In the fourth grade, you could solve $5 \cdot \square = 35$. But you probably didn't know about fractions. So $35 \cdot \square = 5$ would have no solution. Then later you learned that zero complicates things. An equation like $0 \cdot x = b$ might have no solution or infinitely many solutions. Thus in the set of integers, $ax = b$ cannot always be solved. But in the set of positive rationals, $ax = b$ can be solved.

In a multiplicative group, $ax = b$ can always be solved for x.

As another example, recall that $\langle \{1, -1\}, \cdot \rangle$ is a group. In this group, there are only four possible equations of the form $ax = b$. (a and b must be -1 or 1.) They are

$$1 \cdot x = 1 \qquad 1 \cdot x = -1 \qquad -1 \cdot x = 1 \qquad -1 \cdot x = -1$$

Each equation has the solution 1 or -1. So $ax = b$ has solutions in the set.

All three examples above can be verified at the same time. This is done by proving a very general theorem about groups.

Theorem 9.2.1

Let $\langle S, * \rangle$ be a group. Then if a and b are elements of S, the equation $a * x = b$ has a unique solution in S.

PROOF: **1.** Given: $a * x = b$

Since $\langle S, * \rangle$ is a group, a has an inverse a' under $*$:

2. $a' * (a * x) = a' * b$

3. $(a' * a) * x = a' * b$ by associativity

Letting I be the identity for $*$:

4. $I * x = a' * b$

5. $x = a' * b$

6. $a' * b$ is in S because S is closed under $*$.

Look back to see that Theorems 1.4.1 and 1.4.2 are special cases of Theorem 9.2.1 for two important groups: (1) the additive group of real numbers and (2) the multiplicative group of nonzero real numbers.

EXERCISES 9.2

Ⓐ **1–3.** In which sets does the equation $2 + x = 8$ have a solution?

1. set of even numbers

2. set of positive real numbers

3. set of powers of 2

4. In a multiplicative group, what equation always has a solution?

5. True or False? The solution to $64x = \frac{1}{32}$ is an integral power of 2.

6. Suppose m and n are even numbers. Will the solution to $m + x = n$ always be an even number?

Ⓑ **7–10.** Choose two elements a and b from the given set so that the equation $a * x = b$ has no solution in the set. (This is an alternate way of showing that the given set and operation does *not* form a group.)

7. $\{1, 0, -1\}$, $+$

8. $\{0, 1\}$, $\cdot$

9. $\{1, 2, -2, 4, -4\}$, $\cdot$

10. $\{0, 3, 6, 9, 12, 15, \cdots\}$, $+$

11–14. If a and b are chosen from the given set, does $ax = b$ always have a solution in that set?

11. set of all real numbers

12. set of even integers

13. set of odd integers

14. set of all positive real numbers

15–18. Repeat Exercises **11–14** for the sentence $a + x = b$.

Ⓒ **19–24. (a)** Solve each equation. **(b)** Each exercise is related to a group property. Identify that property. **(c)** Generalize the exercise.

19. $563 + x = 259; 259 + y = 563$

20. $1732.4 = 1732.4 \cdot v$

21. $3a = 4; 4b = 17; 3c = 17$

22. $\sqrt{6} = z + \sqrt{6}$

23. $-21 + r = 1; 1 + s = 463; -21 + t = 463$

24. $-17m = 34; 34p = -17$

25–26. Solve each equation. Then indicate a possible group in which you are solving the equation, picking the "smallest" set possible.

25. $128x = \frac{1}{64}$

26. $92 = -46 + y$

9.3 MORE WORK WITH REAL NUMBER PROPERTIES

To form an additive group, you can start with some number and add it to itself again and again. Starting with 7, you get 7, 14, 21, 28, 35, $\cdots$. A group requires an identity, so include 0. A group needs inverses, so include the opposite of each element. The resulting set is

$$\{0, 7, -7, 14, -14, 21, -21, 28, -28, 35, -35, \cdots\}.$$

This set, with addition, forms the group of *integral multiples of* 7.

The same thing can be done with multiplication. Begin with 3, and multiply 3 by itself again and again. Include 1 (the multiplicative identity) and reciprocals. The set which results is

$$\{1, 3, \tfrac{1}{3}, 9, \tfrac{1}{9}, 27, \tfrac{1}{27}, 81, \tfrac{1}{81}, \cdots\}.$$

With multiplication, this set of *integral powers of* 3 forms a group.

We now generalize. At left we begin with the number a and form a group by repeatedly adding. At right we begin with the number x and form a group by repeatedly multiplying.

additive group of integral multiples of a			multiplicative group of integral powers of x
	$a = 1a$		$x = x^1$
	$a + a = 2a$		$x \cdot x = x^2$
	$a + a + a = 3a$		$x \cdot x \cdot x = x^3$
	$\vdots$		$\vdots$
	$0 = 0a$	identities	$1 = x^0$
	$-a = -1a$	inverses	$\frac{1}{x} = x^{-1}$
		$\vdots$	
	$-2a$		$\frac{1}{x^2} = x^{-2}$
	$-3a$		$\frac{1}{x^3} = x^{-3}$

Because the groups are formed in the same way, there are corresponding elements in these groups. In general,

ma corresponds to x^m

na corresponds to x^n

Now add at left (the left group is an additive group); multiply at right. Do the answers correspond?

$$ma + na \qquad\qquad x^m \cdot x^n$$

Using the distributive and power properties, the answers are the $(m + n)$th multiple and the $(m + n)$th power. These do correspond.

$$ma + na = (m + n)a \qquad\qquad x^m \cdot x^n = x^{m+n}$$

When two groups correspond so that answers in one group correspond to answers in the other group, the groups are said to be isomorphic.

Definition

In words:	*More symbolic:*
Two groups are **isomorphic** if and only if	$\langle S, *\rangle$ is **isomorphic** to $\langle T, \#\rangle$ if and only if
a. there is a one-to-one correspondence between their elements;	**a.** there is a 1–1 correspondence between the elements of S and T;
b. the corresponding operations on corresponding elements yield corresponding results.	**b.** if a in S corresponds to x in T and b in S corresponds to y in T, then $a * b$ corresponds to $x \# y$.

The correspondences mentioned on page 234 ensure:

Theorem 9.3.1

The additive group of integral multiples of a is isomorphic to the multiplicative group of integral powers of x.

When two groups are isomorphic, every property in one group corresponds to a property in the other. For the additive group of integral multiples of a and the multiplicative group of integral powers of x, here are three pairs of corresponding properties that you know.

(1) **Distributivity:** $ma + na = (m + n)a$	(1) **Power property:** $x^m \cdot x^n = x^{m+n}$
(2) **Zero multiple** (identity for $+$): $0a = 0$	(2) **Zero power** (identity for $\cdot$): $x^0 = 1$
(3) **Adding inverse multiples:** $ma + (-ma) = 0$	(3) **Multiplying inverse powers:** $x^m \cdot x^{-m} = 1$

A known property of multiples and addition can be used to find the corresponding property of powers and multiplication (and vice versa). For example, you know the multiple of a multiple (associativity) property stated below. A special case is $6 \cdot 5a = 30a$. Isomorphism of the two groups guarantees a corresponding property. A special case is $(x^5)^6 = x^{30}$. In general, this is the power of a power property.

(4) **Multiple of a multiple:** $m(na) = (mn)a$

(4) **Theorem 9.3.2**

Power of a power: $(x^n)^m = x^{mn}$

Examples: Powers of powers

1. $(x^{-1})^{-3} = x^3$ Check: $(x^{-1})^{-3} = \frac{1}{(x^{-1})^3} = \frac{1}{\left(\frac{1}{x}\right)^3} = \frac{1}{\frac{1}{x^3}} = x^3.$

2. $(3^4)^{-2} = 3^{-8}$

3. The square of $(y + 5)^3$ is $(y + 5)^6$.

Corresponding properties of multiples and powers are almost endless. A fifth useful property of multiples follows from viewing distributivity as the multiple of a sum property below. The isomorphism guarantees the property below involving the power of a product. Corresponding to b at the left is the number y at the right.

(5) **Multiple of a sum:** $m(a + b) = ma + mb$

(5) Theorem 9.3.3

Power of a product: $(xy)^m = x^m y^m$

Examples: Powers of products

1. $(xy)^2 = x^2y^2$ Check: $(xy)^2 = xy \cdot xy = x \cdot x \cdot y \cdot y = x^2y^2$.
2. $(3a^2b)^4 = 3^4 \cdot (a^2)^4 b^4 = 81a^8b^4$
3. $(x + y)^4$ can be expanded but not really simplified. It is the power of a sum, not of a product.

In correspondences between addition and multiplication, these correspondences hold true.

addition	⟷	multiplication
sum	⟷	product
multiples	⟷	powers
subtraction	⟷	division
difference	⟷	quotient

This enables us to create new correspondences. Multiples of differences follow from distributivity. To find a corresponding property, replace "multiple" by "power" and "subtraction" by "division."

(6) **Multiple of a difference:** $m(a - b) = ma - mb$

(6) Theorem 9.3.4

Power of a quotient: $\left(\frac{x}{y}\right)^m = \frac{x^m}{y^m}$

For example, $\left(\frac{2}{3}\right)^5 = \frac{2^5}{3^5} = \frac{32}{243}$.

EXERCISES 9.3

Ⓐ **1–2.** What group can be formed by each process?

1. repeatedly adding 10, including 0 and opposites
2. repeatedly multiplying 4, including 1 and reciprocals

3–4. How can each group be formed?

3. $\langle\{0, 2, -2, 4, -4, 6, -6, \cdots\}, +\rangle$
4. $\langle\{1, 2, 0.5, 4, 0.25, 8, 0.125, \cdots\}, \cdot\rangle$

5. Identify three elements of the set of integral powers of 6.

6–10. A property of multiples is given. State a corresponding property of powers.

6. $10a + 10b = 10(a + b)$

7. $3x$ and $-3x$ are opposites.

8. $7t + 14t = 21t$

9. $17(13y) = 221y$

10. $0 \cdot x = 0$

11–37. Simplify.

11. 5^3

12. 5^{-3}

13. $(\frac{1}{2})^{-1}$

14. $(\frac{1}{2})^{-2}$

15. $10^2 \cdot 10^3$

16. $(10^2)^3$

17. $(10^3)^{-2}$

18. $(10^3)^0$

19. $(\frac{3}{4})^{-2} \cdot (\frac{3}{4})^2$

20. $(5^1)^{-3}$

21. $5^1 \cdot 5^{-3}$

22. $(4^0)^6$

23. $\frac{-3^5}{-3^4}$

24. $\frac{2^3}{4^2}$

25. $\frac{4^3}{4^{-3}}$

26. $\frac{2^{-3}}{4^{-2}}$

27. $(3^{-2})^2 \cdot (3^2)^{-2}$

28. $(\frac{1}{2})^{-3}$

29. $((\frac{1}{11})^2)^{-17}$

30. $(101^{-1})^{-4}$

31. $(0.01)^{-3} \cdot (0.01)^4$

32. $x^5 \cdot x^3$

33. $(y^5)^3$

34. $(2z)^4$

35. $2^a \cdot 2^b$

36. $(2^a)^b$

37. $(3m)^{-2}$

38. When are two groups isomorphic?

39. Give an example of two groups which are isomorphic.

40. Why is it helpful to know that two groups are isomorphic?

41–42. Under the isomorphism between groups of multiples and powers, what corresponds to:

41. addition of multiples?

42. the power of a quotient?

43–46. A property of powers is given. State a corresponding property of multiples, with *a* corresponding to *x*, *b* corresponding to *y*.

43. $(x^m)^3 = x^{3m}$

44. $(xy)^7 = x^7y^7$

45. $7^4 \cdot 3^4 = 21^4$

46. $(2^5)^3 = 2^{15}$

Ⓑ **47–52.** Simplify each expression.

47. $(x^2)^3 + (x^4)^5$

48. $\left(\frac{x^2}{y^3}\right)^{-4}$

49. $\left(\frac{2t}{3v}\right)^{-2} \cdot v^4$

50. $(x^3y^2)^{-2}(3x^{-2}y^3)^{-4}$

51. $\left(\frac{3}{m}\right)^{-2} \cdot \left(\frac{m}{3}\right)^5$

52. $(x^my^m)^3$

53–56. Simplify each expression.

53. $(\frac{1}{2})^{-3} \cdot (\frac{1}{3})^{-4}$

54. $((((8^3)^2)^1)^0)^{-1}$

55. $2^{-2} \cdot 3^{-2} \cdot 6^3$

56. $\left(\frac{1}{2.5}\right)^{-3} \cdot \left(\frac{1}{2.5}\right)^2$

© **57–60.** Let $x = \frac{1}{2}$ and $y = -3$. Calculate.

57. $xy + 99.5y$

58. $(xy)^{2xy}$

59. $(10^{4x})^{-y}$

60. $10^{4x} \cdot 10^y$

61–66. Given is a property of multiples of real numbers a and b. Name a corresponding true property of powers of positive numbers x and y.

61. $ma - na = (m - n)a$

62. If $a > 0$ and $m > 0$, then $ma > 0$.

63. If $a < 0$ and $m < n$, then $ma > na$.

64. If $a < b$ and $m > 0$, then $ma < mb$.

65. If b is between a and c, then mb is between ma and mc.

66. A negative multiple of a negative number is positive.

MORE WORK WITH MATRICES

In Section 5.5, we found that the set of 2×2 matrices with multiplication has the following properties: closure, associativity, and existence of an identity matrix $\begin{bmatrix} 1 & 0 \\ 0 & 1 \end{bmatrix}$. These are three of the four group properties. The fourth group property would be the existence of inverse 2×2 matrices under multiplication.

Remember that real numbers a and b are multiplicative inverses if and only if $ab = 1$. Similarly, 2×2 matrices A and B are multiplicative inverses if and only if

$$A \cdot B = \begin{bmatrix} 1 & 0 \\ 0 & 1 \end{bmatrix} = I.$$

There are many pairs of such matrices. For example,

$$\begin{bmatrix} 8 & -5 \\ -3 & 2 \end{bmatrix} \cdot \begin{bmatrix} 2 & 5 \\ 3 & 8 \end{bmatrix} = \begin{bmatrix} 1 & 0 \\ 0 & 1 \end{bmatrix}.$$

A general formula for inverses is given in the next theorem.

Theorem 9.4.1

If $ad - bc \neq 0$, the matrix $\begin{bmatrix} a & b \\ c & d \end{bmatrix}$ has the multiplicative inverse at right.

$$\begin{bmatrix} \frac{d}{ad - bc} & \frac{-b}{ad - bc} \\ \frac{-c}{ad - bc} & \frac{a}{ad - bc} \end{bmatrix}$$

PROOF:

1. Let $A = \begin{bmatrix} a & b \\ c & d \end{bmatrix}$, $B = \begin{bmatrix} w & x \\ y & z \end{bmatrix}$, and suppose A and B are inverses.

2. Then $AB = I$. That is, $\begin{bmatrix} a & b \\ c & d \end{bmatrix} \cdot \begin{bmatrix} w & x \\ y & z \end{bmatrix} = \begin{bmatrix} 1 & 0 \\ 0 & 1 \end{bmatrix}$.

3. Doing the indicated matrix multiplication, we have $\begin{cases} aw + by = 1 \\ cw + dy = 0 \end{cases}$ $\begin{cases} ax + bz = 0 \\ cx + dz = 1 \end{cases}$

4. Now we attempt to solve these two systems for w, y, x, and z in terms of a, b, c, and d. $\begin{cases} acw + bcy = c \\ acw + ady = 0 \end{cases}$ $\begin{cases} acx + bcz = 0 \\ acx + adz = a \end{cases}$

5. Subtracting each top equation from the bottom, $(ad - bc)y = -c$ $(ad - bc)z = a$

6. Only if $ad - bc \neq 0$ can we divide by $ad - bc$. $y = \dfrac{-c}{ad - bc}$ $z = \dfrac{a}{ad - bc}$

7. By a similar process, $w = \dfrac{d}{ad - bc}$ $x = \dfrac{-b}{ad - bc}$

8. Thus, $B = \begin{bmatrix} w & x \\ y & z \end{bmatrix} = \begin{bmatrix} \dfrac{d}{ad - bc} & \dfrac{-b}{ad - bc} \\ \dfrac{-c}{ad - bc} & \dfrac{a}{ad - bc} \end{bmatrix}$.

9. Solving $BA = I$ gives the same result. Multiplying checks the answer. So we have found the inverse of A.

A matrix which has a multiplicative inverse is called *invertible*. As in real number multiplication, the inverse of a matrix A is denoted by the symbol A^{-1}.

Examples: Calculating the inverse of a matrix

1. For the matrix $\begin{bmatrix} 3 & 4 \\ -1 & 2 \end{bmatrix}$, use the formula of Theorem 9.4.1,

$a = 3$, $b = 4$, $c = -1$, and $d = 2$, so $ad - bc = 10$. The inverse is

$$\begin{bmatrix} \frac{2}{10} & \frac{-4}{10} \\ \frac{1}{10} & \frac{3}{10} \end{bmatrix} \text{ or } \begin{bmatrix} 0.2 & -0.4 \\ 0.1 & 0.3 \end{bmatrix}.$$

Check by multiplication: $\begin{bmatrix} 0.2 & -0.4 \\ 0.1 & 0.3 \end{bmatrix} \cdot \begin{bmatrix} 3 & 4 \\ -1 & 2 \end{bmatrix} = \begin{bmatrix} 1 & 0 \\ 0 & 1 \end{bmatrix}$.

2. If $A = \begin{bmatrix} -6 & -11 \\ 3 & 5 \end{bmatrix}$, then $A^{-1} = \begin{bmatrix} \frac{5}{3} & \frac{11}{3} \\ -\frac{3}{3} & -\frac{6}{3} \end{bmatrix} = \begin{bmatrix} \frac{5}{3} & \frac{11}{3} \\ -1 & -2 \end{bmatrix}$. Check it.

Previously discussed matrices have inverses. For example, the inverse of $\begin{bmatrix} 0 & -1 \\ 1 & 0 \end{bmatrix}$ is $\begin{bmatrix} 0 & 1 \\ -1 & 0 \end{bmatrix}$. Notice that $\begin{bmatrix} 0 & -1 \\ 1 & 0 \end{bmatrix}$ is the matrix for R_{90}, while $\begin{bmatrix} 0 & 1 \\ -1 & 0 \end{bmatrix}$ is the matrix for $R_{-90} = R_{270}$, the inverse of R_{90}.

Not all matrices have inverses. One such matrix is $\begin{bmatrix} 3 & 1 \\ 6 & 2 \end{bmatrix}$. Suppose $\begin{bmatrix} w & x \\ y & z \end{bmatrix} \cdot \begin{bmatrix} 3 & 1 \\ 6 & 2 \end{bmatrix} = \begin{bmatrix} 1 & 0 \\ 0 & 1 \end{bmatrix}$. Then $3w + 6x = 1$ and $w + 2x = 0$. But if $3w + 6x = 1$, then $w + 2x = \frac{1}{3}$. Since we cannot have $w + 2x = \frac{1}{3}$ and $w + 2x = 0$ at the same time, $\begin{bmatrix} 3 & 1 \\ 6 & 2 \end{bmatrix}$ has no inverse. In general:

Theorem 9.4.2

If $ad - bc = 0$, then $\begin{bmatrix} a & b \\ c & d \end{bmatrix}$ has no multiplicative inverse.

The number $ad - bc$ thus determines whether or not the matrix $\begin{bmatrix} a & b \\ c & d \end{bmatrix}$ has an inverse. This number is consequently called the *determinant* of the matrix.

Definition

The **determinant** of the matrix $\begin{bmatrix} a & b \\ c & d \end{bmatrix}$ is the number $ad - bc$.

You can abbreviate the word *determinant* as *det*. For example, $\det \begin{bmatrix} 1 & 2 \\ 3 & 4 \end{bmatrix} = 1 \cdot 4 - 2 \cdot 3 = -2$. You should refer back to Theorem 9.4.1 to see that calculating the determinant of a matrix aids in calculating the inverse. We now rephrase Theorems 9.4.1 and 9.4.2.

Theorem 9.4.1 (rephrased)

Let $A = \begin{bmatrix} a & b \\ c & d \end{bmatrix}$. If $\det A$ is not zero, $A^{-1} = \begin{bmatrix} \frac{d}{\det A} & \frac{-b}{\det A} \\ \frac{-c}{\det A} & \frac{a}{\det A} \end{bmatrix}$

Theorem 9.4.2 (rephrased)

If $\det A$ is zero, A has no multiplicative inverse.

From Theorem 9.4.1, notice that you can find A^{-1} as follows. Interchange a and d, take the opposites of b and c, and multiply each resulting element by the reciprocal of $\det A$.

EXERCISES 9.4

Ⓐ **1.** How can one determine if two matrices are inverses of each other?

2–5. Give the determinant of each matrix.

2. $\begin{bmatrix} a & b \\ c & d \end{bmatrix}$ **3.** $\begin{bmatrix} 5 & 1 \\ 2 & -3 \end{bmatrix}$ **4.** $\begin{bmatrix} \frac{1}{2} & \frac{1}{2} \\ \frac{1}{2} & \frac{1}{2} \end{bmatrix}$ **5.** $\begin{bmatrix} -6 & -2 \\ 4 & 7 \end{bmatrix}$

6. Name a matrix not mentioned in this section which has no inverse.

7. What is the significance of the determinant of a matrix?

8. What is the abbreviation for *determinant of M*?

9. A is a matrix with nonzero determinant. What is A^{-1}?

10. What is an invertible matrix?

11–18. Does the matrix have an inverse? If so, calculate it. Check your answer by multiplying.

11. $\begin{bmatrix} 5 & 1 \\ 2 & -3 \end{bmatrix}$ **12.** $\begin{bmatrix} 0.5 & 0.5 \\ 0.5 & 0.5 \end{bmatrix}$ **13.** $\begin{bmatrix} 0 & 1 \\ -1 & 0 \end{bmatrix}$ **14.** $\begin{bmatrix} 0 & k \\ k & 0 \end{bmatrix}$

15. $\begin{bmatrix} 1 & -1 \\ 1 & 1 \end{bmatrix}$ **16.** $\begin{bmatrix} 18 & 17 \\ 19 & 18 \end{bmatrix}$ **17.** $\begin{bmatrix} -2 & 4 \\ 6 & -1 \end{bmatrix}$ **18.** $\begin{bmatrix} 1 & -3 \\ -4 & 2 \end{bmatrix}$

Ⓑ **19.** True or False? $\det \begin{bmatrix} 90 & 75 \\ 63 & 112 \end{bmatrix} = \det \begin{bmatrix} 63 & 112 \\ 90 & 75 \end{bmatrix}$

20. Show that $\left\{ \begin{bmatrix} -1 & 0 \\ 0 & -1 \end{bmatrix}, \begin{bmatrix} 1 & 0 \\ 0 & 1 \end{bmatrix}, \begin{bmatrix} 0 & 1 \\ 1 & 0 \end{bmatrix}, \begin{bmatrix} 0 & -1 \\ -1 & 0 \end{bmatrix} \right\}$ is closed under multiplication.

21. Show that the set of Ex. **20** contains inverses of all its elements.

22. True or False? The matrices for S_2 and S_{-2} are inverses.

23. Examine the matrices for $r_{x=y}$, $r_{x\text{-axis}}$, $r_{y\text{-axis}}$, R_{90}, R_{180}, R_{270}, and I. What property is shared by their determinants?

Ⓒ **24.** Prove: If A and B are 2×2 matrices, $\det A \cdot \det B = \det(AB)$.

25. Use the statement of Ex. **24** to prove $\det A^{-1} = \frac{1}{\det A}$.

26. Show the work as suggested in Steps 4–7 of the proof of Theorem 9.4.1 (page 239) which leads to the formulas for w and x.

9.5 ANOTHER LOOK AT SYSTEM SOLVING

With multiplication, some sets of 2×2 matrices satisfy all 4 group properties. So there are groups of matrices. The largest group of 2×2 matrices involves all those with inverses. It is the first noncommutative group we have discussed.

Theorem 9.5.1

With multiplication, the set of all 2×2 invertible matrices forms a group.

PROOF: Of the four properties needed, associativity holds for *all* matrices, so it holds for 2×2 invertible matrices. The identity $\begin{bmatrix} 1 & 0 \\ 0 & 1 \end{bmatrix}$ is its own inverse, so it is in this set. And all invertible matrices have inverses. The only property which requires some work to show is closure: Is the product of two invertible matrices also invertible? Let A and B be invertible matrices. Then A^{-1} and B^{-1} exist.

Notice $(B^{-1} \cdot A^{-1}) \cdot (A \cdot B) = B^{-1} \cdot (A^{-1} \cdot A) \cdot B$ by associativity

$= B^{-1} \cdot I \cdot B$

$= B^{-1} \cdot B$ $\quad$ I is the identity.

$= I$

So $B^{-1} \cdot A^{-1}$ is the inverse of AB. Thus AB is invertible.

In a group, an equation has exactly one solution. So we know something about equations involving 2×2 matrices.

Theorem 9.5.2

If A and B are 2×2 invertible matrices, the equation $AX = B$ has exactly one solution.

Because of Theorem 9.5.2, the next example has exactly one solution. This is not particularly obvious at first glance.

Example: Solve: $\begin{bmatrix} 3 & 2 \\ 4 & -5 \end{bmatrix} \cdot \begin{bmatrix} j & k \\ \ell & m \end{bmatrix} = \begin{bmatrix} 6 & -2 \\ 9 & -4 \end{bmatrix}$.

SOLUTION: Multiply both sides by the inverse of $\begin{bmatrix} 3 & 2 \\ 4 & -5 \end{bmatrix}$. This inverse matrix must be at left on *each* side of the equation, because the operation is not commutative.

$$\begin{bmatrix} \frac{5}{23} & \frac{2}{23} \\ \frac{4}{23} & -\frac{3}{23} \end{bmatrix} \cdot \begin{bmatrix} 3 & 2 \\ 4 & -5 \end{bmatrix} \cdot \begin{bmatrix} j & k \\ \ell & m \end{bmatrix} = \begin{bmatrix} \frac{5}{23} & \frac{2}{23} \\ \frac{4}{23} & -\frac{3}{23} \end{bmatrix} \cdot \begin{bmatrix} 6 & -2 \\ 9 & -4 \end{bmatrix}$$

$$\begin{bmatrix} 1 & 0 \\ 0 & 1 \end{bmatrix} \cdot \begin{bmatrix} j & k \\ \ell & m \end{bmatrix} = \begin{bmatrix} \frac{48}{23} & -\frac{18}{23} \\ -\frac{3}{23} & \frac{4}{23} \end{bmatrix}$$

This shows that you have correctly calculated the inverse.

$$\begin{bmatrix} j & k \\ \ell & m \end{bmatrix} = \begin{bmatrix} \frac{48}{23} & -\frac{18}{23} \\ -\frac{3}{23} & \frac{4}{23} \end{bmatrix}$$

The same procedure can be used to solve systems.

$\begin{cases} 9x - 2y = 4 \\ 8x + 6y = 3 \end{cases}$ may be written as $\begin{bmatrix} 9 & -2 \\ 8 & 6 \end{bmatrix} \cdot \begin{bmatrix} x \\ y \end{bmatrix} = \begin{bmatrix} 4 \\ 3 \end{bmatrix}$.

Multiply both sides on the left by the inverse of the 2×2 matrix.

$$\begin{bmatrix} \frac{6}{70} & \frac{2}{70} \\ -\frac{8}{70} & \frac{9}{70} \end{bmatrix} \cdot \begin{bmatrix} 9 & -2 \\ 8 & 6 \end{bmatrix} \cdot \begin{bmatrix} x \\ y \end{bmatrix} = \begin{bmatrix} \frac{6}{70} & \frac{2}{70} \\ -\frac{8}{70} & \frac{9}{70} \end{bmatrix} \cdot \begin{bmatrix} 4 \\ 3 \end{bmatrix}$$

$$\begin{bmatrix} 1 & 0 \\ 0 & 1 \end{bmatrix} \cdot \begin{bmatrix} x \\ y \end{bmatrix} = \begin{bmatrix} \frac{30}{70} \\ -\frac{5}{70} \end{bmatrix}$$

$$\begin{bmatrix} x \\ y \end{bmatrix} = \begin{bmatrix} \frac{3}{7} \\ -\frac{1}{14} \end{bmatrix}$$

The idea is simple. In the matrix equation

$$AX = B,$$

just as in the equation $ax = b$ using real numbers, multiply both sides by the inverse of A in order to solve. This leads to a theorem which tells when systems have unique solutions.

Theorem 9.5.3

If $ad - bc \neq 0$, the system $\begin{cases} ax + by = e \\ cx + dy = f \end{cases}$ has exactly one solution.

PROOF: The given system is equivalent to the matrix equation

$$\begin{bmatrix} a & b \\ c & d \end{bmatrix} \cdot \begin{bmatrix} x \\ y \end{bmatrix} = \begin{bmatrix} e \\ f \end{bmatrix}.$$

If $ad - bc \neq 0$, then the 2×2 matrix has an inverse. Multiplying both sides by the inverse gives the unique solution

$$\begin{bmatrix} x \\ y \end{bmatrix} = \begin{bmatrix} a & b \\ c & d \end{bmatrix}^{-1} \cdot \begin{bmatrix} e \\ f \end{bmatrix}.$$

(The theorem doesn't ask what the solution is, so we need no more steps.)

But not every system has exactly one solution.

System (1) $\begin{cases} 3x + 4y = 2 \\ 6x + 8y = 4 \end{cases}$

has many solutions. As you can see, multiplying the first equation by 2 gives the second equation. So any solution to the first is a solution to the second. Graphically, the lines are identical (see graph at left below). The solution set is $\{(x, y): 3x + 4y = 2\}$.

Now look at a second system.

System (2) $\begin{cases} 3x + 4y = 2 \\ 6x + 8y = 5 \end{cases}$ — Multiply by 2 → $\begin{cases} 6x + 8y = 4 \\ 6x + 8y = 5 \end{cases}$

By substitution, $4 = 5$. This indicates there is no solution to the original system (2). Graphically, the lines are parallel and do not intersect (see graph at right below). The solution set is $\emptyset$.

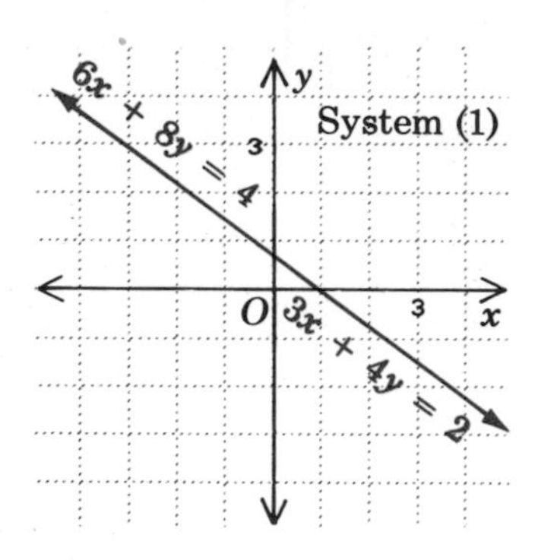

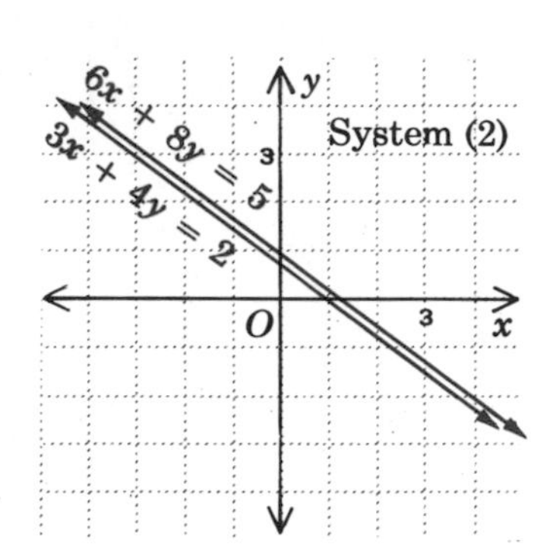

It is useful to be able to predict when an equation will have many solutions or no solution. Systems (1) and (2) above both have the form $\begin{cases} ax + by = e \\ cx + dy = f \end{cases}$, and in each example $ad - bc = 3 \cdot 8 - 4 \cdot 6 = 0$.

Theorem 9.5.4

If $ad - bc = 0$, the system $\begin{cases} ax + by = e \\ cx + dy = f \end{cases}$ has *no solution* or *infinitely many solutions.*

PROOF: The idea is to show that the corresponding lines are parallel. The details are left as an exercise.

Notice that $ad - bc$ is the determinant of the coefficient matrix. For example, systems (1) and (2) are written in matrix form below. Each 2×2 matrix has a zero determinant, indicating no unique solution.

(1) $\begin{bmatrix} 3 & 4 \\ 6 & 8 \end{bmatrix} \cdot \begin{bmatrix} x \\ y \end{bmatrix} = \begin{bmatrix} 2 \\ 4 \end{bmatrix}$ (2) $\begin{bmatrix} 3 & 4 \\ 6 & 8 \end{bmatrix} \cdot \begin{bmatrix} x \\ y \end{bmatrix} = \begin{bmatrix} 2 \\ 5 \end{bmatrix}$

When the determinant is 0, you should find a solution to one of the equations and test it in the other.

$$\begin{cases} 6x - 9y = 10 \\ 62x - 93y = 310 \end{cases} \qquad \begin{bmatrix} 6 & -9 \\ 62 & -93 \end{bmatrix} \cdot \begin{bmatrix} x \\ y \end{bmatrix} = \begin{bmatrix} 10 \\ 310 \end{bmatrix}$$

The determinant of the 2×2 matrix is 0, so there is no unique solution. $(\frac{5}{3}, 0)$ satisfies the first equation; since it does not satisfy the second equation, the system has no solution.

EXERCISES 9.5

Ⓐ **1.** What is the largest group of 2×2 matrices?

2. What is the formula for the inverse of $\begin{bmatrix} a & b \\ c & d \end{bmatrix}$?

3. Describe the process (without doing the work) by which matrices can be used to solve the system: $\begin{cases} 4a + b = 2 \\ 9a - 2b = 4 \end{cases}$.

4–9. Write a matrix equation for each system. Then tell whether the system has no solution, exactly one solution, or many solutions.

4. $3x - y = 2$
$6x - 2y = 4$

5. $-8A - 3B = 10$
$4A + 6B = 5$

6. $8 = 12x - 16y$
$6 = 8x - 12y$

7. $10x + 15y = 30$
$4x + 6y = 12$

8. $x = 4$
$3 = y$

9. $2w = 4z - 9$
$w - 2z = 18$

10–12. What can you say about the graphs of $ax + by = e$ and $cx + dy = f$ when the system has:

10. no solution? **11.** a unique solution? **12.** many solutions?

Ⓑ **13–19.** Use matrices to help find all solutions to the systems of Exercises **3–9.** (You might be able to do the problems without matrices, but you should use matrices this time.)

20. How many solutions does this equation have?

$$\begin{bmatrix} 4 & 2 \\ 9 & 1 \end{bmatrix} \cdot X = \begin{bmatrix} 3 & 2 \\ 0 & 0 \end{bmatrix}$$

21–22. Solve for the unknown matrix.

21. $Y \cdot \begin{bmatrix} 3 & 1 \\ 2 & 4 \end{bmatrix} = \begin{bmatrix} 6 & 0 \\ 9 & 8 \end{bmatrix}$

22. $\begin{bmatrix} 3 & 4 \\ 6 & 2 \end{bmatrix} = \begin{bmatrix} -1 & -2 \\ 3 & 6 \end{bmatrix} \cdot Z$

23–26. Give a corresponding statement involving 2×2 matrices.

23. If $0x = b$, then $b = 0$.

24. If $ax = 0$, then $a = 0$ or $x = 0$.

25. The sentence $0x = 0$ has infinitely many solutions.

26. If $a \neq 0$, the sentence $ax = b$ has a unique solution.

27–29. Solve each system by using matrices.

27. $\begin{aligned} 4A - 2B &= 6 \\ 7A + 4B &= 9 \end{aligned}$

28. $\begin{aligned} 17w + 15z - 2 &= 0 \\ 15w - 17z + 1 &= 0 \end{aligned}$

29. $\begin{aligned} 8w + 6z &= 0 \\ -3z - 4w &= 0 \end{aligned}$

30. Show that the group of Theorem 9.5.1 is not a commutative group.

© **31.** Find 2×2 matrices A, B, and X so that $AX = B$ but $X \neq B \cdot A^{-1}$.

32. If $A = \begin{bmatrix} 1 & 2 \\ 3 & 4 \end{bmatrix}$ and $B = \begin{bmatrix} 5 & 6 \\ 7 & 8 \end{bmatrix}$, find the inverse of AB without calculating AB. HINT: Look at the proof of Theorem 9.5.1.

33. Prove: No 2×2 matrix can stand for a transformation which maps both (2, 3) onto (3, 2) and (4, 6) onto (1, 0).

34. Prove Theorem 9.5.4.

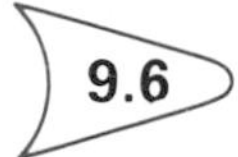

FURTHER WORK WITH TRANSFORMATIONS

We now consider group ideas with transformations. You have studied the identity transformation I, which maps each point onto itself. It is the simplest transformation of all. The next theorem shows that I is named well. It is the identity under the operation of composition.

Theorem 9.6.1

For any transformation T, $T \circ I = I \circ T = T$.

PROOF: We need to show that $T \circ I$, $I \circ T$, and T give the same images for any point P.

$$\begin{aligned} T \circ I(P) &= T(I(P)) = T(P) \\ I \circ T(P) &= I(T(P)) = T(P) \end{aligned}$$

So $T \circ I = I \circ T = T$. They are the same transformation.

Looking at Theorem 9.6.1 another way: The transformation I "does nothing" to a figure. So composing it with another transformation does not affect the other transformation.

When the composite of two transformations is the identity I, the transformations are called *inverses*.

Definition

T and U are **inverse transformations** if and only if for each point P, $T \circ U(P) = P$.

It is common to represent the inverse of a transformation T by the symbol T^{-1}. T and T^{-1} have the effect of "undoing each other." If T is a rotation of 30°, then T^{-1} is a rotation of $-30°$ with the same center. If T is the translation which maps α onto β, then T^{-1} is the translation mapping β onto α. The arrows for T and T^{-1} have the same length but opposite directions.

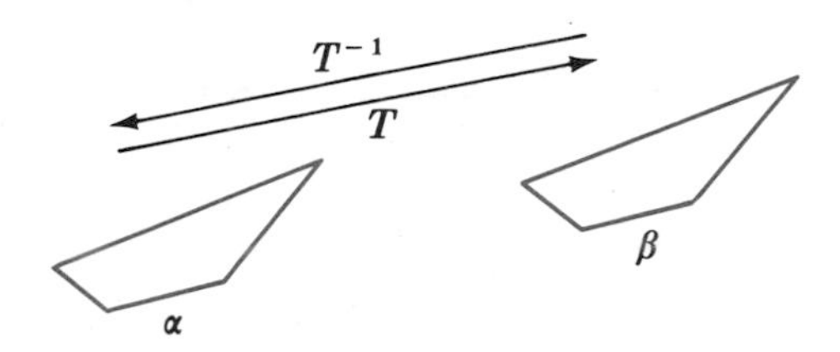

Every transformation has an inverse. The inverse is found by switching all preimage and image points. If S is the size transformation of magnitude 3, center O, mapping polygon $EFGH$ onto polygon $ABCD$, then S^{-1} is the size transformation with center O, magnitude $\frac{1}{3}$.

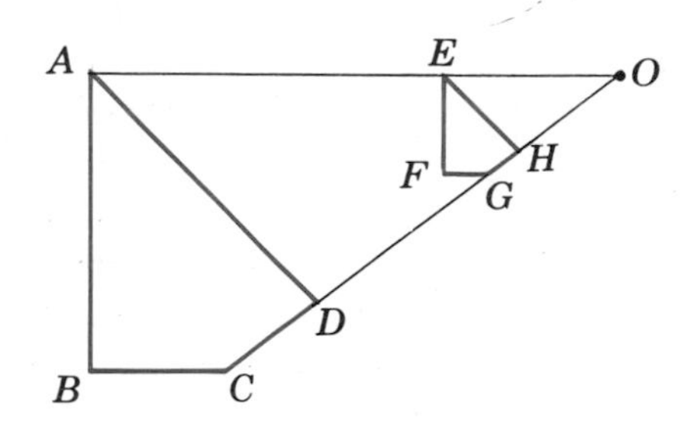

Inverses of reflections are easier to find. If $r(\alpha) = \beta$, then $r(r(\alpha)) = r(\beta) = \alpha$. So a reflection "undoes itself." If r is a particular reflection, then $r \circ r = I$.

Many sets of transformations, with composition as the operation, satisfy all of the group properties. These sets must contain:

(1) I, the identity transformation,

(2) T^{-1}, if T is in the set,

and (3) $T_1 \circ T_2$, if T_1 and T_2 are in the set.

The fourth group property, associativity of $\circ$, is satisfied in every set of transformations. Here is one group.

Theorem 9.6.2

With composition, the set of all translations forms a group.

PROOF: **(1)** The identity is the translation $(x, y) \to (x + 0, y + 0)$. **(2)** The inverse of a translation is a translation. **(3)** The composite of two translations is a translation (Theorem 4.5.2).

You can think of this group as consisting of all transformations which map every figure onto a congruent figure with the same tilt.

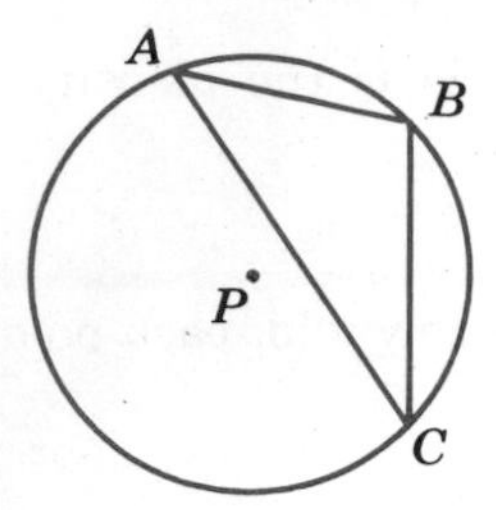

Consider this circle and triangle. What transformations (1) map the circle onto itself *and* (2) map the triangle onto a congruent triangle with the same orientation? These are the rotations with center P. These rotations help to form an important group.

Theorem 9.6.3

With composition, the set of all rotations with a given point as a center forms a group.

PROOF: Let R_x be the rotation of magnitude x with a given point P as center. **(1)** R_0 is the identity. **(2)** R_{-x} is the inverse of R_x because $R_x \circ R_{-x} = R_0$. **(3)** $R_x \circ R_y = R_{x+y}$, so the set is closed. Associativity of $\circ$, the fourth needed group property, is always satisfied by transformations.

Because the set of *all* rotations is not closed under $\circ$ (see Exercise **41**, page 250), there can be no group involving all rotations. Nor is there a group with all size transformations. But if the center is fixed, a group is formed. The proof is very similar to that of the last theorem.

Theorem 9.6.4

With composition, the set of all size transformations with a given point as center forms a group.

Not all transformations of a given type form groups. For example, the identity transformation is not a reflection. As a consequence:

Theorem 9.6.5

With composition, the set of all reflections does *not* form a group.

EXERCISES 9.6

Ⓐ **1.** What is the identity transformation?

2. What symbol is used to denote the identity transformation?

3–8. Which of these sets contain the identity transformation?

3. set of all reflections

4. set of all translations

5. set of all rotations with same point as center

6. $\{R_0, R_{90}, R_{-90}, R_{180}\}$

7. set of all rotations with magnitude 30°

8. set of all size transformations with same point as center

9. What is the composite of two given transformations?

10. When are two transformations inverses under composition?

11. What symbol is used for the inverse of a transformation T?

12–16. Give the inverse (under composition) of each transformation.

12. reflection over line ℓ

13. translation mapping (0, 0) to (3, 4)

14. rotation of $-34°$ about M

15. rotation of 180° about M

16. size transformation of magnitude 34 with center Q

17. Why is the set of all translations closed under composition?

18. Why is the set of all reflections not closed under composition?

19. What properties must be satisfied by a set T of transformations if there is to be a group $\langle T, \circ \rangle$?

20–27. With composition, does the given set form a group?

20. set of all translations

21. set of all reflections

22. set of all rotations

23. set of all size transformations

24. set of all rotations with center (2, 3)

25. set of all size transformations with center $(0, \sqrt{5})$

26. A translation T maps (x, y) onto $(x - 5, y + 2)$. What is the image of (x, y) under T^{-1}?

27. If $S(x, y) = (3x, 3y)$, then $S^{-1}(x, y) =$ ____.

28. Every reflection is its own inverse. What number, other than 1, is its own multiplicative inverse?

Ⓑ **29–34.** These are *review* exercises. Describe each composite. (Assume any pair of size transformations or rotations has the same center.)

29. $S_3 \circ S_6$

30. $S_{-\frac{1}{2}} \circ S_4$

31. $R_4 \circ R_2$

32. $R_{100} \circ R_{120}$

33. $r_\ell \circ r_\ell$

34. $r_\ell \circ r_m$, $\ell \parallel m$

35–38. Tell which group properties are satisfied by the given set and composition.

35. set of rotations with center C, magnitudes $0°$, $120°$, $-120°$

36. $\{I, r_{x\text{-axis}}, r_{y\text{-axis}}, R_{180}\}$

37. set of size transformations with center M and integral magnitudes

38. set of all reflections

39. Demonstrate that transformation composition is *not* commutative.

40. Prove Theorem 9.6.4.

© **41.** Show that the set of *all* rotations is not closed under composition by rotating $\begin{bmatrix} 0 & 1 & 1 & 0 \\ 0 & 1 & 0 & -5 \end{bmatrix}$ $90°$ about $(0, 0)$, then rotating the image $270°$ about $(5, 0)$. Describe the composite of the two rotations.

42. Show that the set of *all* size transformations is not closed under composition by describing $S \circ T$, where S is a size transformation of magnitude 2, center $(0, 0)$, and T is a size transformation of magnitude $\frac{1}{2}$, center $(10, 10)$.

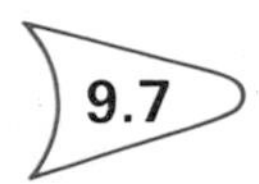

ANOTHER LOOK AT SINES AND COSINES

Recall the matrix-transformation isomorphism theorem (5.5.5): The composite of transformations T_1 and T_2 corresponds to the product of the associated matrices M_1 and M_2.

Composition of transformations	$T_1 \longleftrightarrow M_1$	Multiplication of matrices
	$T_2 \longleftrightarrow M_2$	
	$T_2 \circ T_1 \longleftrightarrow M_2M_1$	

Just as with addition and multiplication of real numbers, this isomorphism implies that *every property of transformations corresponds to a property of associated matrices* (if the transformations have matrices) and vice versa.

If the transformations are rotations with center at the origin, then here are some correspondences.

$$R_x \longleftrightarrow \begin{bmatrix} \cos x & -\sin x \\ \sin x & \cos x \end{bmatrix}$$

$$R_y \longleftrightarrow \begin{bmatrix} \cos y & -\sin y \\ \sin y & \cos y \end{bmatrix}$$

$$R_x \circ R_y = R_{x+y} \qquad \begin{bmatrix} \cos x & -\sin x \\ \sin x & \cos x \end{bmatrix} \cdot \begin{bmatrix} \cos y & -\sin y \\ \sin y & \cos y \end{bmatrix} = \begin{bmatrix} \cos(x+y) & -\sin(x+y) \\ \sin(x+y) & \cos(x+y) \end{bmatrix}$$

Multiplying the matrices at right for R_x and R_y gives an alternate proof of the formulas for $\cos(x + y)$ and $\sin(x + y)$ in Section 8.5.

1st row, 1st column: $\cos x \cos y - \sin x \sin y = \cos(x + y)$

2nd row, 1st column: $\sin x \cos y + \cos x \sin y = \sin(x + y)$

Since R_x and R_{-x} are inverse transformations, their matrices are also inverses. That is,

inverse of matrix for R_x ▶ $\begin{bmatrix} \cos x & -\sin x \\ \sin x & \cos x \end{bmatrix}^{-1} = \begin{bmatrix} \cos(-x) & -\sin(-x) \\ \sin(-x) & \cos(-x) \end{bmatrix}$ ◀ matrix for R_{-x}

But you can calculate the inverse matrix by using Theorem 9.4.1. The determinant is $\cos x \cdot \cos x + \sin x \cdot \sin x$, or 1.

$$\begin{bmatrix} \cos x & -\sin x \\ \sin x & \cos x \end{bmatrix}^{-1} = \begin{bmatrix} \cos x & \sin x \\ -\sin x & \cos x \end{bmatrix}$$

The two right matrices are equal, so corresponding elements are equal. This gives two important properties of sines and cosines.

Theorem 9.7.1

For any x, $\cos(-x) = \cos x$ and $\sin(-x) = -\sin x$.

For example, $\cos(-30^\circ) = \cos 30^\circ = \frac{\sqrt{3}}{2}$;

$\sin(-30^\circ) = -\sin 30^\circ = -\frac{1}{2}$.

EXERCISES 9.7

Ⓐ **1.** What is the matrix-transformation isomorphism theorem?

2. How are the matrices for R_x, R_y, and R_{x+y} related?

3. How are the matrices for R_x and R_{-x} related?

4–7. Give an expression for each number in terms of sines and cosines of x and y.

4. $\sin(-x)$ **5.** $\cos(-x)$ **6.** $\cos(x + y)$ **7.** $\sin(x + y)$

8. If $\cos x = 0.531$, then $\cos(-x) =$ ____.

9. If $\sin x = \frac{3}{5}$, then $\sin(-x) =$ ____.

Ⓑ **10–12.** Calculate.

10. $\cos(-60^\circ)$

11. $\sin(-60^\circ)$

12. $\cos(-45^\circ)$

13. (ve two different expressions for the inverse of $\begin{bmatrix} \cos x & -\sin x \\ \sin x & \cos x \end{bmatrix}$.

14. Find the inverse of the matrix for $r_{x\text{-axis}}$. What does your answer tell you about this transformation?

15. Transformation T has matrix $\begin{bmatrix} 3 & 0 \\ 0 & 2 \end{bmatrix}$. Calculate the matrix for T^{-1}.

16. Use matrices to verify that S_k and $S_{\frac{1}{k}}$ are inverse transformations.

17. Show that the matrices for R_{90} and R_{270} are inverses.

18–20. Calculate.

18. $\cos(-210^\circ)$

19. $\cos(-211^\circ)$

20. $\sin(-840^\circ)$

21. Let $T(\triangle ABC) = \triangle A'B'C'$, where $A = (0, 0)$, $B = (2, 0)$, $C = (2, 3)$ and T has matrix $\begin{bmatrix} 1 & 5 \\ 0 & 1 \end{bmatrix}$. What are the vertices of $\triangle A'B'C'$? What is a matrix for a transformation which maps $\triangle A'B'C'$ onto $\triangle ABC$?

Ⓒ **22–24.** Prove that each set of matrices forms a multiplicative group.

22. the set of matrices of the form $\begin{bmatrix} a & 0 \\ 0 & b \end{bmatrix}$ (These correspond to transformations called *scale* transformations.)

23. the set of matrices of the form $\begin{bmatrix} 1 & k \\ 0 & 1 \end{bmatrix}$ (These correspond to what are called *shear* transformations.)

24. the set of 2×2 matrices in which the sum of the elements in each row is 1 and no column has two equal elements.

25–29. Because of the matrix-transformation isomorphism theorem, every group of transformations which have matrices corresponds to a group of matrices, and vice versa. Name the elements of the group which corresponds to the given group.

25. $\langle\{I, r_{y\text{-axis}}\}, \circ\rangle$

26. $\langle\{I, R_{90}, R_{180}, R_{270}\}, \circ\rangle$

27. $\left\langle\left\{\begin{bmatrix}1 & 0\\0 & 1\end{bmatrix}, \begin{bmatrix}0 & 1\\1 & 0\end{bmatrix}, \begin{bmatrix}-1 & 0\\0 & -1\end{bmatrix}, \begin{bmatrix}0 & -1\\-1 & 0\end{bmatrix}\right\}, \cdot\right\rangle$

28. $\left\langle\left\{\begin{bmatrix}1 & 0\\0 & 1\end{bmatrix}, \begin{bmatrix}-1 & 0\\0 & 1\end{bmatrix}, \begin{bmatrix}1 & 0\\0 & -1\end{bmatrix}, \begin{bmatrix}-1 & 0\\0 & -1\end{bmatrix}\right\}, \cdot\right\rangle$

29. $\langle$the set of matrices of the form $\begin{bmatrix}k & 0\\0 & k\end{bmatrix}$ with $k > 0$, $\cdot\rangle$

ANOTHER LOOK AT LINES, CIRCLES, ETC. 9.8

Flexibility is gained by corresponding geometric ideas with algebraic ideas. The idea is to make the correspondence so good that answers correspond. In fancy words, we want to create an isomorphism between the geometry and the algebra. Here are some corresponding ideas with which you are familiar.

Geometric	*Algebraic*
point on a line	real number
line	set of all real numbers
point in a plane	ordered pair (x, y) of real numbers
line in a plane	$\{(x, y)\colon Ax + By = C\}$
plane	set of all ordered pairs of real numbers
half-plane	$\{(x, y)\colon Ax + By > C\}$
parallelism	sameness of slope
circle	$\{(x, y)\colon (x - h)^2 + (y - k)^2 = r^2\}$
interior of circle	$\{(x, y)\colon (x - h)^2 + (y - k)^2 < r^2\}$
find where two lines intersect	solve 2×2 linear system of equations

The list could be made much longer. We could put some transformations in the left column and their corresponding matrices in the right column. You will study more geometric ideas and their algebraic counterparts in the next chapters.

In most of the cases on page 253, you probably learned the geometric ideas first. Sometimes the numerical, algebraic ideas are first. Here are two ideas from arithmetic and the corresponding geometric ideas. (Both of these geometric ideas were first stated in Section 3.1.)

Algebraic (arithmetic)	*Geometric*
addition	composing translations
multiplication	composing size transformations

As an example of the geometric way to add (composing translations), you may remember adding positive and negative numbers by using arrows. The arrows indicate horizontal slides.

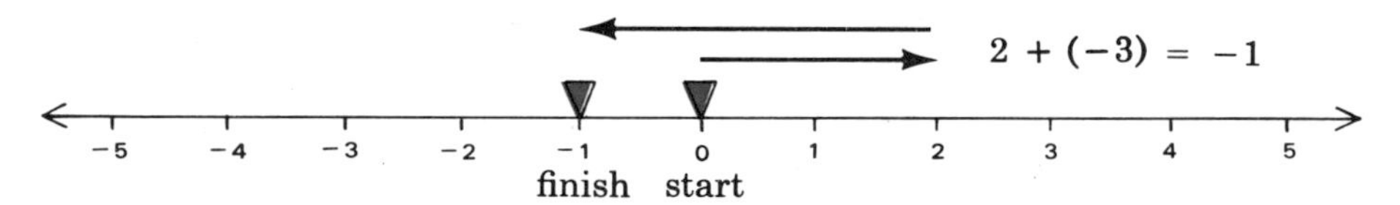

A slide of 2 units to the right followed by a slide of 3 units to the left yields the same result as a slide of 1 unit to the left. (Slides to the left correspond to negative numbers.) The answers correspond because of two isomorphic groups:

$\langle$ set of real numbers, $+ \rangle$ $\qquad$ $\langle$ set of horizontal slides, $\circ \rangle$

a	corresponds to	slide of a units
b	corresponds to	slide of b units
$a + b$	corresponds to	slide of $a + b$ units

The size-transformation view of multiplication is roughly described by the statement "To compose two size transformations with the same center, multiply their magnitudes." This can be done because of an isomorphism between two groups:

$\langle$ set of nonzero real numbers, $\cdot \rangle$ $\qquad$ $\langle$ set of size transformations with center (0, 0), $\circ \rangle$

x	corresponds to	S_x
y	corresponds to	S_y
xy	corresponds to	$S_x \circ S_y = S_{xy}$

For example, $S_{10} \circ S_{20} = S_{200}$, just as $10 \cdot 20 = 200$.

EXERCISES 9.8

Ⓐ **1.** Why might a person want to have an algebraic counterpart of a geometric idea?

2. Why might a geometric picture of addition be useful?

3–20. **(a)** Tell whether the idea is more geometric or algebraic. **(b)** If the idea is geometric, give the corresponding algebraic idea. If the idea is algebraic, what geometric idea does it describe?

3. line in a plane

4. $\{(x, y): (x - 2)^2 + y^2 = 9\}$

5. slope

6. parallelism

7. product of slopes is -1

8. $\{(a, b): 3a - 4b < 12\}$

9. point in a plane

10. real number

11. interior of a circle

12. solve $\begin{cases} 2x - 3y = 4 \\ 8x + 6y = 11 \end{cases}$

Ⓑ **13.** distance in a plane

14. $\{(x, y): 11 > x^2 + y^2\}$

15. $\begin{bmatrix} 1 & 0 \\ 0 & -1 \end{bmatrix}$

16. R_{90}

17. $\begin{bmatrix} 0 & 1 \\ 1 & 0 \end{bmatrix}$

18. S_3

19. $(x, y) \rightarrow (x + a, y + b)$

20. distance on a line

21. A magazine uses the diagram at right to illustrate that 75% of its readers are under age 30. Does this illustrate a correspondence between geometric ideas and algebraic (arithmetic) ideas? If so, how?

22–25. Graph or solve the problem related to the exercise above.

22. Exercise 4 **23.** Exercise 8 **24.** Exercise 12 **25.** Exercise 14

9.9 MORE WORK WITH APPLICATIONS

If you were asked how large your family is, you would answer by using a counting number (positive integer). Such a question would not be answered with a word like *many* or *big*.

In New Guinea in the South Pacific, there are even today tribes which have no names for numbers larger than 2 or 3. They have (in their language) *one*, *two*, and use the word *many* for counts larger than 2. Other tribes may go as high as ten or twenty but no higher.

For us in the United States, the mathematics of counting is isomorphic to the real situation. (For many New Guineans this is not so.) You need a big number system to do this. The positive integers serve as a good *model* for counting.

> The *modeling process* is the attempt to find or create mathematics which is *as isomorphic as possible* to a real situation and apply this mathematics to that situation.

Remember the steps in the modeling process: (1) State the real situation; (2) Simplify it; (3) Translate into mathematics; (4) Work with the mathematics; (5) Translate back; (6) Decide whether the solution is feasible in the real world.

> When people believe that the mathematics is isomorphic to the real situation, they will ignore Steps (5) and (6) and give the answer mathematically.

Real question	*Model*
How warm or cold is it?	number line (temperature)
How much is that worth?	decimals to hundredths (cost)
Will it rain tomorrow?	probability
How big is that farm?	area
How far away is Tokyo?	distance on surface of sphere

... and many, many more

These models may not be considered isomorphic by some people. You may not think that the cost really gives the value of an item. Humidity and wind affect the way a person feels about temperature.

Some models *cannot* be isomorphic. These particularly include models for prediction. Suppose that you wanted to predict what the world record for the women's 800-metre run (about $\frac{1}{2}$ mile) will be in 1980. Some recent world records are given at left and graphed at right. (2:07.3 means 2 minutes, 7.3 seconds.)

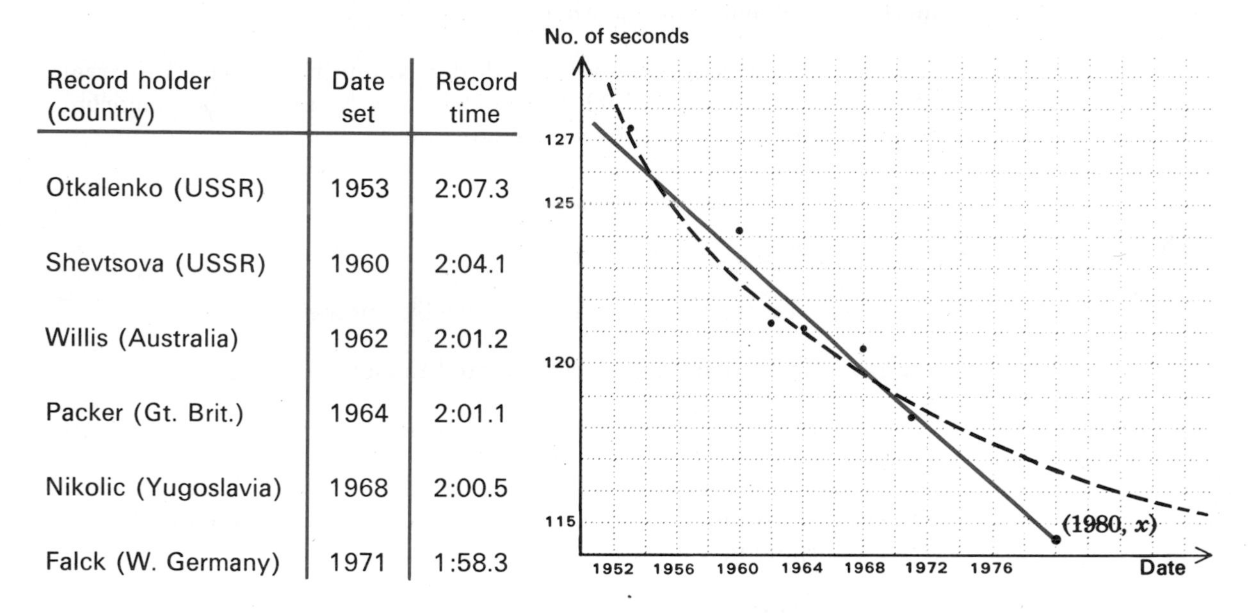

Record holder (country)	Date set	Record time
Otkalenko (USSR)	1953	2:07.3
Shevtsova (USSR)	1960	2:04.1
Willis (Australia)	1962	2:01.2
Packer (Gt. Brit.)	1964	2:01.1
Nikolic (Yugoslavia)	1968	2:00.5
Falck (W. Germany)	1971	1:58.3

We might model the evolution of the world record by the line drawn in red. This line approximately goes through (1972, 118) and (1956, 125). If (1980, x) is on the line, then by equating slopes:

$$\frac{x - 118}{1980 - 1972} = \frac{125 - 118}{1956 - 1972}$$

$$\frac{x - 118}{8} = -\frac{7}{16}$$

$$x - 118 = -\frac{56}{16}$$

$$x = 114.5$$

So a prediction is 1:54.5.

But you might feel that times will not go down as quickly as they have in the past. Then perhaps the dashed curve would be more appropriate as a model. This would give a higher (slower) prediction.

Which model is better? We may not know until 1980. But similar models done by the author for other races suggest that lines are reasonably good models (at the present time) for all but the shortest races.

The process of calculating future or past events from present data is called *extrapolation*. Extrapolation is used by businesses to predict future supply and demand, ecologists to measure possible effects of pollution, colleges to judge the degree of success of an applicant, governments to estimate growth, educators to weigh effects of new methods, and many, many others.

Important decisions may be made by examining a model for extrapolation. The degree to which the model of extrapolation is isomorphic to the real situation is thus very important.

EXERCISES 9.9

Ⓐ **1.** Name six steps involved in the modeling process.

2. How is the modeling process related to isomorphism?

3. Give two real questions for which answers are given by nearly isomorphic models.

4. Give an example of a real situation for which there cannot be an isomorphic mathematical model.

5. What is extrapolation?

6. Give an example of how extrapolation might be used.

Ⓑ **7–9.** *Sports.* Using the curve model of evolution of the world record in the women's 800-metre run (p. 257), predict what the record might be:

7. in 1980. **8.** in 1984. **9.** in 1988.

Ⓒ **10–12.** *Sports.* Using the linear model of evolution of the world record in the women's 800-metre run, predict what the record might be:

10. in 1984. **11.** in 2000. **12.** in 2400.

13–14. Use the following data concerning total population of the United States.

Date	*Population (in millions)*	*Date*	*Population (in millions)*
1900	76	1940	132
1910	92	1950	151
1920	106	1960	179
1930	123	1970	203

13. *Population trends.* Graph the data for the years 1900–1930 only. From this graph, what would you predict for the population in 1940? Why do you think your prediction would be too high?

14. Graph all of the given data and predict what you think the U.S. population will be in 1980.

15. Make up your own question which would involve extrapolation.

CHAPTER SUMMARY

Two interesting and important features of mathematics run through this chapter. (1) *The same situation can be considered by very different types of mathematics.* For instance, algebraic ideas can often be used in place of geometric ideas, and vice versa. Systems can be solved by matrices.

(2) *The same mathematics can be used in many different situations.* In this chapter, group properties are connected with equation solving, system solving, sines and cosines, and corresponding properties of multiples and powers.

The reason that these two features are so widespread is that *isomorphic* structures run through many situations and through much of mathematics. Isomorphic structures are structures which have the same or corresponding properties.

In pointing out examples of isomorphic structures, content from every previous chapter is involved. Thus this chapter serves as a review of the first half of this book. Here is what is done, section by section. The earlier chapter which is reviewed is indicated in parentheses.

9.1 (Chapter 1) A structure called the *group* is introduced. This structure has the group properties you have known for a long time.

9.2 (Chapter 1) The solving of equations $a + x = b$ and $ax = b$ is reviewed and related to a more general theorem about equation solving in groups.

9.3 (Chapters 1 and 2) Sets of multiples with addition are shown to have the same structure as sets of powers with multiplication. The two structures are isomorphic. The isomorphism enables us to list many corresponding properties of multiples and powers, making them easier to remember.

9.4 *and* 9.5 (Chapters 5 and 6) Matrices and multiplication are examined for group properties. These matrix properties are applied to the solution of systems in exactly the same way as real-number properties are applied to the solution of equations in Section 9.2.

9.6 *and* 9.7 (Chapters 4 and 8) Transformations and composition are examined for group properties. You have known (by the matrix-transformation isomorphism theorem of Chapter 5) that structures involving matrices and multiplication are isomorphic to those involving transformations and composition. This is applied to find more properties of sines and cosines.

9.8 (Chapter 7) Correspondences between algebraic ideas and geometric ideas are reviewed. These provide examples of number mathematics which is isomorphic to picture mathematics.

9.9 (Chapter 3) Modeling as used in applications is seen as the attempt to find mathematics and a mathematical structure which is isomorphic or nearly isomorphic to the real situation we are trying to model.

9

CHAPTER REVIEW

1–3. For each group, give (**a**) the identity and (**b**) a second element and its inverse.

1. $\langle$set of real numbers, $+\rangle$

2. $\langle$set of invertible 2×2 matrices, $\cdot\rangle$

3. $\langle\{R_{72}, R_{288}, R_{360}, R_{144}, R_{216}\}, \circ\rangle$

4–5. Tell why each set and operation do not form a group.

4. set of real numbers, $\cdot$

5. $\left\{\begin{bmatrix}1 & 0\\0 & 1\end{bmatrix}, \begin{bmatrix}0 & 1\\-1 & 0\end{bmatrix}, \begin{bmatrix}0 & -1\\1 & 0\end{bmatrix}\right\}, \cdot$

6–8. Simplify.

6. $(2a)^{-3}$

7. $\frac{3^{-2}}{3^2}$

8. $(x^2)^3 + (x^4)^3$

9. A matrix for a transformation is $\begin{bmatrix}3 & 5\\4 & 2\end{bmatrix}$. What is a matrix for the inverse of the transformation?

10. Solve the system $\begin{cases}2a - b = 11\\a - 5b = 3\end{cases}$ using matrices.

11. For what value of c does $\begin{cases}4x - 6y = 5\\2x + cy = 2\end{cases}$ have no solution?

12. Approximate $\sin(-120°)$ to the nearest thousandth.

13. What group involving real numbers is isomorphic to the following group: $\langle$set of horizontal translations, $\circ\rangle$?

14. Multiple choice: The idea of isomorphism is useful because it provides:

a. associativity. **b.** commutativity. **c.** flexibility.

15. Give an example of a use of extrapolation.

CUMULATIVE REVIEW: CHAPTERS 1–9

Ch. 1

1. When are two mathematical sentences equivalent?

2. Name and state the group properties of real number addition.

3–11. Solve.

3. $7 + b = 14$ **4.** $7b = 14$ **5.** $1 - x = 0.75$

6. $\frac{1}{x} = 0.75$ **7.** $0.08c = 0.4$ **8.** $\frac{5}{6} = \frac{25}{y}$

9. $(x - 3)(x + 2) = 0$ **10.** $0a = 3$ **11.** $0a = 0$

12–18. Let $x = 3$, $y = -2$, $a = 2$, and $b = \frac{1}{3}$. Evaluate.

12. $a + y$ **13.** bx **14.** $x - 5y$ **15.** $-ax^2$

16. $2x^2 - 5x + 1$ **17.** $\dfrac{b - \frac{1}{3}}{b + \frac{2}{3}}$ **18.** $(x - 1)(x + 2) - 12b$

19–24. Simplify.

19. $y + [3 - 2(4 - y)]$ **20.** $-(3y)^2y^0$ **21.** $4x - 2x + 5x - x$

22. $x^4 \cdot x^{-2} \cdot x^5 \cdot x^{-1}$ **23.** $\sqrt{3} \cdot \sqrt{\frac{5}{3}}$ **24.** $5\sqrt{2} - \sqrt{8} + \sqrt{18}$

25. Find the arithmetic mean of $\frac{2}{3}$ and $\frac{8}{3}$.

26. Find the geometric means of $\frac{2}{3}$ and $\frac{8}{3}$.

Ch. 2

27. State the trichotomy property.

28. State the transitive property for $<$.

29–37. Solve. Then graph the solution set.

29. $3x > 15$ **30.** $-4y > 2$ **31.** $-z - 2 \leq 7$

32. $253r = 252r + 3$ **33.** $\frac{T}{4} = \frac{3 + T}{2}$ **34.** $6h - 9 > 3h + 12$

35. $\frac{w}{5} = \frac{w}{25} - 8$ **36.** $\frac{2 - m}{3} < 1$ **37.** $-f - 7f = 2(3f - 7)$

38–39. Solve for the given variable.

38. $ax + 2x = 1$ for x **39.** $(y - b)^2 = 9$ for y

40–42. Find each product or square.

40. $(x + 3)(x - 2)$ **41.** $(2a + 5)(3a - 1)$ **42.** $(2x - 5)^2$

43. Give three intervals of a sequence of nested intervals containing $\sqrt{2}$.

Ch. 3

44. If a tire costs t dollars, how much will 4 tires cost?

45. A grandstand ticket costs t dollars, and a box-seat ticket costs 4 dollars more. What is the cost of 4 box-seat tickets?

46–48. Solve. Then graph the solution set.

46. $|x - 3| = 7$

47. $|x - (-2)| > 5$

48. $|x + 2| \leq 5$

49. Find the distance between $(-2, -3)$ and $(10, 2)$.

50. Write a sentence of the form $|x - a| \leq b$ that is a model for: The population p is within 1.5% of 125,000.

51–54. Translate each phrase or sentence into mathematics.

51. 7 more than a number

52. 7 is more than a number.

53. a number decreased by $2\frac{1}{2}$

54. $2\frac{1}{2}$ percent of an amount

Ch. 4

55. A transformation is a 1–1 correspondence between ____.

56. Trace the figure below. Then draw $r_m(\triangle ABC)$.

57. Trace the figure below. Then draw $R_{45}(EFGH)$ using P as center.

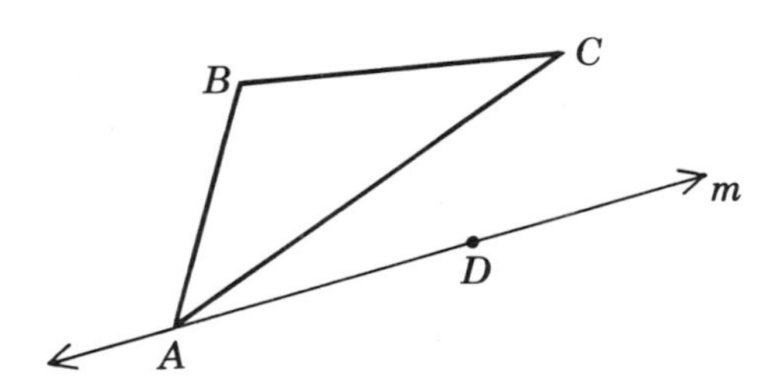

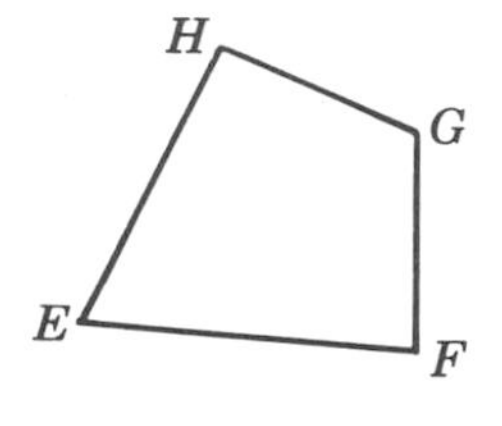

P

58. Trace the figure above. Then draw $t(\triangle ABC)$ where the translation t maps A onto D.

59. Trace the figure above. Then draw $S_2(EFGH)$ using P as center.

60. The composite of two reflections r_x and r_y is a ____ if x and y are parallel and a ____ if x and y intersect.

61. Name three types of transformations which preserve distance and one type which does not.

62. Draw a triangle which is reflection-symmetric but not rotation-symmetric.

63. The dimensions of matrix X are 2×3, and matrix Y has dimensions 3×4. Does $X \cdot Y$ exist? Does $Y \cdot X$ exist?

Ch. 5

64–66. What 2×2 matrix corresponds to each transformation?

64. $r_{x=y}$ **65.** R_{90} **66.** S_{-2}

67–69. Use matrix multiplication to find the image of $(-3, 7)$ under each transformation given in Exercises **64–66.**

70–72. Find the matrix for each composite.

70. $r_{x=y} \circ R_{90}$ **71.** $R_{90} \circ S_{-2}$ **72.** $R_{90} \circ R_{-90}$

73. Find the image of $\triangle ABC$ under the transformation with matrix M. $\triangle ABC = \begin{bmatrix} 2 & -1 & -5 \\ 3 & 5 & 0 \end{bmatrix}$ $M = \begin{bmatrix} 1 & 2 \\ 3 & -1 \end{bmatrix}$

74–77. Let $A = (4, 1)$ and $B = (2, -3)$. Find each of the following.

Ch. 6

74. the slope of $\overleftrightarrow{AB}$

75. the y-intercept of $\overleftrightarrow{AB}$

76. an equation for $\overleftrightarrow{AB}$

77. the midpoint of $\overline{AB}$

78–80. A circle C has center $(2, -5)$ and contains $(-3, 1)$.

78. What is the radius of C?

79. Give an equation for C.

80. Give an equation for the circle that is congruent to C but has center $(0, 0)$.

81–83. Find an equation or inequality for:

81. a line through $(-1, 2)$ that is parallel to $x - 2y = 5$.

82. a line through $(-1, 2)$ that is perpendicular to $x - 2y = 5$.

83. a circle with center $(5, -7)$ that is congruent to $x^2 + y^2 = 16$.

84. the half-plane above the line through $(0, -2)$ and $(8, 2)$.

85. the interior of the circle with center $(3, 2)$ and radius 2.

86–88. On a number line, graph the solution set to each sentence.

Ch. 7

86. $x < -2$ or $x > 3$ **87.** $|z| \leq 4$ **88.** $y > -2$ and $y < 3$

89–91. Solve each system.

89. $y = 3x$
$x - y = 6$

90. $4x + 2y = 6$
$x + 3y = 14$

91. $r + s = 4$
$r + 2s = 2$
$3r - 2s = 22$

92–94. Give the coefficient matrix of each system in Exercises **89–91**.

95. What kind of problems are called linear programming problems?

Ch. 8

96. Give a definition for *cosine of t*.

97. Find each value exactly.

a. $\sin 90^\circ$ **b.** $\cos 270^\circ$ **c.** $\sin(-45^\circ)$

98. Use the table to find approximations.

a. $\cos 72^\circ$ **b.** $\sin 173^\circ$ **c.** $\cos(-108^\circ)$

99. Given $\sin x = 0.8$, find $\cos x$.

100. Use the table to find, approximately, the matrix for R_{75}.

101. Approximate the image of $\begin{bmatrix} 1 & 5 & 3 \\ 1 & 3 & 6 \end{bmatrix}$ under R_{75}.

102. Given $\cos 45^\circ = \sin 45^\circ = \frac{\sqrt{2}}{2}$, $\cos 30^\circ = \frac{\sqrt{3}}{2}$, and $\sin 30^\circ = \frac{1}{2}$, find the exact value of $\sin 75^\circ$.

103–106. Without using tables, graph each point.

103. $[5, 60^\circ]$ **104.** $(2 \cos 90^\circ, 2 \sin 90^\circ)$

105. $[-3, -90^\circ]$ **106.** $(-\frac{1}{2} \cos 45^\circ, -\frac{1}{2} \sin 45^\circ)$

Ch. 9

107. State the group properties for $\langle S, \# \rangle$.

108–109. Tell why each set and operation *do not* form a group.

108. $\{-1, 0, 1\}$; $+$ **109.** set of integers; $\cdot$

110–112. Simplify.

110. $(3x)^4$ **111.** $\left(\frac{x}{2}\right)^3$ **112.** $(y^2)^3$

113. The matrix for transformation T is $\begin{bmatrix} 1 & 0 \\ -2 & 3 \end{bmatrix}$. Find the matrix for T^{-1}.

114. Solve the system $\begin{cases} 2x - 4y = 7 \\ 4x + 2y = 1 \end{cases}$ using matrices.

115–116. For each group give an isomorphic group.

115. $\langle$set of integral powers of 2, $\cdot\rangle$ **116.** $\langle$set of horizontal slides, $\circ\rangle$

Chapter 10 The Complex Numbers

Just as *real numbers* are commonly associated with points on a line, so *complex numbers* are often associated with points on a plane. In this chapter, we discuss some ways of representing complex numbers, operations on these numbers, and relationships between complex numbers and transformations.

Complex numbers can be used in a variety of physical situations. For example, they can be used to represent the speed and direction of the boat shown above, and the speed and direction of both the wind and the current. Operations on complex numbers can give the speed and direction the boat travels as a result of the interaction of these forces.

10.1 THE COMPLEX NUMBER PLANE

As you already know, it is quite useful to associate real numbers with the points on a line. From this association, formulas for the distance between points can be derived, solution sets to equations can be pictured, and the properties of geometric figures can be observed from an algebraic viewpoint.

It is equally useful to associate numbers with the points on a plane. Such numbers are called **complex numbers**. The name arose because at one time mathematicians felt that it was more difficult to deal with complex numbers than real numbers. (Experience and modern developments in mathematics have shown this is not so.)

Definition (part a)

The set of **complex numbers** is a set of numbers which correspond one-to-one to points in the plane.

Other things, such as matrices or ordered pairs, also correspond to points in the plane. Consequently, the definition given above is not enough to fully describe the *complex numbers*. Parts **b** and **c**, given in the next two sections, show how to add and multiply complex numbers.

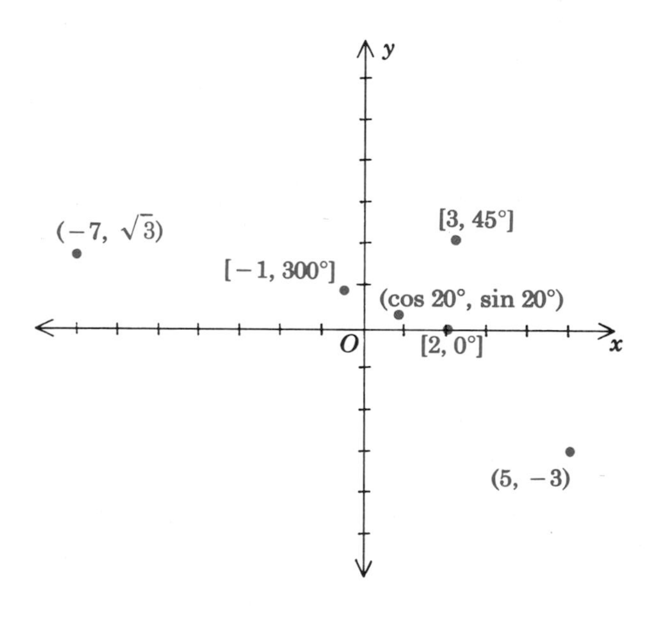

Examples of complex numbers written using rectangular coordinates are $(5, -3)$, $(\cos 20°, \sin 20°)$, and $(-7, \sqrt{3})$. The complex numbers $[3, 45°]$, $[-1, 300°]$, and $[2, 0°]$ are denoted by polar coordinates. The points corresponding to these complex numbers are graphed at the left.

Because ordered pairs are used to represent both complex numbers and points, we speak of *graphing a complex number* when we are really graphing the point corresponding to the complex number. The plane for graphing complex numbers is called the **complex number plane**, just as coordinatized lines are called *real number lines*.

Many concepts that apply to real numbers also apply to complex numbers. One such concept is **absolute value**. Recall that the absolute value of a real number is the distance between its graph and the point whose coordinate is 0.

Definition

The **absolute value of the complex number z**, denoted $|z|$, is the distance of the point z from the origin.

This distance is easily computed in either rectangular or polar coordinates.

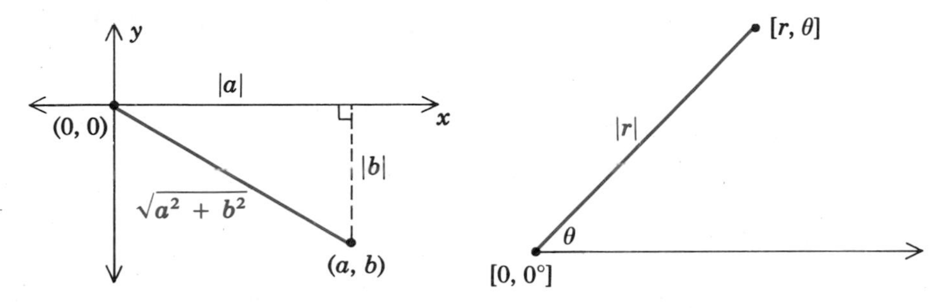

Theorem 10.1.1

Formulas for absolute value:

a. *Rectangular Coordinates:* The absolute value of the complex number (a, b) is $\sqrt{a^2 + b^2}$.

b. *Polar Coordinates:* The absolute value of the complex number $[r, \theta]$ is $|r|$.

Because a, b, and r are real numbers, $\sqrt{a^2 + b^2}$ and $|r|$ are also real numbers. In fact, the absolute value of a complex number is a non-negative real number.

Examples: Calculating absolute value

1. $|(5, -12)| = \sqrt{5^2 + (-12)^2} = \sqrt{25 + 144} = \sqrt{169} = 13$

2. If $z = [-17, 50°]$, then $|z| = 17$.

3. The absolute value of $\left(-\frac{1}{2}, \frac{\sqrt{3}}{2}\right)$ is $\sqrt{\left(-\frac{1}{2}\right)^2 + \left(\frac{\sqrt{3}}{2}\right)^2}$ or $\sqrt{\frac{1}{4} + \frac{3}{4}}$ or 1.

EXERCISES 10.1

Ⓐ 1. How many points of the plane correspond to each complex number?

2. What kinds of coordinates are used to represent a complex number?

3. How is the absolute value of a complex number defined?

4–7. Give the absolute value of each complex number.

4. $(3, 4)$ **5.** $(-2, 0)$ **6.** $[17, 90°]$ **7.** $[17, 21.2°]$

8–11. Simplify.

8. $|(-1, 2)|$ **9.** $|[12, 3°]|$ **10.** $|(-4, -4)|$ **11.** $|(0, 0)|$

12. How many complex numbers have absolute value 0?

13. How many complex numbers have absolute value 1?

14. Can the same point correspond to more than one complex number?

Ⓑ **15.** Name and graph five numbers with absolute value 5.

16. Name and graph 10 complex numbers with absolute value 6. Write five of these numbers using polar coordinates and five using rectangular coordinates.

17–20. Consider the following complex numbers.

a. (0, 8) b. (1, 7) c. (2, 6) d. (3, 5) e. (4, 4)

17. Which has the largest absolute value?

18. Which has the smallest absolute value?

19. Which can also be denoted by $[8, 90°]$?

20. Which can also be denoted by $[4\sqrt{2}, 45°]$?

21. If you wished to calculate the absolute value of a complex number, would you prefer that the number be represented with polar coordinates or with rectangular coordinates?

22–24. Let $z = (-3, 4)$, $w = (-1, 5)$, $u = (0, \frac{1}{4})$, and $v = (-5, 12)$. Calculate.

22. $|z| - |w|$ **23.** $|u| + |v|$ **24.** $4 \cdot |u| + 3 \cdot |v| - 10 \cdot |z|$

Ⓒ **25–28.** Graph the set of all complex numbers z satisfying the equation.

25. $|z| = 3$ **26.** $|z| = -3$ **27.** $|z| < 3$ **28.** $|z| \geq 3$

ADDITION OF COMPLEX NUMBERS

Adding 5 to a real number has the effect of sliding the graph of the number 5 units to the right. For example, $3 + 5$ is 5 units to the right of 3. In Section 9.8, this correspondence between *addition* and *translations (slides)* was identified as one of the isomorphisms between algebraic and geometric ideas.

The operation of addition extends naturally to complex numbers. (Rectangular coordinates are easiest for addition and are used exclusively in this section.) Adding (c, d) to a complex number is defined to correspond to the translation which slides the graph of the number c units horizontally and d units vertically. In the diagram, $(3, -4)$ is the given point and c and d are positive.

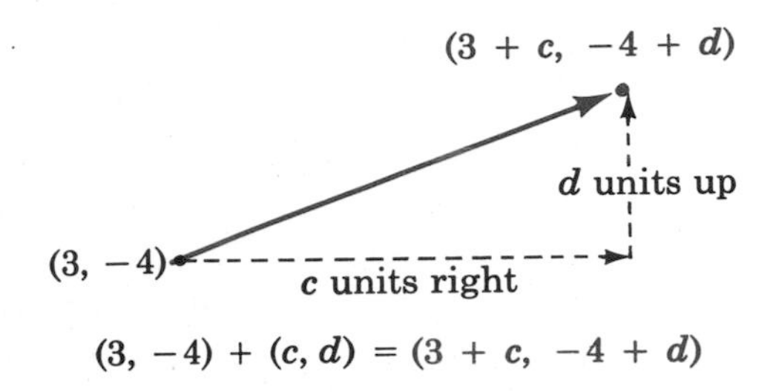

Definition (part b)

For any complex numbers (a, b) and (c, d),

$$(a, b) + (c, d) = (a + c, b + d).$$

Examples: Adding complex numbers

1. $(-7, 11) + (12, 20) = (-7 + 12, 11 + 20) = (5, 31)$
2. $(0, -3) + (-4, 7) = (-4, 4)$
3. Solve for (x, y): $\quad (x, y) + (5, -3) = (20, 0)$

   Adding: $\quad (x + 5, y - 3) = (20, 0)$

   Thus, $x + 5 = 20$ and $y - 3 = 0$,

   so $x = 15$ and $y = 3$. $\quad (x, y) = (15, 3)$

Notice again how *adding a complex number* corresponds to *translating a figure.* Suppose a triangle has vertices $(2, 3)$, $(6, 0)$, and $(-2, 4)$. Let us add $(-2, 8)$ to each vertex.

$$(2, 3) + (-2, 8) = (0, 11)$$

$$(6, 0) + (-2, 8) = (4, 8)$$

$$(-2, 4) + (-2, 8) = (-4, 12)$$

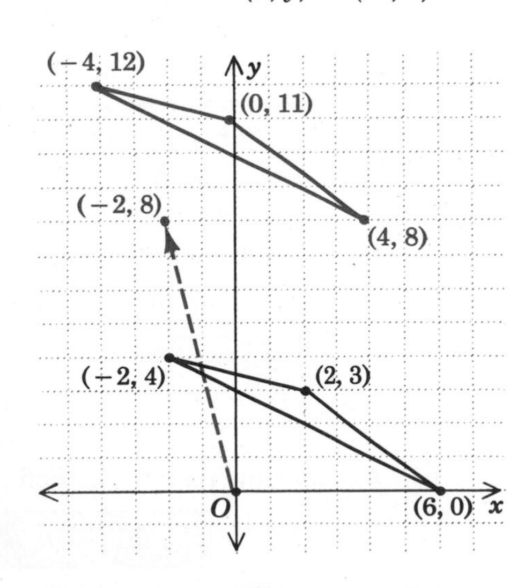

The preimage and image triangles are shown at the right. Addition of $(-2, 8)$ translates a point 2 units to the left and 8 units up.

GRAPHICALLY:

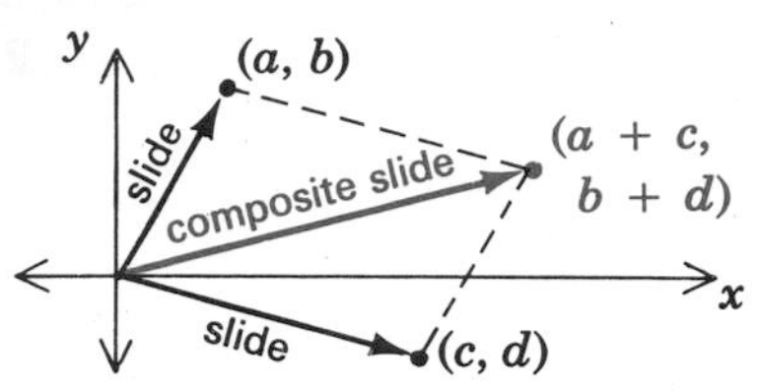

COMPLEX NUMBERS:

add

$$\begin{array}{c} (a, b) \\ (c, d) \\ \hline (a + c,\ b + d) \end{array}$$

TRANSLATIONS:

compose

$$\begin{array}{ll} (x, y) \rightarrow & (x + a,\ y + b) \\ (x, y) \rightarrow & (x + c,\ y + d) \\ \hline (x, y) \rightarrow & (x + a + c,\ y + b + d) \end{array}$$

Theorem 10.2.1

The set of complex numbers with addition is a group, isomorphic to the group of translations with composition.

Because the groups are isomorphic, the properties of complex number addition can be deduced from the properties of translation composition. (They can also be proved directly from the definition on page 269.)

Theorem 10.2.2

Properties of complex number addition: In the set of complex numbers,

a. Addition is closed.

b. Addition is associative.

c. (0, 0) is the additive identity.

d. The additive inverse of (a, b) is $(-a, -b)$.

e. Addition is commutative.

Subtraction is defined, as it is for real numbers, as adding the opposite.

Definition

For any complex numbers (a, b) and (c, d),

$$(\boldsymbol{a}, \boldsymbol{b}) - (\boldsymbol{c}, \boldsymbol{d}) = (a, b) + (-c, -d).$$

This can be simplified.

$$\begin{aligned} (a, b) - (c, d) &= (a, b) + (-c, -d) \\ &= (a + (-c),\ b + (-d)) \\ &= (a - c,\ b - d) \end{aligned}$$

We can now restate the definition.

$$(a, b) - (c, d) = (a - c,\ b - d)$$

EXERCISES 10.2

Ⓐ **1–10.** Add each pair of complex numbers. Graph both given numbers and their sum.

1. $(-2, 3)$, $(2, 3)$ **2.** $(0, \frac{1}{2})$, $(\frac{1}{2}, \frac{3}{2})$

3. $(-8.5, -2)$, $(-2.3, -6)$ **4.** (a, b), $(0, 0)$

5. $(6, -2)$, $(-2, 6)$ **6.** $(4, 6)$, $(-4, -6)$

7. $(3, 4)$, $(2, 8)$ **8.** $(-1, 2)$, $(6, -4)$

9. $(1, 8)$, $(-3, 5)$ **10.** $(-2, -3)$, $(8, 6)$

11–14. Give the additive inverse.

11. $(-4, 3)$ **12.** $(2, 8)$ **13.** $(5, -1)$ **14.** $(-3, -3)$

15. $\langle$set of complex numbers, $+\rangle$ is isomorphic to what other group?

16. Write as one complex number: $(a, b) - (c, d)$.

17. What complex number is the additive identity?

18–27. In Exercises **1–10**, subtract the second number from the first.

Ⓑ **28–33.** Let $u = (17, -2)$, $v = (-8, 6)$, $w = (0, -7)$, $z = (12, -5)$. Write as one complex number or one real number.

28. $(u - v) + w$ **29.** $|v + u + w|$

30. $|v - w|$ **31.** $|u - v| + |v - u|$

32. $(w + z) - w + v - z$ **33.** $z + z + z + z$

34. Add $(1, 4)$ to each vertex of the triangle $\begin{bmatrix} 1 & -2 & -3 \\ 3 & -4 & 0 \end{bmatrix}$. Graph the preimage and image. To what transformation does adding $(1, 4)$ correspond?

35. Add $(6, -1)$ to all points on the unit circle. Graph preimage and image. To what transformation does adding $(6, -1)$ correspond?

36–38. Use u, v, w, and z from Exercises **28–33**.

36. Which is larger, $|u + z|$ or $|u| + |z|$?

37. Which is larger, $|v - w|$ or $||v| - |w||$?

38. True or False? $v - (w + z) = v - w - z$

39. If $[r, \theta]$ is a complex number, what is its additive inverse?

© **40.** Prove: The absolute value of a complex number equals the absolute value of its additive inverse.

41. Prove: The distance from v to w in the complex plane is $|v - w|$. Verify the proof by using the numbers and the answer to Exercise **30**.

10.3 MULTIPLICATION OF COMPLEX NUMBERS

Multiplying by the real number 5 has the effect of magnifying 5 times. This is the size-change model of multiplication discussed earlier. This model applies to multiplication of complex numbers. (Polar coordinates are easiest for multiplication and are used here.)

Definition (part c)

For any complex numbers $[r, \theta]$ and $[s, \phi]$,

$$[r, \theta] \cdot [s, \phi] = [rs, \theta + \phi].$$

Examples: Multiplying complex numbers

1. $[2, 30°] \cdot [3, 45°] = [6, 75°]$
2. $[3, 330°] \cdot [\frac{1}{4}, 80°] = [\frac{3}{4}, 410°]$ or $[\frac{3}{4}, 50°]$
3. $[1, 90°] \cdot [1, 90°] = [1, 180°]$
4. $[-2, 223°] \cdot [5, 137°] = [-10, 0°]$
5. $[4, 200°] \cdot [\frac{1}{4}, -200°] = [1, 0°]$

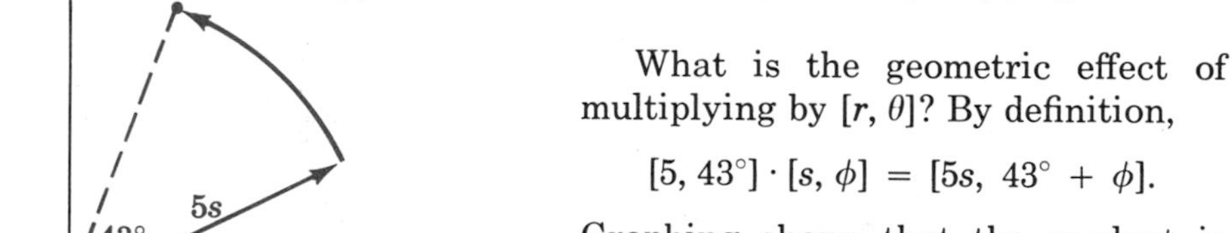

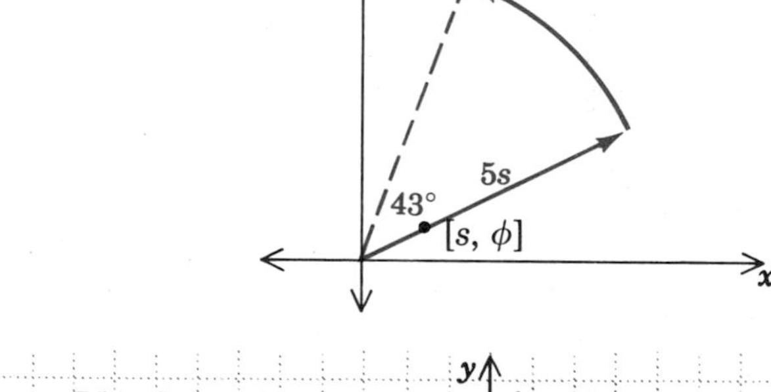

What is the geometric effect of multiplying by $[r, \theta]$? By definition,

$$[5, 43°] \cdot [s, \phi] = [5s, 43° + \phi].$$

Graphing shows that the product is 5 times as far from the origin as $[s, \phi]$ and rotated 43° from $[s, \phi]$.

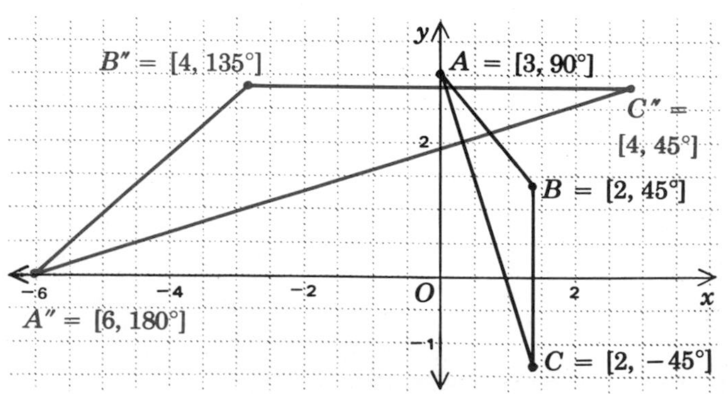

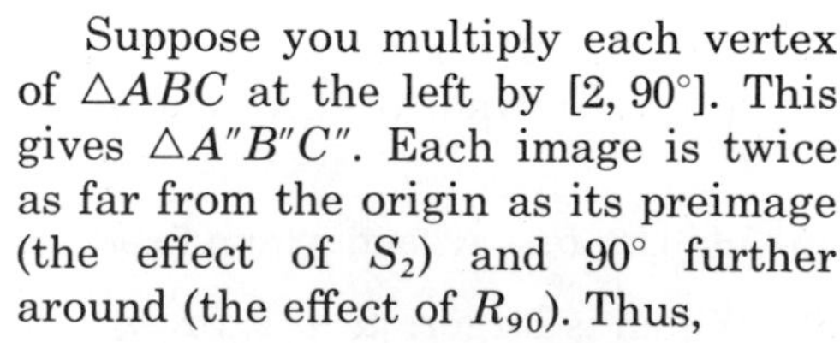

Suppose you multiply each vertex of $\triangle ABC$ at the left by [2, 90°]. This gives $\triangle A''B''C''$. Each image is twice as far from the origin as its preimage (the effect of S_2) and 90° further around (the effect of R_{90}). Thus,

$$\triangle A''B''C'' = R_{90} \circ S_2(\triangle ABC).$$

So $\triangle A''B''C''$ is similar to $\triangle ABC$. The ratio of corresponding sides is 2:1, and $\triangle A''B''C''$ is rotated 90° from $\triangle ABC$.

Theorem 10.3.1

Geometric property of complex number multiplication: Multiplying by $[r, \theta]$ size transforms by r and rotates by θ.

PROOF: By definition, $[r, \theta] \cdot [s, \phi] = [rs, \theta + \phi]$. Now compare $[s, \phi]$ and $[rs, \theta + \phi]$. The point $[rs, \theta + \phi]$ is r times as far from the origin as $[s, \phi]$ and a rotation of θ from $[s, \phi]$.

Any rotation can now be described as multiplication by a single complex number.

Corollary 10.3.2

Multiplying by $[1, \theta]$ rotates by θ.

PROOF: $[1, \theta] \cdot [s, \phi] = [s, \theta + \phi]$, so $[s, \phi]$ is just rotated by θ.

Thus, multiplying by $[1, 0°]$ rotates by $0°$, leaving a point where it is. Hence $[1, 0°]$ is the **identity** for complex number multiplication.

All complex numbers but $[0, 0°]$ have **reciprocals** or **multiplicative inverses.** The inverse numbers correspond to inverse transformations.

Multiplying by	corresponds to rotating by	and size transforming by
$[r, \theta]$	θ	r
reciprocal of $[r, \theta]$	$-\theta$	$\frac{1}{r}$

That is: $[r, \theta] \cdot \left[\frac{1}{r}, -\theta\right] = \left[r \cdot \frac{1}{r}, \theta + (-\theta)\right] = [1, 0°]$. For example, $[3, 100°]$ and $[\frac{1}{3}, -100°]$ are reciprocals.

We have now proved parts **c** and **d** of the following theorem.

Theorem 10.3.3

Properties of complex number multiplication: In the set of complex numbers, excluding $[0, 0°]$,

a. Multiplication is closed.

b. Multiplication is associative.

c. $[1, 0°]$ is the multiplicative identity.

d. The multiplicative inverse of $[r, \theta]$ is $\left[\frac{1}{r}, -\theta\right]$.

e. Multiplication is commutative.

PROOF: **a.** By definition, the product of two complex numbers is a complex number.

b. Complex number multiplication corresponds to applying a transformation. Since transformation composition is associative, so is complex number multiplication.

e. By definition: $[r, \theta] \cdot [s, \phi] = [rs, \theta + \phi]$

Commutativity of real number addition and multiplication: $= [sr, \phi + \theta]$

By definition: $= [s, \phi] \cdot [r, \theta]$

Thus multiplication of complex numbers has many of the same properties as real number multiplication.

EXERCISES 10.3

Ⓐ **1.** Multiplying by $[r, \theta]$ corresponds to what transformation?

2–8. Multiply.

2. $[r, \theta] \cdot [s, \phi]$

3. $[2, 30°] \cdot [5, 10°]$

4. $[6, 100°] \cdot [3, 200°]$

5. $[1, 3°] \cdot [1, 0°]$

6. $[0, 10°] \cdot [17, 410°]$

7. $[\sqrt{2}, 180°] \cdot [\sqrt{2}, -180°]$

8. $[1, 90°] \cdot [1, 90°] \cdot [1, 90°] \cdot [1, 90°]$

9. What is the identity for complex number multiplication?

10. What complex number has no reciprocal under multiplication?

11–14. Give the complex number multiplier needed to:

11. rotate by 60°, size transform by 3.

12. rotate by 120°.

13. size transform by $\sqrt{2}$, rotate by $-70°$.

14. size transform by 6.

15–18. Find the reciprocal of each number.

15. $[2, 50°]$

16. $[\frac{1}{2}, 170°]$

17. $[17, 0°]$

18. $[1, 0°]$

Ⓑ **19–24.** As usual, z^n means $z \cdot z \cdot z \cdots z$, with n factors. Write each power in the form $[r, \theta]$.

19. $[2, 72°]^2$

20. $[1, 120°]^3$

21. $[3, 240°]^3$

22. $[1, 90°]^4$

23. $[1, 90°]^5$

24. $[\sqrt{2}, 60°]^{12}$

25–26. Graph the triangle with vertices [7, 45°], [5, 90°], and [2, 180°]. Multiply each vertex by the given number, and graph the corresponding image. To what transformation does the multiplication correspond?

25. [1, 90°]

26. [$\frac{1}{2}$, 135°]

© **27–30.** Solve for z.

27. $z \cdot [12, 30°] = [2, 15°]$

28. $z = \dfrac{[2, 15°]}{[12, 30°]}$

29. $z \cdot [2, 15°] = [12, 30°]$

30. $z^2 = [4, 180°]$

31. Find four different complex numbers z satisfying $z^4 = [1, 0°]$. (HINT: $[1, 0°] = [1, 360°] = [1, 720°] = \cdots$.)

32. From the definition of multiplication, it can be proved that $[r, \theta]^n = [r^n, n\theta]$. (Special cases are given in Exercises **19–24**.) This theorem is called *De Moivre's Theorem*, named after Abraham De Moivre. Find out when and where this mathematician lived.

33–34. Graph $z, z^2, z^3, z^4, \cdots, z^{10}$ for the given z.

33. $z = [1, 30°]$

34. $z = [1.1, 30°]$

Biologists have discovered that honey bees use polar coordinates! An explorer bee, having found a source of food, returns to the hive to tell the other bees. Using dance-like movements, she describes both the distance from the hive to the food source and the angle of flight (in relation to the sun).

10.4 RELATING ADDITION TO MULTIPLICATION

Rectangular coordinates are more common than polar coordinates, so we need a formula for multiplying complex numbers in rectangular form.

Theorem 10.4.1

If (a, b) and (c, d) are complex numbers, then
$$(a, b) \cdot (c, d) = (ac - bd,\ ad + bc).$$

PROOF: By definition, $$[r, \theta] \cdot [s, \phi] = [rs,\ \theta + \phi].$$

Rewriting in rectangular coordinates (Theorem 8.6.1),

$$(r \cos \theta,\ r \sin \theta) \cdot (s \cos \phi,\ s \sin \phi) = (rs \cos(\theta + \phi),\ rs \sin(\theta + \phi)).$$

Now let $a = r \cos \theta$, $b = r \sin \theta$, $c = s \cos \phi$, and $d = s \sin \phi$.

Then $$(a, b) \cdot (c, d) = (rs \cos(\theta + \phi),\ rs \sin(\theta + \phi)).$$

To simplify the right side, use the formulas from Section 8.5 as shown below. Then substitute back in the equation to complete the proof.

$$\begin{aligned} &rs \cos(\theta + \phi) \\ &= rs(\cos \theta \cos \phi - \sin \theta \sin \phi) \\ &= r \cos \theta \cdot s \cos \phi - r \sin \theta \cdot s \sin \phi \\ &= ac - bd \end{aligned}$$

$$\begin{aligned} &rs \sin(\theta + \phi) \\ &= rs(\sin \theta \cos \phi + \cos \theta \sin \phi) \\ &= r \sin \theta \cdot s \cos \phi + r \cos \theta \cdot s \sin \phi \\ &= bc + ad \text{ (or } ad + bc) \end{aligned}$$

Compare the polar and rectangular forms in the first example.

Examples: Multiplication of complex numbers

1. POLAR:

$$zw = [\sqrt{2}, 45°] \cdot [2, 90°]$$
$$= [2\sqrt{2}, 135°]$$

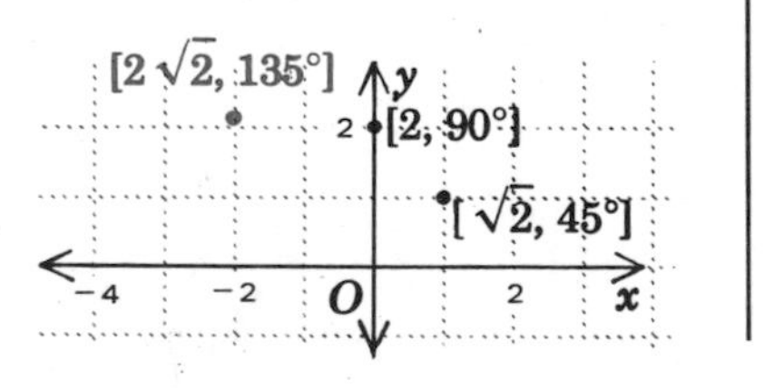

RECTANGULAR:

$$zw = (1, 1) \cdot (0, 2)$$
$$= (1 \cdot 0 - 1 \cdot 2,\ 1 \cdot 2 + 1 \cdot 0)$$
$$= (-2, 2)$$

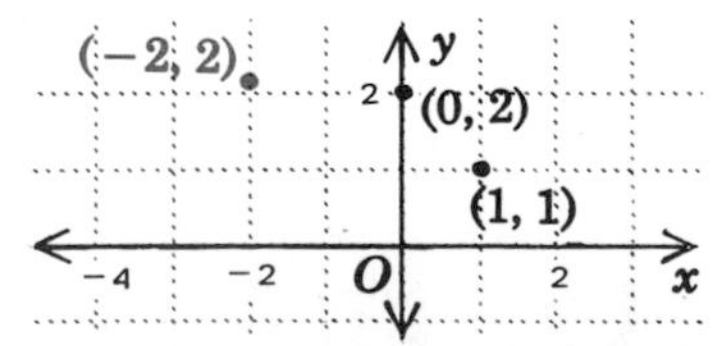

2. $(2, 3) \cdot (1, 5) = (2 \cdot 1 - 3 \cdot 5,\ 2 \cdot 5 + 3 \cdot 1) = (-13, 13)$

3. $(6, 0) \cdot (2, -5) = (6 \cdot 2 - 0(-5),\ 6(-5) + 0 \cdot 2) = (12, -30)$

4. $(\sqrt{2}, \sqrt{3})(\sqrt{2}, \sqrt{3}) = (\sqrt{2} \cdot \sqrt{2} - \sqrt{3} \cdot \sqrt{3},\ \sqrt{2} \cdot \sqrt{3} + \sqrt{3} \cdot \sqrt{2})$
$= (2 - 3,\ \sqrt{6} + \sqrt{6}) = (-1, 2\sqrt{6})$

Addition and multiplication of complex numbers have many properties in common with addition and multiplication of real numbers, including *distributivity*. The proof is left as an exercise.

Theorem 10.4.2

> In the set of complex numbers, multiplication is distributive over addition.

That is, for complex numbers (a, b), (c, d), and (e, f),

$$(a, b)[(c, d) + (e, f)] = (a, b)(c, d) + (a, b)(e, f).$$

Let C stand for the set of complex numbers.

1. With addition, C forms a commutative group. [Theorem 10.2.2]
2. With multiplication, the elements of C not equal to $(0, 0)$ form a commutative group. [Theorem 10.3.3]
3. In C, multiplication is distributive over addition. [Theorem 10.4.2]

So addition and multiplication in C satisfy the properties of Postulates 1–4 of real numbers. Thus, all properties deduced from these four postulates are properties of complex numbers. For example:

- Linear equations such as $ax + b = c$ can be solved as usual.
- The additive identity $(0, 0)$ has a multiplication property like that of zero in the reals. That is, $(0, 0) \cdot (a, b) = (0, 0)$.
- Systems of equations with complex solutions can be solved by the same methods used for real solutions.
- The FOIL theorem and many others hold.
- Fractions in C can be dealt with in the same way as real number fractions.

Some properties of real numbers *are not* held by complex numbers. In particular, the properties of inequality and order have no counterpart in the complex numbers. This is explained in Section 10.8.

EXERCISES 10.4

Ⓐ **1–4.** If u, z, w, and v are complex numbers, is the statement true? Explain your answers.

1. $z(w + v) = zw + vz$ **2.** $(w + u) \cdot (v + z) = wv + wz + uv + uz$

3. $\frac{w}{v} \cdot \frac{u}{z} = \frac{wu}{vz}$ **4.** $\frac{w}{v} + \frac{u}{z} = \frac{w + u}{v + z}$

5. In polar coordinates, $[r, \theta] \cdot [s, \phi] =$ ______.

6. In rectangular coordinates, $(a, b) \cdot (c, d) =$ ______.

7–12. Multiply each pair of complex numbers.

7. $(1, 0), (11, 3)$

8. $(-1, -4), (\frac{1}{2}, \frac{1}{2})$

9. $(-5, 1), (0, 0)$

10. $(6, -2), (6, 2)$

11. $(a, 0), (b, 0)$

12. $(0, 1), (0, 1)$

Ⓑ 13. $(\frac{1}{2}, \frac{1}{3}), (\frac{1}{4}, \frac{1}{5})$

14. $(-0.2, -0.4), (0.3, -0.6)$

15. $(\sqrt{2}, \sqrt{5}), (-\sqrt{2}, \sqrt{5})$

16. $(\frac{2}{5}, -1), (\frac{2}{5}, 1)$

17. Simplify with as little work as possible.

$$(4, 13) \cdot (5, -1) + (4, 13) \cdot (-4, 1)$$

18–19. Multiply the given numbers. Then convert them to rectangular coordinates and multiply. Verify that the products are equal.

18. $[2, 90°], [3, 270°]$

19. $[7, 180°], [-1, 90°]$

20. Prove Theorem 10.4.2.

21. True or False? $(2, 9) \cdot (-\sqrt{3}, \sqrt{2}) = (-\sqrt{3}, \sqrt{2}) \cdot (2, 9)$

Ⓒ 22. It is easy to show that $\frac{1}{16} = 0.0625$ and $\frac{48}{5} = 9.6$. Would you prefer to multiply these numbers as fractions or as decimals? Would you prefer to add them as fractions or decimals? Compare this situation with polar and rectangular coordinates for complex numbers.

10.5 SPECIAL COMPLEX NUMBERS

Since a complex number can be written as an *ordered pair* of real numbers, it is certainly different from a real number. However, certain complex numbers are added and multiplied in the same way real numbers are added and multiplied.

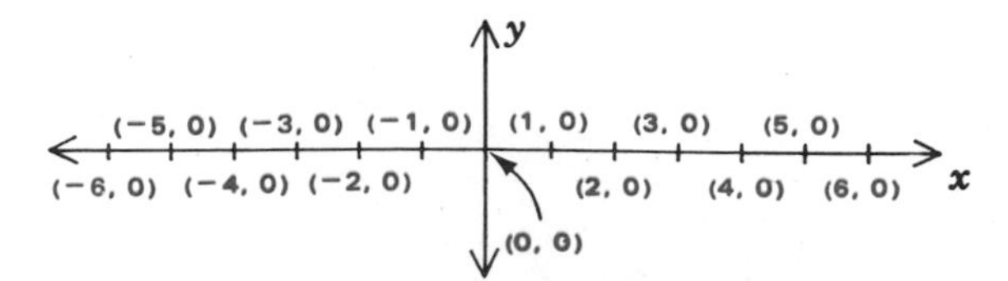

Consider the points on the line through (0, 0) and (1, 0), the x-axis. Let us compare operations on the numbers graphed on this line with the same operations on real numbers.

COMPLEX NUMBERS ON THE x-AXIS:	REAL NUMBERS:
$(a, 0) + (c, 0) = (a + c,\ 0)$	$a + c$
$(a, 0) \cdot (c, 0) = (ac, 0)$	ac

Addition of the complex numbers $(a, 0)$ and $(c, 0)$	corresponds to →	Addition of the real numbers a and c.
Multiplication of the complex numbers $(a, 0)$ and $(c, 0)$	corresponds to →	Multiplication of the real numbers a and c.

The one-to-one correspondence of the numbers, along with the corresponding results of the operations, indicates isomorphic groups.

Theorem 10.5.1

The complex number plane contains a line (the x-axis) upon which addition and multiplication are isomorphic to addition and multiplication of real numbers.

Because of the isomorphism, the line in Theorem 10.5.1 is called the **real axis** of the complex number plane. We consider points of this line to be real numbers and write them in the customary manner.

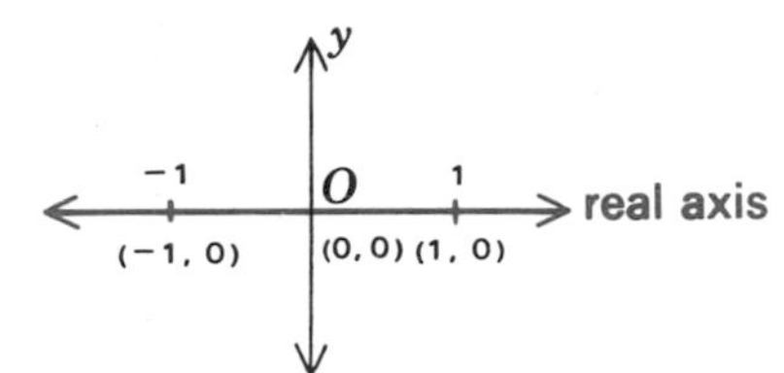

$(a, 0) = a$

So $(0, 0) = 0$ ◀ additive identity for complex numbers

and $(1, 0) = 1.$ ◀ multiplicative identity for complex numbers

Another special complex number is $[1, 90°]$ or $(0, 1)$.

Definition

The symbol i represents $[1, 90°]$ or $(0, 1)$.

Theorem 10.5.2

$$i^2 = -1$$

PROOF: $[1, 90°] \cdot [1, 90°] = [1, 180°] = (-1, 0) = -1$

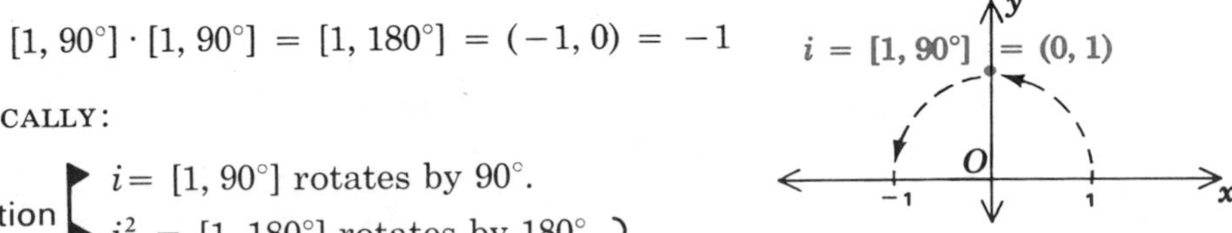

GEOMETRICALLY:

Multiplication by
- $i = [1, 90°]$ rotates by 90°.
- $i^2 = [1, 180°]$ rotates by 180°.
- -1 rotates by 180°.

So $i^2 = -1$.

Let us multiply i by any real number r.

$$r \cdot i = (r, 0) \cdot (0, 1) = (0, r)$$

Since $(0, r)$ is on the y-axis, all real multiples of i lie on the y-axis. Furthermore, the square of ri is a negative real number.

$$(ri)^2 = (0, r) \cdot (0, r) = (-r^2, 0) = -r^2$$

Examples: Squaring ri

1. $(2i)^2 = (0, 2) \cdot (0, 2) = (-4, 0) = -4$

2. $(-7i)^2 = (0, -7) \cdot (0, -7) = (-49, 0) = -49$

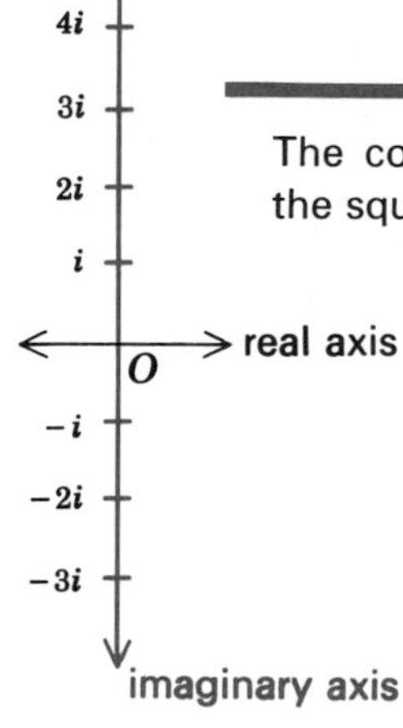

Theorem 10.5.3

The complex number plane contains a line (the y-axis) upon which the squares of all numbers are negative reals.

The y-axis is called the **imaginary axis.** All nonzero numbers on it are **pure imaginary numbers.** This unfortunate but common usage of the word *imaginary* came about because the first mathematicians who worked with complex numbers used *imaginary* to distinguish these numbers from *real* numbers. Yet complex numbers are no less related to reality than real numbers.

EXERCISES 10.5

Ⓐ **1–4.** Give the meaning of each term.

1. the real axis

2. the imaginary axis

3. the imaginary unit i

4. pure imaginary number

5. The complex number $(10, 0)$ is the real number ____.

6. The number $(0, 1)$ is denoted by the symbol ____.

7. In polar coordinates, $i =$ ____.

8. Graph i, $2i$, $3i$, and $4i$.

9. Graph 7, -7, $7i$, and $-7i$.

10. If z is a pure imaginary number, then z^2 is ____.

11. Explain why the use of the word *imaginary* might give someone a false impression.

12–23. Simplify with as little work as possible.

12. $(3, 0) \cdot (2, 0)$ **13.** $(5, 0) + (-11, 0)$

14. $(0, 6) + (0, -4)$ **15.** $(7, 0) \cdot (0, 1)$

16. $(0, 1) \cdot (0, 1)$ **17.** $(0, 1) \cdot (-2.5, 0)$

Ⓑ **18.** $i - 3i$ **19.** $(0, \sqrt{3}) \cdot (0, \sqrt{3})$

20. $4i^2$ **21.** $(2i)^2$ **22.** $-3i \cdot i$ **23.** $-i^2$

24–27. Find a complex number whose square is the given number.

24. -1 **25.** -4 **26.** -3 **27.** 4

28. True or False? $i^2 + 1 = 0$

29–32. Graph each set of numbers.

29. $\{i, i^2, i^3, i^4\}$ **30.** $\{-\sqrt{3} \cdot i, \sqrt{3} \cdot i\}$

31. $\{i\sqrt{2}, -i\sqrt{2}\}$ **32.** $\{2i, (2i)^2, (2i)^3, (2i)^4\}$

Ⓒ **33–34.** In this section a geometric interpretation for $i^2 = -1$ was given. Give a similar interpretation for each equation.

33. $i^3 = -i$ **34.** $i^4 = 1$

35. Prove that a pure imaginary number is the only kind of complex number whose square is a negative real number.

THE $a + bi$ NOTATION

The abbreviations a for $(a, 0)$ and i for $(0, 1)$ make it possible to develop a third notation for complex numbers.

Theorem 10.6.1

In rectangular coordinates, $(a, b) = a + bi$.

PROOF: Verify the calculations:

$$(a, b) = (a, 0) + (0, b)$$
$$= (a, 0) + (b, 0) \cdot (0, 1)$$

Substituting:

$$= a + b \cdot i$$

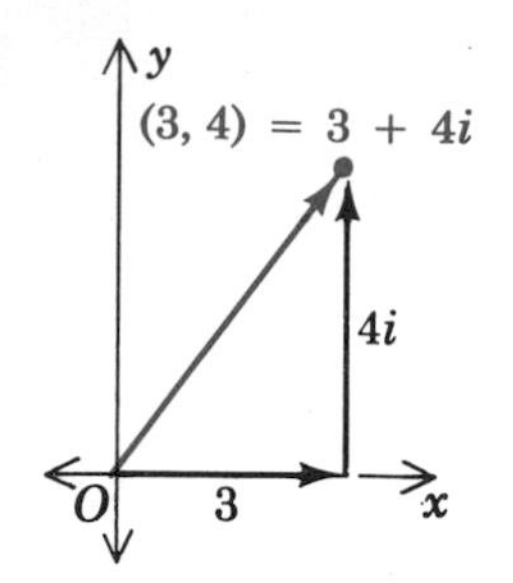

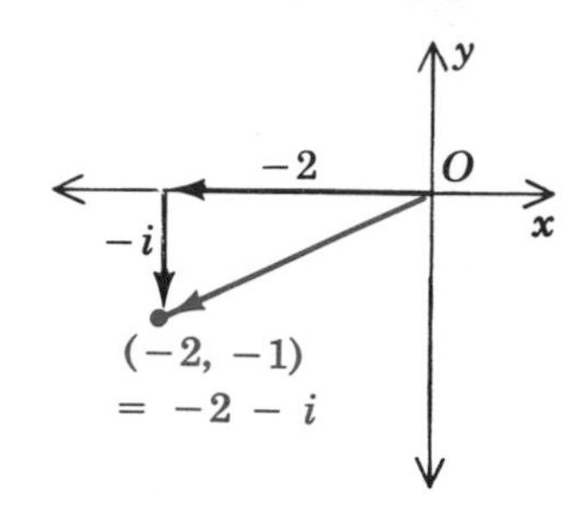

Addition of a and bi corresponds to the composition of horizontal and vertical translations. So every complex number can be expressed as the sum of a real number, a, and a pure imaginary number, bi. *This is the most widely used notation for complex numbers.*

Examples: Converting to and from $a + bi$ notation

1. $(5, 6) = 5 + 6i$

2. $(17, -3) = 17 + (-3)i = 17 - 3i$

3. $86 + i\sqrt{2} = (86, \sqrt{2})$

4. $i - 10 = -10 + 1 \cdot i = (-10, 1)$

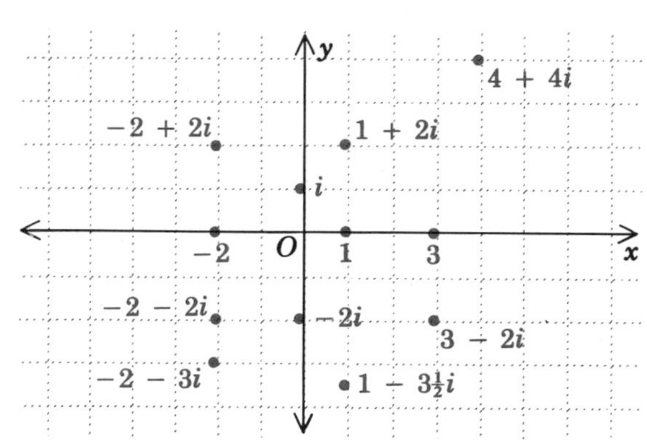

Some complex numbers in $a + bi$ form are graphed at the left. The $a + bi$ notation has two features which make it useful. First, both addition and multiplication are easy in this notation. (Practice with these operations is given in Section 10.7.) Second, the $a + bi$ notation lends itself to work with square roots and quadratic equations, as discussed in Chapter 11.

EXERCISES 10.6

Ⓐ **1–6.** Write each complex number in $a + bi$ notation.

1. $(6, 4)$ **2.** $(4, 6)$ **3.** $(-2, 4)$

4. $(0, 1)$ **5.** $(-1.5, -2)$ **6.** $(1, \sqrt{3})$

7–18. In $a + bi$ notation, what would be the values of a and b?

7. $5 + 9i$ **8.** $9i + 5$ **9.** $i - 2$

10. $3i + 14$ **11.** $7i$ **12.** 462

13. $\frac{1}{2} + \frac{i}{2}$ **14.** $0 - i\sqrt{3}$ **15.** 0

16. $[2, 90°]$ **17.** $[3, 180°]$ **18.** $[5, 0°]$

19–21. Graph each set of numbers in the complex plane.

19. $1 + i,\ 1 + 2i,\ 1 + 3i,\ 1 + 4i$

20. $2 - 3i,\ -2 + 3i,\ 2 + 3i,\ -2 - 3i$

21. $2 - 2i,\ 3 - 2i,\ -4 - 2i,\ -2i$

Ⓑ **22–25.** Write each number in $a + bi$ notation.

22. $(a, 0) + (3, 0) \cdot (0, 1)$

23. $(2, 5) \cdot (-2, 5)$

24. $(3, 0) - (1, 0) \cdot (0, 1)$

25. $(3, 5) \cdot (9, 1) + (9, 2)$

26–29. Write the given number in $a + bi$ notation. Then graph the number. (HINT: First change to rectangular coordinates.)

26. $[\frac{1}{2}, 30°]$

27. $[1000, 72°]$

28. $[3.2, 70°]$

29. $[4, 270°]$

Ⓒ **30.** What is the absolute value of $a + bi$?

31. Prove: If r and θ are polar coordinates for a complex number, then

$$[r, \theta] = r(\cos \theta + i \sin \theta).$$

[The $r(\cos \theta + i \sin \theta)$ idea is used in many books which do not discuss polar coordinates.]

MANIPULATIONS IN $a + bi$ NOTATION

In the $a + bi$ form of a complex number, a, b, and i are themselves complex numbers. So operations with a, b, and i satisfy all the group properties of addition and multiplication. This makes it easy to add and multiply complex numbers in $a + bi$ form.

Examples: Addition and subtraction

1. $5 + (6 + 9i) = 11 + 9i$

2. $3 - 2i + 5i + 6 = 9 + 3i$

3. $4 + (-2)i - 3i = 4 - 5i$

4. $(1 - 3i) - (2 - 2i) = -1 - i$

Examples: Multiplication

5.
$$\begin{aligned}(2 - 3i)(4 + 7i) &= 2 \cdot 4 + 2 \cdot 7i - 3i \cdot 4 - 3i \cdot 7i \\ &= 8 + 14i - 12i - 21i^2 \\ &= 8 + 14i - 12i + 21 \\ &= 29 + 2i\end{aligned}$$

Remember that $i^2 = -1$.

6. $(9 - 4i) \cdot 12 = 108 - 48i$

7. $2i \cdot 4i = 8i^2 = -8$

8. $(3 - 2i) \cdot (3 + 2i) = 9 + 6i - 6i - 4i^2 = 9 + 4 = 13$

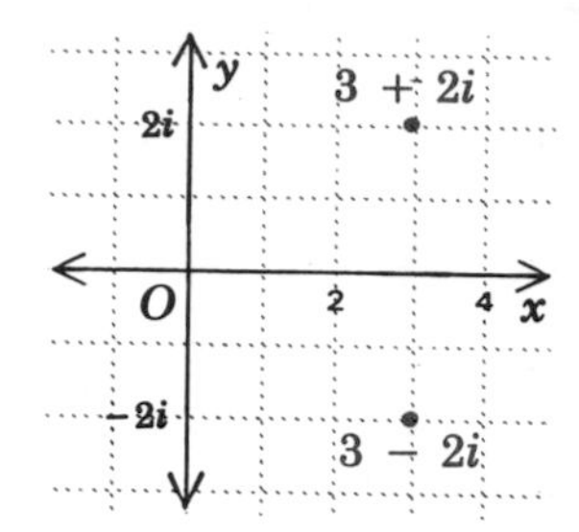

The two numbers multiplied in Example 8 are reflection images of each other over the real axis. Their product is a real number. (In polar coordinates, their first coordinates are equal and their second coordinates add to 0°.) Such numbers are called **conjugate complex numbers.**

Definition

The **conjugate** of $a + bi$ is $a - bi$.

Examples: Conjugates of complex numbers

Number:	$8 + 4i$	$-5 - \frac{1}{2i}$	1 or $1 + 0 \cdot i$	$[r, \theta]$	(a, b)
Conjugate:	$8 - 4i$	$-5 + \frac{1}{2i}$	1 or $1 - 0 \cdot i$	$[r, -\theta]$	$(a, -b)$

Theorem 10.7.1

$(a + bi) \cdot (a - bi)$ is the real number $a^2 + b^2$.

PROOF: $(a + bi)(a - bi) = a^2 - abi + bai - b^2i^2$

$$= a^2 - b^2(-1) = a^2 + b^2$$

The conjugate of a complex number is particularly useful in writing the quotient of two complex numbers in $a + bi$ form.

Examples: Division using conjugates

1. $\dfrac{2 + 3i}{-8 - 4i}$

$$= \frac{2 + 3i}{-8 - 4i} \cdot \frac{-8 + 4i}{-8 + 4i}$$

Multiply numerator and denominator by the conjugate of the denominator.

$$= \frac{-28 - 16i}{64 + 16} = \frac{-28}{80} - \frac{16}{80}i = \boxed{-\frac{7}{20} - \frac{1}{5}i}$$

The final $a + bi$ form makes graphing easier.

2. $\dfrac{2 - i}{2 + i} = \dfrac{2 - i}{2 + i} \cdot \dfrac{2 - i}{2 - i} = \dfrac{4 - 4i + i^2}{4 + 1} = \dfrac{3 - 4i}{5} = \dfrac{3}{5} - \dfrac{4}{5}i$

To check: Does quotient times divisor equal dividend?

$(2 + i)(\frac{3}{5} - \frac{4}{5}i) = \frac{6}{5} - \frac{8}{5}i + \frac{3}{5}i - \frac{4}{5}i^2 = \frac{10}{5} - \frac{5}{5}i = 2 - i$

3. To put the reciprocal of a complex number in $a + bi$ notation

$$\frac{1}{3 - 2i} = \frac{1}{3 - 2i} \cdot \frac{3 + 2i}{3 + 2i} = \frac{3 + 2i}{9 + 4} = \frac{3}{13} + \frac{2}{13}i$$

Sometimes it is more convenient to use a number other than the conjugate as a multiplier.

Examples:

1. $\dfrac{7 + 4i}{i} = \dfrac{7 + 4i}{i} \cdot \dfrac{i}{i} = \dfrac{7i + 4i^2}{i^2} = \dfrac{7i - 4}{-1} = 4 - 7i$

2. $\dfrac{1}{i - 4} = \dfrac{1}{i - 4} \cdot \dfrac{i + 4}{i + 4} = \dfrac{i + 4}{i^2 - 16} = \dfrac{4 + i}{-17} = -\dfrac{4}{17} - \dfrac{1}{17}i$

EXERCISES 10.7

Ⓐ **1–10.** Add the given numbers. Write the answer in $a + bi$ form.

1. $2 + 3i,\ 3 + i$

2. $4 - 2i,\ 7 + 3i$

3. $-9 - i,\ i$

4. $10 + 20i,\ -47$

5. $13 - 2i,\ -8 + 5i$

6. $9 - 7i,\ 7i + 9$

7. $2,\ i,\ -3i,\ 6$

8. $18,\ -7,\ 11i,\ 46i$

9. $8 - i,\ -12 + 4i,\ 6 - 3i,\ i + 2$

10. $1.5 - i,\ 3i + 0.5,\ -i + 8,\ 4 - 0.3i$

11–16. Subtract the second number from the first in Exercises **1–6**.

17–20. Write each expression as one number in $a + bi$ form.

17. $(3 - 2i) + (7 + 4i)$

18. $(3 - 2i) - (7 + 4i)$

19. $i + i^2 + 5$

20. $8 - i + 5i - 3i + 12 + 0.5 - 4i$

21–28. Multiply the numbers given in Exercises **1–8**. Give the answer in $a + bi$ form.

29–34. Write each expression as a complex number in $a + bi$ form.

29. $(3 - 2i) \cdot (7 + 4i)$

30. $(3 - 2i) \cdot (7 + 4i)i$

31. $(i - 2) \cdot (i + 2)$

32. $(2i - 5) \cdot (5 - 2i)$

33. $(2i - 5) + (5 - 2i)$

34. $3(7i - 3) + 4(9 - 9i)$

35. What is the conjugate of $7 - i$?

36. What is the conjugate of $3i + 2$?

Ⓑ **37–40.** Find four true sentences of the form $a + b = c$, $a - b = c$, $ab = c$, or $a \div b = c$ involving the given numbers.

37. $2 + 3i,\ 4 - 5i,\ 6 - 2i$

38. $5 - 3i,\ 34,\ 5 + 3i$

39. $11 + 10i,\ 1 + 4i,\ 3 - 2i$

40. $-8 - 4i,\ -2,\ 4 + 2i$

41–46. Divide the first number by the second in Exercises **1–6**. Denote the answer in $a + bi$ form.

47–50. Write each quotient in $(a + bi)$ or (a, b) form. Check.

47. $\frac{3 - 4i}{6 + i}$

48. $\frac{5i + 2}{5i - 2}$

49. $\frac{a + bi}{i}$

50. $(4, -1) \div (-3, 8)$

51–53. Give the absolute value of each number.

51. $4 - 3i$

52. $-12 - 5i$

53. $1 + i$

54. True or False? The product of a complex number z and its conjugate is the absolute value of z.

55–60. Give the reciprocal of each number in $a + bi$ notation.

55. $2 + i$

56. $3 + 4i$

57. 7

58. $2i$

59. $\frac{1}{4 - i}$

60. $\frac{10}{2 + 3i}$

61–75. Write each expression as a complex number in $a + bi$ form.

61. $(3 - 4i) \cdot (3 - 4i)$

62. $-i(-i) \cdot (-i)$

63. $33 - (2 + i) \cdot (3 - 5i)$

64. $(a - bi) \cdot (c - di)$

65. $(6 - i\sqrt{2}) + (6 + i\sqrt{2})$

66. $(6 - i\sqrt{2}) \cdot (6 + i\sqrt{2})$

67. $(-i - 1) \cdot (2i - 2)$

68. $(i - 2)(i + 2)(2 - i)(2 + i)$

69. $(2, 4) \cdot (3, -1)$

70. $(4 - i)^3$

Ⓒ **71.** $\frac{1}{1 - i} + \frac{1}{1 + i}$

72. $\frac{3 - 2i}{i} + \frac{2 + i}{i - 1} - \frac{6 + i}{i - 2}$

73. $\frac{2 + 3i}{i - 2} - \frac{3i - 2}{2 - i}$

74. $\frac{8 + 4i}{6} - \frac{2 - 3i}{4} + i$

75. $[10, 90°] \cdot [2, 180°]$

76. Prove: If a and b are real numbers, then $(a + bi)^2 + (a - bi)^2$ is a real number.

77. Find the distance between $7 - 2i$ and $8 + 4i$.

ARE THERE POSITIVE OR NEGATIVE COMPLEX NUMBERS?

It is natural to think that the number i is in some sense "positive" and that $-i$ is "negative." But i cannot be thought of in this way.

Theorem 10.8.1

> It is impossible to use inequalities with complex numbers (in general) in a way which satisfies all the properties of inequality and order for real numbers.

PROOF: The proof is indirect. Suppose the set of complex numbers has all the order properties of real numbers. Then, according to the trichotomy property, either $i = 0$, $i > 0$, or $i < 0$.

What if $i = 0$? Then $i^2 = 0^2$, so $-1 = 0$.

What if $i > 0$? By the multiplication properties of order (Postulate 6, page 35), $i^2 > 0 \cdot i$. So $-1 > 0$.

What if $i < 0$? Again by Postulate 6, $i^2 > 0 \cdot i$. So $-1 > 0$.

In each case, we contradict the basic property that $-1 < 0$. This shows that it is impossible to use i in inequalities.

Corollary 10.8.2

> Except for the real numbers, there are no positive or negative complex numbers.

Consider the following statement:

It is impossible to travel to the nearest star.

In this statement, *impossible* means "It can't be done now (but it may be done in the future)." In mathematics, impossibility is different. It is absolute. When something is mathematically impossible, then it *cannot* be done unless the postulates or definitions are changed. Theorem 10.8.1 uses the mathematical meaning of impossibility.

Another example of mathematical impossibility is more famous. With straightedge and compass, you can bisect any angle. Some angles can be **trisected** (split into three congruent parts) with these two tools. However, 2000 years of effort failed to produce a straightedge and compass construction for the trisector of *any* angle.

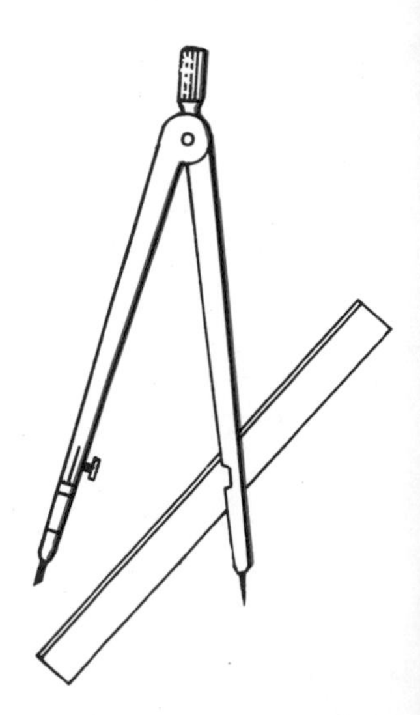

Finally, using algebraic methods, in the last century it was proved impossible to construct such a trisector. Yet editors of mathematics journals still receive letters containing "solutions" to the trisection problem. Since the construction is mathematically impossible, these solutions can *always* be shown to have an error.

EXERCISES 10.8

Ⓐ **1.** There is no real number whose square is negative. Name a complex number whose square is negative.

2. Name one difference between the meaning of the word *impossible* as used in mathematics and as used elsewhere.

3. Why is it impossible for i to be considered a positive number?

Ⓑ **4.** Why are there no positive or negative imaginary numbers?

5–7. Find two complex numbers x and y satisfying the given conditions.

5. graphs of x and y: above the x-axis; graph of xy: below the x-axis

6. graphs of x and y: to the right of the y-axis; graph of xy: to the left of the y-axis

7. graphs of x and y: in quadrant I; graph of xy: in quadrant II

8. Exercise **5** shows that if you consider complex numbers above the x-axis to be positive, then the product of two positive numbers is not always positive. What do Exercises **6** and **7** show?

Ⓒ **9.** From any references, determine who proved it impossible to construct the trisector of an angle. Indicate your source.

10–12. Each phrase refers to a famous mathematical impossibility. Use any references to find out what exactly was proved impossible.

10. squaring the circle

11. duplicating the cube

12. solving the quintic equation

PHYSICAL APPLICATIONS OF COMPLEX NUMBERS

Many applications of complex numbers require a knowledge of physics or electronics which you cannot be expected to have. So we can only present glimpses of some real-world situations (very much idealized) which might lead to complex numbers.

RESOLUTION OF FORCES (VECTORS)

Situation: An airplane heads due east at 500 km per hour and there is a wind from NNE at 100 km per hour. What effect does the wind have on the course of the airplane?

SOLUTION: We represent the plane's course in still air by the arrow t and the wind by the arrow u. These arrows represent **vectors**. The length of t is 500; the length of u is 100. If u begins at (0, 0), it ends at $[100, 247\frac{1}{2}°]$.

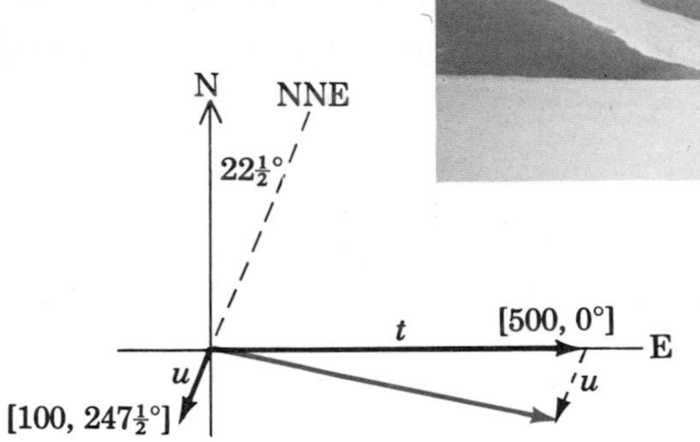

The resulting course is found by adding the endpoints of t and u. (This corresponds to composing the slides represented by t and u.)

In polar coordinates:	$[100, 247\frac{1}{2}°] + [500, 0°]$
In rectangular coordinates:	$= (100 \cos 247\frac{1}{2}°, 100 \sin 247\frac{1}{2}°) + (500, 0)$
Using tables:	$\doteq (-36.7, -92.4) + (500, 0)$
Adding:	$= (463.3, -92.4)$

Looking at the diagram, the result seems reasonable. The wind from NNE pushes the plane south and west from where it was headed. In one hour, the plane is near $(463.3, -92.4)$ in kilometres.

Actually, a more realistic problem is to calculate the direction and time the plane must head at a given speed in order to maintain its desired course. This is also a harder problem.

CIRCULAR MOTION

Examples of circular motion range from astronomical orbits (on the largest scale), to Ferris wheels, to gears, to atomic particle motions (on the smallest scale). Other phenomena, like alternating electrical current and voltage, may be described in terms of circular motion.

In most alternating current circuits, current and voltage both reach their maximum values 60 times a second. However, they need not reach their maximums at the same time. The flow of current in a circuit is affected by three forces, known as *resistance*, *capacitance*, and *inductance*, and the voltage across a pure inductance is always 90° ahead of the current. That is, the current and voltage are 90° *out of phase*.

If the cycles of the current and voltage are thought of in terms of circular motion, the phase relation of the current and voltage may be represented by the positions of the points P (for the current) and Q (for the voltage) on the circle at the right.

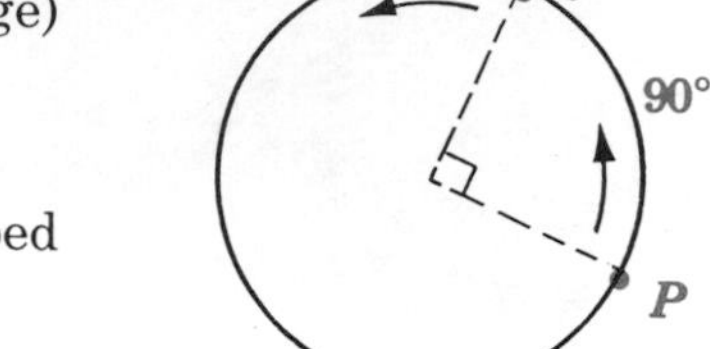

Situation: In the circumstances described above, how are P and Q related?

SOLUTION: Place the center of the circle at the origin. Then Q is the image of P under R_{90}. Since multiplying by $[1, 90°]$, or i, rotates by 90° we have

$$Q = [1, 90°] \cdot P \quad \text{or} \quad Q = iP.$$

The radius of the circle does not matter here. If the circle has radius 5 and $P = 3 + 4i$, then $Q = i(3 + 4i) = -4 + 3i$.

Complex numbers are used in this case to describe the phase relationship of the current and voltage. They are also frequently used to describe the *magnitude* and *phase angle* of alternating current or voltage.

EXERCISES 10.9

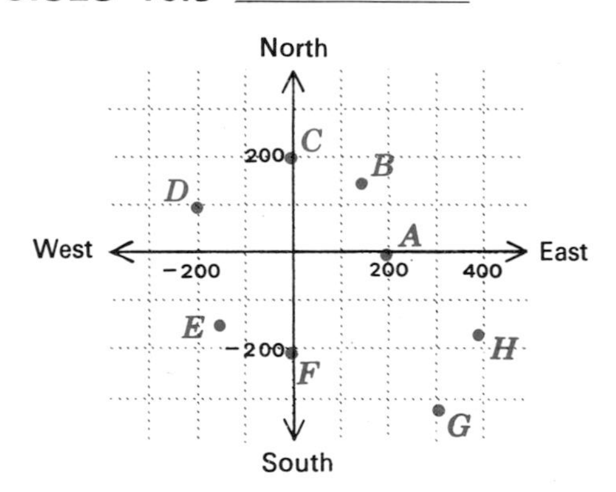

Ⓐ **1–4.** If the given force is represented by an arrow starting at the origin, which point is the endpoint of the arrow?

1. force of 200 in an easterly direction
2. force of 440 from the northwest
3. force of 200 in the SW direction
4. force from the WNW

5. If two forces are acting on an object, how can the resultant force be found?

6. How does multiplication by i transform a point?

7. C is the center of the circle, $C = (0, 0)$, and $m\overset{\frown}{PQ} = 90°$. Which is true?

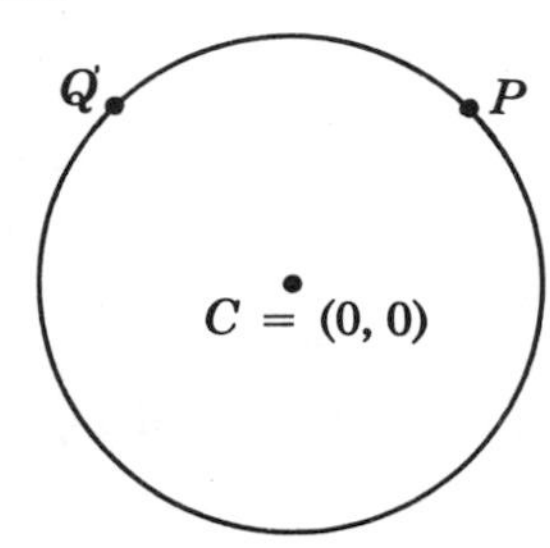

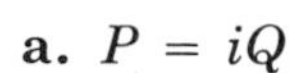

a. $P = iQ$ **b.** $P = i + Q$

c. $Q = iP$ **d.** $Q = i + P$

Ⓑ **8–10.** Graph the forces t and u. Graph and calculate the resultant $t + u$.

8. t is a wind of 100 knots from the northwest acting on a plane headed east at 450 knots. (Consider the plane's heading as u.)

9. t is a force of 200 lbs from the south. u is a force of 300 lbs from the SW.

10. A wind of 30 mph from the NW (t) affects a bird flying south at 25 mph (u).

11. A plane flies 300 km east from city A to city B and then 600 km SSE from city B to city C. How far is city C from city A?

12–14. Refer to the example of circular motion in this section.

12. In an alternating current circuit, the voltage across a pure capacitance is always 90° *behind* the current flowing in the circuit. If the positions of points P (for the current) and R (for the voltage) show the phase relation in this case, how are P and R related?

13. How are Q and R related?

Ⓒ **14.** Actual circuits usually have inductance, capacitance, and resistance. In this case, Q and R are less than 90° from P. Suppose Q and R are each 85° from P. What equation could then relate:

a. P and Q? **b.** P and R? **c.** Q and R?

15. Anita pushes a cabinet 4 metres NW. Then Betty pushes it 3 metres E. Finally Consuela pushes it 5 metres SSE. How far is the final position of the cabinet from its starting point?

16. *Quantum mechanics.* The Paoli spin matrices $\begin{bmatrix} 0 & 1 \\ 1 & 0 \end{bmatrix}$, $\begin{bmatrix} 0 & -i \\ i & 0 \end{bmatrix}$, and $\begin{bmatrix} 1 & 0 \\ 0 & -1 \end{bmatrix}$ are used in studying electron spin. Call any two of these matrices A and B and show that $AB = \begin{bmatrix} -1 & 0 \\ 0 & -1 \end{bmatrix} \cdot BA$.

17. Using any references you can, find out how complex numbers are used in special relativity theory in 4-dimensional space-time coordinates.

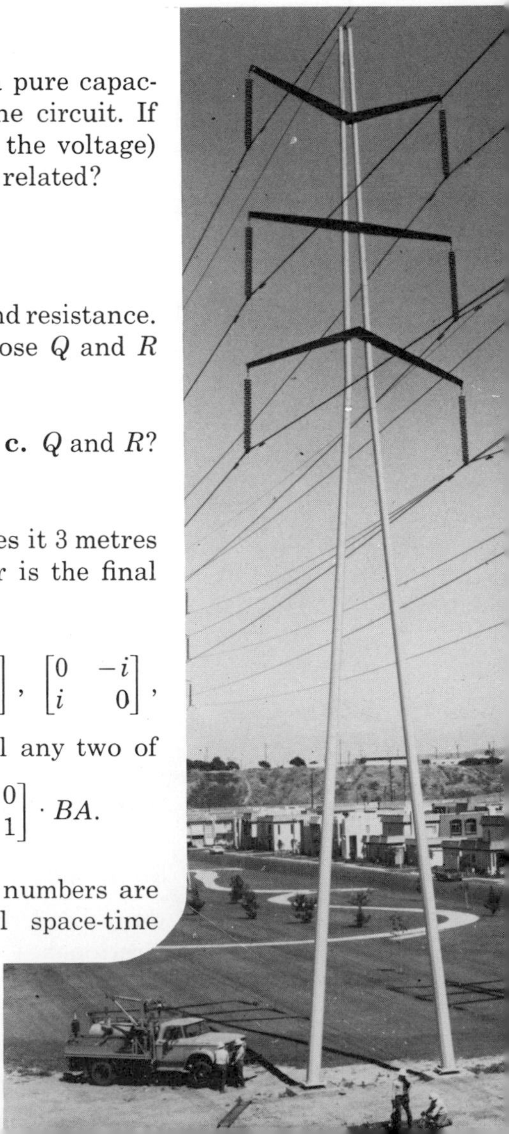

CLASSIFICATION OF COMPLEX NUMBERS

The first numbers you knew of were the *natural numbers* 1, 2, 3, ⋯, also called *positive integers.* The number 0 (also an integer and considered to be a natural number by some mathematicians) is the number of elements in the empty set. Considering opposites of the natural numbers yields the *negative integers,* −1, −2, −3, ⋯. Quotients of integers are *rational numbers* (think of the word *ratio*).

These are rational numbers because they are	0	$\frac{2\pi}{3\pi}$	$-\sqrt{\frac{9}{16}}$	$\frac{\sqrt{8}}{\sqrt{2}}$	$0.0333\cdots$	1.24
equal to these fractions.	$\frac{0}{1}$	$\frac{2}{3}$	$-\frac{3}{4}$	$\frac{2}{1}$	$\frac{1}{30}$	$\frac{124}{100}$

Definition

A **rational number** is a number which can be denoted in the form $\frac{a}{b}$, where a and b are integers and $b \neq 0$.

In the sixth century B.C., the Pythagoreans found that the lengths of certain segments are not rational. Hence these numbers were called **irrational.** Two well-known irrational numbers are $\sqrt{2}$ and π, but many other numbers have also been proved irrational. The following indirect proof that $\sqrt{2}$ is irrational was discovered in 1964 by P. H. Nygaard.

Theorem 10.10.1

It is impossible to represent $\sqrt{2}$ in the form $\frac{a}{b}$ where a and b are integers.

PROOF:

Suppose $\sqrt{2} = \frac{a}{b}$, where a and b are integers and the fraction is in lowest terms.	That is, suppose $\sqrt{2}$ is rational.

If $\sqrt{2} = \frac{a}{b}$, then $b\sqrt{2} = a$, so $2b^2 = a^2$.

Then b^2 and a^2 end in 0, 1, 4, 5, 6, or 9. ← Squares of integers end in one of these digits.

So $2b^2$ ends in 0, 2, or 8. ← Doubling

Since $2b^2 = a^2$, they must both end in 0.

So a^2 ends in 0 and b^2 ends in 0 or 5. In either case, $\frac{a}{b}$ is not in lowest terms, and the supposition (outlined above) cannot be true. So $\sqrt{2}$ is irrational.

Generally, if an integer k is not a perfect square, then $\sqrt{k}$ is irrational. Every decimal represents either a rational or an irrational number. It is possible to show that a number is:

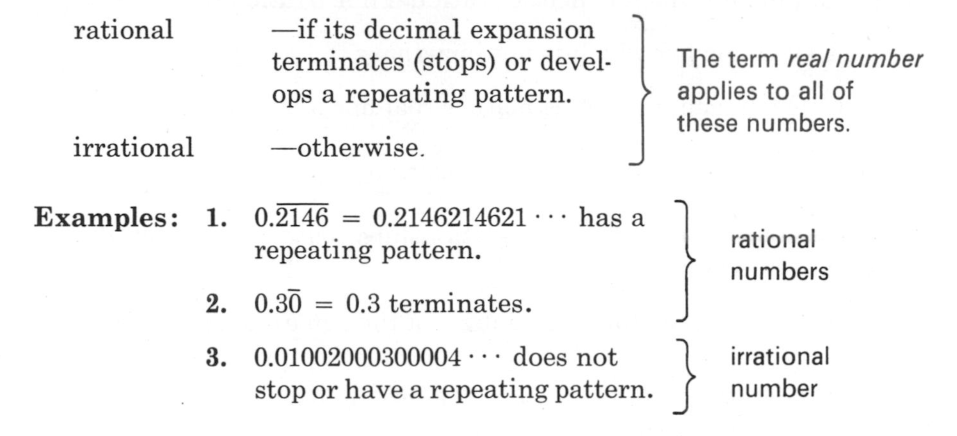

rational —if its decimal expansion terminates (stops) or develops a repeating pattern.

irrational —otherwise.

} The term *real number* applies to all of these numbers.

Examples: **1.** $0.\overline{2146} = 0.2146214621\cdots$ has a repeating pattern.

2. $0.3\overline{0} = 0.3$ terminates.

} rational numbers

3. $0.01002000300004\cdots$ does not stop or have a repeating pattern. } irrational number

This network shows how the various sets of numbers are related.

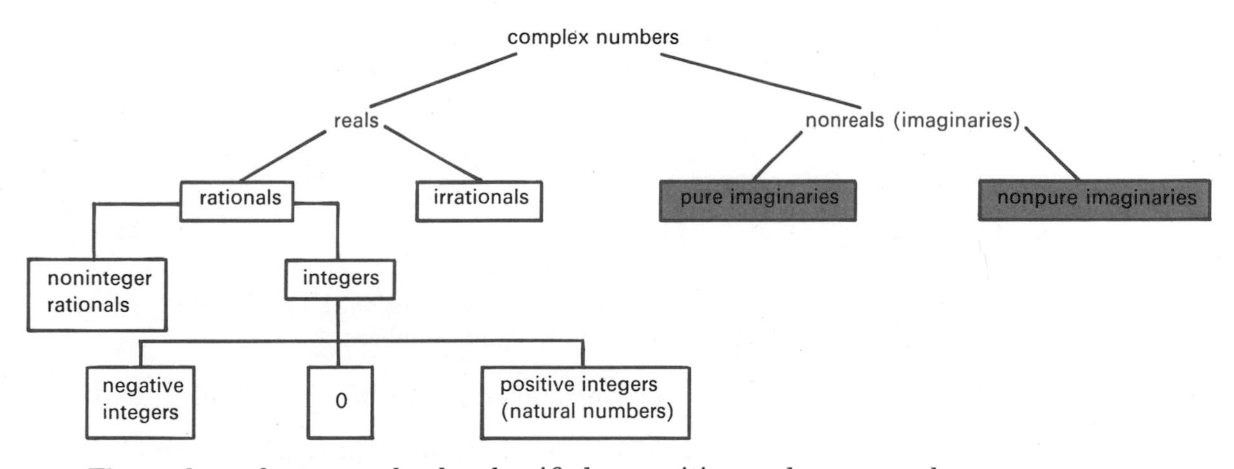

The real numbers can also be classified as positive reals, zero, and negative reals. (There are no positive or negative imaginary numbers.)

EXERCISES 10.10

Ⓐ **1–9.** If possible, give an example.

1. an integer which is neither positive nor negative

2. a real number which is not complex

3. an irrational number **4.** a pure imaginary number

5. a decimal which stands for a rational number

6. a decimal which stands for an irrational number

7. a real number which is neither rational nor irrational

8. a complex number which is not imaginary

9. a complex number which is neither real nor a pure imaginary

10. Give the definition of *rational number*.

11. Draw a diagram indicating relationships between at least 10 different types of numbers.

12. What digits can be the ending digit of the square of an integer?

Ⓑ **13–19.** Show that the given number is a rational number by expressing it in the form $\frac{a}{b}$, where a and b are integers.

13. $0.47 \div 2.3$ **14.** $0.3333\cdots$ **15.** 0.250

16. $\sqrt{20^2 + 21^2}$ **17.** $(3 - 2i)(6 + 4i)$ **18.** $(\frac{1}{2})^{-2}$

19. $0.1111\cdots$ (HINT: Compare with Exercise **14.**)

20–23. Give a terminating or repeating decimal for each number.

20. $\frac{20}{3}$ **21.** $-\frac{1}{64}$ **22.** $3\frac{1}{7}$ **23.** $\frac{1}{125}$

Ⓒ **24.** Discuss why such terms as *negative*, *irrational*, and *imaginary* might have been chosen to apply to some numbers.

25. Show that $\sqrt{3}$ is irrational. (HINT: See the proof of Theorem 10.10.1.)

26. Modify the proof of Theorem 10.10.1 as if the numbers a and b were written in base 3. (This method, which results in a shorter proof, was suggested by Professor Walter Scott of Arizona State University.)

27. Prove: The sum of a rational and an irrational number is never rational.

28–31. Let R be a rational number and let I be irrational. Tell whether the given number is always, sometimes, or never rational.

28. $R - I$ **29.** RI **30.** $\frac{I}{R}$ **31.** I^2

32. Find two irrational numbers whose sum and product are both rational.

33–34. The rational numbers $\frac{7}{5}$, $\frac{17}{12}$, $\frac{41}{29}$, $\frac{99}{70}$, and $\frac{268}{169}$ are better and better approximations to $\sqrt{2}$.

33. Square these numbers to see how close the squares are to 2.

34. Find a pattern to find a better rational approximation than $\frac{268}{169}$.

35–36. Use other references to find out more about the following.

35. transfinite numbers **36.** hypercomplex numbers or quaternions

CHAPTER SUMMARY

10

This chapter deals with writing and manipulating **complex numbers.** These numbers are defined to be in one-to-one correspondence with the points of the plane. Addition corresponds to translations—this gives applications to the resolution of forces. Multiplication corresponds to rotating and size transforming—this gives applications to circuitry.

Two lines in the complex number plane are particularly important. On the *x-axis*, addition and multiplication are isomorphic to addition and multiplication of real numbers. We thus call this axis the *real axis* and say that every real number is also a complex number. The squares of all nonzero numbers on the *y-axis* are negative real numbers; the numbers graphed on this axis are called *pure imaginary numbers,* and the axis is called the *imaginary* axis.

The special complex number (0, 1) or [1, 90°] is called i, and $i^2 = -1$. Every complex number can be written in $a + bi$ form and in this notation addition and multiplication are easy to do. Division is helped by using the *conjugate* $a - bi$ of the number $a + bi$.

Addition and multiplication of complex numbers satisfy commutativity, distributivity, and the group properties. But not all properties of real numbers hold for complex numbers. It is impossible to use inequalities of order (< and >) with complex numbers other than real numbers. So, except for the reals, there are no positive or negative complex numbers.

Impossibility does not have the same meaning in mathematics as in normal use. Impossibility can be logically deduced and only changes if the postulates and definitions of terms are modified. We show that $\sqrt{2}$ is not a *rational number* by proving it impossible to represent $\sqrt{2}$ as a quotient of integers.

The operations with complex numbers are defined to be consistent with operations with real numbers. The *absolute value* of a complex number, defined to be its distance from the origin, is another example of a concept extended from real numbers to complex numbers. In the next chapter, square roots are similarly extended and complex numbers are seen to have applications to sentence solving.

10

CHAPTER REVIEW

1. Addition of complex numbers is isomorphic to composition of ____.

2. How can the graph of $[s, \phi] \cdot [r, \theta]$ be found from the graph of $[s, \phi]$?

3. The absolute value of $7 - 3i$ is ____.

4. The absolute value of $[5, 72°]$ is ____.

5. In the complex plane, the x-axis is called the ____ axis.

6. A positive complex number must be a(n) ____ number.

7. $\sqrt{10}$ and $-0.0101101110\cdots$ are examples of ____ real numbers.

8–14. Write in $a + bi$ notation.

8. $(3, 7)$ **9.** $[3, 30°]$ **10.** $2i(4 + 3i)$

11. the reciprocal of $6i$ **12.** the multiplicative identity

13. the conjugate of $-1 + 3i$

14. the additive inverse of $-3 - 7i$

15–20. If $x = -3 + 6i$ and $y = -2 - 8i$, write each of the following in $a + bi$ notation.

15. $x + y$ **16.** $x - y$ **17.** xy

18. $\frac{1}{x}$ **19.** $\frac{y}{x}$ **20.** ix

21. Multiply: $[2, 27°] \cdot [5, 34°]$.

22. Simplify: $(2 - 3i)(5 + 7i) + (3i - 2)(5 + 7i)$.

23. What does *impossible* mean in mathematics?

24. Graph the forces t and u, and the resultant force, if t is a wind of 70 knots from the east acting on a plane headed northeast at 500 knots. (Consider the plane's course in still air as u.)

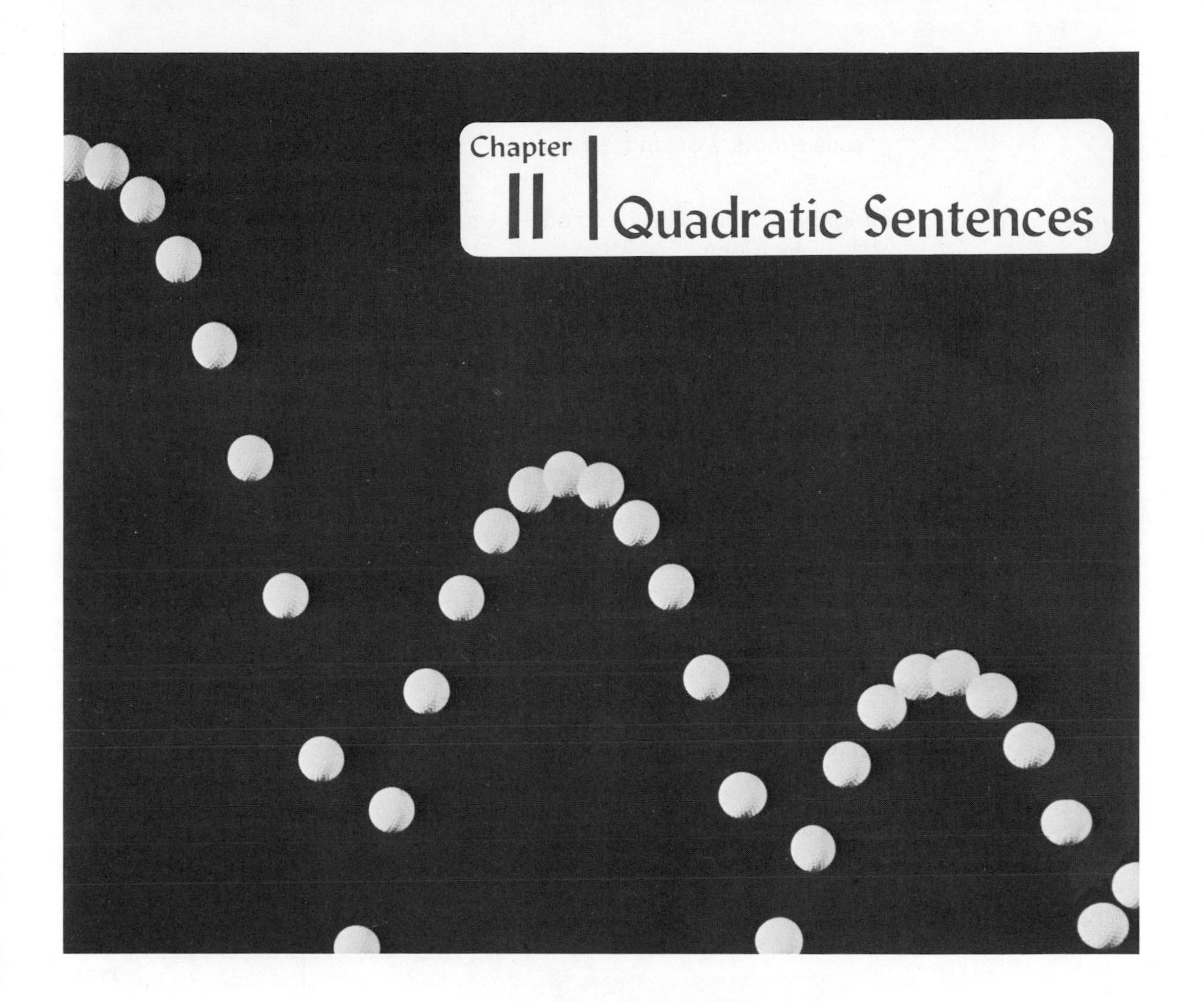

11.1 A MATHEMATICAL APPLICATION OF COMPLEX NUMBERS

The most common applications of complex numbers in mathematics are to the solutions of equations.

The equation $z^2 = -9$ has no real solution. But there are two nonreal solutions, $3i$ and $-3i$. These can be checked by multiplying.

$$(3i)(3i) = 9i^2 = -9$$
$$(-3i)(-3i) = 9i^2 = -9$$

Thus $3i$ and $-3i$ are square roots of -9. Just like every positive number, every negative number has two square roots.

Theorem 11.1.1

Let a be a positive real number. Then the negative number $-a$ has two square roots, $i\sqrt{a}$ and $-i\sqrt{a}$.

PROOF: We verify that $i\sqrt{a}$ and $-i\sqrt{a}$ are square roots of $-a$ by squaring each one.

$$(i\sqrt{a})(i\sqrt{a}) = i^2 \cdot \sqrt{a} \cdot \sqrt{a} = -1 \cdot a = -a$$

$$(-i\sqrt{a})(-i\sqrt{a}) = (-i)^2 \cdot \sqrt{a} \cdot \sqrt{a} = -1 \cdot a = -a$$

Examples: Square roots of negative numbers

1. The two square roots of -5 are $i\sqrt{5}$ and $-i\sqrt{5}$.

2. The square roots of -4 are $i\sqrt{4}$ and $-i\sqrt{4}$. Since $\sqrt{4} = 2$, the square roots should be simplified to $2i$ and $-2i$.

Verify the roots by squaring each one.

Compare the graphs of the square roots of -4 with the graphs of the square roots of 4.

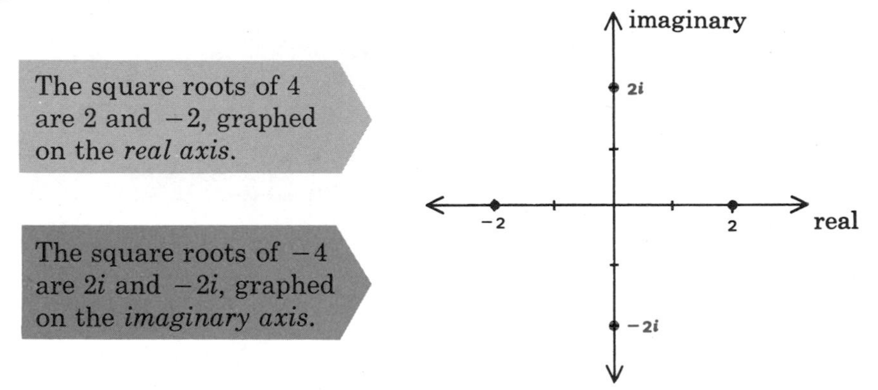

If x is negative, we use the symbol $\sqrt{x}$ to refer to the square root *above* the real axis.

Thus, $\sqrt{-4} = 2i$ and $-\sqrt{-4} = -2i$,

just as $\sqrt{4} = 2$ and $-\sqrt{4} = -2$.

So the symbol $\sqrt{a}$ always denotes exactly *one* of the two square roots of a when a is a real number, not zero.

Examples: $\sqrt{\ }$ Notation

1. $\sqrt{-8} = i\sqrt{8} = 2i\sqrt{2}$

2. $-\sqrt{-75} = -i\sqrt{75} = -5i\sqrt{3}$

We write $i\sqrt{8}$ instead of $\sqrt{8}i$ to avoid confusion about what is under the $\sqrt{\ }$.

In particular, $\sqrt{-1} = i$ and $-\sqrt{-1} = -i$. So, $a + bi = a + b\sqrt{-1}$.

This gives a *fourth* way of denoting any complex number. (The first three were rectangular coordinates, polar coordinates, and $a + bi$ notation.) For example, $3 - 2i = 3 - 2\sqrt{-1}$.

Notice that $\sqrt{-1} \cdot \sqrt{-1} = i \cdot i = i^2 = -1$. Thus we conclude that $\sqrt{-1} \cdot \sqrt{-1} \neq \sqrt{1}$. This leads to a more general conclusion.

You know that $\sqrt{a} \cdot \sqrt{b} = \sqrt{ab}$ if a and b are **positive.**
But, $\sqrt{a} \cdot \sqrt{b} \neq \sqrt{ab}$ if a and b are **negative.**

To avoid making errors, you should convert square roots of negative numbers like $\sqrt{-b}$ into bi notation before computing. For example,

$$\begin{aligned}\sqrt{-2} \cdot \sqrt{-32} &= i\sqrt{2} \cdot i\sqrt{32} \\ &= i^2\sqrt{2} \cdot \sqrt{32} \\ &= -1\sqrt{64} \\ &= -8\end{aligned}$$

Notice that since $\sqrt{64} = 8$, $\sqrt{-2} \cdot \sqrt{-32} \neq \sqrt{64}$.

Examples: Equation solving

1. If $x^2 = -9$, then x is a square root of -9.
   So $x = \sqrt{-9}$ or $x = -\sqrt{-9}$.
   $x = i\sqrt{9}$ or $x = -i\sqrt{9}$
   $x = 3i$ or $x = -3i$

2. If $r^2 = -2$, then $r = \sqrt{-2}$ or $r = -\sqrt{-2}$.
   So $r = i\sqrt{2}$ or $r = -i\sqrt{2}$.

EXERCISES 11.1

Ⓐ 1. The two square roots of 1 are _____ and _____.

2. The two square roots of -1 are _____ and _____.

3. If $a > 0$, $\sqrt{a}$ is graphed on the _____ half of the x-axis.

4. If $a < 0$, $-\sqrt{a}$ is graphed on the ____ half of the ____ -axis.

5. $\sqrt{-6}$ is graphed on the ____ half of the ____-axis.

6. $-\sqrt{-9}$ is graphed on the ____ half of the ____-axis.

7–12. Find and graph all square roots of each number.

7. 4 8. -4 9. 7 10. -7 11. 64 12. -64

13. If $\sqrt{-9} = xi$, $x =$ ____.

14. If $-\sqrt{-16} = yi$, $y =$ ____.

15. $\sqrt{-1}$ is another way of writing ____.

16–24. Express in $a + bi$ notation.

16. $6 - 4\sqrt{-1}$
17. $\frac{1}{4}\sqrt{-1}$
18. $12\sqrt{-1} + 2$
19. $\sqrt{-100}$
20. $\sqrt{-6}$
21. $\sqrt{-4}$
22. $-\sqrt{-4}$
23. $5 - \sqrt{-4}$
24. $6 - 2\sqrt{-3}$

25–30. Square each number.

25. i
26. $5i$
27. $-5i$
28. $-i\sqrt{3}$
29. $\sqrt{-8}$
30. $i\sqrt{2}$

31–38. True or False?

31. The two square roots of any nonzero real number are opposites of each other.

32. Graphed in the complex plane, $\sqrt{-312}$ and $\sqrt{312}$ are equidistant from the origin.

33. $i^2 = (-i)^2$
34. $3i = -\sqrt{-9}$
35. $i\sqrt{2} = \sqrt{-2}$
36. $\sqrt{-1} \cdot \sqrt{-1} = -1$
37. $3 = \sqrt{-3} \cdot \sqrt{-3}$
38. $\sqrt{-3} \cdot \sqrt{-2} = \sqrt{6}$

Ⓑ **39–44.** Solve and express all solutions in $a + bi$ notation.

39. $x^2 = -4$
40. $y^2 = -2$
41. $z^2 + 9 = 0$
42. $41 = a^2$
43. $-49 = b^2$
44. $c^2 + 10 = 0$

45. Multiple choice: $\sqrt{-9} + \sqrt{-25} =$

a. $\sqrt{-34}$ **b.** $-\sqrt{-34}$ **c.** $\sqrt{34}$ **d.** $-\sqrt{34}$ **e.** none of these

© **46.** Show that $2i$ and $-2i$ are the only square roots of -4 by solving the equation $(a + bi)^2 = -4$ for real numbers a and b. (HINT: $-4 = -4 + 0i$.)

47–49. Find all square roots of each number. (HINT: Keep the polar coordinates and remember that $[r, \theta] \cdot [r, \theta] = [r^2, 2\theta]$.)

47. $[16, 30°]$ **48.** $[1, 90°]$ **49.** $[2, 90°]$

MANIPULATIONS INVOLVING RADICALS 11.2

The symbol $\sqrt{\ }$ is called a *radical* sign (from the Latin *radix*, meaning "root"). This section gives you examples and practice with more complicated expressions using this sign. Addition, subtraction, and multiplication of radicals are fairly easy because *all* previous properties of real numbers still apply.

Examples: Adding and subtracting radicals

1. $\sqrt{3} - 30\sqrt{3} = (1 - 30)\sqrt{3}$
$= -29\sqrt{3}$

2. $3\sqrt{-16} - 2\sqrt{-4} = 3i\sqrt{16} - 2i\sqrt{4}$
$= 12i - 4i$
$= 8i$

3. $5\sqrt{10} + \sqrt{40} = 5\sqrt{10} + 2\sqrt{10}$
$= 7\sqrt{10}$

Sometimes simplifying a radical makes addition or subtraction easier.

4. There is *no* way to simplify expressions like:
$5 + \sqrt{2}$, $\sqrt{3} - 8$, and $\sqrt{5} - \sqrt{3}$.

Examples: Multiplying radicals

1. $2\sqrt{3}(4\sqrt{27} - \sqrt{6}) = 8\sqrt{3}\sqrt{27} - 2\sqrt{3}\sqrt{6}$
$= 8\sqrt{81} - 2\sqrt{3} \cdot \sqrt{3} \cdot \sqrt{2}$
$= 72 - 6\sqrt{2}$

2. The FOIL theorem is often helpful.
$(3 - \sqrt{17})(4 + 6\sqrt{17}) = 12 + 18\sqrt{17} - 4\sqrt{17} - 6 \cdot 17$
$= -90 + 14\sqrt{17}$

3. $(2 - 3\sqrt{-6})(5 - 8\sqrt{-6}) = (2 - 3i\sqrt{6})(5 - 8i\sqrt{6})$
$$= 10 - 16i\sqrt{6} - 15i\sqrt{6} + 24i^2\sqrt{6}\cdot\sqrt{6}$$
$$= 10 - 31i\sqrt{6} + 24(-1)(6)$$
$$= -134 - 31i\sqrt{6}$$

4. The product of two irrational numbers can be rational.

$$(2 + \sqrt{5})(2 - \sqrt{5}) = 4 + 2\sqrt{5} - 2\sqrt{5} - 5 = -1$$

When $\sqrt{b}$ is irrational, the two real numbers $a + \sqrt{b}$ and $a - \sqrt{b}$ are called *irrational conjugates*. (See $2 + \sqrt{5}$ and $2 - \sqrt{5}$ in Example **4** above.) The product of two irrational conjugates is always rational, as illustrated in Example **4**.

Like two complex conjugates (whose product is real), irrational conjugates are used to simplify division. For example, we can simplify $\frac{2 - 3\sqrt{5}}{4 + \sqrt{5}}$ by multiplying both numerator and denominator by the conjugate of the denominator.

$$\frac{2 - 3\sqrt{5}}{4 + \sqrt{5}} \cdot \frac{4 - \sqrt{5}}{4 - \sqrt{5}} = \frac{8 - 12\sqrt{5} - 2\sqrt{5} + 15}{16 + 4\sqrt{5} - 4\sqrt{5} - 5} = \frac{23 - 14\sqrt{5}}{11}$$

Notice that the result is a new fraction in which $\sqrt{5}$ appears only once, and only in the numerator. This makes it easy to find a decimal approximation for the result. From tables, $\sqrt{5} \doteq 2.236$.

$$\text{So, } \frac{23 - 14\sqrt{5}}{11} \doteq \frac{23 - 14(2.236)}{11} = \frac{-8.304}{11} \doteq -0.755.$$

Examples: Dividing with radicals

1. $\frac{12 + \sqrt{3}}{2\sqrt{3} - 6} = \frac{12 + \sqrt{3}}{-6 + 2\sqrt{3}} \cdot \frac{-6 - 2\sqrt{3}}{-6 - 2\sqrt{3}} = \frac{-78 - 30\sqrt{3}}{24} = \frac{-13 - 5\sqrt{3}}{4}$

Many applications are simpler, like the following.

2. $\frac{2}{\sqrt{3}} = \frac{2}{\sqrt{3}} \cdot \frac{\sqrt{3}}{\sqrt{3}} = \frac{2\sqrt{3}}{3}$

3. $\frac{1}{\sqrt{-5}} = \frac{1}{\sqrt{-5}} \cdot \frac{\sqrt{-5}}{\sqrt{-5}} = \frac{i\sqrt{5}}{-5}$

4. $\frac{\sqrt{5}}{\sqrt{2}} = \frac{\sqrt{5}}{\sqrt{2}} \cdot \frac{\sqrt{2}}{\sqrt{2}} = \frac{\sqrt{10}}{2}$

5. $\sqrt{-\frac{1}{2}} = i\sqrt{\frac{1}{2}} = i\frac{\sqrt{1}}{\sqrt{2}} = i\frac{\sqrt{1}\cdot\sqrt{2}}{\sqrt{2}\cdot\sqrt{2}} = \frac{i\sqrt{2}}{2}$

EXERCISES 11.2

Ⓐ **1–3.** Tell whether the expression can be simplified.

1. $\sqrt{3} + \sqrt{5}$

2. $\sqrt{2} - \sqrt{8}$

3. $6 - 2\sqrt{6}$

4–6. What could be done to each fraction to form a simpler equivalent fraction?

4. $\frac{5}{\sqrt{2}}$ **5.** $\frac{3 - \sqrt{8}}{2\sqrt{8} + 6}$ **6.** $\frac{4 - i}{2 + \sqrt{-3}}$

7. The irrational conjugate of $3 - 2\sqrt{5}$ is ____.

8–11. True or False? (Assume x and y are positive.)

8. $\sqrt{4x} = 2\sqrt{x}$ **9.** $\sqrt{x} - \sqrt{y} = \sqrt{x - y}$

10. $\frac{\sqrt{x}}{\sqrt{y}} = \sqrt{\frac{x}{y}}$ **11.** $\frac{1}{\sqrt{y}} = \frac{\sqrt{y}}{y}$

Ⓑ **12–29.** Simplify.

12. $\frac{9}{\sqrt{3}}$ **13.** $\frac{1}{\sqrt{7}}$ **14.** $\frac{2}{3\sqrt{6}}$

15. $\sqrt{320}$ **16.** $\sqrt{\frac{3}{2}}$ **17.** $\frac{2\sqrt{27}}{5\sqrt{3}}$

18. $(3 - 2\sqrt{5})(3\sqrt{5} + 1)$ **19.** $(1 + \sqrt{2})^2$ **20.** $(4 - 2\sqrt{3})^2$

21. $(2 + \sqrt{-7})(2 - \sqrt{-7})$ **22.** $(6 - \sqrt{-4})(2 + 2\sqrt{-4})$ **23.** $(8 + \sqrt{8})(7 + \sqrt{7})$

24. $\frac{6 - \sqrt{2}}{3 - \sqrt{2}}$ **25.** $\frac{1}{4 + \sqrt{5}}$ **26.** $\frac{\sqrt{2} - \sqrt{3}}{\sqrt{2} + \sqrt{3}}$

27. $\frac{8}{4 - \sqrt{10}}$ **28.** $\frac{10 - \sqrt{2}}{8 + 9\sqrt{2}}$ **29.** $\frac{3 + 4\sqrt{-9}}{2 + 2\sqrt{-9}}$

30–31. Find an equivalent fraction in which the *numerator* is an integer.

30. $\frac{1 - \sqrt{5}}{2}$ **31.** $\frac{3 + \sqrt{6}}{\sqrt{6} - 6}$

32–33. Simplify so that the denominator contains no radicals. Assume x, y, a, and b are positive.

32. $\frac{\sqrt{x} + \sqrt{y}}{\sqrt{x} - \sqrt{y}}$ **33.** $\frac{\sqrt{a} + \sqrt{b}}{\sqrt{ab}}$

Ⓒ **34.** Let $2x = -1 + \sqrt{5}$. Given that $x^2 + x$ is an integer, which integer is it?

35. Let a and b be any rational numbers. Prove that the set of nonzero numbers of the form $a + b\sqrt{2}$ can form a multiplicative group.

11.3 EQUATIONS INVOLVING RADICALS

This equation is easy to solve. ⟶ $\sqrt{x} = 4$

We just square both sides. ⟶ $x = 16$

The solution, 16, to the second equation checks: $\sqrt{16} = 4$. In general, you do not lose solutions to equations by squaring.

Theorem 11.3.1

If $x = a$, then $x^2 = a^2$.

PROOF: If $x = a$, multiplying both sides by a, we get $ax = a^2$.

If $x = a$, multiplying both sides by x, we get $x^2 = ax$.

Thus, by substitution, $x^2 = a^2$.

The converse of Theorem 11.3.1 is *not true!* It is possible to have $x^2 = a^2$ and not have $x = a$. (For example, let $x = 5$, $a = -5$.) This means that a solution to $x^2 = a^2$ may not be a solution to $x = a$.

$x^2 = a^2$ and $x = a$ are *not* equivalent sentences.

If you square both sides of an equation, you *must check each solution,* even if you are certain you haven't made an error!

For example, when both sides of an equation are squared, the new equation may have solutions which do not "fit" the original equation, as at the right.

$$3 - \sqrt{y - 5} = 10$$

$$-\sqrt{y - 5} = 7 \quad \text{Add } -3$$

$$y - 5 = 49 \quad \text{Squaring}$$

$$y = 54 \quad \text{Add } 5$$

The result, 54, does not check in the original sentence. We call 54 an *extraneous solution.*

$$3 - \sqrt{54 - 5} \neq 10$$

So the original sentence has no solution.

Squaring tends to produce extraneous solutions, but they can be checked. On the other hand, taking square roots of both sides can cause solutions to be lost.

If you do this, you have lost the solution -3.

Given: $x^2 = 9$

Square root: $x = 3$

You must find both square roots to keep all solutions.

Given: $x^2 = 9$

Square roots: $x = 3$ or $x = -3$

Theorem 11.3.2

If $x^2 = a$, then $x = \sqrt{a}$ or $x = -\sqrt{a}$.

Example 1: $x^2 - 5 = 0$

Add 5: $x^2 = 5$

Square roots: $x = \sqrt{5}$ or $x = -\sqrt{5}$

Solution set $= \{\sqrt{5}, -\sqrt{5}\}$

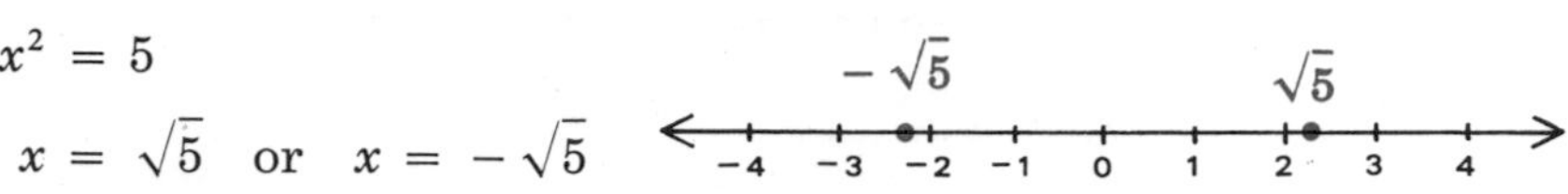

For Example **2**, we replace x by $x + 3$. This shifts the solutions 3 units to the left, as predicted by the graph translation theorem.

Example 2: $(x + 3)^2 - 5 = 0$

Add 5: $(x + 3)^2 = 5$

Square roots: $x + 3 = \sqrt{5}$ or $x + 3 = -\sqrt{5}$

Add -3: $x = -3 + \sqrt{5}$ or $x = -3 - \sqrt{5}$

Solution set $= \{-3 + \sqrt{5}, -3 - \sqrt{5}\}$

$-3 - \sqrt{5}$ $-3 + \sqrt{5}$

−6 −5 −4 −3 −2 −1 0

When solutions to quadratic equations are conjugates, you can abbreviate using the $\pm$ (*plus or minus*) sign. So, for Example **2**, the solutions are $x = -3 \pm \sqrt{5}$. In Example **3** the $\pm$ sign is used wherever possible.

Example 3: $49(t - 8)^2 + 4 = 0$

Add -4: $49(t - 8)^2 = -4$

Multiply by $\frac{1}{49}$: $(t - 8)^2 = -\frac{4}{49}$

Square roots: $t - 8 = \pm\sqrt{-\frac{4}{49}}$

Add 8: $t = 8 \pm \sqrt{-\frac{4}{49}}$

Simplify: $t = 8 \pm \frac{2}{7}i$

The last line is shorthand for: $t = 8 + \frac{2}{7}i$ or $t = 8 - \frac{2}{7}i$.

EXERCISES 11.3

Ⓐ **1–9.** Give all solutions to each sentence.

1. $x^2 = \frac{9}{4}$ **2.** $y^2 = 0$ **3.** $(x - 2)^2 = \frac{9}{4}$

4. $(y - 5)^2 = 0$ 5. $a^2 = 10$ 6. $-9 = b^2$

7. $(c - 3)^2 = 10$ 8. $-9 = (d + 4)^2$ 9. $(e + 6)^2 = 10$

10. True or False? If $x^2 = a^2$, then $x = a$.

11. True or False? If $x = a$, then $x^2 = a^2$.

12. When solving an equation, why should you be careful about squaring both sides?

13–15. Find all solutions to each sentence.

13. $\sqrt{m} = 3$ 14. $\sqrt{n} = -4$ 15. $\sqrt{x} = 2i$

16. Replacing x by $x + 10$ in an equation does what to the solutions?

17. Compare the solutions of $x^2 = 461$ and $(x - 8)^2 = 461$.

Ⓑ **18–33.** Find all solutions to each sentence.

18. $81 = \sqrt{m - 2}$ 19. $0.4 = v\sqrt{3}$

20. $-\sqrt{3x + 5} = \sqrt{2 - x}$ 21. $\sqrt{2450} = m\sqrt{2}$

22. $\sqrt{D + 3} - 8\sqrt{D + 3} = 14$ 23. $\sqrt{y} + 5 = 2(9 - \sqrt{y})$

24. $(a + \frac{3}{4})^2 = 2$ 25. $(a - \frac{3}{4})^2 = 2$

26. $(d - \frac{1}{5})^2 = \frac{2}{3}$ 27. $(d - \frac{1}{5})^2 = -\frac{2}{3}$

28. $3(v - \frac{1}{3})^2 = 12$ 29. $-9(x + \frac{3}{2})^2 = 11$

30. $(x - i)^2 = -4$ 31. $(4 - m)^2 = 8$

32. $20 = (6 - y)^2$ 33. $12 = (\frac{2}{3} + x)^2$

34–36. Simplify if possible.

34. $6 \pm \frac{\sqrt{3}}{3}$ 35. $\frac{15 \pm \sqrt{9}}{4}$ 36. $\frac{2 \pm \sqrt{-4}}{2}$

Ⓒ **37–42.** Find all solutions.

37. $\sqrt{a} > \frac{1}{2}$ 38. $z^2 = -z$ 39. $\sqrt{x} + \sqrt{3} = \sqrt{5}$

40. $x^2 > 3$ 41. $(x - 10)^2 > 3$ 42. $\sqrt{y - 2} = \sqrt{y} - \sqrt{2}$

43. Given $\sqrt{x} + \sqrt{y} = 1$, obtain an equivalent sentence by squaring.

COMPLETING THE SQUARE 11.4

The expression x^2 is the simplest example of a *quadratic expression.* (The word *quadratic* is derived from the Latin *quadratus* meaning "made square.") All quadratic expressions in one variable are equivalent to the one below.

$$ax^2 + bx + c, \quad (a \neq 0)$$

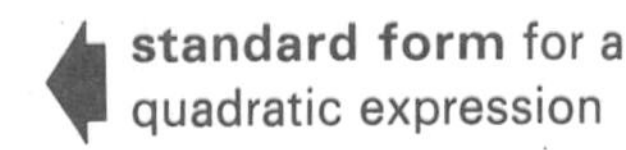

standard form for a quadratic expression

Some of the equations you solved in the last section involved quadratic expressions in *square form.*

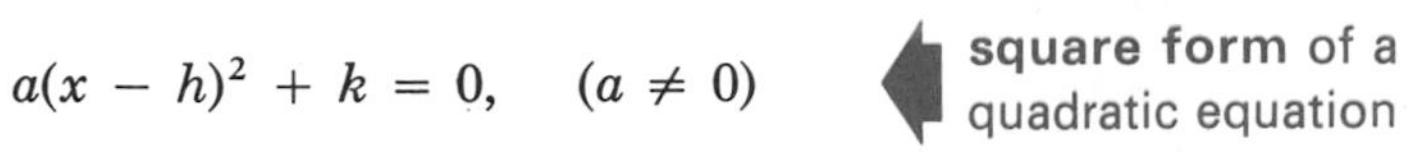

$$a(x - h)^2 + k = 0, \quad (a \neq 0)$$

square form of a quadratic equation

For example: $2(x + 3)^2 - 5 = 0$ is in square form.

When an equation can be converted to this form, it is easy to solve. The process of converting from standard form to square form is called *completing the square* and is *only* performed when the coefficient of x^2 is 1. (Of course, this coefficient can always be made 1 by division.)

Theorem 11.4.1

Completing the square: $x^2 + bx = \left(x + \frac{b}{2}\right)^2 - \left(\frac{b}{2}\right)^2$

PROOF: $\left(x + \frac{b}{2}\right)^2 - \left(\frac{b}{2}\right)^2 = \left(x^2 + bx + \frac{b^2}{4}\right) - \frac{b^2}{4} = x^2 + bx$

Examples:

	Standard form		Square form
1.	$x^2 + 6x$	=	$(x + 3)^2 - 9$
2.	$a^2 - 9a$	=	$(a - \frac{9}{2})^2 - \frac{81}{4}$

To complete the square on $x^2 + bx$, the number in the blank $(x + \_\_)^2$ is $\frac{b}{2}$.

Since $\left(x - \frac{b}{2}\right)^2$ is $\frac{b^2}{4}$ greater than $x^2 + bx$, we must subtract $\frac{b^2}{4}$.

Examples: Completing the square

3. $x^2 + 6x + 34$
$= (x + 3)^2 - 9 + 34$
$= (x + 3)^2 + 25$

4. $y^2 - 5y - 6$
$= (y - \frac{5}{2})^2 - \frac{25}{4} - 6$
$= (y - \frac{5}{2})^2 - \frac{49}{4}$

One application of completing the square is for the solution of equations, as illustrated below.

Given ▶ $x^2 + 6x + 34 = 0$

Complete the square ▶ $x^2 + 6x + 9 - 9 + 34 = 0$

$(x + 3)^2 + 25 = 0$ ← This equation can be solved like those in the last section.

EXERCISES 11.4

Ⓐ **1–2.** Give an example of a quadratic expression:

1. in standard form.

2. in square form.

3–5. Square each binomial.

3. $x + 6$

4. $y - 5$

5. $z + \frac{1}{2}$

6–8. Write in standard form.

6. $(x - 2)^2$

7. $(y + 1)^2$

8. $\left(x + \frac{b}{2}\right)^2$

9. Give an application for "completing the square."

10–21. Convert to square form.

10. $v^2 + 8v$

11. $z^2 - 8z$

12. $x^2 + 5x$

13. $t^2 + t$

14. $r^2 - r$

15. $d^2 - 70d$

Ⓑ **16.** $y^2 + 6y + 10$

17. $y^2 + 6y + 9$

18. $y^2 + 6y + 11$

19. $c^2 - 5c + 1$

20. $c - 5c - 5$

21. $c^2 - \frac{2}{7}c - \frac{5}{7}$

22–25. Convert to standard form.

22. $(h - 3)^2 + 11$

23. $8 - (2 - v)^2$

24. $(x + 1)^2 - 8 = 0$

25. $4 - (3 - 2m)^2 = 0$

Ⓒ **26–27.** Find an equivalent equation of the form $(x - h)^2 + (y - k)^2 = r^2$. (This shows that each equation represents a circle.)

26. $3x^2 + 3y^2 + 8y = 0$

27. $x^2 - 5x + y^2 + 8y - 10 = 0$

28. If $y = x^2 + 4x - 12$ and $y - k = (x - h)^2$, find h and k.

29. If $y = 3x^2 + 2x + 1$ and $y - k = a(x - h)^2$, find a, h, and k.

30–39. Solve by completing the square.

30. $x^2 + 4x = 6$

31. $m^2 - 6m + 1 = 0$

32. $y^2 - 12y = -20$

33. $20 = n^2 + 8n$

34. $z^2 - 5z = 750$

35. $100 = 2p^2 - 24p$

36. $v - v^2 = 1$

37. $w^2 + w + 1 = 0$

38. $d^2 + 11d + 31 = 0$

39. $e^2 - 3e + \frac{25}{4} = 0$

THE QUADRATIC FORMULA

There is a formula which makes it easy to solve *any* quadratic equation. This formula has many applications and *must be memorized.*

Theorem 11.5.1

Quadratic formula theorem: For any quadratic equation expressed in the form $ax^2 + bx + c = 0$, the roots are given by the formula

$$x = \frac{-b \pm \sqrt{b^2 - 4ac}}{2a}.$$

PROOF: The idea is to "complete the square" on the most general quadratic equation.

$$ax^2 + bx + c = 0$$ Given

$$x^2 + \frac{b}{a}x + \frac{c}{a} = 0$$

$$\left(x + \frac{b}{2a}\right)^2 - \frac{b^2}{4a^2} + \frac{c}{a} = 0$$ Complete the square (One half of $\frac{b}{a}$ is $\frac{b}{2a}$.)

$$\left(x + \frac{b}{2a}\right)^2 = \frac{b^2}{4a^2} - \frac{c}{a}$$

$$\left(x + \frac{b}{2a}\right)^2 = \frac{b^2 - 4ac}{4a^2}$$

$$x + \frac{b}{2a} = \frac{\pm\sqrt{b^2 - 4ac}}{2a}$$

$$x = \frac{-b \pm \sqrt{b^2 - 4ac}}{2a}$$

We can rewrite the formula without the $\pm$ sign.

$$x = \frac{-b + \sqrt{b^2 - 4ac}}{2a} \quad \text{or} \quad x = \frac{-b - \sqrt{b^2 - 4ac}}{2a}$$

Examples: Applying the quadratic formula

1. Solve $3x^2 + 4x - 5 = 0$. Let $a = 3$, $b = 4$, $c = -5$.

   Then $b^2 - 4ac = 76$. By the formula,

   $$x = \frac{-b \pm \sqrt{b^2 - 4ac}}{2a} = \frac{-4 \pm \sqrt{76}}{6} = \frac{-4 \pm 2\sqrt{19}}{6} = \frac{-2}{3} \pm \frac{\sqrt{19}}{3}.$$

2. In $y^2 + y - 6 = 0$, $a = 1$, $b = 1$, $c = -6$.

   $$y = \frac{-1 \pm \sqrt{1^2 + 24}}{2} = \frac{-1 \pm \sqrt{25}}{2} = \frac{-1 \pm 5}{2}$$

   So $y = \frac{-1 + 5}{2} = 2$ or $y = \frac{-1 - 5}{2} = -3$.

   You should check both solutions.

3. To solve $4(m^2 - 3m) = -9$, convert into standard form

   $$4m^2 - 12m + 9 = 0.$$

   Now, $a = 4$, $b = -12$, and $c = 9$. Then,

   $$m = \frac{12 \pm \sqrt{144 - 4 \cdot 4 \cdot 9}}{8} = \frac{12}{8} = \frac{3}{2}.$$

4. Let us check with an equation whose solution set is known to be $\{i, -i\}$.

   $$x^2 = -1$$

   Here $x^2 + 1 = 0$. So $a = 1$, $b = 0$, $c = 1$.

   $$x = \frac{0 \pm \sqrt{0 - 4 \cdot 1 \cdot 1}}{2} = \frac{\pm\sqrt{-4}}{2} = \frac{\pm 2i}{2} = \pm i \quad \text{(as expected)}$$

5. Coefficients need not be integers. In $v^2 - \sqrt{2}v - 6 = 0$,

   $$v = \frac{\sqrt{2} \pm \sqrt{2 + 24}}{2}.$$

   So $v = \frac{\sqrt{2} + \sqrt{26}}{2}$ or $v = \frac{\sqrt{2} - \sqrt{26}}{2}$.

The quadratic formula is extremely useful. The formula applies to *any* quadratic equation, even if the coefficients a, b, and c are not real numbers. The formula gives *every* solution to the equation—there are no others.

By observing the formula, we can analyze many properties of the solutions to quadratic equations. Here are the solutions again.

$$\frac{-b + \sqrt{b^2 - 4ac}}{2a} \qquad \frac{-b - \sqrt{b^2 - 4ac}}{2a}$$

Notice that when $b^2 - 4ac$ is zero, $\sqrt{b^2 - 4ac}$ is also zero, and the two expressions on page 310 both simplify to $\frac{-b}{2a}$. There is then only one solution to the equation. (See Example **3**, page 310.)

If $b^2 - 4ac$ is negative, $\sqrt{b^2 - 4ac}$ is imaginary. Thus the solutions also will be imaginary if a and b are real numbers. (See Example **4**.)

If $b^2 - 4ac$ is positive, and a and b are real numbers, there are two real solutions, as in Examples **1** and **2**.

So you can see that the number $b^2 - 4ac$ tells much about the solutions to a quadratic equation. We call this number the **discriminant** of the quadratic equation $ax^2 + bx + c = 0$. The next theorem sums up the preceding observations.

Theorem 11.5.2

Let $D = b^2 - 4ac$, the discriminant of $ax^2 + bx + c = 0$.

a. If $D = 0$,  the equation has exactly *one* solution.

b. If a and b are real and $D > 0$, ➡ the equation has *two real* solutions.

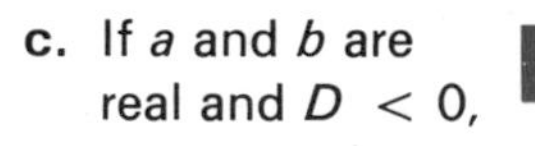

c. If a and b are real and $D < 0$, ➡ the equation has *two imaginary* solutions.

The word *root* is often used as a synonym for *solution*. Then the quadratic formula gives the *roots* of a quadratic equation. (Note that the terms *root* and *square root* do not mean the same thing.)

EXERCISES 11.5

Ⓐ **1.** What does the quadratic formula help to find?

2. State the quadratic formula. Name the discriminant.

3–8. Convert each equation to the form $ax^2 + bx + c = 0$. Give the values of a, b, and c, and find the value of the discriminant.

3. $9 - 4x^2 + 3x = 0$

4. $0 = 2y^2 - 3y$

5. $9(2 - z) = 8(3 + z^2)$

6. $a^2 - 4a + 6 = a^2 - 7a - 9$

7. $(c - 4)(c + 3) = 2$

8. $x^2 = 5$

9. What is a *root* of an equation?

10. How can you check the solutions of a quadratic equation?

11–16. Let D be the discriminant of a quadratic equation $ax^2 + bx + c = 0$ in which a, b, and c are real numbers. What can you say about the solutions to this equation:

11. if $D = 4$? **12.** if $D = 0$? **13.** if $D = -\frac{3}{2}$?

14. if $D = \sqrt{2}$? **15.** if D is positive? **16.** if D is negative?

Ⓑ **17–32.** Solve each equation.

17. $x^2 - 2x + 1 = 0$ **18.** $7c^2 - 2c - 5 = 0$

19. $y(y + 6) + 10 = 0$ **20.** $1 = (z - 4)(z + 3)$

21. $r = \frac{1}{r} + 1$ **22.** $3t^2 = 4t$

23. $2z^2 - 5z + 6 = 4z^2$ **24.** $8m - 6 = 4m^2 - 8m$

25. $100x^2 - 20x = -1$ **26.** $1 - y - 2y^2 = 3$

27. $a + bx + cx^2 = 0$ **28.** $3y^2 - 2\sqrt{3}y = 10$

29. $m^2 + m - 2 = 14$ **30.** $4x = 5x^2 - 1 + 2x$

31. $0 = 3200 - 160t - 160t^2$ **32.** $(w + 25)(w - 4) = (w - 20)(w + 5)$

33–38. Solve the equations of Exercises **3–8**.

Ⓒ **39–44.** Solve. (HINT: For each equation a substitution may help.)

39. $-3m + 2\sqrt{m} + 1 = 0$ **40.** $9d^4 - 13d^2 + 4 = 0$

41. $2(\sin\theta)^2 - 3\sin\theta + 1 = 0$ **42.** $5(\cos x)^2 - 10\cos x = 0$

43. $2 + \frac{8}{x} + \frac{8}{x^2} = 0$ **44.** $z^2 + 6|z| = 40$

45–47. Let r and s be the roots of the equation $ax^2 + bx + c = 0$. Use the quadratic formula to prove:

45. $r + s = \frac{-b}{a}$. **46.** $rs = \frac{c}{a}$. **47.** $|r - s| = \frac{\sqrt{D}}{|a|}$.

48–50. Use the formulas from Exercises **45** and **46** to give the sum and product of the roots for each equation.

48. $4d^2 - 3d + 8 = 0$ **49.** $x^2 + 2x - 1 = 0$ **50.** $-2y^2 - iy + 3$

51. One solution for $461x^2 - 900x - 44 = 0$ is the number 2. Use the formula from Exercise **45** to find the other solution.

52. Find two numbers whose sum is 6 and whose product is 10.

53. *Electricity.* The formula $W = VI - RI^2$ describes current I (in amps), resistance R (in ohms), voltage V (in volts) and power W (in watts) in an electric circuit. In a 110-volt circuit with a resistance of 10 ohms, what current is needed to achieve a power of 100 watts?

54. *Art.* The ancient Greeks, and many artists and architects since then, felt that the most pleasing rectangle is one in which the ratio of length to width equals the ratio of the sum of its length and width to its length. Find each ratio (called the *Golden Ratio*) in this proportion (called the *Divine Proportion*).

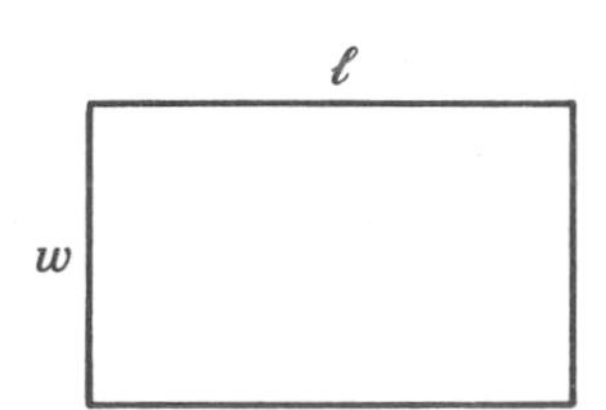

55. The equation $3x^2 + tx + 4 = 0$ has exactly one root. Find t.

56. Prove: The solutions to $ax^2 + bx + c = 0$ are the reciprocals of the solutions to $cx^2 + bx + a = 0$.

A TYPICAL APPLICATION OF QUADRATIC SENTENCES

11.6

If an object is tossed upward into the air with a velocity v (in feet per second), then its height h (measured in feet above or below the point of tossing) after t seconds is approximated by the formula

$$h = vt - \tfrac{1}{2}gt^2.$$

The letter g stands for acceleration due to gravity and is (at sea level on earth) approximately 32 feet per second per second.

If there is no gravitational pull on the object being tossed, then $g = 0$, and the formula becomes $h = vt$. This is identical in form to $d = rt$ (*distance* = *rate* × *time*). The factor $\tfrac{1}{2}gt^2$ must be subtracted because of gravity. The value 32 for g is valid at sea level, but must be changed for other altitudes, or when the object is tossed so far that the gravitational pull changes significantly.

If the original velocity is 24 feet per second, then using $g \doteq 32$,

$$h \doteq 24t - 16t^2.$$

Suppose the object leaves the hand from a height of 4 feet. Then, when the object hits the ground, it will be 4 feet below ($h = -4$) the toss point. For what value of t will $h = -4$?

Using the formula, we get

$$-4 \doteq 24t - 16t^2.$$

$16t^2 - 24t - 4 \doteq 0$ ◀ Convert to standard form

$4t^2 - 6t - 1 \doteq 0$ ◀ Divide by 4

$t \doteq \frac{6 \pm \sqrt{52}}{8} \doteq \frac{6 \pm 7.2}{8}$ ◀ Use quadratic formula

$t \doteq \frac{13.2}{8}$ or $t \doteq \frac{-1.2}{8}$

Choose this solution, since $t > 0$ after the toss.

So, the object will hit the ground approximately $\frac{13.2}{8}$ seconds after it was tossed. In other words, the object will be in the air a little more than 1.6 seconds.

Many other questions might be asked. How high will the object reach? When will it reach this height? For how long will it be over 6 feet in the air? And so on. For these questions, it is helpful to graph the solution set to the sentence $h = 24t - 16t^2$. Time is normally graphed horizontally, height vertically.

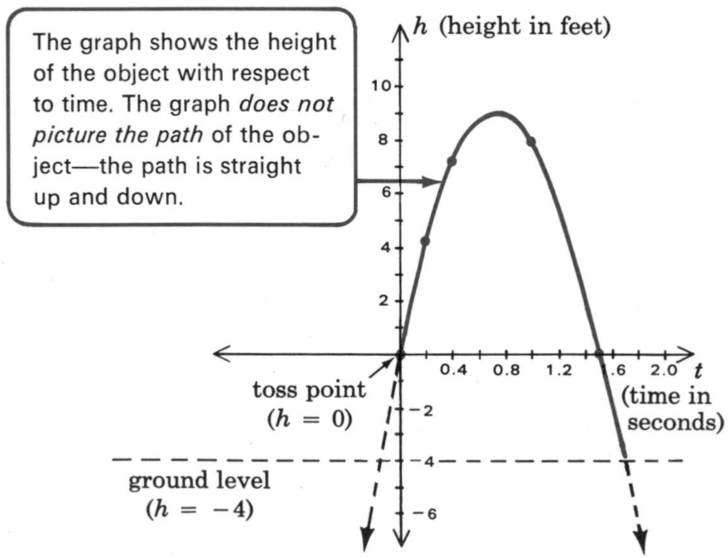

$h = 24t - 16t^2$

(t, h)
(0, 0)
(0.2, 4.16)
(0.4, 7.04)
(1, 8)
(1.5, 0)

You should check these values. These points are indicated on the graph and have been connected by a smooth curve.

In the equation, t can be any real number. But in the real situation, we have found that the object is in the air for only about 1.6 seconds. This part of the graph is shown in red above.

The curve is called a *parabola*. The parabola is one of the very many curves which occur in natural situations. In fact, if the object is not thrown straight up, but is thrown at an angle, its path is almost exactly parabolic.

Questions about the path of the object have mathematical models which involve solutions of quadratic sentences.

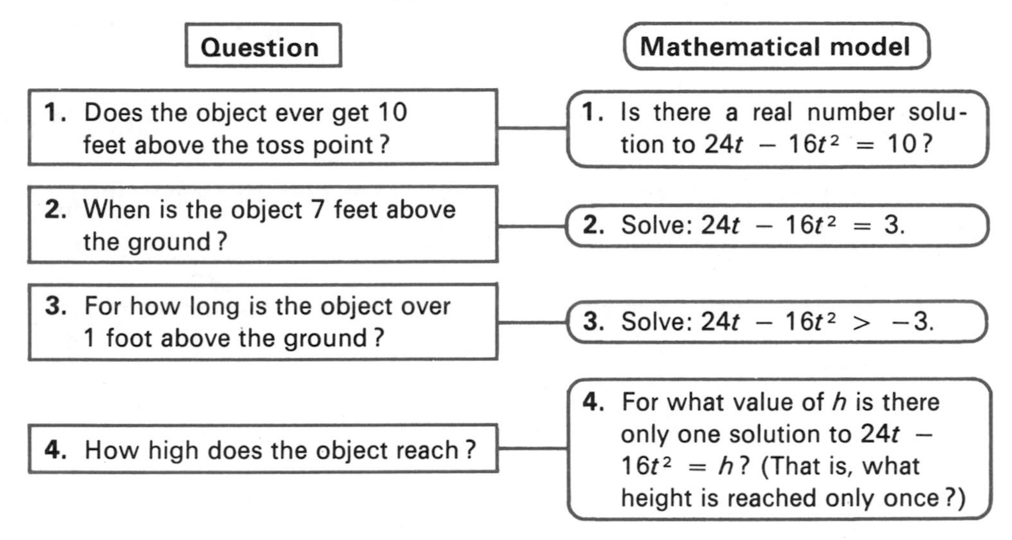

You already can solve equations like those in models **1** and **2**. Notice that question **4** is ingeniously answered by using the equation in model **4**—the only height which is reached exactly once is the maximum height. Proceed as follows.

$$24t - 16t^2 = h \quad \Longleftrightarrow \text{(is equivalent to)} \quad 16t^2 - 24t + h = 0$$

This equation has only one solution for t when the discriminant $b^2 - 4ac$ is 0. Here $a = 16$, $b = -24$, and $c = h$. So $b^2 - 4ac = 576 - 64h = 0$ when h is the maximum height. Solving, we get $h = \frac{576}{64} = 9$. So, the maximum height is 9.

Inequalities like that in model **3** are considered in Section 11.8.

EXERCISES 11.6

Ⓐ **1–4.** Give a *precise* meaning for each letter in $h = vt + \frac{1}{2}gt^2$.

1. h **2.** v **3.** t **4.** g

5–8. If $h = 24t - 16t^2$, find h when t has the given value.

5. $\frac{1}{2}$ **6.** -1 **7.** 0.5 **8.** 1.2

9. The curve graphed on page 314 is called a ____.

10–12. Refer to the graph on page 314 to *estimate* an answer to each question.

10. How high above the *ground* does the object reach?

11. For how long is the object at least 3 feet above the toss point?

12. How long does it take the object to fall to the ground from its highest level?

13. The point (0.6, 8.68) is on the graph. What does this mean in the physical situation?

14–17. Each question below concerns the object mentioned in this section. For each question, give the corresponding mathematical model. (You do not need to answer the question.)

14. At what time is the object 2 feet above the toss point?

15. At what time is the object 2 feet above the ground?

16. How high will the object be after 1 second?

Ⓑ **17.** For how long is the object more than 10 feet above the ground?

18–20. Answer each question in **14–16**. (Use your mathematical models.)

Ⓒ **21–22.** Consider the situation discussed in this section.

21. Solving the sentence $24t - 16t^2 > 4$ tells what about the situation? Solve this sentence.

22. Repeat Exercise **21** for the sentence $-4 \leq 24t - 16t^2 \leq -3$.

23. Graph 16 solutions to $y^2 - 3y = x$. (If correct, this graph should resemble a parabola.)

24. The formula $h = h_0 + vt - 4.9t^2$ describes the approximate height of an object t seconds after being hurled into the air with an initial velocity v from a height h_0, where h_0 is measured in metres. If an object is tossed upward with an initial velocity of 19.5 metres per second from a height of 60 metres, when will the object hit the ground?

25. The formula $h = h_0 + vt - 0.8t^2$ corresponds to that in Exercise **24** if the object is tossed from the moon. Answer the question of Exercise **24** for the moon.

26. Why must the formulas of Exercises **24** and **25** be only approximations?

27. *Skydiving.* Use $h = h_0 + vt - 4.9t^2$ to determine the amount of time in free fall for a skydiver who leaves a plane at an altitude of 2440 metres and opens the parachute at 480 metres.

28. Refer to Exercise **27**. How much more time is spent in free fall if the skydiver leaves the plane at 3000 metres?

EQUATIONS FOR SOME PARABOLAS 11.7

In order to determine whether something is or is not a parabola, we need a definition. (Recall that the distance from a point to a line is the length of the perpendicular from the point to the line.)

Definition

Let d be a line and F be a point not on d. A **parabola** is the set consisting of every point whose distance from F equals its distance from d.

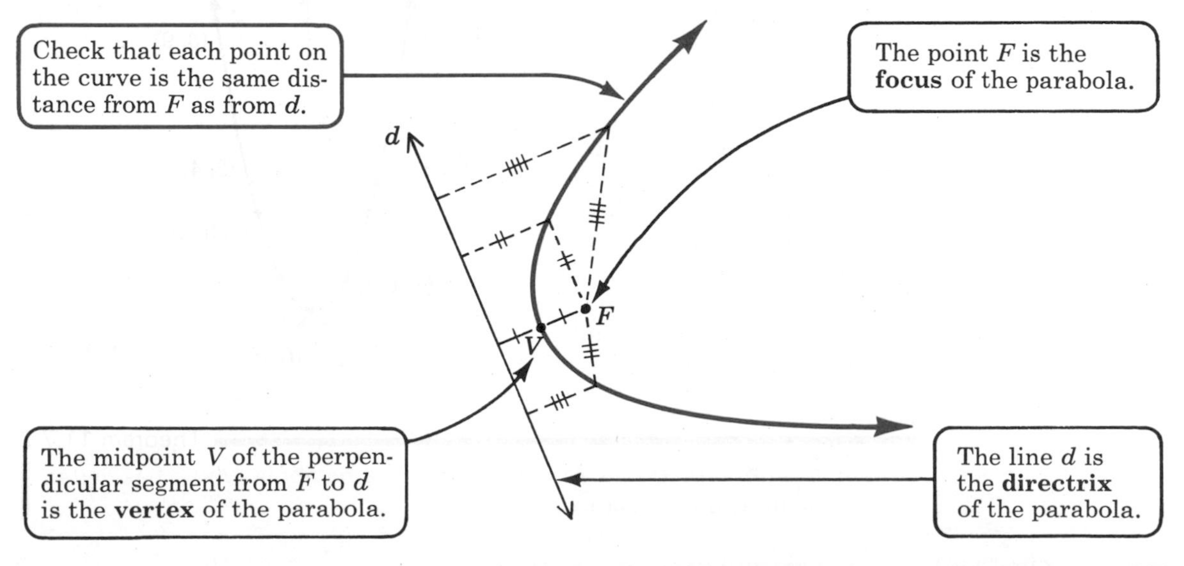

Parabolas have many geometric and algebraic properties. The algebraic properties can be found by studying the equations for parabolas.

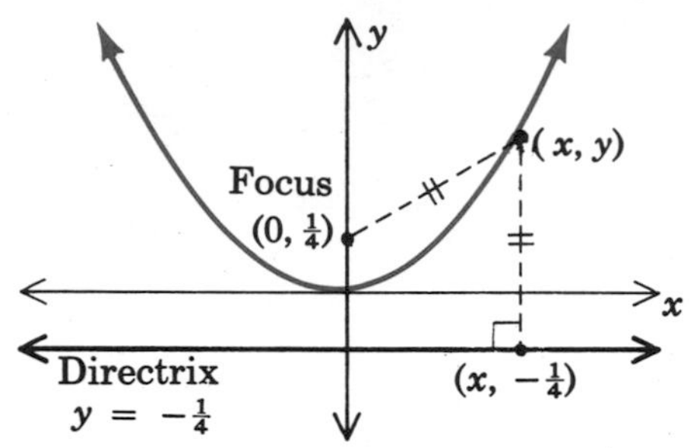

The simplest equation results when the directrix is the line $y = -\frac{1}{4}$ and the focus is $(0, \frac{1}{4})$, as at the left.

If (x, y) is on this parabola, then by the definition,

$$\begin{pmatrix}\text{distance from } (x, y) \\ \text{to } y = -\frac{1}{4}\end{pmatrix} = \begin{pmatrix}\text{distance from } (x, y) \\ \text{to } (0, \frac{1}{4})\end{pmatrix}.$$

$$\sqrt{(x - x)^2 + (y - (-\tfrac{1}{4}))^2} = \sqrt{(x - 0)^2 + (y - \tfrac{1}{4})^2}$$

$$(y + \tfrac{1}{4})^2 = x^2 + (y - \tfrac{1}{4})^2 \quad \blacktriangleleft \text{ Squaring}$$

$$y^2 + \tfrac{1}{2}y + \tfrac{1}{16} = x^2 + y^2 - \tfrac{1}{2}y + \tfrac{1}{16} \quad \blacktriangleleft \text{ Expanding}$$

$$y = x^2 \quad \blacktriangleleft \text{ Simplifying}$$

So, $y = x^2$ is the equation of the parabola whose points are equidistant from the line $y = -\frac{1}{4}$ and the point $(0, \frac{1}{4})$. This result proves the next theorem.

Theorem 11.7.1

The graph of $\{(x, y): y = x^2\}$ is the parabola with focus $(0, \frac{1}{4})$ and directrix $y = -\frac{1}{4}$.

The graph of $y = x^2$ is shown at the right.

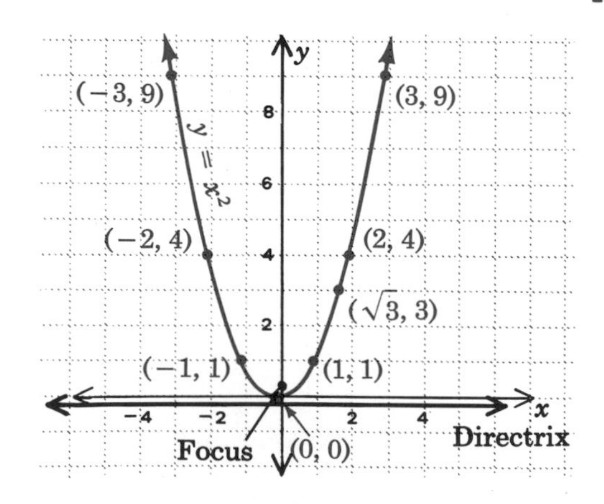

Applying the graph translation theorem (from Section 6.4), we can derive the equation for *any* translation image of this parabola.

This equation is given in the next theorem.

Theorem 11.7.2

The solution set to $y - k = (x - h)^2$ is a parabola which has vertex (h, k) and is congruent to $y = x^2$.

Example 1: The equation $y + 5 = (x - \frac{1}{3})^2$ describes a parabola with vertex $(\frac{1}{3}, -5)$. This parabola is congruent to the parabola $y = x^2$.

Notice that $y - k = (x - h)^2$ is an equation in square form. When graphing an equation which is not in square form, it helps to complete the square first.

Example 2: Graph $\{(x, y): y = x^2 - 4x - 1\}$.

SOLUTION: Complete the square.

$$y = x^2 - 4x - 1$$
$$y = (x - 2)^2 - 4 - 1$$
$$y + 5 = (x - 2)^2$$

Thus, the graph is the parabola with vertex $(2, -5)$, a translation image of $y = x^2$. Plotting points (by substitution) makes the graph more accurate.

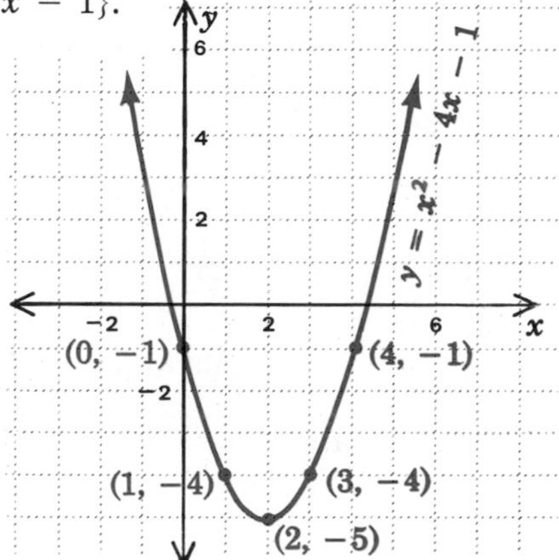

EXERCISES 11.7

Ⓐ **1.** Define *parabola*.

2–4. Give the meaning of each term with regard to a parabola.

2. focus **3.** directrix **4.** vertex

5. Give the focus, directrix, and vertex of the parabola $y = x^2$.

6. What is the graph translation theorem?

7–10. Give the vertex of each parabola.

7. $y - 6 = (x - 2)^2$ **8.** $y = (x + 5)^2$

9. $y + 3 = x^2$ **10.** $y = (x - 4)^2 + 11$

Ⓑ **11.** Trace the figure. Draw 12 points on the parabola with focus P and directrix ℓ.

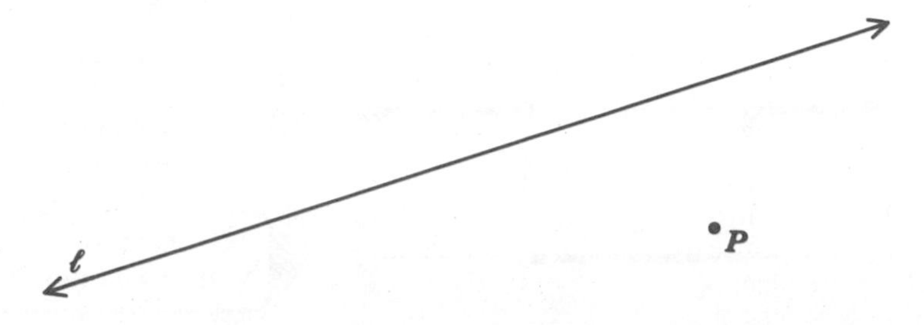

12–15. Graph each parabola from Exercises **7–10**.

16–19. Graph the set of ordered pairs satisfying each sentence.

16. $y - 4 = x^2 + 3$

17. $y = x^2 + 8x - 2$

18. $h = t^2 - 4t + 6$

19. $3y - 3x^2 = 0$

20–25. Find the points of intersection of the parabola $y = x^2 + x - 2$ and:

20. the line $x = 3$.

21. the line $y = 4$.

22. the x-axis.

23. the y-axis.

© **24.** the line $y = 2x$.

25. the parabola $y = x^2$.

26. Name the focus and directrix of the parabola $y + 5 = (x - 2)^2$.

27. A parabola has focus (2, 11) and directrix $y = -1$. Find the vertex.

28. Graph $\{(x, y): x = \sqrt{y}\}$. (HINT: Check restrictions on x and y.)

QUADRATIC INEQUALITIES

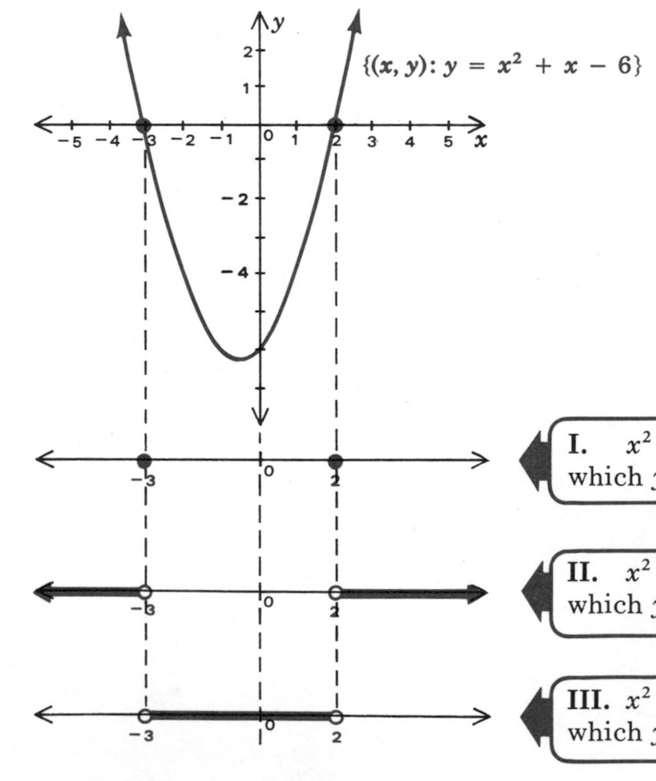

The parabola pictured at the left is the solution set to

$$y = x^2 + x - 6.$$

This graph also helps to identify the solutions to three related sentences in one variable as illustrated below.

I. $x^2 + x - 6 = 0$: The values of x for which $y = 0$ are $x = -3$ or $x = 2$.

II. $x^2 + x - 6 > 0$: The values of x for which y is positive are $x < -3$ or $x > 2$.

III. $x^2 + x - 6 < 0$: The values of x for which y is negative are $-3 < x < 2$.

A **quadratic inequality** is a sentence equivalent to

$$ax^2 + bx + c \; \bullet \; 0$$

where $a \neq 0$ and $\bullet$ is replaced by $<$, $\leq$, $>$, or $\geq$.

Any inequality of this type can be solved by graphing as on page 320. But there is another method which is usually quicker. Notice that 2 and -3 are key values in all three sentences on page 320. These values divide the number line (x-axis) into three parts, A, B, and C.

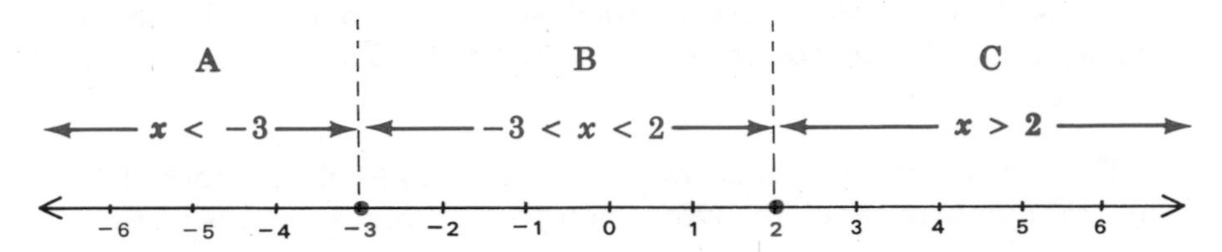

Now, inequalities **II** and **III** can be solved by trying points on each of the parts A, B, and C. If one value works, then all values in that part will work, for the parabola does not cross the x-axis again.

Example: Solve for t: $2t^2 - 3t + 1 \leq 0$.

SOLUTION:

1. First solve $2t^2 - 3t + 1 = 0$. This gives $t = 1$ or $t = \frac{1}{2}$. So, 1 and $\frac{1}{2}$ are key values. They split the number line into 3 parts, labeled A, B, and C.

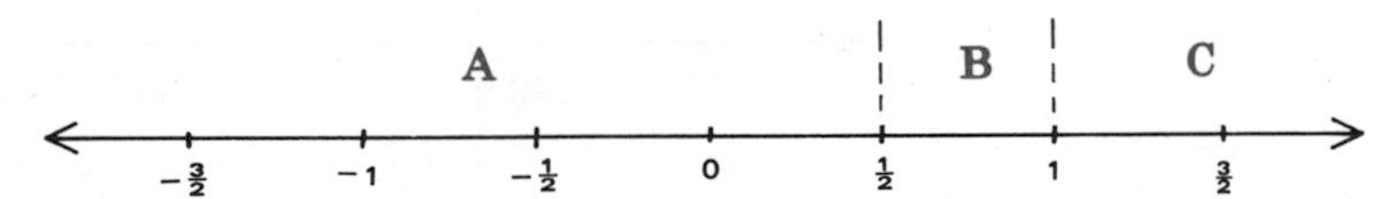

2. Try a number on part A. 0 is easiest. Is $2(0)^2 - 3(0) + 1 \leq 0$? No, it doesn't work. So numbers on part A are not in the solution set.

3. Try a number on part B, say 0.6. Since $2(0.6)^2 - 3(0.6) + 1 = -0.08$, it works. All numbers on part B work.

4. Try 2, a number on part C. Since $2(2)^2 - 3(2) + 1 > 0$, 2 is not a solution. No number on part C will work.

5. The solution set is $\{t: \frac{1}{2} \leq t \leq 1\}$.

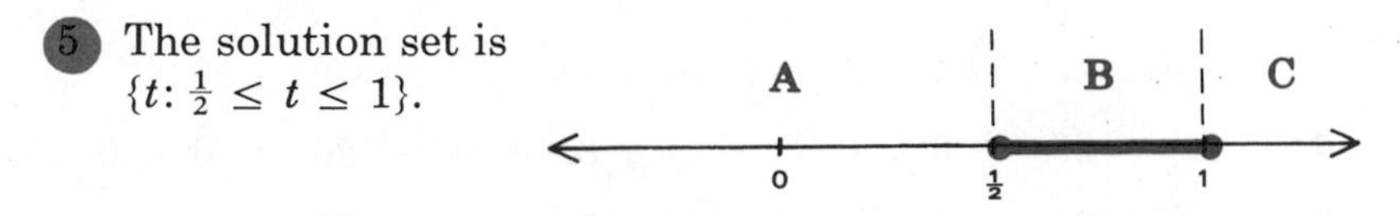

This process for solving quadratic inequalities is easy to apply. But in some cases, the related equation may lead to confusion.

For example, to solve $x^2 + 16 > 8x$, we consider the related equation $x^2 + 16 = 8x$. The only solution of this equation is 4, which splits the number line into *two* parts. You only have to try a point in each part. Since both 3 and 5 work, *all* real numbers other than 4 will work.

To solve $x^2 + 9 > 0$, consider $x^2 + 9 = 0$. This related equation has solutions $3i$ and $-3i$. These nonreal solutions do not split the real number line. This means that the related parabola does not intersect the x-axis.

Thus, either all real numbers work or no real numbers work. Trying any real numbers should convince you that all real numbers work.

EXERCISES 11.8

Ⓐ **1–4.** The equation

$y = x^2 - 2x - 1$

is graphed at the right. Use the graph to find solutions for each sentence.

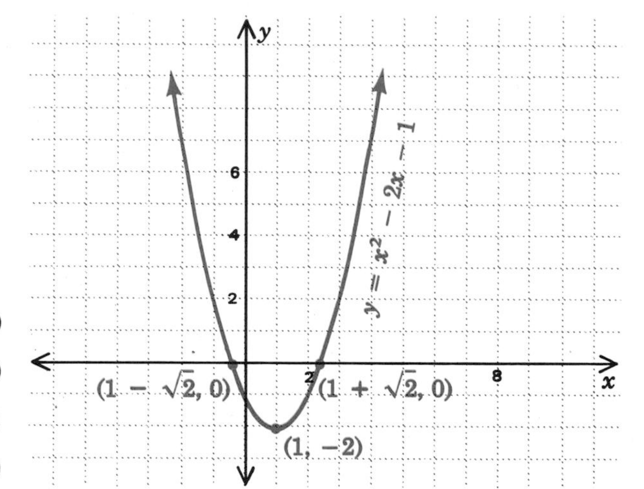

1. $x^2 - 2x - 1 = 0$

2. $x^2 - 2x - 1 < 0$

3. $x^2 - 2x - 1 \leq 0$

4. $x^2 - 2x - 1 > 0$

5. Multiple choice: Which is the solution set to $x^2 - 4x + 3 > 0$?

a. $\{x: x > 1 \text{ or } x < 3\}$ **b.** $\{x: 3 < x < 1\}$

c. $\{x: x > 3 \text{ or } x < 1\}$

6. The equation $x^2 - 4x + 10 = 0$ has no real solutions. What does this tell you about the solutions to $x^2 - 4x + 10 > 0$.

Ⓑ **7–30.** Solve each sentence and graph the solution set.

7. $-8a^2 + 26a - 6 > 0$

8. $-8a^2 + 26a - 6 < 0$

9. $-8a^2 + 26a - 6 \geq 0$

10. $-8a^2 + 26a - 6 \leq 0$

11. $x^2 + 2x > -5$

12. $x^2 + 2x < -5$

13. $0 < (m - 3)^2$

14. $4 < (n - 12)^2$

15. $2x^2 - 4x + 1 < 0$

16. $-3y > y^2$

17. $x^2 - 8x + 12 < 0$

18. $x^2 - 8x + 12 > 0$

19. $15y^2 + 14y \geq 8$

20. $108 + 36v + 3v^2 \leq 0$

21. $(w - 3)^2 - 4 > 0$

22. $10 \leq 2x^2 - 9x + 19$

23. $0.21y^2 + 0.05 \geq 0.22y$

24. $x < (x + 6)(x + 2)$

25. $(2x - 3)(4 - x) \leq -12$

26. $x^2 - x - 1 > 0$

© **27.** $a^2(a - 3)(a + 6) > 0$

28. $(w + 6)^2 < (2w - 3)^2$

29. $(e - 6)(e^2 + 3e - 10) < 0$

30. $(a + 1)(a + 2)(a + 3)(a + 4) > 24$

31. Refer to Exercise **24**, page 316. If an object is tossed upward with an initial velocity of 19.5 metres per second, how long will it be more than 24 metres higher than the toss point?

32. For what values of x does the parabola $y = x^2 - 8x + 10$ lie between the lines $y = 6$ and $y = 7$?

33. What numbers are less than their square roots?

CHAPTER SUMMARY

11

The radical symbol, $\sqrt{\ }$, can be used with negative numbers. If a is positive, $\sqrt{-a} = i\sqrt{a}$.

Equations involving radical expressions can be solved, but you must be cautious. Squaring both sides of an equation does not always result in an equivalent sentence.

For a sentence in which there is a square term, such as $x^2 = a^2$, both square roots of a^2 must be considered to insure getting all solutions. The $\pm$ notation is helpful: $(x = \pm a)$ means $(x = a \text{ or } x = -a)$.

Sentences equivalent to

$$ax^2 + bx + c \ \blacksquare\ 0 \qquad (a \neq 0)$$

where the $\blacksquare$ is replaced with $=, <, \leq, >$, or $\geq$ are *quadratic sentences.*

With complex numbers and the *quadratic formula*, it is possible to solve *any* quadratic *equation.* The solutions are

$$x = \frac{-b \pm \sqrt{b^2 - 4ac}}{2a}.$$

If a, b, and c are real, the *discriminant* $D = b^2 - 4ac$ of a quadratic equation indicates whether the equation has two real solutions (D is positive), one solution (D is 0), or two nonreal solutions (D is negative).

Quadratic inequalities may be solved by using the *roots* of the related quadratic equation as key values.

A *parabola* is the set of points equidistant from a given point and line. The path of an object thrown into the air can be described by a parabola, and many types of problems involving quadratic sentences can be interpreted as problems related to this application.

Any equation of the form $y - k = (x - h)^2$ has a solution set whose graph is a parabola with vertex (h, k). Since any quadratic equation of the preceding type is equivalent to an equation in *square form*, $y = (x - h)^2 + k$, parabolas can be used to picture solutions to quadratic equations.

Completing the square makes it easy to find the vertex of a parabola.

11

CHAPTER REVIEW

1–14. Simplify as much as possible.

1. $\sqrt{-1}$ **2.** $\sqrt{-9}$ **3.** $\sqrt{-5}$ **4.** $\sqrt{-12}$

5. $2\sqrt{8}$ **6.** $3\sqrt{27}$ **7.** $-\sqrt{-36}$ **8.** $\sqrt{-3} \cdot \sqrt{-27}$

9. $\sqrt{3} \cdot \sqrt{5} \cdot \sqrt{-3} \cdot \sqrt{-5}$ **10.** $(\sqrt{-5})^2$ **11.** $\sqrt{-\frac{5}{2}}$

12. $(2 - \sqrt{-2})(2 + \sqrt{-2})$ **13.** $\frac{1}{2 + \sqrt{3}}$ **14.** $\frac{2}{i}$

15. What number should be added to $y^2 - 2y$ to complete the square?

16–26. Find all solutions.

16. $x^2 = 4$ **17.** $\sqrt{x} = 3$ **18.** $(y - 2)^2 = 0$

19. $\sqrt{y - 3} = 5$ **20.** $\sqrt{x + 1} = 3i$ **21.** $3(x - 2)^2 = 4$

22. $(y + 5)^2 - 4 = 0$ **23.** $x^2 + 6x + 13 = 0$ **24.** $3\sqrt{16A} = 9$

25. $y(y - 4) + 8 = 0$ **26.** $cx^2 - ax + b = 0$ (Solve for x.)

27. Suppose that the height (in centimetres) of a ball t seconds after it is batted into the air is given by the expression $4 + 490t - t^2$. What physical problem might you answer by solving the sentence $4 + 490t - t^2 > 65$?

28. Graph the parabola described by $y - 5 = (x + 3)^2$.

29. Solve $x^2 - x - 6 > 0$ and graph the solution set.

30–31. How many real roots does each equation have?

30. $6m = 2 + 5m^2$ **31.** $2z^2 + 2\sqrt{6}z + 3 = 0$

Chapter 12 Quadratic Relations

A quadratic relation is one whose sentence contains terms in x^2, y^2, or xy but no higher powers of x or y. The parabolas and circles you have studied are quadratic relations. The graphs of quadratic relations take on other shapes which have interesting mathematical properties and also occur in nature.

12.1 THE CONIC SECTIONS

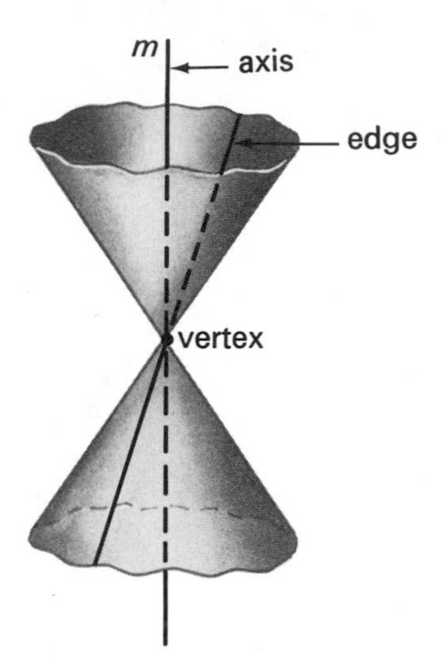

A **right circular cone** is the figure formed when one line revolves (in space) about a second fixed line m which intersects it at a fixed angle. This forms a surface which cannot be drawn completely, for it goes on and on in two directions. (See figure.)

The fixed line m is called the *axis* of the cone, and any position of the rotating line l is called an *edge* of the cone. The intersection of m and l is called the *vertex* of the cone. The two parts of the cone on either side of the vertex are called the *nappes* of the cone.

When a plane intersects a right circular cone and does not contain the vertex of the cone, three types of curves may arise.

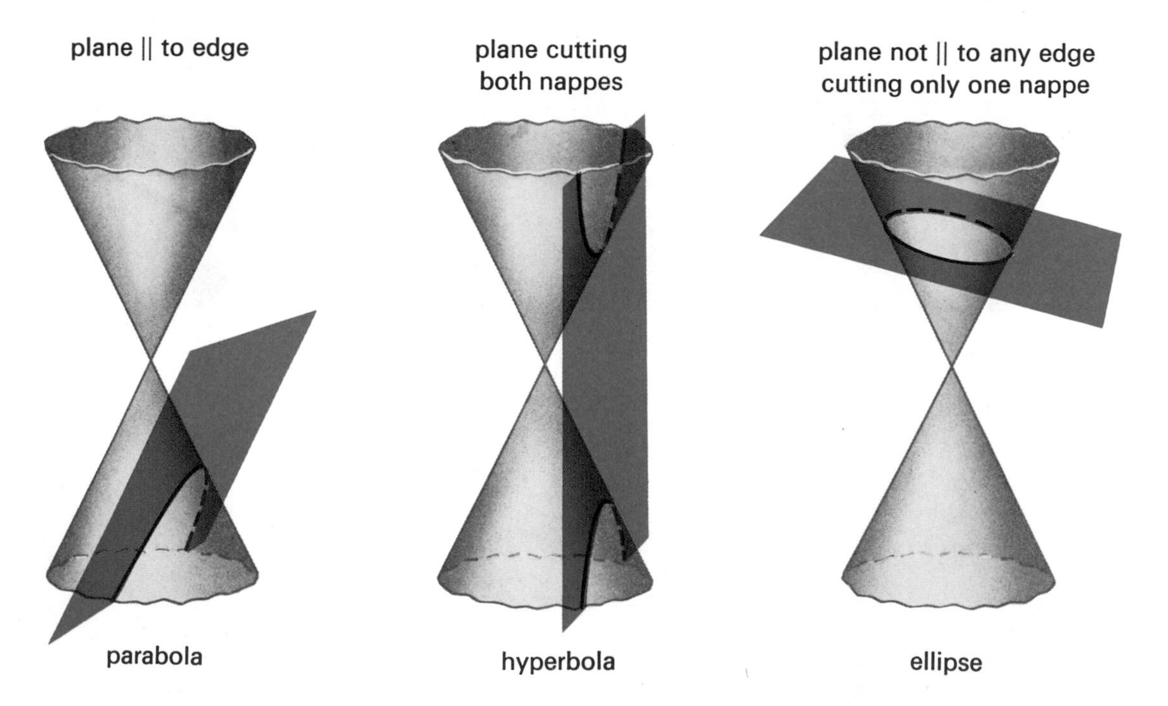

The three types of curves—parabolas, hyperbolas, and ellipses—are known as **conic sections** (short for "conic cross sections"). A circle is also a conic section. It is the special type of ellipse formed when the intersecting plane is perpendicular to the axis of the cone.

If the plane intersects the vertex of the cone, then the intersections are either lines or points. These lines and points are known as **degenerate conic sections.**

line
(degenerate parabola)

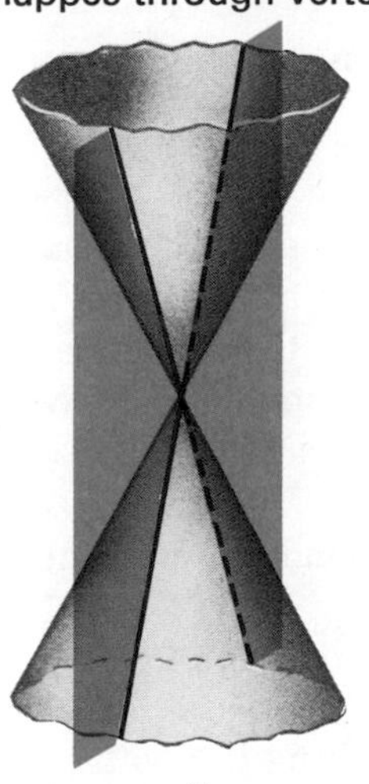

two lines
(degenerate hyperbola)

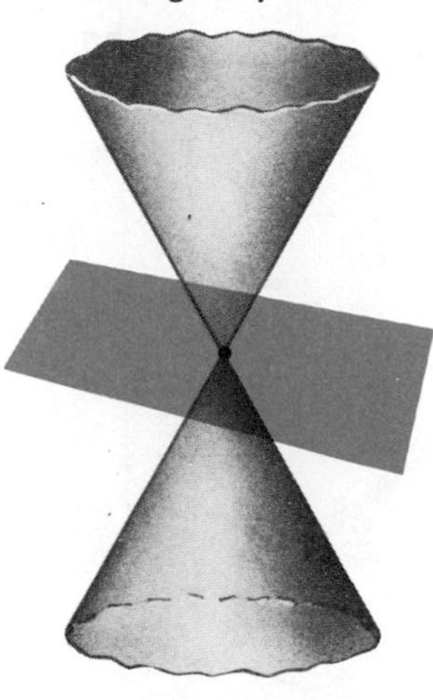

point
(degenerate ellipse)

You already know some equations for conic sections or degenerate conics.

$$(x - 3)^2 + (y + 4)^2 = 100 \quad \longleftarrow \text{circle}$$
$$y - 5 = (x - 2)^2 \quad \longleftarrow \text{parabola}$$
$$x^2 + y^2 = 0 \quad \longleftarrow \text{point}$$
$$3x - 4y = 8 \quad \longleftarrow \text{line}$$

The goal of this chapter is to introduce you to sentences which lead to conic sections you have not previously studied: ellipses and hyperbolas. As usual, we use transformations (including new transformations—the scale transformations) to obtain and compare the graphs.

EXERCISES 12.1

Ⓐ **1.** Draw a picture of a right circular cone. Show the vertex and axis.

2–5. Draw a picture of a plane intersecting a right circular cone in:

2. an ellipse.

3. a circle.

4. a parabola.

5. a hyperbola.

6–8. Draw a picture of a plane intersecting a right circular cone in:

6. a point. **7.** a line. **8.** two intersecting lines.

9. The intersection of a cone and a plane is called a ____.

10. How is a degenerate conic section formed?

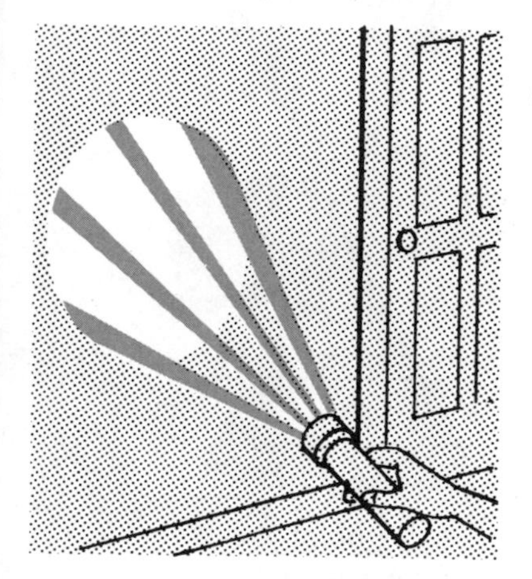

Ⓑ **11–13.** The shape of the space covered by light from a flashlight held in the air is a cone. When that cone of light hits a flat surface, a conic section is outlined. Use an actual flashlight and a wall in a darkened room to tell which conic section is formed when the flashlight is held:

11. perpendicular to the wall.

12. at an angle of 85° to the wall.

13. touching the wall, parallel to it.

14–17. Each sentence is an equation for a conic section you have studied. Name the conic section.

14. $y = x^2 + 4x - 3$ **15.** $x^2 = y$

16. $(x - 2)^2 + (y - 8)^2 = 100$ **17.** $x^2 = 6 - y^2$

Ⓒ **18–21.** Each sentence is an equation of a degenerate conic section. Describe the graph of the solution set.

18. $x^2 + 3y^2 = 0$ **19.** $x^2 + y + 3 = x(x + 1)$

20. $xy = 0$ **21.** $(x - y)(x + 3) = 0$

22. Refer to Exercises 11–13. How should the flashlight be held in order to form a parabola?

23. True or False? Every plane and every cone must have at least one point in common.

24–26. Build a model of a plane intersecting a cone in:

24. a parabola. **25.** an ellipse. **26.** one part of a hyperbola.

ELLIPSES AND HYPERBOLAS

12.2

The descriptions of ellipses and hyperbolas in the last section use 3-dimensional ideas, so they are not helpful in finding equations for these curves. (They would be helpful if we had discussed 3-dimensional graphing.) Thus, it is customary to give definitions for these curves using only 2 dimensions.

Circles are determined by a point (the center) and a number (the radius). Parabolas are determined by a point (the focus) and a line (the directrix). Both ellipses and hyperbolas—although they look totally unlike each other—are determined by *two* points (the *foci*) and a number (the *focal constant*).

From the drawing, notice:

$PF_1 + PF_2 = 10 + 4 = 14.$

$|PF_1 - PF_2| = 10 - 4 = 6.$

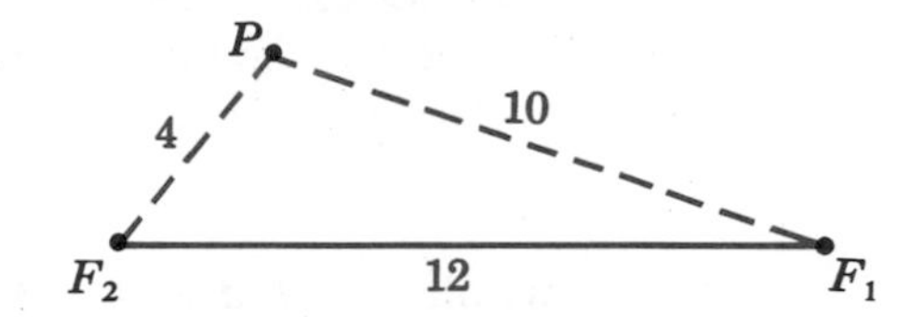

All we have done is calculate the sum and the absolute value of the difference of the distances from P to F_1 and F_2. For any other points in the plane, the sum and difference of these distances could be calculated. If F_1 and F_2 are fixed, the points for which the sum is 14 form an ellipse. The points for which the difference is 6 form a hyperbola.

For now, consider only ellipses. Suppose points F_1 and F_2 (the foci) are 4 units apart and the sum (the focal constant) we want is 12. Then we look for points P with $PF_1 + PF_2 = 12$.

Points P_1 and P_2 are 6 units from each focus. P_3 and P_4 are 4 units from one focus, 8 from the other. The points 5 units from one focus, 7 from the other, are P_5, P_6, P_7, and P_8.

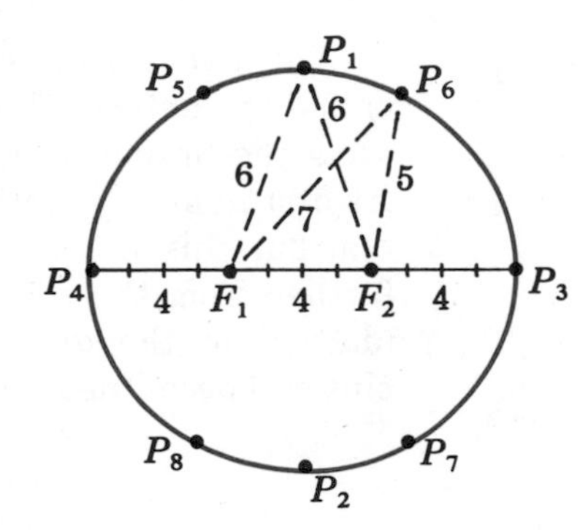

All possible points (for example, those which are 6.3 units from F_1, 5.7 units from F_2) have been drawn in. By definition, these points are said to form an ellipse.

Definition

Let F_1 and F_2 be two points and $2a$ be a constant with $2a > F_1F_2$. The set of points P which satisfy

$$PF_1 + PF_2 = 2a$$

is the **ellipse** with *foci* F_1 and F_2 and *focal constant* $2a$.

In the preceding picture, because of the triangle inequality, we must have $PF_1 + PF_2 > F_1F_2$. Since in an ellipse $PF_1 + PF_2 = 2a$, the condition $2a > F_1F_2$ is needed. In words, in an ellipse, the focal constant must be larger than the distance between the foci. We use $2a$ (instead of a) because later it will make some equations simpler.

Compare the definitions of *ellipse* and *hyperbola*.

Definition

Let F_1 and F_2 be two points and $2a$ a constant with $2a < F_1F_2$. The set of points P which satisfy

$$|PF_1 - PF_2| = 2a$$

is the **hyperbola** with *foci* F_1 and F_2 and *focal constant* $2a$.

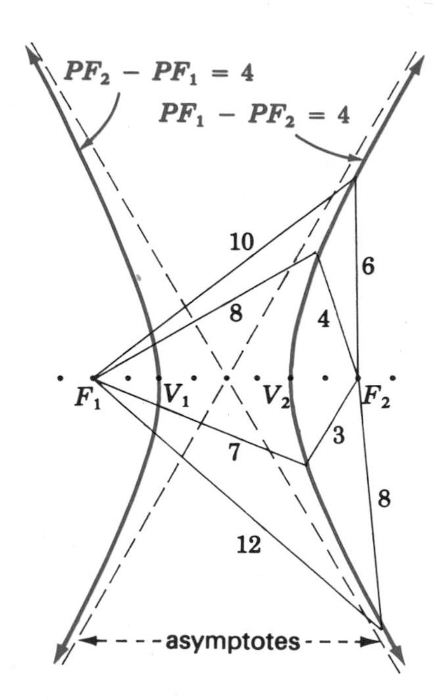

In words, the definition requires that a point on a hyperbola must be located so that if you *subtract* its distance to one focus from its distance to the other focus, you get the focal constant $2a$. In the diagram, $F_1F_2 = 8$, and the focal constant is 4. We look for points which are 4 units closer to one focus than the other. Points at left are closer to F_1; points at right are closer to F_2.

The two unconnected parts of a hyperbola are called **branches**. The segment joining the foci intersects the branches in the **vertices** of the hyperbola. At first glance, each branch may seem to be a parabola, but this is never so. In particular, as one gets farther from the foci on a branch, one of two lines (dashed in the diagram) is approached closer and closer. These lines are called **asymptotes**.

From the drawings, it seems that every ellipse or hyperbola has two symmetry lines. This is easy to prove. All we have to show is that the reflection image (over the desired line) of any point on the curve is also on the curve.

Theorem 12.2.1

> Every ellipse or hyperbola with foci F_1 and F_2 has two symmetry lines: (a) $\overleftrightarrow{F_1F_2}$ and (b) the perpendicular bisector of $\overline{F_1F_2}$.

PROOF: Part (a), for the ellipse:

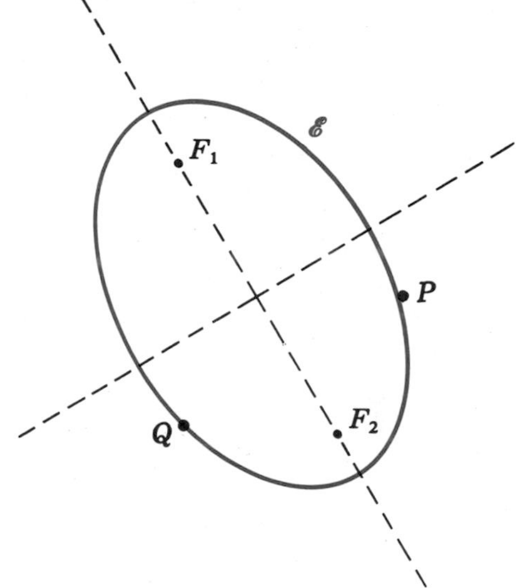

1. Suppose P is on the ellipse $\mathscr{E}$ with foci F_1 and F_2, focal constant $2a$. Then $PF_1 + PF_2 = 2a$.
2. Let $\overleftrightarrow{F_1F_2}$ be the reflecting line and let $Q = r(P)$.
3. $r(F_1) = F_1$; $r(F_2) = F_2$. (Why?)
4. $PF_1 = QF_1$ and $PF_2 = QF_2$ because reflections preserve distance.
5. Substituting back in Step **1**,

$$QF_1 + QF_2 = 2a.$$

6. So Q is on $\mathscr{E}$.
7. Thus, $r(\mathscr{E}) = \mathscr{E}$ and $\mathscr{E}$ is symmetric to $\overleftrightarrow{F_1F_2}$.

The other parts of the theorem can be proved by a similar process.

EXERCISES 12.2

Ⓐ **1–3.** Give the definition of each.

1. ellipse **2.** hyperbola **3.** parabola

4–6. Draw a reasonable approximation to an ellipse. Indicate the:

4. foci. **5.** focal constant. **6.** symmetry lines.

7–12. Draw a reasonable approximation to a hyperbola. Indicate the:

7. foci. **8.** focal constant. **9.** symmetry lines.

10. asymptotes. **11.** vertices. **12.** branches.

13. How does a hyperbola differ from a parabola?

14. The word *foci* is the plural of ____.

Ⓑ **15.** Find 16 points on an ellipse with foci F_1 and F_2, $F_1F_2 = 8$, and focal constant 18.

16. Find 16 points on a hyperbola with foci F_1 and F_2, $F_1F_2 = 5$, and focal constant 4.

17. The points (10, 0), (0, 5), (8, 3), and (6, 4) satisfy

$$x^2 + 4y^2 = 100.$$

Use this information to find 8 other points with integer coordinates which satisfy the equation. Graph these 12 solutions, guess which conic section is the graph of the entire solution set, and name all symmetry lines.

18. The points (1, 24) and (−6, −4) satisfy

$$xy = 24.$$

Find 14 other points with integer coordinates which satisfy the equation. Graph these 16 solutions, guess which conic section is the graph of the entire solution set, and name all symmetry lines.

19. Find 14 points with integer coordinates between −20 and 20 which satisfy this equation for a hyperbola.

$$x^2 - y^2 = 144$$

Graph these points and guess which lines might be asymptotes for this hyperbola.

© **20–22.** Suppose $F_1F_2 = 50$. Let P be any point in the plane.

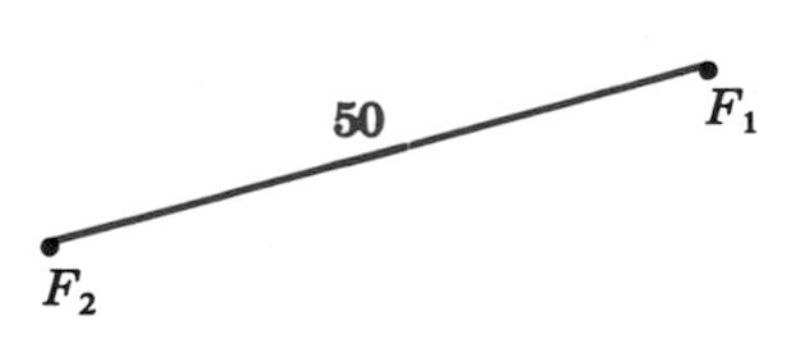

20. Why is it that $PF_1 + PF_2 \geq 50$?

21. Why is it that $PF_1 + 50 \geq PF_2$?

22. Why is it that $50 \geq |PF_1 - PF_2|$?

23–25. Prove the indicated part of Theorem 12.2.1.

23. part (**b**) for an ellipse

24. part (**a**) for a hyperbola

25. part (**b**) for a hyperbola

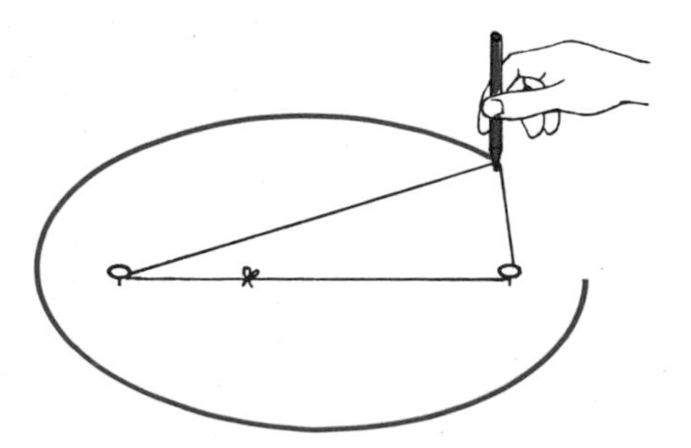

26. With the aid of two thumbtacks and a piece of string, draw an ellipse as shown in the diagram. Explain why the definition of *ellipse* is satisfied by this method of drawing a curve.

EQUATIONS FOR SOME ELLIPSES

We now begin a process of finding simple equations for ellipses. The simplest equations occur when the foci are chosen so that the x-axis and y-axis are the symmetry lines.

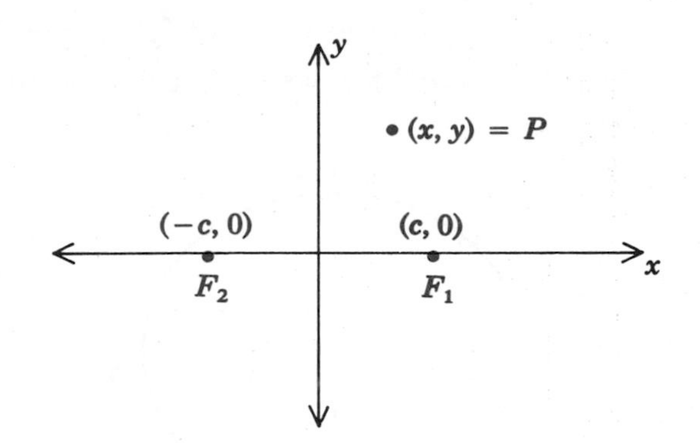

We let $2a$ be the focal constant. With foci $F_1 = (c, 0)$ and $F_2 = (-c, 0)$ as shown, $c > 0$ and $F_1F_2 = 2c$. Since $2a > F_1F_2$, we have $2a > 2c$, and so $a > c$ is necessary.

The condition $PF_1 + PF_2 = 2a$

becomes $\sqrt{(x-c)^2 + (y-0)^2} + \sqrt{(x+c)^2 + (y-0)^2} = 2a.$

Much work is needed to simplify this equation. But the result is very simple. Subtracting one of the square roots from each side,

1. $$\sqrt{(x-c)^2 + y^2} = 2a - \sqrt{(x+c)^2 + y^2}.$$

Squaring each side (the right side is a binomial),

2. $$(x-c)^2 + y^2 = 4a^2 - 4a\sqrt{(x+c)^2 + y^2} + (x+c)^2 + y^2.$$

Expanding the binomials and appropriate subtractions give

3. $$-2cx = 4a^2 - 4a\sqrt{(x+c)^2 + y^2} + 2cx.$$

Additions and multiplication by $\frac{1}{4}$ yield

4. $$a\sqrt{(x+c)^2 + y^2} = a^2 + cx.$$

Squaring for a second time,

5. $$a^2[(x+c)^2 + y^2] = a^4 + 2a^2cx + c^2x^2.$$

Expanding the binomial and subtracting $2a^2cx$ from each side,

6. $$a^2x^2 + a^2c^2 + a^2y^2 = a^4 + c^2x^2.$$

Subtracting a^2c^2 and c^2x^2 from each side, then factoring,

7. $$(a^2 - c^2)x^2 + a^2y^2 = a^2(a^2 - c^2).$$

Since $a > c > 0$, $a^2 > c^2$. So $a^2 - c^2$ is not negative. Let $b^2 = a^2 - c^2$.

8. $$b^2x^2 + a^2y^2 = a^2b^2.$$

9. Dividing by a^2b^2, $\frac{x^2}{a^2} + \frac{y^2}{b^2} = 1.$

Theorem 12.3.1

The graph of $\frac{x^2}{a^2} + \frac{y^2}{b^2} = 1$ is an ellipse. Given $c^2 = a^2 - b^2$, the foci are $(c, 0)$ and $(-c, 0)$, and the focal constant is $2a$.

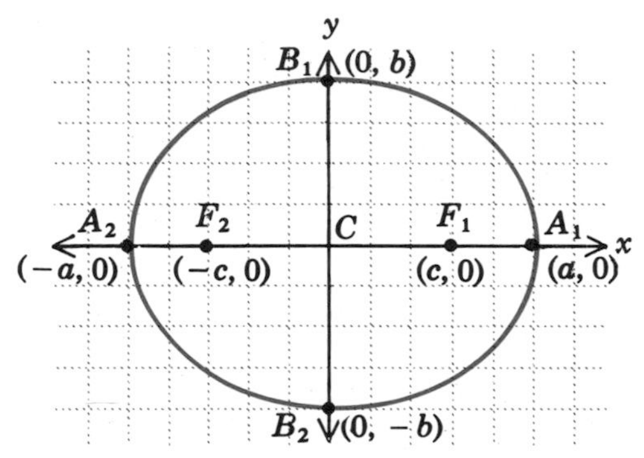

It is easy to check that the points $(a, 0)$, $(-a, 0)$, $(0, b)$, and $(0, -b)$ are on the ellipse $\frac{x^2}{a^2} + \frac{y^2}{b^2} = 1$. This helps graph the ellipse.

The segments $\overline{A_1A_2}$ and $\overline{B_1B_2}$ are the *major* and *minor axes* of the ellipse. (The major axis contains the foci and is always longer.) They lie on the symmetry lines and intersect at the center C of the ellipse. The picture illustrates the following corollary.

Corollary 12.3.2

In the ellipse $\frac{x^2}{a^2} + \frac{y^2}{b^2} = 1$, with $c^2 = a^2 - b^2$,

$2a$ is the length of the major axis (and the focal constant),

$2b$ is the length of the minor axis, and

$2c$ is the distance between the foci.

If $b > a$, then the ellipse will have foci on the y-axis at $(0, c)$ and $(0, -c)$, and the major and minor axes will be switched.

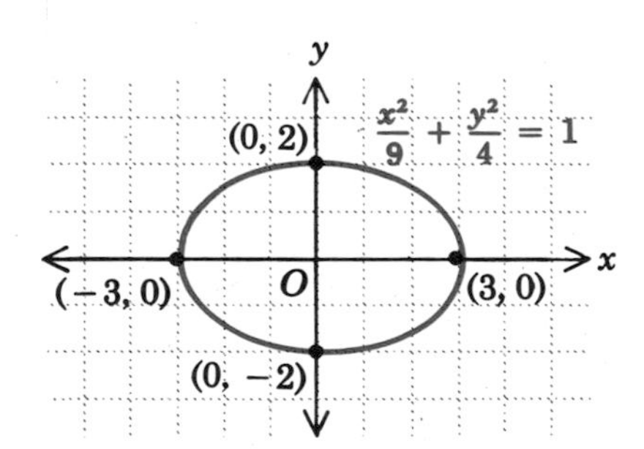

Example 1: Graph the ellipse with equation $\frac{x^2}{9} + \frac{y^2}{4} = 1$.

SOLUTION: Four points on this ellipse are easy to find: $(0, 2)$, $(0, -2)$, $(3, 0)$, $(-3, 0)$. These are the endpoints of the major and minor axes.

Example 2: Find an equation for the ellipse with foci $(5, 0)$ and $(-5, 0)$ and constant 12.

SOLUTION: Since $2a = 12$, $a = 6$ and $a^2 = 36$. Since $c = 5$, $c^2 = 25$. Now $b^2 = a^2 - c^2 = 36 - 25$, so $b^2 = 11$. So an equation is $\frac{x^2}{36} + \frac{y^2}{11} = 1$. This ellipse contains $(6, 0)$, $(-6, 0)$, $(0, \sqrt{11})$, and $(0, -\sqrt{11})$.

EXERCISES 12.3

Ⓐ **1.** Define *ellipse*.

2–5. For the ellipse of Example **1** on page 334, give the following.

2. length of major axis

3. length of minor axis

4. center

5. equations of symmetry lines

6–10. For the ellipse $\frac{x^2}{a^2} + \frac{y^2}{b^2} = 1$, give the following.

6. focal constant

7. length of major axis

8. center

9. length of minor axis

10. four endpoints of major and minor axes

11. A simple equation for an ellipse results when its center is ____ and its foci are ____.

Ⓑ **12.** A sentence equivalent to $\frac{x^2}{9} + \frac{y^2}{4} = 1$ is $4x^2 + 9y^2 =$ ____.

13. A sentence equivalent to $5x^2 + 4y^2 = 20$ is $\frac{x^2}{a^2} + \frac{y^2}{b^2} = 1$, where $a =$ ____ and $b =$ ____.

14. Repeat Exercise **13** if the given sentence is $3u^2 + 4v^2 = 6$.

15–20. Graph the 4 endpoints of the major and minor axes of the ellipse. Sketch the ellipse using these points as guides. (Some of these ellipses have foci on the *y*-axis, but this doesn't change the method of graphing.)

15. $\frac{x^2}{4} + \frac{y^2}{9} = 1$

16. $\frac{x^2}{3} + \frac{y^2}{9} = 1$

17. $\frac{x^2}{9} + y^2 = 1$

18. $1 = \frac{y^2}{25} + \frac{x^2}{64}$

19. $16x^2 + 9y^2 = 144$

20. $a^2 + 4b^2 = 1$

21. Find the foci of the ellipse of Example **1**, page 334.

22. What happens to an ellipse when the foci F_1 and F_2 are the same point?

23. Give a sentence for the interior of the ellipse of Exercise **15**.

24. Give a sentence for the exterior of the ellipse of Exercise **15**.

25. If an ellipse has foci (3, 11) and (7, 14) and focal constant 50, give an equation (perhaps complicated) which any point (x, y) on the ellipse must satisfy.

© **26–32.** Graph the solution set to each sentence.

26. $25x^2 + 16y^2 = 9$

27. $3u^2 + 4v^2 = 6$

28. $\frac{(x-2)^2}{4} + \frac{(y-1)^2}{36} = 1$

29. $100 = 25(y + 3)^2 + 4(x - 5)^2$

30. $x = \sqrt{4 - 4y^2}$

31. $y < \sqrt{9 - 4x^2}$

32. $\sqrt{(x-5)^2 + (y-3)^2} + \sqrt{(x-8)^2 + (y-7)^2} = 8$

33–37. In an ellipse like those in this section, the ratio $\frac{c}{a}$ is called the *eccentricity e* of the ellipse. Find the eccentricity of the ellipse:

33. of Example **1**.

34. of Example **2**.

35. of Exercise **16**.

36. that is the orbit of the earth around the sun (use references).

37. that is the orbit of Halley's comet around the sun.

38. An earth satellite has an orbit which is 250 km from the earth at its farthest point, 150 km at its nearest point. Calculate the eccentricity of this orbit which is (if undisturbed) an ellipse with the earth at one focus. (Use Exercises **33–37** if needed.)

39–42. Look up each word in a dictionary. Explain how each is connected with ellipses. (The latter word is new, having first been used in 1969.)

39. aphelion

40. perihelion

41. apogee

42. perilune

43. From other sources, find out how ellipses are used to construct a "whispering gallery."

44. Is it true that when you look at a circle from an angle, you see an ellipse?

EQUATIONS FOR SOME HYPERBOLAS

Not all automobile speedometers are accurate. A person traveling on a highway with mileage markers can check a speedometer by driving at the same speed for one mile and timing to the second.

$$\text{rate in mph} = \frac{\text{distance in miles}}{\text{time in hours}}$$

$$\text{Using 1 mile and abbreviating: } r = \frac{1}{t \text{ (in hours)}}$$

When time is measured in seconds, the denominator will be 3600 times too big, as there are 3600 seconds in an hour. So multiply the numerator by 3600 to compensate. That is, $r = \dfrac{3600}{t \text{ (in seconds)}}$. Here are some pairs of values which work.

time (sec)	40	45	50	55	60	65	70	75	80	85
rate (mph)	90	80	72	≐65.5	60	≐55.4	≐51.4	48	45	≐42.4

Graphing the ordered pairs, we are graphing the solution set to $tr = 3600$, or more conventionally, $xy = 3600$.

The graph is a hyperbola. The part of the hyperbola in red corresponds to those speeds which are legal on interstate highways in many states.

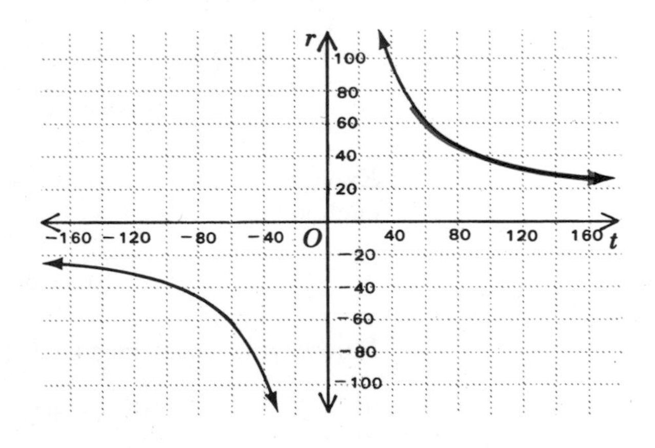

Of course, we have not *proved* that the graph of $\{(x, y): xy = 3600\}$ is a hyperbola. To prove this we would refer to the definition of hyperbola. Let's take a simpler case, and show that $\{(x, y): xy = 2\}$ is a hyperbola. (This is one of the simplest equations for a hyperbola.)

Theorem 12.4.1

The graph of the solution set to $xy = 2$ is the hyperbola with foci $(2, 2)$ and $(-2, -2)$ and focal constant 4.

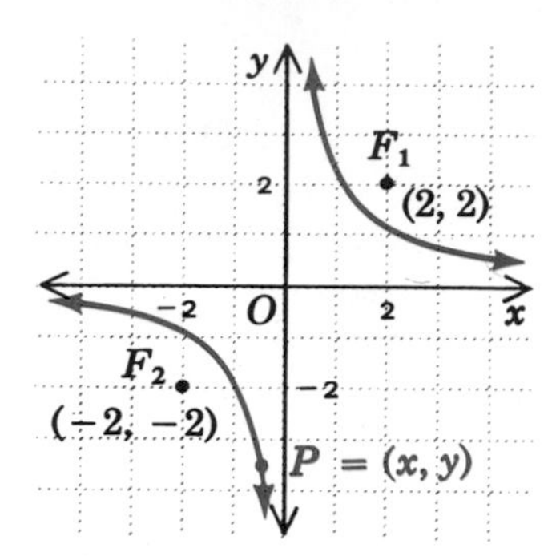

The theorem should seem reasonable from the graph at left. Solutions are easy to find because the equation is so simple. Some points on the graph are $(\sqrt{2}, \sqrt{2})$, $(2, 1)$, $(\frac{2}{3}, 3)$, $(-4, -\frac{1}{2})$, and their images under $r_{x=y}$ and R_{180}.

PROOF: We begin with the definition of *hyperbola*, assuming P is nearer F_2. (The same equation ultimately arises if you assume P is nearer F_1.)

1. $$PF_1 - PF_2 = 2a$$

For this situation, $P = (x, y)$, $F_1 = (2, 2)$, $F_2 = (-2, -2)$, and $2a = 4$.

2. $$\sqrt{(x-2)^2 + (y-2)^2} - \sqrt{(x+2)^2 + (y+2)^2} = 4$$

Adding one of the square roots to each side,

3. $$\sqrt{(x-2)^2 + (y-2)^2} = 4 + \sqrt{(x+2)^2 + (y+2)^2}.$$

Squaring each side (the right side is a binomial),

4. $$(x-2)^2 + (y-2)^2 = 16 + 8\sqrt{(x+2)^2 + (y+2)^2} + (x+2)^2 + (y+2)^2.$$

Expanding the binomials and adding $-x^2 - y^2 - 24 - 4x - 4y$ to each side,

5. $$-8x - 8y - 16 = 8\sqrt{(x+2)^2 + (y+2)^2}.$$

Multiplying both sides by $-\frac{1}{8}$ and then squaring,

6. $$(x + y + 2)^2 = (x+2)^2 + (y+2)^2.$$

Expanding the trinomial and the two binomials,

7. $$x^2 + y^2 + 4x + 4y + 2xy + 4 = x^2 + 4x + 4 + y^2 + 4y + 4.$$

(This is the easiest step—can you see what was done?)

8. $$2xy = 4$$

9. $$xy = 2$$

As $x > 0$ gets larger, y stays positive but gets closer to zero—the point $(200, \frac{1}{100})$ is on the curve. This indicates that the curve gets closer to the x-axis. So the x-axis is an asymptote. By symmetry, the y-axis is an asymptote. Thus the asymptotes may be described by $x = 0$ or $y = 0$ or, more simply, $xy = 0$.

The curve *never* touches or crosses these asymptotes, for it is impossible to have $x = 0$ or $y = 0$ and still have $xy = 2$.

By a long process just like that used in the preceding proof, the next, more general theorem can be proved. We picked $k = 2$ in Theorem 12.4.1 so that no radical signs appeared.

Theorem 12.4.2

When $k > 0$, the graph of the solution set to $xy = k$ is a hyperbola. (This is the hyperbola with foci $(\sqrt{2k}, \sqrt{2k})$ and $(-\sqrt{2k}, -\sqrt{2k})$ and focal constant $2\sqrt{2k}$.)

EXERCISES 12.4

Ⓐ **1.** Define *hyperbola.*

2–7. For the hyperbola $\{(x, y): xy = 2\}$, name the following.

2. foci **3.** asymptotes **4.** symmetry lines

5. vertices **6.** focal constant **7.** center of rotation symmetry

8. Describe the method by which the equation $xy = 2$ was found to be a hyperbola.

9. Find 10 points on the hyperbola $xy = 5$.

10–14. Use the hyperbola $\{(x, y): xy = k\}$.

10. Name the asymptotes. **11.** Name the symmetry lines.

12. Name 5 points on the graph.

Ⓑ **13.** Draw a rough graph.

14. Give a single equation which describes the asymptotes.

15–17. Find at least 10 points on the graph and sketch the entire solution set.

15. $xy = 1$ **16.** $a = \frac{20}{b}$ **17.** $\frac{2}{x} = \frac{y}{6}$

18. A person spends \$10.00 in buying p pencils which cost c cents apiece. Graph all possible pairs (p, c). (Remember that p and c are integers.)

19. A car travels the 2.5 miles around the Indianapolis Speedway in t seconds at an average rate of r mph. Graph all possible pairs (t, r). (Racing fans who bring stopwatches can use this idea to calculate how fast a car is traveling.)

© **20–25.** Find 8 points on the graph and sketch the entire solution set.

20. $(x - 2)y = 2$ **21.** $uv = -6$ **22.** $(a - 5)(b + 3) = 8$

23. $\sqrt{x}\sqrt{y} = 4$ **24.** $xy > 1$ **25.** $xy < 1$

26–28. Give an equation for the hyperbola with:

26. foci $(\sqrt{2}, \sqrt{2})$ and $(-\sqrt{2}, -\sqrt{2})$, constant $2\sqrt{2}$.

27. foci $(\sqrt{8}, \sqrt{8})$ and $(-\sqrt{8}, -\sqrt{8})$, constant $\sqrt{32}$.

28. foci (8, 2) and (12, 6), constant 4. (HINT: Translate.)

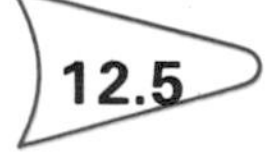

SCALE TRANSFORMATIONS

To find many solutions to $\left(\frac{x}{4}\right)^2 + \left(\frac{y}{3}\right)^2 = 145$, it is easier to think of solutions to $x^2 + y^2 = 145$. Examine this table.

Solutions to $x^2 + y^2 = 145$	Solutions to $\left(\frac{x}{4}\right)^2 + \left(\frac{y}{3}\right)^2 = 145$
(12, 1)	(48, 3)
(−12, 1)	(−48, 3)
(8, 9)	(32, 27)
(−9, −8)	(−36, −24)
$(0, \sqrt{145})$	$(0, 3\sqrt{145})$

You should check *all* 5 pairs in the above equation.

In general (x, y) corresponds to $(4x, 3y)$.

So replacing x by $\frac{x}{4}$ multiplies x-coordinates of solutions by 4; replacing y by $\frac{y}{3}$ multiplies y-coordinates of solutions by 3. We now state an old theorem and suggest a corresponding theorem.

GRAPH TRANSLATION THEOREM:	Does this seem reasonable?
Replacing x by $x - a$, y by $y - b$, translates the graph under the translation mapping (x, y) onto $(x + a, y + b)$.	Replacing x by $\frac{x}{a}$, y by $\frac{y}{b}$, transforms the graph under the transformation mapping (x, y) onto (ax, by).

The transformations which map (x, y) onto (ax, by) are *very important* aids in graphing and are called *scale transformations.*

Definition

A transformation which maps (x, y) onto (ax, by), $ab \neq 0$, is a **scale transformation**.

It is clear that scale transformations have associated matrices, for

$$\begin{bmatrix} a & 0 \\ 0 & b \end{bmatrix} \cdot \begin{bmatrix} x \\ y \end{bmatrix} = \begin{bmatrix} ax \\ by \end{bmatrix}.$$

Theorem 12.5.1

Every scale transformation has a matrix of the form $\begin{bmatrix} a & 0 \\ 0 & b \end{bmatrix}$.

Example 1: Suppose S is a scale transformation with $S(x, y) = (2x, y)$. Find the image of the

polygon $\begin{bmatrix} 1 & 2 & 4 & 4 \\ 3 & -2 & 0 & 3 \end{bmatrix}$.

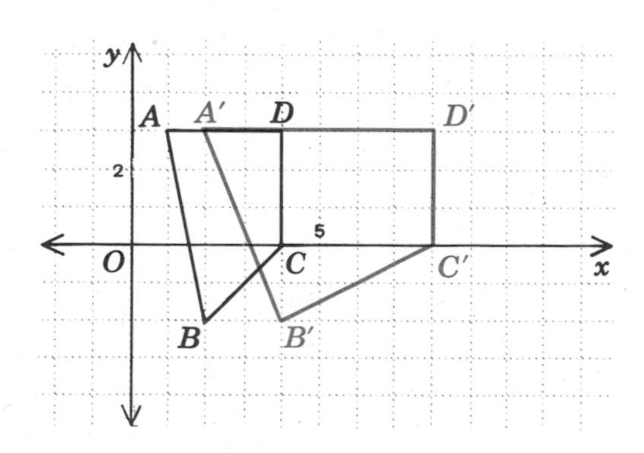

SOLUTION:

S has matrix $\begin{bmatrix} 2 & 0 \\ 0 & 1 \end{bmatrix}$.

$$\begin{bmatrix} 2 & 0 \\ 0 & 1 \end{bmatrix} \cdot \begin{bmatrix} 1 & 2 & 4 & 4 \\ 3 & -2 & 0 & 3 \end{bmatrix}$$

$$= \begin{bmatrix} 2 & 4 & 8 & 8 \\ 3 & -2 & 0 & 3 \end{bmatrix}$$

Example **1** pictures a *horizontal scale transformation* of magnitude 2. Image points are twice as far from the y-axis as preimage points. It is as if the scale on the x-axis were changed—this is how this type of transformation received its name. Other scale transformations are also special. Here are three more examples. Notice that image points can be found with or without matrices.

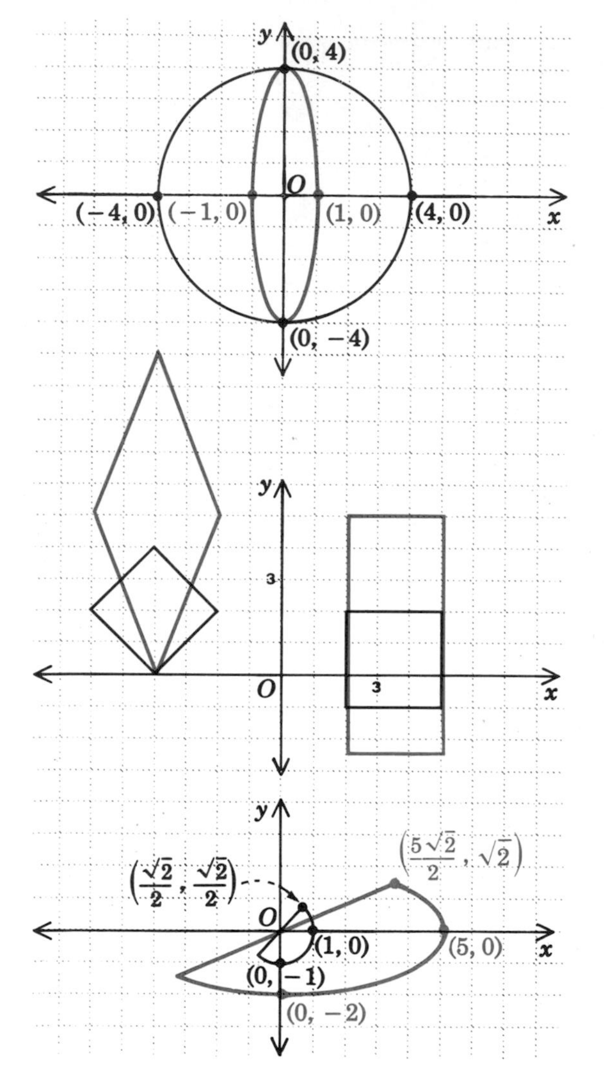

2. *Horizontal scale transformation* of magnitude $\frac{1}{4}$: $(x, y) \rightarrow (\frac{1}{4}x, y)$

$$(4, 0) \rightarrow (1, 0)$$
$$(0, 4) \rightarrow (0, 4)$$
$$(-4, 0) \rightarrow (-1, 0)$$
$$(0, -4) \rightarrow (0, -4)$$

The image of the circle seems to be an ellipse.

3. *Vertical scale transformation* of magnitude $2\frac{1}{2}$: $(x, y) \rightarrow (x, 2\frac{1}{2}y)$

The image of a square is a parallelogram.

A horizontal or vertical scale transformation with a magnitude between 0 and 1 is called a **shrink**. If the magnitude is greater than one, the scale transformation is a **stretch**.

4. *Two-dimensional scale transformation:*

$$(x, y) \rightarrow (5x, 2y)$$

The preimage is a semicircle of the unit circle and a segment of the line $x = y$. Equations for the images may be found by using the following theorem, suggested by the first few paragraphs in this section. Corollaries 12.5.3 and 12.5.4 help to show that the images are a line segment and half of an ellipse.

Theorem 12.5.2

Graph scale transformation theorem: Replacing x by $\frac{x}{a}$ and y by $\frac{y}{b}$ in a sentence applies the two-dimensional scale transformation $(x, y) \rightarrow (ax, by)$ to the graph of that sentence.

Corollary 12.5.3

The image of the unit circle $x^2 + y^2 = 1$ under the scale transformation $(x, y) \rightarrow (ax, by)$ is the ellipse $\frac{x^2}{a^2} + \frac{y^2}{b^2} = 1$.

PROOF: From the theorem, the image is $\left(\frac{x}{a}\right)^2 + \left(\frac{y}{b}\right)^2 = 1$.

But $\left(\frac{x}{a}\right)^2 = \frac{x^2}{a^2}$ and $\left(\frac{y}{b}\right)^2 = \frac{y^2}{b^2}$. Substituting gives the corollary.

You may think of the corollary as indicating that a stretched circle is an ellipse, or that if you graphed a circle on a coordinate system with different scales on the x and y axes, the graph would look like a noncircular ellipse.

Corollary 12.5.4

The image of the line $y = x$ under the scale transformation $(x, y) \to (ax, by)$ is the line $\frac{y}{b} = \frac{x}{a}$.

The equation $\frac{y}{b} = \frac{x}{a}$ was first discussed in Theorem 6.2.2 as the equation of the line through (0, 0) and (a, b). It has slope $\frac{b}{a}$. But $y = x$ has slope 1. This indicates something which is also obvious from Examples **1** and **4**: scale transformations do *not* preserve angle measure. So figures and their images are *not* necessarily similar.

EXERCISES 12.5

Ⓐ **1.** A scale transformation maps (x, y) onto ____.

2–6. Find the image of each point under S if $S(x, y) = (3x, \frac{1}{2}y)$.

2. (6, 2) **3.** (−1, 4) **4.** (6, −3) **5.** (0, 0) **6.** $(102, \frac{1}{2})$

7–11. Match each scale transformation with the best description at right.

7. $(x, y) \to (2x, 3y)$ **a.** horizontal stretch

8. $(x, y) \to (2x, y)$ **b.** horizontal shrink

9. $(x, y) \to (0.9x, 0.9y)$ **c.** vertical stretch

10. $(x, y) \to (x, 0.9y)$ **d.** vertical shrink

11. $(x, y) \to \left(\frac{x}{4}, y\right)$ **e.** 2-dimensional scale transformation

12–15. Give the matrix for the scale transformation of:

12. Exercise **7.** **13.** Exercise 8. **14.** Exercise **10.** **15.** Exercise **11.**

16. What is the graph scale transformation theorem?

17. To apply the scale transformation $(x, y) \to (5x, 6y)$ to the line $9 - 3x = 2y$, you would replace x in the equation by ____ and y by ____.

18–20. The unit circle is the preimage under the transformation T with $T(x, y) = (3x, 2y)$.

18. Give an equation for the image.

19. Describe the image.

20. Name 4 points on the image.

21. Give the equation for the image of $x^2 + y^2 = 1$ under the scale transformation which maps (x, y) onto $\left(\frac{x}{3}, y\right)$.

22. How is the graph of $\frac{y}{4} = x^2$ related to the graph of $y = x^2$? (No graphing is needed to answer.)

23. How is the graph of $\frac{x}{15} - \frac{y}{6} = 3$ related to the graph of $x - y = 3$?

24–25. Multiple choice.

24. Under a scale transformation, the image of a circle is an ellipse.

a. always **b.** sometimes **c.** never

25. Under the scale transformation $(x, y) \to (4x, 9y)$, the image of the unit circle has which equation?

a. $\frac{x^2}{4} + \frac{y^2}{9} = 1$ **b.** $\frac{x^2}{16} + \frac{y^2}{81} = 1$ **c.** $\frac{x^2}{2} + \frac{y^2}{3} = 1$

26. To apply the scale transformation $(x, y) \to (5x, 10y)$ to a relation, what should be done to an equation for the relation?

Ⓑ 27. To apply the scale transformation $(x, y) \to \left(\frac{x}{5}, \frac{y}{10}\right)$ to a relation, what should be done to an equation for the relation?

28. The line $y = 3x$ is the image of the line $y = x$ under a horizontal scale transformation of magnitude ____ or a vertical scale transformation of magnitude ____.

29. Prove that the scale transformation T with $T(w, z) = (4w, 2z)$ is neither an isometry nor a similarity transformation.

30–32. Draw the polygon $\begin{bmatrix} -3 & 2 & 2 & -3 \\ 4 & 4 & 0 & -1 \end{bmatrix}$ and its image under the scale transformation with each matrix.

30. $\begin{bmatrix} 2 & 0 \\ 0 & 1 \end{bmatrix}$ **31.** $\begin{bmatrix} 1 & 0 \\ 0 & 0.5 \end{bmatrix}$ **32.** $\begin{bmatrix} 2 & 0 \\ 0 & -5 \end{bmatrix}$

33–35. Draw the circle $x^2 + y^2 = 36$ and its image under the scale transformations with the matrices of Exercises **30–32**. Find an equation for the image.

36. Draw $y = x^2$ and its image under the scale transformation $(x, y) \rightarrow (4x, 4y)$. What is an equation for the image?

37. Data are often changed in scale in order to be analyzed. How might you change the scale in order to find the average of the following four numbers?

1,462,000 3,246,000 7,777,000 4,829,000

38–41. True or False? Under *every* scale transformation:

38. The image of every horizontal line is horizontal.

39. The image of every vertical line is vertical.

40. Perpendicularity is preserved.

© **41.** The image of a line is a line.

42. The inverse of the scale transformation which maps (x, y) onto $(2x, 3y)$ maps (x, y) onto ____.

43. Use matrices to show that composition of scale transformations is commutative.

44. What is the effect of the scale transformation $(x, y) \rightarrow (ax, by)$ on the area of a polygon?

45. Prove or Disprove: The set of scale transformations with composition forms a group.

46. Prove or Disprove: The set of horizontal scale transformations with composition forms a group.

THE RIGHT SCALE TRANSFORMATION?

12.6 MORE EQUATIONS FOR HYPERBOLAS

The hyperbolas studied in Section 12.4 were special, all of them having foci on the line $y = x$. The resulting equations of the form

$$xy = k$$

do not look like any of the others you have studied. By choosing the foci $(c, 0)$ and $(-c, 0)$ as was done for the ellipse, an equation arises which resembles an equation of an ellipse. Compare this theorem with Theorem 12.3.1.

Theorem 12.6.1

The graph of $\frac{x^2}{a^2} - \frac{y^2}{b^2} = 1$ is a hyperbola. Given $b^2 = c^2 - a^2$, the foci are $(c, 0)$ and $(-c, 0)$, and the focal constant is $2a$.

PROOF: The proof is almost identical to the proof of Theorem 12.3.1, except for two things. First, we are dealing with hyperbolas, so we begin with $|PF_1 - PF_2| = 2a$ which is equivalent to

$$PF_1 - PF_2 = \pm 2a.$$

That is, with $P = (x, y)$, $F_1 = (c, 0)$, and $F_2 = (-c, 0)$,

$$\sqrt{(x - c)^2 + (y - 0)^2} - \sqrt{(x + c)^2 + (y - 0)^2} = \pm 2a.$$

The manipulations are similar to those in Steps **1–7**, page 333. Then in step **8**, $c > a > 0$, so $c^2 > a^2$, and we let $b^2 = c^2 - a^2$. This accounts for the minus sign in the equation.

To graph this hyperbola, notice that $(a, 0)$ and $(-a, 0)$ satisfy the equation of the theorem. Since the foci are on the x-axis, the hyperbola is symmetric to that axis, and $(a, 0)$ and $(-a, 0)$ must be the vertices. If $x = 0$, no real value of y works—the hyperbola does not cross the y-axis. A rough drawing using this information is given below.

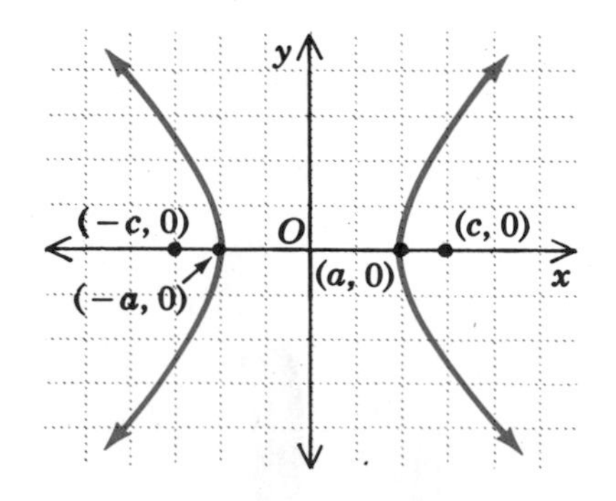

This drawing is a little too rough. The asymptotes are needed to form a better picture. To find general equations for the asymptotes, it is helpful to examine the simplest hyperbola of this kind, $\{(x, y): x^2 - y^2 = 1\}$. Many hyperbolas are related to it, just as many ellipses are related to the unit circle.

Corollary 12.6.2

Every hyperbola with foci $(c, 0)$ and $(-c, 0)$ is a scale transformation image of $x^2 - y^2 = 1$.

PROOF: Using the graph scale transformation theorem, you can apply the scale transformation $(x, y) \rightarrow (ax, by)$ to this hyperbola. An equation for the image is $\left(\frac{x}{a}\right)^2 - \left(\frac{y}{b}\right)^2 = 1$, which is equivalent to that given in Theorem 12.6.1.

Some solutions to $x^2 - y^2 = 1$ are given here. They help graphing. (Because of the reflection-symmetry, we only have to look for solutions in the first quadrant.)

$(1, 0)$

$(2, \sqrt{3}) \doteq (2, 1.73)$

$(3, \sqrt{8}) \doteq (3, 2.83)$

$(4, \sqrt{15}) \doteq (4, 3.87)$

$(5, \sqrt{24}) \doteq (5, 4.90)$

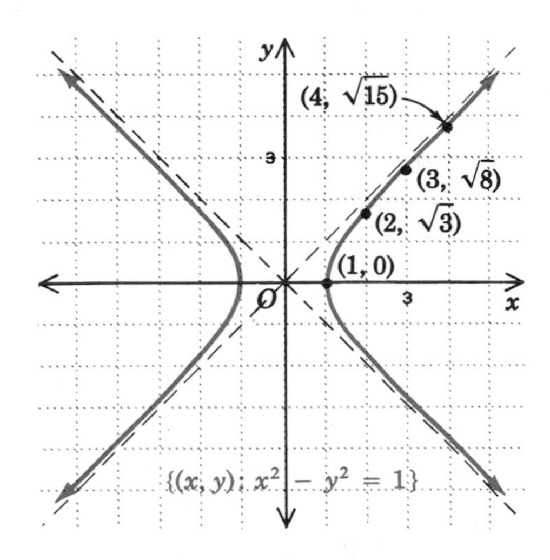

As x gets larger, the points get closer to the line $y = x$. For example, the point $(100, \sqrt{9999}) \doteq (100, 99.995)$ is on the hyperbola.

The hyperbola is symmetric to the x-axis, the line through its foci. So its asymptotes would have to be symmetric. Thus we reflect $y = x$ over the x-axis to get the other asymptote $y = -x$. This can be verified algebraically. When $x^2 - y^2 = 1$,

$$y^2 = x^2 - 1.$$

$$\text{So} \quad y = \pm\sqrt{x^2 - 1}.$$

As x gets larger, $\sqrt{x^2 - 1}$ becomes closer to $\sqrt{x^2}$, which is $|x|$. So y gets closer to x or $-x$.

When $x^2 - y^2 = 1$ is scale transformed onto $\frac{x^2}{a^2} - \frac{y^2}{b^2} = 1$, the asymptotes of $x^2 - y^2 = 1$ are obviously mapped onto the asymptotes of the image. Using Corollary 12.5.4 from the last section, $\frac{y}{b} = \frac{x}{a}$ is the image of $y = x$. The image of $y = -x$ is obtained by reflection.

Theorem 12.6.3

The lines $\frac{y}{b} = \frac{x}{a}$ and $\frac{y}{b} = -\frac{x}{a}$ are the asymptotes of the hyperbola

$$\frac{x^2}{a^2} - \frac{y^2}{b^2} = 1.$$

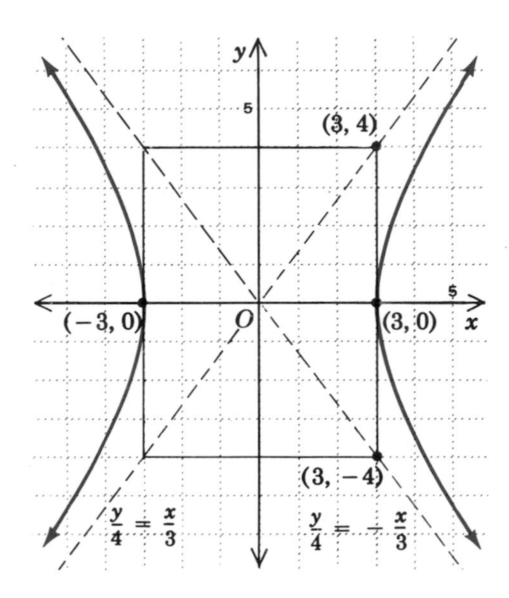

Example: Graph $\{(x, y): \frac{x^2}{9} - \frac{y^2}{16} = 1\}$.

SOLUTION 1: This hyperbola is the image of $x^2 - y^2 = 1$ under the scale transformation $(x, y) \to (3x, 4y)$. Graph $x^2 - y^2 = 1$ and then find the images of the asymptotes and the vertices to sketch the image.

SOLUTION 2: $(3, 0)$ and $(-3, 0)$ are on the x-axis and satisfy the equation. So they are the vertices. From Theorem 12.6.3, the asymptotes are: $\frac{y}{4} = \frac{x}{3}$, through $(0, 0)$ and $(3, 4)$, and $\frac{y}{4} = -\frac{x}{3}$, through $(0, 0)$ and $(3, -4)$. The vertices and asymptotes are easily graphed, and the hyperbola can be sketched. (The rectangle may be helpful.)

EXERCISES 12.6

Ⓐ 1. A hyperbola with foci $(c, 0)$ and $(-c, 0)$ has an equation of the form ______.

2. Why is the hyperbola $\{(x, y): x^2 - y^2 = 1\}$ so useful?

3. Name two solutions to $\frac{x^2}{4} - \frac{y^2}{9} = 1$.

4. Name three solutions to $\frac{x^2}{3} - \frac{y^2}{16} = 1$.

5–7. Give the vertices of each hyperbola.

5. $1 = x^2 - y^2$

6. $\frac{x^2}{a^2} - \frac{y^2}{b^2} = 1$

7. $\frac{u^2}{5} - v^2 = 1$

8–10. For Exercises 5–7, give equations for the asymptotes.

11. Is an asymptote part of a hyperbola?

12. Name two points on the line $\frac{y}{6} = \frac{x}{3}$.

Ⓑ **13–15.** Sketch the solution set to each equation. Identify vertices and asymptotes.

13. $x^2 - y^2 = 4$ **14.** $1 = \frac{x^2}{25} - \frac{y^2}{30}$ **15.** $4u^2 - 9v^2 = 36$

16. Graph $\{(x, y): \frac{x^2}{9} + \frac{y^2}{16} = 1\}$ and $\{(x, y): \frac{x^2}{9} - \frac{y^2}{16} = 1\}$ on the same pair of axes.

17. True or False? $x^2 - y^2 = 1$ and $x^2 - y^2 = 40$ have the same asymptotes.

18. Find the foci of the hyperbola $\{(x, y): x^2 - y^2 = 1\}$. (HINT: Use Theorem 12.6.1.)

19. Use Exercise **18** to find the foci of $\{(x, y): \frac{x^2}{4} - \frac{y^2}{4} = 1\}$.

Ⓒ **20.** Fill in the details in the proof of Theorem 12.6.1.

21. Give a simple equation for the hyperbola with foci (12, 0) and (−12, 0) and focal constant 6.

22. Assuming $F_1 = (-4, 0)$ and $F_2 = (4, 0)$ in the drawing on p. 330, find an equation for the hyperbola drawn.

23. Prove that the hyperbolas with equations $x^2 - y^2 = 1$ and $x^2 - y^2 = 4$ are similar.

24. Prove that the hyperbolas with equations $x^2 - y^2 = 2$ and $xy = 1$ are congruent.

25–28. Each solution set is a subset of $\{(x, y): x^2 - y^2 = 1\}$. Graph.

25. $x = \sqrt{1 + y^2}$ **26.** $x = -\sqrt{1 + y^2}$

27. $y = \sqrt{x^2 - 1}$ **28.** $y = -\sqrt{x^2 - 1}$

29–32. Graph the solution set.

29. $\frac{(x + 3)^2}{4} - \frac{(y - 5)^2}{9} = 1$ **30.** $5x^2 - 9y^2 = 2$

31. $4x^2 - 9y^2 > 36$ **32.** $9x^2 - y^2 \leq 1$

33. Nicole said, "You can find the equations of the asymptotes of a hyperbola just by replacing the constant term by zero." What did she mean? Was she correct?

12.7 MORE EQUATIONS FOR PARABOLAS

Equations of the form $y - k = (x - h)^2$ lead only to parabolas congruent to $y = x^2$. All of these parabolas have a distance of $\frac{1}{2}$ from focus to directrix. Since *any* point and a line not containing it can be chosen as focus and directrix, we have not considered all parabolas.

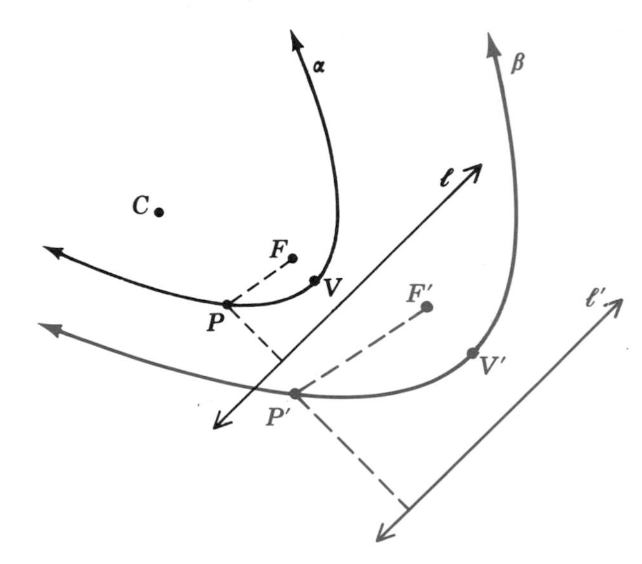

Suppose α is a parabola with focus F and directrix ℓ. Then each point P on α is equidistant from F and ℓ.

At left we have drawn the image, β, of α under a size transformation (magnitude 2, center C). We wish to show that β is a parabola. Since P is equidistant from F and ℓ, its image P' is equidistant from F' and ℓ'. So P' and all other points of β are on the parabola with focus F', directrix ℓ'. Reversing the argument, if a point is on the parabola with focus F', directrix ℓ', then its preimage is on α. This argument shows:

Theorem 12.7.1

Under a size transformation, the image of a parabola is a parabola.

The size transformation S_k of magnitude k, center $(0, 0)$, maps (x, y) onto (kx, ky). So it is the special scale transformation in which the horizontal and vertical magnitudes are equal. This is also seen from the matrix for S_k, $\begin{bmatrix} k & 0 \\ 0 & k \end{bmatrix}$, which is the special case of $\begin{bmatrix} a & 0 \\ 0 & b \end{bmatrix}$ where $a = b = k$.

So the graph scale transformation theorem (12.5.2) can be applied to size transformations.

Theorem 12.7.2

Replacing x by $\frac{x}{k}$ and y by $\frac{y}{k}$ in a sentence applies S_k to the graph of that sentence.

As an example, suppose we begin with the unit circle

$$x^2 + y^2 = 1.$$

Applying S_k to $x^2 + y^2 = 1$, we replace x by $\frac{x}{k}$, y by $\frac{y}{k}$.

$$\left(\frac{x}{k}\right)^2 + \left(\frac{y}{k}\right)^2 = 1$$

$$\frac{x^2}{k^2} + \frac{y^2}{k^2} = 1$$

$$x^2 + y^2 = k^2$$

Equation for the circle with center (0, 0), radius k

Applying size transformations to the parabola $y = x^2$ leads to equations for parabolas by Theorem 12.7.1. We have not previously mentioned these parabolas.

Theorem 12.7.3

When $a \neq 0$, the solution set of $y = ax^2$ is a parabola, the image of $y = x^2$ under $S_{\frac{1}{a}}$.

PROOF: By Theorem 12.7.2, the image of $y = x^2$ under $S_{\frac{1}{a}}$ is

$$\frac{y}{\frac{1}{a}} = \left(\frac{x}{\frac{1}{a}}\right)^2 \quad \text{or} \quad ay = (ax)^2.$$

Then, $\quad ay = a^2x^2.$

Since $a \neq 0$, $\quad y = ax^2.$

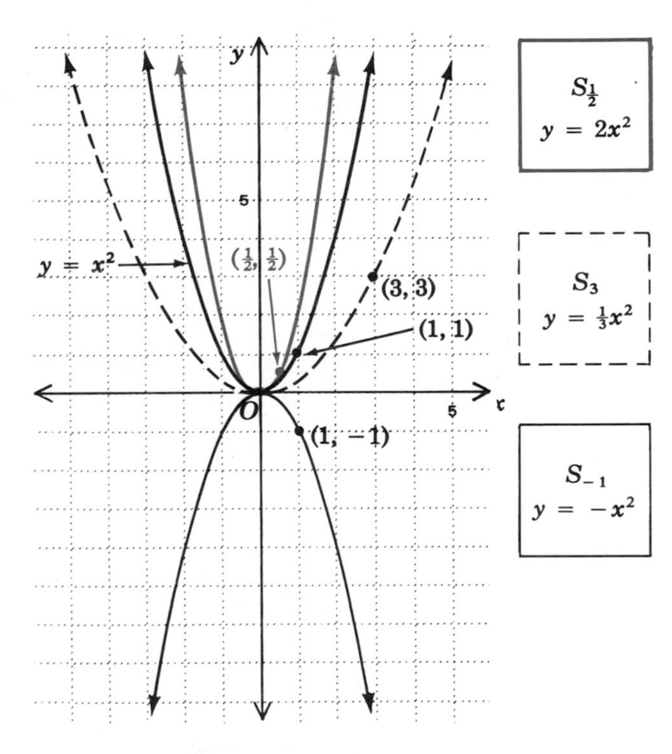

All the parabolas shown are size transformation images of each other. So they are similar. The red parabola appears "narrower" than the dashed parabola because you are seeing more of it. Looking at the parabolas through magnifying lenses of appropriate powers would show that all have the same "shape."

Theorem 12.7.4

All parabolas are similar to each other.

PROOF: Let α and β be any two parabolas with foci and directrices as shown in the next diagram.

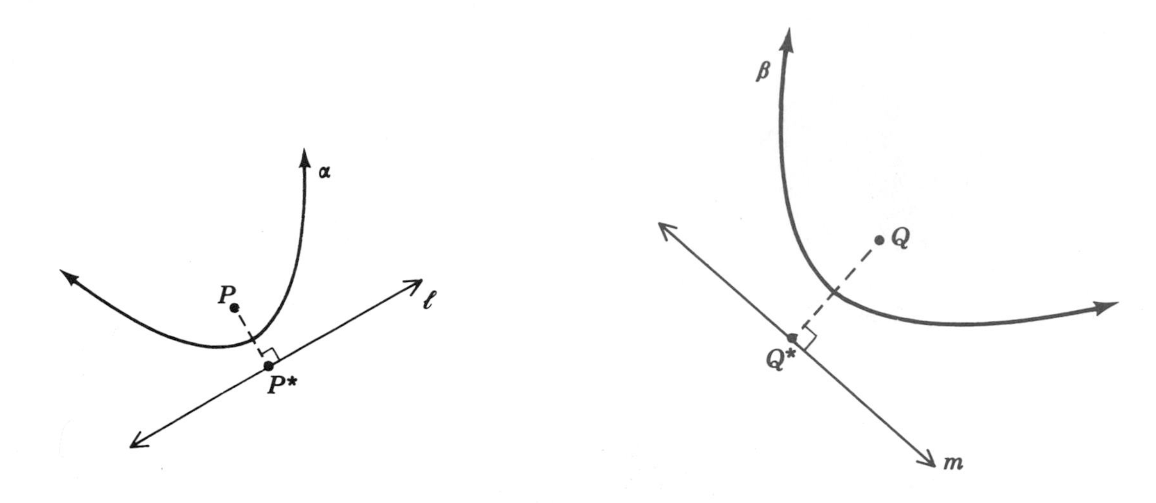

There is a *similarity transformation* S mapping $\overline{PP^*}$ onto $\overline{QQ^*}$. (Use one size transformation of magnitude $\frac{QQ^*}{PP^*}$ and rotations and translations as needed.) Clearly $S(\ell) = m$, and under S, points equidistant from P and ℓ (points on α) are mapped onto points equidistant from Q and m (points on β). That is, $S(\alpha) = \beta$. So $\alpha \sim \beta$.

All hyperbolas are *not* similar. If they were, the angles formed by the asymptotes would have to be the same for all hyperbolas. This you know does not always happen.

All ellipses are *not* similar. In fact, a circle is not similar to any noncircular ellipse. (If you magnify a circle, you always get a circle.) So the similarity of all parabolas is a rather unique property, shared only by circles among the conics.

EXERCISES 12.7

Ⓐ **1.** Define *parabola*.

2. By definition, when are two figures similar?

3–5. True or False?

3. There is a size transformation which maps any parabola onto any other given parabola.

4. If α and β are parabolas, then $\alpha \sim \beta$.

5. If α and β are hyperbolas, then $\alpha \sim \beta$.

6–11. Give a sentence for the image of each relation under the given size transformation.

6. $\{(x, y): x + y = 1\}$; S_3

7. $\{(x, y): y = x^2\}$; $S_{\frac{1}{2}}$

8. $\{(x, y): x^2 + y^2 = 1\}$; S_{-5}

9. $\{(x, y): xy = 10\}$; S_6

10. $\{(x, y): \frac{x^2}{4} + \frac{y^2}{9} = 1\}$; S_{-1}

11. $\{(x, y): y < x^2\}$; S_3

Ⓑ **12.** Are all noncircular ellipses similar? Explain your answer.

13. Explain how all parabolas are proved to be similar.

14–19. Graph the solution set to each sentence.

14. $y = 2x^2$

15. $y = 0.1x^2$

16. $q = -p^2$

17. $y - 5x^2 = 0$

18. $\frac{1}{2}u^2 = v$

19. $3x^2 + y = 0$

20. Graph the solution set to $A = \pi r^2$ for $r > 0$. What does this graph picture?

21–24. Trace the parabola and sketch its image under the indicated size transformation.

21. center V, magnitude $\frac{2}{3}$

22. center V, magnitude 2

23. center V, magnitude -2

24. center A, magnitude 1.5

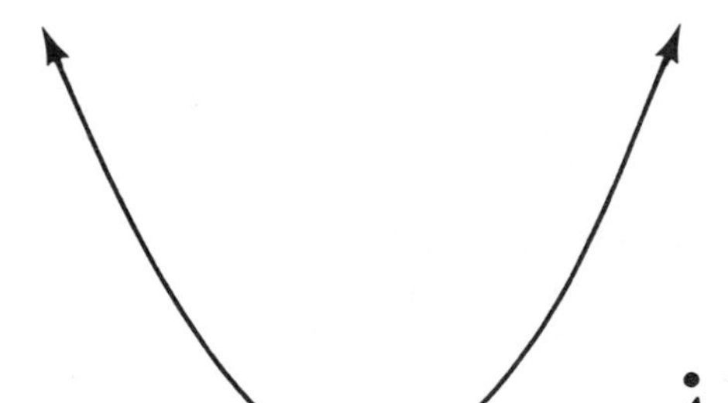

Ⓒ **25.** Prove that the parabola with focus $\left(0, \frac{1}{4a}\right)$ and directrix $y = -\frac{1}{4a}$ has equation $y = ax^2$.

26. Prove that the parabola $y = x^2$ can be shrunk horizontally onto the parabola $y = 4x^2$. (This is a way of mapping one parabola onto another by using a transformation which, in general, does not preserve shape, and the focus of one does not map into the focus of the other.)

27. The argument preceding Theorem 12.7.1 proves more than the theorem specifically states. What more could have been added to the theorem?

12.8 REFLECTION IMAGES OF GRAPHS OF RELATIONS

Recall that to translate a graph a units to the right (that is, to map x onto $x + a$), you replace x by $x - a$ in the sentence. To stretch horizontally a times (to map x onto ax), you replace x by $\frac{x}{a}$ in the sentence. The substitution made in the sentence is the inverse of the transformation's formula.

Suppose we want to reflect a graph. Here are some formulas for reflections.

$r_{x\text{-axis}}$: (x, y) is mapped onto $(x, -y)$.

$r_{y\text{-axis}}$: (x, y) is mapped onto $(-x, y)$.

$r_{x=y}$: (x, y) is mapped onto (y, x).

Because each reflection is its own inverse, the substitutions are the same as the mapping formulas.

Theorem 12.8.1

Given a sentence for a relation α:

a. Replacing y by $-y$ gives a sentence for $r_{x\text{-axis}}(\alpha)$.

b. Replacing x by $-x$ gives a sentence for $r_{y\text{-axis}}(\alpha)$.

c. Switching x and y gives a sentence for $r_{x=y}(\alpha)$.

Example 1: To find the image of $y = x^2$ under $r_{x\text{-axis}}$, use part **a**. The image has the equation $-y = x^2$ (usually written as $y = -x^2$).

Ex. 1

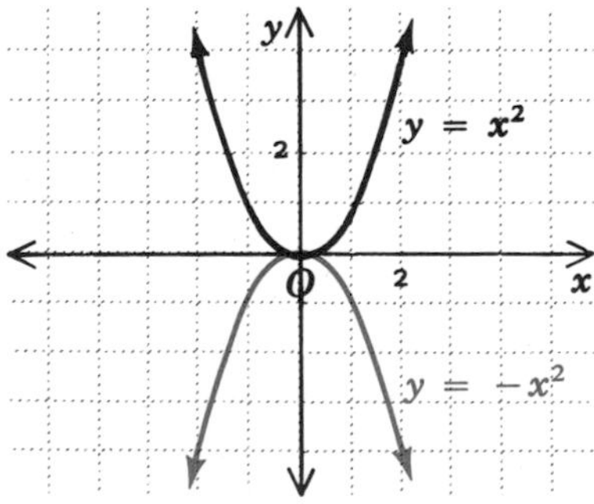

Ex. 2

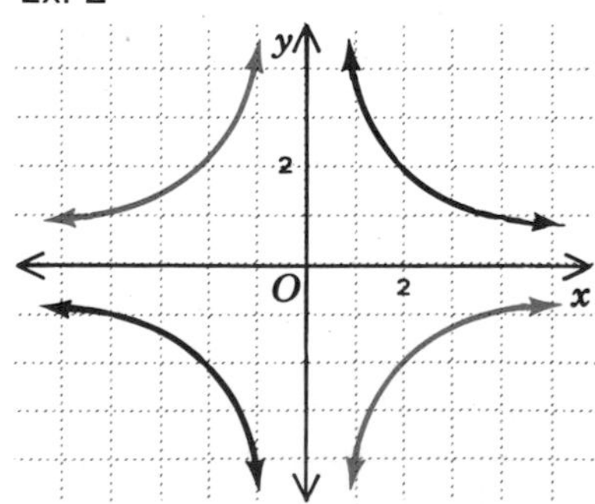

Example 2: The image of $xy = 4$ under $r_{y\text{-axis}}$ has equation $(-x)y = 4$, using part **b** of Theorem 12.8.1. That second equation is equivalent to $xy = -4$. Both relations are graphed above.

Example 3: Switching x and y in $y = 2x^2$ results in the sentence $x = 2y^2$. The graph of $x = 2y^2$ is a parabola symmetric to the x-axis, the reflection image of $\{(x, y): y = 2x^2\}$ over the line $y = x$.

Ex. 3

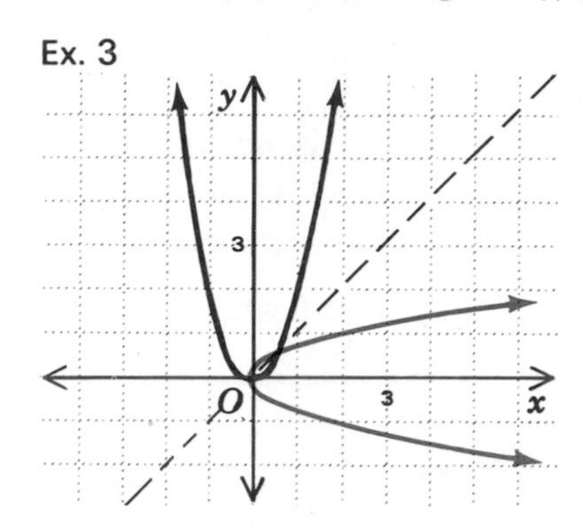

Ex. 4

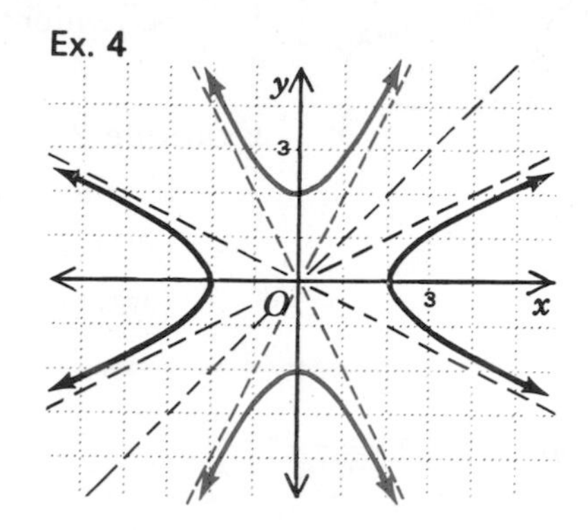

Example 4: The solution set to $\frac{y^2}{4} - x^2 = 1$ is a hyperbola, the reflection image of $\frac{x^2}{4} - y^2 = 1$ over the line $x = y$. Its asymptotes are also reflection images.

From Examples **3** and **4**, you should notice that you now can graph many parabolas and hyperbolas which you did not study before.

If the sentence for $r_\ell(\alpha)$ is equivalent to the sentence for α, then $r_\ell(\alpha) = \alpha$ and α is symmetric to line ℓ. So Theorem 12.8.1 leads to a way of determining when relations are symmetric to the lines we have been considering.

Theorem 12.8.2

Given a sentence for a relation, if the indicated replacement yields an equivalent sentence, the relation is symmetric to the indicated line as follows:

Replacement	Line
y by $-y$	x-axis
x by $-x$	y-axis
x by y, y by x	$x = y$

Example 5: In the relation with sentence $x^2 + y^2 \leq 5$, replacing y by $-y$ gives the sentence $x^2 + (-y)^2 \leq 5$. Since $(-y)^2 = y^2$, this second sentence is equivalent to the given sentence. The given relation is thus symmetric with respect to the x-axis.

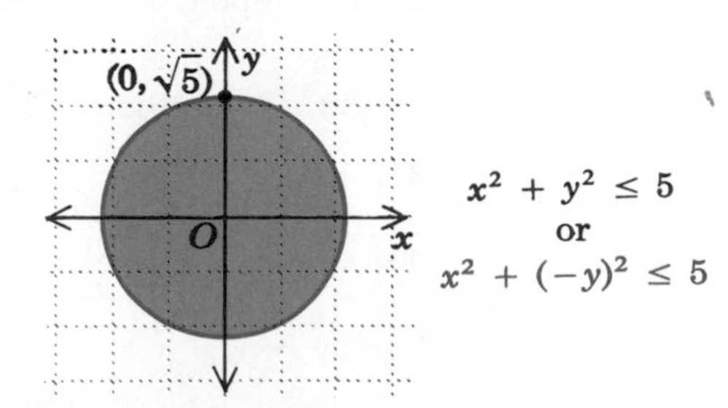

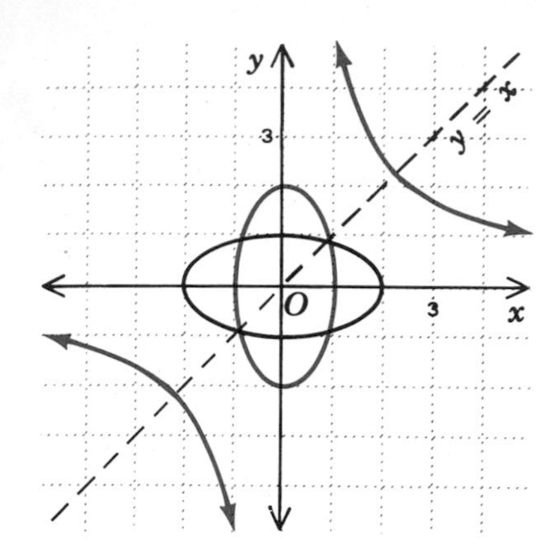

Example 6: The hyperbola $xy = 5$ is symmetric to the line $x = y$ because switching x and y in that sentence results in the sentence $yx = 5$, an equivalent sentence.

Example 7: The ellipse $\frac{x^2}{4} + y^2 = 1$ is *not* symmetric to the line $y = x$ because switching x and y gives the equation $\frac{y^2}{4} + x^2 = 1$, and the second sentence is not equivalent to the first.

EXERCISES 12.8

Ⓐ **1–3.** Give the reflection image of $(-4, 17)$ over the line indicated.

1. the x-axis **2.** the y-axis **3.** $x = y$

4–6. Repeat Exercises **1–3** for the point $(100, 1)$.

7–9. A sentence for a relation involves variables x and y. What should be done to the sentence to obtain a sentence for the reflection image of the relation over the line indicated?

7. the x-axis **8.** the y-axis **9.** $x = y$

10–12. From the sentence for a relation, how can you tell if the relation is symmetric to the lines of Exercises **7–9**?

13–18. Give a sentence for the reflection image of the given relation over the x-axis. Tell if the graph is symmetric to this line.

13. $x = 3y^2$ **14.** $xy = 6$ **15.** $x^2 + (y + 1)^2 = 20$

16. $\frac{x^2}{4} + \frac{y^2}{3} = 9$ **17.** $x + y = 12$ **18.** $y^2 - x^2 = 9$

19–24. Repeat Exercises **13–18** for the line $x = y$.

25–30. Repeat Exercises **13–18** for the y-axis.

Ⓑ **31–38.** Graph the solution set to each sentence.

31. $x = y^2$ **32.** $y^2 - x^2 = 1$ **33.** $x + 2y^2 = 0$

34. $a = 3b^2$ **35.** $\frac{y^2}{25} - \frac{x^2}{16} = 1$ **36.** $9y^2 - 36x^2 = 324$

37. $xy = -6$ **38.** $y = -\frac{1}{x}$

39. Graph $\frac{x^2}{16} - \frac{y^2}{4} = 1$, $\frac{x^2}{16} + \frac{y^2}{4} = 1$, and $\frac{y^2}{4} - \frac{x^2}{16} = 1$ on the same pair of coordinate axes.

40. Give and draw the reflection image of $x = 5$ over the line $x = y$.

© 41. Give the focus and directrix of the parabola $x = y^2$.

42. Give the foci of the hyperbola $\{(x, y): xy = -2\}$.

43. Give the foci of the ellipse $\{(x, y): 9x^2 + y^2 = 9\}$.

44. Find a way to reflect relations over the line $x + y = 0$.

TRANSLATION IMAGES OF CONICS

Even before the last section, you could graph a conveniently located congruent copy of any conic. The general forms are given below.

<table>
<tr><th></th><th>Equation</th><th>Centers and Lines of Symmetry</th><th>Key Points in Graphing</th><th>Asymptotes</th></tr>
<tr><td rowspan="2">Parabola</td><td>$y = ax^2$</td><td>y-axis</td><td rowspan="2">vertex (0, 0)</td><td rowspan="3">none</td></tr>
<tr><td>$x = ay^2$</td><td>x-axis</td></tr>
<tr><td>Ellipse</td><td>$\frac{x^2}{a^2} + \frac{y^2}{b^2} = 1$</td><td rowspan="3">$x$-axis
y-axis
(0, 0)</td><td>endpoints of axes:
$(a, 0)$, $(-a, 0)$
$(0, b)$, $(0, -b)$</td></tr>
<tr><td rowspan="3">Hyperbola</td><td>$\frac{x^2}{a^2} - \frac{y^2}{b^2} = 1$</td><td>vertices:
$(a, 0)$, $(-a, 0)$</td><td>$\frac{y}{b} = \frac{x}{a}$</td></tr>
<tr><td>$\frac{y^2}{b^2} - \frac{x^2}{a^2} = 1$</td><td>vertices:
$(0, b)$, $(0, -b)$</td><td>$\frac{y}{b} = -\frac{x}{a}$</td></tr>
<tr><td>$xy = k$
$(k \neq 0)$</td><td>$x = y$
$x = -y$
(0, 0)</td><td>vertices:
$(\sqrt{k}, \sqrt{k})$,
$(-\sqrt{k}, -\sqrt{k})$</td><td>y-axis
x-axis</td></tr>
</table>

A common feature of these conics is the important role played by (0, 0) either as a vertex or a center of 180°-rotation-symmetry. Also, except for the hyperbola $xy = k$, these conics have horizontal or vertical symmetry lines.

It is possible to rotate conics and find an equation for any conic section in the plane, even if the symmetry lines are tilted. This is studied in more-advanced courses. Here we find equations for *translation* images of these graphs. This insures that horizontal and vertical lines will still play a key role.

We begin with parabolas. Some were studied in Chapter 11.

Theorem 12.9.1

The solution set to $y - k = a(x - h)^2$ is a parabola. Its vertex is (h, k), its symmetry line is $x = h$, and it is congruent to $y = ax^2$.

PROOF: To translate $y = ax^2$, replace x by $x - h$, y by $y - k$. The image will have equation $y - k = a(x - h)^2$, by the graph translation theorem (6.4.1). The symmetry line will be $x - h = 0$ (which is $x = h$). The image of (0, 0) will be (h, k), the new vertex.

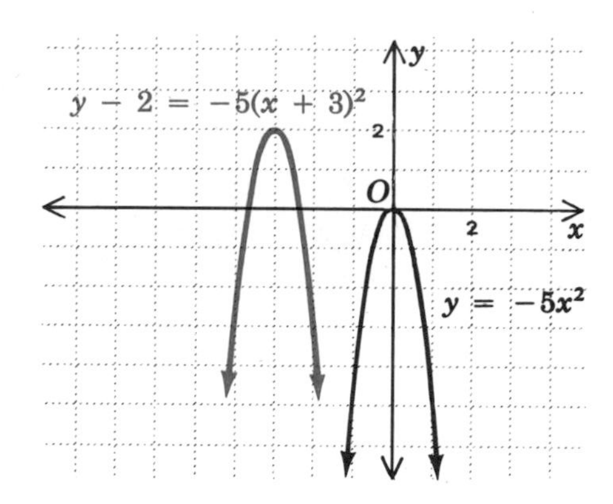

Example 1: Graph $y - 2 = -5(x + 3)^2$.

SOLUTION: This is the image of $y = -5x^2$ under the translation

$$(x, y) \to (x - 3, y + 2).$$

Graphing the preimage makes graphing the image easy. The vertex is $(-3, 2)$. The symmetry line is $x = -3$.

By completing the square, you can always convert the expression

$$ax^2 + bx + c \quad \text{to} \quad a(x - h)^2 + k.$$

So any sentence of the form $\quad y = ax^2 + bx + c$

is equivalent to $\quad y = a(x - h)^2 + k.$

The last sentence is equivalent to the parabola in Theorem 12.9.1. So the graph of $y = ax^2 + bx + c$ is always a parabola.

Example 2: Change $y = 3x^2 + 5x - 4$ to the square form of Theorem 12.9.1.

SOLUTION:

$y = 3(x^2 + \frac{5}{3}x) - 4$ — Use distributivity.

$y = 3[(x + \frac{5}{6})^2 - \frac{25}{36}] - 4$ — Complete square.

$y = 3(x + \frac{5}{6})^2 - \frac{25}{12} - 4$ — Use distributivity again.

$y + \frac{73}{12} = 3(x + \frac{5}{6})^2$ — Add $4 + \frac{25}{12}$.

The graph in the preceding example is a parabola with vertex $(-\frac{5}{6}, -\frac{73}{12})$, congruent to $y = 3x^2$.

All other conics can be treated in the same way. It is extremely easy to graph them when an equation is given in square form. Otherwise, the equations must be modified to this form.

Example 3: Graph $\{(x, y): \frac{(x-2)^2}{4} + \frac{(y-5)^2}{9} = 1\}$.

SOLUTION: This graph is congruent to the ellipse with equation

$$\frac{x^2}{4} + \frac{y^2}{9} = 1.$$

The translation was

$(x, y) \to (x + 2, y + 5)$.

So the center is (2, 5) and the symmetry lines are $x = 2$ and $y = 5$.

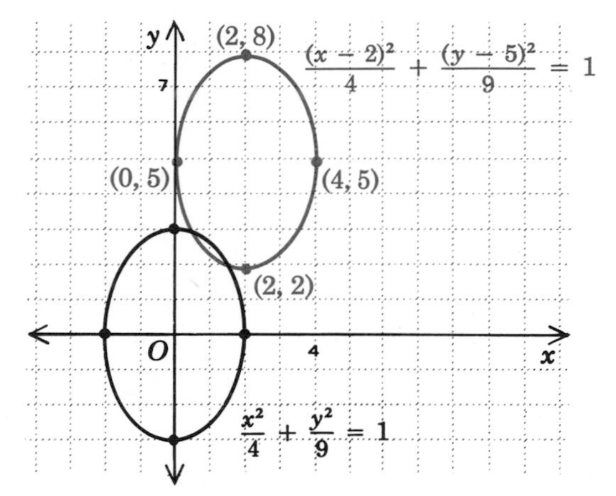

Example 4: Graph the solution set to $9x^2 - y^2 + 18x + 4y - 31 = 0$.

SOLUTION: Given (in rearranged order):

$$9x^2 + 18x - y^2 + 4y - 31 = 0$$

$$9(x^2 + 2x) - (y^2 - 4y) - 31 = 0$$

$$9[(x+1)^2 - 1] - [(y-2)^2 - 4] - 31 = 0$$

$$9(x+1)^2 - 9 - (y-2)^2 + 4 - 31 = 0$$

$$9(x+1)^2 - (y-2)^2 = 36$$

$$\frac{(x+1)^2}{4} - \frac{(y-2)^2}{36} = 1$$

So the graph is the image of $\frac{x^2}{4} - \frac{y^2}{36} = 1$ under the translation $(x, y) \to (x - 1, y + 2)$, a hyperbola with center at $(-1, 2)$. This makes it easy to draw the graph.

EXERCISES 12.9

Ⓐ **1.** State the graph translation theorem.

2–3. For the parabola $y - 2 = 4(x - 5)^2$, name the:

2. vertex.

3. symmetry line.

4–6. Give an equation for the image of each relation under the translation $(x, y) \rightarrow (x + 4, y - 3)$.

4. $\frac{x^2}{9} + y^2 = 1$ **5.** $4y^2 - x^2 = 3$ **6.** $3x = y^2$

7. True or False? The graphs of $4y = x^2$ and $4y = x^2 + 3x + 5$ are congruent.

Ⓑ **8–13.** Draw a rough graph of the solution set to each sentence.

8. $\frac{(p-2)^2}{4} + \frac{m^2}{9} = 1$ **9.** $y = 3(x + 1)^2 - 4$

10. $2x + 1 = 2(y - 1)^2$ **11.** $x^2 - (y + 3)^2 = 1$

12. $(x - 5)(3y + 6) = 12$ **13.** $2y = (x + 7)^2$

14–16. Graph the two relations on the same axes.

14. $\{(x, y): y = x^2 + 10\}$, $\{(x, y): y = x^2 - 5\}$

15. $\{(a, b): b - 3 = 2(a + 1)^2\}$, $\{(a, b): b - 3 = 2(a - 1)^2\}$

16. $\{(c, d): d = -3(c - 2)^2\}$, $\{(c, d): d = 3(c - 2)^2\}$

17–26. Decide whether the graph of the solution set is an ellipse, parabola, or hyperbola.

17. $x^2 + y = 4$ **18.** $\frac{x^2}{36} + \frac{5y^2}{36} = 1$

19. $8x - \frac{4}{y} = 0$ **20.** $4 + \left(\frac{2}{3}x\right)^2 = \left(\frac{2}{3}y\right)^2$

21. $(x + y)^2 - (x - y)^2 = -2$ **22.** $4 - \frac{x^2}{4} = 3 + \frac{y^2}{16}$

23. $y^2 - 8y - x^2 - 4x = 12$ **24.** $y^2 + 15 = 3x^2$

25. $y^2 + 3x^2 = 15$ **26.** $y^2 = 3x^2$

Ⓒ **27–34.** Graph the solution set to each sentence.

27. $y = 5x^2 - 2x + 1$ **28.** $v = 2u^2 - 8u + 6$

29. $3y = 2x^2 + 8x - 10$ **30.** $3x + 6 = y^2 - 4y$

31. $4x^2 - 8y^2 - 16x = 0$ **32.** $3x^2 + 6x + 2y^2 + 5y = 19$

33. $x^2 - y^2 + 2x = 6$ **34.** $3x^2 + 4y^2 - 9x - 12y + 16 = 0$

35–36. Find an equation for the parabola with focus $(-3, 9)$ and directrix $y = 13$ by two different methods

35. Use the definition of parabola and the process on page 318.

36. Determine the vertex of the parabola. Compare the distance between focus and directrix with that in $y = x^2$. Compute the magnitude of a similarity transformation which will map $y = x^2$ onto the given parabola. Use this information to get the equation.

37. *Driving.* The minimum stopping distance d (in feet) of a car traveling at a velocity v (in mph), $v \geq 5$, is approximated by the formula

$$d = \frac{11}{200}v^2 + \frac{12}{11}v - \frac{11}{8}.$$

(NOTE: $\frac{12}{11}v$ is distance before reacting, $\frac{11}{200}v^2 - \frac{11}{8}$ is distance once the brakes have been applied.) Graph this relationship.

38–39. Use examples to answer these questions. Given a sentence for a relation, what transformation results by:

38. replacing x by $-x$, y by $-y$?

39. replacing x by y, y by $-x$?

QUADRATIC SYSTEMS 12.10

Quadratic systems are systems which contain quadratic (and perhaps linear) sentences. As with linear systems, you may (1) find approximations to solutions by graphing, or (2) solve by substitution, or (3) solve by using multiplication and addition properties of equations. No new theorems are needed.

Example 1: By graphing, approximate solutions to the system $\begin{cases} y = 3x + 1 \\ xy = 10. \end{cases}$

SOLUTION: Each relation is graphed. Even the rough graph tells that there are two solutions, one in the 1st quadrant, one in the 3rd quadrant.

Exact solutions may be found by substitution.

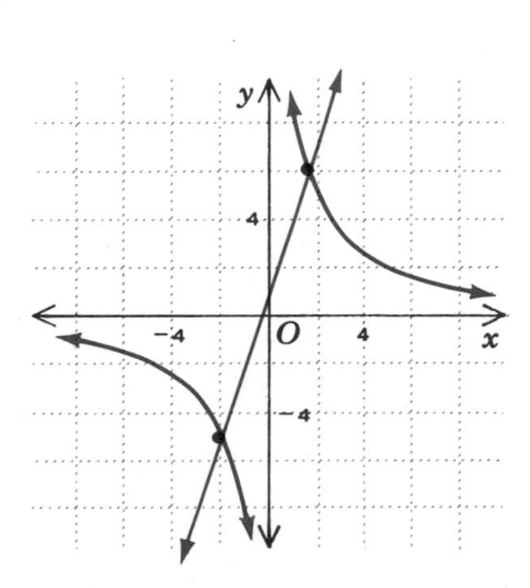

Example 2: Solve the system $\begin{cases} y = 3x + 1 \\ xy = 10. \end{cases}$

SOLUTION: Since $y = 3x + 1$ in any solution, we substitute $3x + 1$ for y in the second equation. This tells us a condition which x must satisfy.

$$x(3x + 1) = 10$$

So,
$$3x^2 + x - 10 = 0.$$

Using the quadratic formula (or by factoring), we find that

$$x = -2 \text{ or } x = \tfrac{5}{3}.$$

When $x = -2$, $y = 3x + 1 = -5$. So one solution is $(-2, -5)$. When $x = \frac{5}{3}$, $y = 3x + 1 = 6$. A second solution is $(\frac{5}{3}, 6)$. You should check that these solutions seem reasonable by referring back to the graph.

The next example is the problem to determine geometrically the points of intersection of an ellipse and a hyperbola. Since both relations are symmetric to the x and y axes, the solution set will also possess this symmetry.

Example 3: Use addition and multiplication properties of equations to solve:

$$\begin{cases} 14x^2 + 4y^2 = 4 \\ 9x^2 - y^2 = 1. \end{cases}$$

SOLUTION: Multiplying the second equation by 4, we get an equivalent system.

$$\begin{cases} 14x^2 + 4y^2 = 4 \\ 36x^2 - 4y^2 = 4 \end{cases}$$

Adding gives a condition which x must satisfy.

$$50x^2 = 8 \qquad \text{So } x = \pm\tfrac{2}{5}.$$

When $x = \dfrac{2}{5}$, $y = \pm\dfrac{\sqrt{11}}{5}$. When $x = -\dfrac{2}{5}$, $y = \pm\dfrac{\sqrt{11}}{5}$.

So there are four solutions:

$$\left(\frac{2}{5}, \frac{\sqrt{11}}{5}\right), \quad \left(\frac{2}{5}, -\frac{\sqrt{11}}{5}\right), \quad \left(-\frac{2}{5}, \frac{\sqrt{11}}{5}\right), \quad \left(-\frac{2}{5}, -\frac{\sqrt{11}}{5}\right).$$

Our last example involves the intersection of two hyperbolas and shows the power of substitution as a way to solve systems.

Example 4: The product of two numbers is 16. If one number is increased by 2 and the other is decreased by 3, their product is 20. Find the numbers.

SOLUTION: Let x and y be the numbers. From the given:

$$\begin{cases} xy = 16 \\ (x + 2)(y - 3) = 20. \end{cases}$$

Solving the first sentence for y yields $y = \frac{16}{x}$. This value of y is substituted in the second sentence.

$$(x + 2)\left(\frac{16}{x} - 3\right) = 20$$

Now the problem is to solve for x. Using the FOIL theorem,

$$16 - 3x + \frac{32}{x} - 6 = 20$$

$$-3x + \frac{32}{x} + 10 = 20$$

$$-3x + \frac{32}{x} - 10 = 0$$

$$-3x^2 + 32 - 10x = 0$$

$$3x^2 + 10x - 32 = 0.$$

Using the quadratic formula, you find $x = -\frac{16}{3}$ or $x = 2$. When $x = -\frac{16}{3}$, $y = \frac{16}{-\frac{16}{3}} = -3$. When $x = 2$, $y = 8$. So there are two pairs of numbers which satisfy the given conditions: ($-\frac{16}{3}$ and -3) or (2 and 8). You should check this.

EXERCISES 12.10

Ⓐ

1. What does it mean to have a solution to a system of sentences?
2. When are two systems equivalent?
3. Name three strategies which can be used to solve systems.
4. Given that $a = 7$, find all solutions to this system. $\begin{cases} 2a - 6 = 2b^2 \\ 3a - |b| = 19. \end{cases}$
5. Given that $x^2 = 8$, find all solutions to this system. $\begin{cases} 3x^2 - 4y^2 = 4 \\ x^2 + y^2 = 13. \end{cases}$
6. Given that $y^2 = 9$, solve: $\begin{cases} y^2 - 4z = -7 \\ y^2 = \frac{36}{z}. \end{cases}$

Ⓑ **7–12.** By graphing, determine the *number* of real solutions to each system. (You do not have to determine the exact solutions.)

7. $x - y = 10$
$y = x^2$

8. $x^2 + y^2 = 1$
$2x^2 + y^2 = 5$

9. $ab = 10$
$b = 4a + 5$

10. $r = (t + 1)^2$
$r - 2 = (t - 1)^2$

11. $y + 1 = 3(x - 2)^2$
$y - 4 = 4(x - 2)^2$

12. $\frac{m^2}{4} + \frac{y^2}{9} = 1$
$m^2 - \frac{y^2}{16} = 1$

13–25. Use any method to find all real solutions to each system.

13. $y = 4 + 3x$
$x(y - 1) = 18$

14. $d = 3 + 4c + c^2$
$d = 9 + c^2$

15. $x^2 + 3y^2 = 28$
$x^2 + y^2 = 20$

16. the system of Exercise **7**

17. the system of Exercise **8**

18. $3u^2 + v^2 = 7$
$2u^2 - v = 4$

19. $x^2 = 9 + y$
$y + 1 = (x - 2)^2$

20. $10 = x^2 + 8y$
$0 = 3x^2 - 6y$

21. $x + y = 1$
$x^2 + y^2 = 1$

22. $u^2 + v^2 = 34$
$uv = 15$

(HINT: Graph to find the number of solutions. Then find all the solutions by trying numbers.)

23. the system of Exercise **10**

24. the system of Exercise **11**

25. the system of Exercise **12**

26. The product of two numbers is 22. If one number is increased by 5 and the other is decreased by 2, their product is 3. Find the numbers.

Ⓒ **27.** Draw two parabolas which intersect in **(a)** exactly one point, **(b)** exactly three points, **(c)** exactly four points, and **(d)** exactly five points.

28–33. Let n be an integer indicating the number of points of intersection of the two given figures. Give all possible values of n when the figures are:

28. two circles.

29. two ellipses.

30. two hyperbolas.

31. an ellipse and a hyperbola.

32. a parabola and an ellipse.

33. a line and a hyperbola.

34. Find all points equidistant from (3, 8), (2, 4), and (−1, 6).

35. One year, a store took in \$6000 by selling certain suits. The next year, the price per suit went up \$5, and 10 fewer suits were sold, so the store took in \$5000 from selling these suits. Each year, all suits were the same price. Find the price per suit each year.

36. On a 120-kilometre trip, increasing the average speed by 20 km/h, a motorist can save 30 minutes. How fast is the car going?

37. Find the values of k for which the hyperbola $xy = k$ is tangent to the ellipse $x^2 + 4y^2 = 4$.

38. The square of the smaller of one pair of consecutive integers is added to the square of the larger of a second pair of consecutive integers, with 2050 the sum. The squares of the other integers in these pairs have a sum of 2020. Find the four integers.

39–40. Solve the system of quadratic inequalities by graphing.

39. $\frac{1}{2} \le x \le 1$
$\frac{1}{2} \le y \le 1$
$xy < \frac{1}{2}$

40. $x^2 + y^2 < 25$
$\frac{x^2}{25} + y^2 > 1$

CHAPTER SUMMARY

12

Conic sections can be formed by intersecting a cone with a plane. If the plane does not contain the vertex of the cone, the intersection may be an ellipse (of which the circle is a special case), hyperbola, or parabola. If the plane contains the vertex, degenerate conic sections—a point, line, or two lines—are formed. In two dimensions, solution sets to equations for conic sections are always *quadratic relations.*

In this chapter, a standard process was used to study each conic section: (1) give a definition for the conic section; (2) from the definition, determine an equation for a conveniently located example of each type; (3) apply translations, scale transformations, or reflections to obtain other equations which give the same type of conic section. You should refer to p. 357 for a summary of the standard equation forms for these conics.

Scale transformations are particularly helpful in showing that all parabolas are similar, in obtaining ellipses, and in calculating equations of asymptotes of hyperbolas. Simple reflection rules can be used to reflect over the x-axis, y-axis, or line $x = y$, and thus to determine symmetry with respect to those lines.

Systems involving quadratic sentences are solved much the same as linear systems, by substitution or by using the addition or multiplication properties of equations. It is often helpful to estimate solutions to such systems by graphing.

12

CHAPTER REVIEW

1–4. Graph the solution set to each sentence. Identify at least 5 points on the graph.

1. $\frac{a^2}{4} + \frac{b^2}{16} = 1$

2. $y - 3 = \frac{1}{2}(x + 1)^2$

3. $\frac{x^2}{25} - \frac{y^2}{9} = 1$

4. $10 + xy = 0$

5–6. Suppose that you have graphed a solution set to a sentence involving x and y. How is the graph modified if in the sentence you:

5. replace x by $\frac{x}{3}$?

6. replace y by $-y$?

7. Graph $y = -2x^2$ and $x = -2y^2$ on the same pair of axes.

8. An ellipse has foci (0, 0) and (4, 3) and focal constant $2a = 10$. Give any equation (not necessarily a simple one) which is satisfied by every point (x, y) on the ellipse and is satisfied by no others.

9. Give equations for the asymptotes of $9y^2 - x^2 = 1$.

10. What is the vertex of $y = 2x^2 + 6x - 8$?

11. Use graphing to determine the number of solutions to the system

$$\begin{cases} x^2 + 4y^2 = 4 \\ y = (x - 2)^2. \end{cases}$$

12. Find all solutions to the system $\begin{cases} 3e^2 - 5m^2 = 2 \\ 4e^2 = 5m^2 + 6. \end{cases}$

13. A circle is a special type of (parabola; hyperbola; ellipse; raft).

$PV = K$	
Pressure (x)	Volume (y)
12	300
16	225
20	180
24	150
30	120
32	112.5

Chapter 13 Functions— A Unifying Concept

FUNCTION—A SPECIAL TYPE OF RELATION

The set of ordered pairs satisfying $xy = 1$ is a relation much like the one depicted above. Such relations have a nice property. If you know the first component for one of the ordered pairs, then you can determine exactly what the second component is. For example, when $xy = 1$ if you let $x = 3$, then you can determine that $y = \frac{1}{3}$. For this value of x, no other value of y works. That is, in this relation, only one ordered pair $(3, \frac{1}{3})$ has first component 3.

The solution set of $x^2 + y^2 = 25$ does not have the property just described. If $x = 3$, then y is not *uniquely* determined. For this value of x, y may be 4 or -4. So, both $(3, 4)$ and $(3, -4)$ are in this relation.

The solution set to $y = x^2$ does have this property. That is, for each value of x, there is only one ordered pair in the relation. Such a relation is called a *function.*

Definition

A **function** is a relation in which no two different ordered pairs have the same first component.

By graphing the three relations just mentioned, we can easily see which are functions.

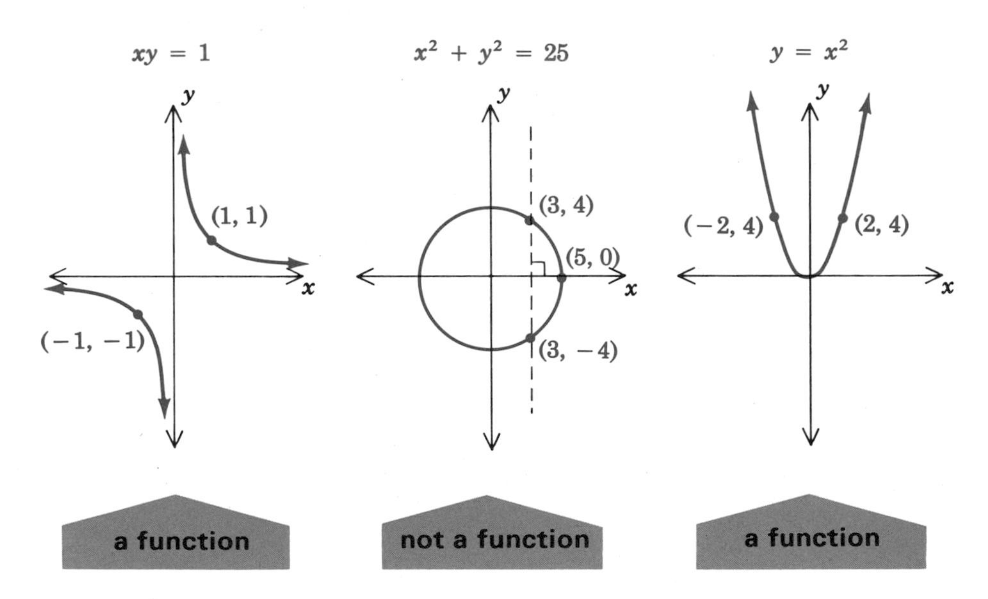

All ordered pairs which have the same first component lie on the same vertical line. (Refer to the middle graph above.) In a function, by definition, there can be no two ordered pairs with the same first component. This proves the next theorem.

Theorem 13.1.1

Vertical-line test for functions: No vertical line can intersect the graph of a function in more than one point.

Many relations have only a finite number of points in their graphs. The following graphs are of three finite relations, two of which are functions.

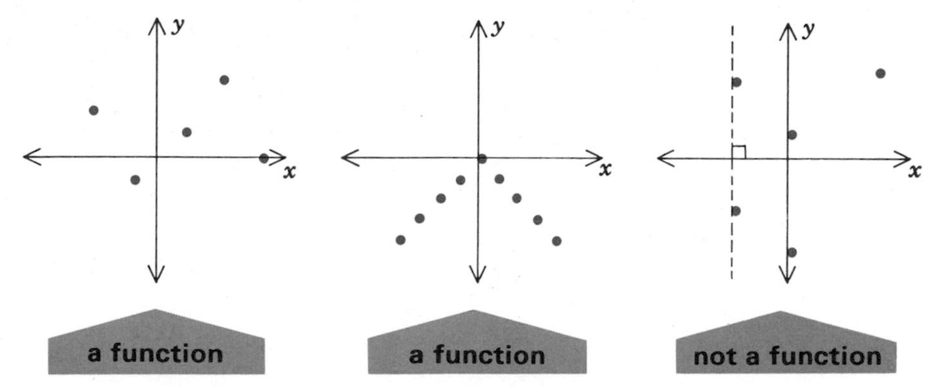

A function *can* have two ordered pairs with the same *second* component, as does the function with equation $y = x^2$, which contains both (2, 4) and $(-2, 4)$. (See graph on page 368.) This means that a horizontal line can intersect the graph of a function more than once.

There are many kinds of functions. Two kinds which you have met are *linear functions* and *quadratic functions.* These are simply linear relations and quadratic relations which also qualify as functions. Every linear function has an equation of the form

$$y = mx + b.$$

The most common quadratic functions have equations of the form

$$y = ax^2 + bx + c \quad \text{or} \quad xy = k.$$

Functions are of tremendous importance not only in mathematics, but in many other fields as well. Whenever the occurrence of an event uniquely determines that another event (or decision) occurs, then we have ordered pairs of corresponding events, and the set of these ordered pairs is a function.

EXERCISES 13.1

Ⓐ **1.** Define *relation.* **2.** Define *function.*

3. From a graph, how can you tell when a relation is a function?

4–11. Tell whether or not each graph is that of a function.

4.

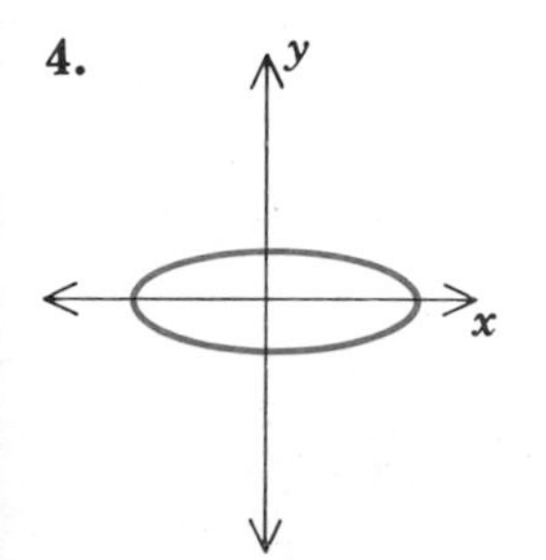

5.

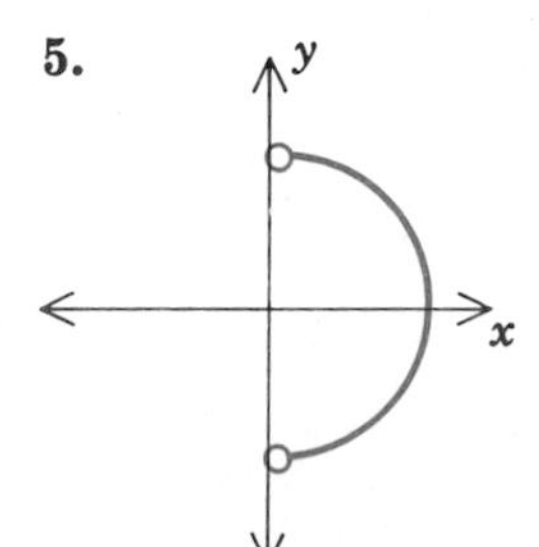

6.

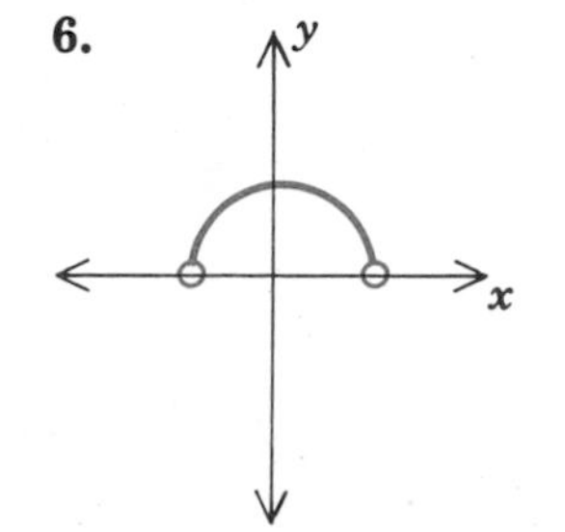

7.

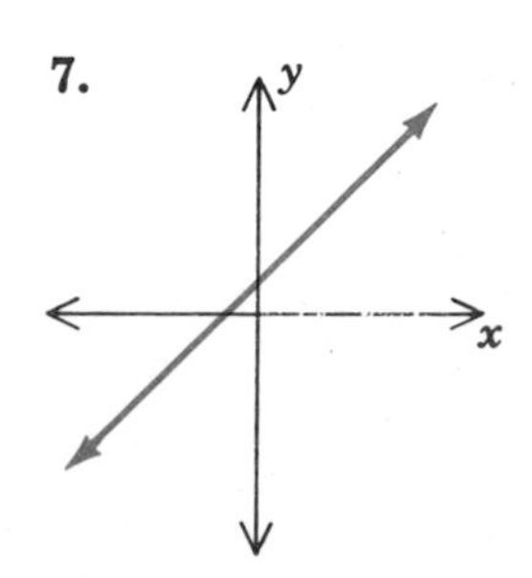

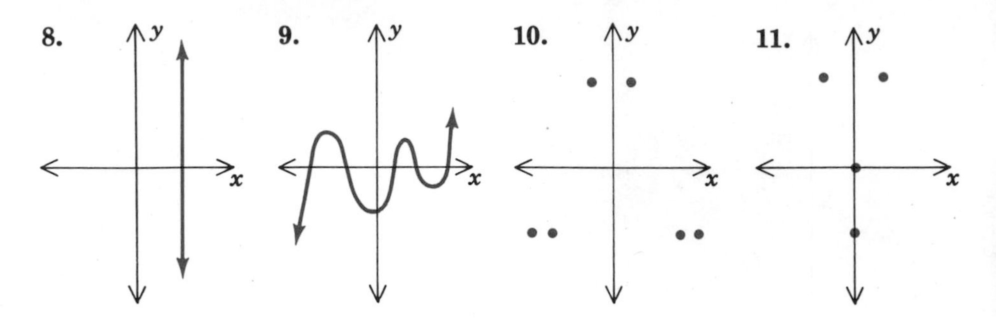

12. What is a linear function?

13. What is a quadratic function?

14–22. In your mind, picture the graph of the solution set for each relation. Then tell whether or not the solution set is a function.

14. $3y + 2x = 14$ **15.** $3y + 2x < 14$ **16.** $x^2 + y^2 = 25$

Ⓑ **17.** $y = 5x^2$ **18.** $x = 5y^2$ **19.** $x^2 + 2y^2 = 2$

20. $xy = 400$ **21.** $x^2 - y^2 = 1$ **22.** $(x - 2)^2 + (y + 5)^2 = 10$

23–32. Tell whether each set of ordered pairs is or is not a function.

23. $\{(2, 4), (3, 4), (5, 4)\}$

24. $\{(6, 2), (2, 5), (5, 9), (9, -\frac{1}{2})\}$

25. $\{(x, y)$: x is any integer and $y = 5\}$

26. $\{(x, y)$: y is any integer and $x = 3\}$

27. $\{(4, 2), (5, 2), (5, 9)\}$

28. $\{(-1, 6), (-2, 7), (-1, 6)\}$

29. $\{(x, y): 9x^2 + 4y^2 = 0\}$

30. $\{(x, y): y = x^3 + x^4\}$

31. solution set of $2y = (x - 8)^2 + (x - 5)^2 - 42$

32. solution set of $x = y^4 - 5y^2 + 8y^6$

33. Give an example of a linear equation which does not describe a function.

34–42. Show that each sentence does not describe a function by finding two different solutions with the same first component. Assume that the order of the components is determined by the alphabetical order of the variables.

34. $x^2 + 2y^2 = 40$ **35.** $xy = 0$ **36.** $x^3 = y^6$

37. $a - |b| = \sqrt{2}$ **38.** $t = \pm\sqrt{r}$ **39.** $xy^2 < 0$

Ⓒ **40.** $x = \sin y$ **41.** $2x = \cos y$ **42.** $\sin x = \cos y$

43. Which conic sections can be graphs of functions? Which cannot?

FUNCTION—A SPECIAL TYPE OF CORRESPONDENCE

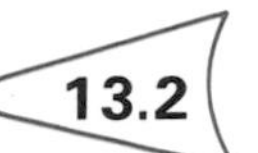

Here are two sets, A and B. $A = \{-2, 2, \frac{3}{4}, 0\}$ $B = \{4, \frac{9}{16}, 0\}$

The diagram at the right shows one way the elements of A might correspond to the elements of B.

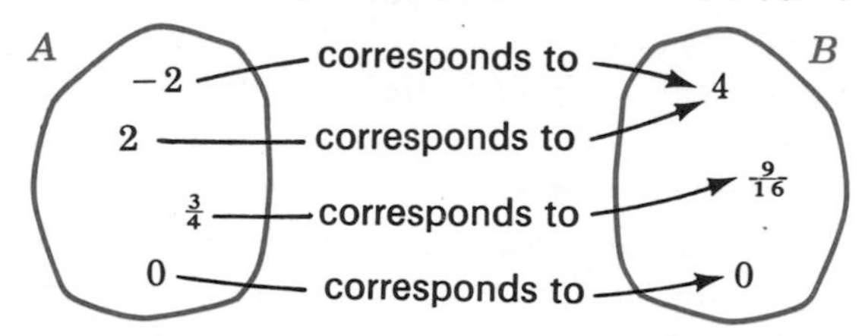

Correspondences are so important in mathematics that many different ways are used to describe them. Here are *five* ways of describing the correspondence above.

Description 1: *Listing using arrows*

$-2 \rightarrow 4$ $2 \rightarrow 4$ $\frac{3}{4} \rightarrow \frac{9}{16}$ $0 \rightarrow 0$

Description 2: *Listing using ordered pairs*

$(-2, 4)$ $(2, 4)$ $(\frac{3}{4}, \frac{9}{16})$ $(0, 0)$

Description 3: *Rule using arrows*

$x \rightarrow x^2$ where x is in $\{-2, 2, \frac{3}{4}, 0\}$

Description 4: *Sentence or formula* Let y be the element in set B which corresponds to the element x in set A. Then

$$y = x^2 \text{ where } x \text{ is in } \{-2, 2, \tfrac{3}{4}, 0\}.$$

Descriptions **2** and **4** show that this correspondence can be graphed.

Description 5: *Graph*

You may recognize this graph as a subset of the parabola $y = x^2$. There are only 4 points because the x-values are from set A, the set $\{-2, 2, \frac{3}{4}, 0\}$.

This set is called the *domain* of the correspondence.

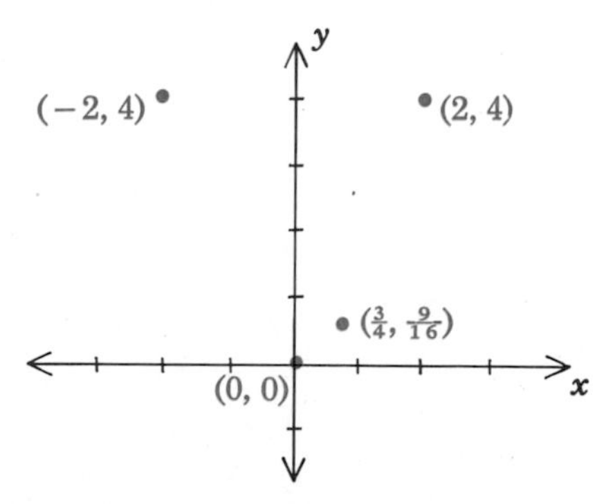

Now look again at the five descriptions. Description **2** shows that any correspondence is a *relation.* A careful look at any of the descriptions shows that this particular correspondence is a *function.*

The next two definitions show how the key ideas of *correspondence*, *relation*, and *function* are related.

Definition

A **correspondence** is a relation.

We can define *function* in terms of correspondences.

Definition (alternate)

A **function** is a correspondence from one set (the **domain**) to a second set (the **codomain**), in which no element of the domain corresponds to more than one element of the codomain.

Below is a function called "adding $\frac{1}{3}$," a correspondence from the set of integers to the set of rational numbers. We list only a few of the infinitely many elements in the domain and codomain.

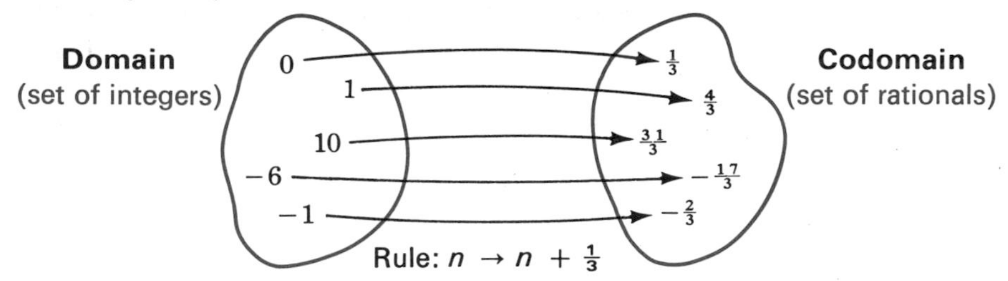

If p stands for the number (in the codomain) which corresponds to n (in the domain), then the equation $p = n + \frac{1}{3}$ is a formula for the correspondence. If we write the correspondence using ordered pairs, a few pairs would be:

$(0, \frac{1}{3})$ $\quad$ $(1, \frac{4}{3})$ $\quad$ $(10, \frac{31}{3})$ $\quad$ $(-6, -\frac{17}{3})$ $\quad$ $(-1, -\frac{2}{3})$

The next two graphs show that this correspondence is part of a linear function you have known for a long time. The domain and codomain are different, but the rule is the same.

$p = n + \frac{1}{3}$		$y = x + \frac{1}{3}$	
Domain:	the set of integers	*Domain:*	the set of reals
Codomain:	the set of rationals	*Codomain:*	the set of reals

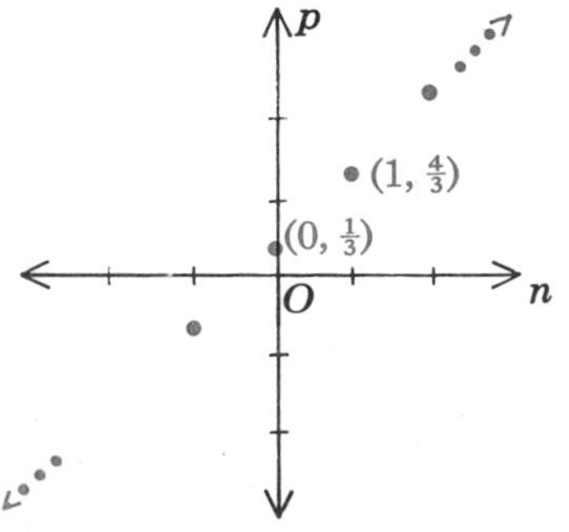

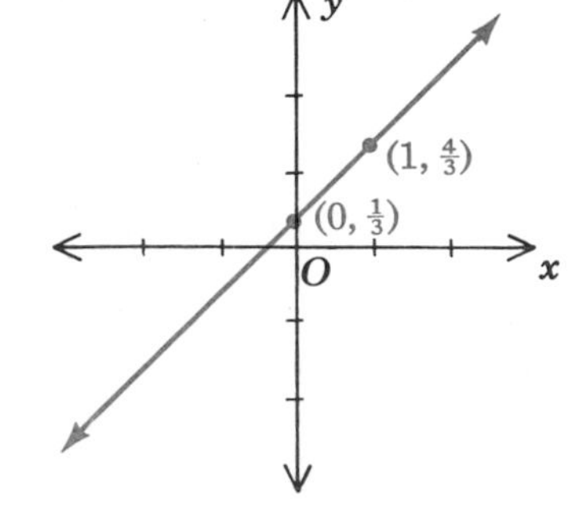

Not every correspondence from a set A to a set B is a function. If an element from A corresponds to more than one element from B, then we have two ordered pairs with the same first component—so the set of ordered pairs cannot be a function.

As an example, the "square root" correspondence from the positive real numbers to all real numbers is *not* a function. A few of the corresponding elements are shown below. (Notice that 4 corresponds to two elements, 2 and -2, in the codomain.)

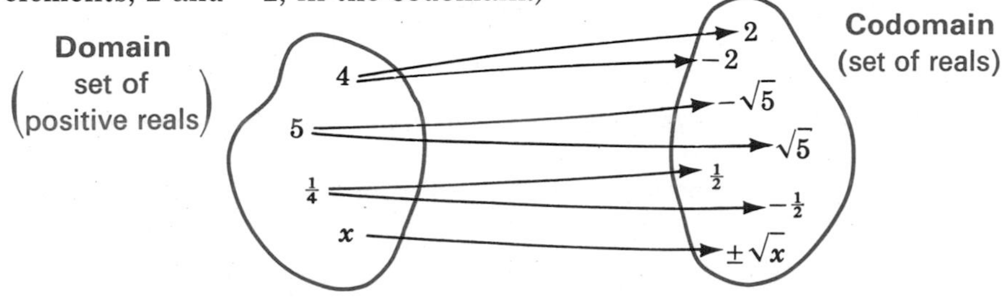

The ordered pairs of a correspondence always involve all members of the domain, but not necessarily all members of the codomain. For example, in the correspondence $p = n + \frac{1}{3}$, the only rational numbers which are possible second components are those which are $\frac{1}{3}$ greater than some integer. No other rationals are used. Nevertheless, it is easier to consider the set of *all* rational numbers as the codomain.

The particular set of elements within the codomain which are used in a correspondence or function is called the **range** of the correspondence or function.

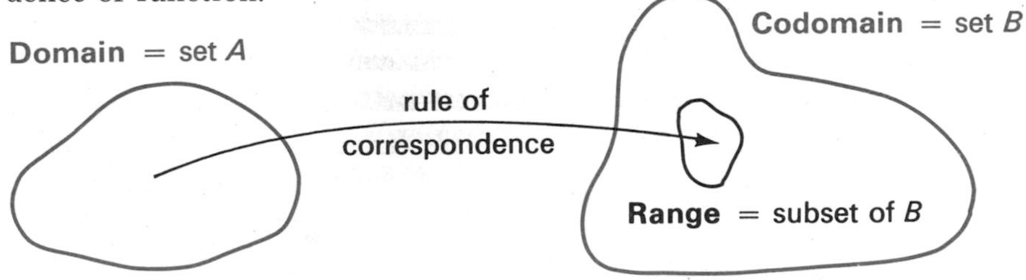

Let's consider an example with elements other than numbers. Suppose 5 students take a test which has 100 possible points. Then, to each student there corresponds a score.

Adam → 78
Brenda → 85
Curt → 46
Della → 91
Eve → 83

Domain = {Adam, Brenda, Curt, Della, Eve}

Codomain = $\{0, 1, 2, 3, \cdots, 98, 99, 100\}$

Range = $\{78, 85, 46, 91, 83\}$

Rule: $x \rightarrow x$'s score on the test.

Since each student receives only one score, this is a function.

EXERCISES 13.2

Ⓐ **1–5.** Consider the correspondence listed below.

$2 \to 4 \qquad 2 \to 5 \qquad 3 \to 5 \qquad 4 \to 2$

1. If you describe this correspondence as a set of ordered pairs, what ordered pairs do you get?
2. The correspondence is *not* a function. Why?
3. Give the domain of the correspondence.
4. Give the range of the correspondence.
5. Give a possible codomain of the correspondence.

6. The words *correspondence* and ____ mean the same thing.
7. Give the definition of *function* as a special kind of *relation.*
8. Give the alternate definition of *function* as a special kind of correspondence.

9–12. Consider the correspondence with rule $x \to x^2$, where x may be any real number.

9. Give the domain.
10. Give the range.
11. Give an equation describing this correspondence.
12. Is this correspondence a function?

13–15. Give the *domain* and *range* of each correspondence graphed below.

13.

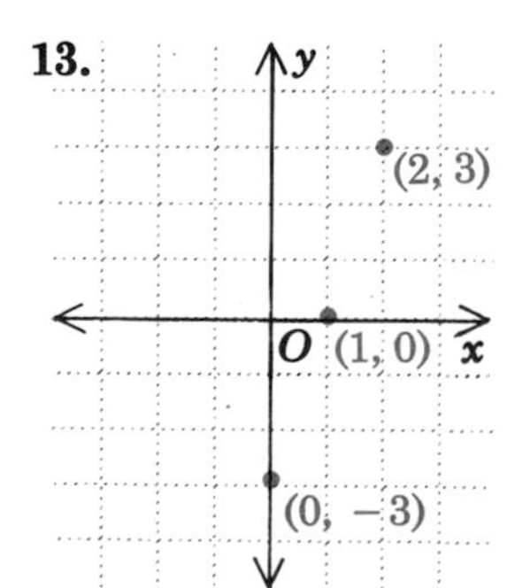

14.

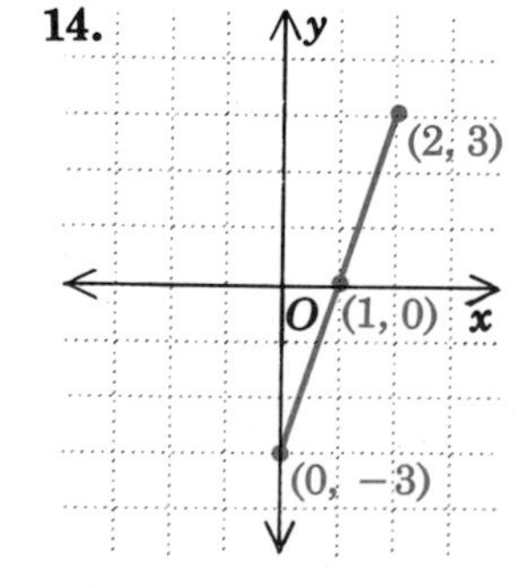

15.

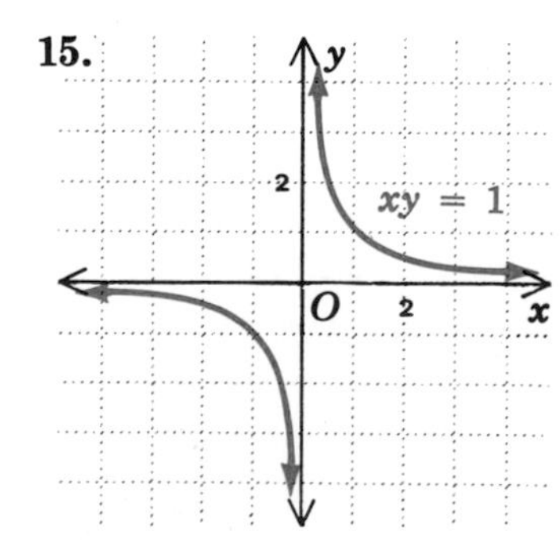

16. Is every correspondence a function?
17. Is every function a correspondence?

18. What is the difference between the codomain and the range of a function?

19. Give an example of a function whose domain is not a set of numbers.

20–26. A function has the given domain and the given rule or equation. Find the range of the function.

20. domain: $\{2, 3, 4, 5\}$ rule: $n \to 2n$

21. domain: $\{4, 6, 8, 10\}$ rule: $n \to \frac{1}{2}n$

Ⓑ 22. domain: the set of integers rule: $p \to 2p$

23. domain: the set of integers rule: $q \to 2q + 1$

24. domain: $\{3, 2, 1, 0\}$ sentence: $y = 5x - 2$

25. domain: the set of reals sentence: $y = 5x - 2$

26. domain: the set of integers rule: $x \to |x|$

27–32. Each equation describes a function whose codomain is the set of real numbers. What real numbers cannot possibly be in the domain?

27. $y = \sqrt{x}$

28. $4y = \sqrt{3 - x}$

29. $xy = 2$

30. $(x - 5)y = 8$

31. $y = x^2 + 3x$

32. $y = 4 + \frac{1}{x}$

33. True or False? Every 1–1 correspondence is a function. Explain your answer.

34. A function has the set of positive integers as its domain and the set of negative integers as its range. Give a possible rule for the function.

Ⓒ **35–38.** Each equation describes a function whose domain is the set of reals. Give the range.

35. $y = -x^2$

36. $y = 2x - 8$

37. $y = |x|$

38. $y - 5 = 3(x + 2)^2$

39–44. For the functions described in Exercises **27–32**, give one real number which cannot possibly be in the range.

45. A function has domain $\{1, 3, 5, 7\}$ and range $\{3, 6, 9, 12\}$. Find a rule for the function.

13.3 TRANSFORMATION—A SPECIAL TYPE OF FUNCTION

The domain and codomain of a function do not have to be sets of numbers. In Section 4.2, a transformation was defined as "a 1–1 correspondence between sets of points."

Since a 1–1 correspondence is a function, an alternate definition of *transformation* can be given in the language of functions.

Definition (alternate)

A **transformation** is a 1–1 function whose domain and range are sets of points.

In this course you have studied transformations *of the plane.* For each point of the plane the corresponding image is exactly one point of the plane. So, if M stands for a plane, a transformation is a function with domain M and range M.

For example, the transformation $r_{x\text{-axis}}$ contains the following pairs of corresponding elements of M.

	Domain = M		Range = M
	(3, 4)	⟶	(3, −4)
	(11, 146)	⟶	(11, −146)
	(−2, −3)	⟶	(−2, 3)
In general,	(x, y)	⟶	$(x, -y)$

Many of the ideas which you learned about transformations are quite general and apply to *all* functions. Among these are:

(1) the *use of one letter* to stand for a transformation (or function).

(2) the idea of a transformation (or function) as a *mapping.*

(3) the *notation* for images (or range elements).

We now discuss these ideas. If T is a transformation, then $T(P)$ stands for the point which corresponds to a point P under the transformation. Now think of a *squaring function,* which we denote by s. If the domain is the real numbers, some ordered pairs would be:

$$2 \rightarrow 4, \qquad -10 \rightarrow 100, \qquad 5 \rightarrow 25.$$

We say s *maps* 2 onto 4, −10 onto 100, and so forth. We write $s(2) = 4$, $s(-10) = 100$, $s(5) = 25$, $s(\frac{1}{8}) = \frac{1}{64}$, and so forth.

s(x) is the number which corresponds to x.

That is, $x \to s(x)$.

For the squaring function, $x \to x^2$.

So we can write, $s(x) = x^2$.

Or, $y = x^2$.

The letter f is most commonly used for functions. For a function f, $f(x)$ is called the *value* of the function f at x. In arrow notation, $f: x \to f(x)$. For example, if $f(x) = x + x^2$, then $f(3) = 3 + 3^2 = 12$. We say that 12 is the *value* of f when x is 3. Values of a function are like images in a transformation.

x		$f(x) = x + x^2$
3	$\longrightarrow$	$f(3) = 12$
10	$\longrightarrow$	$f(10) = 110$
$\frac{1}{2}$	$\longrightarrow$	$f(\frac{1}{2}) = \frac{3}{4}$
-3	$\longrightarrow$	$f(-3) = 6$
0	$\longrightarrow$	$f(0) = 0$

For a function f, $f(x)$ is always the second component of an ordered pair, with x as the first component. Letting y stand for $f(x)$, we have $y = f(x) = x + x^2$. So

$y = x + x^2$ ⟸ is equivalent to ⟹ $f(x) = x + x^2$.

Examples: Notations for functions

1. Let g be a function with $g(x) = 2x^2 - 4x + 1$. That is, g maps x onto $2x^2 - 4x + 1$.

   By substitution:
   $$\begin{aligned} g(0) &= 2(0)^2 - 4(0) + 1 = 1 \\ g(6) &= 2(6)^2 - 4(6) + 1 = 49 \\ g(-2) &= 2(-2)^2 - 4(-2) + 1 = 17 \\ &\vdots \end{aligned}$$

2. Suppose f is a function and $f: m \to 3\sqrt{m} + 6$.

   Then $f: 2 \to 3\sqrt{2} + 6$.

   That is, f maps 2 onto $3\sqrt{2} + 6$.

   Or, $f(2) = 3\sqrt{2} + 6$.

3. The function t with the rule $t(a) = -4a + 5$ is a linear function. In arrow notation, $t: a \to -4a + 5$. Some ordered pairs of t are $(30, -115)$, $(0, 5)$, $(-2, 13)$, and $(1, 1)$. To graph t, we might let $b = t(a)$ and graph the solution set to $b = -4a + 5$.

The following table summarizes the relationships among functions, relations, correspondences, and transformations. Notice that a transformation is a special kind of function, which is a special kind of correspondence or relation.

Word	Meaning
correspondence (relation)	set of ordered pairs
function	set of ordered pairs no two with the same first component
transformation	1–1 function between sets of points

EXERCISES 13.3

Ⓐ **1–3.** Consider: *transformation, function, relation,* and *correspondence.*

1. Which is synonymous with *relation*?

2. Which is a type of *function*?

3. Which term is the most specific?

4. Define *transformation* in terms of *function.*

5–9. Suppose $f: x \to x - 2x^2$. Calculate.

5. $f(2)$ **6.** $f(10)$ **7.** $f(-1)$ **8.** $f(0)$ **9.** $f(-2)$

10–14. Let $g(n) = |n - 5|$. Calculate.

10. $g(0)$ **11.** $g(6)$ **12.** $g(4)$ **13.** $g(5)$ **14.** $g(-4)$

15–19. $h: x \to x + 3$. Find the value of h for each given value of x.

15. 3 **16.** 2 **17.** 11 **18.** 0 **19.** t

20–24. Let $y = f(x)$ and $f(x) = 2\sqrt{x + 3}$. Find y for each value of x.

20. 13 **21.** 3 **22.** -2 **23.** 97 **24.** a

25–30. Name 3 ordered pairs in the function.

25. $f: n \to -n^3$ **26.** $g(x) = 4x - 2$ **27.** $h: x \to |x|$

28. $s(m) = 7m + 7$ **29.** $t(m) = 4\frac{1}{2}$ **30.** $f(a) = \sin a$

Ⓑ **31–33.** The domain of each function is the set of real numbers between 3 and -3. Graph each function.

31. $f(x) = x^2$ **32.** $g(x) = 2 - 4x$ **33.** $h: x \to \frac{1}{3}x$

34–43. The domain of h is the set of complex numbers, and $h: x \to x^2 - 4x + 8$. Calculate.

34. $h(2)$ **35.** $h(i)$ **36.** $h(2 + i)$ **37.** $h(0)$ **38.** $h(3i)$

39. $h(x)$ **40.** $h(a + 1)$ **41.** $h(x + 1)$ **42.** $h(-x)$ **43.** $h(2x)$

44. Given that $f(2) = 4$ and $f(3) = 6$, which is *not* possible?

a. $f(x) = 2x$ **b.** $f(4) = 16$ **c.** $f(x) = 2(x - 2)^2 + 4$

d. $f(3) = 9$ **e.** none of the preceding

45. If $h: x \to x^2 + 4x + 3$, find $h(x - 2)$.

46. If $g: n \to n^2 - 3n + 2$, find two values of n for which $g(n) = 0$.

47. If $f(x) = x^2 + x - 1$, find all solutions to $f(x) = 0$.

Ⓒ **48–55.** Let S be the set of all people. For each appropriate x in S, let $f(x)$ = the father of x, $m(x)$ = the mother of x, $h(x)$ = the husband of x, $w(x)$ = the wife of x, and $s(x)$ = the youngest sister of x. What name should be given to each of the following?

48. f(John Quincy Adams) **49.** h(Marie Curie)

50. h(Queen Victoria) **51.** $f(f$(Benjamin Harrison))

52. $m(f(x))$ **53.** $s(m(x))$ **54.** $s(m(m(x)))$ **55.** $h(w(x))$

COMPOSITES OF FUNCTIONS 13.4

Let f be the function "adding 5." Then $f(x) = x + 5$. Let s be the squaring function $s(x) = x^2$. As with transformations, we may form the *composite* $s \circ f$ of these functions by first applying f, then s.

If $x = 2$ ▶ $s \circ f(2) = s(f(2)) = s(7) = 49$

For *any x* in the domain ▶ $s \circ f(x) = s(f(x)) = s(x + 5) = (x + 5)^2$

In arrow notation ▶ $s \circ f: x \to (x + 5)^2$

So, in the composite function, each domain element is mapped to the square of 5 more than itself.

Recall that the identity transformation maps each point onto itself. Similarly, the **identity function** maps each member of the domain onto itself. That is, if I is the identity function, then for any x in the domain,

$$I(x) = x.$$

If we let y stand for $I(x)$, then $y = x$. You should see that if the domain of I is the set of real numbers, then the graph of the identity function is the line $y = x$.

The *identity function* receives its name because it is the *identity* for the operation of composition. It is the "do nothing" function.

Theorem 13.4.1

Let I be the identity function. Then for any function f,

$$I \circ f = f \circ I = f.$$

PROOF: The proof is identical to that of Theorem 9.6.1. The only difference between the theorems is that this theorem is more general. It applies to *any* functions.

Under the operation of composition, certain functions have *inverses* (or *inverse functions*). As with transformations, an inverse *undoes* what the function did. For instance, if f is the function "adding 5," then

$$f: x \to x + 5.$$

If you add 5 to a number, how can you get back to the original number? The answer is simple—by subtracting 5. The function "subtracting 5" has the rule

$$x \to x - 5$$

and can be denoted by the symbol f^{-1}. If $f(x) = x + 5$, then $f^{-1}(x) = x - 5$. That is, $f^{-1}: x \to x - 5$.

INVERSE FUNCTIONS

x		$f(x) = x + 5$
2	$\to$	7
-1.4	$\to$	3.6
π	$\to$	$\pi + 5$

x		$f^{-1}(x) = x - 5$
7	$\to$	2
3.6	$\to$	-1.4
$\pi + 5$	$\to$	π

The basic relationship between a function and its inverse is,

If $f: a \to b$, then $f^{-1}: b \to a$.

In other words, the components of the ordered pairs of a function are switched in the inverse function.

So, when we graph f and f^{-1}, they are reflection images of each other over the line $y = x$. See the example at the right.

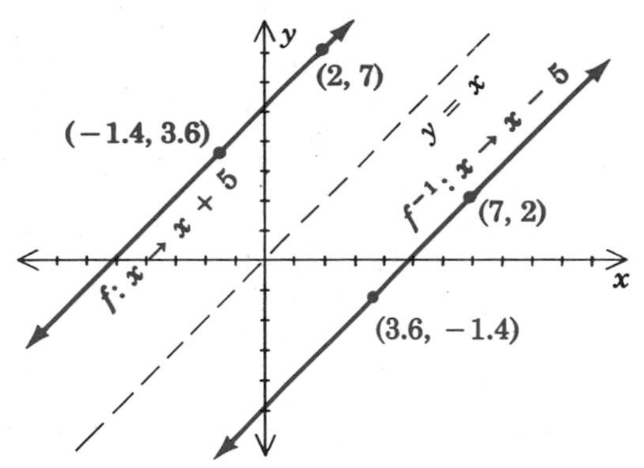

Not every function has an inverse because switching components of ordered pairs sometimes does not yield a function.

For example, if a function contains (3, 6) and (4, 6), then its inverse would have to contain (6, 3) and (6, 4), but no function can contain these two points. We conclude that, to have an inverse, a function cannot map two distinct members of the domain onto the same member of the range. This is summed up in the next theorem.

Theorem 13.4.2

A function has an inverse if and only if it is a 1–1 correspondence between its domain and range.

The squaring function is not a 1–1 correspondence. For example, both 2 and −2 are mapped onto 4. So the squaring function has no inverse. This is verified by examining the graph of $s(x) = x^2$.

When this graph is reflected over the line $y = x$, we see that the image cannot be the graph of a function.

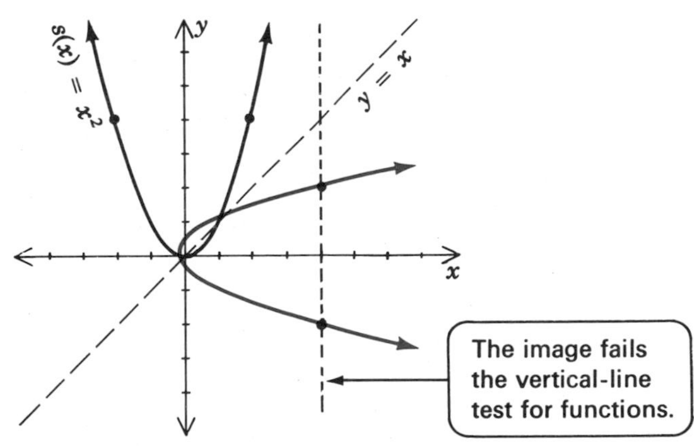

In the graph above, if the line used for the vertical-line test was reflected back over the line $y = x$, it would intersect the graph of the function *horizontally in two points.* This suggests a simpler way to check whether or not a function has an inverse.

Theorem 13.4.3

Horizontal-line test for inverse functions: A function has an inverse if and only if no *horizontal* line intersects it in more than one point.

Finding an equation for the inverse of a function is easy. Use Theorem 12.8.1c to reflect the graph over the line $y = x$.

Theorem 13.4.4

If a function f with equation $y = f(x)$ has an inverse f^{-1}, then an equation for f^{-1} may be found by switching x and y.

Example: Find the inverse of $f: x \to 3x - 2$.

SOLUTION: Equation for f $\Rightarrow y = 3x - 2$

switch x and y

Equations for f^{-1} $\Rightarrow x = 3y - 2$

solve for y

$\Rightarrow y = \frac{1}{3}x + \frac{2}{3}$

EXERCISES 13.4

Ⓐ **1–5.** Let $t(x) = x^2 - 1$. Calculate.

1. $t(1)$ **2.** $t(-2)$ **3.** $t(0)$ **4.** $t(100)$ **5.** $t(-\frac{1}{2})$

6–10. Use function t from Exercises **1–5**, and let $g(x) = x + 6$. Calculate.

6. $g(t(1))$ **7.** $g(t(-2))$ **8.** $g(t(0))$ **9.** $g(t(100))$ **10.** $g(t(-\frac{1}{2}))$

11. In the symbolism $f \circ g$, which function is applied first?

12–14. Use functions g and t from Exercises **1–10**.

12. The function $g \circ t$ maps 10 onto what number?

13. The function $t \circ g$ maps 10 onto what number?

14. $g \circ t$ is called the ____ of g and t.

15. The identity function maps 15 onto what number?

16. Describe the graph of the identity function.

17. A 1–1 function maps 12 onto -3. If the function has an inverse, what can you say about the inverse?

18. When does a function have an inverse?

19. How does the graph of a function show whether or not the function has an inverse?

20. Given the graph of a function, how can you determine the graph of its inverse?

21. What is the meaning of the symbol f^{-1} if f is a function?

22. Given an equation for a function, and given that the function has an inverse, how can you find an equation for the inverse?

23–25. Find an equation for the inverse of each function.

23. $3x + 5y = -12$ **24.** $xy = -5$ **25.** $y = x^3 + 413.2$

Ⓑ **26–30.** Find $f \circ g(x)$ when f and g are as given.

26. $f: x \to x^3$ $g: x \to 3x$

27. $f: n \to 2n + 5$ $g: m \to -7m + 6$

28. $f: a \to a$ $g: x \to 6$

29. $f(x) = x^2 + 3x$ $g(x) = -x^2 + 1$

30. f maps t onto $t + 14$ g maps t onto $3t$

31. Find five ordered pairs of the correspondence $n \to 2^n$ and five ordered pairs in the inverse correspondence.

32. What is the inverse of the function "multiplying by 30"?

33. Find a rule for the inverse of the correspondence $n \to \frac{n}{6}$.

34. Graph the function $y = x^2$ when its domain is the positive real numbers. Graph the inverse of this function, and give its equation.

35. Which of these functions does *not* have an inverse?

a. $y = 4x$ **b.** $y = x + 4$ **c.** $y = x^4$ **d.** all of the preceding

36. Find an equation for the inverse of the linear function $f: x \to 8x + 9$.

Ⓒ **37.** If a linear function has slope 2, what is the slope of its inverse? (HINT: Try some examples.)

38. True or False? If $f(x) = ax$ and $g(x) = \frac{x}{a}$, and $a \neq 0$, then $f \circ g$ is the identity.

39. If L_1 is a linear function with slope m_1, and L_2 is a linear function with slope m_2, what is the slope of $L_1 \circ L_2$? Give at least one example to back up your answer.

40. If $A: x \to x + k$, $B: x \to ax$, $C: x \to x^2$, and $D: x \to x - h$, then $A \circ B \circ C \circ D: x \to$ ______.

13.5 TERMINOLOGY ASSOCIATED WITH FUNCTIONS

For any function f, given $y = f(x)$, we say *y is a function of x.* The variable (often x) which stands for any member of the domain is called the **independent variable**. The variable (often y) which stands for any member of the codomain is called the **dependent variable.** The value of the dependent variable *depends* on what value is chosen for the independent variable.

For example, in the formula

$$A = \frac{s^2\sqrt{3}}{4}$$

each value of s determines a *unique* corresponding value of A. We can think of s as the independent variable and A as the dependent variable. The function f, where

$$f: s \to A \quad \text{or} \quad f(s) = \frac{s^2\sqrt{3}}{4} \quad (s > 0),$$

maps the length of a side onto the area of an equilateral triangle. Of course, the area depends on the length of a side. We could write $f(s) = A$ and say, "*the area is a function of the length of a side.*"

A function may have more than one independent variable. The formula

$$R_{90}(x, y) = (-y, x)$$

indicates that the function R_{90} has two independent variables, x and y. That is, the values (images) of the function depend on both x and y. If we write

$$R_{90}(x, y) = (x', y'),$$

then x' and y' are the two dependent variables.

The familiar operation *addition* may be thought of as a function with *two independent variables*, the *addends* (numbers being added), and *one dependent variable*, the *sum.*

We can describe this function in symbols as at the right.

Name of function ↓	Addends ↓↓		Sum ↓	
a:	(x, y)	$\to$	s	This is more specific.
a:	(x, y)	$\to$	$x + y$	
a:	$(2, 3)$	$\to$	5	Examples
a:	$(200, 14)$	$\to$	214	
a:	$(-3, 5)$	$\to$	2	

Similarly, multiplication, division, and subtraction are also functions with two independent variables and one dependent variable.

The functions which you have graphed have one independent variable and one dependent variable. But the preceding examples show that a function may have any number of independent and dependent variables.

When the range of a function consists of real numbers and there is only one dependent variable, the function may have a **maximum value** or a **minimum value**.

Examples: Maximum or minimum values of functions

1. The finite function $\{(2, 5), (-6, -100), (4, 30)\}$ has maximum value 30 and minimum value -100.

2. $\{(x, y): y = x^2\}$ has minimum value 0, *no* maximum value.

3. If a function is graphed, finding a maximum or minimum is easy. Just look at how high or low the graph goes. See graph **I**.

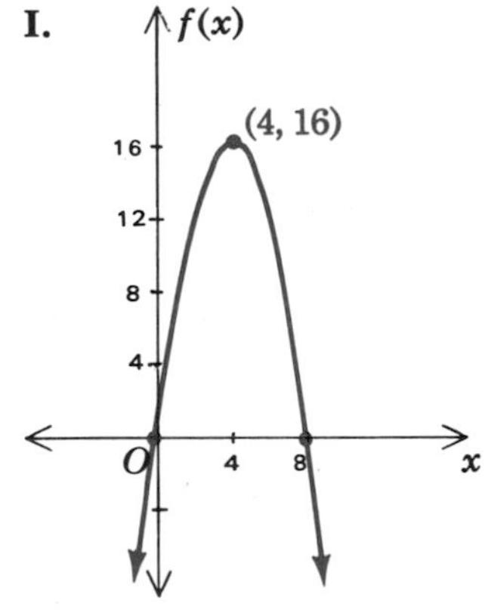

Function: $x \to 8x - x^2$

Domain: {all real numbers}

Maximum value: 16

Minimum value: none

4. Restricting the domain of a function can change the maximum or minimum value. See graph **II**.

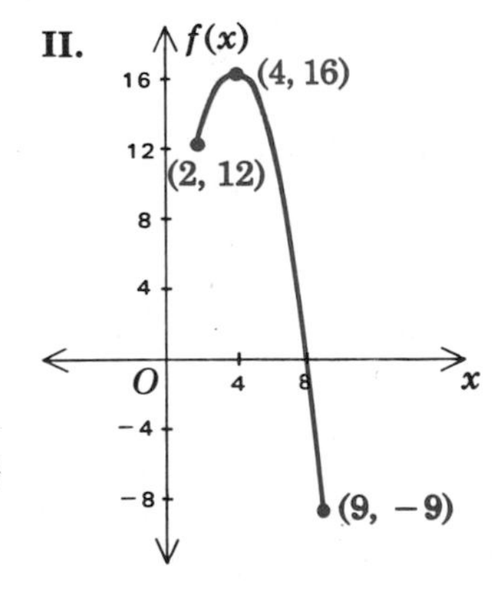

Function: $x \to 8x - x^2$

Domain: $\{x: 2 \leq x \leq 9\}$

Maximum value: 16

Minimum value: -9

5. The linear function $\{(x, y): y = x + 5\}$ has no maximum or minimum value.

EXERCISES 13.5

Ⓐ 1–2. If f is a function and $b = f(z)$, which letter is the:

1. independent variable?
2. dependent variable?

3. Can a function have three independent variables?

4–7. Give the number of dependent and independent variables.

4. $f(x, y) = (2x, 3y)$
5. $f(x, y) = xy$
6. $f(a, b, c, d) = \frac{1}{4}(a + b + c + d)$
7. $f(x) = x^2 - 3x + 6$

8. Those functions which are graphed on the coordinate plane have how many independent variables? Dependent variables?

9. What is the maximum value of a function?

10. Is it possible for a function to have no minimum value?

11. How can you tell the maximum value of a function from its graph?

12. Give an example of a function with both *maximum* and *minimum* values.

13–16. Find the maximum and minimum values if $-3 \leq x \leq 3$.

13. $f\colon x \to x^2$
14. $g(x) = -x^2$
15. $\{(1, 2), (3, 5), (9, -1)\}$
16. $y = 2x - 10$

Ⓑ **17–20.** Give the maximum and minimum values of each function. In each case the domain is the set of real numbers. Graphing may help.

17. $\{(x, y)\colon y = -x^2\}$
18. $\{(a, b)\colon -3a + 6 = b\}$
19. $\{(c, d)\colon d + 7 = (c - 2)^2\}$
20. $f\colon x \to -(x + 8)^2 + 11$

21. If the graph of a function is a parabola with horizontal directrix, the maximum or minimum value is the second coordinate of the _____.

22–25. Find the maximum or minimum value of the function.

22. $y = x^2 - 4x + 3$
23. $y - 8 = -3x^2 + 5$

Ⓒ 24. $y = \sqrt{(x + 3)^2 + 4}$

25. $y = -8x^2 + 2x + 11$

26. Two numbers add to -10. What is the largest product they can have?

27. What is the largest (in area) rectangular garden that can be enclosed by 100 metres of fence?

28. A company now sells 500,000 units of a product at \$9 each. For every dollar increase in the cost of a unit, sales are expected to drop by 50,000 units. What price will give the most income?

29. A transit line has 100,000 customers, each paying 40¢. It is estimated that for every nickel the fare is raised, 5000 customers are lost. Should the transit line raise its fares?

FUNCTIONS OF VARIATION

DIRECT VARIATION

Suppose a worker is paid by the hour and receives $4.50 per hour with no rate increase for overtime. Then the amount of pay, P, depends upon the number of hours, H, worked. So, we could consider H as an independent variable and P as a dependent variable. These variables are related by the simple equation

$$P = 4.50H.$$

Now, if H is doubled, so is P. That is, for working twice as long, this person would receive twice as much pay. If H is multiplied by any number, then P must be multiplied by the same number in order to satisfy the above equation. So, we say that *P varies directly as H.* The function which maps H onto P is called a *function of direct variation.*

Definition

Let k be a constant and $y = kx$. The solution set for this equation is called a **function of direct variation**.

We call k the *constant of variation.* The graphs of functions of direct variation are lines which go through the origin and have slope k. So you have already studied these functions.

Consider some ordered pairs of the function $P = 4.50H$ above.

$(1, 4.50)$ $(4, 18)$ $(12, 54)$ $(10, 45)$ $(\frac{1}{2}, 2.25)$

Take any two of these ordered pairs, (x_1, y_1) and (x_2, y_2). Then

$$\frac{x_1}{x_2} = \frac{y_1}{y_2}.$$

In such cases, we say that x and y are *directly proportional.*

For example, $\frac{12}{10} = \frac{54}{45}.$

That is, the amount this person earns is directly proportional to the number of hours he works.

When two variables are *directly* proportional, multiplying one of them by some number causes the other to be *multiplied* by the same number.

INVERSE VARIATION

Some variables are related so that when one is multiplied by 2, the other is multiplied by $\frac{1}{2}$. To be more general, when one variable is multiplied by k, the other is multiplied by $\frac{1}{k}$. For example, consider the length and width of a rectangle whose area is 100.

$$\text{Since } A = \ell w: \quad 100 = \ell w$$

$$\text{Solving for } w: \quad w = \frac{100}{\ell}$$

Consider w as the independent variable. One ordered pair which works is (25, 4). If we double 25, then we are looking for an ordered pair (50, ?). You can see that the pair is (50, 2). Doubling one variable causes the other to be multiplied by $\frac{1}{2}$. We say *w varies inversely as ℓ*. The function that maps ℓ onto w is called a *function of inverse variation*.

Definition

Let k be a constant and $y = \frac{k}{x}$. The solution set for this equation is called a **function of inverse variation**.

The graphs for functions of inverse variation are hyperbolas which have the x and y axes as asymptotes. In fact, all functions of direct or inverse variation have graphs which are scale transformations of one of those below.

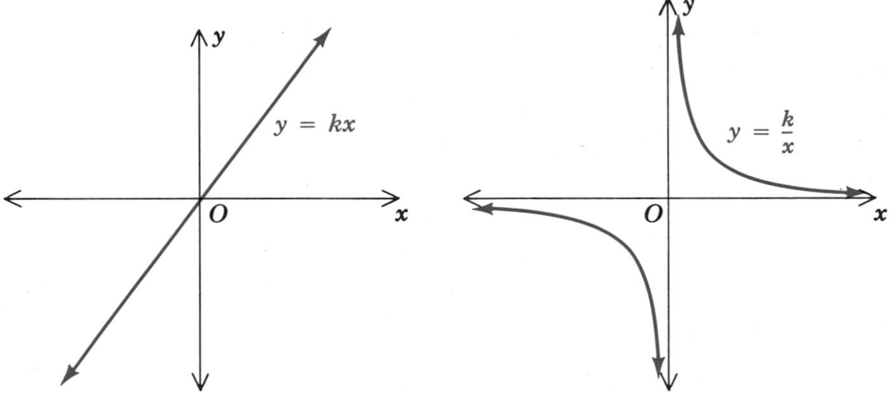

Now, consider some solutions to $w = \frac{100}{\ell}$.

(10, 10), (20, 5), $(3, \frac{100}{3})$, (50, 2), (2, 50), (1, 100)

For any two ordered pairs (x_1, y_1) and (x_2, y_2),

$$y_1 = \frac{100}{x_1} \quad \text{and} \quad y_2 = \frac{100}{x_2}.$$

$$x_1y_1 = 100 \quad \text{and} \quad x_2y_2 = 100$$

$$\text{So,} \quad x_1y_1 = x_2y_2$$

$$\text{Dividing by } x_2y_1, \quad \frac{x_1}{x_2} = \frac{y_2}{y_1}$$

In such cases, we say that x and y are *inversely proportional*.

$$\text{For example,} \quad \frac{50}{20} = \frac{5}{2}.$$

When two variables are *inversely* proportional, multiplying one of them by some number causes the other to be *divided* by the same number.

Suppose $y = \frac{k}{x}$ and $x = d^2$. Then, by substitution, $y = \frac{k}{d^2}$, and we say that y varies inversely as d^2. This relationship occurs when y is sound intensity and d is the distance from a sound source, such as a rock group.

That is, the sound volume is inversely proportional to the square of the distance from the source. So, a person who moves to a position 3 times farther from the source will hear sound $\frac{1}{9}$ as intense.

EXERCISES 13.6

Ⓐ **1.** If y varies *directly* as x, what happens to y when x is doubled?

2. If y varies *inversely* as x, what happens to y when x is doubled?

3–5. The solution set of the given equation is a function of which type of variation—direct or inverse?

3. $y = 10x$ **4.** $x = 10y$ **5.** $xy = 10$

6. In what type of function are elements of the domain directly proportional to elements of the range?

7. Suppose x is directly proportional to y. If x is multiplied by 12, what happens to y?

8. Suppose x is inversely proportional to y. If x is multiplied by -1.5, what happens to y?

9. Write an equation which shows that y varies directly as x.

10. Write an equation which shows that Q varies inversely as $3t$.

11. A function of direct variation contains (3, 15). Find the constant of variation.

12. Repeat Exercise **11** for a function of inverse variation.

13–14. Describe the graphs for functions of:

13. direct variation.

14. inverse variation.

Ⓑ 15. If the area of a rectangle is constant, its length will be ____ proportional to its width.

16. Suppose x is directly proportional to y. If 3 is added to x, what happens to y?

17. If y varies directly as x, and $y = 6$ when $x = 10$, find y when $x = 14$.

18. If T varies inversely as v, and $T = -3$ when $v = 12$, find v when $T = 6$.

19. If y varies directly as $x - 2$, and $y = 10$ when $x = 22$, find y when x is 100.

20–21. Find the constant of variation.

20. The circumference of a circle varies directly as the diameter.

21. The area of a circle varies directly as the square of its radius.

22. The intensity of sound is ____ proportional to the ____ of the distance from the source of sound.

23. The volume of a regular tetrahedron varies directly as the cube of one side. If a regular tetrahedron of side 6 has volume $18\sqrt{2}$, what is the volume of such a tetrahedron of side 8?

24–27. Give the effect on y if (**a**) x is doubled, (**b**) x is tripled, (**c**) x is multiplied by 6, (**d**) x is halved, and (**e**) x is divided by 5.

24. y is directly proportional to x^3.

25. $y = \frac{2}{x^2}$ **26.** $xy = 10$ **27.** $y = \frac{2}{x^3}$

28. If variables A and B are inversely proportional, which is true?

a. AB is constant. **b.** $A + B$ is constant. **c.** $\frac{A}{B}$ is constant.

29. Repeat Exercise **28** if A and B are directly proportional.

30–34. *Laws of physics.* Translate each statement into an equation. Identify the variables used. (Each statement is theoretically true.)

30. The illumination produced on a screen by a point source of light varies inversely as the square of the distance of the screen from the source.

31. *Hooke's law.* The stress on a solid substance is directly proportional to the strain produced (provided the stress is less than the elastic limit of the substance).

32. *Boyle's law.* For low pressures, the pressure of an ideal gas kept at constant temperature varies inversely with the volume of the gas.

33. *Charles' law.* For low pressures, the density of an ideal gas kept at constant pressure varies inversely with the absolute temperature of the gas.

34. *Malus' law.* The intensity of a beam of plane-polarized light varies directly as the square of the cosine of the angle through which the polarizer is rotated from the position that gives maximum intensity.

© **35–37.** Use reference materials if needed.

35. The surface area of a sphere is directly proportional to the square of the radius. Find the constant of variation.

36. The volume of a sphere is directly proportional to the cube of its radius. Find the constant of variation.

37. Distance in metres is directly proportional to distance in yards. Approximate the constant of variation.

38–41. You are sitting in the 20th row at a concert in which the first row is right next to the speakers. How will the intensity of the sound you hear compare to that for a person sitting in the given row? (Assume there are no amplifiers except on the stage.)

38. 5th row **39.** 15th row **40.** 50th row **41.** 1st row

13.7 FUNCTIONS WITH SEVERAL DEFINING SENTENCES

In Chicago, telephone calls are measured in units, based upon the length of the call and the distance between the callers. The basic 1975 rates for an individual phone are given below.

the first 80 units ----------------	\$6.45
each additional unit from 81 to 200---	0.0575
each additional unit over 200-------	0.0525

From this information a function can be constructed:

number of units → amount of phone bill (before taxes).

Because the number of units used may be 0 or any greater integer, the domain of the function is the nonnegative integers. This function is graphed below.

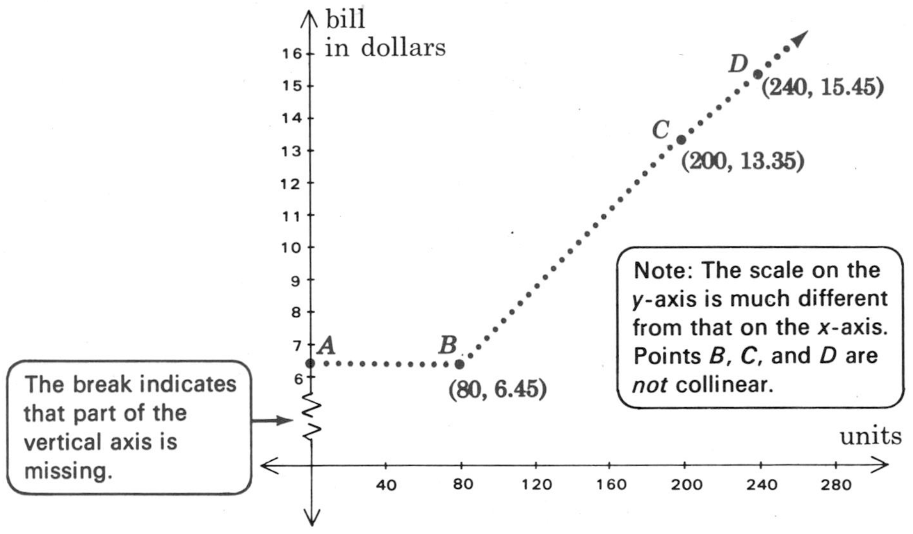

This graph was not hard to construct. You can see that the numbers 0, 80, and 200 are key values of the domain. Bills for these numbers of units were calculated to get points A, B, and C.

Since the bill *increases at a constant rate* from 80 units to 200 units, that part of the graph must lie on $\overline{BC}$. In fact, since the graph goes up 0.0575 for each unit, $\overleftrightarrow{BC}$ has slope 0.0575. ($\overleftrightarrow{BC}$ looks like it has a slope of about 1 because the two axes have different scales.)

When $x > 200$, the line has slope 0.0525. Point D, (240, 15.45), was calculated only to aid in graphing—it is *not* a key point.

You may wonder if there is any single formula to describe this graph. The answer is that there is no *simple*, single formula. But there are equations to describe the three parts of the graph. The phone company could have described its rates as follows.

TELEPHONE RATES		
u = number of units used b = your bill in dollars	(1) If $u \leq 80$,	$b = 6.45$.
	(2) If $81 \leq u \leq 200$,	$b - 6.45 = 0.0575(u - 80)$.
	(3) If $201 \leq u$,	$b - 13.35 = 0.0525(u - 200)$.

The last two equations in the table were found by using the point-slope form for the equation of a line (Theorem 6.6.1).

Most telephone users would probably not be helped by this description of the amount they have to pay. But this type of model is common in mathematics. Many functions have several different rules for finding values, depending on which elements of the domain are used. Some functions of this type involve *absolute value.*

The simplest function involving absolute value can be described by the single equation

$$y = |x|.$$

This function is easily graphed by splitting up the domain into the two parts corresponding to the way absolute value is calculated. (See Theorem 3.3.1.) The graph is an angle.

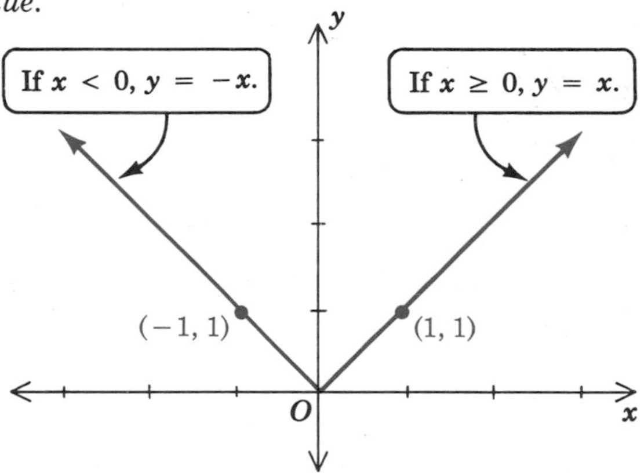

We can find various transformation images for the graph of this function by making substitutions for the variables in the equation.

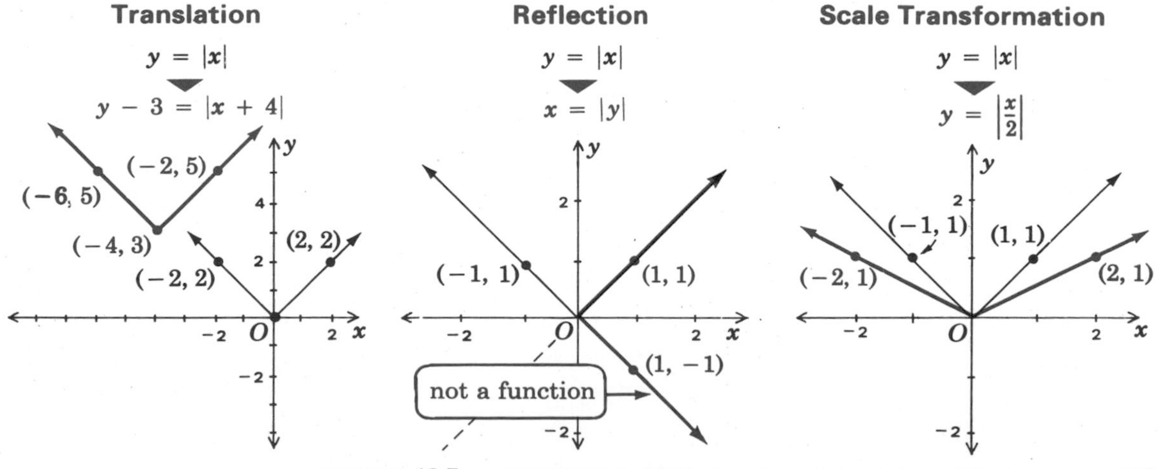

EXERCISES 13.7

Ⓐ **1.** Give an equation for the simplest function involving absolute value.

2. Describe the graph of the function in Exercise **1**.

3–12. A function f is defined by the following equations:

$$\text{If } x \leq 0, \quad f(x) = x^2 - 3x.$$
$$\text{If } 0 < x < 5, \quad f(x) = 2x.$$
$$\text{If } 5 \leq x, \quad f(x) = 12.$$

Calculate:

3. $f(-3)$ **4.** $f(0)$ **5.** $f(2)$ **6.** $f(100)$ **7.** $f(500)$

8. $f(5)$ **9.** $f(\frac{1}{2})$ **10.** $f(2\pi)$ **11.** $f(-2)$ **12.** $f(|-6|)$

Ⓑ **13–17.** Find the monthly telephone bill for the given number of units. Use the formulas of this section.

13. 75 **14.** 100 **15.** 150 **16.** 200 **17.** 300

18–23. Graph the solution set to each sentence. If the sentence describes a function, give the maximum or minimum value of the function.

18. $y + 1 = |x|$ **19.** $y = |x - 2|$ **20.** $y = |2x|$

21. $y \geq |x|$ **22.** $y - 1 = 2|x + 5|$ **23.** $x - 1 = 2|y + 5|$

24–27. Graph each function. In each case, the domain is the set of real numbers.

24. If $x < 1$, $y = x + 1$.
If $x \geq 1$, $y = 2x - 2$.

25. If $x \leq 5$, $f(x) = x$.
If $x > 5$, $f(x) = 5$.

26. $g\colon a \to a^2$ if $-2 \leq a \leq 2$.
$g\colon a \to 4$ if $|a| > 2$.

27. $m(t) = -2$ if t is negative.
$m(t) = 2$ if t is positive.
$m(0) = 0$.

28. A man receives \$5.00 an hour for the first 35 hours worked in a week, and \$7.50 (time and a half) for each additional hour. Graph an appropriate pay function assuming he works no more than 60 hours a week.

29–30. A telephone company charges the rates indicated below.

the first 80 units	\$7.10
each additional unit from 81 to 200	0.0625
each additional unit over 200	0.0575

29. Graph a corresponding rate function. For comparison purposes, on the same set of axes, copy the graph given on page 392.

30. Give equations for the rate function graphed in Exercise **29**.

© **31–33.** Find an equation whose graph is the given angle.

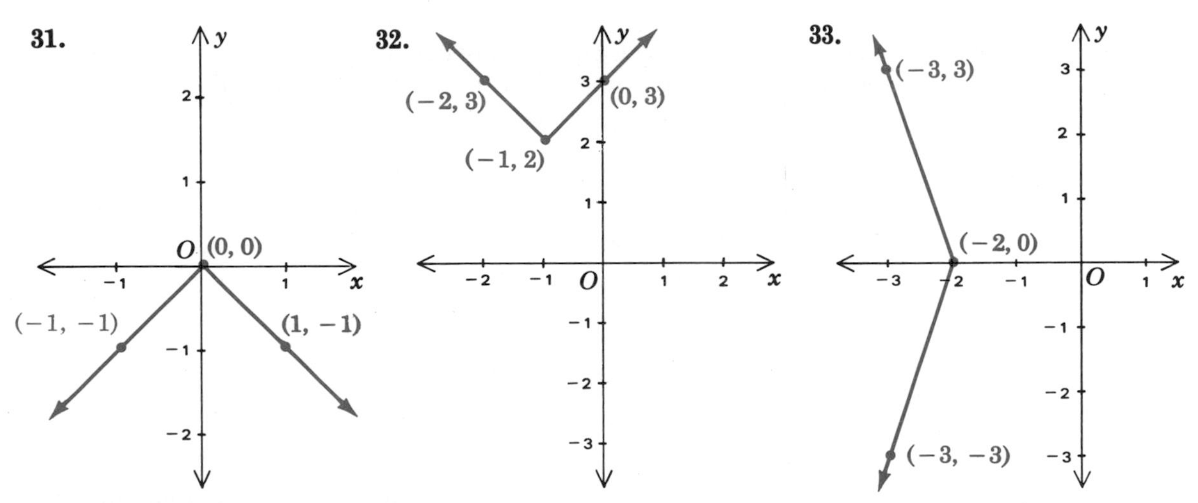

34. Give two different functions containing (2, 5), (1, 6), and (3, 6).

35–37. A telephone company has special package-rate plans for people who use the telephone a lot. Graph the rates for each plan and find equations describing these rates.

35. The basic rate is \$11.25 for the first 200 units, plus 0.0575 for the next 120 units, and 0.0525 for any additional units.

36. The basic rate is \$8.85 for the first 140 units, plus 0.0575 for each of the next 120 units, and 0.0525 for any additional units.

37. You can call as often as you wish for \$22.50. Suppose you use x units per month. For what values of x is it best for you to use the plan described in Exercises **29–30**? When should you use the plan of Exercise **35**? Of Exercise **36**? When should you use the \$22.50 unlimited service?

13.8 FUNCTIONS WITH DISCONNECTED GRAPHS

The symbol [ ] is used with an interesting function which has unexpected applications.

Definition

$[x]$ = the greatest integer less than or equal to x.

Examples: The greatest integer symbol

1. $[4] = 4$	**2.** $[4.1] = 4$	**3.** $[0] = 0$
4. $[-1.3] = -2$	**5.** $[\pi] = 3$	**6.** $[-\pi] = -4$

We now consider the correspondence $x \to [x]$. This correspondence maps each integer onto itself. It also maps all numbers between 3 and 4 onto 3, those between 4 and 5 onto 4, and so forth.

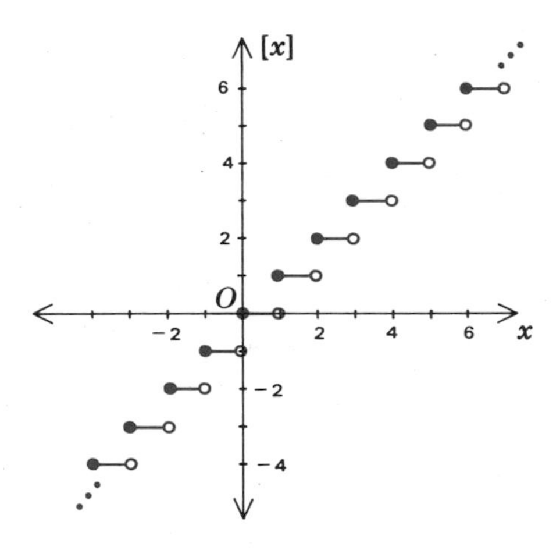

The graph of the correspondence is given at the left. It differs from other graphs you have studied because it is *disconnected.* This occurs because the range of the function consists only of integers. Notice the use of small circles to correspond to points *not* on the graph.

The function with equation $y = [x]$ is known as the **greatest integer function**. Functions with graphs like this one are called **step functions**.

We now consider a seemingly unrelated correspondence. Suppose that on a particular class of mail, the rate is 10¢ for each ounce of weight. Then, if an object weighs one ounce or less, it can be mailed for 10¢. If it weighs between 1 and 2 ounces, it costs 20¢ to mail, and so forth.

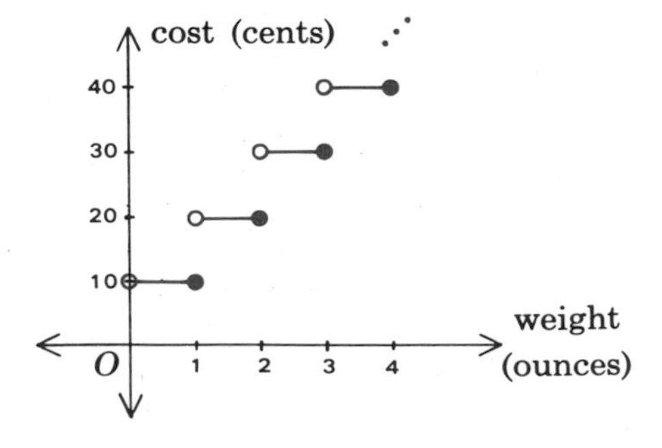

The correspondence

(weight of parcel) → (cost to mail)

is graphed at the left. Values of the function must be multiples of 10¢.

The graph is like the graph of the greatest integer function above, but the small circles are on the left.

An equation for such a graph can be found by analyzing the transformations which map the graph of $y = [x]$ onto this graph.

① Begin with the known function.

$y = [x]$

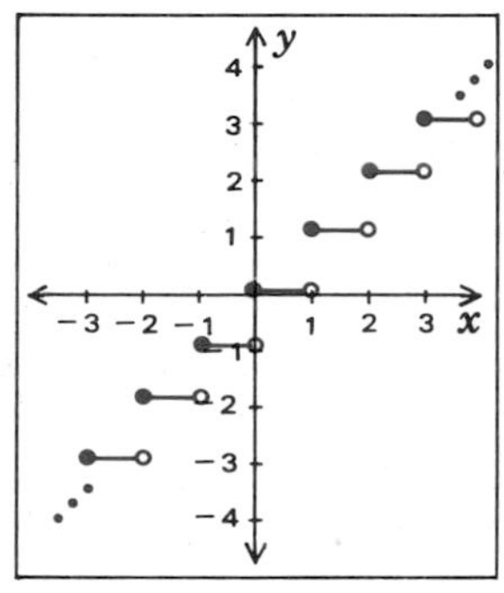

② Reflect over the *x*-axis.

$-y = [x]$

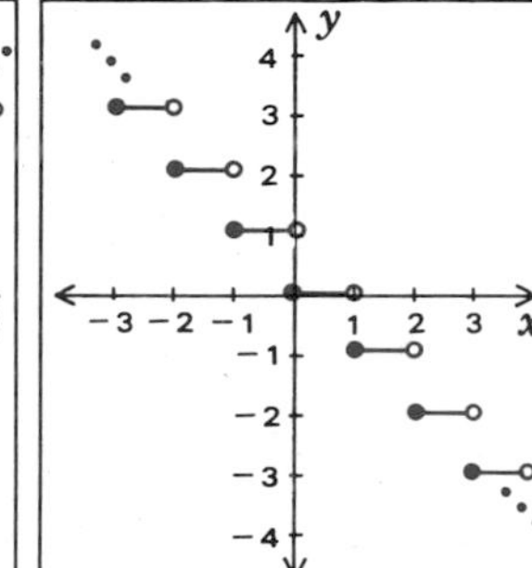

③ Reflect over the *y*-axis.

$-y = [-x]$

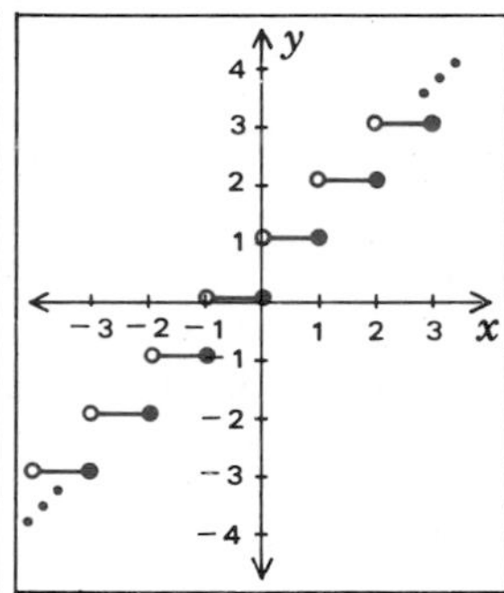

④ Use a vertical scale transformation of magnitude 10.

$-\frac{y}{10} = [-x]$

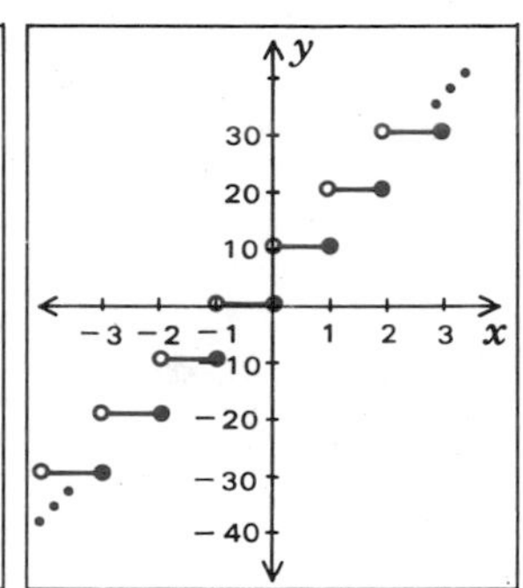

EXERCISES 13.8

Ⓐ **1.** The symbol $[t]$ stands for ______.

2–11. Calculate.

2. $[7]$ **3.** $[7.1]$ **4.** $[6.95]$ **5.** $[-3]$ **6.** $[-3.23]$

7. $[0]$ **8.** $[\frac{7}{100}]$ **9.** $[-\frac{22}{9}]$ **10.** $[\frac{22}{9}]$ **11.** $[7\frac{1}{2} + 3\frac{3}{4}]$

Ⓑ **12.** If the domain of the function $G: x \to [x]$ is the set of real numbers, what is the range of this function?

13. If the domain of $G: x \to [x]$ is the set of positive real numbers, what is the range of G?

14. Find one solution to $[x] = x - \frac{1}{3}$.

15–17. Graph each function. Use the method shown above as an aid.

15. $y + 3 = [x + 2]$ **16.** $y = [2x]$ **17.** $y = \left[\frac{x}{3}\right]$

18. Which of the given expressions stands for the decimal part of a positive number r?

a. $[r] - 1$ **b.** $[r] + r$ **c.** $[r] - r$ **d.** $r - [r]$

19–21. Give an equation whose solution set is graphed.

19.

20.

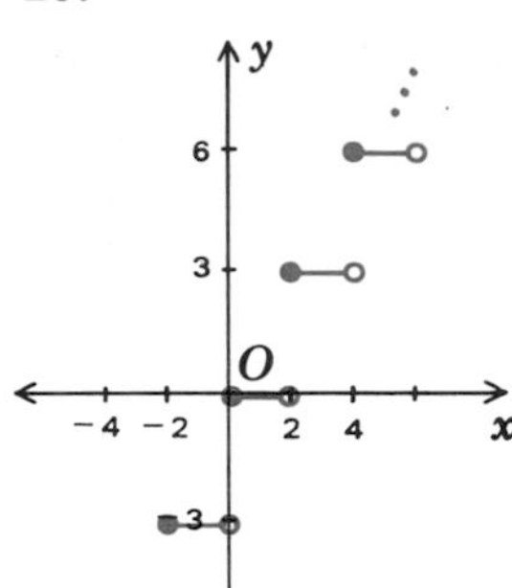

21.

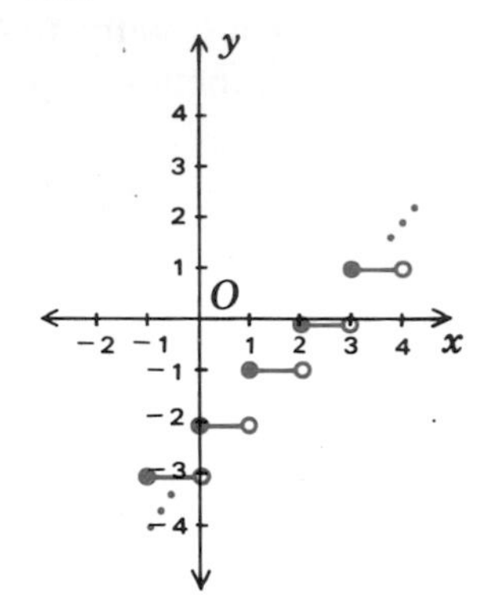

22. Which is always true?

a. $[x + y] = [x] + [y]$

b. $[x + 0.01] = [x]$

c. $[x + 3] - 3 = [x]$

d. $[2x] = 2[x]$

e. none of these

Ⓒ **23.** A cab company charges 40¢ for the first one-fifth mile and 10¢ for each succeeding one-fifth mile. Graph an appropriate function. Find equations which describe this function. How much will it cost to go 3 miles via cab? How much will it cost to go 6 miles via cab?

"The hospital is having a hard time making ends meet."

Medicare, by Reamer Keller, courtesy of Field Newspaper Syndicate

24. Graph the function suggested by the cartoon at the left.

25. A car rental agency charges $7.00 for the first 20 kilometres and 6¢ for each additional kilometre. Graph a rate function and give two equations which together describe the function.

26. A long-distance call costs 80¢ for the first 3 minutes and 25¢ for each additional minute. Graph the time-cost function and give two equations which together describe the function.

27. A state is given one representative in Congress and gets one more for approximately each 500,000 people. Letting P be the population of a state and n be the number of allowed representatives, graph the function $P \to n$. Find a single sentence which describes this function. (The greatest integer symbol will help.)

28. True or False? $y - 4 = [x - 4]$ and $y = [x]$ are equivalent sentences.

29–30. The greatest integer function "rounds down," but the [ ] symbol can be used to give simple sentences for certain related functions. In each case, find the sentence.

29. $x \to$ the smallest integer larger than or equal to x. (This is the "rounding up" function.)

30. $y \to$ the integer nearest y. (This is the standard "rounding" function.)

31. What does the function $z \to \frac{[10z]}{10}$ do to a decimal?

32–34. The day of the week for any date in the last 200 years, or in the future, can be found in the following way.

Number the days of the week as follows

Saturday = 0, Sunday = 1, Monday = 2, Tuesday = 3, · · ·, Friday = 6.

Number the months of the year with

Mar. = 3, Apr. = 4, May = 5, · · ·, Dec. = 12, Jan. = 13, Feb. = 14.

Let: D = the day of the month.

M = the number of the month as above.

N = the year.

Calculate: $D + 2M + \left[\frac{3(M+1)}{5}\right] + N + \left[\frac{N}{4}\right] - \left[\frac{N}{100}\right] + \left[\frac{N}{400}\right] + 2.$

Divide the result found above by 7. The remainder represents the day of the week.

32. Test this formula on today's date.

33. On what day of the week was Pearl Harbor (Dec. 7, 1941)?

34. On what day of the week were you born?

13.9 APPROXIMATING FUNCTIONS BY LINEAR FUNCTIONS

By now you know that there are many different types of functions. A complicated function can be made from simple functions by composing them, or by taking their union.

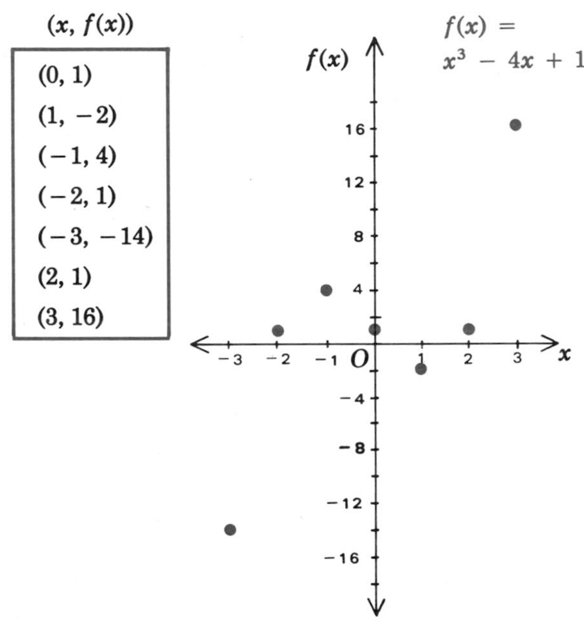

$(x, f(x))$
$(0, 1)$
$(1, -2)$
$(-1, 4)$
$(-2, 1)$
$(-3, -14)$
$(2, 1)$
$(3, 16)$

Of all functions, linear functions are probably the simplest. Thus it is reasonable to use linear functions whenever possible.

The nonlinear function $f(x) = x^3 - 4x + 1$ is somewhat complicated. We can approximate its graph by calculating $f(x)$ for some values of x. Some of the ordered pairs are graphed at the left.

A clearer graph of the function can be found by considering more ordered pairs. If we connect these ordered pairs with line segments, we are approximating the function with linear functions.

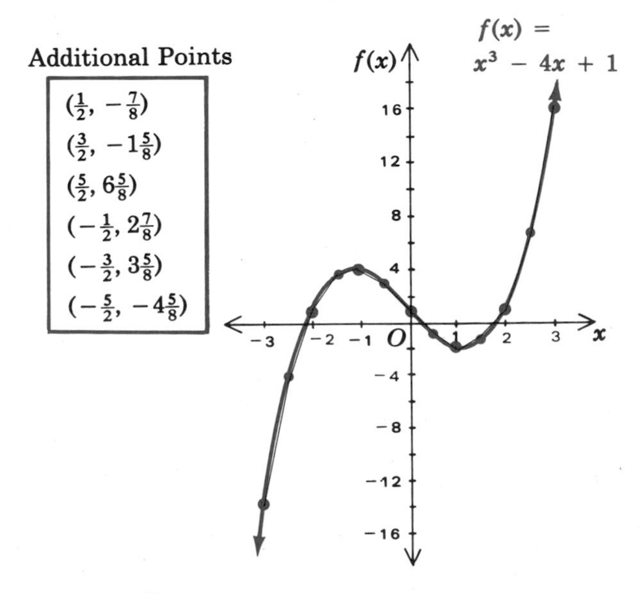

Additional Points
$(\frac{1}{2}, -\frac{7}{8})$
$(\frac{3}{2}, -1\frac{5}{8})$
$(\frac{5}{2}, 6\frac{5}{8})$
$(-\frac{1}{2}, 2\frac{7}{8})$
$(-\frac{3}{2}, 3\frac{5}{8})$
$(-\frac{5}{2}, -4\frac{5}{8})$

You should try to curve the lines to get a smoother graph, as is done in red. This is not only prettier, it is usually more accurate.

Notice that the graph has three x-intercepts. (It crosses the x-axis 3 times.) The largest x-intercept is between $1\frac{1}{2}$ and 2.

Question: *How can we approximate the largest x-intercept more closely?*

This question is not difficult to answer. Enlarging the drawing, we can approximate the graph with the segment connecting the points $(\frac{3}{2}, -1\frac{5}{8})$ and $(2, 1)$.

This segment crosses the x-axis at some point $(a, 0)$. The number a is an approximation for the x-intercept. We find a by considering the slope of the segment.

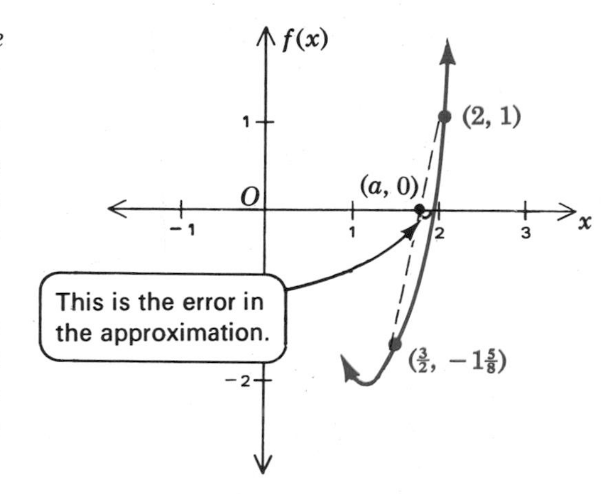

From the points $(\frac{3}{2}, -1\frac{5}{8})$, $(2, 1)$, and $(a, 0)$, we can find the slope.

$$\text{slope} = \frac{0-1}{a-2} \quad \text{or} \quad \text{slope} = \frac{1+1\frac{5}{8}}{2-\frac{3}{2}}$$

These must be equal, so we get

$$\frac{-1}{a-2} = \frac{\frac{21}{8}}{\frac{1}{2}}. \quad \boxed{\text{Using reciprocals,}} \Rightarrow \quad \frac{a-2}{-1} = \frac{\frac{1}{2}}{\frac{21}{8}}$$

$$a - 2 = -1(\tfrac{1}{2} \cdot \tfrac{8}{21})$$

$$a = -\tfrac{4}{21} + 2 = \tfrac{38}{21} \doteq 1.81$$

Thus, the graph's largest x-intercept is about 1.81. Closer estimates are possible by finding more points on the graph. (The actual value is closer to 1.86.) This approximation process has *many* applications.

Example: The table on page 601 gives squares and square roots only for numbers from 1 to 150. How could you approximate $\sqrt{598}$?

SOLUTION: One way to do this is to consider the squaring function. We know $(24)^2 = 576$ and $(25)^2 = 625$. That is, the points $(24, 576)$ and $(25, 625)$ are on the parabola $y = x^2$.

So, we can approximate $\sqrt{598}$ by finding approximately where the parabola crosses the line $y = 598$. That is where $x^2 = 598$. To approximate x, we approximate the parabola by a segment through the known points.

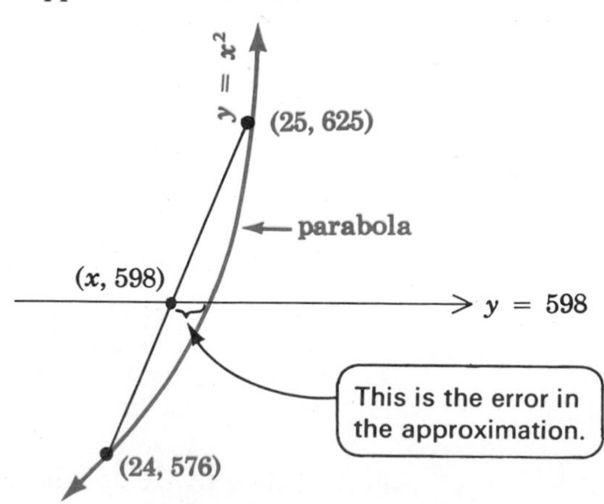

We consider $(x, 598)$ as a point on the segment. Using $(24, 576)$, $(25, 625)$, and $(x, 598)$, we equate slopes:

$$\frac{598 - 576}{x - 24} = \frac{625 - 576}{25 - 24}$$

$$\frac{22}{x - 24} = 49$$

$$x - 24 = \frac{22}{49}$$

$$x = 24\frac{22}{49} \doteq 24.449$$

This is a fair approximation. Actually $\sqrt{598} = 24.454\cdots$.

The process of estimating values of functions by using linear functions is called *linear interpolation.* Linear interpolation is very often used to extend tables (such as those on pages 601–604) beyond what is listed in them. This type of estimation can be helpful in later chapters.

You do not have to graph to do interpolation. In the square-root example, the graph shows what was done, but all of the calculation took only 4 lines.

As another example, suppose you want to approximate $\cos 45.7°$. From the tables $\cos 45° \doteq 0.707$ and $\cos 46° \doteq 0.695$. So you simply equate slopes involving the points $(45, 0.707)$, $(46, 0.695)$, and $(45.7, y)$. Then solve for y, which is the approximation.

$$\frac{0.707 - 0.695}{45 - 46} = \frac{0.695 - y}{46 - 45.7}$$

$$\frac{0.012}{-1} = \frac{0.695 - y}{0.3}$$

$$0.0036 = y - 0.695$$

$$y = 0.6986$$

So, $\cos 45.7° \doteq 0.699$ ← It is customary to round to the number of digits in the table.

EXERCISES 13.9

Ⓐ **1.** Linear functions are used in two ways in this section to approximate other functions. Identify these two ways.

2. Given that the points (a, b), (c, d), and (e, f) are collinear, what relationship must hold between a, b, c, d, e, and f?

3. Describe the idea behind linear interpolation.

4–7. Three collinear points are given. Solve for the variable. (Do it mentally if you can.)

4. $(5, 9), (5.5, x), (6, 15)$

5. $(2, 5), (a, 0), (3, 10)$

6. $(0, 0), (2, 5), (-10, z)$

7. $(6, 400), (x, 500), (9, 700)$

Ⓑ **8–11.** Some information is given. Choose the most accurate approximation without referring to any tables.

8. *Given:* $\sqrt{49} = 7$, $\sqrt{64} = 8$. Then, $\sqrt{56} \doteq$?

a. 7.1 **b.** 7.5 **c.** 7.9

9. *Given:* $(236)^2 = 55696$, $(237)^2 = 56169$. Then, $(236.2)^2 \doteq$?

a. 55800 **b.** 56000 **c.** 56100

10. *Given:* $\sin 10° \doteq 0.173$, $\sin 11° \doteq 0.191$. Then, $\sin 10.3° \doteq$?

a. 0.179 **b.** 0.182 **c.** 0.185

11. *Given:* $\cos 10° \doteq 0.985$, $\cos 11° \doteq 0.982$. Then, $\cos 10.3° \doteq$?

a. 0.989 **b.** 0.984 **c.** 0.983

12. A line contains $(4, 10)$ and $(3, -1)$. Without finding an equation for the line, determine where the line crosses the x-axis.

13. A line contains $(5, -3)$ and $(-2, 7)$. Without finding an equation for the line, determine where the line intersects the line $y = 3$.

14. Use the information of this section to approximate the smallest x-intercept of the function $f: x \to x^3 - 4x + 1$.

15. Consider the function $f: x \to x^3 - 4x + 1$. Find an approximation for the x-intercept which is between 0 and $\frac{1}{2}$.

16–19. Use linear interpolation to find a decimal approximation for each number. Use the two nearest values from tables.

16. $\sqrt{2.2}$ (Two close values are 1.414 for $\sqrt{2}$ and 1.732 for $\sqrt{3}$.)

17. $\sqrt{2.1}$

18. $\sin 38.4°$

19. $\cos 21.8°$

20. Without using tables, use your knowledge of $\sin 45°$ and $\sin 60°$ to approximate $\sin 50°$.

21. Without using tables, use your knowledge of $\cos 30°$ and $\cos 45°$ to approximate $\cos 33°$.

22–23. Would linear interpolation give an exact answer? (You do not have to do the interpolation.)

22. Given 32° F $= 0^\circ$ C and 212° F $= 100^\circ$ C, find the Fahrenheit equivalent of 31.6° C.

23. Given the population of the United States was (according to the census) 151,325,798 on April 1, 1950, and 179,323,175 on April 1, 1960, calculate the population of the U.S. on April 1, 1954.

24–25. Perform the linear interpolations suggested in Exercises **22–23.**

© **26.** Given that $f(x) = 2x^3 - 5x + 2$, $f(1) = -1$, and $f(2) = 8$, find an approximate solution to $2x^3 - 5x + 2 = 0$.

27. Given that $g(m) = m^3 - 6m + 2$, $g(2) = -2$, and $g(3) = 11$, find an approximate solution to $m^3 - 6m + 2 = 0$.

28. Graph $g: x \to x^3 - 9x + 2$, and approximate all x-intercepts to tenths.

29. Graph h where $h(t) = t^3$, and approximate to the nearest tenth the intersection of this function with the line $y = 2$.

CHAPTER SUMMARY

The idea of *function* is one of the most important ideas in all mathematics. A function is a relation with no two different ordered pairs having the same first coordinate.

Many of the relations studied in earlier chapters are also functions. You have seen how *linear* and *quadratic* functions can be graphed.

A function is a special type of correspondence—it involves the ideas of *domain, codomain, range,* and *1–1 functions.*

Transformations are special 1–1 functions, and many transformation concepts apply to functions. These concepts include *function composition, identity functions,* and *inverse functions.*

Applications of functions lead to concepts such as *independent* and *dependent variables, maximum* and *minimum values* of a function, functions of *direct variation* ($y = kx$), and functions of *inverse variation* $\left(y = \frac{k}{x}\right)$.

Many functions, such as the *absolute value functions,* can have more than one defining sentence. There are functions with disconnected graphs, like the *step functions.*

Of all special functions, the *linear functions* studied as early as Chapter 6 are probably most important. Linear functions may be used to approximate other functions. Specific values of the other functions can often be approximated by *linear interpolation.*

CHAPTER REVIEW

1. By looking at its graph, how can you determine whether a relation is a function? Whether a function has an inverse function?

2. If $f: m \to 2m - 1$ and $g: n \to n^2 + 1$, calculate:

   a. $f(3)$. b. $g(f(3))$. c. $f \circ g(x)$.

3. Suppose $f: x \to |x|$, and x may be any integer. Give the domain and range, and graph f.

4–6. Describe, in two words or less, the graph of the given relation.

4. $\{(x, y): 2y = |x|\}$

5. $\left\{(x, y): y = \frac{k}{x}\right\}$

6. $\{(x, y): (x - 3)^2 + 2y^2 = 0\}$

7. Which relations in Exercises **4–6** are functions?

8. The volume of a sphere varies directly as the cube of the radius. If a sphere with radius 3 has volume 36π, what is the volume of a sphere with radius 6?

9. Compute a decimal approximation for the constant of variation in Exercise **8**.

10. Graph the solution set of $y = [x]$ for values of x between -2 and 4, including -2 and 4.

11. $[-5.6] + [3.712] =$ ____

12. Given $\sin 41° \doteq 0.656$ and $\sin 42° \doteq 0.669$, find a decimal approximation for $\sin 41.3°$.

Chapter
14
Exponential Functions

A function in which the domain (independent) variable is an exponent is an *exponential function.* A simple exponential function is

$$y = 2^x.$$

You know how to evaluate 2^x when x is an integer. In this chapter, we discuss both the need for nonintegral exponents and some ways to work with them (particularly using logarithms).

Exponential functions have many applications. For instance, they are used to calculate the age of skeletons such as that of the dodo, shown above. Several other applications are given in this chapter.

Nth ROOTS 14.1

As you know,

$$x \text{ is a } \textbf{square root} \text{ of } t \text{ when } x^2 = t.$$

That is, if t is the square of x, then x is a square root of t.

Similarly,

$$x \text{ is a } \textbf{cube root} \text{ of } t \text{ when } x^3 = t.$$

That is, if t is the cube of x, then x is a cube root of t.

Examples: Cube roots

1. Since $2^3 = 8$, $\quad$ 2 is a cube root of 8.
2. Since $(\frac{4}{5})^3 = \frac{64}{125}$, $\quad$ $\frac{4}{5}$ is a cube root of $\frac{64}{125}$.
3. Since $(-1)^3 = -1$, $\quad$ -1 is a cube root of -1.

Square roots and cube roots are special cases of the following, more general idea.

Definition

> Let n be an integer greater than 1.
>
> x is an ***n*****th root** of t if and only if $x^n = t$.

The definition shows that *if x is an nth root of t, then t is the nth power of x.* There are no special names for nth roots other than *square* roots (when $n = 2$) and *cube* roots (when $n = 3$).

Examples: nth roots

1. Since $2^4 = 16$, $\quad$ 2 is a 4th root of 16.
2. Since $(-2)^4 = 16$, $\quad$ -2 is a 4th root of 16.
3. Since $(\frac{1}{3})^5 = \frac{1}{243}$, $\quad$ $\frac{1}{3}$ is a 5th root of $\frac{1}{243}$.
4. Since $2^{10} = 1024 \doteq 1000$, $\quad$ 2 is close to a 10th root of 1000.
5. Since $(x^2)^8 = x^{16}$, $\quad$ x^2 is an 8th root of x^{16}.

There are two common notations for nth roots. The first of these is a generalization of the symbol $\sqrt{\ }$ for square roots. (The second is given on page 413.)

Definition

> Let n be an integer greater than 1. Then
> $\sqrt[n]{\ }$ stands for the **largest real *n*th root**.

The symbol $\sqrt[n]{\ }$ was first used about 1633 by Albert Girard. Just as $\sqrt{\ }$ and *square root of* are not identical, $\sqrt[n]{\ }$ and *nth root of* are not identical.

A real number may have many nth roots, but only the largest is denoted by $\sqrt[n]{\ }$. With the exception of the use of $\sqrt{-p}$ (where p is a positive real number) to denote pure imaginaries, in this book $\sqrt[n]{x}$ will stand only for real numbers.

Examples: $\sqrt[n]{\ }$ notation

1. 2 is the *largest* real 4th root of 16, so $2 = \sqrt[4]{16}$.

2. $\sqrt[5]{-\frac{1}{243}} = -\frac{1}{3}$ 3. $\sqrt[10]{1000} \doteq 2$ 4. $\sqrt[8]{x^{16}} = x^2$

You can check answers by relating nth roots to nth powers.

Theorem 14.1.1

Let n be an integer greater than 1 and x be a real number.

If $\sqrt[n]{t} = x$, then $x^n = t$.

The converse of Theorem 14.1.1 is *not* true. For example,

$$(-2)^4 = 16 \quad \text{but} \quad \sqrt[4]{16} \neq -2.$$

What is true is that $-\sqrt[4]{16} = -2$.

EXERCISES 14.1

Ⓐ 1. If x is a square root of t, then ____.

2. If u is a cube root of v, then ____.

3. If $a^n = b$, then ____ is the nth power of ____ and ____ is an nth root of ____.

4–7. What does each sentence indicate about nth roots?

4. $2^4 = 16$ 5. $729 = 9^3$ 6. $(\frac{1}{4})^5 = \frac{1}{1024}$ 7. $-128 = (-2)^7$

8–16. Give one indicated nth root of the given number.

8. 32; 5th root 9. $\frac{1}{27}$; cube root 10. $\frac{64}{27}$; cube root

11. -32; 5th root 12. x^8; 4th root 13. 1,000,000; 6th root

14. 10^6; cube root 15. 16; 4th root 16. -1; 9th root

17. $\sqrt[n]{x}$ is another way of writing ____.

18–26. Write your answers to Exercises **8–16** in $\sqrt[n]{\ }$ notation.

27–38. Simplify.

27. $\sqrt[3]{-125}$ **28.** $\sqrt[3]{1000}$ **29.** $\sqrt[5]{-32}$

30. $\sqrt[4]{256}$ **31.** $\sqrt{x^8}$ **32.** $\sqrt[6]{\frac{729}{64}}$

Ⓑ **33.** $\sqrt[3]{343}$ **34.** $(\sqrt{5})^4$ **35.** $\sqrt[3]{10} \cdot \sqrt[3]{10} \cdot \sqrt[3]{10}$

36. $(\sqrt[3]{x})^3$ **37.** $\sqrt{5^4}$ **38.** $-\sqrt[3]{-27}$

39–46. Copy. Place $<$, $=$, or $>$ in the blank.

39. $\sqrt[4]{100}$ ____ $\sqrt[5]{100}$ **40.** -2 ____ $\sqrt[4]{16}$

41. $\sqrt[3]{\sqrt{64}}$ ____ $\sqrt{\sqrt[3]{64}}$ **42.** $\sqrt[3]{3^6}$ ____ $(\sqrt[3]{3})^6$

43. If $x > 1$, $\sqrt[3]{x}$ ____ $\sqrt[5]{x}$. **44.** $\sqrt[5]{1}$ ____ 1

45. $\sqrt[3]{10}$ ____ 3 **46.** $\sqrt[7]{7}$ ____ 1

47–48. Find all numbers z such that $1 \le z \le 1000$ and:

47. $\sqrt[3]{z}$ is an integer. **48.** $\sqrt[4]{z}$ is an integer.

49–51. Solve for n.

49. $\sqrt[n]{1024} = 2$ **50.** $\sqrt[n]{243} = 3$ **51.** $\sqrt[n]{\frac{1}{16}} = \frac{1}{2}$

Ⓒ **52–58.** In the 1700's it was proved that every nonzero complex number has n nth roots. These exercises will help you understand this fact.

52. Graph the two square roots of 49.

53. Graph the two square roots of -49.

54. Verify that $[2, 120°]^3 = [2, 240°]^3 = 8$; then graph the three cube roots of 8. These roots are vertices of what kind of triangle?

55. Show that $i^4 = 1$ and $(-i)^4 = 1$; then graph the four 4th roots of 1.

56. Show that $[1, 45°]$, $[1, 135°]$, and $[1, 225°]$ are three of the four solutions to $z^4 = -1$. Find the fourth solution. (HINT: Graph the three given solutions.)

57. Show that $[1, 72°]$ and $[1, 144°]$ are 5th roots of 1. Find and graph these and the other three 5th roots.

58. Show that $3 + 2i$ and $-2 + 3i$ are 4th roots of the same number. Find the other two 4th roots of that number; graph all four roots.

14.2 GROWTH FUNCTIONS— A NEED FOR MORE EXPONENTS

In 1960, the earth's population was approximately 3 billion. At the 1960 rate of growth, the population will double every 35 years. If a constant rate of growth is assumed, it is possible to graph the correspondence between the years and the approximate populations.

Year		Population (billions)
1960	→	3
1995	→	6
2030	→	12
2065	→	24
2100	→	48

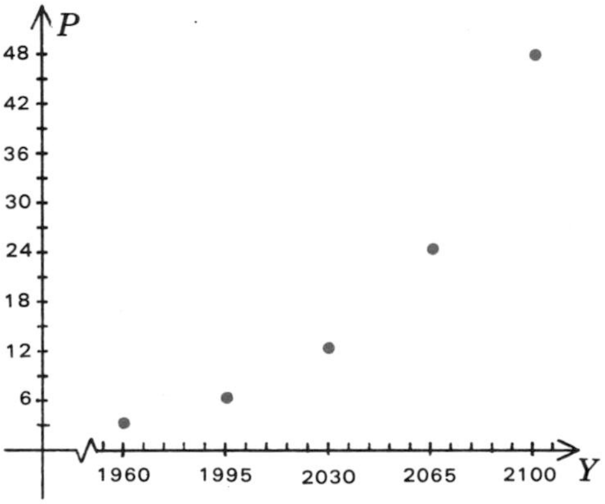

In this graph, there is no population corresponding to the year 2000. But there is an equation which is satisfied by each year Y given above and the corresponding population P.

$$\frac{P}{3} = 2^{\frac{Y-1960}{35}}$$

For example, when $Y = 2065$, the exponent of 2 is 3. Then the right side of the equation is 8, and so $P = 24$, as desired. Substituting 2000 for Y in the equation gives an exponent which is not an integer. So to find the estimated population in 2000, calculations must be done with fractional exponents. (This is the subject of Section 14.3.)

Because the independent variable is in the exponent, the equation above describes an **exponential function**. In an exponential function, the *change in value* of the function is proportional to the *value* of the independent variable. In this example, change in population is directly proportional to the population. Other applications include:

savings: Interest added to an account is directly proportional to the amount in the account.

cooling: The change in rate of cooling of a cup of coffee is directly proportional to the difference between the temperature of the coffee and the room temperature.

radioactive decay: Loss by radiation of radioactive material is directly proportional to the amount of material left.

In most of these applications, the growth or decay is gradual (or *continuous*), not by jumps. For example, the temperature of a cup of coffee does not jump from 120° to 119°—it decreases gradually. When change of this sort is continuous, the function describing it requires the use of fractional exponents.

EXERCISES 14.2

Ⓐ **1.** What is an exponential function?

2–4. *Population growth.* Using the graph on page 410 (or linear interpolation), approximate world population in the given year.

2. 2015 **3.** 2050 **4.** 2085

5–8. Use the equation given on page 410 to find:

5. P when $Y = 1960$. **6.** P when $Y = 2205$.

Ⓑ **7.** Y when $P = 0.75$. **8.** Y when $P = 3072$.

9–11. *Savings.* \$100 is deposited in a bank and 5% interest is added to the account yearly. Find the amount in the account at the end of:

9. 1 year. **10.** 2 years. **11.** 3 years.

12. Which expression tells the amount in the account at the end of n years? (HINT: Use your answers to Exercises **9–11**.)

a. $100 + 0.05n$ **b.** $100 + 5n$ **c.** $(105)^n$ **d.** $100(1.05)^n$

13–15. *Inflation.* If there is inflation at the rate of 8% per year, an item which now costs \$100 will cost \$108 a year from now. At the same rate, how much will that item cost:

13. in 2 years? **14.** in 4 years?

15. Graph five elements of the correspondence $Y \rightarrow C$, where Y is the number of years from now and C is the cost in that year.

16–19. *Radioactive decay.* The isotope carbon 14 decays so that only half of the original quantity is left after 5600 years. (This time is called the *half-life* of the isotope.) What percentage of a quantity of carbon 14 is left:

16. after 11,200 years? **17.** after 16,800 years?

18. When will $\frac{1}{32}$ of an original quantity of carbon 14 remain?

19. Suppose there are now 3 grams of pure carbon 14. Graph six elements of the correspondence $y \rightarrow w$, where y is the number of years from now, and w is the mass of the carbon 14 left.

© **20–22.** The isotope silver 110 decays very quickly; only half of a quantity of pure silver 110 is left after 24 seconds.

20. After about how long will 4% of the original silver 110 remain?

21. After about how long will $\frac{1}{1000}$ of the original remain?

22. Which formula seems to give the percentage of silver 110 left after x seconds?

a. $\frac{1}{24x}$ **b.** $\frac{24}{x}$ **c.** $2^{-\frac{x}{24}}$ **d.** $\frac{24}{100x}$

23–24. The equation on page 410 is the result of assuming a constant rate of population growth.

23. The actual population of the world was about 1,950,000,000 in 1925. What does this tell about the true rate of population growth?

24. Why *must* the equation used in this section be a poor model of population growth over long periods of time?

RATIONAL NUMBERS AS EXPONENTS

The isomorphism between addition and multiplication leads to many corresponding properties, as shown in Section 9.3. Specifically, every property of multiples and addition corresponds to a property of powers and multiplication. We can use this correspondence to give meaning to fractional powers of numbers.

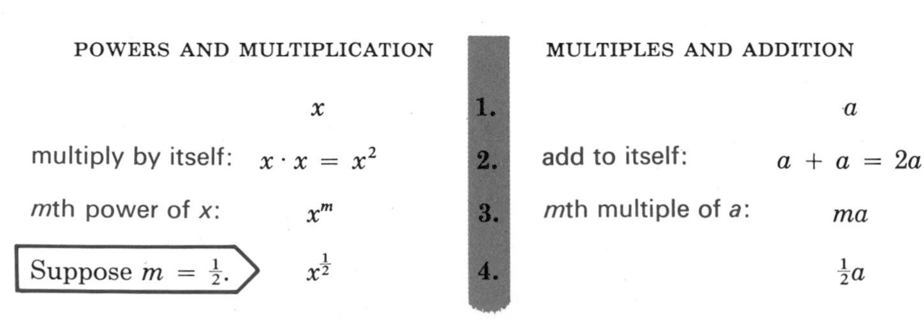

POWERS AND MULTIPLICATION			MULTIPLES AND ADDITION	
	x	1.		a
multiply by itself:	$x \cdot x = x^2$	2.	add to itself:	$a + a = 2a$
mth power of x:	x^m	3.	mth multiple of a:	ma
Suppose $m = \frac{1}{2}$.	$x^{\frac{1}{2}}$	4.		$\frac{1}{2}a$

You know what $\frac{1}{2}a$ means. In order to find out what $x^{\frac{1}{2}}$ means, consider some more corresponding properties.

power of a power: $(x^m)^n = x^{mn}$

multiple of a multiple: $n(ma) = (nm)a$

Now let $m = \frac{1}{2}$ and $n = 2$. $(x^{\frac{1}{2}})^2 = x$ **6.** $2(\frac{1}{2}a) = a$

$x^{\frac{1}{2}}$ multiplied by itself yields x. $\frac{1}{2}a$ added to itself yields a.

So $x^{\frac{1}{2}}$ is a *square root* of x. But there are two square roots of x. Which one is $x^{\frac{1}{2}}$? To avoid confusion, we choose the *positive* square root. Furthermore, to avoid complex roots, we require x to be positive. Thus, $x^{\frac{1}{2}} = \sqrt{x}$. Looking back at correspondence 4, we see that square roots and halves correspond, as was first suggested on page 26.

Suppose $m = \frac{1}{n}$ in correspondence 5. Then, substituting for m:

$$(x^{\frac{1}{n}})^n = x \qquad \textbf{7.} \qquad n\left(\frac{1}{n}a\right) = a$$

So $x^{\frac{1}{n}}$ is an nth *root* of x. But which nth root? In order to have the symbol $x^{\frac{1}{n}}$ stand for exactly one nth root, and to avoid complex roots, we consider x positive and take the positive nth root.

Theorem 14.3.1

> Suppose $x > 0$ and n is an integer greater than 1.
> Then $x^{\frac{1}{n}}$ is defined and $x^{\frac{1}{n}} = \sqrt[n]{x}$.

Theorem 14.3.1 is very helpful, for it shows how fractional exponents and nth roots are related. While $x^{\frac{1}{n}}$ can be defined when x is negative or nonreal, we do not consider such roots in this book.

Examples: Simplifying $x^{\frac{1}{n}}$

1. $16^{\frac{1}{4}}$ is the *positive* 4th root of 16, so $16^{\frac{1}{4}} = \sqrt[4]{16} = 2$.

2. $2^{\frac{1}{2}} = \sqrt{2}$

3. $-9^{\frac{1}{2}} = -\sqrt{9} = -3$

4. $128^{\frac{1}{7}} = \sqrt[7]{128} = 2$

5. $(\frac{64}{27})^{\frac{1}{3}} = \frac{4}{3}$

If we call $\frac{1}{n}a$ the ***n*th part** of a, we see that parts and roots correspond. So to interpret $x^{\frac{m}{n}}$, we look at $\frac{m}{n}a$.

*n*th root:	$x^{\frac{1}{n}}$	*n*th part:	$\frac{1}{n}a$
*m*th power of *n*th root of *x*:	$x^{\frac{m}{n}} = (x^{\frac{1}{n}})^m$	*m*th multiple of *n*th part of *a*:	$\frac{m}{n}a = m\left(\frac{1}{n}a\right)$
*n*th root of *m*th power of *x*:	$= (x^m)^{\frac{1}{n}}$	*n*th part of *m*th multiple of *a*:	$= \frac{1}{n}(ma)$

Theorem 14.3.2

For $x > 0$, $x^{\frac{m}{n}} = (x^{\frac{1}{n}})^m = (x^m)^{\frac{1}{n}}$. $(n \neq 0)$

Nothing in the development above forces m or n to be positive. The theorem holds whether m and n are positive or negative. However, when n is an integer greater than 1, Theorem 14.3.2 may be rewritten using radical notation.

Corollary 14.3.3

For $x > 0$, $x^{\frac{m}{n}} = (\sqrt[n]{x})^m = \sqrt[n]{x^m}$. ($n$ is an integer greater than 1.)

Examples: Using $x^{\frac{m}{n}}$ notation

1. $5^{\frac{126}{17}}$ is the positive 17th root of 5^{126}.
2. $x^{\frac{2}{3}} = (x^{\frac{1}{3}})^2 = (\sqrt[3]{x})^2$ and $x^{\frac{2}{3}} = (x^2)^{\frac{1}{3}} = \sqrt[3]{x^2}$
3. $8^{\frac{2}{3}} = (\sqrt[3]{8})^2 = 2^2 = 4$
4. $8^{-\frac{2}{3}}$ and $8^{\frac{2}{3}}$ are reciprocals. $8^{\frac{2}{3}} = 4$ (Example **3**), so $8^{-\frac{2}{3}} = \frac{1}{4}$.
5. $\left(\frac{16}{9}\right)^{-\frac{3}{2}} = \frac{1}{\left(\frac{16}{9}\right)^{\frac{3}{2}}} = \frac{1}{\left(\sqrt{\frac{16}{9}}\right)^3} = \frac{1}{\left(\frac{4}{3}\right)^3} = \frac{1}{\frac{64}{27}} = \frac{27}{64}$
6. $2500^{\frac{7}{2}} = (\sqrt{2500})^7 = 50^7$

Fractional exponents and properties of powers may be used to simplify some radicals. Recall that $(x^m)^n = x^{mn}$.

Examples: Simplifying radicals

1. $\sqrt[5]{y^{10}} = (y^{10})^{\frac{1}{5}} = y^2$
2. $(\sqrt[3]{7})^6 = (7^{\frac{1}{3}})^6 = 7^2 = 49$
3. $\sqrt[3]{\sqrt{x}} = (x^{\frac{1}{2}})^{\frac{1}{3}} = x^{\frac{1}{6}}$
   $= \sqrt[6]{x}$

In words, the cube root of the square root is the 6th root of the number.

Sometimes it is convenient to convert to radical notation.

Example: Estimating $2^{\frac{7}{2}}$: $2^{\frac{7}{2}} = 2^{3+\frac{1}{2}} = 2^3 \cdot 2^{\frac{1}{2}} = 8\sqrt{2}$

$\doteq 8(1.4) = 11.2$

Rational exponents may be written as decimals. For instance, $2^{\frac{7}{2}} = 2^{3.5}$. This is sometimes very convenient, as you will see in later sections. In particular, it is often necessary to break up a decimal exponent into its integer and fractional parts.

Examples: **1.** $10^{2.34} = 10^{2+0.34} = 10^2 \cdot 10^{0.34}$

2. $x^{6.137} = x^{6+0.137} = x^6 \cdot x^{0.137}$

EXERCISES 14.3

Ⓐ **1.** When x is positive, $x^{\frac{1}{2}}$ is the _____ of x.

2. What does it mean if $\frac{1}{3}$ is an exponent?

3. $x^{\frac{1}{2}} \cdot x^{\frac{1}{2}} =$ _____

4. $x^{\frac{1}{3}} \cdot x^{\frac{1}{3}} \cdot x^{\frac{1}{3}} =$ _____

5. $(x^{\frac{1}{3}})^3 =$ _____

6. $(x^{\frac{1}{3}})^2 =$ _____

7. What is an nth root of a number?

8. Give two 4th roots of 10,000.

9. $(10{,}000)^{\frac{1}{4}} =$ _____

10. $x^{\frac{1}{n}}$ stands for the _____ nth root of x.

11. When $\frac{m}{n}$ is used as an exponent, what is meant?

12. $\sqrt[n]{x^m}$ is what power of x?

13–18. Write in a form with no radical signs.

13. $\sqrt[3]{14}$

14. $\sqrt{T}$

15. $\sqrt[4]{x^3}$

16. $\sqrt[10]{y}$

17. $\sqrt[3]{Z^{15}}$

18. $\sqrt[10]{A^3}$

19–21. Write in a form with a radical sign.

19. $m^{\frac{1}{4}}$

20. $6^{\frac{2}{3}}$

21. $12^{\frac{3}{4}}$

22–45. Write in a form with no exponents and no radicals, if possible.

22. $4^{\frac{1}{2}}$ **23.** $6^{\frac{1}{2}}$ **24.** $4^{-\frac{1}{2}}$ **25.** $6^{-\frac{1}{2}}$

26. $8^{\frac{2}{3}}$ **27.** $8^{-\frac{2}{3}}$ **28.** $8^{\frac{4}{3}}$ **29.** $8^{-\frac{4}{3}}$

30. $16^{\frac{3}{2}}$ **31.** $16^{-1.5}$ **32.** $(\frac{4}{9})^{\frac{1}{2}}$ **33.** $(\frac{4}{9})^{-\frac{1}{2}}$

Ⓑ **34.** $128^{\frac{1}{7}}$ **35.** $343^{\frac{1}{3}}$ **36.** $343^{\frac{2}{3}}$ **37.** $64^{\frac{7}{6}}$

38. $-64^{\frac{7}{6}}$ **39.** $(\frac{1}{64})^{\frac{1}{2}}$ **40.** $(\frac{1}{64})^{\frac{1}{3}}$ **41.** $(\frac{1}{64})^{\frac{2}{3}}$

42. $(\frac{1}{64})^{-\frac{2}{3}}$ **43.** $(0.25)^{0.5}$ **44.** $(0.25)^{1.5}$ **45.** $(\frac{25}{9})^{-3.5}$

46–51. A property of multiples of *a* is given. State a corresponding property of powers of *x*.

46. $\frac{1}{n}(na) = a$ **47.** $\frac{1}{n}(ma) = \frac{m}{n}a$

48. $\frac{1}{3}a + \frac{1}{3}a + \frac{1}{3}a = a$ **49.** $\frac{22}{5}a$ and $-\frac{22}{5}a$ are opposites.

50. $\frac{1}{n}\left(\frac{1}{m}a\right) = \left(\frac{1}{nm}\right)a$ **51.** $2(\frac{1}{4}a) = \frac{1}{2}a$

52–59. Simplify. (All variables are positive.)

52. $(\sqrt{\pi})^4$ **53.** $(\sqrt[3]{\frac{1}{2}})^3$ **54.** $(\sqrt[5]{6})^{200}$

55. $\sqrt[4]{\sqrt[3]{20}}$ **56.** $\sqrt[6]{x} \cdot \sqrt[3]{x} \cdot \sqrt{x}$ **57.** $\sqrt[4]{y^8}$

58. $\sqrt{z^6} + \sqrt[3]{z^6}$ **59.** $2\sqrt[4]{x^{20}} + 3\sqrt[5]{x^{20}}$

60–61. Find all numbers *v* such that $1 \leq v \leq 1000$ and

60. $v^{\frac{1}{5}}$ is an integer. **61.** $v^{\frac{1}{6}}$ is an integer.

Ⓒ **62.** Use the approximation $\sqrt{2} \doteq 1.4$ to evaluate $2^{\frac{3}{2}}$, $2^{\frac{5}{2}}$, and $2^{\frac{7}{2}}$. Then graph the correspondence $x \rightarrow 2^x$ for the following values of x.

$$0, 0.5, 1, 1.5, 2, 2.5, 3, 3.5, 4, 4.5$$

63. Approximate $10^{\frac{1}{3}}$ to the nearest tenth.

64. Estimate world population in the middle of 1977 by using the equation on page 410.

REAL NUMBERS AS EXPONENTS

In Section 14.3, $\frac{1}{2}a$ was examined in order to decide what $x^{\frac{1}{2}}$ means. Similarly, we can use $\sqrt{5}a$ to figure out what the $\sqrt{5}$th power, $x^{\sqrt{5}}$, means. First, consider $\sqrt{5}$.

$\sqrt{5}$ is between 2 and 3.

$\sqrt{5}$ is between 2.2 and 2.3.

$\sqrt{5}$ is between 2.23 and 2.24.

$\vdots$

Thus, $\sqrt{5}$ lies in a sequence of nested intervals. Also, since $2 < \sqrt{5} < 3$, if we multiply by a we have

$2a < \sqrt{5}a < 3a$ if $a > 0$ or $2a > \sqrt{5}a > 3a$ if $a < 0$.

In either case, $\sqrt{5}a$ is between $2a$ and $3a$.

Similarly, $\sqrt{5}a$ is between $2.2a$ and $2.3a$.

$\sqrt{5}a$ is between $2.23a$ and $2.24a$.

$\vdots$

This is a special case of a general property of multiples which is easily proved.

Theorem 14.4.1

Betweenness of multiples: For any real numbers m, n, and p, if $a \neq 0$ and p is between m and n, then pa is between ma and na.

PROOF: From the given, either $m < p < n$ or $n < p < m$.

When $a > 0$, multiplying gives $ma < pa < na$ or $na < pa < ma$.

When $a < 0$, multiplying gives $ma > pa > na$ or $na > pa > ma$.

In all cases, pa is between ma and na.

As you would expect, there is a corresponding property of powers.

Theorem 14.4.2

Betweenness of powers: For any real numbers m, n, and p, if $x > 0$, $x \neq 1$, and p is between m and n, then x^p is between x^m and x^n.

This theorem can be verified as follows for some rational powers of 2 which you already know how to compute or estimate.

$$0.0078125 = 2^{-7}$$
$$0.25 = 2^{-2}$$
$$1 = 2^0$$
$$1.260 \doteq \sqrt[3]{2} = 2^{\frac{1}{3}}$$
$$1.414 \doteq \sqrt{2} = 2^{0.5}$$
$$2 = 2^1$$
$$4 = 2^2$$
$$5.657 \doteq \sqrt{32} = 2^{2.5}$$
$$8 = 2^3$$
$$32 = 2^5$$

Notice that when 2 is a base, the larger the exponent, the larger the power.

Theorem 14.4.2 also applies to irrational powers like $2^{\sqrt{5}}$. The intervals used here for $\sqrt{5}$ were listed previously.

$2^{\sqrt{5}}$ is between 2^2 and 2^3.

$2^{\sqrt{5}}$ is between $2^{2.2}$ and $2^{2.3}$.

$2^{\sqrt{5}}$ is between $2^{2.23}$ and $2^{2.24}$.

$\vdots$

Thus, $2^{\sqrt{5}}$ is the only number which lies in this sequence of nested intervals. This means $2^{\sqrt{5}}$ is a real number, and it also indicates a way of finding a decimal equivalent to $2^{\sqrt{5}}$. In fact $2^{\sqrt{5}} \doteq 4.71$. (An easier method of approximating such powers is discussed later in this chapter.)

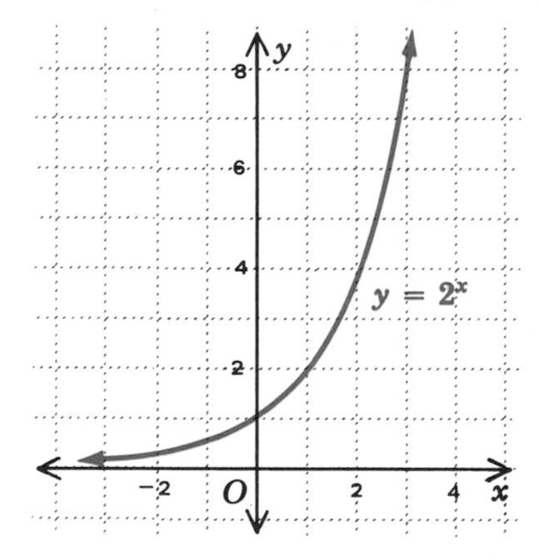

Here is the graph of $\{(x, y): y = 2^x\}$. It is somewhat like the population growth graph on page 410, but the gaps are now filled in. The x-axis is an asymptote on the left side of the graph.

The function $x \to 2^x$ is called the *exponential function with base 2.* Its domain is the set of real numbers; its range, the set of corresponding values of 2^x, is the set of positive real numbers. Thus, every positive real number is some power of 2. For instance, $4.71\cdots$ is the $\sqrt{5}$th power, 8 is the 3rd power, 0.0078125 is the -7th power.

EXERCISES 14.4

Ⓐ **1.** If t is between 1 and 2, then $4t$ is between ____ and ____.

2. If x is between 5 and 6, then 2^x is between ____ and ____.

3. What is a sequence of nested intervals?

4. How can a power like 10^π be approximated?

5. The function $x \to 2^x$ is called the ____.

6. The domain of $y = 2^x$ is ____; the range is ____.

7–9. Solve each sentence.

7. $2^x = 64$

8. $2^y = \sqrt{2}$

9. $2^z = \frac{1}{2}$

10. 64 is the ____ power of 2.

11. $\sqrt{2}$ is the ____ power of 2.

Ⓑ **12–23.** Between what two integers is a solution to each equation?

12. $2^a = 15$

13. $2^b = 100$

14. $2^c = 15.98$

15. $2^d = \frac{1}{3}$

16. $10^e = 473$

17. $10^f = 809{,}007$

18. $10^g = 11$

19. $10^h = 6$

20. $10^k = 60$

21. $10^t = 600$

22. $10^m = 0.12$

23. $10^n = 0.00461$

24. Use the graph on page 418 to better approximate a in Exercise **12**.

25–28. Represent each number as a power of 3.

25. 81

26. $\frac{1}{9}$

27. $\sqrt{3}$

28. $\sqrt[4]{3}$

29–32. Represent each number as a power of 10.

29. 10,000

30. one million

31. 0.01

32. 0.000000001

33–41. Solve each equation.

33. $2^x = 2^{-3}$

34. $4^2 = 4^{2y+1}$

35. $13^{2m+1} = 13^m$

36. $10^p = 0.00001$

37. $9\sqrt{3} = 3^q$

38. $(\sqrt{2})^r = 4\sqrt{2}$

39. $3^s = \frac{81}{6561}$

40. $4 \cdot 2^t = 1024$

41. $36^u = \frac{1}{6}$

42. To which number, 2, 3, 6, or 10, is the solution to $3^x = 20$ closest?

43. To which number, $\frac{1}{4}$, $\frac{1}{2}$, -2, or -4, is the solution to $12^y = 3$ closest?

44. True or False? The solution to $5^t = 15$ is larger than 1.5.

45. True or False? The solution to $9^m = 250$ is larger than 2.5.

Ⓒ **46–48.** Graph each function.

46. $g: x \to 3^x$

47. $h: x \to 10^x$

48. $f: x \to (\frac{1}{2})^x$

14.5 CORRESPONDING SENTENCES WITH MULTIPLES AND POWERS

Ever since Chapter 1, we have emphasized the correspondence between multiplying powers and adding multiples. From this correspondence, many properties have been derived. But can corresponding properties be taken for granted? *Absolutely not!* There must *always* be a theorem or postulate which enables us to deduce these properties. The postulate below serves this purpose.

POSTULATE 9: ORDER ISOMORPHISM PROPERTIES

These two groups are isomorphic.

$\langle$set of all positive reals, $\cdot\rangle$ and $\langle$set of all reals, $+\rangle$

The isomorphism satisfies these two properties.

Power-multiple correspondence: For any real number m,

$$\text{if } x \rightarrow a, \text{ then } x^m \rightarrow ma.$$

Order preservation: If b is between a and c, and $x \rightarrow a$, $y \rightarrow b$, and $z \rightarrow c$, then y is between x and z.

The isomorphism itself guarantees that if numbers correspond as in the postulate, then these correspondences also hold.

1. product $xy \rightarrow a + b$ sum
2. reciprocal y^{-1} or $\frac{1}{y} \rightarrow -b$ opposite
3. quotient $\frac{x}{y} \rightarrow a - b$ difference

The *power-multiple correspondence* gives additional correspondences.

4. identity for $\cdot$ x^0 or $1 \rightarrow 0 \cdot a$ or 0 identity for $+$
5. nth root $x^{\frac{1}{n}} \rightarrow \frac{1}{n}a$ nth part
6. power of power $(x^m)^n = x^{nm} \rightarrow n(ma) = (nm)a$ multiple of multiple

Order preservation was used in the last section to derive betweenness of powers from betweenness of multiples and to interpret $2^{\sqrt{5}}$.

Here is a useful property of nth roots whose proof utilizes Postulate 9 and its consequences.

Theorem 14.5.1

Product of nth roots: If $x > 0$, $y > 0$, and $n > 0$, then

$$x^{\frac{1}{n}}y^{\frac{1}{n}} = (xy)^{\frac{1}{n}}.$$

PROOF: Let $x \to a$ and $y \to b$.

Then from correspondence 5: $\begin{cases} x^{\frac{1}{n}} \to \frac{1}{n}a \\ y^{\frac{1}{n}} \to \frac{1}{n}b \end{cases}$

From correspondence 1: $x^{\frac{1}{n}} \cdot y^{\frac{1}{n}} \to \frac{1}{n}a + \frac{1}{n}b$

But by correspondence 1: $xy \to a + b$

So from correspondence 5: $(xy)^{\frac{1}{n}} \to \frac{1}{n}(a + b)$

Since the correspondence is 1–1 and the images $\frac{1}{n}a + \frac{1}{n}b$ and $\frac{1}{n}(a + b)$ are equal, the preimages $x^{\frac{1}{n}} \cdot y^{\frac{1}{n}}$ and $(xy)^{\frac{1}{n}}$ must be equal.

Theorem 14.5.1 may also be written in radical notation.

$$\sqrt[n]{x} \cdot \sqrt[n]{y} = \sqrt[n]{xy}$$

When $n = 2$, this is the property used to simplify square roots. Now other roots may be simplified.

Example: $\sqrt[3]{32} = \sqrt[3]{8} \cdot \sqrt[3]{4} = 2\sqrt[3]{4}$

The proof of Theorem 14.5.1 shows that

$$x^{\frac{1}{n}}y^{\frac{1}{n}} = (xy)^{\frac{1}{n}} \qquad \text{and} \qquad \frac{1}{n}a + \frac{1}{n}b = \frac{1}{n}(a + b)$$

are **corresponding sentences**. They are a special case of the following theorem, which is itself an immediate consequence of the order isomorphism properties.

Theorem 14.5.2

Corresponding sentence theorem: If

positive real numbers $x, y, z, \cdots$	correspond to	real numbers $a, b, c, \cdots$

so that

multiplication of $x, y, z, \cdots$	corresponds to	addition of $a, b, c, \cdots$,

then these correspondences all hold.

each sentence involving only $x, y, z, \cdots$	$\rightarrow$	a sentence involving only $a, b, c, \cdots$
multiplication	$\rightarrow$	addition
powers	$\rightarrow$	multiples
nth roots	$\rightarrow$	nth parts
reciprocals	$\rightarrow$	opposites
division	$\rightarrow$	subtraction

Examples: Corresponding sentences

1.	$x^2y^2 = (xy)^2$	$\rightarrow$	$2a + 2b = 2(a + b)$
	powers, multiplication	$\rightarrow$	multiples, addition
2.	$z = \sqrt[3]{xy}$	$\rightarrow$	$c = \frac{1}{3}(a + b)$
	cube root, multiplication	$\rightarrow$	3rd part, addition
3.	$\sqrt[5]{\frac{x^2}{y^3}} = z^{10}$	$\rightarrow$	$\frac{1}{5}(2a - 3b) = 10c$
	5th root, powers, division	$\rightarrow$	5th part, multiples, subtraction

A different pair of corresponding sentences leads to a theorem which has already been applied.

Theorem 14.5.3

Range of powers: Let x and y be positive reals with $x \neq 1$. Then there is a real number m with $y = x^m$.

PROOF: The corresponding statement about multiples is: Let a and b be reals with $a \neq 0$. Then there is a real number m with $b = ma$. Is this true? Of course. We simply let $m = \frac{b}{a}$. (Since $a \neq 0$, $\frac{b}{a}$ is real.) Thus, any real number is a multiple of a, and correspondingly, any positive real number is a power of x.

Thus, if x is a positive real number, every positive real number may be represented as a power of x. But why would anyone want to represent numbers as powers? Consider these correspondences.

If $x \to a$, then $x^m \to ma$.

For example: If $2 \to 1$, then $2^m \to m$.

From page 418, $2^{-7} = 0.0078125$, and we know that $2^5 = 32$.

Thus, $0.0078125 \to -7$

and $32 \to 5$.

Then $(0.0078125)(32) \to -7 + 5$ or -2.

But since $2^m \to m$, $2^{-2} \to -2$.

So, without calculation, we know that $(0.0078125)(32) = 2^{-2} = \frac{1}{4}$.

For most numbers, regardless of base, tables are needed to tell which numbers correspond. In the next section we find that 10, not 2, is the most commonly used base in calculations.

EXERCISES 14.5

Ⓐ **1–9.** What idea about addition and multiples corresponds to each given idea? Assume $x \to a$ and $y \to b$.

1. multiplication

2. xy

3. $\frac{x}{y}$

4. nth power of x

5. nth root of y

6. $x^{\frac{1}{n}} \cdot y^{\frac{1}{n}}$

7. reciprocal

8. 1

9. x^0

10–12. Refer to Postulate 9, the order isomorphism properties.

10. What two groups are isomorphic?

11. What is the rule for the isomorphism?

12. What is meant by the order preservation part of the postulate?

13. What theorem of this section implies that any positive real number may be written as a power of 2?

14. Give an example to show why it might be useful to represent numbers as powers of 2.

15. What theorem corresponds to $\frac{1}{n}(a + b) = \frac{1}{n}a + \frac{1}{n}b$?

16. What is the corresponding sentence theorem?

17–19. Simplify.

17. $\sqrt[3]{4} \cdot \sqrt[3]{4}$ **18.** $\sqrt[3]{4} \cdot \sqrt[3]{4} \cdot \sqrt[3]{4}$ **19.** $5^{\frac{1}{10}} \cdot 3^{\frac{1}{10}}$

20. $\sqrt[5]{xy}$ is the product of $\sqrt[5]{x}$ and ____.

Ⓑ **21–29.** Simplify if possible.

21. $\sqrt[3]{9} \cdot \sqrt[3]{3}$ **22.** $\sqrt[3]{\frac{x^3}{y^6}}$ **23.** $\sqrt[5]{64} \cdot \sqrt[5]{0.5}$

24. $\sqrt[4]{x^8y^8}$ **25.** $\sqrt[4]{x^8 + y^8}$ **26.** $\sqrt[5]{y^{-10}z^5}$

27. $(30{,}000)^{\frac{1}{4}}$ **28.** $(\frac{1}{64})^{\frac{1}{3}}$ **29.** $9^{\frac{1}{4}} \cdot 4^{\frac{1}{4}}$

30–42. Find a corresponding sentence by using the corresponding sentence theorem.

30. $xy = z$ **31.** $\frac{x}{y} = z$ **32.** $x^m = y$

33. $xyz = w$ **34.** $\sqrt[3]{y} = x$ **35.** $(xy)^m = x^my^m$

36. $\frac{x}{y} = (zy)^{\frac{1}{5}}$ **37.** $\sqrt[n]{\frac{x}{y}} = \frac{\sqrt[n]{x}}{\sqrt[n]{y}}$ **38.** $z = x^{\frac{1}{10}}y^2$

39. If $x > 0$, there is exactly one positive real number y with $y^n = x$.

40. If m is positive and $x > y > 1$, then $x^m > y^m$.

41. If m is negative and $x > y > 1$, then $x^m < y^m$.

42. If $m > n$ and $x > 1$, then $x^m > x^n$.

43. True or False? $\frac{\sqrt[6]{10}}{\sqrt[3]{10}} = \sqrt{10}$ **44.** True or False? $\frac{\sqrt[3]{x}}{\sqrt[5]{x}} = \sqrt[15]{x}$

Ⓒ **45–52.** Simplify.

45. $\sqrt[3]{81x^6y^3}$ **46.** $\sqrt{a^5b^7}$ **47.** $2\sqrt[3]{x^{27}} + 3\sqrt[7]{x^{21}}$

48. $\sqrt[4]{\sqrt[3]{20}}$ **49.** $\sqrt[4]{\frac{16x^2}{y^4}}$ **50.** $\sqrt[3]{\frac{4a^2}{b}} \cdot \sqrt[3]{\frac{2a}{b^5}}$

51. $\sqrt[6]{4} \cdot \sqrt[3]{4} \cdot \sqrt{4}$ **52.** $\sqrt[12]{100{,}000} \cdot \sqrt[4]{10} \cdot \sqrt[3]{10}$

53–54. Which is larger?

53. $\sqrt[4]{5}$ or $\sqrt[5]{5}$ **54.** $\sqrt[4]{\frac{1}{2}}$ or $\sqrt[5]{\frac{1}{2}}$

In the last few sections you have been working with *logarithms*, even though you may not have known it. In the correspondences given by the order isomorphism properties and their results, such as

$$x \to a$$
$$xy \to a + b$$
$$x^m \to ma$$

and so forth, the numbers at the right are the logarithms of the numbers at the left. It is quite usual to let $x = 10$ and $a = 1$ so that

$$10 \to 1$$

and, in general, $10^m \to m.$

This is a most important correspondence.

Definition

Let $x = 10^m$. The exponent m is called the **common logarithm** of x.

By Theorem 14.5.3, every positive number can be expressed as a power of 10. So every positive number has a common logarithm, as suggested in the list at the right.

Number	Logarithm
10^1	1
10^{-1}	-1
10^2	2
10^{-2}	-2
⋮	⋮

Some logarithms may be found in the following manner.

$$10^{0.4771} \to 0.4771$$

But $10^{0.4771} \doteq 3$. So $3 \to 0.4771$

Since $10^n \to n$

we have: $3 \cdot 10^n \to 0.4771 + n$

For various values of n:

$$30 = 3 \cdot 10^1 \to 0.4771 + 1$$
$$300 = 3 \cdot 10^2 \to 0.4771 + 2$$
$$3000 = 3 \cdot 10^3 \to 0.4771 + 3$$
$$0.3 = 3 \cdot 10^{-1} \to 0.4771 - 1$$
$$0.03 = 3 \cdot 10^{-2} \to 0.4771 - 2 \quad \text{and so on}$$

You can see now why 10 is a convenient base. Let us take another example. The common logarithm of 4.54 is approximately 0.6571.

$$4.54 \to 0.6571$$
$$10^n \to n$$
$$4.54 \cdot 10^n \to 0.6571 + n$$

This represents a number in scientific notation.

For various values of n, $4.54 \cdot 10^n$ is 454, 4,540,000, 4.54, 0.0000454, and so forth. So, given the common logarithm of 4.54, we can find the common logarithm of any of these related numbers.

Example 1: Find the common logarithm of 454,000.

SOLUTION: In scientific notation, $454{,}000 = 4.54 \cdot 10^5$.

$$\begin{array}{rrl} \text{Since} & 4.54 & \rightarrow 0.6571 \\ \text{and} & 10^5 & \rightarrow 5 \\ \text{then} & 4.54 \cdot 10^5 & \rightarrow 0.6571 + 5 \end{array}$$

Thus, the common logarithm of 454,000 is 5.6571.

Example 2: Find the common logarithm of 0.454.

SOLUTION: In scientific notation, $0.454 = 4.54 \cdot 10^{-1}$.

$$\begin{array}{lrl} \text{From above:} & 4.54 & \rightarrow 0.6571 \\ & 10^{-1} & \rightarrow -1 \\ & 4.54 \cdot 10^{-1} & \rightarrow 0.6571 - 1 \\ \text{So,} & 0.454 & \rightarrow 0.6571 - 1 \end{array}$$

Usually this is not simplified.

In scientific notation, every positive number is represented in the form $x \cdot 10^n$, where x is a number between 1 and 10 and n is an integer. If we know the common logarithm of x, we can get the common logarithm for any number that has the same digits in the same order as x. Thus, in the table on pages 603–604, common logarithms are given only for numbers between 1 and 10. From these, the logarithm for any number can be calculated just by adding or subtracting an integer.

Example 3: Find the common logarithm of 2130.

SOLUTION: $2130 = 2.13 \cdot 10^3$

From the tables: $2.13 \rightarrow 0.3284$

Obviously, $10^3 \rightarrow 3$

So, $2130 = 2.13 \cdot 10^3 \rightarrow 0.3284 + 3$

The common logarithm of 2130 is 3.3284.

The decimal part of the common logarithms of 2.13, 213, 0.00213, 213,000, and so forth, is the same. This part, called the **mantissa** of the logarithm, can be found in tables. The integer part, called the **characteristic**, must be calculated without tables. The characteristic is the exponent when the number is written in scientific notation.

The following list gives more numbers and their common logarithms. Use these examples to see how to use the tables on pages 603–604. Notice particularly that the logarithms for 1.50, 1.51, 1.52, 1.53, and so forth, are found on the same row of the tables.

Number		*Scientific Notation*		*Logarithm*
1.50	=	$1.50 \cdot 10^0$	→	0.1761
1.51	=	$1.51 \cdot 10^0$	→	0.1790
1.52	=	$1.52 \cdot 10^0$	→	0.1818
1.53	=	$1.53 \cdot 10^0$	→	0.1847
153	=	$1.53 \cdot 10^2$	→	0.1847 + 2, or 2.1847
0.000153	=	$1.53 \cdot 10^{-4}$	→	0.1847 − 4
91200	=	$9.12 \cdot 10^4$	→	0.9600 + 4, or 4.9600

EXERCISES 14.6

Ⓐ **1.** Under the correspondence $B^m \to m$, B^2 corresponds to ____.

2–7. Tell what each number corresponds to under the correspondence $10^a \to a$.

2. 100 **3.** 1000 **4.** 0.1

5. 0.000001 **6.** 1 million **7.** $10^{0.322}$

8–13. Give the common logarithm of each number in Exercises **2–7**.

14–17. Give the common logarithm.

14. $10^{0.622}$ **15.** $10^{5.611}$ **16.** $\sqrt{10}$ **17.** 10

18. If the common logarithm of 5 is approximately 0.6990, what is the common logarithm of 50?

19–22. Write each number in scientific notation.

19. 3456 **20.** 2.1224 **21.** 0.000653 **22.** 9,780,004

23–24. Simplify.

23. 0.3821 − 1 = ____ **24.** 0.3821 − 2 = ____

25–28. The common logarithm of 4.85 is approximately 0.6857. Find the common logarithm of the given number.

25. 0.485 **26.** 48.5 **27.** 48,500,000 **28.** 0.00485

29. Which common logarithms are normally found in tables?

30. The decimal part of a common logarithm is called the ____ of the logarithm.

31. The integer part of a common logarithm is called the ____ of the logarithm.

Ⓑ **32–55.** Use tables to approximate the common logarithm of each number.

32. 2.78	**33.** 278	**34.** 0.0278	**35.** 8.61
36. 8610	**37.** 8.61×10^6	**38.** 9	**39.** 0.0090
40. 9 trillion	**41.** 4.01	**42.** 0.000401	**43.** 0.401
44. 7.77	**45.** 7,770,000,000	**46.** 77.7	**47.** 5400
48. 3.14	**49.** 1.41	**50.** 5000	**51.** 2500
52. π	**53.** 1.01	**54.** $\sqrt{2}$	**55.** $\sqrt{3}$

56. If a number has 10 digits before the decimal point, what can you tell about its common logarithm?

57. If a number is between 10 and 100, what can you tell about its common logarithm?

58. If $0.01 < x < 0.1$, then the common logarithm of x has characteristic ____.

59. The common logarithm of t is approximately $0.6902 - 1$. Then t is close to which number?

a. 4.9 **b.** 49 **c.** 490 **d.** -4.9 **e.** 0.49

60. The common logarithm of 1,001,329 is approximately ____.

61. The common logarithm of $5.000100020003 \cdots$ is approximately ____.

62–73. Given the correspondence: $x \to$ common logarithm of x, under which $2 \to 0.3010$ and $3 \to 0.4771$, find the common logarithm of each number *without* the aid of tables. (Tables provide a good check of your answers.)

62. $2 \cdot 3$ or 6	**63.** $\frac{2}{3}$	**64.** 2^5 or 32
65. $\sqrt{2}$	**66.** $2 \cdot 3 \cdot 3 \cdot 3$	**67.** 36 or $2^2 \cdot 3^2$
68. 0.0006	**69.** $2^{\frac{1}{5}}$	**70.** $3^{\frac{1}{10}}$
71. $\frac{8}{27}$	**72.** 1.28	**73.** 0.0081

Ⓒ **74–81.** Interpolate to approximate the common logarithm of each number. (Tables are needed.)

74. 1.732	**75.** 9462	**76.** 100.2	**77.** 1.002
78. 1.005	**79.** 0.001234	**80.** 8678	**81.** 0.005555

WHAT NUMBER HAS A GIVEN COMMON LOGARITHM?

These three rules all describe the same correspondence.

$$10^a \to a$$

$$x \to \text{common logarithm of } x$$

$$x \to \log x$$

We can also use the abbreviation $\log x$ to shorten the definition for common logarithm given on page 425.

Definition (restated)

$x = 10^a$ if and only if $a = \log x$. $(x > 0)$

Sometimes $\log x$ is known, but not x. This is like knowing that $\sin \theta = \frac{\sqrt{3}}{2}$, but not knowing θ. Suppose $\log x = 3.6609$. Now

$$x \quad \to \quad \log x = 3.6609.$$

By the first rule above, $x = 10^{3.6609}$. The real question is, How can we write this as a decimal? Three simple ideas are combined to solve this problem.

1. Split 3.6609 into its integer and decimal parts. $3 + 0.6609$
2. Find the numbers whose logarithms are 3 and 0.6609. (Use tables to find the number whose log is 0.6609.) $10^3 \to 3$; $4.58 \to 0.6609$
3. Use the fact that multiplying in the domain corresponds to adding in the range. $4.58 \cdot 10^3 = 4580 \to 3.6609$

So 4580 is the number whose logarithm is 3.6609. We call 4580 the *antilogarithm* of 3.6609.

Definition

If $y = \log x$, then x is the **antilogarithm** of y.
We write $x = \text{antilog } y$.

You should think of an antilogarithm as being the *preimage* and the logarithm as being the *image* under the logarithm correspondence.

Examples: Finding antilogarithms (preimages of logarithms)

1. Find t when $\log t = 0.1875 - 4$.

From tables:

	multiply	1.54	$\to$	0.1875	add
		10^{-4}	$\to$	-4	
$t =$		0.000154	$\to$	$0.1875 - 4$	$= \log t$

2. Find antilog 0.9031. Tables are all that is needed.

log 8.00 = 0.9031 So antilog 0.9031 = 8.

3. Find antilog −0.9031.

The decimals (mantissas) in the tables are all positive. So rewrite the log with a positive decimal part by thinking of it as $(-0.9031 + 1) - 1$ or $0.0969 - 1$.

From tables:

$$\begin{array}{rcr} 1.25 & \rightarrow & 0.0969 \\ 10^{-1} & \rightarrow & -\ 1 \\ \hline 0.125 & \rightarrow & 0.0969 - 1 \end{array}$$

So antilog $-0.9031 = 0.125$.

EXERCISES 14.7

Ⓐ 1. Give two different-looking correspondences for the log function.

2. If $y = \log x$, then x is the ____ of y.

3. *Logarithm* is to *image* as *antilogarithm* is to ____.

4–8. Give the antilogarithm of each number.

4. 1	**5.** −2	**6.** 0	**7.** 6.0000	**8.** x

9. If 7.40 = antilog 0.8692, then ____ = antilog 1.8692.

10. If 4.57 = antilog 0.6599, then ____ = antilog 0.6599 − 2.

11. antilog −2.4568 = antilog (____ − 3)

12. antilog −0.0102 = antilog (____ − 1)

13–30. Use tables (if necessary) to calculate a decimal approximation to the antilogarithm of each number.

13. 0.9703	**14.** 0.8727	**15.** 0.4116
16. 0.0792	**17.** 0.5428	**18.** 0.7160
19. 0.7443	**20.** 0.6911	**21.** 0
Ⓑ **22.** 2.8927	**23.** 3.2989	**24.** 1.2430
25. 0.9440 + 4	**26.** 0.9440 − 4	**27.** −4.9431
28. 0.0899 − 2	**29.** 0.6893 − 1	**30.** −0.4698

31–37. Solve each equation.

31. $\log x = -3.2480$	**32.** $\log y = 2.909$	**33.** $0.8 = \log z$
34. $\log n = -1$	**35.** $\log x = 0.4314$	**36.** $\log y = -0.0991$
37. $\log z = 1.9284$		

38–43. Write each number in the form $m + c$, where m is a decimal between 0 and 1 and c is an integer. **Example:** $-0.3402 = 0.6598 + (-1)$

38. -0.2581

39. -2.46

40. -6.9802

41. $0.2468 + 2 - (0.1619 + 1)$

42. $0.5555 - 1 - (0.6026 + 3)$

43. $-0.3 + 5 - 2(0.2461 - 1)$

Ⓒ **44–49.** Interpolate to approximate the antilogarithm.

44. 2.8423

45. $0.9456 - 5$

46. 3.1416

47. 1.0015

48. 0.21

49. $\frac{5}{3}$

APPLICATIONS TO ARITHMETIC

According to the corresponding sentence theorem, if

$$x \to a, \quad y \to b, \quad \text{and} \quad z \to c,$$

then these are corresponding sentences:

$$z = xy \quad \to \quad c = a + b$$

$$z = \frac{x}{y} \quad \to \quad c = a - b$$

$$z = x^m \quad \to \quad c = ma$$

But you now know we can think of the correspondence as $x \to \log x$, so $a = \log x$, $b = \log y$, and $c = \log z$. Substituting for a, b, and c in the three sentences on the right above, we get sentences which more than correspond—they are *equivalent.*

Theorem 14.8.1

The following pairs of sentences are equivalent.

a. $z = xy$ and $\log z = \log x + \log y$

b. $z = \frac{x}{y}$ and $\log z = \log x - \log y$

c. $z = x^m$ and $\log z = m \log x$

PROOF: **a.** If $x \to a$, $y \to b$, and $z \to c$, as in the corresponding sentence theorem, then $z = xy$ if and only if $c = a + b$.

But $a = \log x$, $b = \log y$ and $c = \log z$.
Substituting, $z = xy$ if and only if $\log z = \log x + \log y$.

Parts **b** and **c** are similarly proved.

Substituting for z in the equations on the right in Theorem 14.8.1 leads to three fundamental properties of logarithms which have simple applications to arithmetic.

Theorem 14.8.1 (alternate form)

Properties of logarithms:

a. $\log xy = \log x + \log y$

b. $\log \frac{x}{y} = \log x - \log y$

c. $\log x^m = m \log x$

Example 1: *Multiplication.* Approximate (0.00369)(86.4) using logs.

SOLUTION: Let $z = xy = (0.00369)(86.4)$.

$z = (0.00369)(86.4)$ — is equivalent to → $\log z = \log 0.00369 + \log 86.4$

$\doteq (0.5670 - 3) + (0.9365 + 1)$

$= 1.5035 - 2$

$\log z \doteq 0.5035 - 1$

To find z, calculate antilog $(0.5035 - 1)$.

$z \doteq 0.319$

Example 2: *Division.* Approximate $\frac{9.18}{0.0032}$ using logs.

SOLUTION: Let $z = \frac{x}{y} = \frac{9.18}{0.0032}$.

$z = \frac{9.18}{0.0032}$ — is equivalent to → $\log z = \log 9.18 - \log 0.0032$

$\doteq 0.9628 - (0.5051 - 3)$

$z \doteq 2870$ ← is equivalent to — $\log z \doteq 0.4577 + 3$

Using logarithms for computations is very similar to modeling in applications.

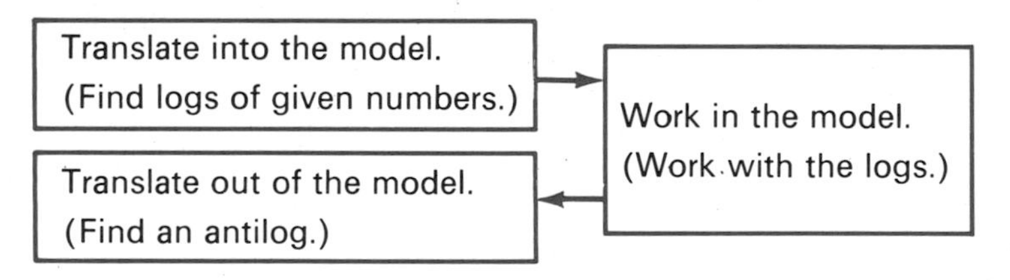

The next three applications of logarithms are most useful because other simple techniques are not available.

Example 3: *Real powers.* Approximate $40^{1.2}$ using logs.

SOLUTION:

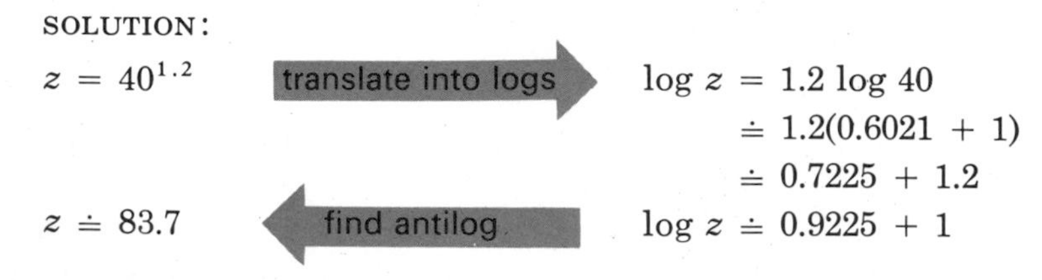

$z = 40^{1.2}$ — translate into logs → $\log z = 1.2 \log 40$

$\doteq 1.2(0.6021 + 1)$

$\doteq 0.7225 + 1.2$

$z \doteq 83.7$ ← find antilog — $\log z \doteq 0.9225 + 1$

Example 4: *Roots.* Find the positive 5th root of 17.

SOLUTION: $z = 17^{\frac{1}{5}} \longrightarrow \log z = \frac{1}{5}\log 17$

$\doteq \frac{1}{5}(1.2304)$

$z \doteq 1.76 \longleftarrow \log z \doteq 0.2461$

Example 5: *Large powers.* Approximate 2^{64}.

SOLUTION: $z = 2^{64} \longrightarrow \log z = 64 \log 2$

$\doteq 64(0.3010)$

$z \doteq 1.84 \cdot 10^{19} \longleftarrow \log z \doteq 19.2640$

So $2^{64} \doteq 1.84 \cdot 10^{19} = 18{,}400{,}000{,}000{,}000{,}000{,}000$.

Example 6: *Tougher arithmetic.* More-complicated problems are not really very difficult. Estimate $\frac{(3.86)^5(0.0012)}{\sqrt{834{,}000}}$.

SOLUTION: Let $N = \frac{x^5y}{z^{\frac{1}{2}}} = \frac{(3.86)^5(0.0012)}{\sqrt{834{,}000}}$.

$N = \frac{x^5y}{z^{\frac{1}{2}}}$ is equivalent to $\log N = 5\log x + \log y - \frac{1}{2}\log z$

So $N = \frac{(3.86)^5(0.0012)}{\sqrt{834{,}000}} \longrightarrow \log N = 5\log 3.86 + \log 0.0012 - \frac{1}{2}\log 834{,}000$

$\doteq 5(0.5866) + (0.0792 - 3) - \frac{1}{2}(5.9212)$

$= 2.9330 + 0.0792 - 3 - 2.9606$

$N \doteq 0.00113 \longleftarrow \log N \doteq 0.0516 - 3$

Example 7: *Solving equations.* Approximate a solution to $14 = \sqrt[3]{7x^2}$.

SOLUTION: $14 = \sqrt[3]{7x^2} \longrightarrow \log 14 = \frac{1}{3}(\log 7 + 2\log x)$

$1.1461 \doteq \frac{1}{3}(0.8451 + 2\log x)$

$1.1461 \doteq 0.2817 + \frac{2}{3}\log x$

$0.8644 \doteq \frac{2}{3}\log x$

$\frac{3}{2}(0.8644) \doteq \log x$

$x \doteq 19.8 \longleftarrow 1.2966 \doteq \log x$

EXERCISES 14.8

Ⓐ 1. Under the corresponding sentence theorem, if x, y, and z are positive, what sentence corresponds to $xy = z$?

2. If $\frac{x}{y} = z$ corresponds to $a - b = c$, how may x and a, y and b, and z and c be related?

3. True or False? Since $6 = 2 \cdot 3$, $\log 6 = \log 2 + \log 3$.

4. True or False? Since $(20.3)^2 = 412.09$, $2 \cdot \log 20.3 = \log 412.09$.

5–14. Find an equivalent equation which involves logarithms. Do not calculate or attempt to solve.

5. $d = ef$ **6.** $g = \sqrt{h}$ **7.** $m^2 = \frac{1}{p}$

8. $y = \sqrt[7]{x^3}$ **9.** $y = x^2$ **10.** $\pi r^2 = A$

11. $N = \sqrt[3]{106}$ **12.** $x = (86.1)^2$

13. $P = (49.6)(215)$ **14.** $V = \frac{4}{3}\pi(0.07)^3$

Ⓑ **15–18.** Use logarithms to approximate each variable in Exercises **11–14**.

19–34. Use logarithms to approximate.

19. $(347)(243{,}000)$ **20.** $(47.1)(0.000839)$ **21.** $\frac{9{,}300{,}000}{841}$

22. $\frac{1}{0.0000101}$ **23.** $2^{\frac{1}{5}}$ **24.** $\sqrt[3]{10}$

25. $9^{1.75}$ **26.** $343^{\frac{2}{3}}$ **27.** $(874)^5$

28. $(1.05)^{20}$ **29.** $(641)(0.00231)(0.06)$ **30.** $\sqrt[3]{(2.46)(61.1)}$

31. $\frac{5.12 \cdot 10^7}{4.06 \cdot 10^{-2}}$ **32.** $\frac{1}{(246)(0.623)}$

33. $\frac{(93{,}000{,}000)(6.28)}{365}$ **34.** $\frac{17^3}{12^4}$

35. Which is larger, $3^{\sqrt{2}}$ or $2^{\sqrt{5}}$?

36. Which is larger, 2^{50} or 10^{15}?

37. Give the first two digits and the number of digits in 3^{20}.

Ⓒ **38.** How many digits are there in $2^{19937} - 1$, the largest known (as of 1975) prime number? What is the first digit? The last digit?

39–46. Solve.

39. $\log 5 + \log x = \log 15$ **40.** $\log y - \log 8 = \log 32$

41. $3 \log 4 = \log x$ **42.** $-\log 5 = \log w$

43. $\log(x + 1) + \log(x - 1) = 2$ **44.** $\log(y - 1) - \log(2y + 3) = -1$

45. $\log(\log z) = 0$ **46.** $\log(\log(\log t)) = 1$

47–48. *Population growth.* Using the formula $\frac{P}{3} = 2^{\frac{Y-1960}{35}}$, discussed on page 410, estimate the growth of the population of the world from:

47. 1975 to 1980. **48.** 1980 to 1985.

49–53. Given $\log \pi \doteq 0.49715$, approximate each log.

49. $\log 2\pi$ **50.** $\log \frac{\pi}{4}$ **51.** $\log 10\pi$

52. $\log \pi r^2$ when $r = 1.8$ **53.** $\log \frac{4}{3}\pi r^3$ when $r = 6$

54. Simplify: $\log C + \log A + \log B + \log I + \log N$.

FURTHER APPLICATIONS OF LOGARITHMS

Because powers are easy to calculate using logarithms, logarithms are useful in obtaining values of exponential functions. One practical application is to compound interest.

Suppose an amount P (the principal) is invested and earns interest at the rate of 6% during a given time period (perhaps each month, each six months, or each year).

At the end of one time period, there is $P + 0.06P = P(1.06)$.

At the end of two time periods, there is $1.06(P(1.06)) = P(1.06)^2$.

⋮

At the end of n time periods, there is $P(1.06)^n$.

In general, if the rate is r, then after n periods of compounding interest, the total amount T is given by

$$T = P(1 + r)^n.$$

In actual problems, it is often necessary to determine r and n before using the formula. For example, if a bank advertises interest of 5% compounded quarterly, the rate for each quarter is not 5% but $\frac{5}{4}\% = \frac{5}{400} = 0.0125$. In two years, the interest is compounded eight times, so after two years in this bank there is

$$P(1 + \tfrac{5}{400})^8 \text{ or } P(1.0125)^8.$$

It is easy to calculate $(1.0125)^8$ using logarithms, so for any principal the amount after two years is easily found.

How long would it take an investment to double at this rate? Letting x be the number of times the interest is compounded, we wish to solve

$$P(1.0125)^x = 2P.$$

Dividing by P: $$(1.0125)^x = 2$$

This tells immediately that the answer does not depend on the amount invested, P, but only on the rate. (You should have expected this result.) We can solve this equation by finding the equivalent equation involving logarithms.

$$x \log 1.0125 = \log 2$$

$$x = \frac{\log 2}{\log 1.0125} \doteq \frac{0.3010}{0.0054} \doteq 56$$ ← can be computed by dividing or by using logarithms again to find antilog (log 0.3010 − log 0.0054)

So it would take about 56 quarters, or about 14 years, to double.

Thus, logarithms can help to solve equations where the unknown is an exponent.

Theorem 14.9.1

If $a^x = b$, then $x = \dfrac{\log b}{\log a}$.

PROOF: $a^x = b$ is equivalent to $x \log a = \log b$, so $x = \dfrac{\log b}{\log a}$.

Example: Solve $2^x = 3$.

SOLUTION: From the theorem, $x = \dfrac{\log 3}{\log 2} \doteq \dfrac{0.4771}{0.3010} \doteq 1.59$.

The formula for growth of money invested at compound interest can also be applied to other situations of either growth or decay, including inflation, population growth, radioactive decay, and changes in light and sound intensity under certain conditions. Examples of some of these are given in the exercises.

EXERCISES 14.9

Ⓐ **1–6.** In the formula $T = P(1 + r)^n$, indicate what you would substitute for each variable and what you would solve for in each situation.

1. Find the amount of money after 6 years if $100 is invested at 8% interest compounded yearly.

2. Find the amount of money after 6 years if $100 is invested at 8% compounded quarterly.

3. How much must you invest at 6% compounded monthly if you wish to have $5000 at the end of 10 years?

4. In how many years will an amount of money triple if it gains 10% yearly?

5. If the dollar loses 3% in purchasing power yearly, in how many years will it lose 25% in purchasing power? (The rate is negative.)

6. A bank advertises that it compounds $4\frac{1}{2}\%$ interest daily. In 10 days how much will \$100,000 gain in interest?

7–10. Give an equivalent equation involving logarithms.

7. $8^x = 3$

8. $5(1.05)^n = 67$

9. $\frac{1}{2}P = P(3.5)^t$

10. $PV^c = T$

11–14. In your head, determine the consecutive integers between which a solution to the equation lies.

11. $10^x = 0.000456$

12. $7^m = 400$

Ⓑ 13. $(\frac{1}{2})^n = 14$

14. $4.5^y = 1000$

15–18. Solve each of the equations of Exercises **11–14**.

19. Solve: $5^x = 3^{x+1}$.

20. Solve: $14^y = 8.72^y$.

21–26. *Compound interest.* Solve each of the problems of Exercises **1–6**.

Ⓒ **27–30.** *Population growth.* Population growth is often assumed to be exponential for short periods of time. If the population is known at two different times, the rate of growth can be calculated for that period. This gives a rate like that in compound interest, and the formula for Exercises **1–6** can be used, where n stands for the number of time periods, P for the original population, and T for the final population.

27. From 1950 to 1960, New York City had a population decline of 1.4 percent per year. If the 1950 population was 7,890,000, and if the rate remained constant, what would you expect the 1970 population to be? The 1970 population census gave 7,770,000 as the population. Was this more or less than would be expected?

28. The U.S. population in 1960 was about 180×10^6, and in 1970, about 209×10^6. At this rate what would the population be in 1980?

29. Under the conditions given in Exercise **28**, what would the U.S. population be in 2000?

30. The world's population growth rate is presently about 2% a year. At this rate, how long will it take the world's population to double?

31–34. *Medicine.* The healing (cicatrization) of wounds is often modeled by exponential functions. If A is the area (in square centimetres) of a wound after t days, one such function might have the equation $A = 107 \cdot 10^{-0.221t}$. Use this formula in the exercises.

31. What was the original area of the wound?

32. What is the area after 1 day?

33. When will the wound be 50% healed?

34. When will the wound be 95% healed?

35–37. *Decay of elements.* The half-life H of a radioactive substance satisfies the equation $M_t = M_0(\frac{1}{2})^{\frac{t}{H}}$, where M_0 is the mass when time $t = 0$ and M_t is the mass at time t.

35. Calculate the half-life of a radioactive substance when after 1 hour only 40% of the substance remains.

36. Date an archaeological artifact which contains 20% of an originally pure amount of carbon 14. The half-life of carbon 14 is approximately 5750 years.

37. Strontium 90 has a half-life of 25 years. How much will be left of 10 grams of strontium 90 after 30 years?

38–39. *Light intensity.* The intensity I of light through a glass of thickness t (in centimetres) satisfies the equation $I = I_0 \cdot 10^{-kt}$, where I_0 is the intensity before entering the glass, and k is a constant which depends on the type of glass being used. Suppose that for ordinary glass, $k \doteq 0.0434$. How thick must the glass be to blot out:

38. $\frac{1}{50}$ of the light?

39. $\frac{1}{10}$ of the light?

40–41. *Depreciation.* Suppose that a car depreciates about $\frac{1}{3}$ of its value in a given year. Then $V \doteq V_0(\frac{2}{3})^n$, where V_0 is the original value and n is the number of years. How much is a \$5000 car worth:

40. after $\frac{1}{2}$ year?

41. after 2.5 years?

LOGARITHMS TO BASES OTHER THAN 10

You know two rules for the log function to the base 10.

$$10^a \to a$$

$$x \to \log x$$

Now let B be the base instead of 10.

$$B^a \to a$$

The correspondence $B^a \to a$ has many of the properties of the log function. So when $x = B^a$, we write

$$x \to \log_B x.$$

$\text{Log}_B\, x$ is short for the logarithm of x to the base B. Summarizing:

Definition

$$\log_B x = a \text{ if and only if } B^a = x.$$
$$(x > 0,\, B > 0,\, B \neq 1)$$

Logs to the base 10 are easy to find with tables because we can write numbers in decimal notation. Logs to the base B are not so convenient; for instance, knowing $\log_B 6.4$ is not usually much help in finding $\log_B 640$. However, the definition can sometimes be useful.

Examples: Logarithms to bases other than 10

1. To calculate $\log_5 125$, think:

   If $\log_5 125 = y$, then $5^y = 125$.

   Solve this in your head. $5^3 = 125$, so $\log_5 125 = 3$.

2. $\log_6 \frac{1}{36} = -2$ because $6^{-2} = \frac{1}{36}$.

Several simple properties of logarithms follow immediately from the definition of $\log_B x$.

Theorem 14.10.1

a. $\log_B B^a = a$ b. $B^{\log_B x} = x$

PROOF: By definition, $\log_B x = a$ if and only if $B^a = x$.

a. Substitute B^a for x on the left side of the definition.

b. Substitute $\log_B x$ for a on the right side of the definition.

There are several special cases of Theorem 14.10.1

	$\log_B 1 = 0$	$\log_B \frac{1}{B} = -1$
That is:	$1 = B^0 \to 0$	$\frac{1}{B} = B^{-1} \to -1$

Examples: Logarithms to bases other than 10

3. $\log_x x^2 = 2$ regardless of the value of x.

4. To find $\log_{81} 27$, let: $x = \log_{81} 27$

Then by definition: $81^x = 27$

Write 81 and 27 as powers of 3: $(3^4)^x = 3^3$

$3^{4x} = 3^3$

Equate the exponents: $4x = 3$

$x = \frac{3}{4}$

Thus, $\log_{81} 27 = \frac{3}{4}$. Check: Does $81^{\frac{3}{4}}$ equal 27?

In each of these examples, the logarithm was a rational number, and tables were not needed. This is not always the case.

5. To approximate $\log_6 12$, let: $x = \log_6 12$

Then: $6^x = 12$

Use Theorem 14.9.1, page 436: $x = \frac{\log 12}{\log 6}$

From the tables: $\doteq \frac{1.0792}{0.7782}$

So $\log_6 12 \doteq 1.39$

Examining the solution above, you can see that $\log_6 12 = \frac{\log 12}{\log 6}$. This can be generalized.

Theorem 14.10.2

Change of base theorem: $\log_B x = \frac{\log x}{\log B}$

Logarithms were invented by the Scottish mathematician John Napier (1550–1617). After 20 years of work to create a table of logarithms of sin x, he published the table in 1614. He did not originally connect logarithms with a base. But before his death, Napier and the English mathematician Henry Briggs (1561–1631) settled upon 10 as a convenient base. In the 17th century, decimals were only beginning to be used, and by revolutionizing computation, logarithms helped to popularize the new decimal system.

Nowadays computers can do all the computation needed, and 10 is *not* the most common base used by mathematicians. The number 2.718 · · ·, always designated by the symbol e, is more commonly used. One of the simplest known formulas for e is this infinite sum of fractions.

$$e = 1 + \frac{1}{1} + \frac{1}{1 \cdot 2} + \frac{1}{1 \cdot 2 \cdot 3} + \frac{1}{1 \cdot 2 \cdot 3 \cdot 4} + \cdots = 2.71828 \cdots$$

When the base e is used, the logarithms are called **natural logarithms**. The shorthand *ln* is used for $\log_e$.

Definition

$$\ln x = \log_e x$$

Example: Calculate ln 5.

SOLUTION: $\ln 5 = \log_e 5 = \frac{\log 5}{\log e}$

$$\doteq \frac{\log 5}{\log 2.718} \doteq \frac{0.6990}{0.4343} \doteq 1.609$$

One application of natural logarithms is to *continuous compounding* of interest. Suppose a bank gives 5% annual interest and \$1 is invested. The time period for compounding the interest determines the total amount (T) in the account after one year.

yearly ➡ $T = 1 + 0.05 = 1.05$

semiannually ➡ $T = \left(1 + \frac{0.05}{2}\right)^2 = 1.050625$

quarterly ➡ $T = \left(1 + \frac{0.05}{4}\right)^4 \doteq 1.050945$

daily ➡ $T = \left(1 + \frac{0.05}{365}\right)^{365} \doteq 1.051267$

Notice that the more times interest is compounded, the larger T gets. But T does not increase beyond bound. Even compounding daily, T is still less than \$2 (less than double the original \$1).

As one compounds more often, perhaps each second, perhaps ten times a second, T gets nearer and nearer to $e^{0.05}$. Powers of e are easily calculated because tables of natural logarithms are widely available. At 5% annual interest continuously compounded, after one year each dollar will become

$$e^{0.05} \doteq 1.052.$$

In general, if an amount P is invested at rate r compounded continuously for n time periods, the total T is given by this formula.

$$T = Pe^{rn}$$

EXERCISES 14.10

Ⓐ **1.** Since $2^5 = 32$, $\log_2 32 =$ _____.

2. Since $27^2 = 729$, $\log_{27}$ _____ $=$ _____.

3–5. Find an equivalent equation involving logs not to the base 10.

3. $64^{-\frac{1}{3}} = \frac{1}{4}$

4. $5^{30} = x$

5. $0.343 = (0.7)^3$

6. Define $\log_B x$.

7. What is e?

8. What is a natural logarithm?

9. What is $\ln x$?

10–27. Simplify.

10. $\log_3 9$

11. $\log_9 3$

12. $\log_4 64$

13. $\log_{64} 4$

14. $\log_3 81$

15. $\log_3 \frac{1}{81}$

16. $\log_{\frac{1}{3}} 81$

17. $\log_{10} 1000$

18. $\log_2 128$

19. $\log_2 2^{50}$

20. $\log_2 2^{0.016}$

21. $\log_2 1$

22. $\log_2 2$

23. $\log_e e^2$

24. $\log_e e$

25. $\log_e 1$

26. $\log_7 1$

27. $\log_{\frac{1}{2}} 1$

28. True or False? $\log_2 6 + \log_2 4 = \log_2 24$

29. Multiple Choice: $\log_9 18 =$ _____.

a. 2 **b.** $\log 2$ **c.** $\log 18 - \log 9$ **d.** $\dfrac{\log 18}{\log 9}$

30. If $\log_e 10 = \dfrac{\log 10}{x}$, then $x =$ _____.

31. If \$1 is continuously compounded at 4% a year, how much will there be after 1 year?

Ⓑ **32–37.** Given $\ln 2 \doteq 0.693$ and $\ln 3 \doteq 1.099$, calculate or solve.

32. $\ln 4$

33. $\ln 12$

34. $\ln \frac{1}{2}$

35. $e^x = \frac{1}{4}$

36. $e^x = 3^{10}$

37. $e^x = \frac{2}{3}$

38–43. Use tables to help approximate.

38. $\log_6 4$

39. $\log_{103} 225$

40. $\log_7 0.01$

41. $\ln 10$

42. $\ln 7$

43. $\ln 0.1$

44. Give an example of an infinite sequence of numbers which continually increases but never gets above 3.

45–53. Simplify without tables.

45. $4^{\log_4 7}$ **46.** $6^{\log_6 36}$ **47.** $\log_x \sqrt[3]{x}$

48. $b^{\log_b x}$ **49.** $(7^{\log_7 3})^{\log_3 10}$ **50.** $\dfrac{\ln 25}{\ln 5}$

51. $\log_6 4 + \log_6 9$ **52.** $\log_3 15 - \log_3 45$ **53.** $\log_4 2 \cdot \log_2 4$

© **54.** *Atmospheric contamination.* It is estimated that the amount A of radioactivity from a nuclear explosion decreases exponentially so that $A = A_0 e^{-2t}$, where t is measured in days. How long will it take for the radioactivity to reach $\frac{1}{100}$ of its original intensity A_0?

55. What is your opinion of the applicability of the idea of Exercise **54** to a description of the intensity of normal air pollution?

56. Under certain conditions, atmospheric pressure P (in pounds per square inch) at h feet above sea level approximately satisfies the formula $P = 14.7e^{-0.000039h}$. Find P at 1 mile above sea level.

57–59. For these exercises, first carefully draw a graph of $y = \dfrac{1}{x}$ for values of x between 1 and 4.

57. Estimate (to the nearest tenth) the area of the region bounded by the x-axis, $x = 1$, $x = 2$, and $y = \dfrac{1}{x}$.

58. Estimate the area of the region bounded by the x-axis, $x = 1$, $x = 3$, and $y = \dfrac{1}{x}$.

59. Your answers to Exercises **57** and **58** should be close to the values of ln 2 and ln 3 given in Exercises **32–37**. Calculate ln 4, and give a possible geometric interpretation. Generalize.

60. A surprising application of natural logarithms is to the number of prime integers. It has been proved that if $N(x)$ is the number of primes less than x, then $\dfrac{x}{\ln x} \div N(x)$ approaches 1 as x increases. Calculate $\dfrac{x}{\ln x} \div N(x)$ for $x = 50$ and $x = 100$.

61. *Investment.* If \$100 is invested at 6% interest compounded continuously for 5 years, how much is received at the end of that period? How does this compare with what would be received if the interest were compounded annually?

62. If \$500 is compounded continuously at 6% a year, in how many years will it double?

63. The length of the part of the parabola $y = x^2$ between (0, 0) and (x, y) is $\frac{x}{2}\sqrt{4x^2 + 1} + \frac{1}{4}\ln(2x + \sqrt{4x^2 + 1}) - \frac{1}{2}\ln x$. Approximate (to the nearest tenth) the length of the part of this parabola between (0, 0) and (3, 9).

64. Prove Theorem 14.10.2.

65. Prove: $\log_b a \cdot \log_c b = \log_c a$

66–68. Use Exercise 65 as a hint to complete these exercises.

66. $\log_6 3 \cdot \log_3 \frac{1}{6} =$ ____

67. $\log 5 \cdot \log_5 10 =$ ____

68. Prove: $\log_b a$ and $\log_a b$ are reciprocals.

69. Napier's name is associated not only with logarithms, but also with a method of multiplication and a type of diagram used in navigation. Use references to find out about these.

GRAPHS OF EXPONENTIAL AND LOGARITHMIC FUNCTIONS

The correspondence $x \to \log x$ is a function. The notation used with the *logarithmic function* differs from the usual function notation.

Instead of $f(2) = 0.3010$	we write	$\log 2 = 0.3010$.
Instead of $f\colon x \to \log x$	we write	$\log\colon x \to \log x$.
Equivalently,		$\log\colon 10^a \to a$.
Switching ordered pairs,	we have	inverse of $\log\colon a \to 10^a$.

Thus, the inverse of the log function is the exponential function with base 10.

Theorem 14.11.1

Let f be the exponential function with base 10. Then f and log are inverses.

Graphs of inverse functions are reflection images of each other over $y = x$. So we can graph $y = 10^x$ and then reflect to get the graph of the log function. This shows that the domain of the log function is the positive reals and the range is the reals.

Logarithmic functions with other bases are also graphed using the corresponding exponential functions.

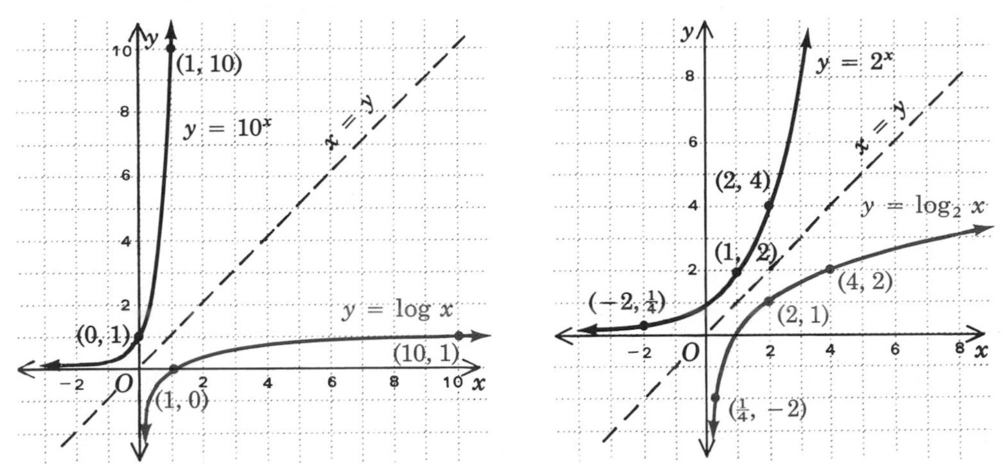

Exponential functions with base $B > 1$ increase so fast that domain values are difficult to read on a graph. This problem is solved by using graph paper with a **logarithmic scale** on the y-axis; the paper is called *semilogarithmic*. Since the resulting graph is linear, it is easier to draw accurately, as well as to read.

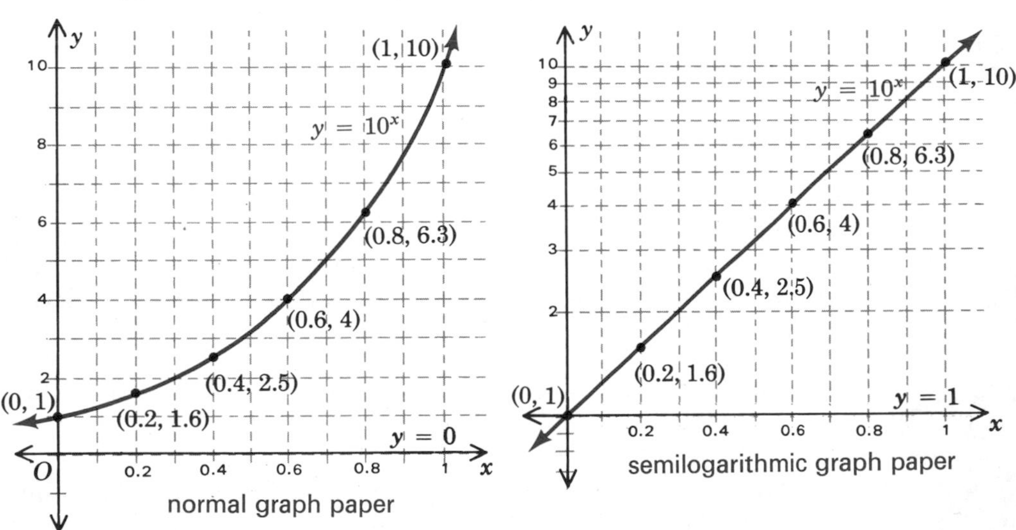

EXERCISES 14.11

Ⓐ **1.** The log function maps x onto ____.

2. Name 5 points on the graph of the log function.

3. Name 5 points on the graph of the inverse of the log function.

4. The functions with equations $y = \log x$ and ____ are inverses.

5. The functions $f: x \to 3^x$ and $g: x \to$ _____ are inverses.

6. How can the graph of a function be used to graph the inverse function?

7. How is a function such as $\log_4$ graphed?

Ⓑ 8. Graph $x \to 4^x$.

9. Graph $\log_4$.

10. Graph f where $f(x) = e^x$.

11. Graph $y = \ln x$.

12–16. What feature of the graph of $\log_B$ illustrates each property?

12. The domain of $\log_B$ is the set of positive real numbers.

13. If $B > 1$, the bigger a number is, the bigger its logarithm.

14. The range of $\log_B$ is the set of real numbers.

15. $\log_B 1 = 0$ for any B

16. If $B > 1$, $\log_B x < x$.

17. From the graph of the log function, when does it look like interpolation would be least accurate?

18. Graph $x \to (\frac{1}{2})^x$ and $\log_{\frac{1}{2}}$ on the same graph.

Ⓒ 19. Graph $y = 3^x$ on normal and on semilogarithmic graph paper.

20. Logarithmic graph paper uses logarithmic scales on both axes. Using such paper, graph $\{(x, y): y = x^2\}$. Describe your result.

21. The slide rule was invented by the English mathematician Oughtred in 1620. To use it to multiply, one of two identical logarithmic scales is slid along the other. How does this relate to translations and addition?

22. *Music.* The frets on a guitar are spaced to form a logarithmic scale. Relate this to Exercises **29–32**, page 541.

23–24. Logarithms may be used to compare quantities which differ vastly in magnitude. This makes the numbers more manageable. Differences in magnitudes correspond to ratios of sizes. Use other references to answer each question.

23. *Astronomy.* How many times brighter is a star of magnitude 1 than a star of magnitude 0?

24. *Earthquakes.* An earthquake registering 6.5 on the Richter scale is quite powerful. How many times more powerful is it than an earthquake registering 5.5?

25. By graphing, estimate a solution to the system $\begin{cases} y = \log x \\ y = 3x. \end{cases}$

26. Use the idea of Exercise **25** to estimate a solution to $\log x = 5x$.

27. *Biology*. The cross section of the shell of the chambered nautilus, shown here, forms a logarithmic spiral. Using any sources, (**a**) find an equation for a logarithmic spiral; (**b**) find one other occurrence of such a spiral in nature.

CHAPTER SUMMARY

14

The number x is an nth root of t if and only if $x^n = t$. Numbers may have more than one nth root. The radical sign $\sqrt[n]{\ }$ stands for the largest nth root of a number.

There is an order isomorphism between the groups

$$\langle \text{set of positive reals}, \cdot \rangle$$

and $$\langle \text{set of reals}, + \rangle$$

such that

if $x \neq 1$ corresponds to $a \neq 0$,

then $$x^m \to ma.$$

This isomorphism is used to give meaning to rational and real exponents.

nth root ▶ $x^{\frac{1}{n}} \to \frac{1}{n}a$ ◀ nth part

mth power of nth root ▶ $x^{\frac{m}{n}} \to \frac{m}{n}a$ ◀ mth multiple of nth part

If p is between m and n, then

x^p is between x^m and x^n	$\to$	pa is between ma and na

The numbers at the right (in the range of the isomorphism) are **logarithms** of the numbers at the left (in the domain). Any positive real number can be represented as a power of a positive base B, where $B \neq 1$ and $B \to 1$. Then

number ▶ $B^n \to n$ ◀ logarithm of number

The isomorphism guarantees corresponding sentences. When logarithms are used, these sentences are equivalent. This makes logarithms useful for computing.

$$z = xy \to \log z = \log x + \log y$$

$$z = \frac{x}{y} \to \log z = \log x - \log y$$

$$z = x^m \to \log z = m \log x$$

For computing, B is often 10, but the base $e = 2.71828\cdots$ is common in advanced mathematics. In general,

$y = \log_B x$ if and only if $B^y = x$.

$\log_{10} x$ is abbreviated $\log x$ and

$\log_e x$ is abbreviated $\ln x$.

Tables are needed to find logarithms of most numbers and to find numbers (antilogarithms) from logarithms.

logarithmic function — exponential function

$B^n \to n$ ◀ inverse functions ▶ $n \to B^n$

The graphs of the log and exponential functions are reflection images of each other over the line $y = x$. Exponential functions can be applied to compound interest, population growth, decay of radioactive materials, and many other situations. The equivalent equations

$$B^y = x \quad \text{and} \quad y \log B = \log x$$

permit logarithms to be used to advantage in solving sentences in which the unknown is an exponent; they are indispensable in these applications.

14

CHAPTER REVIEW

1–3. Simplify.

1. $\sqrt[3]{-64}$ 2. $(\sqrt[6]{7^3})^2$ 3. $\sqrt[5]{32y^5x^8}$

4–9. Calculate.

4. $\log_9 \frac{1}{27}$ 5. $\log_2 64$ 6. $\sqrt[4]{2^{12}}$

7. $64^{\frac{2}{3}}$ 8. $6^{\log_6 10}$ 9. $(\frac{1}{8})^{-\frac{2}{3}}$

10–13. Solve.

10. $\log_{10} x = 4$ 11. $3^{2y} = \sqrt{3}$ 12. $30 = 10^x$

13. $x^{10} = 8$ where $x > 0$

14. Define $\log_B a$.

15–16. Write an equivalent sentence involving logarithms.

15. $\sqrt[7]{n} = t^{0.2}$ 16. $A = 17 \cdot 12^{10}$

17. If \$100 is invested at 5% interest compounded quarterly, how much will there be at the end of 5 years?

18–21. Approximate using tables.

18. $\log 0.00702$ 19. $\log_4 7$

20. $\dfrac{578}{0.000372}$ 21. antilog 4.8230

22–24. Given $\ln 2 \doteq 0.693$ and $\ln 3 \doteq 1.099$, approximate each number.

22. $\ln \frac{1}{2}$ 23. $\ln 18$ 24. $\ln 3e$

25. Explain the statement: There is an isomorphism between $\langle$set of positive reals, $\cdot\,\rangle$ and $\langle$set of all reals, $+\,\rangle$.

26. Give the domain and range of each function: $x \to 3^x$; $x \to \log_3 x$.

Chapter 15 Trigonometry and Circular Functions

RADIAN MEASURE 15.1

As noted in Chapter 14, in mathematics and its applications base e is used more often than base 10 for logarithms. Similarly, the *degree* is not always used in measuring angles or magnitudes of rotation. A more widely used unit is the *radian* (abbreviated *rad*).

The radian unit is related to the degree unit by the following definition.

Definition

$$\pi \textbf{ radians} = 180 \text{ degrees}$$

As usual, $\pi \doteq 3.1416$. Multiplying both sides of the definition by $\frac{1}{\pi}$ gives the degree equivalent of a radian.

$$1 \text{ rad} = \frac{180}{\pi} \text{ degrees}$$

$$\doteq 57.30 \text{ degrees}$$

By multiplying, any measurement in radians can be converted to a measurement in degrees.

Examples: Conversion from radians to degrees

By definition, $\pi \text{ rad} = 180 \text{ degrees.}$

1. Multiply by $\frac{1}{4}$: $\frac{\pi}{4} \text{ rad} = \frac{180}{4} \text{ degrees} = 45^\circ$

2. Multiply by $\frac{5}{6}$: $\frac{5\pi}{6} \text{ rad} = \frac{5}{6}(180) \text{ degrees} = 150^\circ$

3. $1 \text{ rad} \doteq 57.30 \text{ degrees}$

Multiply by 3: $3 \text{ rad} \doteq 3(57.30) \text{ degrees} = 171.90^\circ$

Examples: Conversion from degrees to radians

Again we multiply both sides of the definition.

Since $180^\circ = \pi \text{ rad}$

1. $360^\circ = 2(180)^\circ = 2\pi \text{ rad}$

2. $90^\circ = \frac{1}{2}(180)^\circ = \frac{1}{2}\pi \text{ rad or } \frac{\pi}{2} \text{ rad}$

3. $60^\circ = \frac{1}{3}(180)^\circ = \frac{1}{3}\pi \text{ rad}$

4. $1^\circ = \frac{1}{180}(180)^\circ = \frac{\pi}{180} \text{ rad}$

5. $500^\circ = \frac{500}{180}(180)^\circ = \frac{25\pi}{9} \text{ rad}$

Notice that conversion is easy for factors or multiples of 180°.

Magnitudes of rotations and angles are often given in radians. The word *radian* or abbreviation *rad* is usually omitted, as in the examples below. Recall that $(\cos x, \sin x)$ is the image of $(1, 0)$ under R_x, the rotation of magnitude x.

Examples: Sines and cosines of radian magnitudes

1. $\sin \frac{\pi}{3} = \sin 60^\circ = \frac{\sqrt{3}}{2}$

2. $\cos \frac{3\pi}{2} = \cos 270^\circ = 0$

3. $\sin 1 \doteq \sin 57.30^\circ \doteq 0.843$

4. $\cos(-\pi) = \cos(-180^\circ) = -1$

There are two major reasons why radians are preferred to degrees. The first is that lengths of arcs are easier to compute (see Exercises **41–46**). The second is that formulas for sines and cosines are easier to use with radians than with degrees. (These formulas are given in the exercises for Section 17.6.)

EXERCISES 15.1

Ⓐ **1.** What is the definition of *radian*?

2. 2π radians $=$ _____ degrees

3. 0 radians $=$ _____ degrees

4. $360° =$ _____ rad

5. $57.30° \doteq$ _____ rad

6. Give two reasons why in mathematics and its applications, radians are preferred to degrees.

7–14. Convert from degrees to radians or vice versa.

7. $90°$ **8.** $-90°$ **9.** $45°$ **10.** $135°$

11. 4π **12.** $\frac{\pi}{6}$ **13.** $\frac{5\pi}{6}$ **14.** $\frac{2\pi}{3}$

15. The measures of two complementary angles add to _____ radians.

16. The measures of two supplementary angles add to _____ rad.

Ⓑ **17–28.** Calculate.

17. $\cos \pi$ **18.** $\cos \frac{\pi}{3}$ **19.** $\sin \frac{2\pi}{3}$ **20.** $\cos \frac{3\pi}{4}$

21. $\sin\left(-\frac{3\pi}{4}\right)$ **22.** $\cos \frac{\pi}{6}$ **23.** $\sin \frac{11\pi}{6}$ **24.** $\sin 14\pi$

25. $\cos \frac{-5\pi}{2}$ **26.** $\sin \frac{3\pi}{2}$ **27.** $\cos \frac{11}{6}\pi$ **28.** $\cos(-5\pi)$

29. What is the image of (1, 0) under a rotation of $-\frac{\pi}{3}$ rad?

30–35. O is between A and D, and O is between B and F. Congruent angles are marked in the diagram and $\overline{OC} \perp \overline{OD}$. Give the radian measure of each angle.

30. $\angle COD$ **31.** $\angle COB$

32. $\angle DOE$ **33.** $\angle COE$

34. $\angle AOF$ **35.** $\angle EOB$

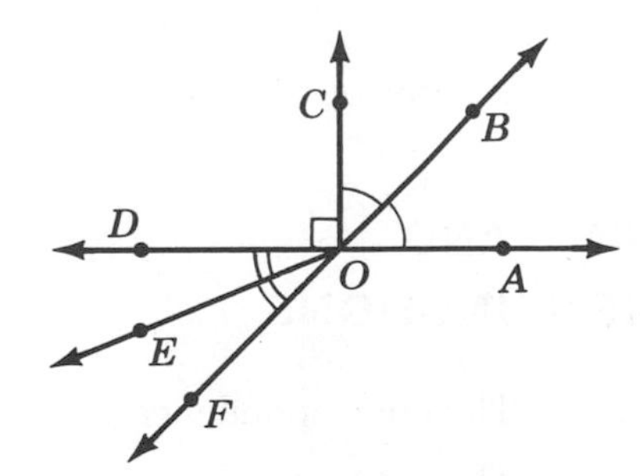

36–38. Give a matrix (with decimal approximations for elements) for the rotation with the given magnitude.

36. π **37.** $\frac{4\pi}{3}$ **38.** $\frac{-2\pi}{3}$

Ⓒ **39.** Explain why $\sin(x + 2\pi) = \sin x$ for any value of x.

40. Explain why $\cos(\pi - x) = -\cos x$ for any value of x.

41–46. For these exercises, use the following theorem.
In circle O with radius r,
length of $\widehat{AB} = r \cdot$ radian measure of $\widehat{AB}$.

Example: In a circle of radius 7, $\widehat{AB}$ has measure 60° or $\frac{\pi}{3}$ rad. So the length of $\widehat{AB}$ is $7 \cdot \frac{\pi}{3} \doteq 7\left(\frac{3.14}{3}\right) \doteq 7.33$, just a little more than the radius.

In a circle with radius 5, what is the length of an arc with the given measure?

41. 360° **42.** 180° **43.** 90°

44. 45° **45.** 135° **46.** 225°

47–50. To the nearest tenth, find the length of an arc with the given measure in a circle of the given radius. Draw a figure. (Use the theorem given with Exercises **41–46.**)

47. 312° arc, radius 10 **48.** 48° arc, radius 10

49. 135° arc, radius $\frac{1}{2}$ **50.** 135° arc, radius $\frac{7}{2}$

51–53. True or False? (Use Exercises **41–46.**)

51. Doubling the measure of an arc doubles its length.

52. A 60° arc in a circle of radius 30 is three times as long as a 60° arc in a circle of radius 10.

53. In any circle, the length of an arc is directly proportional to the measure of the arc.

15.2 THE SINE AND COSINE FUNCTIONS

The correspondence $x \to \sin x$ is called the **sine function.**

The correspondence $x \to \cos x$ is called the **cosine function.**

The domain of each of these functions is the set of real numbers. (That is, x can be any real number.) Because $\sin x$ and $\cos x$ are coordinates of points on the unit circle, the range of each of these functions is the set of real numbers between -1 and 1, inclusive.

Either function is usually graphed by thinking of x as corresponding to radian measure. (The degree equivalents are given in the table and on the graph to help you.) Seventeen ordered pairs of the sine function are tabulated and graphed here.

	0°	30°	45°	60°	90°	120°	135°	150°	180°	210°	225°	240°	270°	300°	315°	330°	360°
x	0	$\frac{\pi}{6}$	$\frac{\pi}{4}$	$\frac{\pi}{3}$	$\frac{\pi}{2}$	$\frac{2\pi}{3}$	$\frac{3\pi}{4}$	$\frac{5\pi}{6}$	π	$\frac{7\pi}{6}$	$\frac{5\pi}{4}$	$\frac{4\pi}{3}$	$\frac{3\pi}{2}$	$\frac{5\pi}{3}$	$\frac{7\pi}{4}$	$\frac{11\pi}{6}$	2π
$\sin x$	0	$\frac{1}{2}$	$\frac{\sqrt{2}}{2}$	$\frac{\sqrt{3}}{2}$	1	$\frac{\sqrt{3}}{2}$	$\frac{\sqrt{2}}{2}$	$\frac{1}{2}$	0	$-\frac{1}{2}$	$-\frac{\sqrt{2}}{2}$	$-\frac{\sqrt{3}}{2}$	-1	$-\frac{\sqrt{3}}{2}$	$-\frac{\sqrt{2}}{2}$	$-\frac{1}{2}$	0

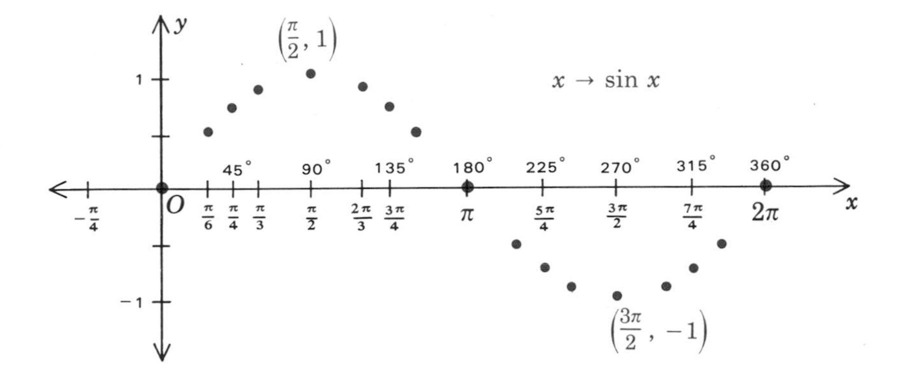

There are four questions to consider.

1. What does the entire graph look like?

2. Could the shape of the graph have been predicted?

3. What does the graph of $x \to \cos x$ look like?

4. Are there simple applications?

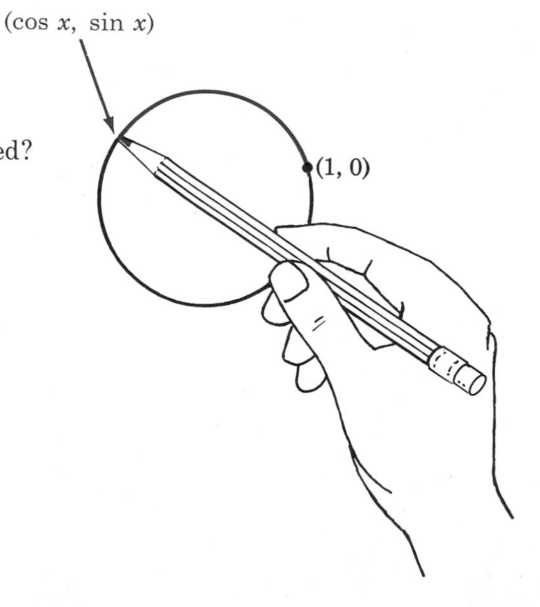

Think of a point starting at (1, 0) and moving counterclockwise at a constant speed around the unit circle. When the point moves x radians, it is at ($\cos x$, $\sin x$). As the point moves, consider the second coordinate, $\sin x$.

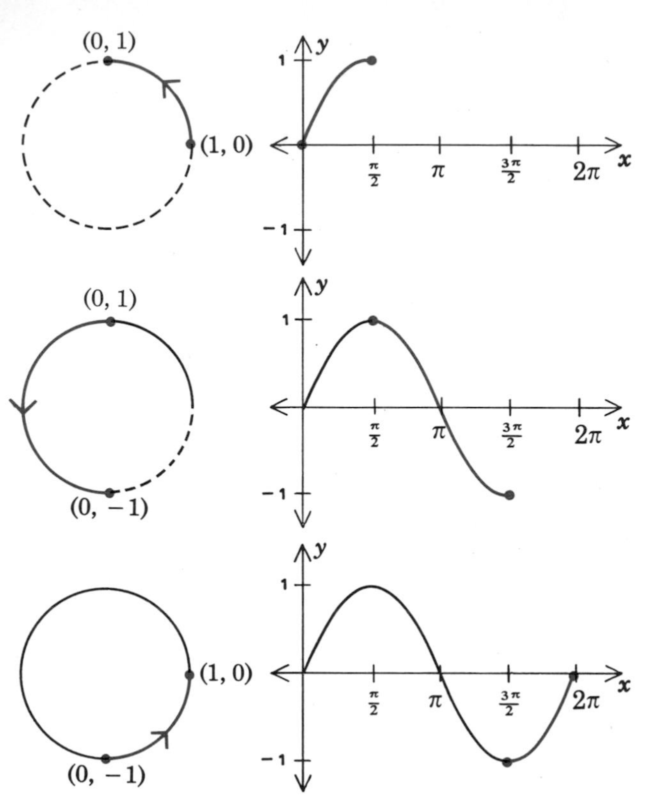

As x, the length of the arc traced by the moving point, increases from 0 to $\frac{\pi}{2}$ radians, the point goes from (1, 0) to (0, 1). So $\sin x$ increases from 0 to 1.

As x increases from $\frac{\pi}{2}$ to $\frac{3\pi}{2}$, the point goes from (0, 1) to (0, −1). The value of the second coordinate, $\sin x$, decreases most rapidly when x is near π and the moving point is near (−1, 0).

As x increases from $\frac{3\pi}{2}$ to 2π, the point moves from (0, −1) to (1, 0). So $\sin x$ (always the second coordinate) increases from −1 to 0.

Now what happens? As x continues to increase, the point continues around and around the circle. The value of the second coordinate—$\sin x$—repeats itself each 2π radians, or 360°. The result is a function whose values repeat every 2π. Here is the graph.

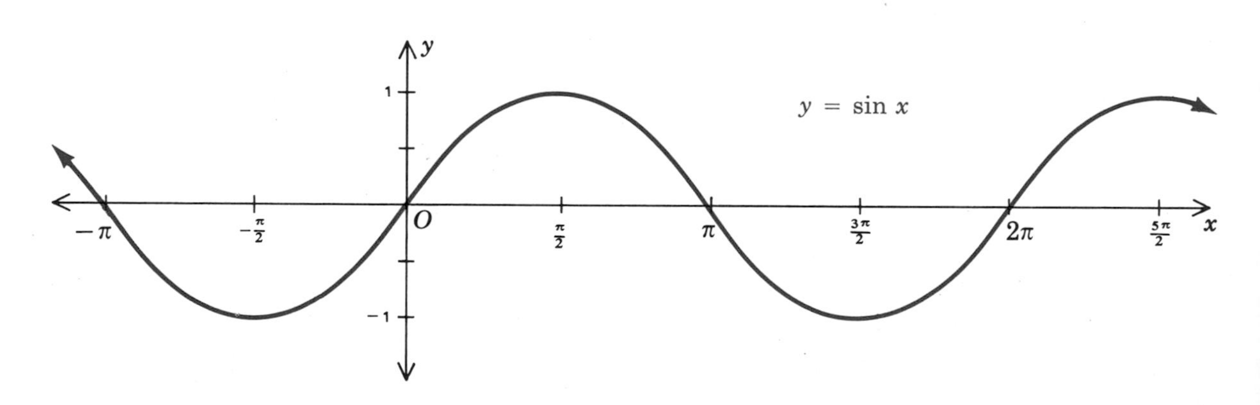

Given the graph of $y = \sin x$, by replacing x with $x - a$ or $\frac{x}{a}$, or replacing y with $y - b$ or $\frac{y}{b}$, you get translation or scale transformation images of this graph. You are familiar with the effects of these substitutions from earlier work. For example, replacing x with $x + \frac{\pi}{2}$ gives

$$y = \sin\left(x + \frac{\pi}{2}\right).$$

The graph of this equation is a translation image $\frac{\pi}{2}$ units to the *left* of the graph of $y = \sin x$. But, using Theorem 8.5.1b,

$y = \sin\left(x + \frac{\pi}{2}\right)$ **is equivalent to** $y = \sin x \cos \frac{\pi}{2} + \cos x \sin \frac{\pi}{2}$

$$= \sin x \cdot 0 + \cos x \cdot 1$$

$$= \cos x$$

So the graph of $y = \cos x$ is a translation image of the graph of $y = \sin x$. Thus the sine and cosine functions have congruent graphs. These graphs are examples of *sine waves.*

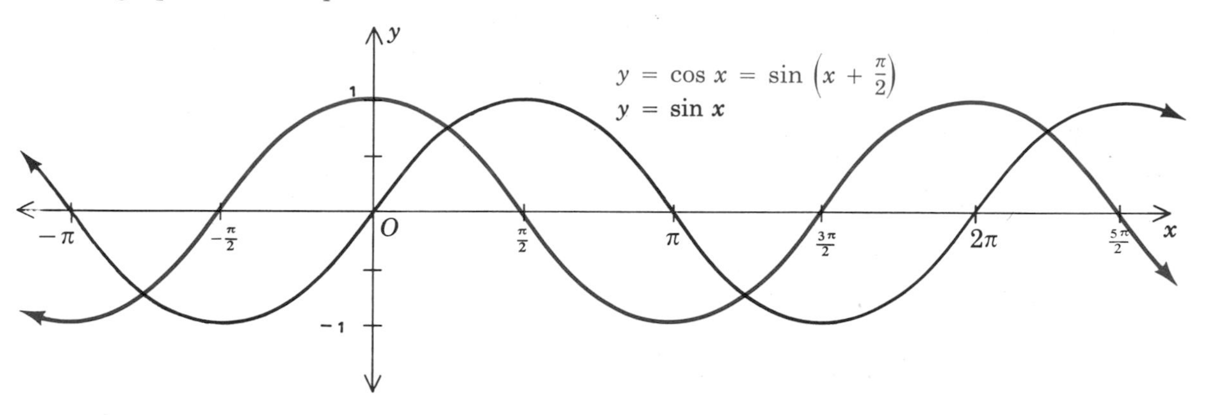

Definition

A **sine wave** is any graph which can be mapped onto the graph of $y = \sin x$ by a composite of isometries and scale transformations.

Pure sound tones travel in sine waves; these can be pictured on an oscilloscope. The height of a point on a constantly vibrating string, or a weight suspended from a spring, describes a sine curve (the independent variable is time). The time of sunset for a given location also leads to a sine curve. (See Exercise **34**.) Indeed, the variety of applications of sines and cosines is much greater than can be covered in a single book.

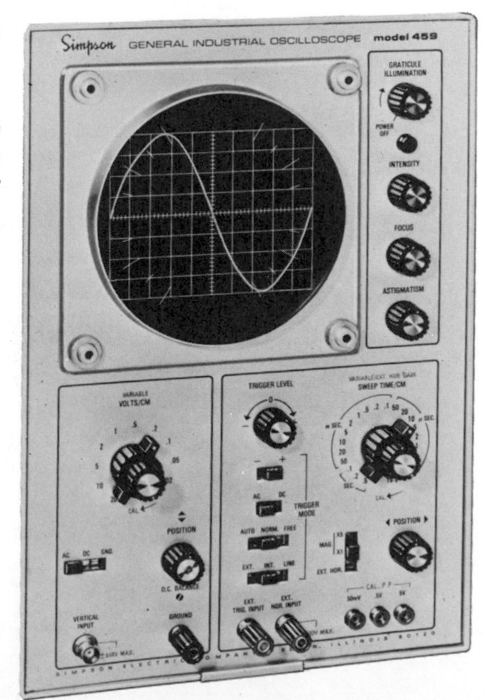

EXERCISES 15.2

1. The sine function maps x onto _____.

2. Name five ordered pairs in the sine function.

3. Name five ordered pairs in the cosine function.

4. When $x = -\frac{\pi}{4}$, $\sin x =$ _____ and $\cos x =$ _____.

5–8. Which word, *positive* or *negative*, belongs in the blank?

5. When $0 < x < \frac{\pi}{2}$, $\cos x$ is ____ and $\sin x$ is ____.

6. When $\frac{\pi}{2} < x < \pi$, $\cos x$ is ____ and $\sin x$ is ____.

7. When $\pi < x < \frac{3\pi}{2}$, $\cos x$ is ____ and $\sin x$ is ____.

8. When $\frac{3\pi}{2} < x < 2\pi$, $\cos x$ is ____ and $\sin x$ is ____.

9–11. Tell whether $\sin x$ increases or decreases and give its starting and ending values as x makes the indicated change.

9. x increases from 0 to $\frac{\pi}{2}$.

10. x increases from π to $\frac{3\pi}{2}$.

11. x decreases from 0 to $-\frac{\pi}{2}$.

12–14. Repeat Exercises **9–11** for $\cos x$.

15. How often does the pattern of values of $\sin x$ repeat?

16. How are the graphs of $y = \sin x$ and $y = \cos x$ related?

17. What is a sine wave?

18. Give one physical example of a sine wave.

Ⓑ **19.** Graph 17 ordered pairs of the cosine function corresponding to the 17 values of x given on page 453.

20. Use tables to help accurately graph 15 points on the sine function for values of x between 0 and $\frac{\pi}{2}$ inclusive.

21. Name two symmetry lines of the graph of $y = \sin x$. Are there any symmetry lines other than the ones you have named?

22. The graph of $y = \sin x$ has rotation-symmetry. What is the center and magnitude of a rotation which maps this graph onto itself?

23. Sine waves have translation-symmetry. What does this mean?

24. Does the graph of the cosine function have rotation-symmetry? Explain your answer.

25. In this section, it was shown that $\sin\left(x + \frac{\pi}{2}\right) = \cos x$. What general theorem was used?

© **26–31**. Graph the solution set to each sentence.

26. $y = -\sin x$ **27.** $y = 2 \cos x$ **28.** $y = \sin 2x$

29. $y + 1 = \sin x$ **30.** $y = \cos(x - \pi)$ **31.** $3y = \sin \frac{x}{3}$

32. *Weather*. New York City's average *monthly* temperatures (based on the years 1931 to 1960) are given below. Graph this data.

Jan.	Feb.	Mar.	Apr.	May	June	July	Aug.	Sept.	Oct.	Nov.	Dec.
33	33	41	51	62	71	77	75	69	58	47	36

33. Refer to Exercise **32**. Do you think a graph of average *daily* temperatures would approximate a sine wave?

34. The following lists the time of sunset each Sunday of 1966 for Denver, Colorado. Accurately graph an appropriate function.

1/2	4:46	4/3	6:26	7/3	7:32	10/2	5:42
1/9	4:53	4/10	6:33	7/10	7:31	10/9	5:31
1/16	5:00	4/17	6:40	7/17	7:27	10/16	5:20
1/23	5:08	4/24	6:47	7/24	7:22	10/23	5:10
1/30	5:16	5/1	6:54	7/31	7:15	10/30	5:01
2/6	5:24	5/8	7:01	8/7	7:07	11/6	4:53
2/13	5:33	5/15	7:08	8/14	6:59	11/13	4:46
2/20	5:41	5/22	7:14	8/21	6:49	11/20	4:41
2/27	5:49	5/29	7:20	8/28	6:39	11/27	4:37
3/6	5:57	6/5	7:25	9/5	6:28	12/4	4:35
3/13	6:04	6/12	7:29	9/12	6:17	12/11	4:35
3/20	6:12	6/19	7:32	9/19	6:03	12/18	4:36
3/27	6:19	6/26	7:33	9/26	5:53	12/25	4:40

15.3 SYMMETRIES OF SINE WAVES

Recall that a figure is symmetric if it can be mapped onto itself by an isometry T. (Refer to Section 4.9.) Sine waves possess many kinds of symmetry. These include:

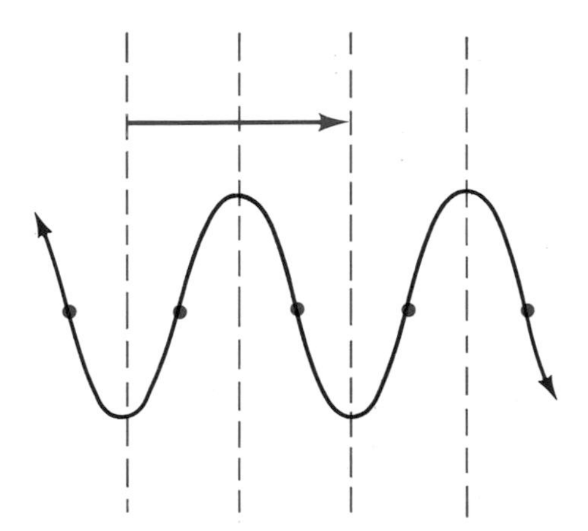

1. **Rotation-symmetry**
   A rotation of π with any of the marked points as center maps the wave onto itself.
2. **Translation-symmetry**
   The arrow indicates the magnitude and direction of one translation which maps the wave onto itself.
3. **Reflection-symmetry**
   The dashed lines indicate symmetry lines.

The graphs of both the sine and the cosine functions are translation-symmetric. Furthermore, the translations are horizontal. Each has magnitude 2π. Thus, if (x, y) is in either function, so is $(x + 2\pi, y)$. Functions of this type are called *periodic*.

Definition

If the graph of a function is translation-symmetric under a horizontal translation, the function is called a **periodic function**.

Notice that the translation mentioned in the definition is horizontal. The graph of $x \to [x]$, shown below, is translation-symmetric, but the function is not periodic—its values do not repeat.

However, the function $x \to x - [x]$ is periodic. Some points of the function are $(3, 0)$, $(3\frac{1}{3}, \frac{1}{3})$, $(3\frac{2}{3}, \frac{2}{3})$, $(4, 0)$, $(4\frac{1}{3}, \frac{1}{3})$, $(4\frac{2}{3}, \frac{2}{3})$, and so forth. This function maps a number onto its decimal or fraction part.

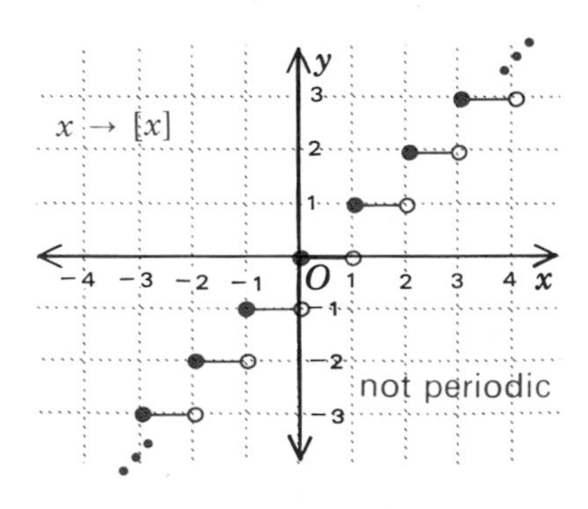

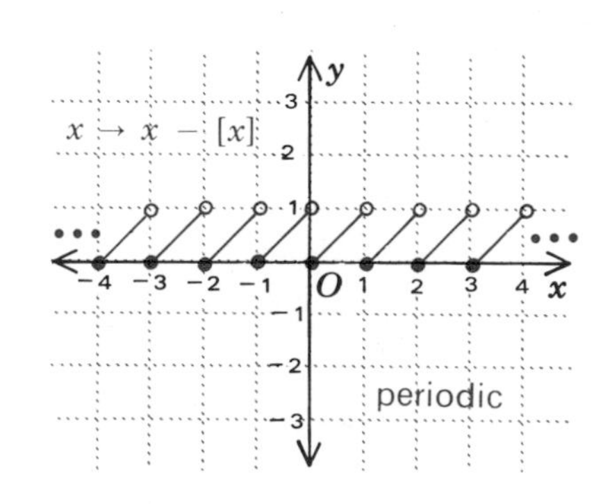

In a periodic function, the magnitude of each symmetry translation is called a **period** of the function. For $x \to x - [x]$, the periods are 1, 2, 3, 4, $\cdots$. For the sine and cosine functions, 2π, 4π, 6π, $\cdots$ are periods. The smallest period is called the **fundamental period** of the function; all other periods are integral multiples of this period.

Theorem 15.3.1

The fundamental period of the sine and cosine functions is 2π.

Any motion that can be pictured as a sine wave is periodic. So particles on vibrating strings, springs (forgetting friction), and sound waves have periodic motion. This makes periodicity a useful idea in applications.

Periodic functions are very much like events which occur at regular time intervals, and this is how they received their name. Many events related to astronomy, such as eclipses, phases of the moon, orbits of planets, tides, and our measurement of time and dates, are periodic. Periodic biological events include heartbeats, hibernation, migrations, and the daily openings and closings of some flowers.

Theorem 15.3.2

For any real x: **a.** $\cos(\pi - x) = -\cos x$; **b.** $\sin(\pi - x) = \sin x$.

PROOF: Part **a.** By Theorem 8.5.1a,

$$\begin{aligned}\cos(\pi - x) &= \cos \pi \cos(-x) - \sin \pi \sin(-x)\\ &= -1 \cdot \cos(-x) - 0 \cdot \sin(-x)\\ &= -\cos(-x) = -\cos x\end{aligned}$$

Part **b** can be similarly proved by applying Theorem 8.5.1b.

Theorem 15.3.2 can be verified using graphs of the cosine and sine functions.

a. Rotating $(x, \cos x)$ 180° about $\left(\frac{\pi}{2}, 0\right)$ gives the image

$(\pi - x, \cos(\pi - x))$.

So $\cos(\pi - x)$ and $\cos x$ are opposites.

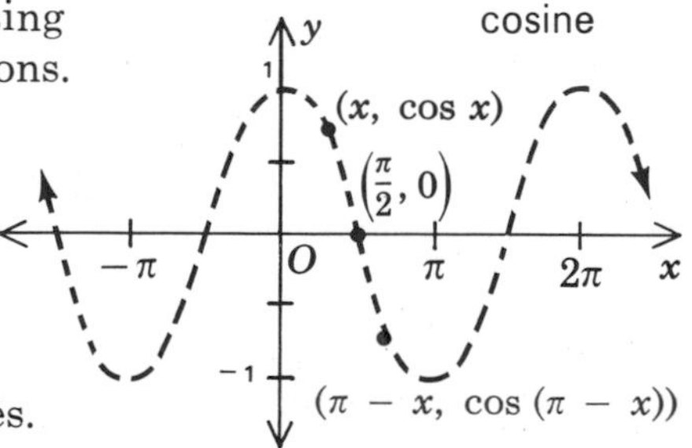

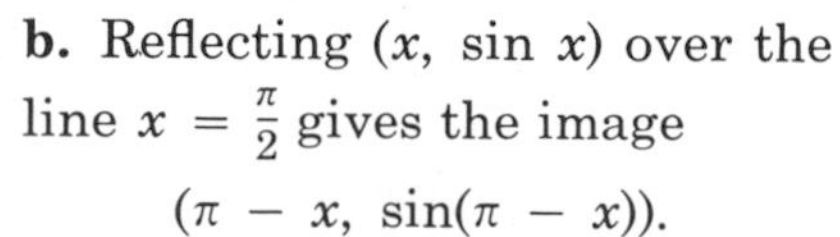

b. Reflecting $(x, \sin x)$ over the line $x = \frac{\pi}{2}$ gives the image

$(\pi - x, \sin(\pi - x))$.

So $\sin x = \sin(\pi - x)$.

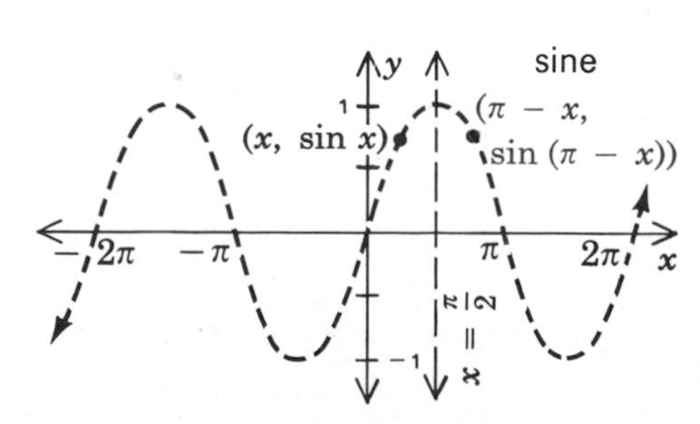

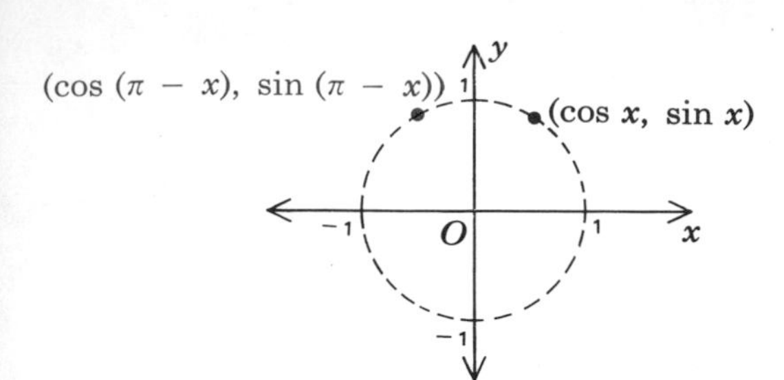

Still another way to verify Theorem 15.3.2 is to reflect $(\cos x, \sin x)$ over the y-axis. The image is $(\cos(\pi - x), \sin(\pi - x))$.

So $\cos(\pi - x) = -\cos x$

and $\sin(\pi - x) = \sin x$.

The numbers x and $\pi - x$ add to π. If they stand for angle measures, the angles are supplementary, for their measures add to π rad, or 180°. Interpreting Theorem 15.3.2 as involving angle measures results in an important corollary.

Corollary 15.3.3

a. The cosines of supplementary angles are opposites.

b. The sines of supplementary angles are equal.

Examples: Sines and cosines of supplements

1. $\sin 160° = \sin 20° \doteq 0.342$

2. $\cos \frac{3\pi}{4} = -\cos \frac{\pi}{4} = -\frac{\sqrt{2}}{2}$

EXERCISES 15.3

Ⓐ **1.** When is a figure rotation-symmetric?

2. When is a figure translation-symmetric?

3. A sine wave has ____ symmetry lines.

4. What is a periodic function?

5. What is a period of a periodic function?

6. Name two periods of the cosine function.

7. What is the fundamental period of the cosine function?

8. $\cos(\pi - x)$ and $\cos x$ are ____.

9. $\sin(\pi - x)$ and $\sin x$ are ____.

10. The ____ of supplementary angles are equal.

11. The ____ of supplementary angles are opposites.

12. The reflection image over the y-axis of $(\cos 41°, \sin 41°)$ is ____.

13–14. If $\cos 41° \doteq 0.755$ and $\sin 41° \doteq 0.656$, approximate:

13. $\cos 139°$.

14. $\sin 139°$.

15. Give five periods and the fundamental period of this function.

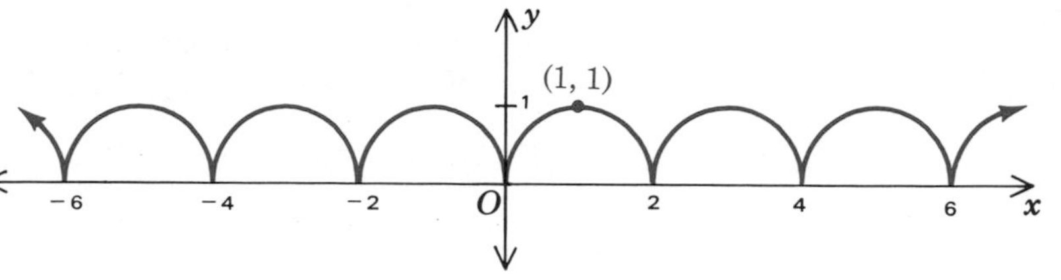

16. Draw the graph of a function which is translation-symmetric but not periodic.

Ⓑ **17–19.** Consider the function $f: x \to x - [x]$. (See page 458.)

17. Name 5 ordered pairs of this function.

18. Name 5 solutions to $f(x) = \frac{1}{3}$.

19. Give the fundamental period of this function.

20. True or False? If 7 is a period of a function, so is 14.

21–23. Use tables to help approximate a solution if $90° < x < 180°$.

21. $\cos x = -0.25$

22. $\sin x = \frac{1}{3}$

23. $\cos x = -0.880$

24. The symmetry of the unit circle to the y-axis results in Theorem 15.3.2. What theorem mentioned in Chapter 9 is a result of the symmetry of the unit circle to the x-axis?

25. What theorem mentioned in Chapter 8 is a result of the symmetry of the unit circle to the line $x = y$?

26. Prove Theorem 15.3.2b.

Ⓒ **27–30.** The *amplitude* of a sine wave is half the difference of the maximum and minimum values of the function. For example, the amplitude of $x \to \sin x$ is 1. Give the amplitude and fundamental period of each function; then graph.

27. $y = 2 \cos 3x$

28. $2y = \sin \frac{x}{4}$

29. $y = 3 \cos(x - \pi)$

30. $y = \sin 2\left(x + \frac{\pi}{6}\right)$

31. A function is an *even function* if its graph is symmetric to the y-axis. Which of these functions are even?

a. $y = x$
b. $y = x^2$
c. $y = x^3$
d. $y = x^4$
e. $y = x^5$
f. $y = x^6$
g. $y = \sin x$
h. $y = \cos x$

32. A function is an *odd function* if its graph is symmetric under a rotation of π rad about (0, 0). Which functions of Ex. **31** are odd?

33. In an even function f, $f(x)$ and $f(-x)$ are ____. (See Ex. **31**.)

34. In an odd function g, $g(x)$ and $g(-x)$ are ____. (See Ex. **32**.)

35. Give 5 examples of periodic events which occur in nature and are not mentioned in this section.

15.4 TRIGONOMETRY— THE LAW OF COSINES

Sines and cosines have nice applications to triangles and other polygons. The study of these applications is called *trigonometry* (from the Greek words for *triangle* and *measure*).

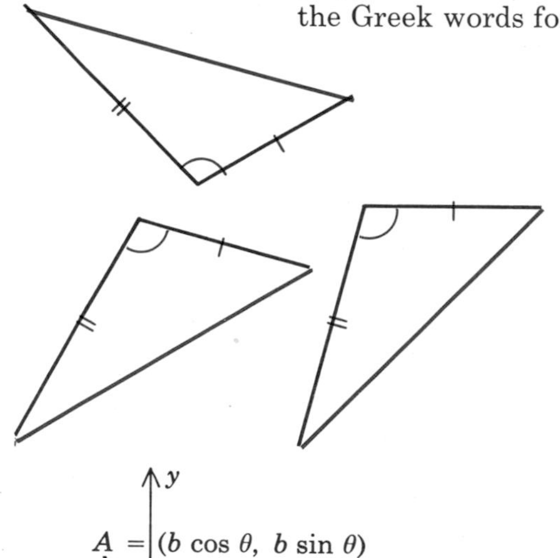

A first application arises from the SAS theorem of geometry: *All triangles with two given sides and a given included angle are congruent.* This theorem implies that the measures of two sides and the included angle determine the length of the third side. So it is natural to ask,

> Given SAS in a triangle, how can the length of the third side be calculated?

Any triangle can be rotated and translated so the vertex of the given angle is at the origin and one side is on the nonnegative ray of the x-axis, as shown here.

The lengths a and b are given and $m\angle C = \theta$. The problem is to determine c, the length of $\overline{AB}$.

1. The coordinates of A and B are easy to find.

$$A = [b, \theta] = (b \cos \theta,\ b \sin \theta)$$
$$B = (a, 0)$$

2. By the distance formula:

$$AB = c = \sqrt{(b \cos \theta - a)^2 + (b \sin \theta - 0)^2}$$

3. Squaring and expanding:

$$c^2 = b^2(\cos \theta)^2 - 2ab \cos \theta + a^2 + b^2(\sin \theta)^2$$

4. $$= a^2 + b^2[(\cos \theta)^2 + (\sin \theta)^2] - 2ab \cos \theta$$

But for any number θ, $(\cos\theta)^2 + (\sin\theta)^2 = 1$, so

5. $$c^2 = a^2 + b^2 - 2ab\cos\theta.$$

Triangles are usually lettered as we have done here, with a the side (or the length of the side) opposite $\angle A$, b the side opposite $\angle B$, and c the side opposite $\angle C$. Furthermore, $\cos C$ is used to mean $\cos(m\angle C)$. (The *cosine of the angle* really means the *cosine of the measure of the angle.*) Applying these conventions to the formula above gives the following well-known theorem.

Theorem 15.4.1

Law of cosines: In any $\triangle ABC$, $c^2 = a^2 + b^2 - 2ab\cos C$.

Examples: Using the law of cosines

1. Find c in $\triangle ABC$ at the right.

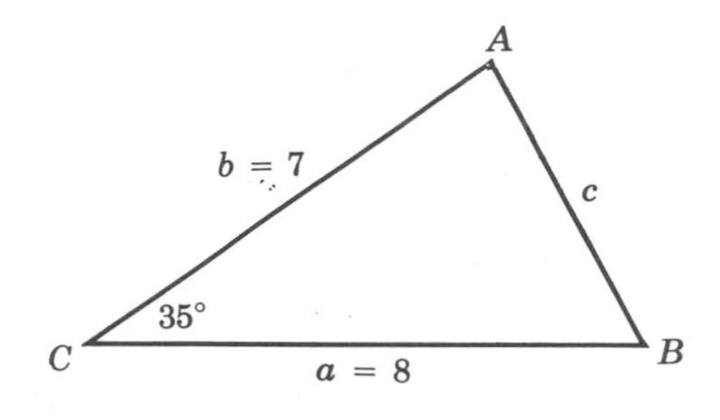

SOLUTION: $c^2 = 8^2 + 7^2 - 2\cdot 8\cdot 7\cdot\cos 35^\circ$

$\doteq 64 + 49 - 112(0.819)$

$= 113 - 91.728$

$= 21.272$ or 21.3

So $c \doteq 4.6$.

2. Find the diagonal of a regular pentagon with side 10.

SOLUTION: The sum of the measures of the angles of a pentagon is 540°, so each angle of a regular pentagon measures 108°. By the law of cosines,

$$c^2 = 10^2 + 10^2 - 2\cdot 10\cdot 10\cos 108^\circ$$

$$= 100 + 100 - 200\cos 108^\circ$$

By Corollary 15.3.3a, $\cos 108^\circ = -\cos 72^\circ$.

Substituting: $c^2 \doteq 200 - 200(-\cos 72^\circ)$

$= 200 - 200(-0.309)$

$= 200 + 61.8 = 261.8$

So $c \doteq 16.2$

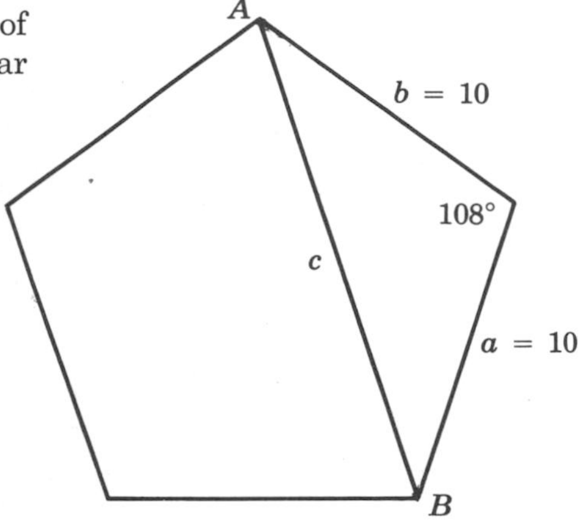

The law of cosines is very useful because it holds for *any* triangle. In a right triangle, if $\angle C$ is the right angle, then $\cos C = 0$. So

$$c^2 = a^2 + b^2.$$

Thus, the Pythagorean theorem is a special case of the law of cosines.

The law of cosines makes it possible to find the measures of the angles of a triangle, given the three sides (SSS).

Example: Find the measure of the largest angle in $\triangle MNP$.

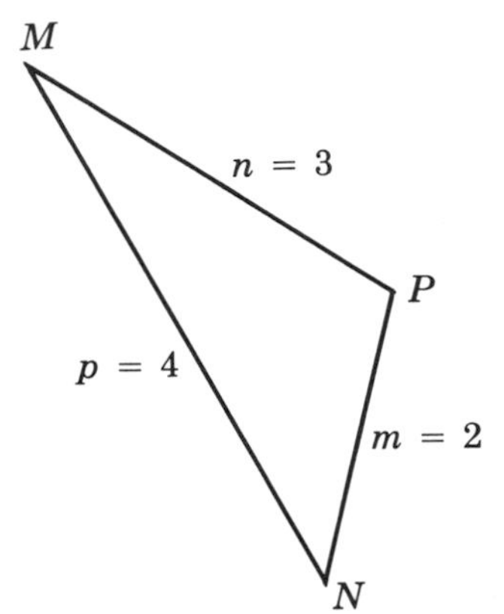

SOLUTION: Since (from geometry) the largest angle is opposite the longest side, we want $m\angle P$.

By the law of cosines: $4^2 = 2^2 + 3^2 - 2 \cdot 2 \cdot 3 \cos P$

$$16 = 13 - 12 \cos P$$

$$-0.25 = \cos P$$

$\cos P < 0$, so $\angle P$ is obtuse.

By Corollary 15.3.3a: $0.25 = \cos(180^\circ - m\angle P)$

From tables: $75.5^\circ \doteq 180^\circ - m\angle P$

$$105.5^\circ \doteq m\angle P$$

EXERCISES 15.4

Ⓐ 1. What is the meaning of *trigonometry*?

2. How are triangles lettered in order to make it easier to understand trigonometric formulas?

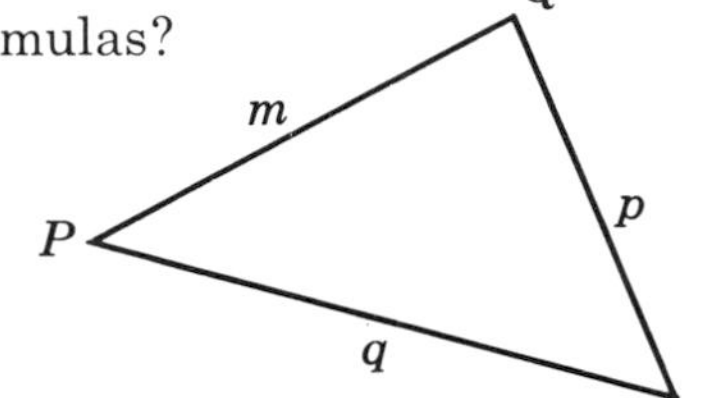

3. State the law of cosines.

4. State a formula relating the measures of $\angle Q$, p, m, and q.

5. What is a shorthand for $\cos(m\angle Q)$?

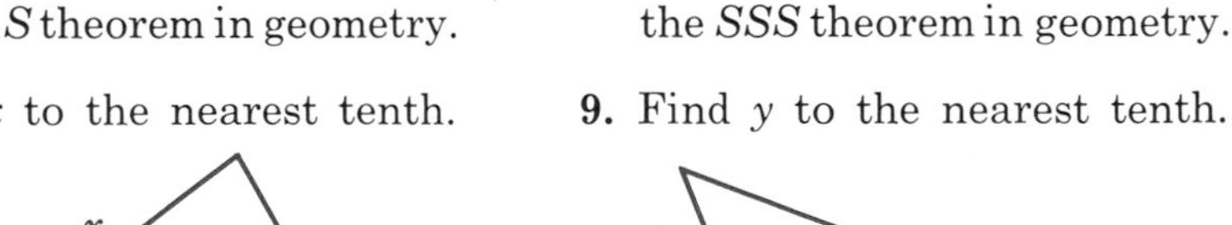

Ⓑ 6. Relate the law of cosines to the SAS theorem in geometry.

7. Relate the law of cosines to the SSS theorem in geometry.

8. Find x to the nearest tenth.

9. Find y to the nearest tenth.

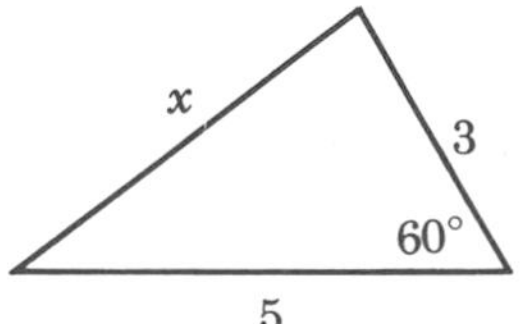

10
y
112°
20

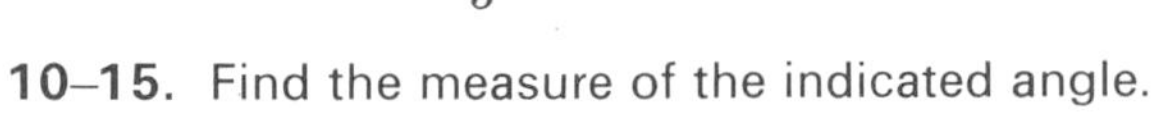

10–15. Find the measure of the indicated angle.

10. $\angle A$

11. $\angle B$

12. $\angle C$

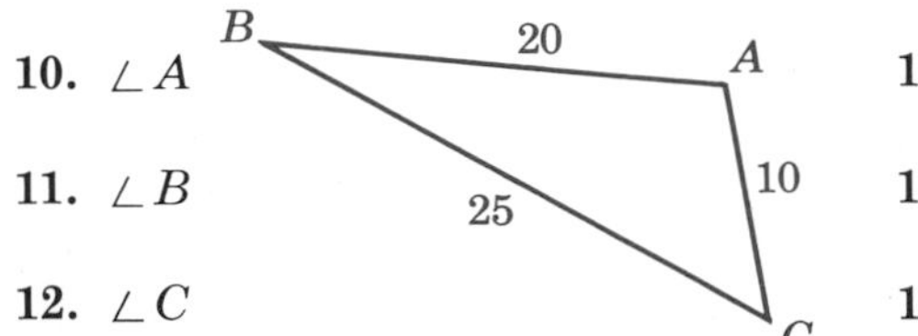

13. $\angle X$

14. $\angle Y$

15. $\angle Z$

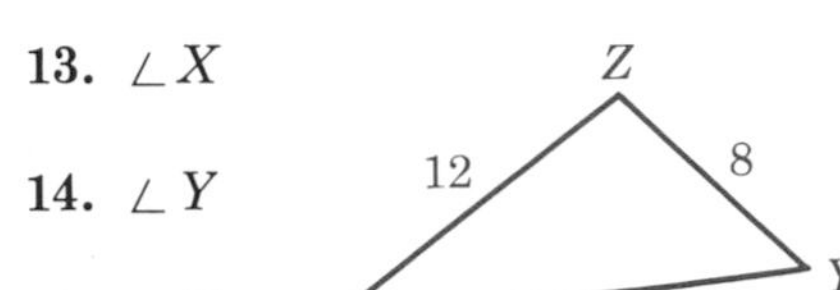

16–17. Refer to parallelogram $ABCD$.

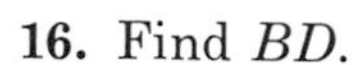

16. Find BD. **17.** Find AC.

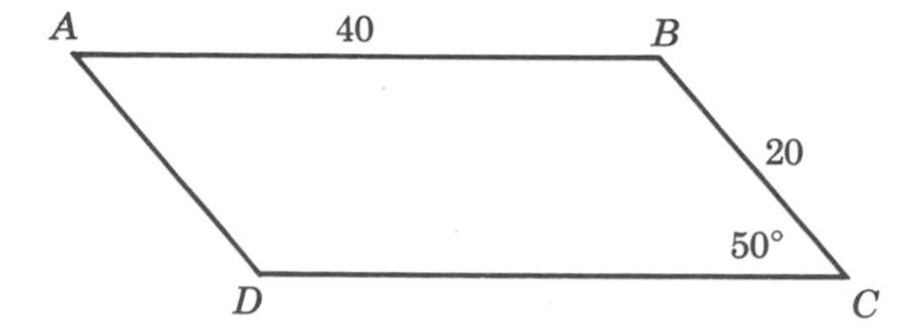

18. Find the length of a chord of an 18° arc in a circle of radius 6.

19. Solve the equation of Theorem 15.4.1 for $\cos C$.

20. One plane leaves an airport at 1:00 P.M., traveling due east at 500 km/h. A second plane leaves 30 minutes later, traveling northwest at 400 km/h. How far apart will the planes be at 2:00 P.M.?

© **21.** Find the distance between the points with polar coordinates $\left[4, \frac{\pi}{6}\right]$ and $\left[10, -\frac{\pi}{5}\right]$. (HINT: Look for an easy way.)

22. A plane travels 500 mph due east for 30 minutes, then turns 20° to the north and flies for 12 minutes, then turns 20° to the north again and flies for 18 minutes. At the end of the hour, how far is the plane from its starting point? (Assume a constant speed for the plane.)

23. A triangle has sides 25, 30, and 60. Use the law of cosines to find the measures of the three angles of the triangle. Explain your result.

24. The law of cosines could be called the *Pythagorean theorem with a correction term.* Explain why this description is appropriate.

25. Use the law of cosines to prove: In any parallelogram with sides a and b and diagonals x and y, $2a^2 + 2b^2 = x^2 + y^2$. (HINT: Call the angle measures C and $\pi - C$ and use Corollary 15.3.3a.)

TRIGONOMETRY— THE LAW OF SINES

15.5

Given SAS or SSS in a triangle, the law of cosines can be used to find the measures of all other parts. Since the law of cosines involves only one angle, it is not useful when only ASA or AAS is known. But a second famous theorem, the law of sines, can be applied in these situations.

Theorem 15.5.1

Law of sines: In any $\triangle ABC$, $\dfrac{\sin A}{a} = \dfrac{\sin B}{b} = \dfrac{\sin C}{c}$.

PROOF: As in the proof of the law of cosines, page 462, translate and rotate $\triangle ABC$ so $A = (b \cos C, b \sin C)$ and $B = (a, 0)$. Now apply the translation $T(x, y) = (x - a, y)$ to $\triangle ABC$.

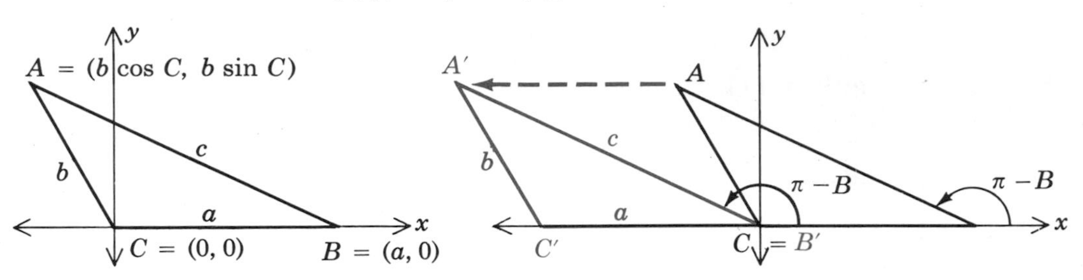

T maps B onto the origin and

$$T(A) = A' = (b \cos C - a,\ b \sin C).$$

But A' has polar coordinates $[c, \pi - B]$.

$$\text{So } A' = (c \cos(\pi - B),\ c \sin(\pi - B)).$$

These two sets of rectangular coordinates of A' must be identical.

That is: $(b \cos C - a,\ b \sin C) = (c \cos(\pi - B),\ c \sin(\pi - B))$

From Theorem 15.3.2: $= (-c \cos B,\ c \sin B)$

Equate the second coordinates: $b \sin C = c \sin B$

Divide by bc: $\dfrac{\sin C}{c} = \dfrac{\sin B}{b}$

Similarly, we can show that $\dfrac{\sin A}{a} = \dfrac{\sin B}{b}$, completing the proof.

Equating the first coordinates of A' instead of the second coordinates gives another important theorem. Since this theorem involves three sides and two angles of a triangle, it is very useful for checking answers.

Theorem 15.5.2

Triangle-check theorem: In any $\triangle ABC$, $b \cos C + c \cos B = a$.

PROOF: Equate the first coordinates of A': $b \cos C - a = -c \cos B$.
Adding a and $c \cos B$ to both sides completes the proof.

Examples: Using the law of sines and the triangle-check theorem

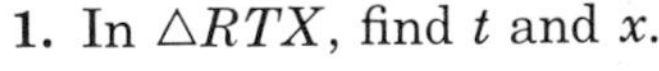

1. In $\triangle RTX$, find t and x.

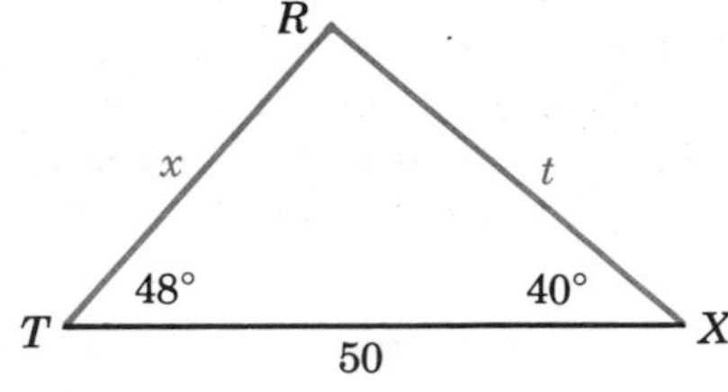

SOLUTION: First, note that $m\angle R = 92°$.

To find x: $\frac{\sin 40°}{x} = \frac{\sin 92°}{50}$

$$\frac{0.643}{x} \doteq \frac{0.999}{50}$$

$$x \doteq \frac{50(0.643)}{0.999} \doteq 32.2$$

To find t: $\frac{\sin 48°}{t} = \frac{\sin 92°}{50}$

$$\frac{0.743}{t} \doteq \frac{0.999}{50}$$

$$t \doteq \frac{50(0.743)}{0.999} \doteq 37.2$$

2. To check the results in Example **1**, we can use the triangle-check theorem. Let $r = a$, $t = b$, and $x = c$. So the question is, does $t \cos X + x \cos T$ equal 50?

$$t \cos X + x \cos T = 37.2 \cos 40° + 32.2 \cos 48°$$
$$\doteq 37.2(0.766) + 32.2(0.669)$$
$$\doteq 28.495 + 21.542 = 50.037$$

The lengths of the sides were found to the nearest tenth, so the answer checks.

The law of sines, in its simplest form, involves two sides and the opposite angles. If the sides and one angle are known, the situation is *SSA*. For some values of a, b, and $m\angle A$, exactly one triangle exists; for other values, no triangle exists. But for still other values, two triangles are possible, and this is why there is no *SSA* congruence theorem.

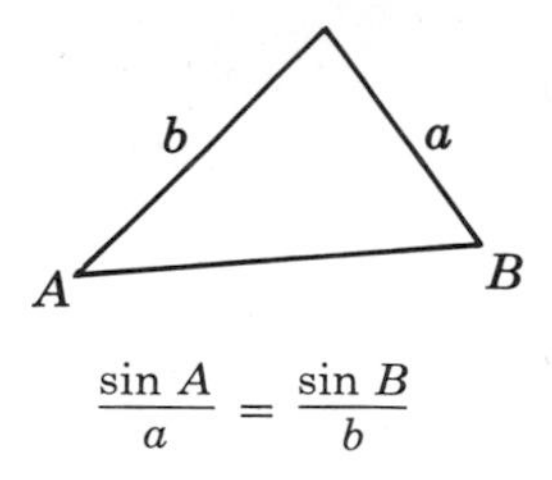

$$\frac{\sin A}{a} = \frac{\sin B}{b}$$

Examples: Two special situations

1. no triangle possible

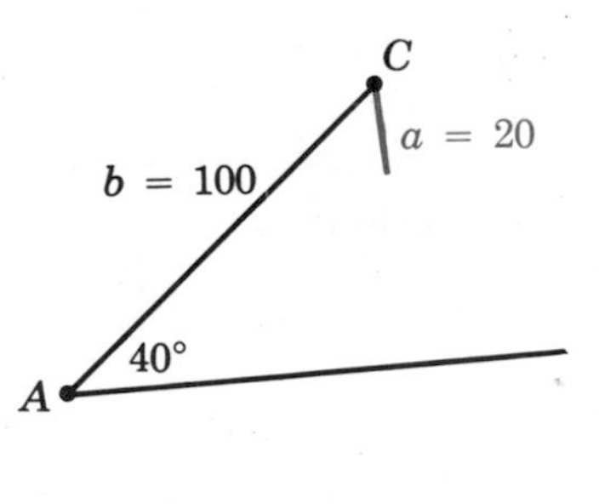

$a = 20$, $b = 100$, $m\angle A = 40°$

2. two triangles possible

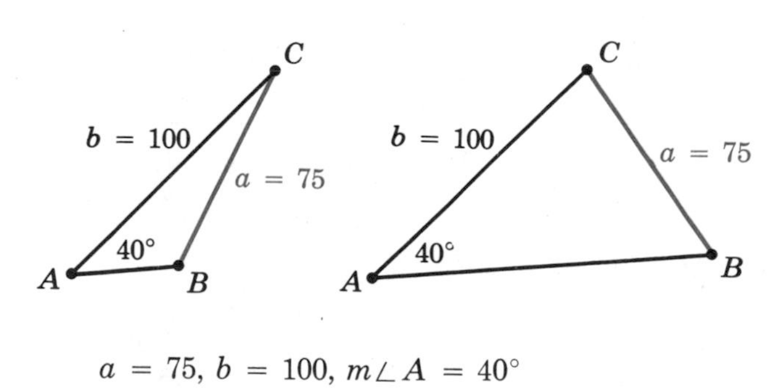

$a = 75$, $b = 100$, $m\angle A = 40°$

The law of sines can be used to verify these situations.

1. Find all triangles ABC with $m\angle A = 40°$, $b = 100$, and $a = 20$.

SOLUTION: By the law of sines: $\frac{\sin 40°}{20} = \frac{\sin B}{100}$

$$100 \cdot \frac{0.643}{20} \doteq \sin B$$

$$3.215 \doteq \sin B$$

Since $\sin B \leq 1$ always, no value of B works.

2. Find all triangles ABC with $m\angle A = 40°$, $b = 100$, and $a = 75$.

SOLUTION: By the law of sines:

$$\frac{\sin 40°}{75} = \frac{\sin B}{100}$$

$$100 \cdot \frac{0.643}{75} \doteq \sin B$$

$$0.857 \doteq \sin B$$

From the tables, $m\angle B \doteq 59°$. But supplementary angles have the same sine. So we could also have $m\angle B \doteq 121°$.

The process of finding measures of angles and sides in a triangle, with some given information, is called *solving the triangle*. With the law of cosines and the law of sines and enough given information, any triangle can be solved. This table summarizes the past two sections.

Given	To find	Procedure	Example
SAS	3rd side	Use law of cosines.	p. 463
	2nd angle	Find 3rd side; use law of cosines or law of sines.	
SSS	angle	Use law of cosines.	p. 464
ASA or *AAS*	2nd side	Use law of sines.	p. 466
SSA	*2nd angle	Use law of sines.	pp. 467–8
	*3rd side	Find 2nd angle; use law of sines.	

* There may be no solution, one solution, or two solutions.

EXERCISES 15.5

Ⓐ **1–6.** Refer to the diagram. Name the rectangular coordinates of the given point.

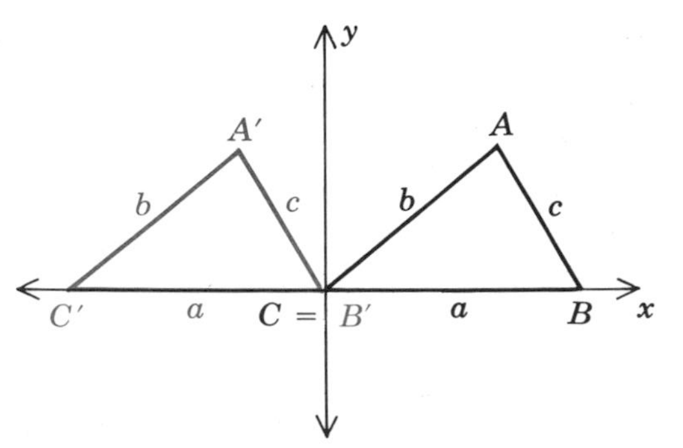

1. C **2.** B

3. A **4.** C'

5. B' **6.** A'

7. Refer to Exercises **1–6**. What is a formula for the translation which maps $\triangle ABC$ onto $\triangle A'B'C'$?

8. State the law of sines.

9. In $\triangle XYZ$, $x \cos Y + y \cos X =$ ____.

10. How does the triangle-check theorem get its name?

11. Given $m\angle V$ and $m\angle W$ in $\triangle VWX$, how can you find $m\angle X$?

12–15. State an equation which yields the desired number when solved.

12. AB

13. AC

14. $m\angle P$

15. $m\angle T$

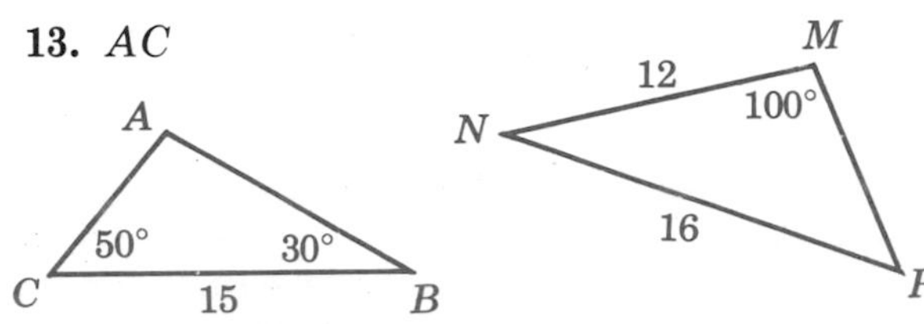

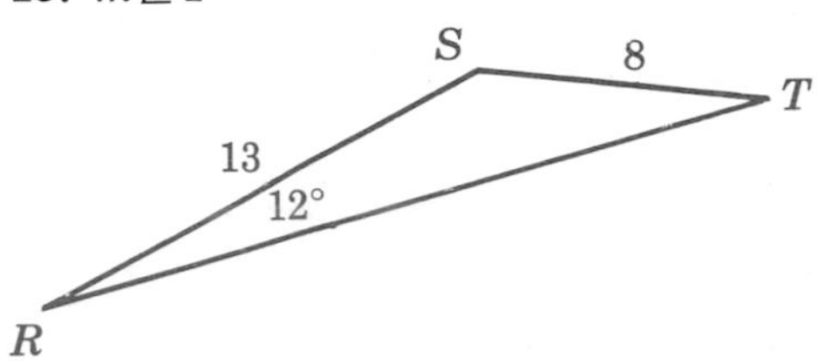

16–17. Refer to the drawings with Exercises **12–15**.

16. Give the 2-step process which would enable MP to be found.

17. Give the 2-step process which would enable RT to be found.

18. What is meant by the phrase *solving a triangle*?

19–21. Check whether a triangle exists with the given measures.

19. $m\angle C \doteq 120°$, $m\angle B \doteq 41°$, $m\angle A \doteq 19°$, $a = 6$, $b = 12$, $c = 15.9$

20. $d = 3$, $e = 4$, $f = 5$, $m\angle D \doteq 36°$, $m\angle E \doteq 54°$

21. $m\angle G \doteq 68°$, $m\angle H \doteq 53°$, $g = 15$, $h = 13$, $f = 14$

Ⓑ **22–27.** Find the side or the angle referred to in Exercises **12–17.**

28–29. Solve (find all missing parts of) the given triangle.

28.

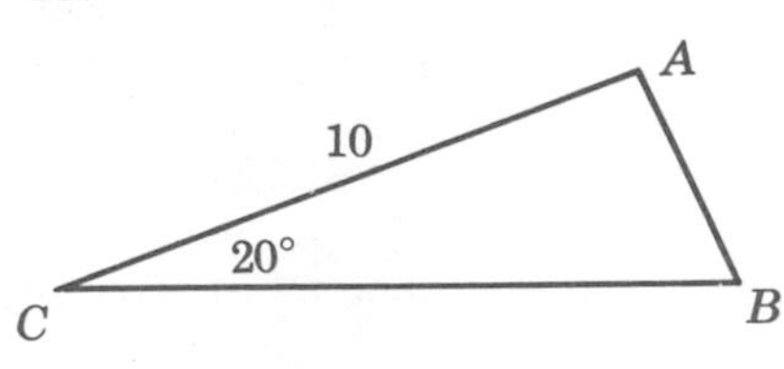

29.

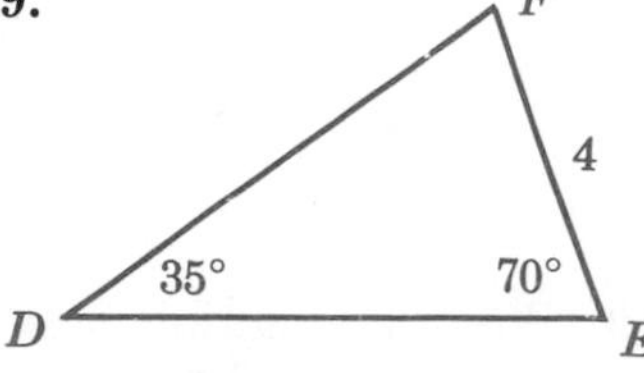

30–32. Find $m\angle B$ and draw a reasonably accurate figure.

30. $a = 14$, $b = 7$, $m\angle A = 23°$

31. $a = 12$, $b = 5$, $m\angle A = 30°$

32. $a = 20$, $b = 42$, $m\angle A = 30°$

33. *Surveying.* Equipped with a tape measure and an angle measuring device, a camper wishes to approximate the width of a lake. Beginning at a point A, she walks 200 feet to a point she calls B. At each point she looks at a tree T on the other side of the lake. By drawing lines on the ground, she measures $\angle TAB$ and $\angle TBA$. If $m\angle TAB = 88°$ and $m\angle TBA = 83°$, about how far is it from A to T?

34. Explain how, if A and B stood for forest ranger stations, the idea of Exercise **33** could be used to locate the distance to a forest fire.

P

M

N

35. Measure the sides and the angles of $\triangle MNP$, at the left, and use tables to verify the law of sines.

© 36. *Navigation.* Two ships S and T pick up a distress signal from a third ship D. It is possible to find the direction of this signal, but the distance of the signal cannot be found directly. S and T determine that D is located 30° south of east from S and 20° south of east from T, and they find that they are 100 km apart with S 40° east of north from T. If S can travel at 30 km/h and T at 25 km/h, how long will it take each ship to reach ship D?

B
A
118°
121°
7
49°
72°
C
D
18

37. *Astronomy.* How far is the earth from Mars when Mars rises 4 hours after the sun? (Assume circular orbits for the earth and Mars with radii 9.3×10^7 and 1.41×10^8 miles respectively.)

38. Find AB and BC in quadrilateral $ABCD$.

39. What correction should be made in this statement? In $\triangle ABC$, $\log \sin A + \log a = \log \sin B + \log b = \log \sin C + \log c$.

40. In a triangle, the sines of two angles are _____ proportional to the lengths of the opposite sides.

41. Refer to the two special situations on page 467. What should be the length of a in order to have only one triangle possible?

THE SECANT AND COSECANT FUNCTIONS

Cosines and sines are the foundations upon which trigonometry is based. But for certain calculations it is easier to use reciprocals of cosines and sines. These have special names.

Definitions

The **secant** of x, abbreviated *sec* x, is $\frac{1}{\cos x}$, provided $\cos x \neq 0$.

The **cosecant** of x, abbreviated *csc* x, is $\frac{1}{\sin x}$, provided $\sin x \neq 0$.

Values of $\sec x$ and $\csc x$ are given in the table on page 602. For values not in the table, use the ideas of these examples.

Examples: Calculating secants and cosecants

1. $\sec \frac{\pi}{4} = \dfrac{1}{\cos \frac{\pi}{4}} = \dfrac{1}{\frac{\sqrt{2}}{2}} = \dfrac{2}{\sqrt{2}} = \sqrt{2} \doteq 1.414$

2. $\sec 216° = \dfrac{1}{\cos 216°} \doteq \dfrac{1}{-0.809} \doteq -1.236$

   OR $\sec 216° = \dfrac{1}{\cos 216°} = \dfrac{1}{-\cos 36°} = -\sec 36° \doteq -1.236$

3. $\csc 0$ is not defined because $\sin 0$ has no reciprocal.

4. $\csc(-1°) = \dfrac{1}{\sin(-1°)} = \dfrac{1}{-\sin 1°} \doteq \dfrac{1}{-0.017} \doteq -57.30$

   OR $\csc(-1°) = \dfrac{1}{\sin(-1°)} = \dfrac{1}{-\sin 1°} = -\csc 1° \doteq -57.30$

Because $\sec x$ and $\cos x$ are reciprocals, we can use properties of cosines and reciprocals to determine some characteristics of $\sec x$.

1. When $\cos x$ is positive, $\sec x$ is positive.
When $\cos x = 0$, $\sec x$ is undefined.
When $\cos x$ is negative, $\sec x$ is negative.

2. Since $|\cos x| \leq 1$, $|\sec x| \geq 1$ always.
The smaller $|\cos x|$ is, the larger $|\sec x|$ is.

3. $\sec x = \cos x$ only when $\cos x = 1$ or $\cos x = -1$.

Putting these properties together, the *secant function*, $x \rightarrow \sec x$, can be graphed. The graph of the cosine function is used as a guide. Each of the three properties above can be seen in the graph.

1. For any x, $y = \cos x$ and $y = \sec x$ are on the same side of the x-axis; there is an asymptote of $y = \sec x$ when $\cos x = 0$.

2. The closer $y = \cos x$ is to the x-axis, the farther $y = \sec x$ is from that axis.

3. The graphs intersect when $\cos x = 1$ or $\cos x = -1$.

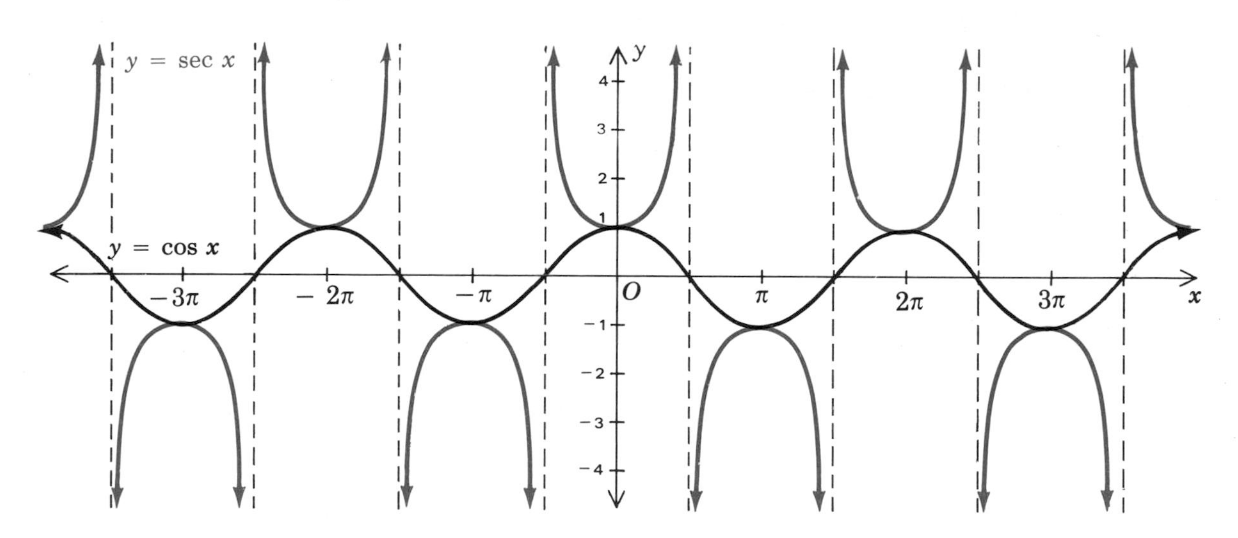

The *cosecant function*, $x \to \csc x$, is likewise related to the sine function. Graphing it is left as an exercise.

EXERCISES 15.6

Ⓐ 1. The numbers $\sec x$ and ____ are reciprocals.

2. The numbers $\csc x$ and ____ are reciprocals.

3. The abbreviation *sec* is short for ____.

4. The abbreviation *csc* is short for ____.

5. When is $\sec x$ undefined?

6. When is $\csc x$ undefined?

7. Name one value of x for which $\sec x$ is undefined.

8. Name one value of x for which $\csc x$ is undefined.

9–32. Calculate. Use tables only if necessary.

9. $\sec \frac{\pi}{3}$

10. $\sec \frac{\pi}{2}$

11. $\sec \frac{\pi}{4}$

12. $\sec \frac{2\pi}{3}$

13. $\csc \frac{\pi}{3}$

14. $\csc \frac{\pi}{2}$

15. $\csc \frac{\pi}{4}$

16. $\csc \frac{2\pi}{3}$

Ⓑ 17. sec 127° 18. sec(−12°) 19. sec 202° 20. sec 639°

21. csc 127° 22. csc(−12°) 23. csc 202° 24. csc 639°

25. $\sec \frac{3\pi}{4}$ 26. $\sec \frac{5\pi}{2}$ 27. $\sec \frac{13\pi}{6}$ 28. $\sec\left(-\frac{\pi}{3}\right)$

29. $\csc \frac{3\pi}{4}$ 30. $\csc \frac{5\pi}{2}$ 31. $\csc \frac{13\pi}{6}$ 32. $\csc\left(-\frac{\pi}{3}\right)$

33. Sketch a graph of the solution set to $y = \csc x$.

34. Name five points on the graph of the cosecant function.

35–39. Refer to the secant function, $x \to \sec x$, and its graph. Name:

35. the domain. 36. the range.

37. all lines of symmetry. 38. all centers of rotation-symmetry.

39. five periods and the fundamental period.

40–44. Answer Exercises **35–39** for the cosecant function.

Ⓒ 45. Graph $y = \sec 2x$. 46. Graph $\frac{y}{3} = \csc \frac{x}{2}$.

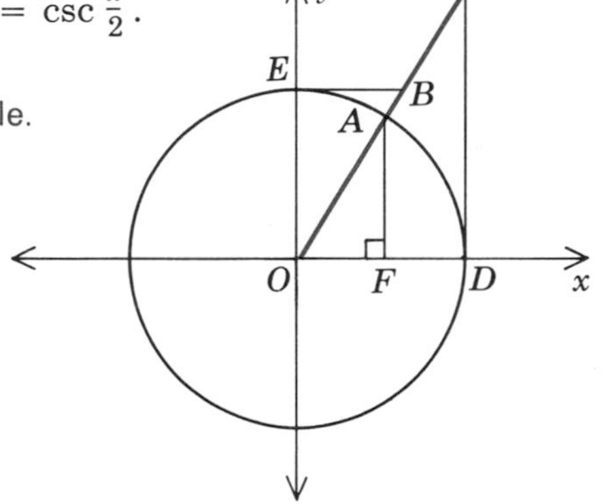

47–48. Let $\overleftrightarrow{CD}$ and $\overleftrightarrow{BE}$ be tangent to the unit circle. If $0 < x < \frac{\pi}{2}$ and $A = (\cos x, \sin x)$, prove:

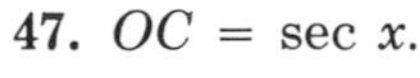

47. $OC = \sec x$.

48. $OB = \csc x$.

(NOTE: It is from this geometric interpretation that the words *secant* and *cosecant* arose.)

THE TANGENT AND COTANGENT FUNCTIONS

Six functions are commonly studied and applied in trigonometry.

They are:	(1) $x \to \cos x$	(2) $x \to \sin x$
their reciprocals:	(3) $x \to \sec x$	(4) $x \to \csc x$
and two functions formed by division:	(5) $x \to \tan x$	(6) $x \to \cot x$

These six functions are known as **circular functions** because sines and cosines are coordinates of points on the unit circle.

Here is how tan x and cot x are calculated.

Definitions

The **tangent** of x, abbreviated *tan x*, is $\frac{\sin x}{\cos x}$ if $\cos x \neq 0$.

The **cotangent** of x, abbreviated *cot x*, is $\frac{\cos x}{\sin x}$ if $\sin x \neq 0$.

Values of tan x and cot x are given in the table on page 602. For values not in the table, you should use the ideas of these examples.

Examples: Calculating tangents and cotangents

1. $\tan \frac{\pi}{4} = \dfrac{\sin \frac{\pi}{4}}{\cos \frac{\pi}{4}} = \dfrac{\frac{\sqrt{2}}{2}}{\frac{\sqrt{2}}{2}} = 1$

2. $\tan 0 = \frac{\sin 0}{\cos 0} = \frac{0}{1} = 0$

3. $\cot 111^\circ = \frac{\cos 111^\circ}{\sin 111^\circ} = \frac{-\cos 69^\circ}{\sin 69^\circ} \doteq \frac{-0.358}{0.934} \doteq -0.384$

   OR $\cot 111^\circ = -\cot 69^\circ \doteq -0.384$

4. $\cot 2\pi$ is not defined because $\sin 2\pi = 0$. (We cannot divide by 0.)

From the definitions, it is easy to see that tan x and cot x are reciprocals. Thus, these numbers are reciprocals:

$\sin x$ and $\csc x$ $\qquad$ $\cos x$ and $\sec x$ $\qquad$ $\tan x$ and $\cot x$

Because reciprocals are easy to approximate by means of logarithms, many tables list only values of sines, cosines, and tangents.

The tangents of x and $x + \pi$ are the same for any x. The cotangents of x and $x + \pi$ are also the same. Here are proofs.

$$\tan(x + \pi) = \frac{\sin(x + \pi)}{\cos(x + \pi)} = \frac{\sin x \cos \pi + \cos x \sin \pi}{\cos x \cos \pi - \sin x \sin \pi}$$

$$= \frac{\sin x \cdot (-1) + \cos x \cdot (0)}{\cos x \cdot (-1) - \sin x \cdot (0)} = \frac{-\sin x}{-\cos x} = \tan x$$

Similarly, $\quad \cot(x + \pi) = \dfrac{\cos(x + \pi)}{\sin(x + \pi)} = \dfrac{-\cos x}{-\sin x} = \cot x.$

So π is the fundamental period for these functions, and they can be graphed if the values are known for any interval of length π.

Furthermore, $\quad \tan(-x) = \dfrac{\sin(-x)}{\cos(-x)} = \dfrac{-\sin x}{\cos x} = -\tan x.$

So we calculate $\tan x$ when $0 \leq x \leq \frac{\pi}{2}$. Then we use $\tan(-x) = -\tan x$ to find values of $\tan x$ when $-\frac{\pi}{2} \leq x \leq 0$. This gives us values for the needed interval of length π.

x	0	$\frac{\pi}{6}$	$\frac{\pi}{4}$	$\frac{\pi}{3}$	$\frac{\pi}{2}$
$y = \tan x$	0	$\frac{\sqrt{3}}{3}$	1	$\sqrt{3}$	not defined

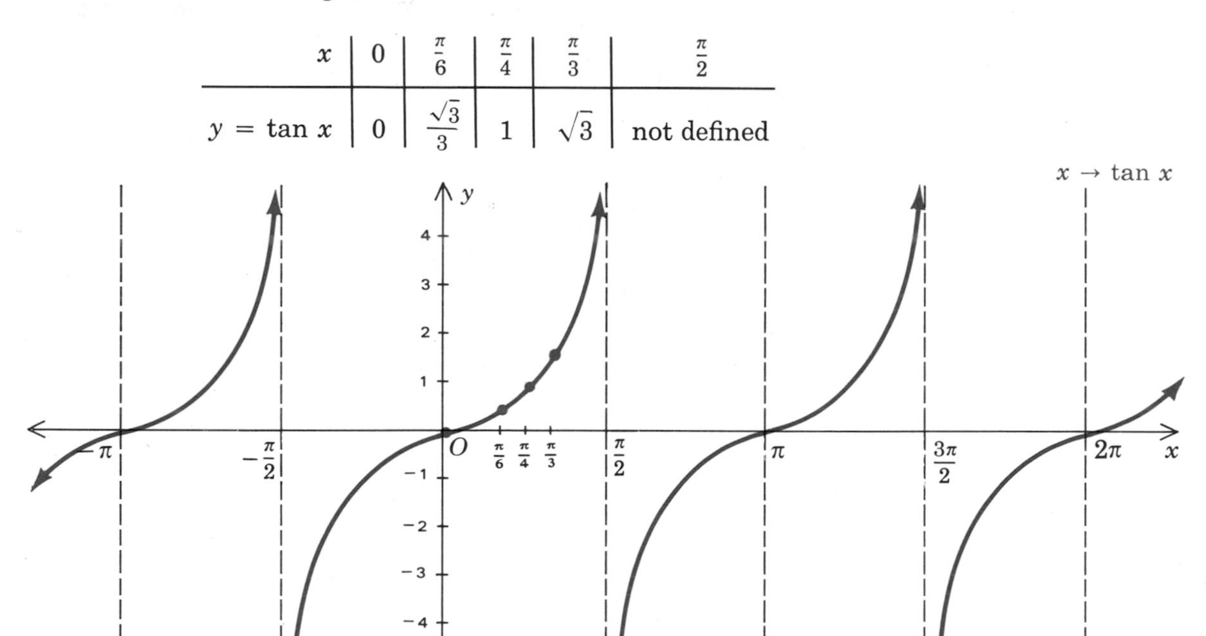

The graph of the cotangent function is congruent to the graph above but is not a translation image. Drawing it is left as an exercise.

EXERCISES 15.7

Ⓐ **1.** By definition, $\tan x$ is ____ divided by ____.

2. By definition, $\cot x$ is ____ divided by ____.

3. $\tan x \cdot \cot x =$ ____

4. The abbreviation *cot* is short for ____.

5. When is $\tan x$ undefined?

6. When is $\cot x$ undefined?

7. Name all values of x between 0 and 2π (inclusive) for which $\tan x$ is undefined.

8. Name all values of x between 0 and 2π (inclusive) for which $\cot x$ is undefined.

9–32. Calculate. Use tables only if necessary.

9. $\tan \frac{\pi}{3}$	**10.** $\tan \frac{\pi}{2}$	**11.** $\tan \frac{\pi}{4}$	**12.** $\tan\left(-\frac{\pi}{4}\right)$
13. $\cot \frac{\pi}{3}$	**14.** $\cot \frac{\pi}{2}$	**15.** $\cot \frac{\pi}{4}$	**16.** $\cot\left(-\frac{\pi}{4}\right)$
Ⓑ **17.** $\tan 127°$	**18.** $\tan(-12°)$	**19.** $\tan 202°$	**20.** $\tan 639°$
21. $\cot 127°$	**22.** $\cot(-12°)$	**23.** $\cot 202°$	**24.** $\cot 639°$
25. $\tan \frac{3\pi}{4}$	**26.** $\tan 0$	**27.** $\tan\left(-\frac{13\pi}{6}\right)$	**28.** $\tan\left(-\frac{\pi}{3}\right)$
29. $\cot \frac{3\pi}{4}$	**30.** $\cot 0$	**31.** $\cot\left(-\frac{13\pi}{6}\right)$	**32.** $\cot\left(-\frac{\pi}{3}\right)$

33. Name five points on the graph of $x \rightarrow \cot x$.

34. Sketch a graph of the solution set to $y = \cot x$.

35–39. Refer to the tangent function $x \rightarrow \tan x$ and its graph. Name:

35. the domain.

36. the range.

37. all lines of symmetry.

38. all centers of rotation-symmetry.

39. the fundamental period.

40–44. Answer Exercises **35–39** with respect to the cotangent function.

Ⓒ **45.** Graph $y = \tan 3x$.

46. Graph $2y = \cot x$.

47–48. Refer to Exercises **47–48** on page 473. Prove that if $0 < x < \frac{\pi}{2}$ and $A = (\cos x, \sin x)$, then:

47. $CD = \tan x$.

48. $EB = \cot x$.

(NOTE: From this geometric interpretation, the words *tangent* and *cotangent* arose.)

49. Draw any obtuse triangle ABC which is not isosceles. Measure the angles and sides, and use tables to verify that

$$\frac{a - b}{a + b} = \frac{\tan \frac{1}{2}(A - B)}{\tan \frac{1}{2}(A + B)}.$$

(This formula is known as the *law of tangents*.)

50. Let line ℓ contain the origin. Let $A = (1, 0)$, $B = (0, 0)$, and let C be the point where ℓ intersects the unit circle in the first quadrant. Prove that $\tan(m\angle ABC)$ is the slope of this line.

TRIGONOMETRY— THE RIGHT TRIANGLE

Every right triangle has two legs and two acute angles. The drawing shows how either acute angle can be used to identify the legs.

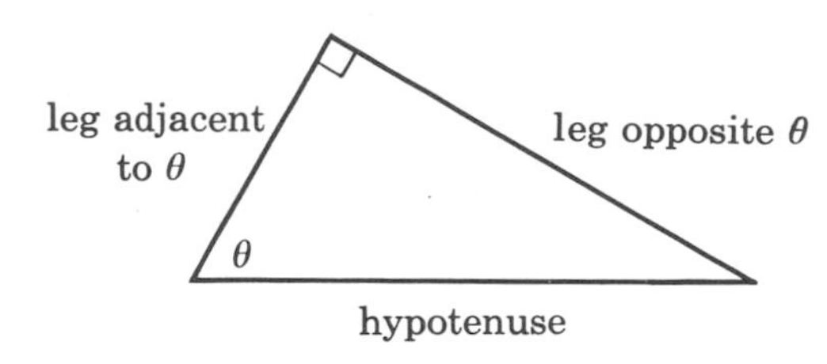

Six ratios can be formed using the lengths of the sides. One such ratio is $\frac{\text{length of leg opposite } \theta}{\text{length of hypotenuse}}$, usually written $\frac{\text{leg opposite } \theta}{\text{hypotenuse}}$.

In this section it is shown that each of the six possible ratios is associated with one of the trigonometric functions.

First we apply the law of sines to $\triangle ABC$, in which $m\angle C = \frac{\pi}{2}$.

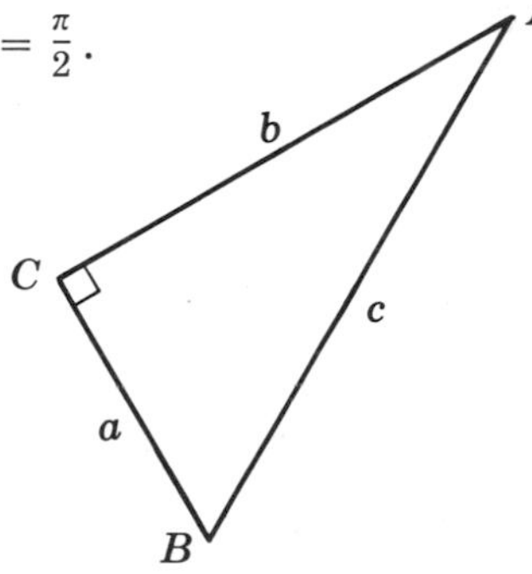

$$\frac{\sin B}{b} = \frac{\sin C}{c}$$

But $\sin \frac{\pi}{2} = 1$, so: $\quad \frac{\sin B}{b} = \frac{1}{c}$

Multiplying both sides by b: $\quad \sin B = \frac{b}{c}$

Similarly, it can be shown that $\sin A = \frac{a}{c}$.

Theorem 15.8.1a

> Let θ be an acute angle in a right triangle. Then
>
> $$\sin \theta = \frac{\text{leg opposite } \theta}{\text{hypotenuse}}.$$

This theorem can be used to approximate sines. For example, to estimate sin 20°, construct a right triangle with a 20° angle. Measuring a and c, approximate $\frac{a}{c}$. Since $\sin A = \frac{a}{c}$, you have approximated sin 20°. (The ratio does not depend on the size of the right triangle, because all right triangles with 20° angles are similar.)

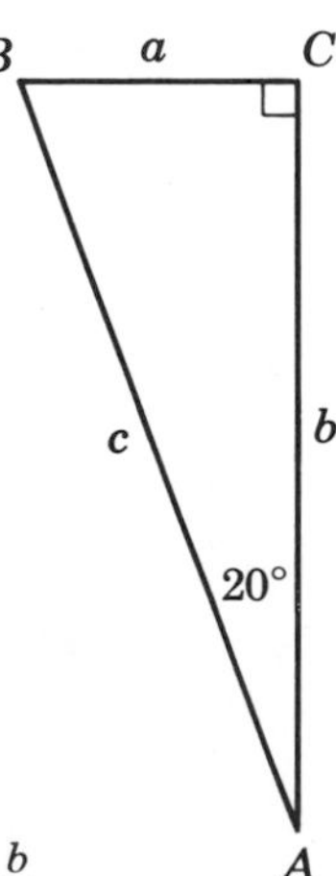

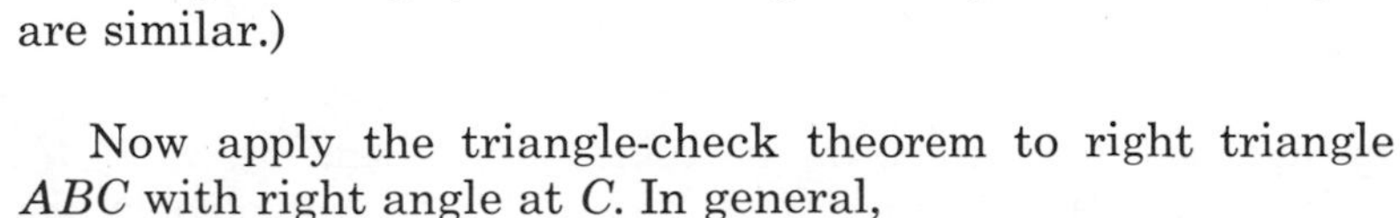

Now apply the triangle-check theorem to right triangle ABC with right angle at C. In general,

$$b \cos C + c \cos B = a; \quad \text{but } m\angle C = \frac{\pi}{2}, \text{ so } b \cos C = b \cdot 0 = 0.$$

Thus: $\quad c \cos B = a$

Divide by c: $\quad \cos B = \frac{a}{c} \qquad$ Relettering the triangle gives $\cos A = \frac{b}{c}$.

Theorem 15.8.1b

Let θ be an acute angle in a right triangle. Then

$$\cos \theta = \frac{\text{leg adjacent to } \theta}{\text{hypotenuse}}.$$

Expressions for the other functions can now be found.

Theorem 15.8.1c–f

Let θ be an acute angle in a right triangle. Then

c. $\tan \theta = \dfrac{\text{leg opposite } \theta}{\text{leg adjacent to } \theta}$. **d.** $\cot \theta = \dfrac{\text{leg adjacent to } \theta}{\text{leg opposite } \theta}$.

e. $\sec \theta = \dfrac{\text{hypotenuse}}{\text{leg adjacent to } \theta}$. **f.** $\csc \theta = \dfrac{\text{hypotenuse}}{\text{leg opposite } \theta}$.

PROOFS:

c. $\tan \theta = \dfrac{\sin \theta}{\cos \theta} = \dfrac{\frac{\text{leg opp. } \theta}{\text{hyp.}}}{\frac{\text{leg adj. to } \theta}{\text{hyp.}}} = \dfrac{\text{leg opp. } \theta}{\text{leg adj. to } \theta}$

d. $\cot \theta$ is the reciprocal of $\tan \theta$; use Theorem 15.8.1c.

e. $\sec \theta$ is the reciprocal of $\cos \theta$; use Theorem 15.8.1b.

f. $\csc \theta$ is the reciprocal of $\sin \theta$; use Theorem 15.8.1a.

The six ratios can be applied to $\angle X$ in $\triangle XYZ$ below.

$$\sin X = \frac{\text{leg opp. } X}{\text{hyp.}} = \frac{3}{5} = 0.600$$

$$\cos X = \frac{\text{leg adj. } X}{\text{hyp.}} = \frac{4}{5} = 0.800$$

$$\tan X = \frac{\text{leg opp. } X}{\text{leg adj. } X} = \frac{3}{4} = 0.750$$

$$\cot X = \frac{\text{leg adj. } X}{\text{leg opp. } X} = \frac{4}{3} = 1.333\cdots$$

$$\sec X = \frac{\text{hyp.}}{\text{leg adj. } X} = \frac{5}{4} = 1.250$$

$$\csc X = \frac{\text{hyp.}}{\text{leg opp. } X} = \frac{5}{3} = 1.666\cdots$$

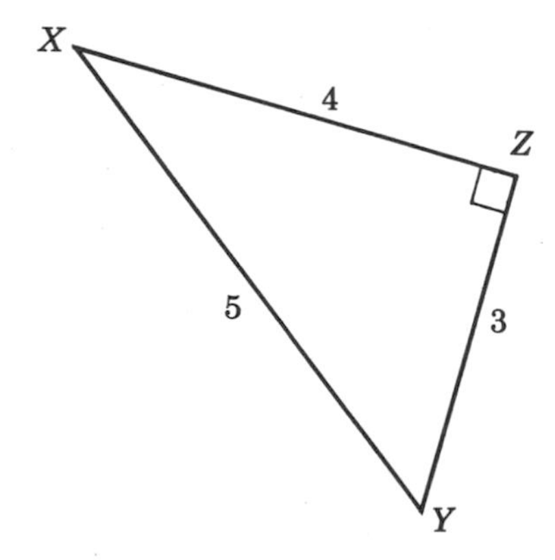

Finding any of these values in the tables shows that $m\angle X \doteq 37°$. (You should check this.) Since $\angle X$ and $\angle Y$ are complementary, $m\angle Y \doteq 53°$.

The terms *cosine, cotangent,* and *cosecant* were invented by Edmund Gunter (1581–1626). *Complement's sine* was shortened to *cosine.* Similar abbreviations led to *cotangent* and *cosecant.*

The relationships between functions of complementary angles can be verified using $\triangle XYZ$ on page 478.

$$\cos Y = \frac{\text{leg adj. } Y}{\text{hyp.}} = \frac{3}{5} = \sin X = \text{sine (complement of } Y)$$

$$\cot Y = \frac{\text{leg adj. } Y}{\text{leg opp. } Y} = \frac{3}{4} = \tan X = \text{tangent (complement of } Y)$$

$$\csc Y = \frac{\text{hyp.}}{\text{leg opp. } Y} = \frac{5}{4} = \sec X = \text{secant (complement of } Y)$$

EXERCISES 15.8

Ⓐ **1–6.** Match each numbered term with the best lettered choice.

1. sine

2. cosine

3. tangent

4. cotangent

5. secant

6. cosecant

a. $\dfrac{\text{hypotenuse}}{\text{leg opposite}}$ **b.** $\dfrac{\text{hypotenuse}}{\text{leg adjacent}}$

c. $\dfrac{\text{leg opposite}}{\text{leg adjacent}}$ **d.** $\dfrac{\text{leg opposite}}{\text{hypotenuse}}$

e. $\dfrac{\text{leg adjacent}}{\text{leg opposite}}$ **f.** $\dfrac{\text{leg adjacent}}{\text{hypotenuse}}$

7–18. Use $\triangle PQM$ to calculate.

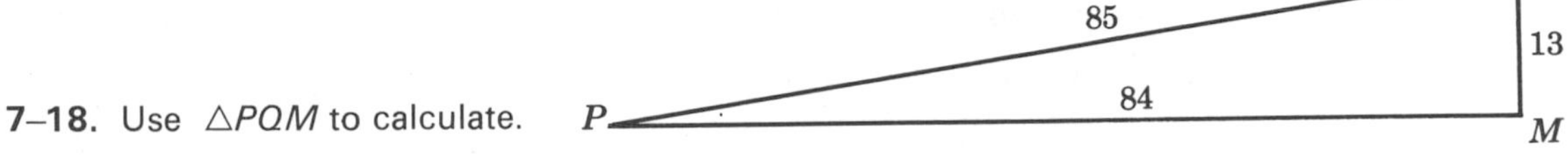

7. $\sin P$ **8.** $\sin Q$ **9.** $\cos P$ **10.** $\cos Q$

11. $\tan P$ **12.** $\cot P$ **13.** $\tan Q$ **14.** $\cot Q$

15. $\sec P$ **16.** $\csc Q$ **17.** $\csc P$ **18.** $\sec Q$

19. Theorem 15.8.1a is a special case of what theorem?

20. Theorem 15.8.1b is a special case of what theorem?

21. The word *cosine* was originally short for ____.

22. $\cos 50° = \sin$ ____ **23.** $\cot 19° = \tan$ ____

24. $\sec 43° = \csc$ ____ **25.** $\sin 62° = \cos$ ____

26. In right triangle ABC, with $m\angle C = \frac{\pi}{2}$, $\tan B =$ ____ A.

27–34. Use tables to give a decimal approximation.

27. $\sec 12°$ **28.** $\csc 89°$ **29.** $\tan 46°$ **30.** $\cot 4°$

31. $\tan 61°$ **32.** $\cot 28°$ **33.** $\sec 50°$ **34.** $\csc 40°$

Ⓑ **35.** If $\sin X = \frac{5}{13}$ and $0 \le X \le \frac{\pi}{2}$, calculate $\cos X$, $\tan X$, $\cot X$, $\sec X$, and $\csc X$. (HINT: Draw a right triangle.)

36. If $\tan X = 2$ and $0 \le X \le \frac{\pi}{2}$, calculate $\sin X$, $\cos X$, $\cot X$, $\sec X$, and $\csc X$.

37–39. Find the measures of the angles in a right triangle with sides:

37. 3, 4, and 5. **38.** 20, 21, and 29. **39.** 2, 3, and $\sqrt{13}$.

40. A right triangle has legs 6 and 11. Find its angles.

41. Approximate $\sin\frac{2\pi}{9}$, $\cos\frac{2\pi}{9}$, and $\tan\frac{2\pi}{9}$ by drawing a right triangle with an angle of measure $\frac{2\pi}{9}$ and measuring appropriate sides.

42–49. Simplify.

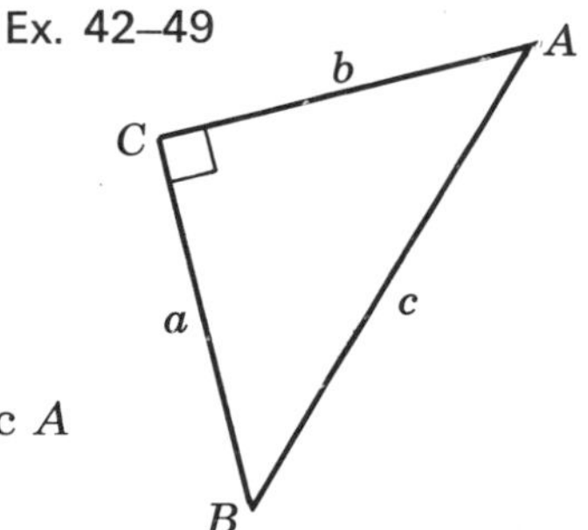

42. $c \sin A$ **43.** $c \cos A$

44. $(\sin B)^2 + (\cos B)^2$

45. $b \tan A$ **46.** $a \sec B$

Ⓒ **47.** $\sqrt{1 + (\tan B)^2}$

48. $\sin A \cdot \cos A \cdot \tan A \cdot \cot A \cdot \sec A \cdot \csc A$

49. $\sin A \cdot \cos B + \cos A \cdot \sin B$

APPLICATIONS OF RIGHT TRIANGLE TRIGONOMETRY

Suppose a person 150 feet away from a building finds that the top of the building is 56° above the horizon. How high is the building?

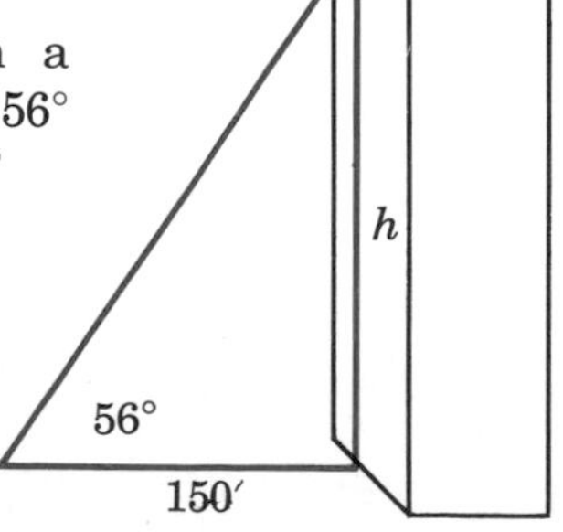

The height is easy to estimate. In the right triangle shown,

$$\tan 56^\circ = \frac{h}{150}$$

$$150(1.483) \doteq h$$

$$222 \doteq h$$

This is the height from eye level to the top of the building, so 5 or 6 feet should be added. However, measuring errors might be greater than 5 or 6 feet, so perhaps 225 feet is a reasonable estimate.

This problem could have been solved using the law of sines, since two angles and a side are known. But using the tangent is easier. (It is typical of problems involving right triangles that although the laws of sines and cosines apply, it may be easier to use other theorems.)

Example 1: How long must a ladder be if, when placed at a 70° angle to the ground, it hits a building at a point 10 m above the ground?

SOLUTION: A diagram is helpful. An equation is usually easier to solve if the variable is in the numerator instead of in the denominator. So we choose the ratio

$$\frac{\ell}{10} = \csc 70^\circ$$

$$\ell \doteq 10(1.064) \doteq 10.6$$

A ladder 11 meters long will do.

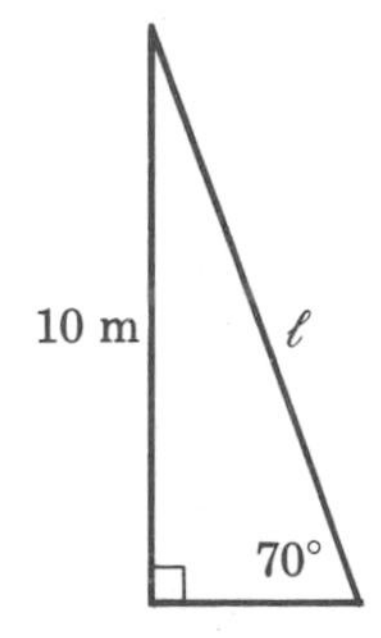

The next example shows an application of the circular functions to geometry; other applications are given in the exercises.

Example 2: Find a formula for the area of a parallelogram in terms of the lengths of two sides and the included angle. (The height is not known.)

SOLUTION: Draw the altitude h. You know

that Area of ▱ $= ah$

But $\frac{h}{b} = \sin \theta$, so $h = b \sin \theta$.

Substituting, Area of ▱ $= ab \sin \theta$

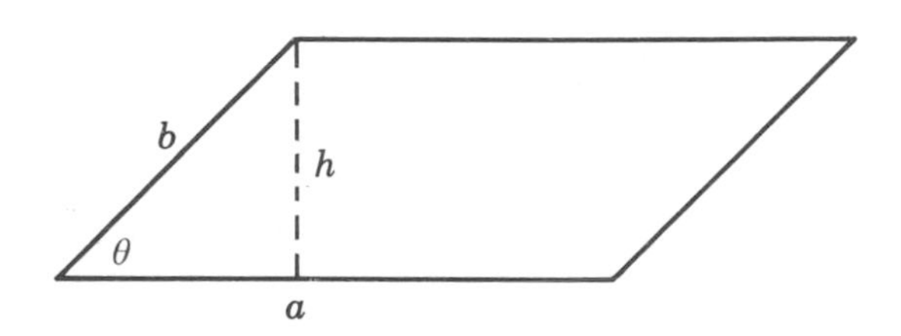

EXERCISES 15.9

Ⓐ 1. Give an easy way of approximating a.

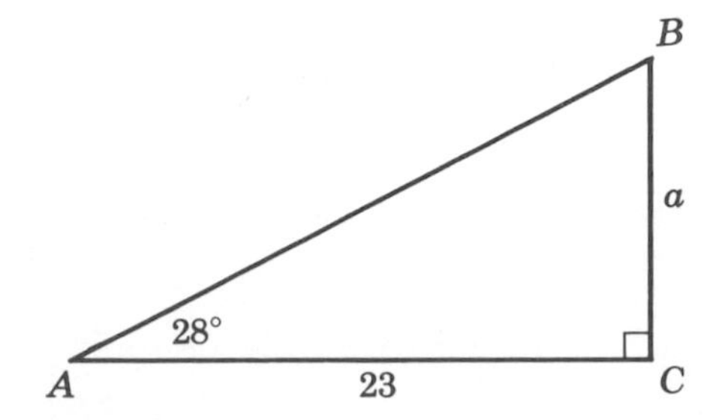

2. Give an easy way of approximating e.

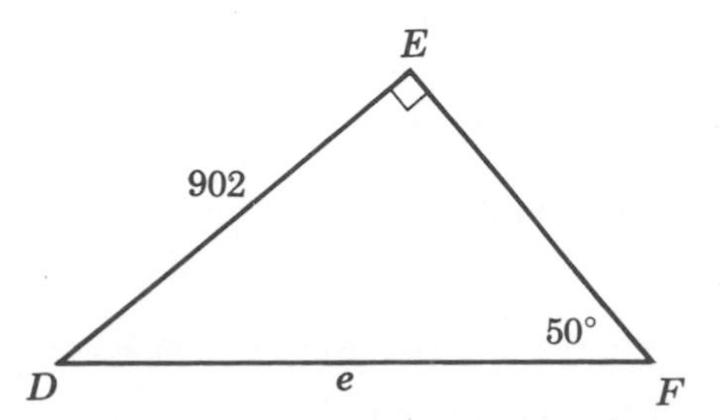

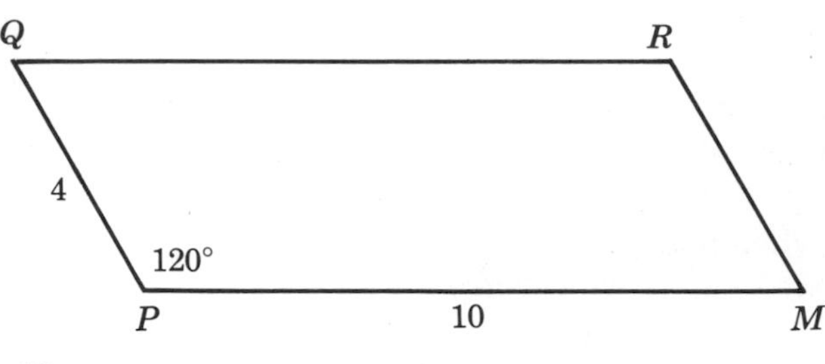

3. What area formula is found in this section?

4. Without using tables, find the area of ▱ $MPQR$.

5. Give the area of $\triangle MPQ$.

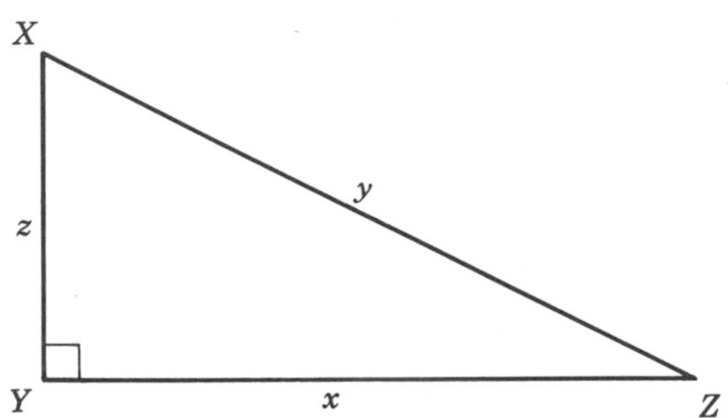

Ⓑ **6–10.** In $\triangle XYZ$ at left, $m\angle Y = \frac{\pi}{2}$.

6. If $m\angle X = 71°$ and $y = 100$, find x.

7. If $m\angle X = 71°$ and $y = 100$, find z.

8. If $y = 200$ and $x = 175$, find $m\angle X$.

9. If $z = 0.1$ and $y = 0.3$, find $m\angle Z$.

10. If $m\angle X = 10°$ and $z = 50$, find y.

11. Refer to Exercise **1**. Find a.

12. Refer to Exercise **2**. Find e.

13. Standing 305 metres from a television tower, a person has to look up 41° to see the top of the tower. About how high is the tower?

14–17. Find the polar coordinates of the point.

14. (2, 3)

15. (−1, 5)

16. (−6, −2)

17. (1.3, −2.9)

18. Find the area of the parallelogram with vertices at (0, 0), (5, 0), (1, 9), and (6, 9).

Ⓒ **19–23.** Verify the given formula by **(a)** selecting an appropriate figure for which the area or perimeter can be found without using the formula and **(b)** comparing your result with what you get using the formula.

19. The area of a triangle with sides a and b and included angle θ is $\frac{1}{2}ab \cdot \sin \theta$. (Use a right triangle to verify.)

20. The area of a regular n-gon with each side of length s is $\frac{1}{4}ns^2 \cdot \cot \frac{\pi}{n}$. (Verify with a square.)

21. The area of *any* quadrilateral with diagonals d and e and angle θ between the diagonals is $\frac{1}{2}de \cdot \sin \theta$.

22. The perimeter of a regular n-gon inscribed in a circle of radius r is $2nr \cdot \sin \frac{\pi}{n}$.

23. The perimeter of a regular n-gon circumscribed about a circle of radius r is $2nr \cdot \tan \frac{\pi}{n}$.

24–28. Derive each formula in Exercises **19–23.**

29. Given the formula in Exercise **19**, derive a formula for the area of an equilateral triangle when the length of one side is known.

30. Given the formulas in Exercises **22** and **23**, find the perimeters of regular 20-gons inscribed and circumscribed about a circle with radius $\frac{1}{2}$. Use your results to approximate π.

CHAPTER SUMMARY

15

The correspondence $x \to \sin x$ is the *sine function*; $x \to \cos x$ is the *cosine function*. Usually, x is given in *radian measure*, which is related to degree measure by this formula:

$$180^\circ = \pi \text{ radians} \doteq 3.14 \text{ radians}.$$

The graphs of these functions are *sine waves* and have many symmetries. The values of each function repeat each 2π. So the graph is translation-symmetric under a horizontal translation and the function is *periodic* with *fundamental period* 2π.

Four other numbers are defined in terms of sine and cosine.

definition	function	fund. period
$\tan x = \frac{\sin x}{\cos x}$	$x \to \tan x$	π
$\cot x = \frac{\cos x}{\sin x}$	$x \to \cot x$	π
$\sec x = \frac{1}{\cos x}$	$x \to \sec x$	2π
$\csc x = \frac{1}{\sin x}$	$x \to \csc x$	2π

The six functions given above are *circular functions*, which have many applications. One application is to *trigonometry*, the measurement of sides and angles of polygons. In any $\triangle ABC$:

$$c^2 = a^2 + b^2 - 2ab \cos C$$ ◀ **law of cosines**

$$\frac{\sin A}{a} = \frac{\sin B}{b} = \frac{\sin C}{c}$$ ◀ **law of sines**

$$b \cos C + c \cos B = a$$ ◀ **triangle-check theorem**

When these theorems are restricted to right triangles, six important ratios result. If θ is an acute angle:

$$\sin \theta = \frac{\text{side opposite } \theta}{\text{hypotenuse}}$$

$$\csc \theta = \frac{\text{hypotenuse}}{\text{side opposite } \theta}$$

$$\cos \theta = \frac{\text{side adjacent to } \theta}{\text{hypotenuse}}$$

$$\sec \theta = \frac{\text{hypotenuse}}{\text{side adjacent to } \theta}$$

$$\tan \theta = \frac{\text{side opposite } \theta}{\text{side adjacent to } \theta}$$

$$\cot \theta = \frac{\text{side adjacent to } \theta}{\text{side opposite } \theta}$$

Using trigonometry, many distances and angles can be approximated without direct measurement.

CHAPTER REVIEW

1. $\frac{3\pi}{2}$ radians = _____ degrees

2. 1.5 radians $\doteq$ _____ degrees

3. $\frac{360}{\pi}$ degrees = _____ radians

4. 7° = _____ rad

5–10. Copy and complete the following chart.

	function	range	fund. period	lines of symmetry	points of symmetry	undefined for x =	reciprocal function
5.	sin						
6.	cos						
7.	tan						
8.	cot						
9.	sec						
10.	csc						

11. State the law of cosines.

12. State the law of sines.

13. In which cases can the law of cosines be used to start solving a triangle?

a. *SSA* **b.** *SAS* **c.** *ASA* **d.** *AAS* **e.** *SSS*

14. In which cases listed in Exercise **13** can the law of sines be used to start solving a triangle?

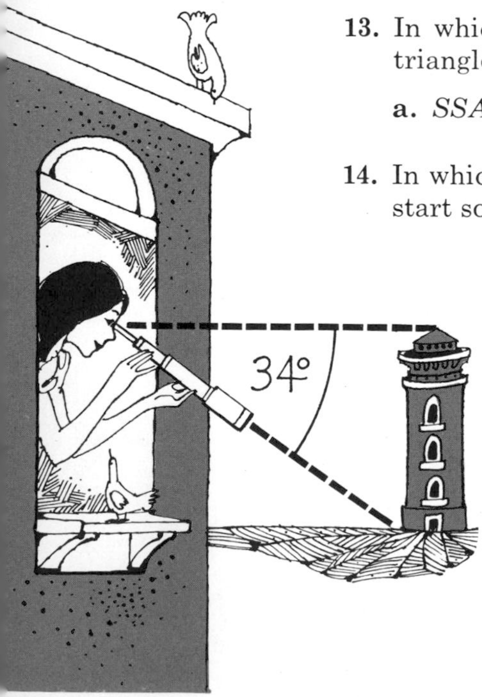

15. From a window even with the top of a tower and 60 metres from it, a person has to look down 34° to see the base of the tower. About how high is the tower?

16. On the same graph, sketch $\sin x$ and $\csc x$ for $-\frac{\pi}{2} \leq x \leq \frac{\pi}{2}$.

17–19. Find $\sin x$, $\cos x$, and $\tan x$ for the given x.

17. $\frac{3\pi}{2}$

18. $\frac{2\pi}{3}$

19. $\frac{5\pi}{4}$

20. In $\triangle BED$, $m\angle B = 130^\circ$, $b = 525$, and $e = 421$. Find d.

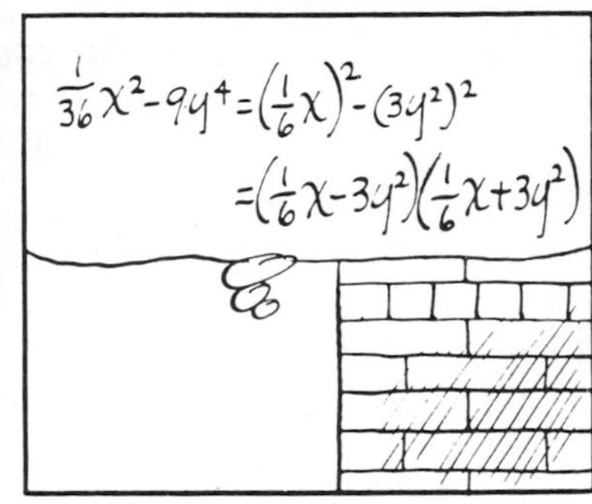

Chapter 16 | Advanced Manipulative Techniques

Some applications of mathematics involve complicated expressions. These expressions have sometimes occurred in earlier chapters; now they are studied in a little more detail.

FACTORING

By the multiplication process, if you begin with 3 and 2, you will wind up with 6. If you begin with 6 and end with 3 and 2, the process is called *factoring*. The same words apply to expressions.

multiplication

$$(2x - 3)(3x + 4) \qquad 6x^2 - x - 12$$

factoring

An expression is said to be in **factored form** if, by the order of operations, the last operation performed is multiplication. For example, $(2x - 3)(3x + 4)$ is in factored form.

The simplest type of factoring is an application of the distributive property. Look for a factor common to each term.

Examples: Factoring with common factors

	Original		*Factored form*
1.	$18x^2 - 27y$	$=$	$9(2x^2 - 3y)$
2.	$a^5 + a^4$	$=$	$a^4(a + 1)$
3.	$9d^2 + 3ed - 6d^3$	$=$	$3d(3d + e - 2d^2)$

As the example $6x^2 - x - 12 = (2x - 3)(3x + 4)$ shows, it is not necessary to have a common factor in order to be able to factor. In fact, *every* quadratic expression of the form $ax^2 + bx + c$ can be factored. The next theorem gives the factors. (The proof is left as an exercise.)

Theorem 16.1.1

Let r and s be the solutions to $ax^2 + bx + c = 0$. Then

$$ax^2 + bx + c = a(x - r)(x - s).$$

Examples: Factoring using Theorem 16.1.1

4. To factor $4x^2 - 4x - 15$, solve $4x^2 - 4x - 15 = 0$ using the quadratic formula. The solutions are $\frac{5}{2}$ and $-\frac{3}{2}$. Let $r = \frac{5}{2}$, $s = -\frac{3}{2}$.

Then $\qquad 4x^2 - 4x + 5 = 4(x - \frac{5}{2})(x + \frac{3}{2})$.

If possible, the expression at right is cleared of fractions by multiplying. Since $4 = 2 \cdot 2$:

$$= 2(x - \tfrac{5}{2}) \cdot 2(x + \tfrac{3}{2})$$

$$= (2x - 5)(2x + 3).$$

5. The solutions to $x^2 + x - 1 = 0$ are $-\frac{1}{2} + \frac{\sqrt{5}}{2}$ and $-\frac{1}{2} - \frac{\sqrt{5}}{2}$.

$$x^2 + x - 1 = \left[x - \left(-\frac{1}{2} + \frac{\sqrt{5}}{2}\right)\right]\left[x - \left(-\frac{1}{2} - \frac{\sqrt{5}}{2}\right)\right]$$

$$= \left(x + \frac{1}{2} - \frac{\sqrt{5}}{2}\right)\left(x + \frac{1}{2} + \frac{\sqrt{5}}{2}\right)$$

Sometimes you may want to factor $ax^2 + bx + c$ without solving the quadratic equation $ax^2 + bx + c = 0$. Example **5** shows that this is not always realistic—the factors will involve irrationals when the solutions are irrational. However, Example 4 could have been done by a trial-and-error process.

Example: Trying to factor a quadratic expression by trial and error

6. To factor $8a^2 - 3 + 10a$,

commute for convenience: $8a^2 + 10a - 3$.

If there is a factorization with integer coefficients, it must have the form

$$(4a + \_\_)(2a + \_\_) \quad \text{or} \quad (8a + \_\_)(a + \_\_)$$

where the blanks must be filled by numbers which multiply to -3. Here are the choices.

$(4a - 3)(2a + 1)$	$(8a - 3)(a + 1)$
$(4a + 3)(2a - 1)$	$(8a + 3)(a - 1)$
$(4a - 1)(2a + 3)$	$(8a - 1)(a + 3)$
$(4a + 1)(2a - 3)$	$(8a + 1)(a - 3)$

When you multiply using the FOIL theorem, only one choice gives a middle term of $10a$.

$$(4a - 1)(2a + 3) = 8a^2 + 10a - 3$$

If all choices do not work, then factorization into integral linear expressions is impossible.

Certain forms and their factors occur so often that we call attention to them by a theorem.

Theorem 16.1.2

a. Perfect-square trinomial: $x^2 + 2xy + y^2 = (x + y)(x + y) = (x + y)^2$

b. Difference of two squares: $x^2 - y^2 = (x + y)(x - y)$

PROOF: Verify the factors by multiplying the binomials.

Examples: Common forms

7. $x^2 + 2x + 1 = (x + 1)(x + 1) = (x + 1)^2$

8. To factor $m^6 + 8m^3 + 16$, notice that if $x = m^3$ and $y = 4$, then $2xy = 8m^3$. So this is a perfect-square trinomial.

$$m^6 + 8m^3 + 16 = (m^3 + 4)^2$$

9. $81x^2 - y^{10}$ is the difference of the squares of $9x$ and y^5. Thus

$$81x^2 - y^{10} = (9x + y^5)(9x - y^5).$$

Although $x^2 - y^2$ is easy to factor, $x^2 + y^2$ cannot be factored without using complex numbers. Theorem 10.7.1, page 284, displays the factorization of $x^2 + y^2$.

$$x^2 + y^2 = (x + iy)(x - iy)$$

Examples: Using more than one factoring idea

10. The first pair of terms is the difference of two squares. The second pair of terms has a common factor.

$$\begin{aligned} x^2 - y^2 + 3x + 3y &= (x - y)(x + y) + 3(x + y) \\ &= (x + y)[(x - y) + 3] \quad \text{Common factor} \\ &= (x + y)(x - y + 3) \end{aligned}$$

11. $$\begin{aligned} 12a^2 - 60a + 75 &= 3(4a^2 - 20a + 25) \quad \text{Common factor} \\ &= 3(2a - 5)^2 \quad \text{Perfect-square trinomial} \end{aligned}$$

12. $$\begin{aligned} x^4 - y^4 &= (x^2 - y^2)(x^2 + y^2) \quad \text{Difference of two squares (twice)} \\ &= (x - y)(x + y)(x^2 + y^2) \\ &= (x - y)(x + y)(x + iy)(x - iy) \quad \text{If complex numbers are allowed} \end{aligned}$$

Why factor? One reason is to help reduce fractions. This is studied in Section 16.4. A second reason is that factoring can help solve some equations. For example, from Example **6** you know

$$8a^2 + 10a - 3 = 0 \text{ is equivalent to } (4a - 1)(2a + 3) = 0.$$

By the zero product theorem (1.6.3), at least one factor is 0.

So $\quad 4a - 1 = 0 \quad$ or $\quad 2a + 3 = 0$

$\qquad a = \frac{1}{4} \quad$ or $\quad a = -\frac{3}{2}$.

Both values check. So the solution set to $8a^2 + 10a - 3 = 0$ is $\{\frac{1}{4}, -\frac{3}{2}\}$.

EXERCISES 16.1

Ⓐ **1.** When is an expression in factored form?

2. Which expression is not in factored form?

a. $(x + y)(x - y)$ **b.** $(x + y) - (x - y)$ **c.** $3(x + y)$

3–6. Find a common factor, and use the distributive property to factor.

3. $3x + 9x^2$

4. $ab + ac - ad^2$

5. $8xy - 12y^2 + 16y^3$

6. $62x^2 - 124$

7. Given that $(3x + 1)(2x - 4) = 6x^2 - 10x - 4$, solve the equation $6y^2 - 10y - 4 = 0$ in your head.

8. Upon what theorem about real numbers is the strategy of factoring to solve equations based?

9. Which expression cannot be factored without using imaginary numbers?

a. $a^2 - b^2$ **b.** $a^2 - 2ab + b^2$ **c.** $a^2 + b^2$

10–12. Factor each expression of Exercise **9**.

13–17. True or False?

13. $5x^2 - 7x - 6 = (5x - 3)(x + 2)$

14. $a^2 + 6a + 6 = (a + 2)(a + 3)$

15. $1 - 6y - 9y^2 = (1 - 3y)(1 - 3y)$

16. $2y^2 - 8 = (2y - 4)(y + 2)$

17. $w^2 + 49 = (w + 7)(w + 7)$

18–33. Find all solutions to each equation. Factor, if possible. Check answers.

18. $(2 - y)(y + 6) = 0$

19. $(2x + 4)(3x - 1) = 0$

Ⓑ **20.** $(x^2 - 1)(x^2 + 1) = 0$

21. $(a - 1)(a + 1) = 1$

22. $10t^2 + 19t + 7 = 0$

23. $10x^2 - 19x + 7 = 0$

24. $7u^2 + 19u + 10 = 0$

25. $7y^2 - 19y + 10 = 0$

26. $0 = x^2 - 7x - 18$

27. $0 = h^2 + 1.5h + 0.5$

28. $8k^2 + 1 = 6k$

29. $72k^2 + 9 = 54k$

30. $3ab + 9a + 2b = -6$

31. $5x^2 = 10x$

32. $4m + m^2 = 0$

33. $2p^7 = 7p^6$

34–51. Factor into an expression with integer coefficients.

34. $x^2 - 9$

35. $16 - y^2$

36. $ax + bx + ay + by$

37. $9 - 4a^2$

38. $28y^2 - 7x^2$

39. $2k - 6m + ak - 3am$

40. $(x + y)(3x - y) + (x + y)(2x - 3y)$

41. $2(c - 1)^2 - 3(c - 1) - 2$

42. $270h^2 + 240h + 50$

43. $x^2y - 24xy + 143y$

44. $7a^2 - 64ab + 9b^2$

45. $m^2 + 6mp + 9p^2$

46. $2r^2 - 8t^2 + 15rt$

47. $-12uv + 4u^2 + 9v^2$

48. $x^2y^2 + 2xy + 1$

49. $10(z - 3) + xz - 3x$

50. $t^8 - 1$

51. $16a^4 - 24a^2b + 9b^2$

© **52. Verify that $4x^2 + 5x + 1 = (4x + 1)(x + 1)$ by substituting the numbers 1, 2, 3, 4, $\cdots$, 10 for x on both sides. In this way, show that factoring polynomials corresponds to factoring integers.**

53. Prove Theorem 16.1.1. HINT: Use the fact that $a(x - r)(x - s) = a(x^2 - sx - rx + rs) = a[x^2 - (r + s)x + rs]$. Then apply the results of Exercises 45–46, page 312.

54–57. Find all solutions to each equation by factoring, if possible.

54. $x^4 + 49 = 14x^2$

55. $2y + 5\sqrt{y} - 12 = 0$

56. $2(\sin x)^2 = \sin x$

57. $30 - 43 \log x + 4(\log x)^2 = 0$

58–59. *Trigonometric identities.* An equation is called an identity if it is true for all values of x. $3x + 2x = 5x$ is an identity. A trigonometric identity is $(\sin x)^2 + (\cos x)^2 = 1$. Use factoring to prove these identities, and verify each identity when $x = \frac{\pi}{6}$. We adopt here the standard notations $\sin^n x$, $\cos^n x$, $\cdots$ for $(\sin x)^n$, $(\cos x)^n$, $\cdots$.

58. $\sin^4 x - \cos^4 x = \sin^2 x - \cos^2 x$

59. $\cos x \tan x - \sin^3 x = \sin x \cos^2 x$

16.2 SOLVING POLYNOMIAL EQUATIONS

The equation below is easy to solve.

$$(x - 4)(x - 3)(x + 2)(x - 1) = 0$$

Using the zero product theorem, at least one factor is 0. So $x = 4$ or $x = 3$ or $x = -2$ or $x = 1$. The solution set is $\{4, 3, -2, 1\}$.

When the four binomials above are multiplied, the result is

$$x^4 - 6x^3 + 3x^2 + 26x - 24 = 0.$$

Although this equation is equivalent to the preceding one, the four solutions are not as apparent. In general, these types of equations are difficult to solve. But there is a process by which any *rational* solution can be found. It uses the next theorem.

Theorem 16.2.1

Rational root theorem: If $\frac{p}{q}$ is a solution to

$$a_nx^n + a_{n-1}x^{n-1} + \cdots + a_1x + a_0 = 0$$

where $a_n, \cdots, a_0$ are any integers and $\frac{p}{q}$ is in lowest terms, then p is a factor of a_0 and q is a factor of a_n.

Before proving this theorem, we give an example of its use.

Suppose $$4x^5 + 2x^4 - 6x^3 + 12x^2 - 3x - 1 = 0.$$

Now a_n is the coefficient of x^n, the highest power of x. In this case, $a_n = 4$. a_0 is the constant, so $a_0 = -1$. The theorem says that for any rational solution $\frac{p}{q}$ in lowest terms, p must be a factor of -1 and q must be a factor of 4. So $p = \pm1$ and q is ±1, ±2, or ±4. This allows only 6 possible values for $\frac{p}{q}$.

$$1, -1, \tfrac{1}{2}, -\tfrac{1}{2}, \tfrac{1}{4}, -\tfrac{1}{4}$$

By substitution, each of the 6 potential solutions is tested. Only $\frac{1}{2}$ works, indicating that $\frac{1}{2}$ is the only rational solution. (There may be other solutions, but they would have to be irrational or nonreal.)

PROOF OF THEOREM 16.2.1: Suppose $\frac{p}{q}$ is a solution to the given equation. Then

1. $a_n\left(\frac{p}{q}\right)^n + a_{n-1}\left(\frac{p}{q}\right)^{n-1} + \cdots + a_1\left(\frac{p}{q}\right) + a_0 = 0.$

Multiplying both sides by q^n,

2. $a_np^n + a_{n-1}p^{n-1}q + \cdots + a_1pq^{n-1} + a_0q^n = 0.$

With appropriate additions,

3. $a_np^n = q(-a_{n-1}p^{n-1} - \cdots - a_1pq^{n-2} - a_0q^{n-1}).$

So q is a factor of a_np^n. But q and p have no common factors, for $\frac{p}{q}$ is in lowest terms. So q and p^n have no common factors. So q must be a factor of a_n.

4. To prove that p is a factor of a_0, solve for a_0q^n in Step 2.

$$a_0q^n = p(-a_np^{n-1} - a_{n-1}p^{n-2}q - \cdots - a_1q^{n-1})$$

So p is a factor of a_0q^n. As before, p cannot be a factor of q or of q^n, so p is a factor of a_0.

Example 1: Find all rational solutions to $a^3 - a^2 - a - 2 = 0$.

SOLUTION: If the solution is $\frac{p}{q}$ in lowest terms, p must be a factor of -2, and q must be a factor of 1. So $\frac{p}{q}$ can only be one of these:

$$1, -1, 2, -2.$$

It is easy to check that 2 is the only rational solution.

Polynomial equations are equations equivalent to

$$a_n x^n + a_{n-1}x^{n-1} + \cdots + a_1 x + a_0 = 0.$$

The rational root theorem applies only when the coefficients a_0, a_1, $\cdots$, a_n are integers. If $a_n \neq 0$, this equation has *degree n*. You have worked with polynomial equations of degree 1 or 2 (even some without integer coefficients). These and a few others have special names.

Degree	*Equation*	*Name*
1	$a_1 x + a_0 = 0$	linear
2	$a_2 x^2 + a_1 x + a_0 = 0$	quadratic
3	$a_3 x^3 + a_2 x^2 + a_1 x + a_0 = 0$	cubic
4	$a_4 x^4 + a_3 x^3 + a_2 x^2 + a_1 x + a_0 = 0$	quartic or biquadratic
5	$a_5 x^5 + a_4 x^4 + \cdots + a_1 x + a_0 = 0$	quintic

There are other formulas similar to the quadratic formula for finding *all* solutions to cubic and quartic equations. These complicated formulas involve only a finite number of additions, multiplications, and rational powers using the coefficients and were known in the 1600's. Other formulas were sought for all polynomial equations. However, in 1824 the Norwegian mathematician Abel proved the *impossibility* of finding such a formula for solutions to the quintic. A little later the French mathematician Galois generalized Abel's result for higher degree polynomial equations. Their landmark proofs require more mathematics than we have discussed, so cannot be given here.

The rational root theorem may help find solutions to equations for which there is no formula for all solutions. These are *exact* solutions. *Approximations* to irrational solutions can always be found by substituting again and again. The first example of this was done in Section 1.1. Here is a second example.

Example 2: Estimate a solution to $x^3 - 5x + 1 = 0$ correct to the nearest tenth.

SOLUTION: There are no rational solutions. The only possible solutions are 1 or -1. We graph $f: x \to x^3 - 5x + 1$ to get some idea of when $x^3 - 5x + 1$ is near 0.

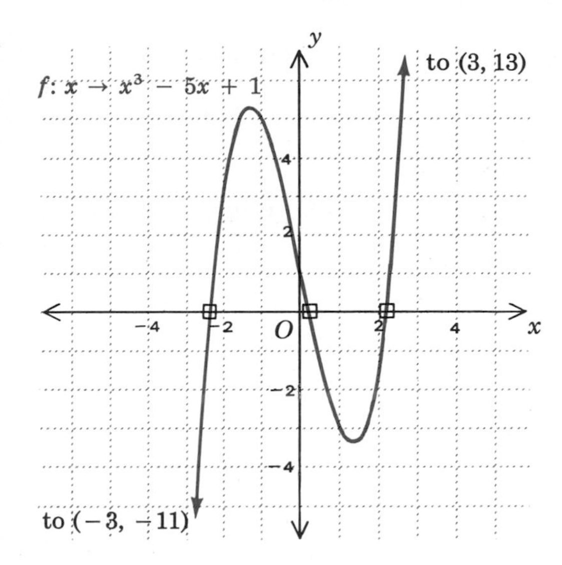

The three squares on the graph indicate that $x^3 - 5x + 1$ is 0 when $x \doteq -2.5$, 0.2, or 2.2. We substitute to approximate the solution near 0.2.

If $x = 0.1$: $x^3 - 5x + 1 = 0.5001$.

If $x = 0.2$: $x^3 - 5x + 1 = 0.008$.

If $x = 0.3$: $x^3 - 5x + 1 = -0.473$.

So, correct to the nearest tenth, $x = 0.2$. By substituting 0.20, 0.21, 0.22, etc., you can find the best approximation to the nearest hundredth.

EXERCISES 16.2

Ⓐ **1.** State the rational root theorem.

2–5. Using the rational root theorem, what are the only possible rational roots to each equation?

2. $y^5 + \sqrt{2}y^3 - 1 = 0$ **3.** $2z^4 - 7z^3 + 4z + 1 = 0$

4. $12a - a^5 + 13 = 0$ **5.** $x^3 + 4x - 8 = 0$

6. If the graph at right is of a function $f: x \to a_n x^n + \cdots + a_0$, estimate a solution to

$$a_n x^n + \cdots + a_0 = 0.$$

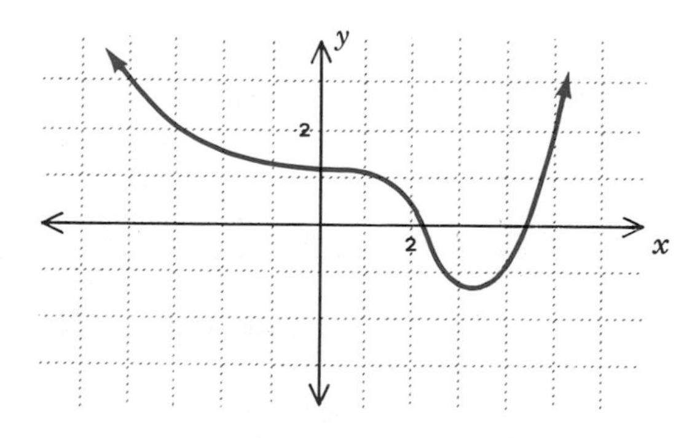

7. What is a polynomial equation?

8. What is the degree of a polynomial equation?

9–11. Give an example of an equation of the given type.

9. quartic **10.** quintic **11.** cubic

12. Whose name and what country is associated with the impossibility of getting a formula for solving a quintic equation? (HINT: There is a statue to the mathematician in the center of Oslo.)

Ⓑ 13–15. Find all rational roots of the equations of Exercises 3–5.

16–19. Find all rational solutions to each sentence.

16. $2a^3 - 9a^2 + a + 12 = 0$

17. $2x^3 + 5x^2 = 1$

18. $3m^4 + m^3 - 11m^2 = 4m - 4$

19. $0 = y^5 + 5y^4 - 6$

20–21. Estimate, correct to the nearest tenth, the indicated solution to the equation $x^3 - 5x + 1 = 0$ studied in Example 2 of this section.

20. largest solution

21. smallest solution

22–23. Estimate, correct to the nearest tenth, one solution to each sentence.

22. $2x^3 + x + 1 = 0$

23. $y^4 = 3y + 5$

Ⓒ 24. Describe all types of symmetry in the graph of the function f at the top of page 493.

25. Prove your answer to Exercise 24.

26. One solution to $x^2 - 3 = 0$ is $\sqrt{3}$. Use this information and the rational root theorem to show that $\sqrt{3}$ is irrational.

27. Use the idea of Exercise 26 to prove that $\sqrt[3]{7}$ is irrational.

16.3 DIVISION OF POLYNOMIALS

Knowing that $$(x + 3)(2x - 5) = 2x^2 + x - 15,$$

when $x \neq -3$, we have $$2x - 5 = \frac{2x^2 + x - 15}{x + 3}.$$

Now the question is, Given $\frac{2x^2 + x - 15}{x + 3}$, how can we get $2x - 5$? The process is much like normal division. Examine the examples.

Examples: Division of polynomials

1. Divide $2x^3 - 18x^2 + 47x - 35$ by $x - 5$.

$$
\begin{array}{r|l}
 & 2x^2 - 8x + 7 \quad \leftarrow \text{quotient} \\
x - 5 & 2x^3 - 18x^2 + 47x - 35 \\
 & 2x^3 - 10x^2 \\
\hline
 & -8x^2 + 47x \\
 & -8x^2 + 40x \\
\hline
 & 7x - 35 \\
 & 7x - 35 \\
\hline
\end{array}
$$

2. As in division, not all problems "come out even."

$$
\begin{array}{r|l}
 & 5x^2 - 12x + 41 \\
2x^2 + 3x - 8 & 10x^4 - 9x^3 + 6x^2 + 80x + 50 \\
 & 10x^4 + 15x^3 - 40x^2 \\
\hline
 & -24x^3 + 46x^2 + 80x \\
 & -24x^3 - 36x^2 + 96x \\
\hline
 & 82x^2 - 16x + 50 \\
 & 82x^2 + 123x - 328 \\
\hline
 & -139x + 378
\end{array}
$$

When 45 is divided by 7, the quotient is 6 and the remainder is 3. To check this, you might write $45 = 6 \cdot 7 + 3$. In general,

$$\text{dividend} = (\text{quotient})(\text{divisor}) + \text{remainder}.$$

This same relationship holds for polynomials. Example **2** may be checked by multiplying and adding on the right side of the equation.

$$
\begin{aligned}
&10x^4 - 9x^3 + 6x^2 + 80x + 50 \\
&\qquad = (5x^2 - 12x + 41)(2x^2 + 3x - 8) + (-139x + 378)
\end{aligned}
$$

As a further check, you can substitute a value for x and verify the last equation.

If the remainder is 0, then the polynomial can be factored. Here is the check for Example **1**.

$$2x^3 - 18x^2 + 47x - 35 = (x - 5)(2x^2 - 8x + 7)$$

If we substitute 5 for x, the right side is obviously 0. So the value of the left side must also be 0. So we have *5 as a solution* to

$$2x^3 - 18x^2 + 47x - 35 = 0,$$

and also *$x - 5$ is a factor* of the polynomial. This correspondence between solutions and factors holds in general. This famous theorem generalizes Theorem 16.1.1.

Theorem 16.3.1

Factor theorem: A number r is a solution to $a_nx^n + a_{n-1}x^{n-1} + \cdots + a_1x + a_0 = 0$ if and only if $x - r$ is a factor of $a_nx^n + a_{n-1}x^{n-1} + \cdots + a_1x + a_0$.

PROOF: This proof uses the graph translation theorem. Notice that 0 is a solution if and only if $a_0 = 0$ (there is no constant term), and then x is a factor of the given polynomial. Using the graph translation theorem, we can increase solutions by r if we replace x by $x - r$. Then r is a solution and $x - r$ is a factor of the polynomial.

The factor theorem can sometimes help find *non*rational solutions to equations. On page 492, we found that 2 was a solution to the equation $0 = a^3 - a^2 - a - 2$. By the factor theorem, $a - 2$ is a factor of $a^3 - a^2 - a - 2$. Dividing gives $a^2 + a + 1$ as the quotient.

$$0 = a^3 - a^2 - a - 2 = (a - 2)(a^2 + a + 1)$$

By the zero product theorem,

$$a - 2 = 0 \text{ or } a^2 + a + 1 = 0.$$

Now the equations can be solved as usual. The solution set is

$$\left\{2, \frac{-1 + i\sqrt{3}}{2}, \frac{-1 - i\sqrt{3}}{2}\right\}.$$

In this way, if you can find one solution to a cubic equation, factoring gives linear and quadratic equations, which can always be solved.

Another application of the factor theorem allows $x^3 - a^3$ to be factored. Since a is a solution to $x^3 - a^3 = 0$, $x - a$ is a factor of $x^3 - a^3$. The division is shown at the right.

$$\begin{array}{r l}
 & x^2 + ax + a^2 \\
x - a \,) & x^3 \qquad\qquad\quad - a^3 \\
 & x^3 - ax^2 \\
 & \quad ax^2 \\
 & \quad ax^2 - a^2x \\
 & \qquad\quad a^2x - a^3 \\
 & \qquad\quad a^2x - a^3
\end{array}$$

For $x^3 + a^3 = 0$, $-a$ is a solution, so $x + a$ is a factor. A similar division process shows that $x^2 - ax + a^2$ is the other factor. Thus:

Theorem 16.3.2

a. $x^3 - a^3 = (x - a)(x^2 + ax + a^2)$.

b. $x^3 + a^3 = (x + a)(x^2 - ax + a^2)$.

For example, let $a = 2$. Then, as you can verify by multiplying,

$$x^3 - 8 = (x - 2)(x^2 + 2x + 4);$$
$$x^3 + 8 = (x + 2)(x^2 - 2x + 4).$$

EXERCISES 16.3

Ⓐ 1. A student divided $4m^3 + 11m^2 + 7m + 2$ by $m + 2$ and got $4m^2 + 3m + 1$ for a quotient. Was this correct?

2. True or False? $x^3 + a^3$ divided by $x + a$ is $x^2 + ax + a^2$.

3. How can you check a division problem when the remainder is not 0?

4. If $x^3 - a^3 = (x - a) \cdot P$, then $P =$ ____.

5. $\frac{x^3 - a^3}{x - a} =$ ____

6. $\frac{m^3 + p^3}{m + p} =$ ____

7. If $x - 2$ is a factor of $5x^3 - 2x - 36$, what can you say about the equation $5x^3 - 2x - 36 = 0$?

8. One solution to $6y^4 + 5y - 1 = 0$ is -1. Name a factor of $6y^4 + 5y - 1$.

9. What is the factor theorem?

10. Without dividing, choose *two* factors of $x^3 + 6x^2 + 3x - 10$ from:

a. $x + 2$. **b.** $x - 2$. **c.** $x + 1$. **d.** $x - 1$.

Ⓑ 11. Without dividing, choose the correct answer. When $2x^4 - 3x^2 + 1$ is divided by $x + 1$, the quotient is:

a. $2x^3 + 1$. **b.** $2x^3 - 3x + 1$. **c.** $2x^3 - x + 1$.

d. $2x^3 - 2x^2 - x + 1$. **e.** none of these.

12–19. Divide the first polynomial by the second polynomial.

12. $3x^2 - 4x + 6;\ x - 2$

13. $4y^3 - 10y^2 - 15y - 1;\ y + 1$

14. $10a^3 - 21a^2 - 25;\ 2a - 5$

15. $8B^3 + 2B^2 - 5B - 6;\ B + 3$

16. $x^4 - 16;\ x - 2$

17. $4y^3 - 11y^2 + 7y - 2;\ 4y^2 - 3y + 1$

18. $m^5 - 1;\ m + 1$

19. $z^4 + 4z^3 + 6z^2 + 4z + 1;\ z^2 + 2z + 1$

20–21. Find the other solutions to each equation.

20. $5x^3 - 5x^2 + 4x - 4 = 0$; 1 is a solution.

21. $2p^4 + 13p^3 + 12p^2 - 17p - 10 = 0$; 1 and $-\frac{1}{2}$ are solutions.

22–23. Use the rational root theorem to find one solution to each equation. Find the others with the aid of the factor theorem.

22. $x^3 = 1$

23. $z^3 - 8z - 3 = 0$

24–27. Factor each expression.

24. $y^3 + 8$

25. $27 - 64m^3$

26. $8x^3 - 1$

27. $A^6 + 1000B^3$

© **28.** Factor $x^6 - 1$ as much as possible.

29. Prove that $x^n - a^n$ is divisible by $x - a$ for any positive integer n.

30–33. Find a polynomial equation with the given solutions.

30. $2, -3, 1$

31. $5, 8, -\frac{1}{2}$

32. $\sqrt{2}, \sqrt{3}$

33. $i, 2i, 3i, 4i$

34. Use Theorem 16.3.2a to factor 973. (HINT: $973 = 10^3 - 3^3$.)

35. Use Theorem 16.3.2b to factor 1027.

36. Since $x^6 + 5x^3 + 4$ is divisible by $x + 1$, 1,005,004 is divisible by ______.

37–38. *Trigonometric identities.* Prove that for all values of x:

37. $\sin^3 x - \cos^3 x = (\sin x - \cos x)(1 + \cos x \sin x)$.

38. $\sin^3 x + \cos^3 x = (1 - \cos x \sin x)(\sin x + \cos x)$.

16.4 FRACTIONAL EXPRESSIONS

A **fractional expression** is an expression in which the last indicated operation is division. Examples include:

$$\frac{2}{3} \qquad \frac{\pi + 1}{2} \qquad \frac{4x^2 - 3x}{5} \qquad \frac{\frac{9}{2} + t}{\frac{9}{2} - t} \qquad 31t \div 47 \qquad \frac{1}{m}$$

Throughout this chapter, variables are assumed not to have values which would cause denominators to be zero.

To emphasize its importance, we repeat a fundamental property of fractions which is well-known to you.

Theorem 16.4.1

Fundamental fraction property: For any complex number $\frac{a}{b}$, if $k \neq 0$,

$$\frac{a}{b} = \frac{ka}{kb}$$

PROOF: $\frac{a}{b} = \frac{a}{b} \cdot 1$

$= \frac{a}{b} \cdot \left(k \cdot \frac{1}{k}\right)$ $\quad$ $k \neq 0$ implies k has a reciprocal.

$= \frac{a}{b} \cdot \frac{k}{k}$

$= \frac{ak}{bk}$ $\quad$ Multiplying fractions

If you begin with $\frac{a}{b}$ and end with $\frac{ka}{kb}$, the fundamental fraction property implies that you can multiply the numerator and denominator of a fraction by the same nonzero number to achieve an equal expression. This is helpful when a fraction is divided by a fraction.

1. $\dfrac{\frac{3}{5}}{\frac{2}{9}} = \dfrac{\frac{3}{5} \cdot 45}{\frac{2}{9} \cdot 45} = \dfrac{27}{10}$

2. $\dfrac{\frac{1}{x}}{\frac{3}{x^2}} = \dfrac{\frac{1}{x} \cdot x^2}{\frac{3}{x^2} \cdot x^2} = \dfrac{x}{3}$

3. $\dfrac{\frac{2a + 1}{3}}{\frac{a - 4}{a + 6}} = \dfrac{\frac{2a + 1}{3} \cdot (a + 6) \cdot 3}{\frac{a - 4}{a + 6} \cdot (a + 6) \cdot 3} = \dfrac{(2a + 1)(a + 6)}{(a - 4) \cdot 3} = \dfrac{2a^2 + 13a + 6}{3a - 12}$

The same process works with more complicated expressions · · ·

4. $\dfrac{\frac{1}{a} + \frac{1}{b}}{\frac{1}{a} - \frac{1}{b}} = \dfrac{\left(\frac{1}{a} + \frac{1}{b}\right) \cdot ab}{\left(\frac{1}{a} - \frac{1}{b}\right) \cdot ab} = \dfrac{\frac{1}{a} \cdot ab + \frac{1}{b} \cdot ab}{\frac{1}{a} \cdot ab - \frac{1}{b} \cdot ab} = \dfrac{b + a}{b - a}$

5. $\dfrac{\frac{x}{2} + y}{3y + \frac{x}{6}} = \dfrac{\left(\frac{x}{2} + y\right) \cdot 6}{\left(3y + \frac{x}{6}\right) \cdot 6} = \dfrac{3x + 6y}{18y + x}$

· · · and with expressions containing negative exponents · · ·

6. $\dfrac{x^3}{x^{-4}} = \dfrac{x^3 \cdot x^4}{x^{-4} \cdot x^4} = \dfrac{x^7}{x^0} = x^7$

7. $\dfrac{m^{-2} + 3}{m^{-2} - 4} = \dfrac{(m^{-2} + 3) \cdot m^2}{(m^{-2} - 4) \cdot m^2} = \dfrac{1 + 3m^2}{1 - 4m^2}$

If you begin with $\frac{ka}{kb}$ and end with $\frac{a}{b}$, the fundamental fraction property shows that dividing both the numerator and denominator by a common factor forms an equal fraction which is usually simpler. For this, both numerator and denominator *must* be factored.

8. $\dfrac{34}{85} = \dfrac{17 \cdot 2}{17 \cdot 5} = \dfrac{2}{5}$

9. $\dfrac{x^2 - 5x + 4}{x^2 - 3x + 2} = \dfrac{(x - 4)(x - 1)}{(x - 2)(x - 1)} = \dfrac{x - 4}{x - 2}$

10. $\dfrac{6 \cdot 5 \cdot 4 \cdot 3 \cdot 2 \cdot 1}{4 \cdot 3 \cdot 2 \cdot 1} = 30$

11. $\dfrac{8x - 12}{3 - 2x} = \dfrac{4(2x - 3)}{-1(2x - 3)} = -4$

12. $\dfrac{4a^2 + 16a + 16}{8a + 16} = \dfrac{2 \cdot 2 \cdot (a + 2)(a + 2)}{2 \cdot 2 \cdot 2 \cdot (a + 2)} = \dfrac{a + 2}{2}$

You must be careful *not* to *add* or *subtract* the same number from the numerator and denominator of a fraction.

13. $\dfrac{x^2 + 3}{y^2 + 3} \neq \dfrac{x^2}{y^2}$ and also $\dfrac{x^2 + 3}{y^2 + 3} \neq \dfrac{x^2}{y^2} + 1$. There is no equivalent expression which is simpler than $\dfrac{x^2 + 3}{y^2 + 3}$.

How can you check that one process is correct, another not correct? The answer is simple: substitute. A simplified expression should have the same value as the original for every possible value of each variable. For example, refer back to Example 4. We found:

$$\frac{\frac{1}{a} + \frac{1}{b}}{\frac{1}{a} - \frac{1}{b}} = \frac{b + a}{b - a}.$$

It you let $a = 1$, $b = 2$, then:

$$\frac{\frac{1}{1} + \frac{1}{2}}{\frac{1}{1} - \frac{1}{2}} = \frac{2 + 1}{2 - 1}.$$

Both sides of the equation at the right equal 3. So the answer checks. Any other nonzero values of a and b, where $a \neq b$, will give equal values for the two expressions.

EXERCISES 16.4

Ⓐ 1. State the fundamental fraction property.

2–5. By what number could numerator and denominator be multiplied in order to form a simpler, equivalent expression?

2. $\dfrac{\frac{x + 1}{4}}{\frac{x - 3}{5}}$

3. $\dfrac{m^{-10}}{2m^{-14}}$

4. $\dfrac{x - y + \frac{x - 2y}{3}}{x + y - \frac{x + 3y}{4}}$

5. $\dfrac{a^{-2} + b^{-2}}{a^{-1} + b^{-1}}$

6–11. True or False?

6. $\dfrac{104 + 20}{104 - 10} = 2$

7. $\dfrac{104 \cdot 20}{104 \cdot 10} = 2$

8. $\dfrac{104 \div 20}{104 \div 10} = 2$

9. $\dfrac{104 - 20}{104 - 10} = 2$

10. $\dfrac{t - \frac{t^2 - 1}{t}}{1 - \frac{t - 1}{t}} = 1$

11. $\dfrac{2 - \frac{3}{x} - \frac{2}{x^2}}{2 - \frac{5}{x} - \frac{3}{x^2}} = \dfrac{x - 2}{x - 3}$

12. How can you check whether or not two fractional expressions are equivalent?

13–21. Simplify if possible.

13. $\frac{\frac{7}{4}}{5}$ **14.** $\frac{\frac{5}{2}}{\frac{3}{4}}$ **15.** $\frac{\frac{9}{16x}}{\frac{3}{8x}}$ **16.** $\frac{x^2y}{xy^3}$ **17.** $\frac{3x^8}{6x^4}$

18. $\frac{3 \cdot 4 \cdot 5}{3 \cdot 4}$ **19.** $\frac{(a+4)^2}{(a-4)^2}$ **20.** $\frac{a^3 - b^3}{a - b}$ **21.** $\frac{(a-3)(a-2)}{a(a-3)}$

Ⓑ **22–25.** Simplify the expressions of Exercises **2–5**.

26–31. Simplify. Check your answers.

26. $\frac{3y + 9}{4y^2 + 8y - 12}$ **27.** $\frac{z^2 - 1}{2z - 2}$ **28.** $\frac{16 - w^2}{12 + 5w - 2w^2}$

29. $\frac{x^4 - y^4}{y^4 - x^4}$ **30.** $\frac{7x^2 - 34x - 5}{7xy^2 + y^2}$ **31.** $\frac{6m - 6p}{6m^2 - p^2 - mp}$

32–34. Use the fundamental fraction property to *rationalize denominators*. That is, find an equivalent fraction with a rational denominator.

32. $\frac{3 - 2\sqrt{2}}{4\sqrt{2} + 1}$ **33.** $\frac{7}{\sqrt{6}}$ **34.** $\frac{5}{1 - 2\sqrt{23}}$

35–37. Rationalize numerators. (See directions of Exercises **32–34**.)

35. $\frac{-9 + \sqrt{15}}{2\sqrt{15}}$ **36.** $\frac{\sqrt{x} - \sqrt{y}}{\sqrt{x} + \sqrt{y}}$ **37.** $\frac{9 - 3\sqrt{41}}{2 + \sqrt{41}}$

38. If it takes one person h hours to do a job alone and a second person j hours, then assuming their rates are unaffected by working together, it will take them $\frac{1}{\frac{1}{h} + \frac{1}{j}}$ hours to do it together. Find an equivalent, simpler fraction.

39. Check your answer to Exercise **38** and interpret the result when $h = 6$ and $j = 8$.

40–45. Find an equivalent, simpler fraction.

40. $\dfrac{\frac{3}{a} - \frac{2}{b}}{\frac{6}{a} + \frac{4}{b}}$

41. $\dfrac{\frac{x}{2} - 1.5}{\frac{x}{3} - 1}$

42. $\dfrac{\frac{1}{z^2 + 20z + 51}}{\frac{1}{6 + 2z}}$

43. $\dfrac{4 - 2x^{-1}}{8 + 4x^{-2}}$

44. $\dfrac{a^{-2} - 14 + 4a^{-1}}{a^{-1} + 6}$

45. $\dfrac{\frac{x - 4}{x + 3}}{\frac{x^2 - 4x + 4}{x^2 + 6x + 9}}$

© **46.** The fundamental fraction property can be considered as a property of multiplication and division. What is the corresponding property of addition and subtraction?

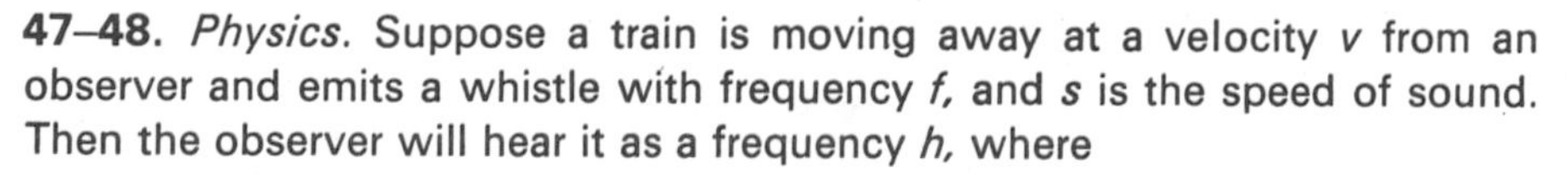

47–48. *Physics.* Suppose a train is moving away at a velocity v from an observer and emits a whistle with frequency f, and s is the speed of sound. Then the observer will hear it as a frequency h, where

$$h = \frac{f}{1 + \frac{v}{s}}.$$

The change in velocity relative to an observer accounts for the change in pitch of the train whistle as the train passes. This effect is known as the Doppler effect, named after C. J. Doppler (1803–1853).

47. Find an equivalent, simpler fraction. Why do you think the given formula is more common than the simplified fraction?

48. Calculate h when $f = 512$ (near middle C) and $v = 64$ mph, given $s = 736$ mph (a cold day).

49–55. *Trigonometric identities.* Prove that each statement is true for all allowable values of x or y. Check by letting $x = \frac{\pi}{3}$, $y = \frac{\pi}{6}$. HINT: Use the definitions of tan x, cot x, sec x, and csc x.

49. $\dfrac{\tan x}{\sec x} = \sin x$

50. $\dfrac{\cot x}{\csc x} = \cos x$

51. $\dfrac{1}{\csc^2 x - 1} = \tan^2 x$

52. $\dfrac{1}{\sec^2 x - 1} = \cot^2 x$

53. $\tan x + \tan y = \dfrac{\sin(x + y)}{\cos x \cos y}$

54. $\cot x + \cot y = \dfrac{\sin(x + y)}{\sin x \sin y}$

55. $\tan(x + y) = \dfrac{\tan x + \tan y}{1 - \tan x \tan y}$

OPERATIONS WITH FRACTIONAL EXPRESSIONS

Rather complicated fractions can be multiplied by using the familiar theorem which you have used for years.

$$\frac{a}{b} \cdot \frac{c}{d} = \frac{ac}{bd}$$

Examples:

1. $\dfrac{m - 8}{m + 8} \cdot \dfrac{m - 5}{m - 8} = \dfrac{(m - 8)(m - 5)}{(m + 8)(m - 8)}$

You might be tempted to multiply the binomials, but the numerator and denominator have a common factor which makes it possible for the fraction to be simplified.

$$= \frac{m - 5}{m + 8}$$

This cannot be simplified further—there is no common factor. (Substitution for m can tell you that the fraction is not always equal to $\frac{-5}{8}$.)

Because common factors allow fractions to be simplified, you should always factor *before* multiplication.

2. $\dfrac{a^3 + b^3}{a^2 - b^2} \cdot \dfrac{a^2 + 2ab + b^2}{a^2 - ab + b^2}$

$= \dfrac{(a + b)(a^2 - ab + b^2)}{(a + b)(a - b)} \cdot \dfrac{(a + b)(a + b)}{a^2 - ab + b^2}$ Factoring

$= \dfrac{(a + b)(a^2 - ab + b^2)(a + b)(a + b)}{(a + b)(a - b)(a^2 - ab + b^2)}$ Multiplying (a step which is usually not written)

$= \dfrac{(a + b)(a + b)}{a - b}$ Dividing by common factors

Notice how difficult this would have been if the numerators and denominators had been multiplied before factoring.

Here is another example. In this case, it helps to simplify the more complicated fraction.

3. $\dfrac{\frac{1}{x} - \frac{1}{y}}{\frac{1}{x} + \frac{1}{y}} \cdot \dfrac{x + y}{x - y} = \dfrac{xy\left(\frac{1}{x} - \frac{1}{y}\right)}{xy\left(\frac{1}{x} + \frac{1}{y}\right)} \cdot \dfrac{x + y}{x - y}$

$= \dfrac{y - x}{y + x} \cdot \dfrac{x + y}{x - y}$ Notice that $y - x = -(x - y)$.

$= -1$

When fractions have the same denominator, they are easily added or subtracted by applying distributivity.

4. $\frac{a}{c} + \frac{b}{c} = a \cdot \frac{1}{c} + b \cdot \frac{1}{c}$

$= (a + b)\frac{1}{c}$

Both steps in red are almost always done mentally.

$= \frac{a + b}{c}$

5. $\frac{x - 8}{y^2 + 2} - \frac{2 + 4x}{y^2 + 2} = \frac{x - 8 - (2 + 4x)}{y^2 + 2}$

$= \frac{-3x - 10}{y^2 + 2}$

Notice that all of $2 + 4x$ is subtracted.

If the fractions have different denominators, the obvious strategy is to find equivalent fractions with the same *common denominator.*

6. $\frac{5}{3x - 3y} + \frac{4y}{x^2 + 3xy - 4y^2}$

To find this denominator, factoring is necessary.

$= \frac{5}{3(x - y)} + \frac{4y}{(x + 4y)(x - y)}$

Inspecting both factored denominators, we see that a common denominator is $3(x - y)(x + 4y)$. We convert each fraction to an equivalent fraction with this common denominator.

$= \frac{5(x + 4y)}{3(x - y)(x + 4y)} + \frac{3 \cdot 4y}{3(x + 4y)(x - y)}$

Notice that for each fraction, the *numerator and denominator* are multiplied by a factor of the common denominator which is missing from the original denominator. Now the fractions can be added.

$= \frac{5x + 20y + 12y}{3(x - y)(x + 4y)}$

$= \frac{5x + 32y}{3(x - y)(x + 4y)}$ ← No simplification is possible because the numerator cannot be factored.

7. $\frac{9}{ab} - \frac{4}{a^2b}$

$= \frac{9a}{a^2b} - \frac{4}{a^2b} = \frac{9a - 4}{a^2b}$

a^2b is the common denominator.

EXERCISES 16.5

Ⓐ **1–4.** Simplify.

1. $\dfrac{a^2(b - c)}{a(c - b)}$

2. $\dfrac{(x - 5)^2(x + 3)}{(x + 3)(x + 5)(x - 5)}$

3. $\dfrac{8b}{c^2} - \dfrac{8a}{c^2}$

4. $\dfrac{9}{x + 1} - \dfrac{2 - x}{x + 1}$

5–9. To rewrite the expression as a single fraction, what common denominator should be used?

5. $\dfrac{9}{x - 3} - \dfrac{2}{x}$

6. $\dfrac{4}{9m^2} + \dfrac{9}{30m^2}$

7. $\dfrac{4a}{a - 1} + \dfrac{2a - 2}{a + 2}$

8. $\dfrac{(y + 2)^2}{(y - 2)(y - 3)} - \dfrac{(y - 4)(y - 3)}{(y - 2)(y - 1)}$

9. $\dfrac{1}{x} + \dfrac{2}{x^2} + \dfrac{3}{x^3}$

10. How can the answer to Exercise **2** be checked?

Ⓑ **11–14.** Rewrite each expression as a single fraction. Check your answer.

11. $\dfrac{3a - 1}{4} - \dfrac{a - 5}{6}$

12. $\dfrac{x - 1}{x} - \dfrac{y - 1}{y}$

13. $\dfrac{3k}{k^2 - k} + \dfrac{3}{1 - k}$

14. $\dfrac{x - 5}{x^2 + 4x + 4} - \dfrac{x}{x^2 - 4}$

15–19. Simplify each expression of Exercises **5–9**.

20–32. Rewrite as a single fraction and check your answer.

20. $\dfrac{y}{9 - y^2} - \dfrac{3}{y^2 - 9}$

21. $\dfrac{1}{2} + \dfrac{6 - 2x}{x + 3}$

22. $4 - \dfrac{2 - 4z}{z}$

23. $\dfrac{1}{a + 3} - \dfrac{1}{a}$

24. $\dfrac{v^2 - 9}{v^2 - 5v + 6} \cdot \dfrac{v^2 + 5v + 6}{v^2 - 4}$

25. $\dfrac{w^3 - 1}{w + 1} - w^2$

26. $\dfrac{\frac{3}{a} - \frac{2}{b}}{\frac{3}{a} + \frac{2}{b}} \cdot \dfrac{\frac{a}{3} + \frac{b}{2}}{\frac{a}{3} - \frac{b}{2}}$

27. $\dfrac{\frac{x}{2} - 1}{x^2 + 11x + 10} \cdot \dfrac{\frac{3x}{5} + 6}{2x - 4}$

28. $\dfrac{2}{3c^2 - 7c + 4} + \dfrac{y}{6c - 8}$

29. $\dfrac{2x^2 - 4x + 5}{3} - \dfrac{3 - x^2 + 4x}{10}$

Ⓒ **30.** $\dfrac{1}{a + b\sqrt{2}} + \dfrac{1}{a - b\sqrt{2}}$

31. $\dfrac{-18y}{y^3 + 27} - \dfrac{y - 1}{3 - y} + \dfrac{6 - 5y}{y^2 - 9}$

32. $\dfrac{4d - 5}{5d - 4} + \dfrac{16d - 20}{20d^2 - 16d} - \dfrac{2d + 3}{3d + 2}$

33–36. *Trigonometric identities.* Prove that each statement is true for all allowable values of x.

33. $\tan^2 x + 1 = \sec^2 x$

34. $\cot^2 x + 1 = \csc^2 x$

35. $\sec^2 x + \csc^2 x = \sec^2 x \csc^2 x$

36. $\sin^2 x + \frac{1}{\sin^2 x} + \cos^2 x + \frac{1}{\cos^2 x} - \tan^2 x - \cot^2 x = 3$

SENTENCES INVOLVING FRACTIONAL EXPRESSIONS

Sentences involving fractions can be solved by using the multiplication properties of equations or inequalities.

Example 1: $\frac{8}{16 - 3x} = \frac{x}{2}$

Multiply both sides by $2(16 - 3x)$, a common denominator of the fractions.

$$2(16 - 3x)\frac{8}{16 - 3x} = \frac{x}{2}(2)(16 - 3x)$$

$$2 \cdot 8 = x(16 - 3x)$$

$$3x^2 - 16x + 16 = 0$$

By the quadratic formula or by factoring, $x = 4$ or $x = \frac{4}{3}$.

This procedure works with more-complicated sentences.

Example 2: $\frac{3}{y - 3} = \frac{9}{2y^2 - 7y + 3} + 1$

Factor: $\frac{3}{y - 3} = \frac{9}{(2y - 1)(y - 3)} + 1$

The factoring helps determine an appropriate multiplier. Notice that both sides of the equation are multiplied by $(2y - 1)(y - 3)$.

$$(2y - 1)(y - 3) \cdot \left(\frac{3}{y - 3}\right) = \left[\frac{9}{(2y - 1)(y - 3)} + 1\right](2y - 1)(y - 3)$$

$$(2y - 1)3 = 9 + (2y - 1)(y - 3)$$

$$6y - 3 = 9 + 2y^2 - 7y + 3$$

$$0 = 2y^2 - 13y + 15$$

By the quadratic formula or by factoring, $y = 5$ or $y = \frac{3}{2}$. Each value checks.

With inequalities, the same procedure is followed. But two cases are needed, depending on whether the sides are multiplied by a positive or negative number.

Example 3: $\frac{4}{z-6} < 3$

Clearly we want to multiply by $z - 6$.

Case 1. Let $z - 6$ be positive. Then $z - 6 > 0$. So multiplying the given sentence by $z - 6$ will not change the sense of the inequality.

$$z - 6 > 0 \quad \text{and} \quad \frac{4}{z-6} < 3.$$

So $\quad z > 6 \quad$ and $\quad 4 < 3z - 18.$

So $\quad z > 6 \quad$ and $\quad \frac{22}{3} < z. \longrightarrow$ In short, $z > \frac{22}{3}$.

Case 2. Let $z - 6$ be negative. Then $z - 6 < 0$. So multiplying the given sentence by $z - 6$ will change the sense of the inequality.

$$z - 6 < 0 \quad \text{and} \quad \frac{4}{z-6} < 3.$$

Then $\quad z < 6 \quad$ and $\quad 4 > 3z - 18.$

$z < 6 \quad$ and $\quad \frac{22}{3} > z. \longrightarrow$ In short, $z < 6$.

So $z > \frac{22}{3}$ or $z < 6$.

EXERCISES 16.6

Ⓐ **1–6.** By what should both sides be multiplied to obtain an equivalent sentence which has no fractions?

1. $\frac{3}{4x - 2} = \frac{11}{2x + 5}$

2. $\frac{6}{x - 2} - \frac{x}{x - 2} = x$

3. $y < 3 - \frac{6}{y + 2}$

4. $\frac{B}{B - 4} + \frac{2}{5} = \frac{3}{B + 4}$

5. $\frac{24}{z} - \frac{1}{z^3} - \frac{2}{z^2} = 0$

6. $\frac{m - 2}{m - 3} - \frac{m^2 - 8}{m^2 - 9} = 6$

7. What caution must be taken with inequalities?

8. In which of Exercises **1–6** might it be best to simplify one side of the sentence before multiplying to get rid of fractions?

Ⓑ **9.** Solve:

$$\frac{4}{x^2 - 4} = \frac{36}{13}.$$

10. Solve for n, given n is negative.

$$\frac{n + 5}{n - 1} < 3$$

11–16. Solve the sentences of Exercises **1–6**.

17–22. Find all solutions.

17. $\frac{1}{x} < 3$

18. $\frac{6}{3k - 5} - \frac{8}{3k + 5} = \frac{64}{9k^2 - 25}$

19. $\frac{\sqrt{A} + 1}{10} = \frac{4}{\sqrt{A}}$

20. $\frac{t + 3}{2t - 4} + \frac{3}{2 - t} = \frac{t + 1}{2}$

21. $5x^{-2} - 6x^{-1} + x^0 = 0$

22. $\frac{3v^2 - 9v}{4} = \frac{6v^3 - 2}{8v}$

Ⓒ **23–24.** In some systems of sentences which involve fractions, the strategy of this section is not helpful. A better method is to substitute, a method mentioned as early as Section 2.4. For instance, in Exercise **23**, let $a = \frac{1}{x + 3}$, $b = \frac{1}{y - 2}$. Solve each system.

23. $\frac{1}{x + 3} + \frac{2}{y - 2} = 5$

$\frac{3}{x + 3} - \frac{1}{y - 2} = 5$

24. $\frac{4}{m} = 8 + \frac{3}{p}$

$\frac{10}{p} - \frac{1}{m} - \frac{5}{2} = 0$

25–26. If an object has mass m_0 at rest, then at velocity v, it will have mass m (see formula at right). In the formula, c is the speed of light, approximately 3×10^5 kilometres per second.

$$m = \frac{m_0}{\sqrt{1 - \frac{v^2}{c^2}}}$$

25. Solve for v in terms of m and m_0.

26. What velocity is necessary to double an object's mass?

27–29. Two cars A and B (A faster than B) are running on an elliptical racetrack at constant but different velocities. If t_A and t_B are the times it takes for the cars to travel a lap, and T is the length of time between meetings of the cars, then

$$\frac{1}{T} = \frac{1}{t_A} - \frac{1}{t_B}.$$

27. If $t_A = 30$ seconds and $t_B = 60$ seconds, what is T?

28. If one car travels a lap in 72 sec and the other in 70 sec, how often will they meet? (Answer to the nearest second.) How many laps will have been covered from their first to their second meeting?

29. Solve for t_B in terms of T and t_A.

30. The earth travels around the sun in approximately 365 days. Mars travels around the sun in approximately 687 days. When the earth is *between* Mars and the sun, Mars is said to reach opposition, and we get the best views of the planet. How often does Mars reach opposition?

31–32. The number π can be approximated in the following way.

1st approximation: $\frac{4}{1}$ 2nd approx: $\frac{4}{1} - \frac{4}{3}$

3rd approx: $\frac{4}{1} - \frac{4}{3} + \frac{4}{5}$ 4th approx: $\frac{4}{1} - \frac{4}{3} + \frac{4}{5} - \frac{4}{7}$

and so on.

The nth approximation requires adding n fractions. The *error* E after these additions satisfies the sentence $E < \frac{4}{2n + 1}$.

31. Solve for n.

32. How many fractions must be added to come within 0.001 of π?

33–36. If a person goes from X to Y at rate G and back on the same route at rate B, then the average rate R (total distance ÷ total time) satisfies $\frac{1}{R} = \frac{\frac{1}{G} + \frac{1}{B}}{2}$.

33. If $G = 50$ and $B = 45$, calculate R.

34. Solve for B in terms of R and G.

35. (Use Exercise **34**.) A person travels from X to Y at 48 km/h but wishes to average 64 km/h for the round trip. At what velocity must the trip back from Y to X be made?

36. Repeat Exercise **35** if the person wishes to average 96 km/h for the round trip. Explain the unusual result to this problem.

16.7 PUZZLE PROBLEMS INVOLVING RATES

Mathematics is often applied to problems which do not arise from a real situation and are not related to any mathematical theory. Perhaps the problem resembles a real situation, perhaps not. We call these *puzzle problems.*

Many puzzle problems involve rates and apply the familiar formula.

$$\text{rate of travel} = \frac{\text{distance traveled}}{\text{time traveled}}.$$

That is, $$r = \frac{d}{t}.$$

Multiplying by t, $$d = rt.$$

The units must be consistent in order for this formula to hold. A typical example follows.

Example: Coming home from work, a woman goes directly to an expressway, upon which she drives at 60 mph, then to another street on which she averages 25 mph. If it takes 30 minutes to get home and the odometer shows she has traveled 20 miles, how many miles does she drive on the expressway?

SOLUTION: Are the units consistent? In the problem, the time is given in *minutes*, the rate in miles per *hour*. To solve, change 30 minutes to $\frac{1}{2}$ hour. Will a picture help?

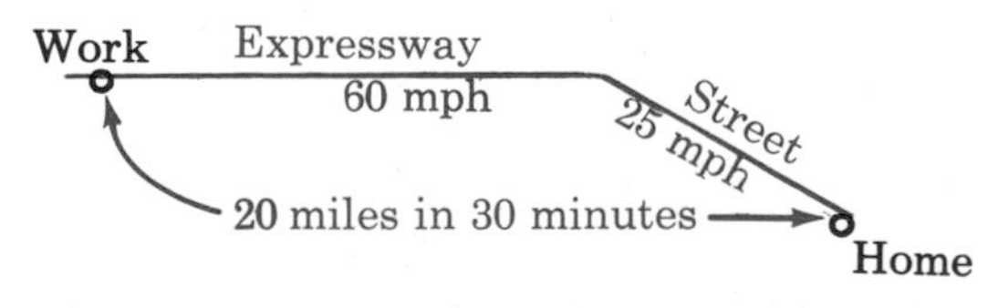

Here is the most important question: What is asked for?

Let D = number of miles driven on the expressway.

Then $20 - D$ = number of miles driven on the street.

We could find these distances if we knew some times.

Let T = number of *hours* driven on the expressway.

Then $\frac{1}{2} - T$ = number of hours driven on the street.

Has all given information been used? No. Rates are given. Can all of this information be summarized? A table is not necessary but may help.

	distance	rate	time
on expressway	D	60	T
on street	$20 - D$	25	$\frac{1}{2} - T$

Using the formula $d = rt$, each row of the table translates into an equation:

$$D = 60T$$
$$20 - D = 25(\tfrac{1}{2} - T).$$

This is a system which can be solved in many ways. The solution is $(D, T) = (\frac{90}{7}, \frac{3}{14})$. Hence the woman drives $\frac{90}{7}$, or $12\frac{6}{7}$ miles on the expressway.

This problem was solved in detail so that you could see the mathematics and the type of thinking which help in solving these problems. Asking good questions is essential. In the preceding example, some questions which you might ask yourself are in red.

Rates occur in many problems not connected with distance and time. When you buy something in a store, you are paying a rate: cost per item. The formula resembles the $d = rt$ formula.

$$\text{total cost of items} = (\text{cost per item}) \cdot (\text{number of items}).$$

Of course, the units must match. The items must be the same, at the same price. Mixtures of substances are also connected with rates. Suppose an ore contains 15 percent lead. We can think of this percentage as being the rate at which lead is in the ore. The formula becomes

$$\text{total amount of lead in ore} = \left(\begin{matrix}\text{percent of}\\ \text{lead in ore}\end{matrix}\right) \cdot \left(\begin{matrix}\text{amount}\\ \text{of ore}\end{matrix}\right).$$

Interest rates follow the same pattern.

$$\text{total interest} = (\text{rate of interest}) \cdot (\text{amount invested})$$

Here are five problems which involve different rates. But each can lead to the same equation or system of equations.

$$\begin{cases} 56 = 0.04x + 0.06y \\ 1200 = x + y \end{cases} \quad \text{or} \quad 56 = (0.04x) + 0.06(1200 - x)$$

Problem A: A woman invests \$1200, part at 4%, part at 6%. If she receives \$56 income on the investment, how much was invested at 4%?

	total	at 4%	at 6%
amt. invested	1200	x	y
interest	56	$0.04x$	$0.06y$

or

total	at 4%	at 6%
1200	x	$1200 - x$
56	$0.04x$	$0.06(1200 - x)$

Problem B: In a year, a jogger calculates that he ran for 1200 hours, each mile run in either 15 min or 10 min (4 mph or 6 mph). If he covered a total of 5600 miles, how far did he run at 4 mph?

Problem C: A 4% solution of mercury bichloride was used in an experiment. Unknowingly, a chemist mixed this solution with a 6% solution to fill up a vessel with a volume of 1200 cubic centimetres. To find out how much of the 4% solution was used in the experiment, the mercury bichloride was isolated from the other liquid in the vessel. 56 cubic centimetres of mercury bichloride were found. How much mercury was in the original 4% solution?

Problem D: Some candy costs 4¢, some 6¢. A store sells 1200 pieces of candy and receives \$56. How many pieces were sold for 4¢?

Problem E: A foreign country has two coins, worth 4¢ and 6¢ in our currency. If a collection of 1200 of their coins is worth 56 of our dollars, how many coins in the collection are 4¢ coins?

Problems like **C** given above could actually occur. Then ideas from puzzle problems would help in a real situation. Or puzzle problems may be interesting to you by themselves. Or they may be fun to solve. For these reasons, puzzle problems are found in all branches of mathematics and are common in popular books on mathematics.

EXERCISES 16.7

Ⓐ **1.** In solving a problem, what is the most important question to ask?

2. Suppose a problem is difficult. Give 3 questions you might ask to help yourself.

3–11. Fill in the chart for the given problem without introducing any new variables.

3–5. How much water should be added to 30 cubic centimetres of a 3% tincture of iodine solution to dilute it to a 2.5% solution?

	Start	Add	Finish
Entire solution	30	x	**3.**
Amt. of water	0.97(30)	**4.**	**5.**

6–8. While traveling on a highway at 88 km/h, a man noticed a speeding car which passed his car and was about 0.5 kilometre ahead in 1 minute. How fast was the other car going?

	d	r	t
First car	**7.**	88	$\frac{1}{60}$
Speeding car	**8.**	x	**6.**

9–11. A collection of 150 nickels and quarters is worth $30.00 face value. How many nickels are in the collection?

	Total	Nickels	Quarters
Number of coins	**9.**	N	Q
Value of coins	30.00	**10.**	**11.**

12. Make a chart which might aid in solving Problem **C** in this section.

13. Repeat Exercise **12** for Problem **B** in this section.

Ⓑ **14–16.** Solve the problem given in:

14. Exercises **3–5.** **15.** Exercises **6–8.** **16.** Exercises **9–11.**

17. How long does it take a ray of sunlight (going at 1.86×10^5 miles per second approximately) to reach the earth, which is 9.3×10^7 miles from the sun?

18. Ida travels k kilometres at 80 km/h. Marge travels the same distance at 96 km/h. How much quicker will Marge's trip be?

19. (Refer to Exercise **18.**) If Ida and Marge leave at the same time and arrive 9 minutes apart at their destination, how far is the trip?

20. A fugitive travels on an interstate highway at the 55-mph speed limit in order not to be noticed and has a 10-minute head start on the police. If the police travel at 70 mph on the same highway, in how many miles will they catch up with the fugitive?

21. (Refer to Exercise **20**.) The fugitive is trying to get to another state 40 miles away. How fast must the police travel in order to catch the fugitive within the state?

22. The range of a pair of walkie-talkies is 1 kilometre. Two people, each carrying a set, move away from each other at constant rates of 5 km/h and 4 km/h. How soon will they be out of communication?

23. A freight train leaves an army base at 50 mph. An hour later an error is found on the shipment, and a helicopter is dispatched from the base to overtake the train. If the helicopter travels at 150 mph, how far will it have to travel to catch up to the train?

24. (You may want to try to solve this problem without algebra.) Two cars move towards each other at rates of 60 mph and 65 mph along the same highway. If they meet in 12 minutes, how far apart were they to begin with?

25. A suit cost a store C dollars. The store marked the price up 40% for selling. It then announced a sale in which all suits were lowered 20% in price. If the final price was $72.80 to a customer, how much profit did the store make? What was the percentage of profit on the store's cost?

26. Tickets for a game cost $1.75 or $2.25. If 812 tickets were sold with total receipts of $1500, was the athletic director justified in saying that some error was made.

27. Mrs. Khan owns 30 shares of stock in company A and 100 shares of stock in company B. From these companies she receives $200 yearly in dividends. Mr. Yung owns 50 shares of stock in A and 200 shares in B. He receives $370 yearly in dividends. Determine how much of a dividend per share is given out by each company.

28. Two cars travel in the same direction, one at 88 feet per second, the other at 66 feet per second. In how many minutes will they be 1 mile apart?

29. Sign in shoe store: "All shoes in store reduced to either $2.99 or $4.99 a pair." If the store netted $415 from the sale of 100 pairs of shoes, how many pairs were sold at the cheaper price?

30. Solve Problems **A–E** of this section.

31. A woman invested a sum of money at 8%. She invested a second sum $2000 greater than the first sum at 7%. If the annual income of each investment was the same, how much did she invest at 7%?

32. Two bars of soap and four cans of cleanser cost \$1.34. In the same store, 6 bars of the same soap and 9 cans of the same cleanser cost \$1.20. How much does a bar of soap cost? How much does a can of cleanser cost?

33. Tobacco stems are about 8% potash in weight. How many kilograms of tobacco stems must be bought to obtain 10 kilograms of potash?

34. How much water should be added to 80 grams of a solution which is 5% alcohol in order to change it to a solution which is 3.2% alcohol?

35. How many litres of 10% brine solution must be added to 6 litres of a 5% solution in order to get an 8% solution?

36. A chemist in a laboratory wants to form 20 cubic centimetres of a 30% acid solution. How much of a 50% solution should she mix with water in order to do this?

37. An owner of a professional tiddlywinks team pays the 12 regulars one fee per game, the 13 substitutes a second fee \$20 less than the first. If \$1240 was paid out, how much did each substitute get?

38. How many grams of an alcohol-water mixture which is 12% alcohol can be made from 50 grams of pure alcohol?

39. A solution of milk is 6 percent butterfat. How much butterfat should be removed to leave exactly one litre of milk which is 2 percent butterfat? (Possible method: reverse the situation and add butterfat instead of subtracting it.)

© **40.** In 1968, Debbie Meyer swam the 200-metre freestyle in 2 minutes, 10.5 seconds. In 1974, Shirley Babashoff set a new record by swimming the 200-metre freestyle in 2 minutes, 2.9 seconds. If these races had been swum in the same pool at the same time, by approximately what distance would Shirley Babashoff have been ahead of Debbie Meyer when Shirley finished the race? What assumptions must be made about the swimming in order to arrive at your approximation?

41. Let p be the speed of an object and s be the speed of sound in the surrounding atmosphere. The object is then said to be traveling at "Mach $\frac{p}{s}$." For example, if $p = 2s$, then $\frac{p}{s} = 2$ and the object is traveling at Mach 2, twice the speed of sound. (This unit of speed is named after Ernst Mach [pronounced "mock"], an Austrian physicist, philosopher, and psychologist [1838–1916].) In a test, a guided missile is shot at Mach 2. Two minutes later an antiballistic missile is shot at Mach 2.5 along the same path. In how many minutes will the missiles collide?

42. A "Local" leaves Union Station and runs at an average rate of 35 mph. A half hour later, an "Express" leaves that station at an average rate of 56 mph on a parallel track. Indira arrives in time for the Local. Her destination is Suburb Station, which is 25 miles away. Should she take the Local or wait for the Express?

43. A painter has filled a small paint holder with equal amounts of red and white paint. What part (percentage) of the paint in this holder must be removed and replaced by white paint in order to make a mixture which is $\frac{3}{5}$ white paint?

44. A stamp dealer advertises to sell a stamp collection that contains 1200 stamps with a total catalog value of exactly $25. Values of stamps are always given in catalogs to the nearest penny, and no stamp has a catalog value of less than 2¢. At most how many stamps in this collection have catalog value greater than 2¢?

45. Derive the formula used in Exercises **33–36** on page 509.

46. Examine Exercises **20–45**. Which of these problems seem to you to be problems which might arise from actual situations? Which are obviously made up as puzzles.

MORE PUZZLE PROBLEMS 16.8

In Section 3.1, we used the joining model for addition to help represent various age or time situations. For instance, if A is your age now, $A + 15$ will be your age 15 years from now.

Example 1: Mary is twice as old as her brother was 3 years ago. In six years she will be only $\frac{4}{3}$ as old as her brother is then. How old is each of them now?

SOLUTION: Let M = present age of Mary in years, b = present age of Mary's brother. A table helps clarify the problem. Information which is not given is in red and is easily obtained.

	3 years ago	now	six years from now
Mary's age	$M - 3$	M	$M + 6$
brother's age	$b - 3$	b	$b + 6$

From the first sentence of the given: $M = 2(b - 3)$.

From the second sentence of the given: $M + 6 = \frac{4}{3}(b + 6)$.

This system is easily solved. Its solution is left to you.

One of the fundamental principles of physics implies that when two forces are exerted upon an object in the same direction, the total force is the sum of the individual forces. This is the slide model for addition. For example, if a plane in still air has a velocity of 350 mph and there is a 40 mph following wind, we add to get the actual velocity of 390 mph. Forces in opposite directions are subtracted; the same plane traveling in the opposite direction would only go at 310 mph.

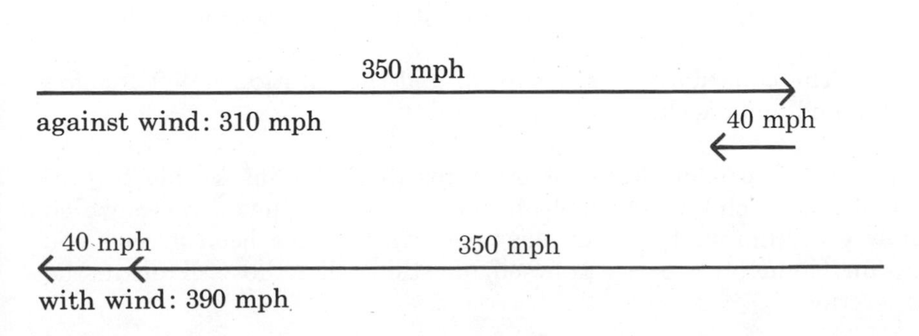

Example 2: Cabin A is 20 kilometres upstream from cabin B. If it takes 50 minutes for a motorboat to go from A to B and 80 minutes for the boat to go back (at the same rate in still water) from B to A, what is the rate of the current?

SOLUTION: Let b = rate of boat in still water in kilometres per *hour*. Let c = rate of current. A table helps.

	d (in km)	r (in km/h)	t (in hours)
with current	20	$b + c$	$\frac{5}{6}$
against current	20	$b - c$	$\frac{8}{6}$

Each row in the table leads to an equation. The two equations form a system which can be solved for b and c.

$\begin{cases} 20 = \frac{5}{6}(b + c) \\ 20 = \frac{8}{6}(b - c) \end{cases}$ Solving gives $\begin{cases} b = 19.5 \\ c = 4.5 \end{cases}$ The rate of the current is 4.5 km/h.

A special application of rate is to *work problems.*

Example 3: Machine A turns out 1000 chocolate bars in an hour. A newer machine B turns out 1200 chocolate bars in 40 minutes. In how many minutes will the two machines together turn out a total of 4000 chocolate bars?

SOLUTION: Let t = time both machines operate in *minutes*. Machine A turns out 1000 bars an hour, or $\frac{1000}{60}$ bars a minute, its rate. In t minutes it turns out $\frac{1000}{60}t$ bars. Machine B turns out 30 bars a minute, and $30t$ bars in t minutes. So we want the value of t which satisfies:

$$4000 = \frac{1000}{60}t + 30t$$

4000: total number of bars
$\frac{1000}{60}t$: total number produced by A
$30t$: total number produced by B

The equation is easily solved, and the solution is left for you to find and check.

There are so many kinds of problems that it is impossible to give examples for each type of problem. In fact, many of the exercises which follow are different from any examples which have been given. You may find it helpful to ask yourself questions like those given in the last section.

EXERCISES 16.8

Ⓐ **1–2.** If x is the age of a person now, give the age of that person at each time listed.

1. 3 years ago
2. n years from now

3–4. If a plane travels at x kilometres an hour in still air, how fast will it travel:

3. against a head wind of h kilometres per hour?
4. with a tail wind of t kilometres per hour?

5. Why would the method of Example **3** be unreasonable for this problem: Ava can do a type of problem in 10 minutes. José can do the same type of problem in 12 minutes. How long would it take them to do that type of problem together?

Ⓑ 6. In 10 years, Ann will be twice as old as her sister is then. If Ann is now 6 years older than her sister, what are their present ages?

7. A father is 22 years older than his son. Five years ago he was three times as old as his son was then. Find their present ages.

8. Of two sisters, one is old enough to vote in national elections, yet their combined ages do not exceed 35 years. If the age of one sister is half the age of the second, find their ages.

9. Central High scored 12 more points than their opponents, South High, in a football game. Last year, Central was beaten by 5 points. In the two games, South scored a total of 42 points. Name at least two sets of possible scores for the games.

10. If person x drinks six times as much milk as person y, and together they consume 168 litres a year, how much milk does y consume in an average month?

11. A man traveled 60 km through swamp and forest, 5 times as long through swamp as through forest. He traveled twice as many kilometres through swamp as there were chimpanzees in his trunk, and he had as many chimpanzees in his trunk as he had koala bears in his glove compartment. How far did he travel altogether?

12. A person finds that 90 metres of fencing is not enough to fence a yard, which is rectangularly shaped, with the length $1\frac{1}{2}$ times the width. What can be deduced about the width?

13. Sonja Kovalevsky, a great Russian mathematician, died of influenza at the height of her career. If she had lived 9 more years, her age would have been twice the age she was 16 years before her death. How old was she when she died?

14. A laundry worker was normally able to finish the daily quota in 8 hours. One day an assistant was assigned to help. Together they were able to finish the quota in 5 hours. At that rate, how long would it have taken the assistant to do the job alone?

15. A woman rows 18 kilometres downstream in 3 hours. She finds that it takes 6 hours to row back. What is the rate of rowing in still water, and what is the rate of the stream? What assumptions do you have to make in order to make this problem manageable?

16. In a small town, 30% of the town's school-age children attend the parochial schools, 65% the public schools, and 500 students attend the private school. If 100 school-age children are not in school, how many school-age children are in the town?

17. June is 10 pounds heavier than her sister Jean, 3 pounds lighter than her sister Joan, $\frac{7}{8}$ the weight of her mother, Jane, and $\frac{2}{3}$ the weight of her father, John. All 5 people got on a scale and tipped the scales at 625 pounds. How much did each person weigh?

18. One IBM machine can sort 1000 cards in a minute, a second can sort 1500 cards in 80 seconds. Together, how many cards can they sort in x minutes? How long would it take the two machines to sort 3800 cards? What assumptions do you have to make to solve this problem?

19. Construction company A can build 40 new houses in 12 months. Company B can build 30 new houses in a year. If the two companies merge, how long will it take the companies together to build 85 houses, assuming that the capacities of the two companies are not affected by the merger?

20. Finish solving Example **1** of this section.

21. Finish solving Example **3** of this section.

22. A batter in baseball presently has 50 hits in 175 at bats, for a batting average of exactly $\frac{50}{175} = 0.285\cdots$. How many consecutive hits are needed to raise the batting average above 0.300?

23. Bookstore A in town X gives a 10% discount on books; bookstore B in town Y gives an 8% discount. If town X has a 3% sales tax and town Y has a 1% sales tax, where are books cheapest? What factors other than cost might affect the decision of where to buy books?

24. It is approximately 882 miles from Chicago to New York. Flight schedules for some planes normally have these planes going from Chicago to New York in 1 hr. 45 min. and back in 2 hr. 15 min. What is the normal expected velocity of air movement from west to east? (The great velocity is due to the "jet stream.") What is the expected average velocity of the plane in still air?

25. (See Exercise 24.) It took a plane $5\frac{1}{2}$ hours to travel from Boston to Los Angeles. At the same time a plane of the same type took $4\frac{1}{4}$ hours to travel from Los Angeles to Boston, a distance of 4000 kilometres. Pose an interesting question, make necessary simplifications to help answer your question, and finally answer your question.

26. Approximately 8% of the items produced by a company are found defective before shipping. How many items should be manufactured in order to ship 1000 nondefective items?

© 27. A plane carries enough fuel for 12 hours of flight. A group of people wish to charter the plane for a party. How far can the plane fly against a 160 km/h head wind on its outbound trip and with this wind on its return trip if its normal speed is 640 km/h?

28. When a motorboat travels against the current at full speed, it is going at the same rate as when it travels with the current at half speed. Find the ratio of the boat's speed to the speed of the current.

29. The hands of a clock form opposite rays at 6:00. When next will they form opposite rays? (The answer is not 7:05.)

30. Suppose you are running up and back from one place to another. Do you think a constant wind would help or hurt your total time?

MATHEMATICAL PROBLEMS 16.9

Suppose that the thousands digit of a four-digit number is a, the hundreds digit is b, the tens digit is c, and the units digit is d. We have a numeral

a	b	c	d

How is the value of the number related to the digits a, b, c, and d? Do we multiply them? Add them?

Sometimes it is best to try a simpler problem. Suppose the thousands digit is 7, the hundreds digit is 5, the tens digit is 6, and the units digit is 4. How is the number 7564 related to the four numbers 7, 5, 6, and 4. Clearly we multiply 7 by 1000 (it is the thousands digit), multiply 5 by 100, multiply 6 by 10, multiply 4 by 1, and add the products.

$$7564 = 7 \cdot 1000 + 5 \cdot 100 + 6 \cdot 10 + 4 \cdot 1$$

In general, we have the following theorem, which can itself be generalized.

Theorem 16.9.1

If a four-digit number (base 10) has thousands digit T, hundreds digit h, tens digit t, and units digit u, then the value of the number is $1000T + 100h + 10t + u$.

With this theorem, problems involving digits can be solved. What is the value of the number which looks like $u\ t\ h\ T$? You should recognize this as the number of Theorem 16.9.1 with its digits reversed. Its value is, by the theorem, $1000u + 100t + 10h + T$.

The theorem can be generalized to deal with decimal places, to deal with numbers of more or less than 4 digits, or to cover numbers in other bases. Each of these generalizations is left as an exercise.

What we have done is to translate information about the digits of a number into a formula for the value of the number itself. Other translations are very common, and you should be familiar with them.

In words	*Possible translation*	
1. three *consecutive* integers	$n, n + 1, n + 2$ or $n - 1, n, n + 1$	
2. even integer	$2n$	Where n is any integer
3. four consecutive *even* integers	$2n, 2n + 2, 2n + 4, 2n + 6$	
4. odd integer	$2n - 1$	
5. integer divisible by 14	$14n$	

Examples of consecutive even integers are $-8, -6, -4$, etc. Odd integers follow the same pattern: 17, 19, and 21 are three consecutive odd integers. Here is a typical problem.

Example: Prove that the sum of any three consecutive even integers is divisible by 6.

SOLUTION: Three consecutive even integers are $2n$, $2n + 2$, and $2n + 4$.

$$2n + (2n + 2) + (2n + 4) = 6n + 6$$
$$= 6(n + 1)$$

Now because $n + 1$ is an integer, $6(n + 1)$ is a multiple of 6. So the sum of these three even integers is divisible by 6.

The solution of problems requires knowing the meaning of the terms used. In the exercises, it is expected that you are familiar with certain geometric terms and theorems. Should you have forgotten some of those, you may find it helpful to examine a geometry text of your own or in your school library.

EXERCISES 16.9

Ⓐ **1–6.** Consider the 5-digit number denoted by $a\,b\,c\,d\,e$. Translate each phrase or sentence into mathematics.

1. the product of the digits

2. the sum of the digits

3. the value of the number

4. the thousands digit

5. the value of the number with the digits reversed

6. the value of the number if the tens and hundreds digits are switched

7. When are two angles complementary?

8. An angle has measure x. What is the measure of a supplement to the angle?

9. The sum of the measures of the angles of a triangle is ____.

10. The sum of the measures of the angles of a quadrilateral is ____.

11. The smallest of four consecutive integers is $n - 2$. Name the other three.

12. One of three consecutive odd integers is x. Name the other two.

13. The largest of three consecutive even integers is $2n$. Name the other two.

Ⓑ **14.** The measures of two supplementary angles are in the ratio 23:13. Find the measure of the larger angle.

15. The measure of one angle exceeds 3 times the measure of a second complementary angle by 15. Find the measure of each angle.

16. The measures of the angles of a triangle are in the ratio 3:4:5. (This symbolism means that if the measure of the smallest is $3x$, then the other two measures are $4x$ and $5x$.) Find the measures. Are the sides of the triangle in the same ratio?

17. Find the measures of the angles of quadrilateral $ABCD$ pictured at right.

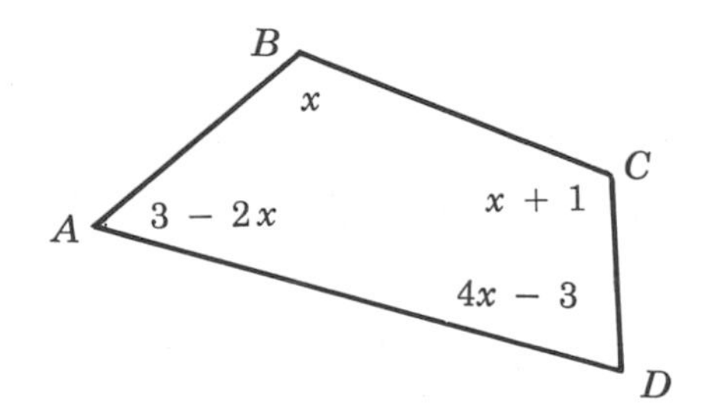

18. Two consecutive odd integers are in the ratio 3:4. Find the integers.

19. Two consecutive even integers are in the ratio 1:2. Find the integers.

20. Prove that the sum of three consecutive integers is always divisible by 3.

21. Multiple choice: Prove your answer.
The sum of four consecutive integers is divisible by 4:

a. always. **b.** sometimes. **c.** never.

22. Of seven consecutive odd integers, the ratio of the last to the first is 9:7. Name these seven integers.

23. The three angles of a triangle are in the ratio 4:3:3. Find the number of degrees in each.

24. Is there any number which is tripled when it is decreased by 8?

25. X is a 2-digit number and Y is the number formed by reversing the digits of X. Prove or Disprove: $X + Y$ is divisible by 11.

26. See Exercise **25**. Prove or Disprove: $X - Y$ is divisible by 9.

27. Repeat Exercise **25** for a 4-digit number.

28. Repeat Exercise **26** for a 5-digit number.

29. The sum of the digits of a 2-digit number is added to the number itself. The result equals the original number with its digits interchanged. Find all numbers for which this is possible.

30. Fill in the blank with the largest possible integer and prove: If the digits of a 3-digit number are reversed and the resulting number is subtracted from the given number, then the difference is divisible by _____.

31. The sum of the digits of a 4-digit number is 9. The tens digit is 5 times the units digit. How many numbers satisfy these conditions?

32. A 3-digit number has digits h, t, and u (obvious meanings). What is the value of the number formed by removing the units digit and placing it before the hundreds digit?

33. Prove: If the sum of the digits of a 4-digit number is divisible by 9, then the number is divisible by 9.

34. Think of a number. Divide it by -4, subtract -3 from the quotient, then multiply the difference by -2. If you get the answer 16, then you are thinking of the correct answer to this problem. What number do you wish you had thought of in the first place?

35. The sum of two numbers is -15. Their difference is -4. Solve this problem two different ways, first using two equations in two variables, then using only one equation in one variable.

36. The sum of two numbers is P. Their difference is Q. Find the two numbers. Check your answer by trying specific values of P and Q.

37. Prove: There is only one 2-digit number in which the sum of the digits of the number is one half the number itself.

© 38. Prove: If the sum of the units and hundreds digits of a 4-digit number equals the sum of the tens and thousands digits, then the number is divisible by 11.

39. Write the theorem in base 8 corresponding to Theorem 16.9.1.

40. Extend Theorem 16.9.1 to cover digits to the right of the decimal point.

41. Generalize Theorem 16.9.1 to cover any base.

42. How could Exercise **38** be modified so that it would be a theorem true in base 8?

43. The square of a 2-digit number is subtracted from the square of the number formed by reversing the digits. Answer True or False for each possibility: The difference is always divisible by **(a)** 11, **(b)** 9, **(c)** the sum of the digits, or **(d)** the difference of the digits.

44. Of any three consecutive positive integers, prove that the sum of the reciprocals of the first and last less twice the reciprocal of the middle can be reduced to a simple fraction with 1 in its numerator. Give a specific example to verify your proof.

16

CHAPTER SUMMARY

Two types of expressions are studied in this chapter: *polynomials* and *fractions*. Techniques for each of these types can be useful in working with the other type.

If a polynomial equation $a_nx^n + a_{n-1}x^{n-1} + \cdots + a_1x + a_0 = 0$ with integer coefficients has a rational root $\frac{p}{q}$ in lowest terms, then p is a factor of a_0 and q is a factor of a_n. This *rational root theorem* is very useful because of the *factor theorem.* If r is a root of the equation, then $x - r$ is a factor of the polynomial. Dividing the polynomial by $x - r$ gives a new polynomial whose degree is one less. Then a solution to the related equation may be easier to find.

If a polynomial can be factored, then the solutions to related equations and inequalities can be found without need of any formulas. Factoring also helps to simplify fractions because common factors of the numerator and denominator of a fraction may be removed without affecting the value of the fraction. Likewise, factoring assists in finding common denominators and thus aids in addition, subtraction, and the solution of sentences involving fractions.

Certain polynomials occur rather frequently, and their factorizations should be memorized.

$$a^2 + 2ab + b^2 = (a + b)^2$$

$$a^2 - b^2 = (a - b)(a + b)$$

$$a^3 - b^3 = (a - b)(a^2 + ab + b^2)$$

$$a^2 + b^2 = (a + bi)(a - bi)$$

$$a^3 + b^3 = (a + b)(a^2 - ab + b^2)$$

A large collection of puzzle problems is given in this chapter. These problems sometimes resemble a real situation, sometimes they do not. Travel, costs, percentages, solutions (or mixtures), money, age, and work production are subjects of some of these problems. The chapter also includes mathematical problems involving digits, consecutive integers, and geometry.

CHAPTER REVIEW

1–4. Factor each expression as much as possible into expressions with integer coefficients.

1. $8x^3 + y^3$

2. $v^4 - 81$

3. $18n^2 - 7nx - x^2$

4. $bd - 4c + 12cd - 2$

5–6. Use factoring to find all solutions to each equation.

5. $0 = 21m^2 - m - 10$

6. $x^3 = 1$

7. Divide $3x^3 + 16x^2 - 27x + 49$ by $x + 7$.

8–11. Simplify.

8. $\dfrac{\frac{5A - 2}{8}}{\frac{3 + A}{3}}$

9. $\dfrac{9 - 9x + 2x^2}{9 - x^2}$

10. $\dfrac{10}{3B + 4} - \dfrac{10 - B}{3B - 4}$

11. $\dfrac{3M - 6}{\frac{2M}{5} + 4} \cdot \dfrac{M^2 + 1\ M + 10}{M - 2}$

12–13. Solve each sentence.

12. $\dfrac{4}{y} - \dfrac{3}{y + 1} = \dfrac{3}{35}$

13. $\dfrac{w^3 - 1}{w - 1} + w = 9$

14. Find all solutions to $2v^3 = v^2 + 3v + 1$. (HINT: One solution is rational.)

15. The selling price of an item is reduced by 40% and the item now sells for $13.98. What was the original selling price?

16. How many ounces of water should be added to 60 ounces of a 5% saline solution to change it to a 4% solution.

17. Flying with the wind, it takes a plane 3 hours to travel the 800 kilometres from city A to city B. Flying at the same time, a second, similar plane takes 4 hours to travel from city B to city A. If there were no wind, the planes would be traveling at the same speed. How strong is the wind?

18. The digits of a 4-digit number are reversed, and the resulting number is added to the original number. Prove or Disprove: The sum is divisible by 11.

Chapter 17 Sequences, Sums, and Statistics

EXAMPLES OF SEQUENCES

A sequence involves objects, called *terms*, which have been placed in a particular order. (The order may not be according to size.) Here is one example of a sequence.

$$2, -\tfrac{1}{2}, 4, -\tfrac{1}{4}, 6, -\tfrac{1}{6}, 8, -\tfrac{1}{8}, \cdots$$

The three dots indicate that there are more terms than have been written.

One problem with the three dots is that you can't be sure what follows. For example, suppose you write the following.

$$1, 2, 4, \cdots$$

You might be thinking of any one of many different sequences. Some possibilities are given below.

(I) 1, 2, 4, 8, 16, ⋯ — sequence of powers of 2

(II) 1, 2, 4, 7, 11, ⋯ — sequence in which the differences between successive numbers increase by 1

(III) 1, 2, 4, 6, 12. — finite sequence of numbers which are divisors of 12

(IV) 1, 2, 4, 6, 8, 9, ⋯ — sequence of positive integers which are *not* odd primes

We need a precise way of describing a sequence. We can think of a sequence as a function. The number 1 corresponds to the first term, the number 2 to the second term, and so forth. The positive integer n corresponds to the nth term.

Domain (Term numbers)	1st	2nd	3rd	4th	5th	6th	⋯
Range for sequence (I)	1	2	4	8	16	32	⋯
Range for sequence (II)	1	2	4	7	11	16	⋯
Range for sequence (III)	1	2	4	6	12		
Range for sequence (IV)	1	2	4	6	8	9	⋯

Definitions

A **finite sequence** is a function whose domain is the set of integers from 1 to k, inclusive.

An **infinite sequence** is a function whose domain is the set of *all* positive integers.

We often name a sequence by a single letter, such as S. Then S_n names the nth term of the sequence. In writing a sequence, we usually write only the range elements which are called **terms** of the sequence.

$$S_1, S_2, S_3, S_4, S_5, \cdots$$

This notation is slightly different from the normal function notation, which would be $S(1)$, $S(2,)$ $S(3)$, ⋯ .

We can describe a sequence by giving a rule of correspondence, an *explicit formula* for the nth term.

Examples: Explicit rules for sequences

1. Suppose $S_n = 2n - 1$.

$$S_1 = 2 \cdot 1 - 1 = 1$$
$$S_2 = 2 \cdot 2 - 1 = 3$$
$$S_3 = 2 \cdot 3 - 1 = 5$$
$$S_4 = 2 \cdot 4 - 1 = 7$$
$$\vdots \quad \vdots \quad \vdots$$

We get terms of the sequence by substituting various positive integers for n.

The resulting terms are the ordered, positive, odd numbers.

$$1, 3, 5, 7, \cdots$$

2. Suppose $t_n = \frac{1}{2}n(n + 1)$.

$$t_1 = \tfrac{1}{2} \cdot 1 \cdot 2 = 1$$
$$t_2 = \tfrac{1}{2} \cdot 2 \cdot 3 = 3$$
$$t_3 = \tfrac{1}{2} \cdot 3 \cdot 4 = 6$$
$$t_4 = \tfrac{1}{2} \cdot 4 \cdot 5 = 10$$
$$\vdots \quad \vdots \quad \vdots$$

3. The sequence below is called the *factorial sequence, f.*

$$f_1 = 1 = 1$$
$$f_2 = 2 \cdot 1 = 2$$
$$f_3 = 3 \cdot 2 \cdot 1 = 6$$
$$f_4 = 4 \cdot 3 \cdot 2 \cdot 1 = 24$$
$$f_5 = 5 \cdot 4 \cdot 3 \cdot 2 \cdot 1 = 120$$
$$\vdots \quad \vdots \quad \vdots$$

The nth term of this sequence is the *product* of all integers from 1 to n, inclusive.

Any term of this sequence can be represented by using the symbol !, called the *factorial* symbol.

Definition

If n is a positive integer, $n!$ is the product of all integers from 1 to n, inclusive.

The factorial symbol was first introduced in 1808 by Christian Kramp (1760–1826).

Examples: The factorial symbol

$1! = 1 \qquad 2! = 2 \cdot 1 = 2 \qquad 3! = 3 \cdot 2 \cdot 1 = 6$ and so forth.

In general, $\quad n! = n(n - 1)(n - 2)(n - 3) \cdots 3 \cdot 2 \cdot 1.$

Some sequences are more easily described by how you get from one term to the next than by giving a formula for the nth term. For example, if you know 5!, then to get 6! it is easier to multiply 5! by 6 than to multiply $6 \cdot 5 \cdot 4 \cdot 3 \cdot 2 \cdot 1$.

In a sequence, the term after S_n is S_{n+1}, called the "n-plus-first term," or "$(n + 1)$st term." For the sequence of positive odd numbers, we begin with 1 and add 2 to each S_n to get S_{n+1}.

$$S_1 = 1$$
$$S_{n+1} = S_n + 2$$

← This is an abbreviated way to describe the sequence of positive odd numbers.

Such a description is called a *recursive definition* (or *formula*, or *rule*) for a sequence. Notice that there are two parts. The first part tells how the sequence starts. The second part tells how to get the $(n + 1)$st term from the previous terms.

Examples: Recursive rules for sequences

1. The sequence of positive even numbers, in increasing order, can be described with a recursive rule.

   $2, 4, 6, 8, \cdots$ — sequence

   $$E_1 = 2$$
   $$E_{n+1} = E_n + 2$$
   — recursive rule

2. In a famous sequence called the *Fibonacci sequence*, *F*, each term is the sum of the *two* preceding terms.

   $1, 1, 2, 3, 5, 8, 13, 21, \cdots$ — Fibonacci sequence

   The numbers in this sequence are called *Fibonacci numbers*.

   Notice that the nature of this sequence makes it necessary to give two beginning terms.

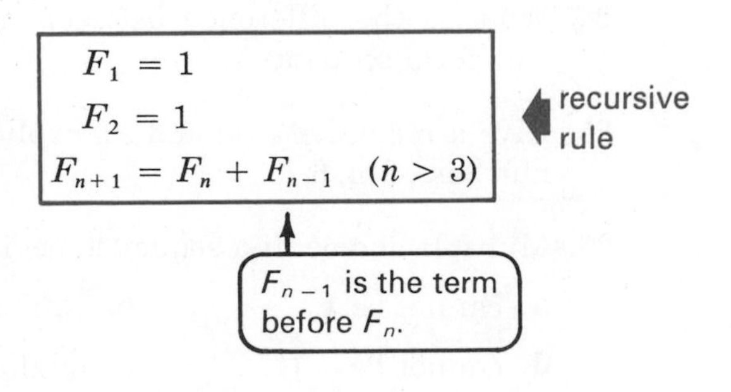

3. Find a recursive definition for 11, 9, 7, 5, 3, 1, −1, · · · .

SOLUTION: Call the sequence S. Two characteristics determine this sequence.

(1) The first term is 11. ▶ $S_1 = 11$

(2) Subtracting 2 from a term gives the next term. ▶ $S_{n+1} = S_n - 2$

These form a recursive rule for S.

EXERCISES 17.1

Ⓐ **1–4.** Let S be the sequence with $S_n = 2n - 2$. Calculate.

1. S_1 **2.** S_2 **3.** S_3 **4.** S_4

5–8. Let $t_n = n^2$. Calculate.

5. t_1 **6.** t_3 **7.** t_{10} **8.** $t_4 - t_3$

9. The 14th term of a sequence v is denoted by _____.

10. The expression $n!$ stands for the _____ of all integers from 1 to n, inclusive, and is called n _____.

11–18. Calculate.

11. 3! **12.** 4! **13.** 5! **14.** 6!

15. 2! **16.** 1! **17.** $\frac{4!}{3!}$ **18.** $\frac{5!}{6!}$

19–22. If $t_1 = 0$ and $t_{n+1} = 2t_n + 5$, find each term named below.

19. t_2 **20.** t_3 **21.** t_4 **22.** t_6

23. Give an example of a recursive definition for a sequence.

24. What is the difference between a recursive rule and an explicit rule for a sequence?

25. Give a recursive rule and an explicit rule for the sequence of even numbers, 2, 4, 6, · · · .

26. Multiple choice. If a sequence begins 1, 1, 2, 2, · · · , the 5th term:

a. cannot be 1. **b.** cannot be 2. **c.** is 3.

d. cannot be −1. **e.** might be any number.

27. What is the precise definition of *sequence?*

28–30. Consider the sequences A, B, C, and D, below.

A: $-1, -4, -7, \cdots$ $\quad$ B: $\frac{1}{2}, -2, -7, \cdots$

C: $10, 17, 31, \cdots$ $\quad$ D: $-1, 1, 3, 5, \cdots$

In which sequence(s) is the given statement true?

28. $a_1 = -1$ $\quad$ **29.** $a_{n+1} = 2a_n - 3$ $\quad$ **30.** $a_{n+1} = a_n + 2$

Ⓑ **31.** Calculate the first ten members of the factorial sequence.

32–40. Give the first six terms of the sequence with the given formula.

32. $s_n = 5n + 1$ $\quad$ **33.** $t_n = (-1)^n$ $\quad$ **34.** $u_n = (5n + 1)(-1)^n$

35. $v_n = \frac{n}{n + 1}$ $\quad$ **36.** $w_n = (2n - 1)!$ $\quad$ **37.** $x_n = i^n$

38. $y_1 = 2$, $y_{n+1} = 3 \cdot y_n$ $\quad$ **39.** $a_n = \frac{2}{10^n}$ $\quad$ **40.** $z_1 = 256$, $z_{n+1} = \sqrt{z_n}$

41. Give two possible rules for a sequence which begins $1, 3, 5, \cdots$.

42. Give a rule for a sequence which contains no positive terms.

43–48. Give a recursive rule for each sequence.

43. $10, 13, 16, 19, \cdots$ $\quad$ **44.** $\frac{1}{2}, \frac{3}{2}, \frac{5}{2}, \frac{7}{2}, \cdots$

45. $5, 15, 45, 135, 405, \cdots$ $\quad$ **46.** $-1, -3, -5, -7, \cdots$

47. $1.1, 1.2, 1.3, 1.4, \cdots$ $\quad$ **48.** $20, 15, 10, 5, 0, -5, \cdots$

49. Name the first 15 Fibonacci numbers.

Ⓒ **50.** The *Lucas numbers* are related to the Fibonacci numbers and are defined by the recursive rule at the right. Give the first 10 Lucas numbers.

$$L_1 = 1$$
$$L_2 = 3$$
$$L_{n+1} = L_n + L_{n-1}$$

51. Suppose $F_n = \dfrac{\left(\frac{1 + \sqrt{5}}{2}\right)^n - \left(\frac{1 - \sqrt{5}}{2}\right)^n}{\sqrt{5}}$.

Verify that F_1, F_2, and F_3 are the first three Fibonacci numbers.

52. Who was Fibonacci?

53. What simple sequence is defined by the rule $d_n = \dfrac{\left[\frac{10^n}{3}\right]}{10^n}$?

17.2 LINEAR (ARITHMETIC) SEQUENCES

Since a sequence is a function, equations for functions lead to equations for sequences. Here is an equation for a linear function.

$$y = 3x - 2$$

A rule for the corresponding sequence is found by replacing x with n and y with A_n.

$$A_n = 3n - 2$$

The domain must be restricted to the set of positive integers (by definition). Now, substituting $1, 2, 3, 4, 5, \cdots$ for n, we find that the sequence is

$$1, 4, 7, 10, 13, \cdots.$$

Graphing (n, A_n) is just like graphing (x, y) where $y = 3x - 2$. The only difference is that, for the sequence, the domain is restricted to the positive integers.

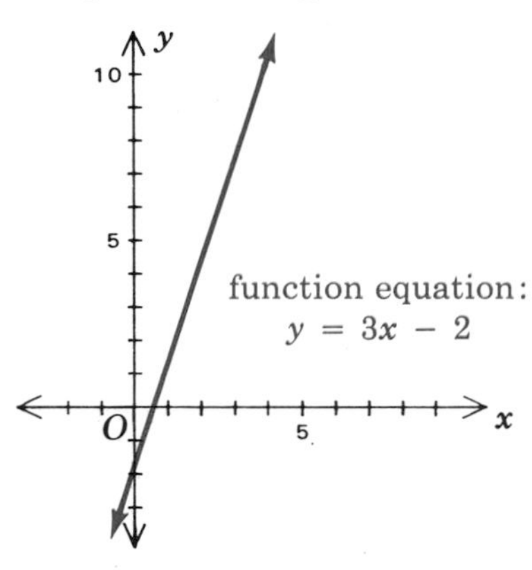

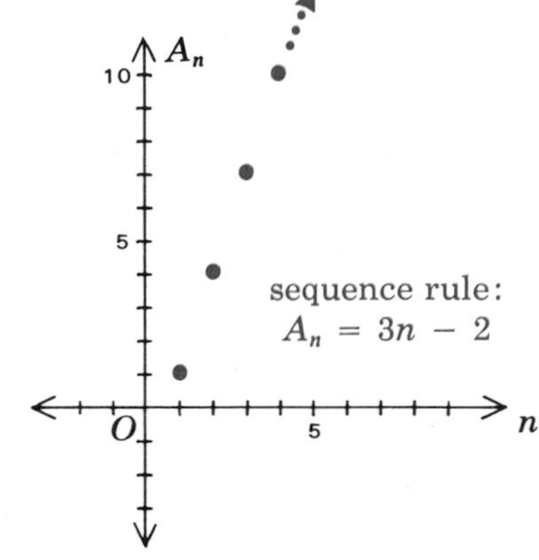

Sequences of this type are naturally called *linear sequences*, because they are subsets of linear functions.

Definition

A **linear sequence** (sometimes called an **arithmetic sequence** or an **arithmetic progression**) is a sequence A with a rule of the form

$$A_n = mn + b.$$

Examples:

	Rule	Linear sequence	
1.	$A_n = n$	$1, 2, 3, 4, \cdots$	increasing positive integers
2.	$B_n = 2n$	$2, 4, 6, 8, \cdots$	increasing positive even integers
3.	$C_n = 2n - 1$	$1, 3, 5, 7, \cdots$	increasing positive odd integers

In each of these examples, the sequence is formed by adding a fixed number to one term to get the next term. This is true of all *linear sequences.*

Theorem 17.2.1

In a linear (arithmetic) sequence, the difference between two consecutive terms is constant.

PROOF: Let $A_n = mn + b$ where m and b are constants. Two consecutive terms are A_{n+1} and A_n.

$$\begin{aligned} A_{n+1} - A_n &= [m(n+1) + b] - (mn + b) \\ &= mn + m + b - mn - b \\ &= m \end{aligned}$$

Since m is a constant, the theorem is proved.

The letter d (for *difference*) is usually used (rather than m) to denote the *constant difference* between terms. In Example **1** on page 534, the first term is 1 and $d = 1$. In Examples **2** and **3** the first terms are different, but $d = 2$ in each.

Given the first term and the constant difference, it is helpful to be able to get an explicit rule for the sequence. This is like being given a point and the slope of a line, then finding the equation.

Theorem 17.2.2

A linear (arithmetic) sequence A with first term A_1 and constant difference d has the explicit rule

$$A_n = A_1 + (n - 1)d.$$

PROOF: The point-slope form for an equation of a line (Theorem 6.6.1) is

$$y - k = m(x - h).$$

In this case, the sequence has slope d and contains $(1, A_1)$. Substituting (remember to replace y by A_n and x by n), we get

$$A_n - A_1 = d(n - 1).$$

Then adding A_1 to each side, we get $A_n = A_1 + (n - 1)d$, which is the desired rule.

Examples: Finding terms of linear sequences

1. Let A be the sequence $6, 4, 2, 0, -2, \cdots$. The 100th term of A is found by letting $A_1 = 6$, $d = -2$, and $n = 100$ in the formula $A_n = A_1 + (n - 1)d$.

$$A_{100} = 6 + (100 - 1)(-2) = -192$$

2. If you pay \$200 down and \$50 a month for a used car, then letting P_n be the *total paid after n months*, a sequence P will be formed.

$$250, 300, 350, 400, \cdots$$

Since $P_1 = 250$ and $d = 50$, $P_n = 250 + (n - 1)50$.

For example, $P_7 = 250 + (6)50 = 550$.

The most general linear sequence, with first term A_1 and constant difference d, looks like this:

$$A_1, \quad A_1 + d, \quad A_1 + 2d, \quad A_1 + 3d, \quad \cdots, \quad A_1 + (n - 1)d, \quad \cdots.$$

Each term is found by adding d to the previous term. So there is a simple recursive rule for this sequence, given A_1,

$$A_{n+1} = A_n + d.$$

This rule shows that linear sequences are related to addition. In the next section we consider sequences related to multiplication.

EXERCISES 17.2

Ⓐ 1. Which sequence could *not* be a linear sequence?

a. 1, 4, 7, 10, 13, ⋯

b. 2.3, 1.3, 0.3, −0.7, −1.7, −2.7, ⋯

c. 1, 2, 4, 8, 16, ⋯

d. $-\frac{1}{2}, \frac{1}{2}, \frac{3}{2}, \frac{5}{2}, \frac{7}{2}, \cdots$

2–3. Give the first 5 terms of the linear sequence A with constant difference d.

2. $A_1 = 2$ and $d = 3$

3. $A_1 = 10$ and $d = -\frac{1}{2}$

4–6. Give the first 5 terms of the sequence for which:

4. $B_1 = 1$; $B_{n+1} = B_n - 1$.

5. $C_1 = 1$; $C_{n+1} = C_n + 1$.

6. first term $= A_1$; constant difference $= d$.

7. Name two synonyms for *linear sequence*.

8. Which is a rule for the arithmetic sequence 3, 7, 11, 15, 19, ⋯ ?

a. $D_1 = 4$; $D_n = 3$

b. $D_1 = 4$; $D_{n+1} = D_n + 3$

c. $D_1 = 3$; $D_{n+1} = D_n + 4$

9. Give the 3rd term of the linear sequence $A_1, A_1 + d, \cdots$.

10. Give the nth term of the arithmetic progression $A_1, A_1 + d, \cdots$.

Ⓑ **11–18.** Find an explicit rule for the nth term, and use this to find the indicated term of the linear sequence.

11. $1, 4, 7, 10, \cdots$; 100th term

12. $12, 11.5, 11, \cdots$; 32nd term

13. $a_1 = 6$;
$a_{n+1} = a_n + 5$; 14th term

14. $b_1 = -2$;
$b_{n+1} = b_n - 11$; 25th term

15. $c_1 = 7$;
$d = 14$; c_{16}

16. $s_3 = 11$;
$d = -3$; s_{100}

17. $a_{11} = 5$;
$a_{14} = 68$; a_1

18. $b_5 = 100$;
$b_7 = 90$; b_6

19. A girl is given 500 stamps to start a collection. If she adds 5 stamps a week, how many will she have at the end of n weeks?

20. Mrs. Lyles begins with \$1000 in a checking account and withdraws \$15 a week. Give the formula for the amount left after w weeks.

21. How many months will it take to pay \$4000 when \$490 is paid at the start and \$65 every month thereafter?

22. A gas company charges a basic monthly rate plus a certain amount per unit. If the use of 122 units gives a bill of \$12.83 and the use of 508 units gives a bill of \$18.62, what is the basic monthly rate and what is the cost per unit?

23. What is the first term and common difference of the linear sequence A with $A_{122} = 1283$ and $A_{508} = 1862$?

24–26. Graph the sequences of Exercises **11–13**.

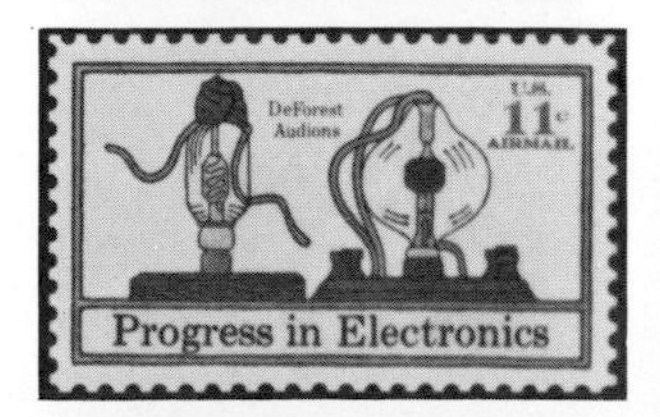

27. How is the constant difference of a linear sequence related to the slope of its graph?

Ⓒ **28.** Prove or Disprove: If a, b, and c are three consecutive terms of an arithmetic sequence, then b is the arithmetic mean of a and c.

29. Prove or Disprove: If A is an arithmetic sequence, then $A_7 + A_{10} = A_8 + A_9$. (HINT: It may help to try some examples first.)

30. Generalize Exercise **29**.

EXPONENTIAL (GEOMETRIC) SEQUENCES

Linear sequences are formed by beginning with some number and *adding* a constant to each term to get the next term. If, instead, we *multiply* each term by a constant to get the next term, then an *exponential* or *geometric sequence* is formed.

Examples: Exponential (geometric) sequences

1. Begin with 2 and multiply by 3.

$$2, \quad 6, \quad 18, \quad 54, \quad 162, \quad 486, \quad \cdots$$

2. If $G_1 = 70$ and $G_{n+1} = \frac{1}{10}G_n$, then the sequence G is

$$70, 7, 0.7, 0.07, \cdots.$$

geometric sequences

Such sequences are called *exponential* because each geometric sequence is a subset of an exponential function. This can be seen by graphing both sequence G from Example **2** and the corresponding exponential function, which has the equation $y = 700(\frac{1}{10})^x$.

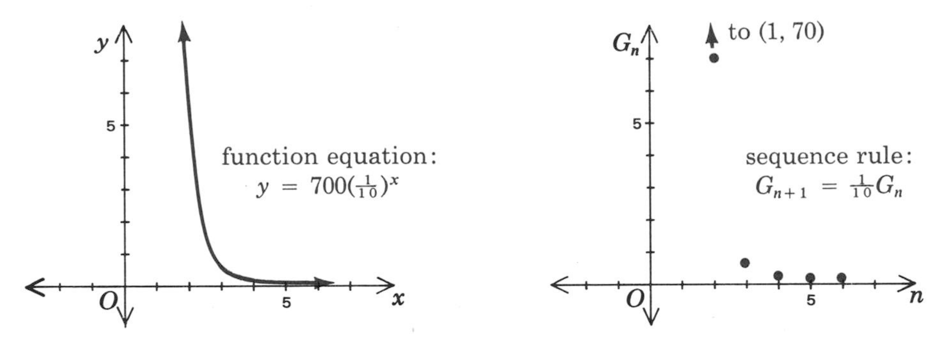

Compare the definition of exponential sequence, below, with that for linear sequence. The letters were chosen to show the similarities.

Definition

An **exponential sequence** (sometimes called a **geometric sequence** or a **geometric progression**) is a sequence G with a rule of the form

$$G_n = bm^n.$$

Examples:

	Rule	Exponential sequence	
3.	$A_n = 2^n$	2, 4, 8, 16, 32, $\cdots$	powers of 2
4.	$B_n = 5 \cdot 2^n$	10, 20, 40, 80, 160, $\cdots$	5 times each power above

Theorem 17.3.1

In an exponential (geometric) sequence, the ratio of two consecutive terms is constant.

PROOF: Let $G_n = bm^n$. Then $G_{n+1} = bm^{n+1}$. Now, G_n and G_{n+1} are consecutive terms and their ratio is

$$\frac{G_{n+1}}{G_n} = \frac{bm^{n+1}}{bm^n} = m. \longleftarrow \text{constant ratio of consecutive terms}$$

The letter r (rather than m) is usually used for the constant *ratio* between terms. In Example **1** on page 538 we had $r = 3$ and in Example **2**, $r = \frac{1}{10}$. In both Examples **3** and **4**, $r = 2$.

Given the first term and the constant ratio, it is helpful to be able to get an explicit rule for the sequence. The following theorem shows how this can be done.

Theorem 17.3.2

The exponential (geometric) sequence G with first term G_1 and constant ratio r has the explicit rule

$$G_n = G_1 \cdot r^{n-1}.$$

PROOF: From the definition of exponential sequence we have,

$$G_n = b \cdot r^n.$$

Then $\quad G_1 = b \cdot r^1$

Dividing $\quad \frac{G_n}{G_1} = \frac{br^n}{br^1} = r^{n-1}$

Multiplying both sides by G_1 gives $G_n = G_1 \cdot r^{n-1}$, which is the desired rule.

Examples: Finding terms of geometric sequences

1. In the sequence $9, 6, 4, \frac{8}{3}, \frac{16}{9}, \cdots$, the constant ratio is $\frac{2}{3}$ and so the nth term is $9 \cdot (\frac{2}{3})^{n-1}$.

2. A ball is dropped from a height of 100 feet and it bounces up to 0.9 of its previous height after each bounce. If h_n is the height after n bounces, h is the sequence

$$90, 81, 72.9, 65.61, \cdots.$$

In general, $h_n = 90(0.9)^{n-1}$. On the eighth bounce the ball will rise to $90(0.9)^7$ feet, or approximately 43 feet.

The most general exponential sequence, with first term G_1 and constant ratio r, can be written as follows.

$$G_1, \quad G_1r, \quad G_1r^2, \quad G_1r^3, \quad \cdots, \quad G_1r^{n-1}, \quad \cdots$$

Each term is found by multiplying the previous term by r. So there is a simple recursive rule, given G_1,

$$G_{n+1} = G_n \cdot r.$$

This rule shows how closely exponential sequences are related to multiplication.

EXERCISES 17.3

Ⓐ **1.** An exponential sequence can be formed by ____ the nth term by a constant to get the $(n + 1)$st term.

2–6. Give the first 5 terms of the exponential sequence G with constant ratio r.

2. $G_1 = 2$, $r = 3$

3. $G_1 = 1$, $G_{n+1} = 5 \cdot G_n$

4. $G_1 = 64$, $G_{n+1} = \frac{3}{4}G_n$

5. $G_1 = 2$ and $r = -3$

6. $G_1 = 4$ and $G_2 = 20$

7. Name two synonyms for *exponential sequence.*

8–10. For the geometric sequence $a, ar, \cdots$, give the:

8. 3rd term.

9. 5th term.

10. nth term.

Ⓑ **11–17.** Find an explicit rule for the nth term, and use this to find the indicated term of the exponential sequence.

11. 6561, 2187, 729, $\cdots$; 13th term

12. 1, 1.5, 2.25, $\cdots$; 10th term

13. $a_1 = \sqrt{2}$; $a_{n+1} = a_n\sqrt{3}$; a_7

14. $b_1 = -2$; $b_{n+1} = 3b_n$; b_{100}

15. $c_4 = 8$; $c_7 = 27$; c_1

16. 9th term: $\frac{64}{729}$; constant ratio: $\frac{2}{3}$; 14th term

17. 1st term: 1; constant ratio: $a + b$; 10th term

18. A ball is dropped from a height of 5 metres and loses 20% of its height on each bounce. Give its height after 5 bounces and after n bounces.

19. A diamond was purchased for \$1000. If its value increases 5% each year, give the first 5 terms of the geometric sequence v which indicates its value v_n after n years. What is the constant ratio?

20. Suppose each bacterium splits into two every half hour. If there are 3 bacteria to begin with, how many will exist after 24 hours?

21–22. Explain how each of the following could be a geometric sequence.

21. $7, -7, 7, -7, 7, \cdots$

22. $x, x, x, x, \cdots$

23–25. Graph the sequences of Exercises **11**, **12**, and **14**.

© **26.** Prove: If $a_1, a_2, a_3, \cdots$ is a geometric sequence, then $\log a_1, \log a_2, \log a_3, \cdots$ is an arithmetic sequence.

27. Square S_{n+1} is formed by joining the midpoints of the sides of square S_n. If S_1 has area 12, find the area of S_6.

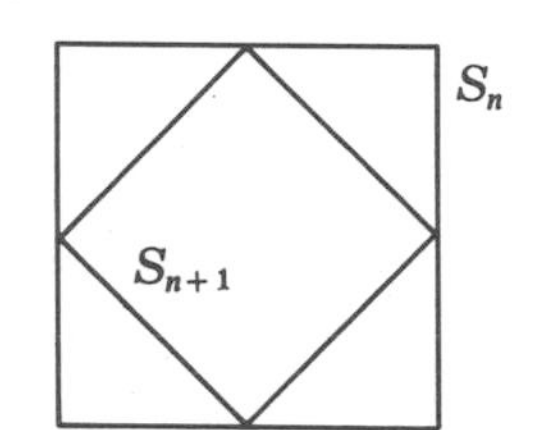

28. Triangle T_{n+1} is formed by joining the midpoints of the sides of T_n. If T_1 has perimeter 24 and area 20, find the perimeter and the area of T_{10}.

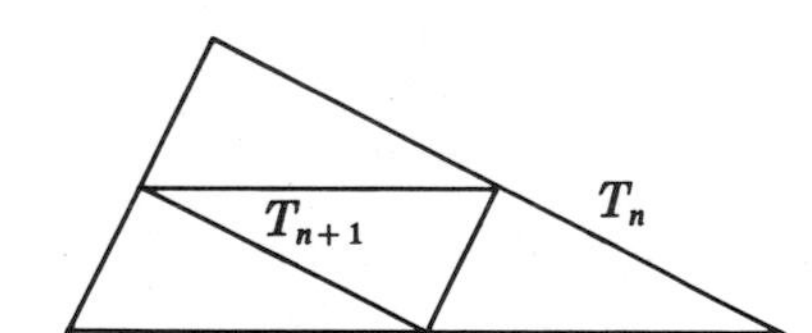

29–32. *Music.* Notes in music are carefully related to the frequency of A below middle C. This frequency varies from orchestra to orchestra (according to the conductor's choice) but is usually near 438 beats per second. If F_n is the frequency of a note on a piano, then F_{n+1}, the frequency of the note just above, is given by

$$F_{n+1} = (2)^{\frac{1}{12}} F_n.$$

29. Do the frequencies of the notes form an exponential sequence?

30. Find the frequency of middle C (3 notes above A).

31. Find the frequency of G below middle C (2 notes below A).

32. Prove that one note has exactly twice the frequency of the note an octave (12 notes) below.

17.4 SUMS OF FINITE SEQUENCES

SUMS OF LINEAR SEQUENCES

There is a well-known story about the famous mathematician Karl Friedrich Gauss (1777–1855). When he was in third grade, his class misbehaved and the teacher gave the following problem as punishment.

"Add the integers from 1 to 100."

It is said that Gauss solved the problem in almost no time at all. The teacher (who had hoped the problem would keep the students working for a long time) was quite disturbed. Gauss' method of solution is the basis for the proof of the next theorem.

Theorem 17.4.1

The sum of the integers from 1 to n is $\frac{1}{2}n(n + 1)$.

PROOF:

Reverse the order of the terms

Add each term in equations **1** and **2** to the term above it.

1. Let $S = 1 + 2 + \cdots + (n-1) + n$

2. Also, $S = n + (n-1) + \cdots + 2 + 1$

3. Adding, $2S = (1 + n) + (2 + n - 1) + \cdots + (n - 1 + 2) + (n + 1)$

4. $= \underbrace{(n + 1) + (n + 1) + \cdots + (n + 1) + (n + 1)}_{n \text{ terms}}$

5. $= n(n + 1)$

6. So, $S = \frac{1}{2}n(n + 1)$

The sum of the integers from 1 to 100 is $\frac{1}{2}(100)(101) = 5050$. (This is the answer Gauss gave.) Similarly, the sum of the integers from 1 to 4 is $\frac{1}{2}(4)(5) = 10$, a result easy to check.

Using the same idea, we can get a formula for the sum of the first n terms of any linear sequence. For example, suppose you want to find the sum of the first 30 terms of the arithmetic sequence below.

$$4, 11, 18, 25, \cdots$$

First, calculate the 30th term (it is 207).

Now, $S = 4 + 11 + \cdots + 200 + 207$

Also, $S = 207 + 200 + \cdots + 11 + 4$

So, $2S = \underbrace{211 + 211 + \cdots + 211 + 211}_{30 \text{ terms}}$

$$S = \tfrac{1}{2}(30)(211) = 3165$$

The next theorem gives the sum of n terms of *any* linear sequence. The proof is left for you in the exercises.

Theorem 17.4.2

The sum S of the first n terms of a linear (arithmetic) sequence is

$$S = \tfrac{1}{2}n(A_1 + A_n).$$

That is, the sum of the first n terms of any linear sequence is n times the *average* of the first term and the last (nth) term.

SUMS OF EXPONENTIAL SEQUENCES

Suppose → $S = G_1 + G_1r + G_1r^2 + \cdots + G_1r^{n-1}$. ← This is the sum of the first n terms of an exponential sequence.

Multiplying by $-r$ → $-rS = -G_1r - G_1r^2 - \cdots - G_1r^{n-1} - G_1r^n$

By addition property of equations → $S - rS = G_1 - G_1r^n$

By distributivity → $S(1 - r) = G_1(1 - r^n)$

Multiplying by $\dfrac{1}{1-r}$ → $S = G_1\left(\dfrac{1 - r^n}{1 - r}\right)$

Theorem 17.4.3

Let G be an exponential (geometric) sequence with ratio r. Then the sum S of the first n terms of G is

$$S = G_1\left(\frac{1 - r^n}{1 - r}\right).$$

Examples: Sums of finite exponential sequences.

1. $2 + \frac{2}{3} + \frac{2}{9} + \cdots + \frac{2}{729}$ is the sum of the first 7 terms of the exponential sequence with $G_1 = 2$ and $r = \frac{1}{3}$. Using Theorem 17.4.3, we can evaluate this sum.

$$S = 2 \cdot \frac{1 - \left(\frac{1}{3}\right)^7}{1 - \frac{1}{3}} = 2 \cdot \frac{1 - \frac{1}{3^7}}{\frac{2}{3}} = 3\left(1 - \frac{1}{3^7}\right)$$

$$= 3 - \frac{1}{3^6} = \frac{2186}{729}$$

2. The sum S of the first 100 terms of the geometric sequence with $G_1 = 5$ and $r = -2$ is

$$S = 5 - 10 + 20 - 40 + \cdots + 5(-2)^{99}.$$

By Theorem 17.4.3,

$$S = 5 \cdot \frac{1 - (-2)^{100}}{1 - (-2)} = \frac{5}{3}(1 - 2^{100}).$$

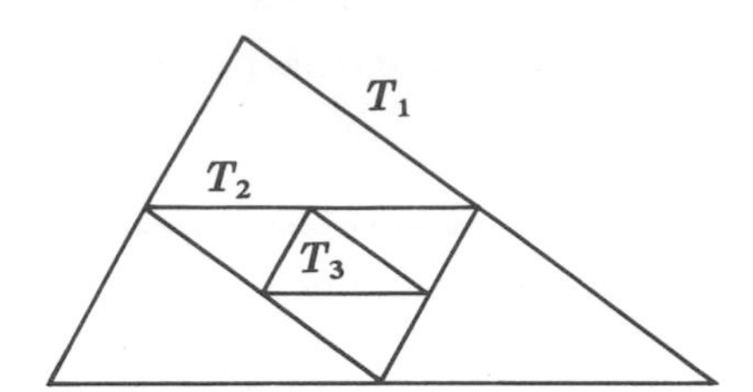

3. At the left, the midpoints of the sides of each triangle T_n are joined to form the next smaller triangle T_{n+1}. If triangle T_1 has perimeter 20, find the sum S of the perimeters of the first 10 triangles formed in this way.

SOLUTION: Notice that each triangle has half as large a perimeter as the previous triangle. Thus we wish to calculate

$$S = 20 + 10 + 5 + \cdots + 20(\tfrac{1}{2})^9.$$

By Theorem 17.4.3,

$$S = 20 \cdot \frac{1 - (\frac{1}{2})^{10}}{1 - \frac{1}{2}} = 40[1 - (\tfrac{1}{2})^{10}] = 40\left(\frac{2^{10} - 1}{2^{10}}\right)$$

$$= 40(\tfrac{1023}{1024}) = \tfrac{5115}{128} = 39\tfrac{123}{128}$$

EXERCISES 17.4

Ⓐ **1–4.** Give a formula for the sum of the:

1. integers from 1 to n.

2. n smallest positive odd integers.

3. first n terms of a linear sequence L with difference d.

4. first n terms of an exponential sequence E with ratio r.

5. The sum of the integers from 1 to 10 inclusive is ____.

6. The sum of the odd integers from 1 to 39 inclusive is ____.

7–10. Assume that the terms are from either a linear sequence or an exponential sequence. Find the sum.

7. $1 + 4 + 7 + \cdots + 28$

8. $2 + 4 + 8 + \cdots + 4096$

9. $27 - 9 + 3 - \cdots - \frac{1}{81}$

10. $99 + 98 + 97 + \cdots + 40$

Ⓑ **11.** The sum of all odd integers with two digits is ____.

12. The sum of the integers from 1 to ____ is 325.

13. If n is an integer, find the sum of all integers of the form $3n + 2$ between 1 and 100.

14. If k is an integer, find the sum of all integers of the form 3^k between 0 and 100.

15–20. The terms are from either a linear sequence or an exponential sequence. Find the sum.

15. $\sqrt{3} + \sqrt{6} + \cdots + \sqrt{384}$

16. $9 + 8.9 + 8.8 + \cdots + 2$

17. $1 - 5 + 25 - \cdots - 5^9$

18. $-2 - 4 - 6 - \cdots - 200$

19. $6 - 4 + \frac{8}{3} - \cdots - \frac{64}{81}$

20. $14 + 98 + \cdots + 2 \cdot 7^8$

21. Find the sum of the first n positive even integers.

© **22.** Prove that the sum of the integral powers of 2 from 2^0 to 2^{n-1} is $2^n - 1$. Give a specific example for the case of $n = 6$.

23–26. At the right, rhombi and rectangles are formed by connecting midpoints of each figure to get the next smaller figure. The original rectangle is 12 by 16.

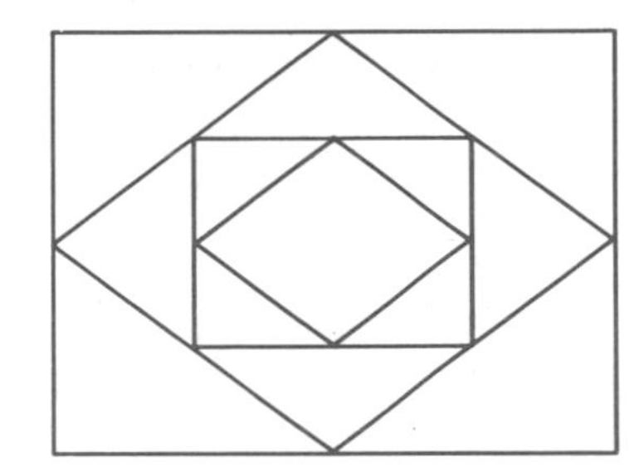

23. What is the sum of the perimeters of the first 10 rectangles formed? (Include the largest rectangle.)

24. What is the sum of the perimeters of the first 10 rhombi formed?

25. What is the sum of the areas of the first 20 rectangles and rhombi?

26. Into how many separate regions is the largest rectangle divided when the figure contains 100 rectangles and 100 rhombi?

27. Explain how the pattern at the right is related to one of the theorems of this section.

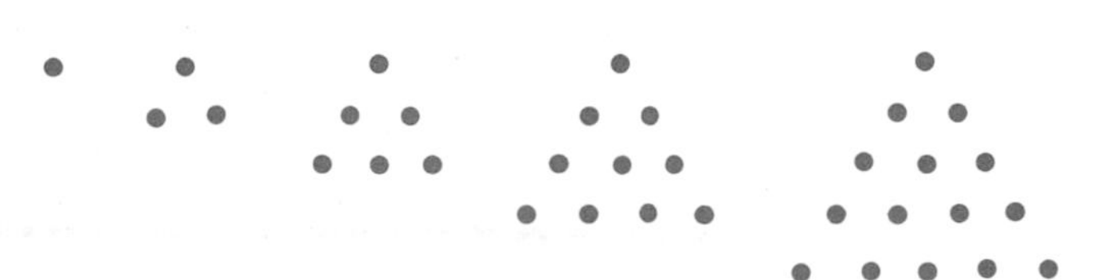

28. A ball is dropped from a height of 100 metres and bounces up to 90% of its height on each bounce. When it hits the ground for the 10th time, what is the total distance it has traveled?

29. Prove Theorem 17.4.2. (HINT: Refer to the method used for the special cases on page 542.)

30. Prove: The sum of the first n positive odd integers is n^2. (HINT: This is a corollary to Theorem 17.4.2.)

31. Find a formula for the sum S of the first n terms of an arithmetic sequence in terms of its first term A_1 and the constant difference d.

17.5 NOTATION FOR SUMS

Consider the linear sequence 8, 11, 14, $\cdots$. *Any* term of this sequence can be calculated from the formula $S_n = 3n + 5$.

The sum of the first 1000 terms of this sequence is

$$8 + 11 + 14 + \cdots + 3005.$$

We would like a shorthand notation for such sums. The Greek capital letter $\sum$ (for sum) is used for this purpose.

"The sum of the numbers $3n + 5$ for integral values of n from $n = 1$ to $n = 1000$"

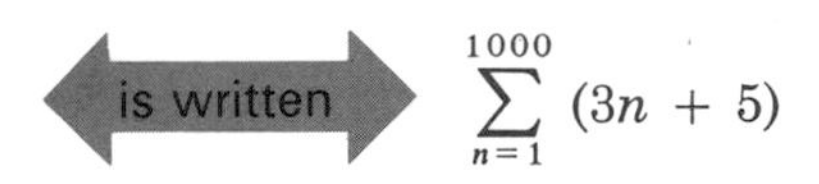

$$\sum_{n=1}^{1000} (3n + 5)$$

In other words,

$$\sum_{n=1}^{1000} (3n + 5) = 8 + 11 + 14 + \cdots + 3005.$$

The variable n is called an *index variable.* In this book, index variables will have *only* integral values. Here is an example with i as an index variable. (In this case, i is *not* the complex number $\sqrt{-1}$.)

$\sum_{i=5}^{11} 2^i$ **is shorthand for** "The sum of the numbers 2^i for integral values of i from $i = 5$ to $i = 11$"

That is, $\sum_{i=5}^{11} 2^i = 32 + 64 + 128 + 256 + 512 + 1024 + 2048.$

Each of the theorems of the last section can be restated using $\sum$ notation. Notice that i is used as the index variable to avoid confusion with the variable n. Compare these restatements with the original statements.

Theorem 17.4.1 (restatement)

$$\sum_{i=1}^{n} i = \tfrac{1}{2}n(n + 1)$$

(Remember the index variable takes on *only integral values.*)

Theorem 17.4.2 (restatement)

If A is an arithmetic sequence, then $\sum_{i=1}^{n} A_i = \tfrac{1}{2}n(A_1 + A_n)$.

Theorem 17.4.3 (restatement)

If G is a geometric sequence with ratio r, then

$$\sum_{i=1}^{n} G_i = G_1 \frac{(1 - r^n)}{1 - r}.$$

EXERCISES 17.5

Ⓐ **1.** Multiple choice: $2 + 4 + 6 + 8 + 10 + 12 + 14 =$

a. $\sum_{i=2}^{14} 2i$ **b.** $\sum_{i=2}^{14} i$ **c.** $\sum_{i=1}^{7} 2i$

2. Multiple choice: $\sum_{i=1}^{3} (3i + 2) =$

a. $5 + 8 + 11$ **b.** $3 + 5 + 7$ **c.** $4 + 5 + 6$

3. Multiple choice: $\sum_{i=4}^{8} 2^i =$

a. $4 + 8$ **b.** $16 + 32 + 64 + 128 + 256$

c. $2 + 3$ **d.** $16 + 256$ **e.** none of these

4. Multiple choice: $\sum_{i=4}^{6} (2i + 3) =$

a. 15 **b.** 26 **c.** 30 **d.** 39

5. In the symbolism $\sum_{n=2}^{8} 6n$, n is called the ____.

6. How many terms are to be added in $\sum_{n=5}^{11} n^2$?

7–8. Abbreviate each statement using $\sum$ notation. The sum of:

7. the numbers $2 - 8i$ for integral values of i from 1 to 50.

8. the numbers 5^n for integral values of n from 3 to 7.

Ⓑ **9–21.** What number does each expression represent?

9. $\sum_{n=1}^{4} 3^n$ **10.** $\sum_{i=0}^{5} 6i$ **11.** $\sum_{k=1}^{10} k$ **12.** $\sum_{i=3}^{6} (4i - 5)$

13. $\sum_{n=0}^{3} \sin(n\pi)$ **14.** $\sum_{i=1}^{8} \frac{i}{2}$ **15.** $\sum_{n=1}^{100} (2n + 1)$ **16.** $\sum_{k=1}^{20} (\frac{1}{2}k - \frac{3}{2})$

17. $\sum_{i=1}^{40} (10 - 6i)$ **18.** $\sum_{i=1}^{6} (3 \cdot 2^i)$ **19.** $\sum_{k=3}^{11} 4^{k-1}$ **20.** $\sum_{n=1}^{20} 5(\frac{1}{3})^n$

21. $\sum_{n=1}^{15} S_n$, where $S_n = 7n$

22–24. Suppose $S_1 = 30$, $S_2 = 50$, $S_3 = 40$, $S_4 = 40$, and $S_5 = 70$. (Do not look for a pattern.) Calculate.

22. $\sum_{i=1}^{3} S_i$ **23.** $\sum_{i=1}^{5} (S_i)^2$ **24.** $\left(\sum_{i=1}^{5} S_i\right)^2$

25–27. Repeat Exercises **22–24** for $S_1 = 6$, $S_2 = 9$, $S_3 = -2$, $S_4 = -5$, and $S_5 = 0$.

28–30. Translate each statement into mathematical notation using $\sum$. Then evaluate your result for $n = 3$.

28. The sum of the squares of the integers from 1 to n is

$$\frac{n(n+1)(2n+1)}{6}.$$

29. The sum of the cubes of the integers from 1 to n is the square of the sum of the integers from 1 to n.

30. The sum of the reciprocals of the integers from 1 to 2^n is greater than or equal to $\frac{n}{2} + 1$.

© **31–33.** What number does each expression represent?

31. $\sum_{i=2}^{7} a_i$, where $a_i = 10(1.01)^{i-1}$

32. $\sum_{k=1}^{10} (2^k - 2k)$

33. $3\left(\sum_{i=1}^{100} 3i - \sum_{i=1}^{100} i\right)$

34. Calculate $\sum_{i=1}^{n} 10^{-i}$ for $n = 1$, $n = 2$, $n = 3$, and $n = 4$. What number does this sum approach as n gets larger and larger?

35–36. Write each expression without using $\sum$ or factorial notation.

35. $\sum_{n=1}^{5} \left(\frac{x^n}{n!}\right)$

36. $\sum_{r=0}^{2} \left(\frac{n!}{r!(n-r)!} a^{n-r} b^r\right)$

17.6 SUMS OF INFINITE SEQUENCES

In the sequence 1, 2, 4, 8, 16, 32, $\cdots$ the three dots mean that the sequence is *infinite*. But what does "infinite" mean? In this case, it means that for *any* positive integer you might think of, no matter how large, there is a corresponding term of the sequence. There is a tenth term, a millionth term, a 432,986,310th term, and so on.

Now suppose + signs are put between terms of this sequence.

$$1 + 2 + 4 + 8 + 16 + 32 + \cdots$$

Is a number represented by this "infinite sum"? To answer this question, we form a sequence, S, of *partial sums*. (They are sums of parts of the sequence.) Let S_n be the sum of the first n terms.

S_n				Partial sums
S_1	$=$	1	$=$	1
S_2	$=$	$1 + 2$	$=$	3
S_3	$=$	$1 + 2 + 4$	$=$	7
S_4	$=$	$1 + 2 + 4 + 8$	$=$	15
$\vdots$		$\vdots$		$\vdots$

As n gets larger, if S_n gets closer and closer to some number, say L, then we write

$S_n \to L$ which is read "S_n approaches L as a *limit*."

If there is such a number (or limit), that number, L, is called the *sum of the infinite sequence*. You can see that the partial sums of the above sequence, S, do *not* get closer to some number. The terms of this sequence keep on increasing, and for any number you might mention, there is a term which is larger.

Some sequences of partial sums do have limits. Consider the infinite exponential sequence

$$\frac{6}{10}, \frac{6}{100}, \frac{6}{1000}, \frac{6}{10{,}000}, \cdots.$$

Here is the sequence, T, of partial sums.

$$T_1 = \frac{6}{10} = 0.6$$

$$T_2 = \frac{6}{10} + \frac{6}{100} = 0.66$$

$$T_3 = \frac{6}{10} + \frac{6}{100} + \frac{6}{1000} = 0.666$$

$$T_4 = \frac{6}{10} + \frac{6}{100} + \frac{6}{1000} + \frac{6}{10{,}000} = 0.6666$$

$$\vdots$$

As n gets larger, T_n approaches $\frac{2}{3}$ as a limit. That is,

$$T_n \to \frac{2}{3}.$$

We write $\frac{2}{3} = \frac{6}{10} + \frac{6}{100} + \frac{6}{1000} + \frac{6}{10{,}000} + \cdots.$

You are accustomed to seeing this as an infinite decimal.

$$\frac{2}{3} = 0.6666\cdots$$

Even though you have seen many infinite decimals before, you may not have thought of them as infinite sums.

The examples just considered involved exponential sequences. In the sequence $1 + 2 + 4 + \cdots$ there was no limit. In $\frac{6}{10} + \frac{6}{100} + \frac{6}{1000} + \cdots$ there was a limit. When does an exponential sequence have a limit? From Theorem 17.4.3, we know that

$$G_1 + G_1 r + \cdots + G_1 r^{n-1} = G_1 \cdot \frac{1 - r^n}{1 - r} = \frac{G_1}{1 - r}(1 - r^n).$$

This is the sum of the first n terms of the infinite exponential sequence G with ratio r. When $|r| < 1$, r^n gets smaller and smaller as n gets larger. That is, if r is between -1 and 1, then

as n gets larger, $\quad r^n \to 0$

So, $\quad (1 - r^n) \to 1$

Multiplying, $\quad \frac{G_1}{1 - r}(1 - r^n) \to \frac{G_1}{1 - r}$

This informally demonstrates the next theorem. (A formal proof would require more advanced mathematics.)

Theorem 17.6.1

If $|r| < 1$, the sum of *all* terms of the infinite exponential (geometric) sequence G with ratio r is $\frac{G_1}{1 - r}$.

Examples: Applications of Theorem 17.6.1

1. In the exponential sequence 0.6, 0.06, 0.006, $\cdots$, the ratio is $\frac{1}{10}$ and the first term is $\frac{6}{10}$. So the sum of all terms is

$$\frac{G_1}{1 - r} = \frac{\frac{6}{10}}{1 - \frac{1}{10}} = \frac{\frac{6}{10}}{\frac{9}{10}} = \frac{2}{3}.$$

← This agrees with the result on page 549.

2. A fraction for any infinite repeating decimal can be found. For example,

$$8.521212121\cdots$$
$$= 8.5 + 0.021212121\cdots$$
$$= 8.5 + 0.021 + 0.00021 + 0.0000021 + \cdots$$

← This part is an exponential sequence. So Theorem 17.6.1 applies.

$$= 8.5 + \frac{0.021}{1 - 0.01}$$
$$= 8.5 + \frac{0.021}{0.99} = \frac{85}{10} + \frac{21}{990} = \frac{1406}{165}$$

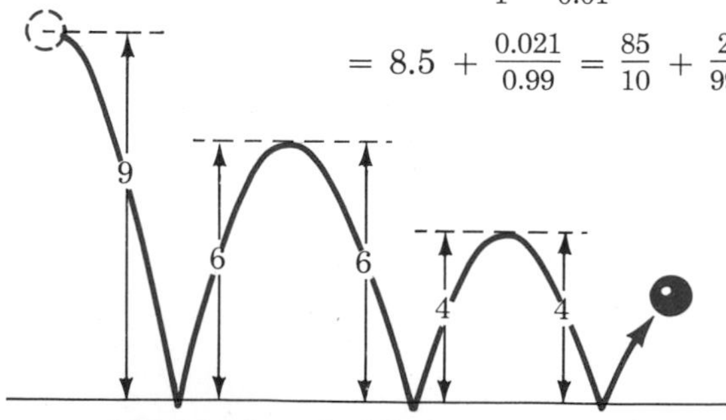

The numbers in black represent *vertical* distances traveled.

3. A ball is dropped from a height of 9 metres. On each bounce it rebounds to $\frac{2}{3}$ of its previous height. If it is allowed to bounce *until it stops*, how far will the ball have traveled?

SOLUTION:

$$\text{Distance falling} = 9 + 6 + 4 + \tfrac{8}{3} + \cdots = \frac{9}{1 - \frac{2}{3}} = 27$$

$$\text{Distance rising} = 6 + 4 + \tfrac{8}{3} + \tfrac{16}{9} + \cdots = \frac{6}{1 - \frac{2}{3}} = 18$$

$$\text{Total distance} = 27 + 18 = 45.$$

EXERCISES 17.6

Ⓐ **1–3.** Each infinite decimal given below can be considered to be the sum of an infinite exponential sequence. Give the terms of such a sequence.

1. $0.7777\cdots$ **2.** $0.252525\cdots$ **3.** $0.0198198198\cdots$

4–7. Give the sum of each infinite exponential sequence.

4. first term: G_1
common ratio: r

5. first term: 6
common ratio: $\frac{1}{3}$

6. $1, 0.5, 0.25, 0.125, \cdots$

7. $0.6, 0.06, 0.006, 0.0006, \cdots$

8. Give an example of an exponential sequence whose sum is not a real number.

9. Does the exponential sequence $1, -2, 4, -8, 16, \cdots$ have a sum?

10. An infinite exponential sequence has a _____ if the common ratio, r, satisfies $|r| < 1$.

Ⓑ **11–16.** Give a fraction in lowest terms for each repeating decimal.

11. $0.11111\cdots$ **12.** $0.454545\cdots$ **13.** $0.261261261\cdots$

14. $4.11111\cdots$ **15.** $0.0454545\cdots$ **16.** $2.000261261261\cdots$

17. Find a fraction for the repeating decimal $0.999\cdots$, and thus, find a number which can be represented by two different decimals.

18. Find a fraction for the repeating decimal $5.199999\cdots$. Find a second decimal for that fraction.

19–22. Give the sum of each infinite exponential sequence.

19. $1, -\frac{1}{2}, \frac{1}{4}, -\frac{1}{8}, \frac{1}{16}, \cdots$

20. $x, x^2, x^3, x^4, \cdots; |x| < 1$

21. $9, 8, \cdots$

22. $\frac{2}{3}, \frac{4}{9}, \frac{8}{27}, \frac{16}{81}, \cdots$

23. A ball is dropped from a height of 10 metres and rebounds to $\frac{3}{4}$ of its height. If the ball is allowed to bounce until it stops, how far will the ball have traveled?

24. Repeat Exercise **23** if the ball is dropped from 20 metres. Make a guess at the answer before you begin.

25. How has Exercise **23** been idealized from the real situation?

26–27. Use the drawing at the right. One side of equilateral triangle E_1 is divided into 3 congruent segments by A and B. $\overline{AB}$ is a side of equilateral triangle E_2. Suppose this process continues without end, forming an infinite sequence E, and suppose $AB = 1$.

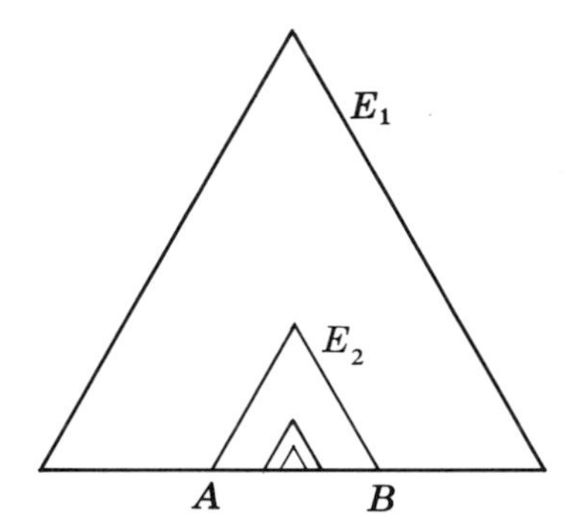

26. What is the sum of the perimeters of all triangles E_n?

© **27.** What is the sum of the areas of all triangles E_n?

28–30. Approximations to sines, cosines, logarithms, and similar numbers are often calculated by adding the first n terms of an infinite sequence. See the examples below. (∞ is the symbol for infinity.)

$$\ln(1 + x) = \sum_{n=1}^{\infty}\left[(-1)^{n+1}\frac{x^n}{n}\right] = x - \frac{x^2}{2} + \frac{x^3}{3} - \frac{x^4}{4} + \cdots$$

x is in radians here.

$$\sin x = \sum_{n=1}^{\infty}\left[(-1)^{n+1}\frac{x^{2n-1}}{(2n-1)!}\right] = x - \frac{x^3}{3!} + \frac{x^5}{5!} - \frac{x^7}{7!} + \cdots$$

$$\cos x = \sum_{n=1}^{\infty}\left[(-1)^{n+1}\frac{x^{2n-2}}{(2n-2)!}\right] = 1 - \frac{x^2}{2!} + \frac{x^4}{4!} - \frac{x^6}{6!} + \cdots$$

For these exercises, a calculator will be helpful, if available. (Check your answers against the approximations given in tables.)

28. Approximate ln 2 to tenths.

29. Approximate sin 1 (radians) to hundredths.

30. Approximate cos 1 (radians) to hundredths.

Ten top students in a school take a College-Board exam and receive the scores shown at the right.

Suppose you wished to describe these scores quickly. One way is to calculate a single number which in some way describes the entire set of scores.

Three common numbers used for this purpose are the *mean*, the *median*, and the *mode*.

College-Board Scores for Ten Students

Set I
750
742
736
725
725
690
662
660
650
640

Definitions

Let S be a sequence of n numbers. Then, the

mean of S = the *average* of all terms of S = $\dfrac{\sum_{i=1}^{n} S_i}{n}$.

median of S = the *middle* term of S when the terms are placed in increasing order.

mode of S = the number which occurs most often in the sequence.

For the given College-Board scores, the *mean* score is $\frac{6980}{10} = 698$. The *median* is considered to be halfway between the two middle scores, 690 and 725. So it is 707.5. The *mode* is the most common score, 725.

The mean, median, and mode are called *measures of central tendency*, because they are intended to give a number which in some sense is at the "center" of the sequence.

The *mean* is most often used when the terms of the sequence are fairly closely grouped, as in finding bowling averages.

The *median* is used when there are a few low or high terms which could greatly affect the mean, as with personal incomes.

The *mode* is particularly useful when many of the terms are the results of rounding, as often occurs when recording the ages of people.

These three measures of central tendency are examples of *statistical measures*.

Definition

A **statistical measure** is a single number which is used to describe an entire set of numbers.

Here is a second set of numbers which might be the College-Board scores of ten students in a different school.

Look back at the previous set of scores. Which set of scores do you think is better?

Actually, the mean, median, and mode are identical to those in the first set. But, these scores are more widely dispersed than the scores given earlier.

College-Board Scores for Ten Students

Set II	
800	
792	
786	
725	
725	725 = mode
690	707.5 = median
662	698 = mean
610	
600	
590	

One statistical measure of *dispersion* is standard deviation.

Definition

Let S be a sequence of n numbers. Let m be the *mean* of S. Then the **standard deviation** of S is

$$\sqrt{\frac{\sum_{i=1}^{n}(S_i - m)^2}{n}}.$$

Finding a Standard Deviation

From the definition, we see that the *standard deviation* of a sequence S can be found as follows:

1. calculate the mean of S,
2. subtract the mean from each term of S,
3. square these differences,
4. add up the squares,
5. divide the sum by n (the number of terms), and
6. find the square root of this quotient.

When this is done for the two sets of College-Board scores, we get:

standard deviation of set **I** $= \sqrt{\frac{16014}{10}} = \sqrt{1601.4} \doteq 40.0$

standard deviation of set **II** $= \sqrt{\frac{58814}{10}} = \sqrt{5881.4} \doteq 76.7$

Notice that the larger the standard deviation, the more widely dispersed are the scores. Although hard to calculate by hand, standard deviations are easily calculated by machines and are very widely used.

The four measures mentioned in this section—*mean*, *median*, *mode*, and *standard deviation*—are by no means the only *statistical measures* in common use. There are many others.

Statistics is a large and relatively new branch of mathematics. It has well-known applications in the social, biological, and physical sciences. In fact, statistical methods have even been used to determine authorship of unsigned writings and to analyze languages.

Although you probably know that statistics can be, and have been, used to distort information and mislead people, the wide use of statistical methods indicates the confidence which people have in statistics which are properly used and interpreted.

EXERCISES 17.7

Ⓐ **1–3.** Consider the sequence 1, 2, 3, 4, 5, 7, 7, 7. Find the:

1. mean. **2.** median. **3.** mode.

4–6. Repeat Exercises **1–3** for the sequence 11, 28, 15, 40.

7. How can you calculate the standard deviation of a sequence?

8. Calculate the mean and standard deviation of 30, 40, 40, 40, 50.

9. Calculate the mean and standard deviation of 20, 30, 40, 50, 60.

10. Why should you expect the standard deviation in Exercise **9** to be larger than that in Exercise **8**?

11. What is a statistical measure?

12. Name two measures of central tendency.

13. Name a measure of dispersion.

Ⓑ **14.** What measure of central tendency is calculated in finding a bowling average?

15. Why is *median income* often considered a better measure of the wealth of a community than *mean income*?

16. The mean of 30 scores is 87. For 40 other scores the mean is 80. Find the mean for all 70 scores.

17–22. For each set of scores, find the (**a**) mean, (**b**) median, (**c**) mode, and (**d**) standard deviation.

17. 10, 12, 12, 12, 14, 15, 17, 20

18. 31, 82, 46, 11, 29, 50, 59, 22, 59, 71

19. 72, 90, 86, 94, 100, 68, 98, 89, 71

20. 1, 7, 21, 35, 35, 21, 7, 1

21. 1, 2, 4, 8, 16, 32, 64, 128, 256, 512

22. 15, 17, 19, 21, 23, 25, 27, 29, 31, 33, 35, 37, 39, 41, 43, 45

© **23–25.** What happens to the value of the (**a**) mean, (**b**) median, (**c**) mode, and (**d**) standard deviation of a set of scores under each change?

23. Each score is multiplied by 100.

24. 14 is subtracted from each score.

25. Each score is multiplied by k, and b is added to the product.

26. Find a set of 2 numbers with mean 50 and standard deviation 10.

27. Find a set of 5 numbers with mean 50 and standard deviation 10.

17.8 PASCAL'S TRIANGLE

Very often an idea from one part of mathematics has applications to another part of mathematics. The triangular array at the top of page 557 is such an idea. (The top element of the array is called *row* 0 because this is convenient in applications of the array.)

This array first appeared in 1544 in the work of Michael Stifel, a German mathematician. But the array is known as *Pascal's triangle*, named after Blaise Pascal (1623–1662), the French mathematician and philosopher who discovered many properties relating the elements (numbers) in the array.

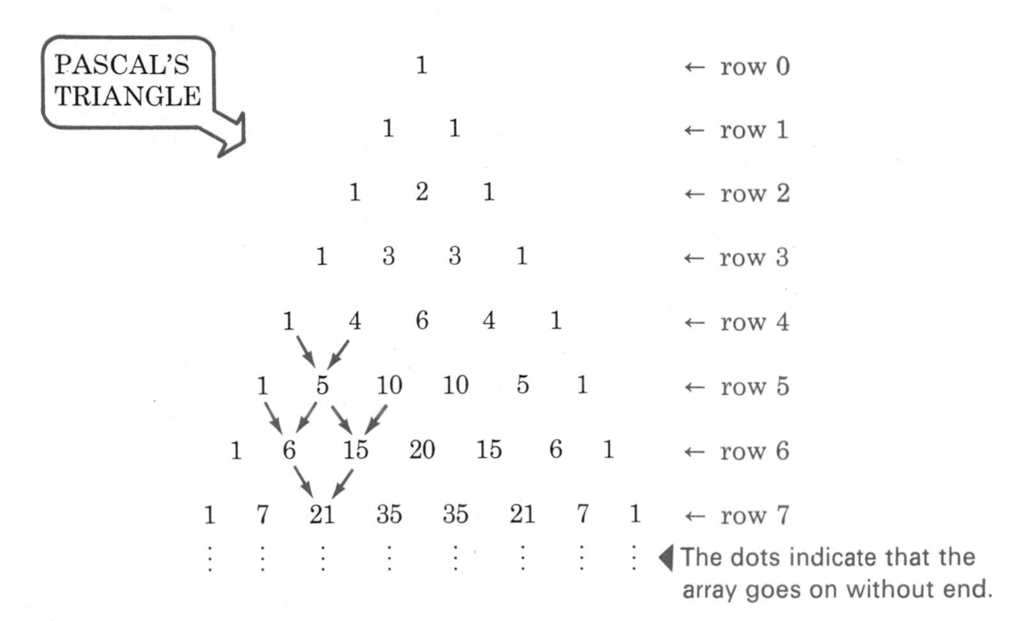

Pascal's triangle is formed in a very simple way. If x and y are located next to each other on a row, the element just below and directly between them is $x + y$ as illustrated below.

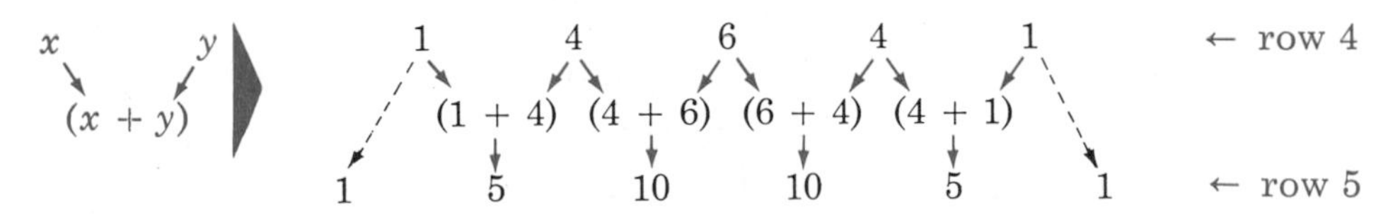

This is also shown by the red arrows between rows 4 and 7 of the triangle above. All other elements in the array follow the same pattern.

You can think of Pascal's triangle as a *two-dimensional sequence*. Each element is determined by *a row* and its position in that row. We use a standard symbol to indicate these elements.

Definition

The $(r + 1)$st element in the nth row of Pascal's triangle is denoted by $\binom{n}{r}$.

For example, the 7th row consists of the following elements.

$$\binom{7}{0} \quad \binom{7}{1} \quad \binom{7}{2} \quad \binom{7}{3} \quad \binom{7}{4} \quad \binom{7}{5} \quad \binom{7}{6} \quad \binom{7}{7}$$

That is, $\binom{7}{0} = 1$, $\binom{7}{1} = 7$, $\binom{7}{2} = 21$, and so forth. We found these values by referring to row 7 as it was given above. The top row has one element $\binom{0}{0}$.

The method of construction of Pascal's triangle lends itself to a recursive definition of the triangle. Since the triangle is a two-dimensional sequence, the recursive rule involves two variables.

Definition

Pascal's triangle is the two-dimensional sequence with

(1) $$\binom{n}{0} = \binom{n}{n} = 1$$

(2) $$\binom{n+1}{r+1} = \binom{n}{r} + \binom{n}{r+1}$$

where n and r are any integers with $0 \leq r \leq n$.

Formula **1** in the definition gives the "sides" of the triangle. Formula **2** is a symbolic way of stating that adding two adjacent elements in one row gives an element in the next row.

Using the definition, in order to determine the elements in the 14th row of the triangle, you would have to construct the first 13 rows.

The next theorem was first proved by Isaac Newton and shows how to calculate $\binom{n}{r}$ without constructing the triangle. The theorem is a surprising application of factorials and requires that we define,

definition of zero factorial 

$$\boxed{0! = 1.}$$

Theorem 17.8.1

$$\binom{n}{r} = \frac{n!}{r!(n-r)!}$$

Before proving this theorem, we give some examples of its use.

Examples: Calculating $\binom{n}{r}$

1. $$\binom{4}{2} = \frac{4!}{2!(4-2)!} = \frac{4 \cdot 3 \cdot 2 \cdot 1}{2 \cdot 1(2 \cdot 1)} = 6$$

This agrees with $\binom{4}{2}$ being the 3rd element in the 4th row of the triangle.

2. $$\binom{11}{3} = \frac{11!}{3!(11-3)!} = \frac{11 \cdot 10 \cdot 9 \cdot 8 \cdot 7 \cdot 6 \cdot 5 \cdot 4 \cdot 3 \cdot 2 \cdot 1}{3 \cdot 2 \cdot 1 \cdot 8 \cdot 7 \cdot 6 \cdot 5 \cdot 4 \cdot 3 \cdot 2 \cdot 1} = 165$$

Notice how easily the fraction can be simplified because of the common factors.

3. $$\binom{7}{0} = \frac{7!}{0!(7-0)!} = \frac{7!}{1 \cdot 7!} = 1$$

PROOF OF THEOREM 17.8.1:

All we have to do is to show that the factorial formula given in Theorem 17.8.1 satisfies the two relationships which define Pascal's triangle.

1. **(a)** $\dfrac{n!}{0!(n-0)!} = \dfrac{n!}{0!n!} = \dfrac{n!}{1 \cdot n!} = 1$, so $\dfrac{n!}{0!(n-0)!} = \dbinom{n}{0}$.

(b) $\dfrac{n!}{n!(n-n)!} = \dfrac{n!}{n!0!} = \dfrac{n!}{n!(1)} = 1$, so $\dfrac{n!}{n!(n-n)!} = \dbinom{n}{n}$.

Thus the formula works for the "sides" of Pascal's triangle.

2. In the "middle" of the triangle, the formula will stand for $\dbinom{n}{r}$ if it satisfies $\dbinom{n+1}{r+1} = \dbinom{n}{r} + \dbinom{n}{r+1}$. So we add the possible formulas for $\dbinom{n}{r}$ and $\dbinom{n}{r+1}$.

$$\frac{n!}{r!(n-r)!} + \frac{n!}{(r+1)!(n-r-1)!}$$

$$= \frac{n!(r+1)}{(r+1)!(n-r)!} + \frac{n!(n-r)}{(r+1)!(n-r)!}$$

$$= \frac{n!(r+1+n-r)}{(r+1)!(n-r)!}$$

$$= \frac{(n+1)!}{(r+1)!(n-r)!}$$

This is the factorial expression for $\dbinom{n+1}{r+1}$ as required.

Important applications of Pascal's triangle are given in the remaining sections of this chapter.

EXERCISES 17.8

Ⓐ **1.** Write down rows 0 through 7 of Pascal's triangle.

2. What are the rules by which Pascal's triangle is defined?

3. Write down rows 8 through 10 of Pascal's triangle. (It is a good idea to keep rows 0 through 10 handy for reference.)

4. The symbol $\dbinom{n}{r}$ denotes what element in which row of Pascal's triangle?

5–14. Calculate.

5. $\binom{n}{r}$ 6. $\binom{8}{2}$ 7. $\binom{7}{4}$ 8. $\binom{3}{2}$ 9. $\binom{10}{5}$

10. $0!$ 11. $\binom{6}{6}$ 12. $\binom{15}{0}$ 13. $\binom{15}{14}$ 14. $\binom{20}{2}$

Ⓑ **15.** If $\binom{10}{5} + \binom{10}{6} = \binom{x}{y}$, then $x =$ ____ and $y =$ ____.

16. If $\binom{9}{2} + \binom{a}{b} = \binom{10}{2}$, then $a =$ ____ and $b =$ ____.

17. True or False? $\binom{99}{17}$ is an integer.

18. True or False? $\frac{n!}{(n-2)!}$ is always an integer when $n \geq 2$.

19. If $10 \cdot 9! = x!$, then $x =$ ____.

20. If $(n - r)(n - r - 1)! = y!$, then $y =$ ____.

21. What symmetry is possessed by Pascal's triangle?

Ⓒ **22–27.** Properties of elements in Pascal's triangle are many, and new ones are still being discovered. Give at least 4 examples which illustrate each property described below.

22. The sum of the elements in row n is 2^n.

23. The third element in the nth row is the sum of the integers from 1 to $n - 1$.

24. If $-$ and $+$ signs are alternated between elements in any row (except row 1), the sum of the elements in the row is 0.

25. The sum of the squares of all elements in row n is the middle element in some row of the triangle.

26. Prove $\binom{n}{r} = \binom{n}{n-r}$. What does this equality imply about Pascal's triangle?

27. Find the mean and standard deviation of all numbers in the 8th row of Pascal's triangle.

THE BINOMIAL THEOREM

A well-known exponential sequence has first term 1 and the binomial $a + b$ as its constant ratio.

$$1, a + b, (a + b)^2, (a + b)^3, (a + b)^4, \cdots$$

The powers of $(a + b)$ can be written as polynomials—sums of products of powers of a and b. The results are known as *binomial power expansions.*

$$(a + b)^0 = 1$$

$$(a + b)^1 = a + b$$

$$(a + b)^2 = (a + b)(a + b) = a^2 + 2ab + b^2$$

$$(a + b)^3 = (a + b)(a^2 + 2ab + b^2) = a^3 + 3a^2b + 3ab^2 + b^3$$

$$(a + b)^4 = (a + b)(a^3 + 3a^2b + 3ab^2 + b^3) = a^4 + 4a^3b + 6a^2b^2 + 4ab^3 + b^4$$

$$\vdots \qquad\qquad \vdots \qquad\qquad \vdots$$

Looking at the expansions (in red), it looks like there is no pattern. But if the a's and b's are ignored, and only the coefficients are written, then Pascal's triangle appears!

Powers of $(a + b)$	Pascal's triangle	Row
$(a + b)^0$	1	0
$(a + b)^1$	1 1	1
$(a + b)^2$	1 2 1	2
$(a + b)^3$	1 3 3 1	3
$(a + b)^4$	1 4 6 4 1	4
$\vdots$	$\vdots$ $\vdots$ $\vdots$ $\vdots$ $\vdots$	$\vdots$

Now, look back at the binomial power expansions. We can write these expansions using the $\binom{n}{r}$ symbolism.

$$(a + b)^0 = \binom{0}{0}$$

$$(a + b)^1 = \binom{1}{0} a + \binom{1}{1} b$$

$$(a + b)^2 = \binom{2}{0} a^2 + \binom{2}{1} ab + \binom{2}{2} b^2$$

$$(a + b)^3 = \binom{3}{0} a^3 + \binom{3}{1} a^2b + \binom{3}{2} ab^2 + \binom{3}{3} b^3$$

$$(a + b)^4 = \binom{4}{0} a^4 + \binom{4}{1} a^3b + \binom{4}{2} a^2b^2 + \binom{4}{3} ab^3 + \binom{4}{4} b^4$$

$$\vdots \qquad\qquad \vdots$$

We can now make some additional observations about the expansion of $(a + b)^n$:

(1) In each term, the exponents of a and b add to n.

(2) If the power of b is r, then the coefficient of the term is $\binom{n}{r}$.

(3) All the powers of a from a^n to a^0 occur in order.

This information is summarized in a famous theorem.

Theorem 17.9.1

Binomial theorem: The $(r + 1)$st term in the expansion of $(a + b)^n$ is $\binom{n}{r} a^{n-r}b^r$. The sum of all these terms is $(a + b)^n$. That is,

$$(a + b)^n = \sum_{r=0}^{n} \binom{n}{r} a^{n-r}b^r.$$

PROOF: A formal proof requires a knowledge of mathematical induction, a powerful proof technique not discussed in this book. You are asked to verify the theorem for some special cases in the exercises.

The binomial theorem can be used to expand powers of *any* binomial.

Examples:

1. To expand $(5x - 2y)^3$, think of $5x$ as a, $-2y$ as b.

$$(a + b)^3 = \binom{3}{0} a^3 + \binom{3}{1} a^2b + \binom{3}{2} ab^2 + \binom{3}{3} b^3$$

Substituting,

$$(5x - 2y)^3 = 1(5x)^3 + 3(5x)^2(-2y) + 3(5x)(-2y)^2 + 1(-2y)^3$$
$$= 125x^3 - 150x^2y + 60xy^2 - 8y^3$$

2. To expand $(x^2 + 1)^4$, think of x^2 as a, 1 as b.

$(x^2 + 1)^4$

$$= \binom{4}{0}(x^2)^4 + \binom{4}{1}(x^2)^3 \cdot 1 + \binom{4}{2}(x^2)^2 \cdot 1^2 + \binom{4}{3}(x^2)^1 \cdot 1^3 + \binom{4}{4} \cdot 1^4$$
$$= x^8 + 4x^6 + 6x^4 + 4x^2 + 1$$

You can check these results by letting $x = 2$ and $y = 3$, or by using some other small numbers. Note that linear sequences are formed by the exponents of each variable in each expansion.

Due to their use in the binomial theorem, the numbers in Pascal's triangle are known as *binomial coefficients.* The binomial theorem has a surprising number of applications in estimations, counting problems, probability, and statistics. One statistical application is discussed in the next section.

EXERCISES 17.9

Ⓐ **1.** What are the binomial coefficients?

2. Tell how the powers of $a + b$ are related to Pascal's triangle.

3–6. Expand each binomial power.

3. $(a + b)^2$ **4.** $(a + b)^3$ **5.** $(a + b)^4$ **6.** $(a + b)^5$

7–10. In the expansion of $(a + b)^7$, give the coefficient of:

7. a^6b **8.** a^4b^3 **9.** ab^6 **10.** b^7

11. State the binomial theorem.

Ⓑ **12–19.** Expand each binomial power.

12. $(a - b)^3$ **13.** $(x + 1)^5$ **14.** $(2 - m)^4$ **15.** $(x + y)^6$

16. $(3x + y)^3$ **17.** $(a - 2b)^4$ **18.** $(v - 3)^5$ **19.** $(p + q)^{10}$

20. Verify the binomial expansion for $(a + b)^4$ by squaring $a^2 + 2ab + b^2$.

21. Multiply the binomial expansion for $(a + b)^4$ by $a + b$ to check the expansion for $(a + b)^5$.

Ⓒ **22.** Calculate 11, 11^2, 11^3, 11^4, 11^5, and 11^6. Tell how these powers are related to the binomial coefficients.

23–24. Convert to an expression in the form $(a + b)^n$.

23. $\sum_{r=0}^{n} \binom{n}{r} x^{n-r}3^r$ **24.** $\sum_{i=0}^{n} \binom{n}{i} y^{n-i}(2a)^i$

25. Use the binomial theorem to quickly approximate $(1.002)^{10}$ to the nearest hundredth. (HINT: $1.002 = 1 + 0.002$)

26. Repeat Exercise **25** for $(1.005)^8$.

17.10 COUNTING SUBSETS

The set $\{a, b, c\}$ has the following subsets.

$\{\ \}$	$\{a\}\ \{b\}\ \{c\}$	$\{a, b\}\ \{b, c\}\ \{a, c\}$	$\{a, b, c\}$
1 with 0 elements	3 with 1 element	3 with 2 elements	1 with 3 elements

Again, notice that the numbers from Pascal's triangle appear (in red).

The next theorem generalizes the results just observed.

Theorem 17.10.1

The number of subsets of r elements which can be formed from a set of n elements is $\binom{n}{r}$.

PROOF: The proof consists of showing that the numbers of subsets satisfy the same relationships as those which define the Pascal triangle. A new symbol is helpful.

Let ${}_nC_r$ be the number of subsets of r elements from a set of n elements.

1. If a set has n elements, there is one subset with 0 elements (the null set) and one subset with n elements (the set itself).

   Thus, $\quad {}_nC_0 = 1 = \binom{n}{0}$ and ${}_nC_n = 1 = \binom{n}{n}$.

2. Now ${}_{n+1}C_{r+1}$ is the number of subsets with $r + 1$ elements from a set S which contains $n + 1$ elements. Suppose the $(n + 1)$st element of S is x. Then,

   ${}_{n+1}C_{r+1}$ = (the number of subsets of S containing x) + (the number of subsets of S not containing x)

   = (the number of subsets containing r elements from the other n elements of S) + (the number of subsets containing $r + 1$ elements from the other n elements of S)

   $= {}_nC_r + {}_nC_{r+1}$

3. Thus ${}_nC_r$ satisfies the defining relationships of $\binom{n}{r}$. So we conclude that ${}_nC_r = \binom{n}{r}$.

For example, a set with 10 elements has $\binom{10}{3}$ or 120 subsets with exactly 3 elements.

The symbol $_nC_r$, which was introduced as an aid in the proof of Theorem 17.10.1, is actually often used in place of $\binom{n}{r}$. In proving the theorem, we showed that $_nC_r$ represents the number of ways in which r elements can be chosen from n given elements.

Using Theorem 17.10.1, we can conclude that the *total* number of subsets of a set with n elements is

$$_nC_0 + {}_nC_1 + {}_nC_2 + \cdots + {}_nC_n.$$

$$\binom{n}{0} + \binom{n}{1} + \binom{n}{2} + \cdots + \binom{n}{n} = \sum_{i=0}^{n} \binom{n}{i}$$

$$= \sum_{i=0}^{n} \binom{n}{i} 1^i 1^{n-i}$$ ← We can do this because $1^x = 1$ for any x.

$$= (1 + 1)^n$$ ← By the binomial theorem with $a = 1$ and $b = 1$

$$= 2^n$$

When $n = 3$, $2^n = 8$. This agrees with the example at the top of page 564.

Theorem 17.10.2

A set with n elements has 2^n subsets.

EXERCISES 17.10

Ⓐ **1–4.** If a set has 6 elements, how many subsets contain:

1. 0 elements? **2.** 2 elements? **3.** 4 elements? **4.** 5 elements?

5–8. Repeat Exercises **1–4** for a set having 8 elements.

9–12. How many subsets does a set with the given number of elements have?

9. 5 **10.** 6 **11.** 1 **12.** 10

13. The symbol $_nC_r$ is another way of writing _____.

Ⓑ **14–16.** List all the subsets of each given set.

14. $\{x, y\}$ **15.** $\{1, 2, 3, 4\}$ **16.** $\{a, b, 1, 2, 3\}$

17. A set S has n elements, one of which is the number 4. How many subsets of S do not contain 4?

18. In the set $\{a, b, c, d, e\}$, how many 3-element subsets contain the element d? How many do not contain d?

17.11 PROBABILITY

Suppose a hat contains 10 slips of paper numbered 1 through 10. As an experiment, you pick a slip blindfolded. The *probability* of getting the slip numbered 6 is $\frac{1}{10}$.

This means that if the experiment is repeated *many* times, you could expect the event "getting the 6" to occur $\frac{1}{10}$ of the times (over the long run). The probability of getting an even-numbered slip is $\frac{5}{10}$ (because there are 5 even-numbered slips).

Definition

If a situation has a total of t equally likely possibilities and e of these possibilities satisfy conditions for a particular event, then

$$\textbf{probability} \text{ of that event } = \frac{e}{t}.$$

Probabilities are often easy to calculate. Here is an example which does not seem so easy. However, ideas from earlier sections will help.

Suppose you take a 5-question, True-False test on a subject you know *nothing* about, so you guess. If a question is as likely to be true as false, and you need 75% to pass, what is your probability of passing?

The equally likely possibilities are the ways you could answer the questions, R (for right) and W (for wrong). For example, $RRRRW$ would mean that you had the first 4 questions right, the last one wrong. There are 32 such possibilities.

RRRRR	RWRRR	WRRRR	WWRRR
RRRRW	RWRRW	WRRRW	WWRRW
RRRWR	RWRWR	WRRWR	WWRWR
RRRWW	RWRWW	WRRWW	WWRWW
RRWRR	RWWRR	WRWRR	WWWRR
RRWRW	RWWRW	WRWRW	WWWRW
RRWWR	RWWWR	WRWWR	WWWWR
RRWWW	RWWWW	WRWWW	WWWWW

Counting gives the following information.

1 possibility has 0 R's
5 possibilities have 1 R
10 possibilities have 2 R's
10 possibilities have 3 R's
5 possibilities have 4 R's
1 possibility has 5 R's

Number correct	Probability
0	$\frac{1}{32}$
1	$\frac{5}{32}$
2	$\frac{10}{32}$
3	$\frac{10}{32}$
4	$\frac{5}{32}$
5	$\frac{1}{32}$

Notice that there are 6 possibilities with 4 R's or 5 R's. These would be passing. Since there are 32 possibilities in all, the *probability of passing* is

$$\tfrac{6}{32} \quad \text{or about} \quad 0.19.$$

In a True-False test, the same situation—choosing T or F—occurs again and again. Each such choosing is called a *trial.* The numbers in Pascal's triangle always occur when calculating probabilities involving repeated trials, each of which has two equally likely outcomes.

Combining Theorems 17.10.1, 17.10.2, and the definition of probability, we get a very useful theorem.

Theorem 17.11.1

If a situation consists of n trials with the same two equally likely outcomes for each trial, then the probability of one of these outcomes occurring exactly r times is

$$\frac{\binom{n}{r}}{2^n}.$$

For example, let each trial be the tossing of a fair coin. Then the expression in the theorem denotes the probability of getting r heads in n tosses. If the coin is tossed 4 times, there are 2^4 possible ways of getting H (heads) and T (tails).

HHHH	HTHH	THHH	(TTHH)
HHHT	(HTHT)	(THHT)	TTHT
HHTH	(HTTH)	(THTH)	TTTH
(HHTT)	HTTT	THTT	TTTT

Of these, $\binom{4}{2}$, or 6, have 2 H's. They are circled. In these 6 ways, the 2 H's are shown in all possible positions they could have. (These positions correspond to all possible 2-element subsets of a 4-element set.) This verifies that the probability of getting 2 heads in 4 tosses of a fair coin is

$$\frac{\binom{4}{2}}{2^4} \quad \text{or} \quad \tfrac{6}{16}.$$

EXERCISES 17.11

Ⓐ **1–4.** How many different arrangements of H's and T's could occur if a coin is tossed:

1. 4 times? **2.** 2 times? **3.** 5 times? **4.** 10 times?

5–8. If you toss a coin 4 times, in how many ways could you get:

5. 0 heads? **6.** 1 head? **7.** 2 heads? **8.** 3 heads?

9–12. Repeat Exercises **5–8** for 5 tosses of the coin.

13. What is meant by the *probability* of an event?

14–15. If a fair coin is tossed twice, give the probability of:

14. 2 heads. **15.** 1 head, 1 tail.

16. If a set contains n elements and a subset is chosen at random, what is the probability that the subset has r elements?

17–20. On a True-False exam in which answers are randomly guessed, what is the probability of:

17. 5 correct out of 5? **18.** 8 correct out of 10?

Ⓑ **19.** passing a 6-question exam if 4 right are required to pass?

20. failing a 7-question exam if 5 right are required to pass?

21–22. Give the probabilities of getting exactly (**a**) 0, (**b**) 1, (**c**) 2, and (**d**) 3 tails in:

21. 3 tosses of a coin. **22.** 10 tosses of a coin.

23. Give the probabilities of getting exactly $0, 1, 2, \cdots, 8$ heads in 8 tosses of a fair coin.

24–27. Slips of paper, numbered from 1 to 24, are tossed into a hat. One slip is picked at random. Give the probability that its number:

24. is divisible by 2. **25.** is divisible by 5.

26. is prime. **27.** satisfies $3x + 2 > 11$.

28–31. A card is picked at random from a deck of 52 cards. Give the probability that the card is:

28. the ace of spades. **29.** a king, a queen, or a jack.

30. a ten or a heart. **31.** a red card or an ace.

Ⓒ **32.** How would you expect Theorem 17.11.1 to be modified if there were 3 equally likely outcomes for each trial?

33. Find the probability of passing a 10-question, True-False quiz if 70% is passing and answers are guessed randomly.

If a fair coin is tossed 5 times, we can graph the probabilities of getting 0, 1, 2, 3, 4, or 5 heads. (These values are the same as those given in the table on page 566 for the True-False test.)

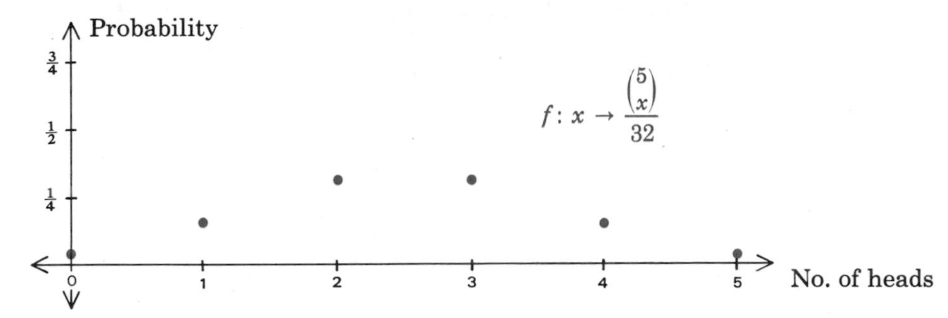

If the fair coin is tossed 10 times, the possible numbers of heads are 0, 1, 2, $\cdots$, 10, so there are 11 points in the graph of corresponding probabilities. The individual probabilities are all less than $\frac{1}{4}$ and are listed below the graph.

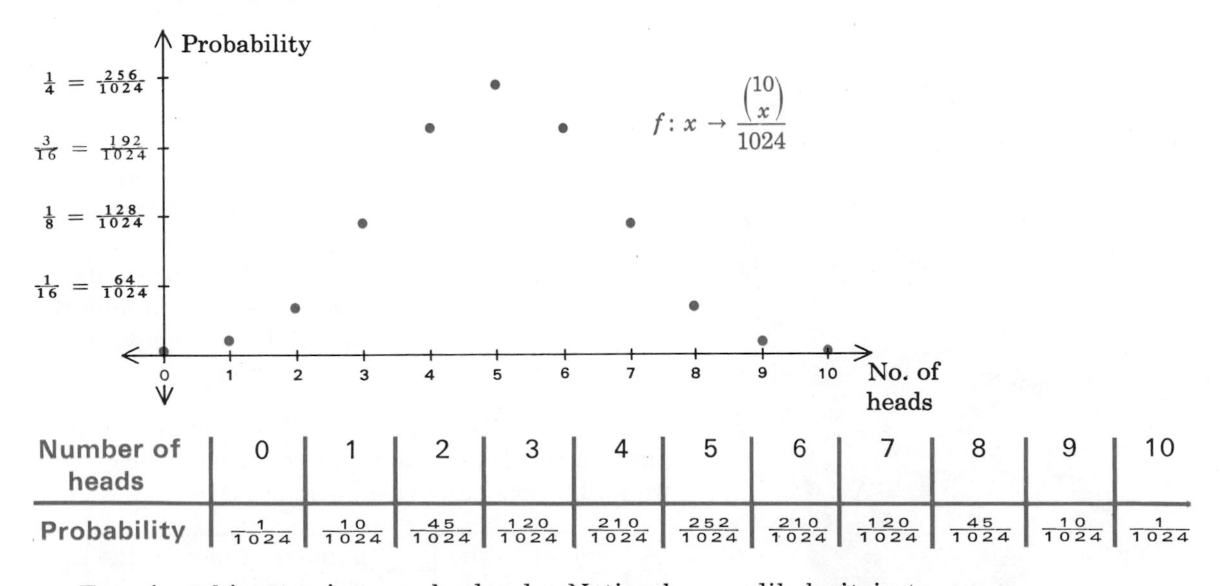

Number of heads	0	1	2	3	4	5	6	7	8	9	10
Probability	$\frac{1}{1024}$	$\frac{10}{1024}$	$\frac{45}{1024}$	$\frac{120}{1024}$	$\frac{210}{1024}$	$\frac{252}{1024}$	$\frac{210}{1024}$	$\frac{120}{1024}$	$\frac{45}{1024}$	$\frac{10}{1024}$	$\frac{1}{1024}$

Examine this 11-point graph closely. Notice how unlikely it is to get no heads or 10 heads in a row (the probability for each is less than $\frac{1}{1000}$). Even for 9 heads in 10 tosses the probability is less than $\frac{1}{100}$. The number 1024 is 2^{10} and the probability of x heads is

$$\frac{\binom{10}{x}}{1024},$$

as given by Theorem 17.11.1. The 11 probabilities are easy to calculate because the numerators in the fractions are the numbers in the 10th row of Pascal's triangle. That is, they are binomial coefficients. For this reason, the functions being graphed are called *binomial density functions.*

There are not enough points in the first (6-point) graph to see any pattern emerging. But the points of the 11-point binomial distribution could be connected by a fairly smooth curve. As the number of tosses is increased, lower rows in Pascal's triangle will correspond to the probabilities, and the points more closely outline a bell-shaped curve.

Here is the bell-shaped curve in the position where its equation is simplest—symmetric to the y-axis with y-intercept $\frac{1}{\sqrt{2\pi}}$.

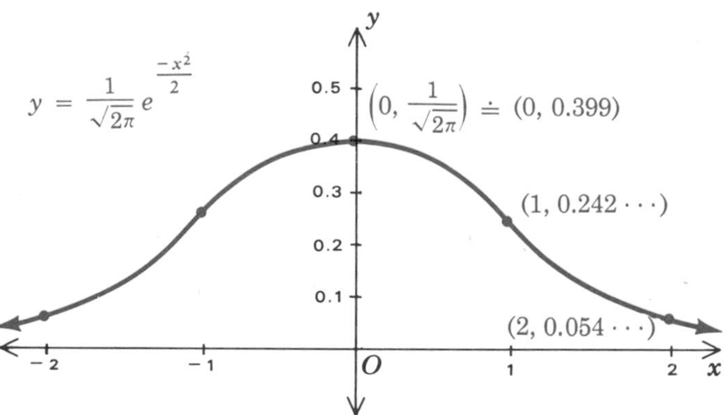

The function which determines this graph is called a *normal density function,* and the curve is called a *normal curve.* Notice that its equation, shown on the graph, involves the famous constants $e \doteq 2.718$ and $\pi \doteq 3.14$. Every normal curve is the image of the above graph under a composite of translations or scale transformations.

Normal curves are models for many natural phenomena. The graph of the correspondence below would be very close to a normal curve.

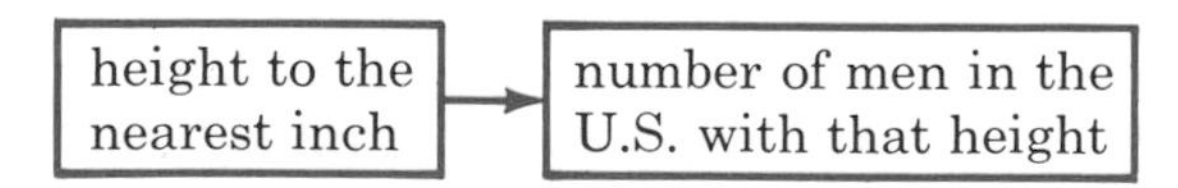

The curve would have its highest point around 5′ 10″ or 5′ 11″.

Normal curves are often good mathematical models for the distribution of scores on an exam. The graph at the top of the next page shows an actual distribution of scores on a 40-question test given by the author to 209 geometry students. (It was a hard test.) A possible corresponding normal curve is shown in black dashes.

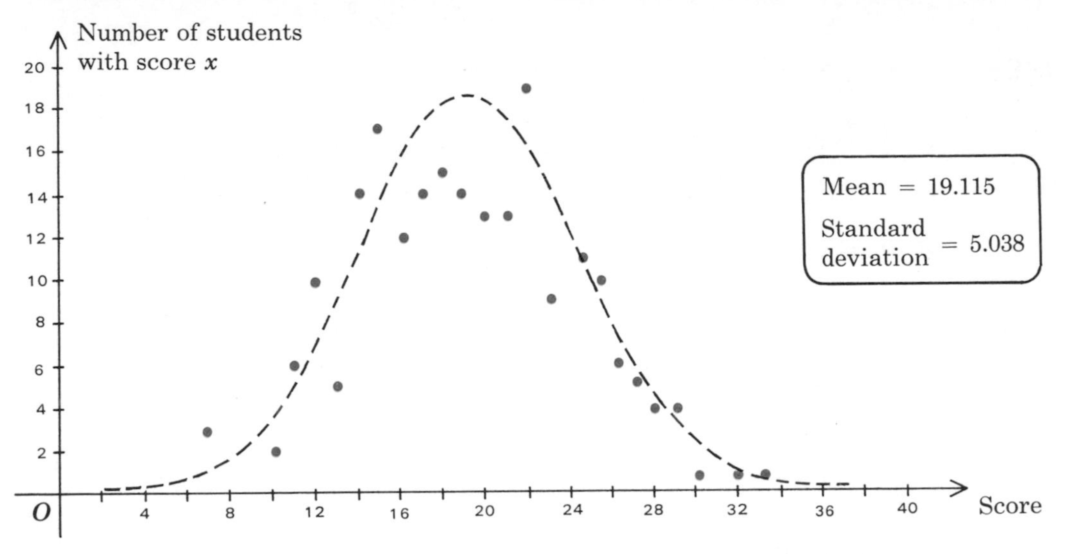

For other tests, the scores are *standardized* or *normalized*. This means that a person's score is not the number of correct answers, but some score chosen so that the distribution of scores is a normal curve.

College-Board scores are standardized so that the mean is 500 and the standard deviation is 100. Many IQ tests are normalized so that the mean IQ is 100 and the standard deviation is 15. One advantage of normalizing scores is that you need to know no other scores to know how a person's score compares with the scores of others.

The next graph shows percentages of scores in certain intervals of a normal distribution with mean m and standard deviation s. (An appropriate equation is also given.) Each percentage gives the probability of scoring in a particular interval. Actual values for endpoints of these intervals are given below the graph for particular applications.

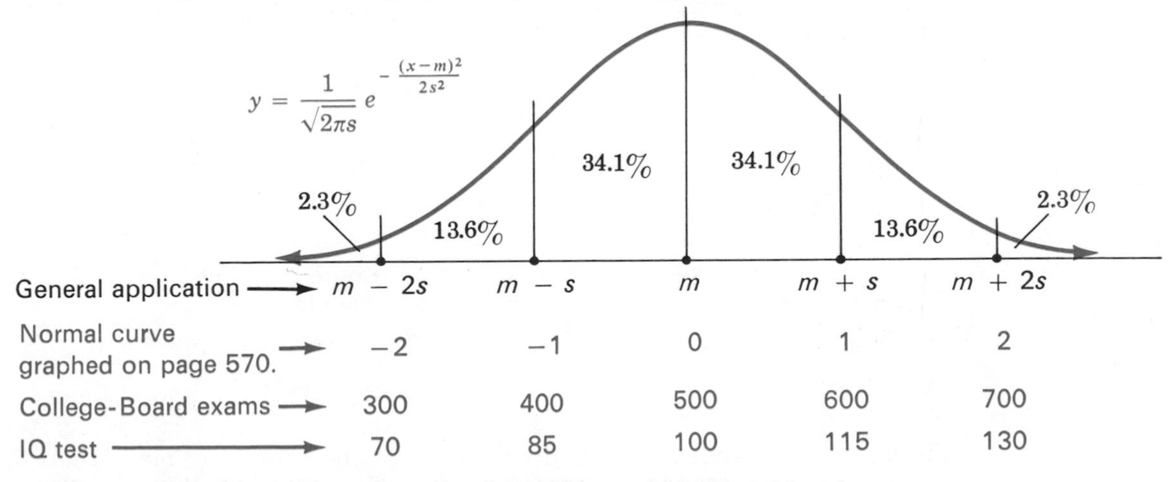

The graph indicates that about 34.1% of IQ's are between 100 and 115. Other information may be similarly read from the graph.

EXERCISES 17.12

Ⓐ **1.** How is a probability function formed?

2. Give an equation for a *normal curve.*

3. Give one application in which normal curves are used.

4–7. If a fair coin is tossed 10 times, give the probability of getting:

4. more than 7 heads.

5. exactly 5 heads.

6. no heads.

7. all heads.

8–11. Approximately what percentage of people score lower than you on a normal curve if you:

8. score 500 on a College-Board exam?

9. score 700 on a College-Board exam?

10. have an IQ of 115?

11. have an IQ of 70?

12. What is the mean and standard deviation on IQ scores?

13. What does it mean when scores are normalized? Standardized?

14. Give one advantage of standardizing scores.

Ⓑ **15.** Construct the graph of the binomial density function related to tossing a fair coin 6 times.

16–17. Give an equation (with the proper values of *m* and *s*) for the normal curve which describes a distribution for:

16. IQ scores.

17. College-Board scores.

18. Name five points on the graph of $\{(x, y): y = \frac{1}{\sqrt{2\pi}} e^{\frac{-x^2}{2}}\}$. (HINT: Three points are given in this section.)

19–22. Some exam scores were standardized to have a mean of 50 and a standard deviation of 10. What percentage of people scored:

19. between 40 and 50?

20. between 50 and 70?

21. over 50?

22. under 30?

Ⓒ **23.** In a normalized distribution, 0.2% of the scores lie more than 3 standard deviations away from the mean. This implies that 1 out of ____ people has an IQ over ____.

CHAPTER SUMMARY

A *sequence* is a 1–1 correspondence with a certain set of positive integers as the domain. A sequence may be described either by an *explicit rule* for the nth term or by a *recursive rule* which tells how to get any term from the previous terms.

Specific sequences include the *factorial* sequence and the *Fibonacci* sequence. We studied two common types of sequences. The *linear* (arithmetic) sequences are formed by adding a constant difference d:

$$A_1, A_1 + d, A_1 + 2d, \cdots, A_1 + (n-1)d, \cdots.$$

The *exponential* (geometric) sequences are formed by multiplying by a constant ratio r:

$$G_1, G_1r, G_1r^2, \cdots, G_1r^{n-1}, \cdots.$$

In each of these sequences the nth terms have the indicated formulas.

There are formulas for sums of finite linear sequences and for finite and infinite exponential sequences. The latter formulas are helpful in finding a fraction equal to an infinite repeating decimal. When discussing such sums, the following notation is useful.

$$\sum_{i=1}^{n} a_i = a_1 + a_2 + a_3 + \cdots + a_n$$

Pascal's triangle is one example of a *two-dimensional* sequence. The $(r+1)$st element in the nth row is denoted by $\binom{n}{r} = \frac{n!}{r!(n-r)!}$. $\binom{n}{r}$ is the coefficient of $a^{n-r}b^r$ in the binomial expansion of $(a+b)^n$ (see the binomial theorem). $\binom{n}{r}$ is also the number of subsets of r elements taken from a set of n elements—and $\binom{n}{r}$ is related to the probability of getting r heads in n tosses of a coin. Thus, Pascal's triangle is related to each theme of this chapter.

A *statistical measure* is a number which is used to describe a set of numbers. Measures of central tendency include the *mean*, *median*, and *mode*. *Standard deviation* is a measure of dispersion.

The graph of a distribution of scores often resembles the bell-shaped graph of values in Pascal's triangle, or the graph of probabilities related to these values. It is convenient to normalize or standardize scores based upon a knowledge of a curve called the *normal curve*.

CHAPTER REVIEW

17

1. Write the first 10 terms of the sequence described by $t_1 = 1$ and $t_{n+1} = 3t_n - 1$.

2. Tell whether each sequence is linear or exponential.

   a. $0, 4, 8, 12, \cdots$ **b.** $-1, 2, -4, 8, -16, \cdots$

   c. $-3, -1, 1, 3, \cdots$ **d.** $\frac{1}{3}, \frac{1}{15}, \frac{1}{75}, \frac{1}{375}, \cdots$

3. If $S_1 = 4$ and $S_{n+1} = \frac{1}{2}S_n^{\,2}$, give the first 5 terms of sequence S.

4. If $a_n = 3n - 1$, calculate $\sum_{i=1}^{20} a_i$.

5. Give a fraction in lowest terms for each repeating decimal.

a. $0.818181\cdots$ **b.** $3.916666\cdots$

6–7. For the linear sequence 11, 10, 9, 8, 7, $\cdots$,

6. give an *explicit* definition. **7.** give a *recursive* definition.

8. A painting was bought for \$200 and is expected to increase 10% in value each year. Give an expression which indicates how much the painting will be worth n years after it was bought.

9. Write all the elements in row 9 of Pascal's triangle.

10–11. Explain how the answer to Exercise **9** is related to:

10. a power of $(a + b)$. **11.** subsets of a set.

12–13. Consider the sequence 4, 8, 9, 10, 10.

12. Find the *median*, *mode*, and *mean*.

13. Find the *standard deviation*.

14–16. Calculate.

14. $\frac{8!}{5!}$ **15.** $\sum_{i=1}^{5} i!$ **16.** $\binom{8}{4}$

17. Expand $(x - 3y)^4$.

18. If a subset of $\{a, b, c, d\}$ is picked at random from all the subsets of this set, what is the probability that the subset contains exactly 3 elements?

19. Write an equation which describes a normal distribution for which the mean is 0 and the standard deviation is 1.

CUMULATIVE REVIEW: CHAPTERS 10–17

1–4. Give the absolute value of each complex number. **Ch. 10**

1. $(-4, 3)$ **2.** $(0, 5)$ **3.** $[\frac{1}{2}, 80°]$ **4.** $[-\sqrt{2}, 33\frac{1}{3}°]$

5. How many complex numbers have absolute value 5?

6–9. Add each pair of complex numbers.

6. $(-3, 2)$, $(3, 2)$ **7.** $(-2, 1)$, $(4, -6)$

8. (a, b), $(0, 0)$ **9.** $(\frac{3}{2}, -\frac{1}{2})$, $(-\frac{3}{2}, \frac{1}{2})$

10–13. In Exercises **6–9**, subtract the second number from the first.

14. Add (2, 3) to each vertex of the triangle $\begin{bmatrix} 2 & -3 & -1 \\ 2 & 0 & -2 \end{bmatrix}$. To what transformation does adding the complex number (2, 3) correspond?

15–18. Multiply the complex numbers in each pair.

15. $[4, 25°] \cdot [2, 5°]$ **16.** $[7, 200°] \cdot [1, 180°]$

17. $[\sqrt{3}, 160°] \cdot [-\sqrt{3}, -160°]$ **18.** $[r, \theta] \cdot [s, \phi]$

19. Graph the triangle with vertices $[3, 0°]$, $[4, 45°]$, and $[2, 90°]$. Multiply each vertex by $[2, 45°]$, and graph the image triangle. To what transformation does multiplying by $[2, 45°]$ correspond?

20–23. Multiply each pair of complex numbers in Exercises **6–9**.

24–27. Put in $a + bi$ form.

24. $(-2, 5)$ **25.** $[10, 30°]$ **26.** $[1, 90°]^4$ **27.** $\frac{1}{i}$

28–31. Compute and give the result in $a + bi$ form.

28. $(-6 + 2i) + (3 - i)$ **29.** $(-6 + 2i) - (3 - i)$

30. $(3 - 7i) \cdot (-2 + 3i)$ **31.** $\frac{1 + 3i}{4 - 2i}$

32–43. Simplify. **Ch. 11**

32. $\sqrt{-25}$ **33.** $\sqrt{-4} \cdot \sqrt{-9}$ **34.** $\sqrt{-18}$

35. $\sqrt{2} \cdot \sqrt{-2}$ **36.** $-\sqrt{-49}$ **37.** $(\sqrt{-3})^2$

38. $(2 - 3\sqrt{7})(2\sqrt{7} - 1)$ **39.** $(2 - \sqrt{3})^2$ **40.** $\sqrt{\frac{1}{2}}$

41. $\sqrt{180}$

42. $\frac{2}{\sqrt{5}}$

43. $\frac{5 - \sqrt{3}}{2 + \sqrt{3}}$

44–53. Find all solutions.

44. $x^2 = 9$

45. $x^2 = -9$

46. $x^2 = -3$

47. $\sqrt{x} - 3 = 0$

48. $(a + \frac{3}{2})^2 = 4$

49. $\sqrt{n - 2} = 3$

50. $-3x^2 + 4x + 2 = 0$

51. $4m^2 = 7m - 3$

52. $x^2 + 2x + 4 = 0$

53. $\sqrt{3}x^2 - 2x - \sqrt{3} = 0$

54. Find an equation for a parabola that is congruent to $y = x^2$ and has vertex (6, 5).

55. Find the vertex of the parabola $y = x^2 - 2x + 1$.

56. If $h = 24t - 16t^2$, find all values of t for which $h = 6$.

57–58. Solve each sentence and graph the solution set.

57. $-a^2 + 4a < 12$

58. $(2m - 3)(3m + 1) < 0$

Ch. 12

59–65. Graph the solution set to each sentence.

59. $\frac{x^2}{25} + \frac{y^2}{36} = 1$

60. $(x - 2)^2 + (y + 3)^2 = 4$

61. $16x^2 - 9y^2 = 144$

62. $y^2 - x^2 = 9$

63. $4x^2 + 9y^2 - 16x + 18y - 11 = 0$

64. $xy = 6$

65. $(x - 3)(y + 5) = 8$

66–67. Find all solutions to each system.

66. $y = 2x - 3$
$x^2 + y^2 = 5$

67. $2x^2 + y^2 = 22$
$3x^2 - 2y^2 = 19$

68–72. Let $E = \left\{(x, y): \frac{x^2}{9} + \frac{y^2}{4} = 1\right\}$. Find an equation for:

68. $r_{x\text{-axis}}(E)$.

69. $r_{x=y}(E)$.

70. $R_{90}(E)$.

71. $t(E)$ if $t(x, y) = (x + 2, y + 3)$.

72. $s(E)$ if $s(x, y) = (3x, 5y)$.

Ch. 13

73–77. Is the set a function? If not, list two ordered pairs to show why.

73. $\{(3, 3), (2, 2), (0, 0), (-1, -1)\}$

74. $\{(5, 7), (6, 8), (7, 8)\}$

75. $\{(2, 5), (2, 6), (3, 7)\}$

76. $\{(x, y): x^2 + y^2 = 1\}$

77. $\{(x, y): y = x^2 + 2x + 1\}$

78–80. A function has the given domain and the given rule or equation. Find the range of the function.

78. domain: $\{1, 2, 3, 4\}$ rule: $x \to 3x$

79. domain: $\{-1, 0, 1, \frac{3}{2}\}$ equation: $y = 2x - 1$

80. domain: set of reals rule: $x \to |x|$

81. Function f has sentence $y = \sqrt{x}$ and codomain the set of reals. What real numbers cannot possibly be in the domain of f?

82. Let $f(x) = x^2 - 2x$. Calculate: $f(0)$, $f(-1)$, $f(\frac{1}{2})$, and $f(i)$.

83–84. Given f and g, find $f \circ g(x)$.

83. $f: x \to x^2$; $g: x \to \sqrt{x}$

84. $f: x \to x^2 - 9$; $g: x \to 2x + 1$

85. Find an equation for the inverse of this function: $3x - 4y = 12$.

86. Give the maximum or minimum value (if any) of this function: $y = (x - 2)^2 + 5$.

87. If y varies inversely as x, and $y = 6$ when $x = 30$, find y when $x = -2$.

88–90. Given that the domain is the set of reals, graph each function.

88. $f(x) = x^2 - 2x$

89. $g: t \to |t + 2|$

90. $\begin{cases} y = x^2 \text{ if } x \geq 0 \\ y = -x^2 \text{ if } x < 0 \end{cases}$

91–102. Simplify.

Ch. 14

91. $\sqrt[3]{-1000}$

92. $\sqrt[5]{32x^5}$

93. $\sqrt{x^4}$

94. $(\sqrt{2})^4$

95. $-\sqrt[3]{-125}$

96. $-\sqrt[4]{16}$

97. $8^{\frac{2}{3}}$

98. $(\frac{4}{9})^{-\frac{1}{2}}$

99. $25^{-1.5}$

100. $\sqrt[3]{16} \cdot \sqrt[3]{4}$

101. $\sqrt{\frac{x^4}{y^8}}$

102. $\sqrt[7]{a^{-14}b^7}$

103–105. Solve.

103. $25^x = 5^{-\sqrt{2}}$

104. $x = \log_2 16$

105. $\log_{10} x = 3$

106. What property of powers corresponds to $\frac{1}{2}(\frac{1}{3}a) = \frac{1}{6}a$?

107–108. Give a relationship between a, b, and c when:

107. $\log a + \log b = \log c$.

108. $a \log b = \log c$.

109–114. Approximate using tables of logarithms.

109. $(0.0187)(523)$ **110.** $\frac{1675}{4.2}$ **111.** $(563)^{12}$

112. $\sqrt[3]{71}$ **113.** $\log_5 2$ **114.** $\ln 5$

115–117. Given $\ln 2 = 0.693$ and $\ln 3 = 1.099$, calculate.

115. $\ln 6$ **116.** $\ln 9$ **117.** $\ln \frac{2}{3}$

Ch. 15

118–121. Convert from radians to degrees or vice versa.

118. $\frac{\pi}{5}$ **119.** 60° **120.** $\frac{3}{4}\pi$ **121.** 30°

122–127. Calculate without using tables.

122. $\sin \frac{\pi}{4}$ **123.** $\cos \pi$ **124.** $\tan \frac{\pi}{6}$

125. $\cot \frac{2}{3}\pi$ **126.** $\sec \frac{\pi}{2}$ **127.** $\csc \frac{\pi}{3}$

Ex. 128

x 6 60° 8

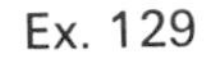

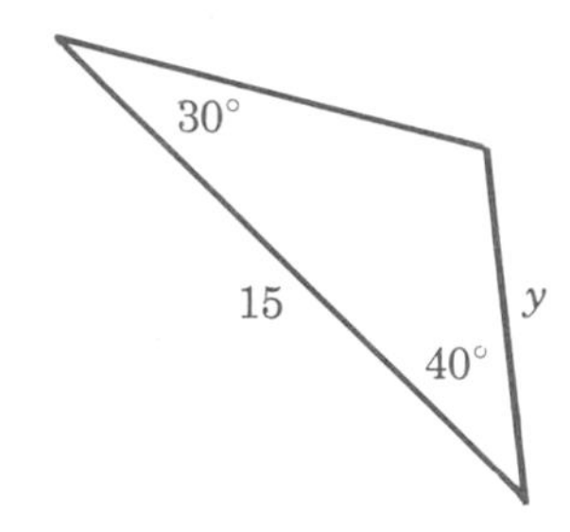

128. Use the law of cosines to calculate x. (Leave answer in radical form.)

129. Use the law of sines to calculate y to the nearest tenth.

130. In $\triangle ABC$, $m\angle C = \frac{\pi}{2}$, $m\angle B = 34^\circ$, and $AB = 50$. Find a to the nearest tenth.

131–134. Answer with one or more of the following functions: sin, cos, tan, cot, sec, csc.

131. Which functions have a fundamental period of π?

132. Which functions have a maximum value of 1?

133. What is the reciprocal function of cos?

134. Which functions are undefined at $\frac{\pi}{2}$?

Ch. 16

135–140. Factor.

135. $9x^2 - 25$ **136.** $x^3 + 64$ **137.** $p^{10} - 3p^8$

138. $5t^2 - 31t + 6$ **139.** $4a^2 + 8ab + 4b^2$ **140.** $ax^2 - 2ax + a$

141–146. Solve.

141. $(v + 1)(v - 3) = 0$ **142.** $4x^2 - 9 = 0$ **143.** $x^2 - 5x - 6 = 0$

144. $\frac{2}{x + 1} = x$ **145.** $\frac{6}{x^2 + 5} = \frac{1}{x}$ **146.** $3x^{-2} - 2x^{-1} = 5$

147. By the rational root theorem, what are the only possible rational roots of $n^3 - 2n^2 + n - 4 = 0$?

148. Divide $5x^3 - 18x^2 - 8x - 3$ by $x - 3$.

149–154. Simplify.

149. $\frac{y^2 - 9}{y^2 + 6y + 9}$ **150.** $\frac{\frac{x^2 - 1}{x}}{\frac{x - 1}{x^2}}$ **151.** $\frac{\frac{1}{a} - \frac{1}{b}}{\frac{1}{a} + \frac{1}{b}}$

152. $\frac{2x + 1}{2x + 2} \cdot \frac{x + 1}{4x^2 - 1}$ **153.** $\frac{3}{4x} + \frac{8}{5y}$ **154.** $\frac{4}{x - 1} - \frac{x + 2}{x - 1}$

155. How much water should be added to 10 grams of a 3% tincture of iodine solution to dilute it to a 2% solution?

156. $794 is received from the sale of 400 tickets, some at $1.75, the rest at $2.25. How many tickets were sold at $2.25?

157–160. Calculate.

Ch. 17

157. $5!$ **158.** $\frac{6!}{3!}$ **159.** $\sum_{n=1}^{5} (2n - 1)$ **160.** $\binom{8}{5}$

161. For the infinite geometric sequence $3, \frac{3}{2}, \frac{3}{4}, \cdots$, find the sum of the first n terms.

162. Find the sum of all the terms of the sequence of Exercise **161**.

163. Find the sum of the first 400 positive odd integers.

164. If $a_1 = 6$ and $a_{n+1} = \frac{1}{3}a_n$, give the first 4 terms of the sequence.

165. Expand $(2x + y)^5$.

166–169. Consider the sequence 3, 7, 8, 10, 10. Find the:

166. median. **167.** mode.

168. mean. **169.** standard deviation.

170. If a fair coin is tossed 8 times, what is the probability of **(a)** all heads; **(b)** 4 heads and 4 tails?

The representatives of seventy-two countries voted yes, and this was more than two thirds of the total.

Zastępcy z siedemdziesiąt-dwa kraj głosowali tak, i to było więcej niż dwa-trece od całkowitość.

I rappresentanti di settantadue paesi hanno votato si, e questo è stato fu più dei due terzi del totale.

$72 > \frac{2}{3}T$

Chapter 18 Summary—The Many Facets of Mathematics

Before you read further, you should look at the titles of the sections in this chapter. These titles indicate general facets or realms of mathematics. In each section there are many specific ideas which you have studied earlier. The purpose of this chapter is to review these ideas by placing them in a larger overall picture as indicated by the section titles.

MATHEMATICS AS A LANGUAGE

18.1

Mathematics has a written language, much like English or Spanish or any other language. Words in English are symbols which represent many things, such as actions, concepts, and descriptions. Symbols in mathematics correspond to words in English and stand for numbers, relations, and sets, among other things. It took you a long time to learn to read English. But there are words which you still do not know. So it is not surprising that it takes a long time to understand the symbols used in mathematics.

It is often necessary to translate from one language to another. Throughout this book, there have been problems stated in English. These were translated into mathematics so they could be solved more easily. Once a mathematical solution was found, it was often necessary to translate back into English.

In all languages, there are definitions of symbols and words in terms of other symbols and words. For example, the symbol $\sqrt{}$ is defined in terms of a simpler idea, the idea of multiplication. The phrase "sin x" is defined from an easier idea, the rotation. In mathematics these definitions are more precise than in many other languages.

English has its synonyms, words which mean virtually the same thing. Mathematics has its expressions which stand for the same number or concept. For example, if m and n are lines which intersect at a 45° angle, then $r_n \circ r_m$ is a synonym for R_{90} (or perhaps for R_{-90}). The word *is* can be translated as the symbol =, and we can write $r_n \circ r_m = R_{90}$.

The comparisons between English and mathematics could be continued further. Like English, mathematics has expressions, sentences, compound sentences, etc. In each language, difficult ideas can sometimes be represented by simple words or symbols. And so on. The exercises which follow emphasize translations, definitions of terms, and meanings of symbols. The symbol in parentheses following each exercise indicates the section(s) in which you can find the topic studied in more detail. (NOTE: Exercises are not labeled Ⓐ, Ⓑ, and Ⓒ.)

EXERCISES 18.1

1–5. Translate each symbol into English.

1. $\geq$ *(2.1)* **2.** $\sum_{i=1}^{n} a_i$ *(17.5)* **3.** $[x]$ *(13.8)*

4. $n!$ *(17.1)* **5.** $\sqrt[3]{}$ *(14.1)*

6–35. Give a definition of each term, using simpler terms.

6. reflection image of a point (*4.1*)
7. group (*9.1*)
8. transformation (*4.2*)
9. function (*13.1*)
10. relation (*6.1*)
11. variable (*6.1*)
12. $\cos x$ (*8.1*)
13. $\tan x$ (*15.7*)
14. ellipse (*12.2*)
15. rational number (*10.10*)
16. parabola (*11.7*)
17. $\log_B x$ (*14.10*)
18. circle (*6.3*)
19. linear programming problem (*7.5*)
20. polar coordinates of a point (*8.6*)
21. the cosecant of a number (*15.6*)
22. pure imaginary number (*10.5*)
23. constant (*6.1*)
24. solution to a system (*7.2*)
25. equivalent sentences (*1.1*)
26. rotation (*4.4*)
27. identity function (*5.5, 9.6, 13.4*)
28. size transformation (*4.8*)
29. slope of a line (*6.5*)
30. sequence of nested intervals (*2.7*)
31. congruent (*4.7*)
32. reflection-symmetric (*4.9*)
33. similar (*4.8*)
34. isometry (*4.6*)
35. isomorphic groups (*9.3*)

36–40. Translate each sentence into mathematics.

36. The distance a car travels varies directly as the average rate of the car. (*13.6*)
37. If two angles are supplementary, their sines are equal. (*15.3*)
38. On a number line, the distance between x and 2 is greater than 5. (*3.4*)
39. The product of two numbers is 6, and the second number is 6 less than the first. (*3.6*)
40. The composite of two reflections over parallel lines is a translation. (*4.6*)

41–48. State the named theorem, property, etc.

41. FOIL theorem *(2.5)* **42.** nested interval property *(2.7)*

43. law of sines *(15.5)* **44.** law of cosines *(15.4)*

45. matrix-transformation isomorphism theorem *(5.5)*

46. distributive property *(1.6)* **47.** binomial theorem *(17.9)*

48. quadratic formula *(11.5)*

49–73. Each expression stands for a number. If the number is real, rewrite it in the language of decimal notation. If the number is imaginary, rewrite the number in $a + bi$ language. Approximate if necessary.

49. -3^0 *(1.7)* **50.** $4.6 \cdot 10^{-3}$ *(1.7)* **51.** $(\frac{1}{2})^{-3}$ *(1.7)*

52. $\sum_{i=1}^{100} i$ *(17.4, 17.5)* **53.** $\sqrt{-5}$ *(11.1)* **54.** $10^{2.469}$ *(14.6)*

55. $\sin 461°$ *(8.3)* **56.** $\sin \frac{5\pi}{4}$ *(15.1)* **57.** $2^{3.5}$ *(14.8)*

58. $\log 0.00502$ *(14.6)* **59.** $\log_3 6$ *(14.10)* **60.** $-\sqrt{9} + 4$ *(1.8)*

61. $\frac{4}{\sqrt{2} + 1}$ *(11.2)* **62.** $\frac{3}{i} + 2$ *(10.7)* **63.** $\frac{5 - 4i}{3 + 2i}$ *(10.7)*

64. antilog 6.3 *(14.7)* **65.** $\sqrt{15{,}000}$ *(1.8)* **66.** $\sqrt{\frac{9}{2}} + \sqrt{\frac{25}{2}}$ *(11.2)*

67. $|-4| - |-3|$ *(3.3)* **68.** $[-4.6]$ *(13.8)* **69.** $\sqrt[3]{729}$ *(14.1)*

70. $[4, 70°] \cdot [2, 35°]$ *(10.3)* **71.** $(3 - i)^2$ *(10.7)*

72. $(4.6 \cdot 10^{-9})(3.1 \cdot 10^{-6})$ *(1.7)* **73.** $(-3)^{-1} - (-4)^{-1}$ *(1.7)*

74. How does the meaning of the word *impossible* differ in mathematics from its usual use? *(10.8)*

75. Translate $[3, 160°]$ into rectangular coordinates. *(8.7)*

76. Translate 160° into radians. *(15.1)*

77. Write $3.12121212 \cdots$ as a fraction in lowest terms. *(17.6)*

78. What is a real number? *(1.9)*

79. Which does not refer to the same complex number? *(8.6, 10.1, 10.5)*

a. $[-1, 90°]$ **b.** $-i$ **c.** $(0, -1)$ **d.** -1 **e.** $[1, 270°]$

80. Name the three types of figures formed by the intersection of a plane with a right circular cone. *(12.1)*

18.2 MATHEMATICS AS A LANGUAGE (continued)

In any language, people normally want to express themselves in as simple a way as possible. This is done by simplifying and rewriting expressions and sentences.

Mathematical expressions which are easy to work with in one situation may be difficult in another. So various techniques are necessary: factoring, simplifying fractional expressions, working with powers of the same number, completing the square, and so on. But the idea is the same: *to find an expression which gives the same values as the original expression and in which these values are "easier" to calculate.*

Expressions are the "nouns" in mathematics, and the symbols $=$, $\doteq$, $>$, $\cong$, $\sim$, etc., are the "verbs." Placing verbs between nouns yields sentences. There are a great variety of sentences: linear, quadratic, polynomial, those with more than one variable, formulas, equalities and inequalities, those involving functions, etc. Again the idea is the same: *to find a sentence which has the same solutions as the original sentence and in which these solutions are "easier" to find.* We often graph solution sets to get a picture—a different view—of what is going on.

Simplified expressions and sentences are said to be *equivalent* to their originals. Finding equivalent expressions or sentences comprises what is called *manipulative mathematics.* Many people think that manipulating symbols is all there is to mathematics. The exercises here review these ideas, but the next sections show other facets of mathematics.

EXERCISES 18.2

1. What is meant by "solving a sentence"? *(1.1)*

2–18. Solve each sentence.

2. $9 - x = 8 - 2(x - 4)$ *(2.3)*

3. $(2t + 1)^2 = 5$ *(11.4)*

4. $\frac{1}{y + 1} = \frac{2}{2y + 3}$ *(2.3)*

5. $\frac{m}{3} - 4m \leq 2m - \frac{m}{6}$ *(2.3)*

6. $3E^2 - 4E - 2 < 2$ *(11.8)*

7. $ax^2 + bx = c$ (Solve for x.) *(11.5)*

8. $\frac{3}{5}t = \sqrt{t + 4}$ *(11.3)*

9. $|3E| - 2 \geq 0$ *(7.1)*

10. $\frac{9}{1 - A} + \frac{6}{2 - A} = 11$ *(16.6)*

11. $P = \sqrt{\frac{2\pi}{t}}$ (Solve for t.) *(11.3)*

12. $2x - 6 < \frac{4}{3} < 2x + 6$ *(2.3)*

13. $3x - 8y = 6$ (Solve for y.) *(2.4)*

14. $\begin{bmatrix} a^2 & a \\ 4 & 6 \end{bmatrix} \cdot \begin{bmatrix} 2 \\ 3 \end{bmatrix} = \begin{bmatrix} 9 \\ 26 \end{bmatrix}$ *(5.2, 11.5)*

15. $10^x = 4$ *(14.6)*

16. $30^Y = 14$ *(14.9)*

17. $\log_2 u = 8$ *(14.10)*

18. $V^9 = 462$ *(14.8)*

19–24. Graph the solution set to each sentence on a number line.

19. $-4t < -2$ *(2.6)*

20. $-y = |y|$ *(7.1)*

21. $\sin x = 0$ *(15.2)*

22. $v^2 = v + 1$ *(11.5)*

23. $\tan x = 1$ *(15.7)*

24. $|11 - d| > \frac{2}{3}$ *(3.4)*

25–30. List or graph all solutions to each system.

25. $\begin{aligned} 3x + 5y &= 2 \\ x - y &= 9 \end{aligned}$ *(7.3)*

26. $\begin{aligned} a^2 - b^2 &= 9 \\ ab &= 4 \end{aligned}$ *(12.10)*

27. $\begin{bmatrix} 9 & -2 \\ 4 & -1 \end{bmatrix} \cdot \begin{bmatrix} v \\ w \end{bmatrix} = \begin{bmatrix} 11 \\ 2 \end{bmatrix}$ *(9.5)*

28. $\begin{aligned} \frac{3x - 3}{y} &= 2 \\ 4y &= 6x + 3 \end{aligned}$ *(7.3)*

29. $\begin{aligned} y &= 5x \\ x^2 + y^2 &= 25 \end{aligned}$ *(12.10)*

30. $\begin{aligned} a + 2b - 3c &= 11 \\ 3a - b + 2c &= 8 \\ a + 4b - 6c &= -6 \end{aligned}$ *(7.4)*

31. Find all rational roots of $3v^3 - v^2 - 64v + 80 = 0$. *(16.2)*

32–35. Factor each expression.

32. $9x^2 + 18x$ *(16.1)*

33. $77 - 8a + 4a^2$ *(16.1)*

34. $64y^6 - x^6$ *(16.3)*

35. $2ab^2 - 4b^2 + 3ab - 6b$ *(16.1)*

36–39. Write each expression as a single simple fraction.

36. $\frac{4}{2 + \sqrt{3}} - \frac{4}{2 - \sqrt{3}}$ *(16.5)*

37. $\frac{2}{x^2 + 2x - 3} - \frac{2}{x^2 + 5x + 6}$ *(16.5)*

38. $\frac{ab^2}{3m^2n} \cdot \frac{b^{-3}n^2}{6m^4a^9}$ *(16.5)*

39. $\dfrac{\frac{1}{x^2} + \frac{2}{x^3} + \frac{1}{x^4}}{(x + 1)^2}$ *(16.4)*

40–44. Simplify.

40. $4x - 9y - (x - y + 12) - 2x(3 + y) - (4 - x)(3 + 2y)$ *(1.6, 2.5)*

41. $(x^1)^2 + (x^0)^1 + (x^{-1})^0 + (x^2)^1 + (x^1)^0 + (x^0)^{-1}$ *(9.3)*

42. $-3^2 + 2 \cdot 7$ *(1.5)*

43. $\left(\frac{a}{b} + \frac{b}{a}\right) \div (a^2 + b^2)$ *(16.4, 16.5)*

44. $\sum_{i=1}^{100} (3i + 1)$ *(17.4)*

45. If $3x^2 - 4x + 2 = a(x - h)^2 + k$, find a, h, and k. *(11.4)*

46–47. Write as one matrix if possible.

46. $\begin{bmatrix} -3 & 1 & 2 \\ 4 & 1 & 2 \end{bmatrix} \cdot \begin{bmatrix} 6 \\ 3 \\ -1 \end{bmatrix}$ *(5.2)*

47. $\begin{bmatrix} 2 & 4 & 6 \\ 6 & -9 & 1 \end{bmatrix} \cdot \begin{bmatrix} 1 & 0 \\ -3 & 2 \end{bmatrix}$ *(5.2)*

48. If $\tan x = 0.394$, approximate $\sin x$. *(15.8)*

49. Expand $(x + 2y)^4$. *(17.9)*

50. If $z^2 = -2$, graph z in the complex plane. *(10.1)*

51. Divide $2x^4 + 6x^3 - 11x^2 + 4x - 3$ by $x + 3$. *(16.3)*

52. For this system, name the solution for which $x + 3y$ is largest: $2x + y \leq 5$; $x \geq 0$; $y \geq 0$; $x + 2y \leq 3$. *(7.5)*

18.3 MATHEMATICS AS A STUDY OF RELATIONSHIPS

Chapter 13 covered a variety of situations involving *functions*. *Transformations* and *operations* are special types of functions. Functions themselves are special *relations*—special sets of ordered pairs, special *correspondences*. And although we have not mentioned this previously, the symbols $=$, $<$, $\cong$, and so on, also stand for relations.

Relations (functions, correspondences, transformations, . . .) can be described by sentences (equations, formulas, inequalities, . . .) or by rules of correspondence. Some relations have graphs. Many manipulative exercises deal with these descriptions and are designed to give information about relations.

You should realize that relations run through virtually every topic of the preceding chapters. A short summary is given here.

RELATIONS

I. "Verbs"

- A. Equality *(1.1–1.3)*
- B. Inequality *(2.1)*
- C. Congruence *(4.7)*
- D. Similarity *(4.8)*

II. Correspondences

A. Between multiplication and addition (*1.4, 1.7, 9.3, 14.3–14.5*)

B. Between numbers and points (*2.6, 10.1*)

C. Between transformations and matrices (*5.3–5.7, 8.4, 9.7*)

D. Isomorphisms (*9.3, 9.7–9.9, 10.2, 10.3, 10.5, 14.5*)

III. Ordered pairs of real numbers

A. Linear relations (*6.2, 6.5, 6.8, 13.9*)

B. Quadratic relations (*11.7, Chapter 12*)

C. Circular functions (*15.2, 15.6, 15.7*)

D. Exponential and logarithmic functions (*14.2, 14.11*)

E. Absolute value relations (*13.7*)

F. Step functions (*13.8*)

G. Sequences (*17.1–17.3*)

H. Density functions (*17.12*)

IV. Operations

A. With real numbers (*1.2–1.7, 9.3, 14.3–14.5, 14.8*)

B. With complex numbers (*10.2–10.7*)

C. With matrices (*5.2, 9.4*)

D. With transformations (*4.5, 4.6, 9.6*)

E. With functions (*13.4*)

V. Transformations

A. Isometries (*4.1–4.6, 6.4*)

B. Similarities (*4.8, 10.3, 12.7*)

C. Scale transformations (*12.5*)

Mathematicians attempt to study and invent relations which have applications either to mathematics or outside mathematics. (It is easy to invent relations which might have no application.) When studying these relations, such ideas as slope, symmetry, periodicity, maximum and minimum points, and intercepts are used to describe the relation and to gain information about it. The branch of mathematics which studies relations (and particularly functions) is known as *analysis*. Today, it is one of the two largest branches of mathematics.

EXERCISES 18.3

1–2. Name a set of points which is in one-to-one correspondence with the:

1. set of real numbers. *(2.6)* **2.** set of complex numbers. *(10.1)*

3. There is a one-to-one correspondence between the set of integral powers of a number and ________. (9.3)

4. Name five ways in which a correspondence may be described. Choose a correspondence and describe it in these five ways. *(13.2)*

5–10. Graph the relation with the given sentence or rule. Name **(a)** all intercepts, **(b)** key points, such as vertices, if any, **(c)** any symmetry lines, and **(d)** any centers of rotation-symmetry.

5. $(x - 3)^2 + (y + 2)^2 = 10$ *(6.3)* **6.** $y - 6 \geq 4(x - 3)$ *(6.8)*

7. $x \to \cos x$ *(15.2)* **8.** $[x + 3] = y$ *(13.8)*

9. $b = a^2$ *(11.7)* **10.** $b = 2^a$ *(14.11)*

11–16. Give at least one similarity and one difference in the *graphs* of each pair of relations.

11. $4y - 3x = 11$; $4y - 3x = 10$ *(6.6, 9.5)*

12. $y = |x|$; $x = |y|$ *(12.8, 13.7)*

13. $w = \frac{1}{2}(v - 3)^2$; $w = 2(v - 3)^2$ *(12.7, 12.9)*

14. $4x^2 + y^2 = 1$; $4x^2 - y^2 = 1$ *(12.3, 12.6)*

15. $y = \sec x$; $y = \csc x$ *(15.6)*

16. $3y - 2x < 6$; $2x - 3y < -6$ *(6.8)*

17–22. Give a sentence for the relation that satisfies the conditions.

17. linear function containing $(4, 8)$ and $(-3, 0)$ *(6.6)*

18. linear function perpendicular to $y = 3x + 6$ containing $(-8, -3)$ *(6.6)*

19. parabola congruent to $y + 4 = 3(x - 1)^2$ with vertex at the origin (Give two answers.) *(12.7)*

20. ellipse with $(6, 0)$, $(-6, 0)$, $(0, 2)$, and $(0, -2)$ as endpoints of its axes *(12.3)*

21. sine curve which is the image of $y = \sin x$ under a size transformation of magnitude 3 *(12.7, 15.2)*

22. quadratic function containing (1, 2) with x and y axes as asymptotes *(12.4)*

23–26. Give a rule of correspondence for each transformation.

23. $r_{x\text{-axis}}$ *(5.3)*

24. R_{60} *(8.4)*

25. translation which maps (2, 9) onto (1, 160) *(4.3)*

26. scale transformation which maps $x^2 + y^2 = 1$ onto $4x^2 + 9y^2 = 36$ *(12.5)*

27–28. Graph.

27. $[30, -10°]$ *(8.6)*

28. $(\cos 235°, \sin 235°)$ *(8.1)*

29–32. Give the maximum and/or minimum values of each function. *(13.5)*

29. $y = 9|x + 5|$ *(13.7)*

30. $m^2 + 3m - 4 = n$ *(12.7)*

31. $y = \sin(t - \pi) + 3$ *(15.2)*

32. $s_n = (-1)^n$ *(17.1)*

33. Approximate the three x-intercepts of $f: x \rightarrow x^5 - 2x$. *(13.9)*

34. What are the domain and the range of the function $g: x \rightarrow (x + 3)^2$, if x can be any positive number? *(13.2)*

35–38. Let $f: x \rightarrow x^2 - 4x + 2$ and $g: a \rightarrow 3 - a^2$. Calculate.

35. $f(-2)$ *(13.3)*

36. $g(-\frac{1}{2})$ *(13.3)*

37. $f(g(6))$ *(13.4)*

38. $g \circ f(x)$ *(13.4)*

39–41. Describe the composite of:

39. two reflections over intersecting lines. *(4.6)*

40. two translations. *(4.5)*

41. two size transformations. *(5.7)*

42. Give an equation for a hyperbola with asymptotes $y = 3x$ and $y = -3x$ which does not intersect the x-axis. *(12.6)*

43. Name a relation which is not a hyperbola but whose graph has an asymptote. *(14.2, 14.11, 15.6, 15.7, 17.12)*

44. Name a relation which contains $(5, -13)$ and which has a disconnected graph. *(13.8)*

45–49. **(a)** Tell whether the statement is true when the blank is replaced by the word *congruent*. **(b)** Then repeat the exercise, replacing the blank with *similar*.

45. All parabolas are __________. *(12.7)*

46. All ellipses are __________. *(12.7)*

47. All sine curves are __________. *(15.3)*

48. All circles are __________. *(4.8)*

49. All lines are __________. *(4.7)*

50. Give an equation of a parabola which is symmetric to $y = -4$. *(12.9)*

51–53. Give a rule or formula for:

51. $\sin(x + y)$. *(8.5)*

52. the distance between (a, b) and (c, d). *(3.5)*

53. the midpoint of $\overline{AB}$ if $A = (x_1, y_1)$ and $B = (x_2, y_2)$. *(6.7)*

MATHEMATICS AS A STUDY OF COMMONALITIES

As has been noted, *analysis* is a large branch of mathematics. A second large branch of mathematics is known as *algebra*. Although most students think of algebra as solving equations and simplifying expressions (as in Section 18.2), mathematicians do not look upon algebra in this way. Algebraists are primarily interested in *structures*—sets with operations possessing certain properties. Such words as

associativity
commutativity
identity
inverse
closure

are part of the working vocabulary of the algebraist. One structure studied by algebraists, the *group*, has been used in this book to point out *isomorphisms* (identical structures) between seemingly different sets and operations. Stressed have been the correspondences between:

multiplying matrices	and	composing transformations
operating on complex numbers	and	composing transformations
multiplying positive reals	and	adding real numbers
substituting in equations	and	transforming graphs

These correspondences point out how geometrical ideas and pictures help in studying relations and numbers. Conversely, they show that algebraic ideas can be used to study geometry.

As an example, *transformations* are aids in a variety of topics. People who use transformations in geometry think of a transformation as a geometric idea. Analysts (those who study analysis) consider transformations as special functions, often without a geometric picture.

Algebraists would most likely associate transformations with a large and growing branch of mathematics called *linear algebra*, where transformations are studied along with matrices. Like many other concepts (such as set, number, point, relation), transformations point out how difficult it is to split mathematics up into branches—they indicate an essential unity of mathematics.

Any large subject must be broken down to be studied. And mathematics is a large subject. So courses are entitled "Algebra" and "Geometry" and "Calculus," and many others, even though all these courses are interrelated and each uses ideas from the others.

This does not mean that a person must be very good in every part of mathematics in order to be a mathematician. Most mathematicians have their specialties—they are acquainted with other parts of mathematics but would not feel able to nor want to work in these other parts.

EXERCISES 18.4

1–4. Give the property of addition of real numbers which corresponds to each property of multiplication of positive real numbers.

1. If $ax = b$, then $x = \frac{b}{a}$. *(1.4)* **2.** $\frac{1}{a} \cdot \frac{1}{b} = \frac{1}{ab}$ *(1.4)*

3. $a^0 = 1$ *(1.7)* **4.** $x^m \cdot y^m = (xy)^m$ *(9.3)*

5–7. Give the corresponding property involving multiplication of positive real numbers. *(9.3, 14.5)*

5. $\frac{1}{3}x + \frac{1}{3}y = \frac{1}{3}(x + y)$ *(14.5)* **6.** $a(b + c) = ab + ac$ *(1.6)*

7. The nth term of the arithmetic sequence A with difference d is $A_1 + (n - 1)d$. *(17.3)*

8–9. Give the corresponding property of addition. Then give an equivalent equation involving logarithms.

8. $x^2 \cdot x^3 = x^5$ *(1.7)* **9.** $N = \sqrt[3]{m}$ *(14.8)*

10–11. Give an equivalent equation involving logarithms and use this equation to solve the original equation. *(14.8)*

10. $N = 383 \cdot 47^{\frac{1}{3}}$ *(14.8)* **11.** $150^x = 300$ *(14.9)*

12–13. Give a corresponding sentence involving matrices.

12. $R_{30} \circ R_{60} = R_{90}$ *(5.5, 8.4)* **13.** $\begin{aligned} 3x + 4y &= 2 \\ -8x - 2y &= 0 \end{aligned}$ *(9.5)*

14–15. Give a corresponding sentence involving transformations.

14. $\begin{bmatrix} 1 & 0 \\ 0 & -1 \end{bmatrix} \cdot \begin{bmatrix} -1 & 0 \\ 0 & 1 \end{bmatrix} = \begin{bmatrix} -1 & 0 \\ 0 & -1 \end{bmatrix}$ *(5.4, 5.6)*

15. $\begin{bmatrix} -1 & 0 \\ 0 & -1 \end{bmatrix} = \begin{bmatrix} 0 & 1 \\ -1 & 0 \end{bmatrix} \cdot \begin{bmatrix} 0 & 1 \\ -1 & 0 \end{bmatrix}$ *(5.6)*

16–19. Apply the given transformation to the graph of the solution set for the given sentence. What is a sentence for the image?

16. $y = 3x^2$; reflect over the line $y = x$. *(12.8)*

17. $y = 3x^2$; translate so that $T(0, 0) = (4, -3)$. *(6.4, 12.9)*

18. $x^2 + y^2 = 1$; scale transform so that $T(1, 1) = (2, 3)$. *(12.5)*

19. $y = e^x$; reflect over the y-axis. *(14.11)*

20–22. Name a group of transformations isomorphic to each group.

20. $\langle$set of nonzero complex numbers, multiplication$\rangle$ *(10.3)*

21. $\left\langle \left\{ \begin{bmatrix} 1 & 0 \\ 0 & 1 \end{bmatrix}, \begin{bmatrix} 0 & 1 \\ 1 & 0 \end{bmatrix}, \begin{bmatrix} -1 & 0 \\ 0 & -1 \end{bmatrix}, \begin{bmatrix} 0 & -1 \\ -1 & 0 \end{bmatrix} \right\}, \cdot \right\rangle$ *(9.7)*

22. $\langle$set of real numbers, addition$\rangle$ *(9.8)*

23–31. A set and an operation are given. (**a**) Tell whether the set is closed under the operation. (**b**) Give an identity for the operation in the set. (**c**) Tell whether each element has an inverse under the operation. (**d**) Give an example of an element and its inverse. (**e**) Is a group formed?

23. set of invertible 2×2 matrices; multiplication *(9.5)*

24. set of real numbers; multiplication *(1.4)*

25. set of matrices of the form $\begin{bmatrix} k & 0 \\ 0 & k \end{bmatrix}$, $k \neq 0$; multiplication *(9.4)*

26. set of reflections; composition *(4.6)*

27. set of integral powers of $\frac{1}{4}$; multiplication *(9.3)*

28. set of irrational numbers; addition *(10.10)*

29. set of complex numbers; multiplication *(10.3)*

30. set of rotations with (1, 3) as center; composition *(9.6)*

31. $\{i, i^2, i^3, i^4\}$; multiplication *(10.5–10.7)*

32. In a group $\langle S, *\rangle$, what equation can always be solved? Verify your answer with an example from the group of invertible 2×2 matrices and multiplication. *(9.2, 9.4)*

33. What transformation corresponds to adding $2 - 3i$? *(10.2)*

34–39. Indicate all reflection, rotation, or translation symmetries of the given figure. *(4.9)*

34. unit circle *(6.3)*

35. hyperbola *(12.2)*

36. graph of $y = |x|$ *(13.7)*

37. graph of $y = \cos x$ *(15.3)*

38. graph of $y + x^2 = 0$ *(12.8)*

39. square with vertices (0, 0), $(a, 0)$, $(0, a)$, and (a, a) *(4.9)*

40. How can the graph of a function indicate whether or not the function has an inverse? *(13.4)*

41. Which of these functions has an inverse? *(14.11, 15.2, 15.7)*

a. $y = \log x$ **b.** $y = \sin x$ **c.** $y = \tan x$

42. Let a and b be real numbers. What properties of addition of real numbers are needed to solve $a + x = b$? *(1.4)*

43. When do two linear equations have parallel graphs? When are their graphs perpendicular? *(6.5, 6.6)*

44. Why are there no positive or negative imaginary numbers? *(10.8)*

45. The product of two numbers is 42; their sum is 13. Find the numbers by three different methods: **(a)** in your head, **(b)** by solving an appropriate sentence or system, and **(c)** by graphing. *(12.10)*

46–48. Give the meaning of $\binom{n}{r}$ as it relates to:

46. the power of a binomial. *(17.9)*

47. subsets of a set. *(17.10)*

48. Pascal's triangle. *(17.8)*

49. One of the most famous algebraists of recent times was Amalie Emmy Noether (1882–1935). Using any references, look up her biography and find the names of two algebraic structures (other than groups) which she studied. *(18.4)*

18.5 MATHEMATICS AS AN AID IN APPLICATIONS

There are many more people who apply mathematics than there are mathematicians, and there are thousands of books written about mathematical applications. In this book, a great number of simpler applications have been given—a few to go along with just about every topic. The following list (not meant to be complete) indicates the variety.

Mathematical topic	Applications
nested intervals	successive approximation, estimation
transformations	symmetry, models, carbon copies
absolute value	distance
special functions	telephone rates, postal rates
exponential functions	population growth, element decay
logarithms	computational arithmetic
sine waves	sound waves
trigonometry	measuring inaccessible distances
conic sections	orbits of planets, thrown objects

Puzzle problems were studied particularly in Chapter 16. "Real" applications are mentioned in the table above, and such applications are a primary reason why mathematics is considered important, is so widely used, and is liked by many people. On the other hand, the puzzles interest many students in mathematics. These students, like chess players or crossword-puzzle fans, enjoy the challenge of a puzzle and often do not care whether there is some practical application.

EXERCISES 18.5

1. Give a sequence of nested intervals containing $\sqrt{12}$. Indicate how this sequence can be related to successive approximations. *(2.7)*

2. A football team gains 13 yards on a play, but it is called back because of a penalty, and the team is penalized 5 yards. How much did the penalty hurt? Generalize this exercise and relate it to absolute value. *(3.3)*

3. Draw the front of a house which is reflection-symmetric. *(4.9)*

4. One ship is 40° north of west and 200 miles from a radar station; a second ship is 20° south of east and 150 miles from the same station. How far are the ships from each other? *(15.4)*

5. A shipment weighs 3250 pounds on a scale which is 99% accurate. What is the interval within which the true weight lies? Express this interval using absolute value ideas. *(3.4)*

6. Of three consecutive integers, prove that the difference of the squares of the largest and smallest is divisible by the third. Give an example with all three integers larger than 10. *(16.9)*

7. A relationship between the time t (in seconds) for a complete swing of a pendulum whose length is L (in feet) is $gt^2 = 4\pi^2 L$. The acceleration due to gravity g (in feet per second per second) is very close to 32 at sea level. Solve for t in terms of L. *(11.3)*

8. Factor $x^3 + 1$ and use this to find two factors of 1001. *(16.3)*

9. How much water must be added to 5 grams of alcohol in order to make a solution which is only 70% alcohol (by weight)? *(16.7)*

10. A store charges 10¢ to make a copy of a sheet of paper for the first 10 copies, 5¢ each for copies 11 to 99, and 3¢ a copy thereafter. Graph and give equations for an appropriate function and find out how many copies can be made for \$5.00. *(13.7)*

11. A woman drove 400 kilometres averaging one speed and 200 kilometres averaging 5 km/h faster. If the trip took her 10 hours, how fast did she travel at each speed? *(16.7)*

12. A certain class of mail costs 15¢ an ounce. Give a linear equation which relates weight w and cost c when w is an integer. *(3.6)*

13. Refer to Exercise **12**. Relate w and c, taking into account how postage weights are usually determined. *(13.8)*

14. A person has 18 U.S. coins with a total value of $1.72. Give all possible combinations of coins, and give a sentence by which a particular combination can be checked to see if it is possible. *(16.7)*

15. If the inflation rate of a country is 5% a year, how long will it take for that country's currency to be worth only half of what it is now? *(14.9)*

16. If $250 is invested at 5% interest compounded quarterly, how much will there be at the end of 4 years? *(14.9)*

17. Knowing that $10^{0.301} \doteq 2$ and $10^{0.477} \doteq 3$, use linear interpolation to approximate a solution to $10^x = 2.5$. Compare this with what you get by using the given information and the fact that $2.5 = \frac{10}{2^2}$. Compare both results with the table on page 603. *(13.9, 14.6)*

18. Explain how the law of sines can be used to solve certain surveying problems. *(15.5)*

19. What is the difference between the "median family income" and the "mean family income" in a city? Which do you feel is a better statistic? *(17.7)*

20. What is meant by a *mathematical model* to a real problem? What is the modeling process? *(3.2, 9.9)*

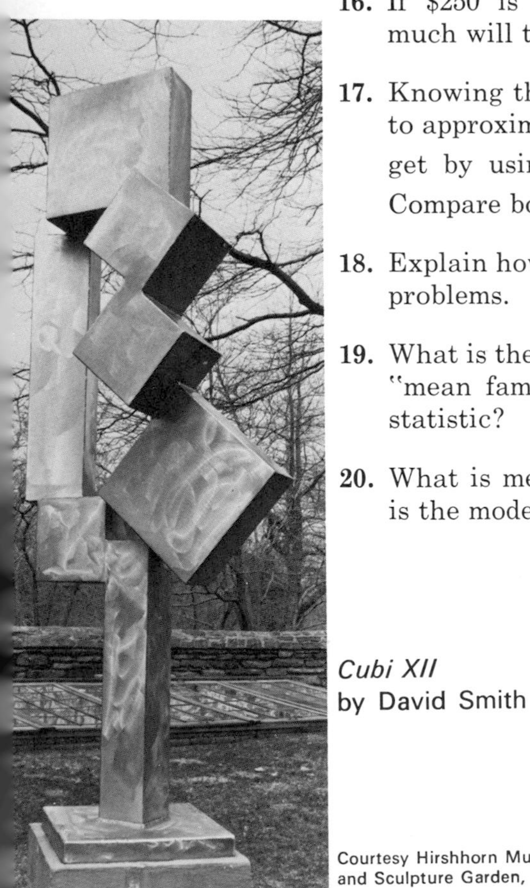

Cubi XII
by David Smith

Courtesy Hirshhorn Museum and Sculpture Garden, Smithsonian Institution

21. Name the steps involved in solving a real problem by mathematics. Give your opinion of the difficulty of each step. *(3.2)*

22. A triangular plot of ground has dimensions 400 metres by 300 metres by 150 metres. What is the smallest angle in this plot? What is the area of the plot? *(15.4)*

23. The volume of a cube is 0.064 cubic metres. Approximate the length of a side. *(14.3, 14.5)*

24. Janet starts her savings with \$25 and saves \$10 each month. How much has she saved after m months? *(17.2)*

25. An object thrown into the air with initial velocity v from a height h_0 will reach altitude h after t seconds, where $h = h_0 + vt - 16t^2$. If an object is thrown from a platform 20 feet high and hits the ground 2.5 seconds later, what was its initial velocity? What was the maximum height reached? *(11.6)*

26. The weight of a uniformly dense pipe varies directly as the cube of its length. If a $\frac{2}{3}$-metre length of pipe weighs 8 kilograms, how much will a similar 1-metre length weigh? *(13.6)*

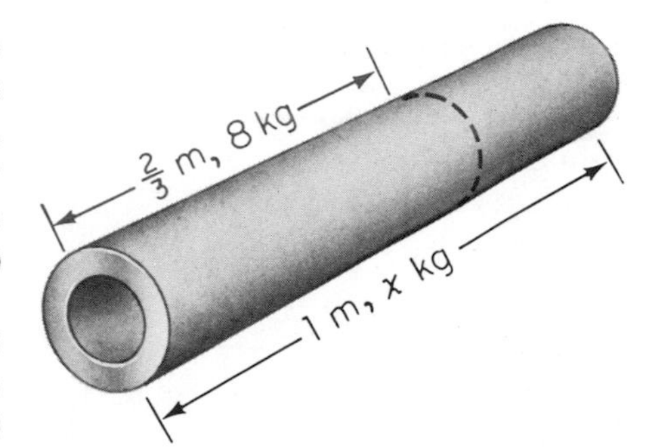

27. On standardized IQ tests, what percentage of people have IQ's over 115? *(17.12)*

28. City B is 500 miles due east of city A. If plane schedules indicate that it takes 1 hour, 20 minutes to go from B to A and 1 hour, 10 minutes from A to B, what is the expected average velocity of the wind from west to east? *(16.8)*

29. A ball is bounced from a height of 2 metres, then picked up after the second bounce at the top of its flight, 1 metre off the ground. How far has the ball traveled? *(17.4)*

30. Name four applications of multiplication. *(3.1)*

31. If a business sells a items of Product 1 for \$3 each, b items of Product 2 for \$4.50 each, and c items of Product 3 for \$8 each, how much money will be taken in? *(2.2, 3.6)*

32. What is extrapolation? Give an example of a problem in which extrapolation might be used. *(9.9)*

33. There is a wind of $t = 8$ knots from the southwest. A bird flies SSE at a speed which would be $u = 15$ knots in still air. Graph t, u, and $t + u$. What does $t + u$ stand for? *(10.9)*

34–39. Using any references, find out the kind of work each person did and name a mathematical topic from this book which the person might have applied in that line of work. *(18.5)*

34. Caroline Herschel **35.** Walter Carlos **36.** Lise Meitner

37. Maria Goeppert Mayer **38.** Mary Leakey **39.** Max Ernst

18

CHAPTER SUMMARY

Mathematics has certain general facets which are common to all courses in mathematics. In this chapter, we have taken another look at the common threads which run throughout this book:

- ☐ Mathematics as a language
- ☐ Mathematics as a study of relationships
- ☐ Mathematics as a study of commonalities
- ☐ Mathematics as an aid in applications

These themes have not only provided a means of unifying the content of this course, but they also point out the essential unity of all mathematics.

CHAPTER REVIEW

1. It is often necessary to translate from English to mathematics. When a solution is found, it may then be necessary to ______.

2. In working with expressions, we want to find an expression which ______ as the original expression and in which these values are ______ to calculate.

3. In working with sentences, we want to find a sentence which ______ as the original sentence and in which these solutions are ______ to find.

4. Transformations and operations are special types of ______, which are themselves special types of ______.

5. Name three mathematical "verbs."

6. Name three correspondences considered in this course.

7. Name four sets of elements for which operations have been considered in this course.

8. The branch of mathematics which studies relations (particularly functions) is called ______.

9. In general, what is a mathematical structure? Give one example.

10. What does *isomorphism* mean?

11. Why are transformations important?

12. List three mathematical topics studied in this course and indicate a possible application for each topic.

LIST OF SYMBOLS

Symbol	Page
$\{A: \quad \}$	2
$\{ \quad \}, \emptyset$	2
x^m	21
$\sqrt{\quad}$	26
$\doteq$	27
$<, \leq, \geq, >$	34
$\lvert x \rvert$	70
$r_m, r_m(P)$	92
$T(A)$	93
$\circ$	103
R_x	103
$\cong$	111
$\sim$	116
S_k	147
sin	205
cos	205
$[r, \theta]$	220
$\langle S, * \rangle$	230
A^{-1}	239
det	240
T^{-1}	247
i	279
$a + bi$	281
$\sqrt{-k}$	298
$\pm$	305
$f(x)$	377
$f: x \rightarrow y$	377
$f^{-1}(x)$	380
$[x]$	396
$\sqrt[n]{\quad}$	407
$x^{\frac{1}{n}}$	413
$x^{\frac{m}{n}}$	414
log	429
antilog	429
$\log_B$	439
e	441
ln	441
rad	449
sec	471
csc	471
tan	473
cot	473
S_n	529
$n!$	530
$\sum_{n=1}^{k} S_n$	546
$\binom{n}{r}$	557
${}_nC_r$	564

LIST OF POSTULATES

Postulate	Page
1. Group Properties of Real Number Addition	12
2. Group Properties of Nonzero Real Number Multiplication	12
3. Commutativity	13
4. Distributive Property—Closure of Multiples Under Addition	18
5. Power Property—Closure of Powers Under Multiplication	21
6. Order Properties	35
7. Ruler Postulate	51
8. Nested Interval Property	56
9. Order Isomorphism Properties	420

LIST OF NAMED THEOREMS

		PAGE
1.6.1	Zero multiple property	18
1.6.3	Zero product theorem	18
1.7.1	Zero power theorem	22
1.8.1	Square-root multiplication	26
1.8.2	Square-root division	27
2.5.1	FOIL theorem	48
3.5.2	Pythagorean theorem	78
3.5.3	Distance formula theorem	79
5.5.5	Matrix-transformation isomorphism theorem	140
5.7.3	Matrix basis theorem	146
6.4.1	Graph translation theorem	162
6.5.1	Slope-intercept form	164
6.6.1	Point-slope form	169
6.7.1	Midpoint formula	174
8.4.1	Rotation matrix theorem	214
9.3.2	Power of a power	235
9.3.3	Power of a product	236
9.3.4	Power of a quotient	236
10.1.1	Formulas for absolute value	267
10.2.2	Properties of complex number addition	270
10.3.1	Geometric property of complex number multiplication	273
10.3.3	Properties of complex number multiplication	273

		PAGE
11.4.1	Completing the square	307
11.5.1	Quadratic formula theorem	309
12.5.2	Graph scale transformation theorem	342
13.1.1	Vertical-line test for functions	368
13.4.3	Horizontal-line test for inverse functions	381
14.4.1	Betweenness of multiples	417
14.4.2	Betweenness of powers	417
14.5.1	Product of *n*th roots	421
14.5.2	Corresponding sentence theorem	422
14.5.3	Range of powers	422
14.8.1	Properties of logarithms	432
14.10.2	Change of base theorem	440
15.4.1	Law of cosines	463
15.5.1	Law of sines	465
15.5.2	Triangle-check theorem	466
16.1.2a	Perfect-square trinomial	487
16.1.2b	Difference of two squares	487
16.2.1	Rational root theorem	491
16.3.1	Factor theorem	496
16.4.1	Fundamental fraction property	498
17.9.1	Binomial theorem	562

SQUARES AND SQUARE ROOTS*

x	x^2	$\sqrt{x}$	x	x^2	$\sqrt{x}$	x	x^2	$\sqrt{x}$
1	1	1.000	**51**	2,601	7.141	**101**	10,201	10.050
2	4	1.414	**52**	2,704	7.211	**102**	10,404	10.100
3	9	1.732	**53**	2,809	7.280	**103**	10,609	10.149
4	16	2.000	**54**	2,916	7.348	**104**	10,816	10.198
5	25	2.236	**55**	3,025	7.416	**105**	11,025	10.247
6	36	2.449	**56**	3,136	7.483	**106**	11,236	10.296
7	49	2.646	**57**	3,249	7.550	**107**	11,449	10.344
8	64	2.828	**58**	3,364	7.616	**108**	11,664	10.392
9	81	3.000	**59**	3,481	7.681	**109**	11,881	10.440
10	100	3.162	**60**	3,600	7.746	**110**	12,100	10.488
11	121	3.317	**61**	3,721	7.810	**111**	12,321	10.536
12	144	3.464	**62**	3,844	7.874	**112**	12,544	10.583
13	169	3.606	**63**	3,969	7.937	**113**	12,769	10.630
14	196	3.742	**64**	4,096	8.000	**114**	12,996	10.677
15	225	3.873	**65**	4,225	8.062	**115**	13,225	10.724
16	256	4.000	**66**	4,356	8.124	**116**	13,456	10.770
17	289	4.123	**67**	4,489	8.185	**117**	13,689	10.817
18	324	4.243	**68**	4,624	8.246	**118**	13,924	10.863
19	361	4.359	**69**	4,761	8.307	**119**	14,161	10.909
20	400	4.472	**70**	4,900	8.367	**120**	14,400	10.954
21	441	4.583	**71**	5,041	8.426	**121**	14,641	11.000
22	484	4.690	**72**	5,184	8.485	**122**	14,884	11.045
23	529	4.796	**73**	5,329	8.544	**123**	15,129	11.091
24	576	4.899	**74**	5,476	8.602	**124**	15,376	11.136
25	625	5.000	**75**	5,625	8.660	**125**	15,625	11.180
26	676	5.099	**76**	5,776	8.718	**126**	15,876	11.225
27	729	5.196	**77**	5,929	8.775	**127**	16,129	11.269
28	784	5.292	**78**	6,084	8.832	**128**	16,384	11.314
29	841	5.385	**79**	6,241	8.888	**129**	16,641	11.358
30	900	5.477	**80**	6,400	8.944	**130**	16,900	11.402
31	961	5.568	**81**	6,561	9.000	**131**	17,161	11.446
32	1,024	5.657	**82**	6,724	9.055	**132**	17,424	11.489
33	1,089	5.745	**83**	6,889	9.110	**133**	17,689	11.533
34	1,156	5.831	**84**	7,056	9.165	**134**	17,956	11.576
35	1,225	5.916	**85**	7,225	9.220	**135**	18,225	11.619
36	1,296	6.000	**86**	7,396	9.274	**136**	18,496	11.662
37	1,369	6.083	**87**	7,569	9.327	**137**	18,769	11.705
38	1,444	6.164	**88**	7,744	9.381	**138**	19,044	11.747
39	1,521	6.245	**89**	7,921	9.434	**139**	19,321	11.790
40	1,600	6.325	**90**	8,100	9.487	**140**	19,600	11.832
41	1,681	6.403	**91**	8,281	9.539	**141**	19,881	11.874
42	1,764	6.481	**92**	8,464	9.592	**142**	20,164	11.916
43	1,849	6.557	**93**	8,649	9.644	**143**	20,449	11.958
44	1,936	6.633	**94**	8,836	9.695	**144**	20,736	12.000
45	2,025	6.708	**95**	9,025	9.747	**145**	21,025	12.042
46	2,116	6.782	**96**	9,216	9.798	**146**	21,316	12.083
47	2,209	6.856	**97**	9,409	9.849	**147**	21,609	12.124
48	2,304	6.928	**98**	9,604	9.899	**148**	21,904	12.166
49	2,401	7.000	**99**	9,801	9.950	**149**	22,201	12.207
50	2,500	7.071	**100**	10,000	10.000	**150**	22,500	12.247

* Square roots are given to nearest thousandth.

APPROXIMATIONS TO VALUES OF CIRCULAR FUNCTIONS

(for degrees 0° to 90° and radians 0 to $\frac{\pi}{2}$)

deg	rad	sin	cos	tan	cot	sec	csc		
0°	.000	.000	1.000	.000	———	1.000	———	1.571	90°
1°	.017	.017	1.000	.017	57.29	1.000	57.30	1.553	89°
2°	.035	.035	0.999	.035	28.64	1.001	28.65	1.536	88°
3°	.052	.052	.999	.052	19.08	1.001	19.11	1.518	87°
4°	.070	.070	.998	.070	14.30	1.002	14.34	1.501	86°
5°	.087	.087	.996	.087	11.43	1.004	11.47	1.484	85°
6°	.105	.105	.995	.105	9.514	1.006	9.567	1.466	84°
7°	.122	.122	.993	.123	8.144	1.008	8.206	1.449	83°
8°	.140	.139	.990	.141	7.115	1.010	7.185	1.431	82°
9°	.157	.156	.988	.158	6.314	1.012	6.392	1.414	81°
10°	.175	.174	.985	.176	5.671	1.015	5.759	1.396	80°
11°	.192	.191	.982	.194	5.145	1.019	5.241	1.379	79°
12°	.209	.208	.978	.213	4.705	1.022	4.810	1.361	78°
13°	.227	.225	.974	.231	4.331	1.026	4.445	1.344	77°
14°	.244	.242	.970	.249	4.011	1.031	4.134	1.326	76°
15°	.262	.259	.966	.268	3.732	1.035	3.864	1.309	75°
16°	.279	.276	.961	.287	3.487	1.040	3.628	1.292	74°
17°	.297	.292	.956	.306	3.271	1.046	3.420	1.274	73°
18°	.314	.309	.951	.325	3.078	1.051	3.236	1.257	72°
19°	.332	.326	.946	.344	2.904	1.058	3.072	1.239	71°
20°	.349	.342	.940	.364	2.747	1.064	2.924	1.222	70°
21°	.367	.358	.934	.384	2.605	1.071	2.790	1.204	69°
22°	.384	.375	.927	.404	2.475	1.079	2.669	1.187	68°
23°	.401	.391	.921	.424	2.356	1.086	2.559	1.169	67°
24°	.419	.407	.914	.445	2.246	1.095	2.459	1.152	66°
25°	.436	.423	.906	.466	2.145	1.103	2.366	1.134	65°
26°	.454	.438	.899	.488	2.050	1.113	2.281	1.117	64°
27°	.471	.454	.891	.510	1.963	1.122	2.203	1.100	63°
28°	.489	.469	.883	.532	1.881	1.133	2.130	1.082	62°
29°	.506	.485	.875	.554	1.804	1.143	2.063	1.065	61°
30°	.524	.500	.866	.577	1.732	1.155	2.000	1.047	60°
31°	.541	.515	.857	.601	1.664	1.167	1.942	1.030	59°
32°	.559	.530	.848	.625	1.600	1.179	1.887	1.012	58°
33°	.576	.545	.839	.649	1.540	1.192	1.836	0.995	57°
34°	.593	.559	.829	.675	1.483	1.206	1.788	0.977	56°
35°	.611	.574	.819	.700	1.428	1.221	1.743	0.960	55°
36°	.628	.588	.809	.727	1.376	1.236	1.701	0.942	54°
37°	.646	.602	.799	.754	1.327	1.252	1.662	0.925	53°
38°	.663	.616	.788	.781	1.280	1.269	1.624	0.908	52°
39°	.681	.629	.777	.810	1.235	1.287	1.589	0.890	51°
40°	.698	.643	.766	.839	1.192	1.305	1.556	0.873	50°
41°	.716	.656	.755	.869	1.150	1.325	1.524	0.855	49°
42°	.733	.669	.743	.900	1.111	1.346	1.494	0.838	48°
43°	.750	.682	.731	.933	1.072	1.367	1.466	0.820	47°
44°	.768	.695	.719	0.966	1.036	1.390	1.440	0.803	46°
45°	.785	.707	.707	1.000	1.000	1.414	1.414	0.785	45°
		cos	sin	cot	tan	csc	sec	rad	deg

COMMON LOGARITHMS OF NUMBERS BETWEEN 1.00 AND 9.99

N +	.00	.01	.02	.03	.04	.05	.06	.07	.08	.09
1.0	.0000	.0043	.0086	.0128	.0170	.0212	.0253	.0294	.0334	.0374
1.1	.0414	.0453	.0492	.0531	.0569	.0607	.0645	.0682	.0719	.0755
1.2	.0792	.0828	.0864	.0899	.0934	.0969	.1004	.1038	.1072	.1106
1.3	.1139	.1173	.1206	.1239	.1271	.1303	.1335	.1367	.1399	.1430
1.4	.1461	.1492	.1523	.1553	.1584	.1614	.1644	.1673	.1703	.1732
1.5	.1761	.1790	.1818	.1847	.1875	.1903	.1931	.1959	.1987	.2014
1.6	.2041	.2068	.2095	.2122	.2148	.2175	.2201	.2227	.2253	.2279
1.7	.2304	.2330	.2355	.2380	.2405	.2430	.2455	.2480	.2504	.2529
1.8	.2553	.2577	.2601	.2625	.2648	.2672	.2695	.2718	.2742	.2765
1.9	.2788	.2810	.2833	.2856	.2878	.2900	.2923	.2945	.2967	.2989
2.0	.3010	.3032	.3054	.3075	.3096	.3118	.3139	.3160	.3181	.3201
2.1	.3222	.3243	.3263	.3284	.3304	.3324	.3345	.3365	.3385	.3404
2.2	.3424	.3444	.3464	.3483	.3502	.3522	.3541	.3560	.3579	.3598
2.3	.3617	.3636	.3655	.3674	.3692	.3711	.3729	.3747	.3766	.3784
2.4	.3802	.3820	.3838	.3856	.3874	.3892	.3909	.3927	.3945	.3962
2.5	.3979	.3997	.4014	.4031	.4048	.4065	.4082	.4099	.4116	.4133
2.6	.4150	.4166	.4183	.4200	.4216	.4232	.4249	.4265	.4281	.4298
2.7	.4314	.4330	.4346	.4362	.4378	.4393	.4409	.4425	.4440	.4456
2.8	.4472	.4487	.4502	.4518	.4533	.4548	.4564	.4579	.4594	.4609
2.9	.4624	.4639	.4654	.4669	.4683	.4698	.4713	.4728	.4742	.4757
3.0	.4771	.4786	.4800	.4814	.4829	.4843	.4857	.4871	.4886	.4900
3.1	.4914	.4928	.4942	.4955	.4969	.4983	.4997	.5011	.5024	.5038
3.2	.5051	.5065	.5079	.5092	.5105	.5119	.5132	.5145	.5159	.5172
3.3	.5185	.5198	.5211	.5224	.5237	.5250	.5263	.5276	.5289	.5302
3.4	.5315	.5328	.5340	.5353	.5366	.5378	.5391	.5403	.5416	.5428
3.5	.5441	.5453	.5465	.5478	.5490	.5502	.5514	.5527	.5539	.5551
3.6	.5563	.5575	.5587	.5599	.5611	.5623	.5635	.5647	.5658	.5670
3.7	.5682	.5694	.5705	.5717	.5729	.5740	.5752	.5763	.5775	.5786
3.8	.5798	.5809	.5821	.5832	.5843	.5855	.5866	.5877	.5888	.5899
3.9	.5911	.5922	.5933	.5944	.5955	.5966	.5977	.5988	.5999	.6010
4.0	.6021	.6031	.6042	.6053	.6064	.6075	.6085	.6096	.6107	.6117
4.1	.6128	.6138	.6149	.6160	.6170	.6180	.6191	.6201	.6212	.6222
4.2	.6232	.6243	.6253	.6263	.6274	.6284	.6294	.6304	.6314	.6325
4.3	.6335	.6345	.6355	.6365	.6375	.6385	.6395	.6405	.6415	.6425
4.4	.6435	.6444	.6454	.6464	.6474	.6484	.6493	.6503	.6513	.6522
4.5	.6532	.6542	.6551	.6561	.6571	.6580	.6590	.6599	.6609	.6618
4.6	.6628	.6637	.6646	.6656	.6665	.6675	.6684	.6693	.6702	.6712
4.7	.6721	.6730	.6739	.6749	.6758	.6767	.6776	.6785	.6794	.6803
4.8	.6812	.6821	.6830	.6839	.6848	.6857	.6866	.6875	.6884	.6893
4.9	.6902	.6911	.6920	.6928	.6937	.6946	.6955	.6964	.6972	.6981
5.0	.6990	.6998	.7007	.7016	.7024	.7033	.7042	.7050	.7059	.7067
5.1	.7076	.7084	.7093	.7101	.7110	.7118	.7126	.7135	.7143	.7152
5.2	.7160	.7168	.7177	.7185	.7193	.7202	.7210	.7218	.7226	.7235
5.3	.7243	.7251	.7259	.7267	.7275	.7284	.7292	.7300	.7308	.7316
5.4	.7324	.7332	.7340	.7348	.7356	.7364	.7372	.7380	.7388	.7396

COMMON LOGARITHMS OF NUMBERS BETWEEN 1.00 AND 9.99 (continued)

N +	.00	.01	.02	.03	.04	.05	.06	.07	.08	.09
5.5	.7404	.7412	.7419	.7427	.7435	.7443	.7451	.7459	.7466	.7474
5.6	.7482	.7490	.7497	.7505	.7513	.7520	.7528	.7536	.7543	.7551
5.7	.7559	.7566	.7574	.7582	.7589	.7597	.7604	.7612	.7619	.7627
5.8	.7634	.7642	.7649	.7657	.7664	.7672	.7679	.7686	.7694	.7701
5.9	.7709	.7716	.7723	.7731	.7738	.7745	.7752	.7760	.7767	.7774
6.0	.7782	.7789	.7796	.7803	.7810	.7818	.7825	.7832	.7839	.7846
6.1	.7853	.7860	.7868	.7875	.7882	.7889	.7896	.7903	.7910	.7917
6.2	.7924	.7931	.7938	.7945	.7952	.7959	.7966	.7973	.7980	.7987
6.3	.7993	.8000	.8007	.8014	.8021	.8028	.8035	.8041	.8048	.8055
6.4	.8062	.8069	.8075	.8082	.8089	.8096	.8102	.8109	.8116	.8122
6.5	.8129	.8136	.8142	.8149	.8156	.8162	.8169	.8176	.8182	.8189
6.6	.8195	.8202	.8209	.8215	.8222	.8228	.8235	.8241	.8248	.8254
6.7	.8261	.8267	.8274	.8280	.8287	.8293	.8299	.8306	.8312	.8319
6.8	.8325	.8331	.8338	.8344	.8351	.8357	.8363	.8370	.8376	.8382
6.9	.8388	.8395	.8401	.8407	.8414	.8420	.8426	.8432	.8439	.8445
7.0	.8451	.8457	.8463	.8470	.8476	.8482	.8488	.8494	.8500	.8506
7.1	.8513	.8519	.8525	.8531	.8537	.8543	.8549	.8555	.8561	.8567
7.2	.8573	.8579	.8585	.8591	.8597	.8603	.8609	.8615	.8621	.8627
7.3	.8633	.8639	.8645	.8651	.8657	.8663	.8669	.8675	.8681	.8686
7.4	.8692	.8698	.8704	.8710	.8716	.8722	.8727	.8733	.8739	.8745
7.5	.8751	.8756	.8762	.8768	.8774	.8779	.8785	.8791	.8797	.8802
7.6	.8808	.8814	.8820	.8825	.8831	.8837	.8842	.8848	.8854	.8859
7.7	.8865	.8871	.8876	.8882	.8887	.8893	.8899	.8904	.8910	.8915
7.8	.8921	.8927	.8932	.8938	.8943	.8949	.8954	.8960	.8965	.8971
7.9	.8976	.8982	.8987	.8993	.8998	.9004	.9009	.9015	.9020	.9025
8.0	.9031	.9036	.9042	.9047	.9053	.9058	.9063	.9069	.9074	.9079
8.1	.9085	.9090	.9096	.9101	.9106	.9112	.9117	.9122	.9128	.9133
8.2	.9138	.9143	.9149	.9154	.9159	.9165	.9170	.9175	.9180	.9186
8.3	.9191	.9196	.9201	.9206	.9212	.9217	.9222	.9227	.9232	.9238
8.4	.9243	.9248	.9253	.9258	.9263	.9269	.9274	.9279	.9284	.9289
8.5	.9294	.9299	.9304	.9309	.9315	.9320	.9325	.9330	.9335	.9340
8.6	.9345	.9350	.9355	.9360	.9365	.9370	.9375	.9380	.9385	.9390
8.7	.9395	.9400	.9405	.9410	.9415	.9420	.9425	.9430	.9435	.9440
8.8	.9445	.9450	.9455	.9460	.9465	.9469	.9474	.9479	.9484	.9489
8.9	.9494	.9499	.9504	.9509	.9513	.9518	.9523	.9528	.9533	.9538
9.0	.9542	.9547	.9552	.9557	.9562	.9566	.9571	.9576	.9581	.9586
9.1	.9590	.9595	.9600	.9605	.9609	.9614	.9619	.9624	.9628	.9633
9.2	.9638	.9643	.9647	.9652	.9657	.9661	.9666	.9671	.9675	.9680
9.3	.9685	.9689	.9694	.9699	.9703	.9708	.9713	.9717	.9722	.9727
9.4	.9731	.9736	.9741	.9745	.9750	.9754	.9759	.9763	.9768	.9773
9.5	.9777	.9782	.9786	.9791	.9795	.9800	.9805	.9809	.9814	.9818
9.6	.9823	.9827	.9832	.9836	.9841	.9845	.9850	.9854	.9859	.9863
9.7	.9868	.9872	.9877	.9881	.9886	.9890	.9894	.9899	.9903	.9908
9.8	.9912	.9917	.9921	.9926	.9930	.9934	.9939	.9943	.9948	.9952
9.9	.9956	.9961	.9965	.9969	.9974	.9978	.9983	.9987	.9991	.9996

Index

A

Abel, Niels Henrik, 492
Absolute value
of a complex number, 267
of a real number, 70
Absolute-value functions, 392–395
Absolute-value sentences, 74, 182–184
Accuracy, 73
Addition
applications of, 60–64
of complex numbers, 269–272, 283–286
of fractional expressions, 504
properties of, 12, 270
of radicals, 301
of real numbers, 5–8, 11–15
Addition property
of equations, 6
of order, 35–36
Additive groups, 230, 232–238
Additive identity
for complex numbers, 270
for real numbers, 5, 12
Additive inverse
of a complex number, 270
of a real number, 5, 12
Algebra, 590–591
Amplitude, 461
Analysis, 587, 590
Angle(s)
and magnitudes of rotation, 100, 108
measure of, 449–452
of a triangle, finding, 462–470, 477–480
Antilogarithm, 429
Approximations
to irrational numbers, 417
to irrational solutions, 492–493
to powers, 418
to solutions, 3
to square roots, 27
successive, 55–58
Arc length, 452
Arithmetic means, 26
Arithmetic sequences, 534–537
sums of, 542–548
Associativity
for complex numbers, 270, 273
of composition, 247
for groups, 229
for matrices, 139
for real numbers, 12
Asymptotes, 330
Average, 26, 553
Axis (axes)
of a cone, 326
coordinate, 77
of an ellipse, 334
imaginary, 280
real, 279

B

Base
of an exponential function, 418
of a logarithm, 425, 439–444
BASIC (computer language), 17
Betweenness, 51
of multiples and powers, 417
Binomial, 48
Binomial coefficients, 563
Binomial density, 569–570
Binomial theorem, 561–563
Boyle's law, 391
Briggs, Henry, 440

C

Cartesian coordinates, 77
Cayley, Arthur, 125, 197
Center
of a circle, 157–158
of a rotation, 99
of a size transformation, 114–115
of symmetry, 120
Characteristic, 426
Charles' law, 391
Circle(s), 157–160, 253
as a conic section, 326
equations for, 157–160
exterior of, 177–178
interior of, 177–178
unit, 158, 204
Circular functions, 473
Closure properties
for complex numbers, 270, 273
for groups, 229
for real numbers, 12
Codomain, 372
Coefficient(s), 17
binomial, 563
Coefficient matrix, 193
Common factors, 486
Common logarithms, 425–438
computing with, 431–435
table of, 603–604
Commutative group, 231
Commutativity
for complex numbers, 270, 273
lack of, of composition, 106
lack of, of matrix multiplication, 139
for real numbers, 13
Completeness property, 57

Completing the square, 307–309
Complex number(s), 265–296
absolute values of, 267
adding, 269–272, 283–286
applications of, 288–291
conjugate of, 284
dividing, 284–286
graphing, 266–268
inverse of, 270, 273
multiplying, 272–278, 283–286
notation for, 266, 281–283
order for, lack of, 287–288
subtracting, 270
Complex number plane, 266–268, 278–281
Composites
of functions, 379–383
of reflections, 107–114, 116
of transformations, 102–114, 116, 147
Composition, 103–104, 246–250
Compound sentences, 182–187
Computer language, 17
Congruence, 111–114
Conic sections, 326–366
Conjugate
of a complex number, 284
irrational, 302
Constant, 152
of variation, 387
Constant difference, 535
Constant ratio, 538–539
Coordinate(s)
Cartesian, 77
of a point on a line, 51
of a point in a plane, 77, 219–226
polar, 219–226
rectangular, 77, 223
Corollary, 18
Correspondence, 372, 587
function as, 371–375, 378
one-to-one, 50–55, 78
Corresponding sentences, 421–422, 431
Cosecant, 471–473, 478–479
Cosine(s), 204–208, 250–253, 452–457, 478–479, 552
of supplementary angles, 460
using tables of, 209–214
of $(90 - x)$, 209
of $(x + y)$, 217–219
of $(-x)$, 251
of $(\pi - x)$, 459
Cotangent, 473–476, 478–479
Cube roots, 407

D

Dantzig, George, 197
Decimals
infinite, 57, 549–552
nonterminating, 293
repeating, 293
terminating, 293
Degree (unit), 449–452
Degree of an equation, 492
De Moivre, Abraham, 275
De Moivre's theorem, 275
Denominator
common, 504
rationalizing [illegible], 501
Density functions, 569–570
Dependent variable, 384
Descartes, René, 7[illegible]
Determinant, 240
Dimension(s)
of a matrix, 126, 129
of a sentence, 152
of a system, 193–194
Diophantine equation, 154
Direct proportion, 387
Direct variation, 387
Direction
of orientation, 88–89
of rotation, 99
of translation, 96
Directrix, 317–318
Discriminant, 311
Distance
from a point to a line, 317
between points on a line, 69–72
between points in a plane, 77–82
Distance formula, 79
Distributive property, 18
for complex numbers, 277
Divine proportion, 313
Division
of complex numbers, 284–286
of fractional expressions, 499–506
logarithms used for, 432
of polynomials, 494–498
of powers, 236
of radicals, 302
of real numbers, 10
of square roots, 27
by zero not defined, 18
Domain, 372
Doppler, C. J., 502
Doppler effect, 502

E

Eccentricity, 336
Edge of a cone, 326
Ellipses, 329–336, 342–343, 359
Empty set, 2–3
Equation(s), 5–11
of circles, 157–160
degree of, 492
Diophantine, 154
of ellipses, 333–336
with fractional expressions, 506–509
of horizontal lines, 154
of hyperbolas, 337–340, 346–349
linear, 37–47
of lines, 136, 154–155, 164–173

logarithms used in solving, 433
matrix, 242–246
of oblique lines, 155
of parabolas, 317–319, 350–353
in point-slope form, 169
polynomial, 490–494
quadratic, 304–320, 492
radical, 304–306
in slope-intercept form, 164
systems of, 186–196, 199–202, 242–246, 361–365
with variables as exponents, 435–438
for vertical lines, 154

Equivalent
sentences, 2, 40–41, 431
systems, 187

Estimation
modeling, 73–76
of solutions, 3, 187–188

Exponent(s), 21
negative, 22–23
properties of, 21–25
rational, 412–416
real, 417–419
in scientific notation, 25, 425–427
variables in, 435–438
zero as, 22

Exponential functions, 406, 410–412, 418
graphing, 444–447
and logarithms, 435–438

Exponential sequences, 538–541
sums of finite, 542–548
sums of infinite, 548–552

Expression(s)
fractional, 498
linear, 38
quadratic, 307, 485–490

Extraneous solution, 304
Extrapolation, 258
Extremes, 9

F

Factor theorem, 496
Factorial sequence, 530
Factorial symbol, 530–531

Factoring
differences of two cubes, 496
differences of two squares, 487
perfect-square trinomials, 487
polynomials, 485–490, 496
sums of two cubes, 496

Factors, 486
Feasible region, 199
Fibonacci numbers, 531
Fibonacci sequence, 531

Finite sequences, 529
sums of, 542–548

Focal constant, 329–330, 334, 339, 346

Focus (foci)
of an ellipse, 329–330, 334
of a hyperbola, 329–331, 339, 346
of a parabola, 317–318

FOIL theorem, 47–50
Fourier, Joseph, 197

Fractional expressions, 498
adding, 504
dividing, 499–506
multiplying, 503
rationalizing denominators of, 501
sentences involving, 506–509
subtracting, 504

Function(s), 367–405
absolute value, 392–395
circular, 452–462, 471–476
composite, 379–383
as correspondences, 371–375, 378
density, 569–570
even, 461
exponential, 406, 410–412, 435–438, 444–447
greatest integer, 396–399
growth, 410–412
identity, 380
inverse, 380–383
linear, 369, 400–404
logarithmic, 425–431, 439–447
maximum or minimum value of, 385
notation for, 371–377
odd, 462
quadratic, 369
step, 396–399, 458
terminology for, 384–386
transformations as, 376–379
variation, 387–388
vertical-line test for, 368

G

Galois, Evariste, 492
Gauss, Karl Friedrich, 197, 542
Geometric means, 26, 29

Geometric sequences, 538–541
sums of finite, 543–548
sums of infinite, 548–552

Girard, Albert, 407
Golden ratio, 313
Graph scale transformation theorem, 342
Graph translation theorem, 162

Graphing
absolute-value sentences, 183, 392–395
circles, 157–160
circular functions, 453–455, 472, 475
complex numbers, 266–268
compound sentences, 182–186
conics, 313–320, 329–361
exponential functions, 444–447
functions of variation, 388

Graphing (*continued*)
inequalities, 177–179, 320–323
inverse relations, 354–357, 381
linear equations, 154–157, 164–173
logarithmic functions, 444–447
ordered pairs, 77–78, 151
quadratic equations, 313–320
quadratic systems, 361–365
real numbers, 50–55, 150–151
relations, 367–375
step functions, 396–399
systems of equations, 187–188, 361–365
systems of inequalities, 199–202
Greatest integer function, 396–399
Group(s), 11–15, 229–231
additive, 230, 232–238
isomorphic, 234–238, 250–255 270, 279, 420–424
of matrices, 242–246
multiplicative, 229–238
noncommutative, 242
of transformations, 247–250
Grouping symbols, 15–16
Growth functions, 410–412

H

Half-plane, 177
Hamilton, W. R., 15
Hooke's law, 391
Horizontal-line test, 381
Hurwicz, Leonid, 197
Hyperbolas, 329–332, 337–340, 346–349, 359

I

***i*,** 279
Identities, trigonometric, 490, 498, 502, 506
Identity
additive, 5, 12, 270
for group operations, 229
for matrix multiplication, 138
multiplicative, 8, 12, 273
Identity function, 380
Identity matrix, 138
Identity transformation, 138, 246
Image, 87, 132
Imaginary number, 280, 293, 297–301
Independent variable, 384
Index variable, 546
Inequalities
and complex numbers, 287–288
graphing, 177–179, 320–323
linear, 37–47
and order, 34–37
quadratic, 320–323
systems of, 199–202
Infinite sequences, 529
sums of, 548–552
Integers, 30, 292–293
Interpolation (linear), 400–404
Intersection of sets, 182, 186–187
Interval(s), 51–52, 73–77
congruent, 113
endpoints of, 51
length of, 69–72, 74
midpoint of, 73–75
nested, 56, 74, 417–418
Inverse
additive, 5, 12, 270
of element of a group, 229
of a function, 380–383
of a matrix, 238–241
multiplicative, 8–9, 12, 273
of a transformation, 247
Inverse proportion, 388–389
Inverse variation, 387–388
Invertible matrix, 239
Irrational conjugates, 302
Irrational numbers, 292–293
decimal approximations for, 417
as powers, 418
Isometries, 107–114
properties of, 112
Isomorphic groups, 234–238, 250–255, 270, 279, 420–424
Isomorphism, 141

K

Kantorovich, L. V., 197
Koopmans, T. C., 197
Kovalevsky, Sonja, 520
Kramp, Christian, 530

L

Law of cosines, 462–465
Law of sines, 465–470
Length
of an arc, 452
of an interval, 69–72, 74
Limit, 549
Line(s)
coordinatized, 51
equations for, 136, 154–155, 164–173
half-plane of, 177
parallel, 165, 169
perpendicular, 170–171
reflecting, 87
of symmetry, 119, 330–331
Linear functions, 369, 400–404
Linear programming, 197–202
Linear sequences, 534–537
sums of, 542–548
Logarithmic function, 425–431, 439–447
graphing, 444–447
Logarithmic spiral, 447
Logarithms, 425–448
changing base of, 440

common, 425–438
natural, 441
properties of, 432
Lucas numbers, 533

M

Mach, Ernst, 516
Magnitude
of a rotation, 99
of a size transformation, 114–115
of a translation, 97
Malus' law, 391
Mantissa(s), 426
table of, 603–604
Mapping, 94
Mathematical model, 65–68, 256–259, 594
Matrix (matrices), 125–128
coefficient, 193
determinant of, 240
identity, for multiplication, 138
invertible, 239
multiplicative inverse of, 238–241
multiplying, 128–131, 138–141
for a network, 127–128
for reflections, 135–138, 145
to represent points, 126
to represent polygons, 126
for rotations, 143–145, 212–216
for scale transformations, 341
for size transformations, 145–146
for transformations, 131–148, 212–216, 250–253, 341
for translations, 145
Matrix basis theorem, 146
Matrix equations, 242–246
Matrix multiplication, 128–131, 138–141
applied to transformations, 131–135
properties of, 138–139
Matrix-transformation isomorphism, 140–141
Maximum value of a function, 385
Mean, 553
Mean proportionals, 26
Means
arithmetic and geometric, 26
of a proportion, 9
Median, 553
Midpoint
of an interval, 73–75
of a segment, 174–176
Midpoint formula, 174
Minimum value of a function, 385
Mode, 553
Modeling, 65–68, 594
distance on a line, 69–72
distance in a plane, 77–82
estimation, 73–76
and isomorphism, 256–258
Multiples, 17–19, 417, 420–424
additive group of, 234–238
and roots, 412–416
Multiplication
applications of, 61–64
of complex numbers, 272–278, 283–286
of fractional expressions, 503
logarithms used for, 432
of matrices, 128–131, 138–141
of polynomials, 47–50
of powers, 235–236
properties of, 12
of radicals, 301–303
of real numbers, 8–15, 17–21
of roots, 421
of square roots, 26
Multiplication properties of order, 35–36
Multiplication property
of equations, 9
of negative one, 19
of zero, 18
Multiplicative groups, 229–238
Multiplicative identity
for complex numbers, 273
for matrices, 138
for real numbers, 8, 12
Multiplicative inverse
of a complex number, 273
of a matrix, 238–241
of a real number, 8–9, 12

N

***n*th roots,** 407–409, 413–414
product of, 421
Napier, John, 440, 444
Nappe, 326
Natural logarithms, 441
Natural numbers, 292–293
Negative size transformation, 115
Nested intervals, 56, 417–418
Networks, 127–128
Newton, Isaac, 558
Noether, Amalie Emmy, 594
Normal curves, 570–571
Normal density, 570
Normalized scores, 571
Null set, 2–3
Nygaard, P. H., 292

O

One-to-one correspondence, 50–55, 78
Operations, order of, 15–17
Opposite
of a multiple, 19, 23
of a real number, 5, 12
Order
and inequality, 34–37
lack of, for complex numbers, 287–288

Order *(continued)*
on a number line, 51
of operations, 15–17
properties of, 34–37
Order isomorphism, 420
Order preservation property, 420
Ordered pairs, 77
as a complex number, 266
relation as a set of, 152
Ordered triple, 195–196
Orientation, 89
Origin, 77
Oughtred, William, 446

P

Parabolas, 315, 317–320, 350–353, 358–359
Parallel lines, 165, 169
Pascal, Blaise, 556
Pascal's triangle, 556–563
Pereira, Irene Rice, 68
Perfect-square trinomials, 487
Period, 459
Periodic function, 458–459
Perpendicular lines, 170–171
Pi, 74
Point matrix, 126
Point-slope form, 169
Point-symmetry, 145
Points
betweenness of, 51
coordinates of, on a line, 51
coordinates of, in a plane, 77, 219–226
distance between, 69–72, 77–82
Polar coordinates, 219–226
Polynomial equations, 490–494
Polynomials, 49
dividing, 494–498
factoring, 485–490, 496
multiplying, 47–50
Postulates
list of, 599
purpose of, 11–12
Power(s), 21–25, 420–424
betweenness of, 417
of binomials, 561–563
dividing, 236
logarithms used to find, 432–433
multiplicative group of, 234–238
multiplying, 235–236
of a power, 235, 413–414
of a product, 236
of a quotient, 236
range of, 422
of a real number, 21–25
of a root, 414
Power-multiple correspondence, 420
Power property, 21
Preimage, 87, 132
Probability, 566–572
Proportion, 9, 387–389
Divine, 313
Pure imaginary number, 280
Pythagorean theorem, 78, 463

Q

Quadrant, 78
Quadratic equation(s), 304–313, 492
in square form, 307
in two variables, 313–320
Quadratic expression, 307
factoring, 485–490
Quadratic formula, 309–313
Quadratic functions, 369
Quadratic inequalities, 320–323
Quadratic relation(s), 325–366
Quadratic systems, 361–365

R

Radian (unit), 449–452
Radical equations, 304–306
Radical sign, 301
Radicals, 301–303
Radius, 157–158
Range
of a correspondence or function, 373
of powers, 422
Ratio(s)
constant, 538–539
Golden, 313
trigonometric, 477–480
Rational numbers, 30, 292–293
decimal expansion of, 293
as exponents, 412–416
Rational root theorem, 491
Rationalizing a denominator, 501
Real number(s), 29–31, 293
adding, 5–8, 11–15
completeness of, 57
decimal expansion of, 293
dividing, 10
as exponents, 417–419
graphing, 50–55, 150–151
logarithms of, 425–443
multiplying, 8–15, 17–21
powers of, 21–25
roots of, 26–29, 407–409, 413–414
subtracting, 6
Real number lines, 50–55
Reciprocal
of a complex number, 273
of a power, 22–23
of a real number, 8–9, 12
of zero, lack of, 18
Rectangular coordinates, 77, 223
Reflecting line(s), 87, 119
intersecting, 108
parallel, 107–108

Reflection(s), 86–92, 248
composites of, 107–114, 116
matrices for, 135–138, 145
notation for, 91–92
properties of, 87–89
Reflection-symmetry, 119
of conic sections, 330–331
of relations, 354–357, 381
of sine waves, 458–462
Relation(s), 152, 586–587
functions as, 367–370, 378
quadratic, 325–366
Right circular cone, 326
Right triangle
finding hypotenuse of, 78–79
trigonometry of, 477–483
Root(s) (of numbers)
logarithms used to find, 433
of negative numbers, 297–301
of a power, 414
power of, 414
product of, 26, 421
quotient of, 27
of real numbers, 26–29, 407–409, 413–414
of a root, 414
table of, 601
Roots (of equations)
of polynomial equations, 491–493
of quadratic equations, 309–313
Rotation(s), 99–102, 204–208
center of, 99
and complex number multiplication, 273
as composite of reflections, 108
composites of, 103–104
direction of, 99
groups of, 248
magnitude of, 99
matrices for, 143–145, 212–216
and values of sines and cosines, 211–214
Rotation-symmetry, 120
of sine waves, 458–462
Row-by-column multiplication, 128
Rudolff, Christoff, 62
Ruler postulate, 51

S

Scale transformations, 252, 340–349
Scientific notation, 25, 425–427
Scott, Walter, 294
Secant, 471–473, 478–479
Sentences, 1–5, 150–154
compound, 182–187
corresponding, 421–422, 431
equivalent, 2, 40–41, 431
involving absolute value, 74, 182–184
involving fractional expressions, 506–509
linear, 37–47
with two or more variables, 44–47
Sequence(s), 528–533
arithmetic, 534–537
describing, 530–531
exponential, 538–541
factorial, 530
Fibonacci, 531
finite, 529, 542–548
geometric, 538–541
infinite, 529, 548–552
limit of, 549
linear, 534–537
of nested intervals, 56
sums of, 542–552
Servois, F. J., 15
Set(s)
counting subsets of, 564–565
empty (null), 2–3
intersection of, 182, 186–187
solution, 2, 186
union of, 182
Set notation, 2
Shear transformations, 252
Similar figures, 116–117
Similarity transformations, 116–117
of parabolas, 351–352
Simplex algorithm, 197
Sine(s), 204–208, 250–253, 452–457, 477–479, 552
of supplementary angles, 460
using tables of, 209–214
of $(90 - x)$, 209
of $(x + y)$, 217–219
of $(-x)$, 251
of $(\pi - x)$, 459
Sine waves, 455
symmetries of, 458–462
Size transformation(s), 114–119
center of, 114–115
composites of, 116, 147
groups of, 248
magnitude of, 114–115
matrices for, 145–146
of parabolas, 350–351
Slope(s)
of a line, 165–166
of parallel lines, 165
of perpendicular lines, 170–171
Slope-intercept form, 164
Solution set
of a sentence, 2
of a system of equations, 186
Solutions
describing, 2, 187
estimating, 3, 187–188
of systems, 186, 195
Solving triangles, 462–470
Square form of a quadratic equation, 307
Square roots, 26–29, 407, 413
division of, 27
graphing, 298
multiplication of, 26
of negative numbers, 297–301
table of, 601

Standard deviation, 554–555
Standard form of quadratic expressions, 307
Standardized scores, 571
Statistical measure, 553
Statistics, 553–556
Step functions, 396–399, 458
Stifel, Michael, 556
Stigler, George, 197
Subsets
counting, 564–565
Substitution method for solving
linear systems, 190
quadratic systems, 362
Subtraction
of complex numbers, 270
of real numbers, 6
Summation notation, 546–548
Symbols, list of, 599
Symmetric figures, 119
Symmetry, 119–122, 145
center of, 120
lines of, 119, 330–331
Systems, 186–189
dimensions of, 193–194
equivalent, 187
graphing, 187–188, 199–202
and matrices, 242–246
quadratic, 361–365
solving, 190–196, 242–246

T

Tangent, 473–476, 478–479
Terms of a sequence, 528–532
Theorem(s), 12
list of, 600
Transformation(s), 91–95, 587
composites of, 102–114, 116, 147
as functions, 376–379
identity, 138, 246
inverse, 247
as mappings, 94
and matrix multiplication, 131–135
reflection, 86–92, 107–114, 116, 135–138, 145
rotation, 99–104, 108, 143–145, 204–208, 212–216, 248, 273
scale, 252, 340–349
shear, 252
similarity, 116–117, 351–352
size, 114–119, 145–147, 248, 350–351
translation, 96–98, 104–108, 145, 161–164, 247, 357–361
2 × 2 matrices for, 131–148, 212–216, 250–253, 341
Transitive property of order, 35
Translation(s), 96–98
as composite of reflections, 107–108
composites of, 104–105
and conics, 357–361
and graphs, 161–164
groups of, 247
magnitude of a, 97
matrices for, 145
Translation-symmetry, 120
of sine waves, 458–462
Triangles, solving, 462–470
Trichotomy property, 34–35
Trigonometric identities, 490, 498, 502, 506
Trigonometry, 462–470
of right triangles, 477–483
Trinomial(s), 49
factoring, 485–490
perfect-square, 487
Truth set, 2

U · V

Union of sets, 182
Unit circle, 158, 204
Variables, 150
dependent, 384
independent, 384
index, 546
Variation
direct, 387
inverse, 387–388
Vectors, 288–291
Vertex (vertices)
of a cone, 326
of a hyperbola, 330
of a parabola, 317–318
Vertical-line test, 368

X · Y · Z

***x*-axis,** 77, 279
***y*-axis,** 77, 280
***y*-intercept,** 165
Zero, 292–293
as the additive identity, 5, 12
division by, not defined, 18
as an exponent, 22
multiples of, 18
multiplication by, 18–19
Zero determinant, 240
Zero factorial, 558
Zero multiple, 18
Zero power theorem, 22
Zero product theorem, 18–19

Answers to Selected Exercises

Generally, the odd-numbered Ⓐ and Ⓑ exercises are answered. TA denotes that a *typical* answer is given, but there are other good answers.

1.1 Pages 3–5

1. d **3.** $5 + x = 2$ **5.** $8 > 2t$ **7.** No **9.** { }, ∅
11. TA: $d = 50.6$ **13.** TA: $-2.5, -3, -4$ **15.** TA: $0, -1, -2$
17. $6 + n > 8$ **19.** TA: $x + 1 < x$ **21.** $B = 8900$, 8900, {8900}
23. No solution, ∅ **25.** 4 and 5 **27.** TA: $x^2 = 36$ **29.** a

1.2 Pages 6–8

1. -10 **3.** $\frac{2}{3}$ **5.** -1.3 **7.** 0 **9.** -4
11. $\frac{7}{6}$ **13.** -349.4 **15.** Addition **17.** $-3 + 2 + 6$ **19.** $2 + (-x) = -2$
21. 7 **23.** 3.5 **25.** -8 **27.** $-\frac{1}{2}$
29. Add -3.1, $\{-1.7\}$ **31.** TA: Add $\frac{3}{4}$, $\{-\frac{23}{36}\}$ **33.** TA: Add $-(19 + 42)$, $\{51\}$
35. TA: Add -210.3, $\{211.8\}$ **37.** Add $-\sqrt{10}$, $\{-5 - \sqrt{10}\}$ **39.** $-6 - v$
41. $d = -a + 9 + \frac{1}{2}e$ **43.** $a = -x - y$ **45.** $-14 + b - d$
47. The sum of the measures of two supplementary angles is 180. **49.** $y - 3 + z$

1.3 Pages 10–11

1. 1 **3.** Multiplicative inverse **5.** $-\frac{1}{5}$ **7.** $\frac{10}{13}$ **9.** 8
11. $\frac{2}{15}$ **13.** Multiplication **15.** $12 \cdot \frac{3}{2}$ **17.** $y(-\frac{1}{6}) = -7$ **19.** 2
21. $\frac{5}{6}$ **23.** If $a \neq 0$, then $x = y$ and $ax = ay$ are equivalent equations. **25.** $\frac{3}{2}$
27. Mult. $\frac{1}{3}$, {156} **29.** Mult. $\frac{1}{2}$, {50} **31.** TA: Mult. $7y$, $\{\frac{14}{5}\}$ **33.** TA: Mult. $\frac{1}{24}$, $\{\frac{3}{4}\}$
35. $b = \frac{ad}{c}$ **37.** Let r be the rate in km/h. Then $r = \frac{m}{h}$.

1.4 Pages 13–14

1. Def. of subtraction **3.** Assoc. prop. of add. **5.** Identity for add.
7. 933 **9.** b **11.** Closure, associativity, identity, inverses
13. d **15.** Postulates indicate relationships between undefined terms and are used to prove other relationships.
17. Def. of division **19.** Comm. and assoc. of add. **21.** Comm. of mult.

23. $-9 + (-3) = -12$
$-3 + (-9) = -12$
$-12 - (-3) = -9$
$-12 - (-9) = -3$

25. $a \cdot b = ab$
$b \cdot a = ab$
$\frac{ab}{a} = b$
$\frac{ab}{b} = a$

27. $\frac{3}{4} \cdot 2 = \frac{3}{2}$
$2 \cdot \frac{3}{4} = \frac{3}{2}$
$\frac{3}{2} \div 2 = \frac{3}{4}$
$\frac{3}{2} \div \frac{3}{4} = 2$

1.5 Pages 16–17

1. *See page 15.* **3.** -30 **5.** 16 **7.** $\frac{(100 + 10)}{(100 + 5)}$ **9.** $\sqrt{[(6^2) + (8^2)]}$
11. -16 **13.** $\sqrt{5}$ **15.** $-\frac{5}{2}$ **17.** 0 **19.** Not a real number
21. TA: If $m = 2$, $\sqrt{8} \neq 4$. **23.** TA: If $a = 3$ and $x = 2$, $25 \neq 13$.

1.6 Pages 19–20

1. For any real numbers a, b, and x, $(a + b)x = ax + bx$. Servois **3.** $3B - 7$ **5.** $\{6\}$ **7.** The set of all real numbers **9.** $\{0\}$ **11.** $-2, -9$ **13.** $7z$ **15.** $-5A$ **17.** 300 **19.** 812 **21.** -43 **23.** 49 **25.** 62 **27.** 0 **29.** $\frac{7}{6}D$ **31.** $28 - 10W$ **33.** $4x - 1$ **35.** $1 - 2y$ **37.** $-0.53t$ **39.** Substitute numbers for the variables and see if the values are the same for the original and simplified expressions. **41.** -10 **43.** 5, 2

1.7 Pages 23–24

1. $4q$ **3.** -16 **5.** 32 **7.** -125 **9.** y^{15} **11.** a^2 **13.** c^0 **15.** b **17.** 1 **19.** $-64, 16, -4, 1, -\frac{1}{4}, \frac{1}{16}, -\frac{1}{64}$ **21.** $\frac{8}{27}, \frac{4}{9}, \frac{2}{3}, 1, \frac{3}{2}, \frac{9}{4}, \frac{27}{8}$ **23.** The coefficient is 2 and the exponent is -4. **25.** 1 **27.** $\frac{16}{7}$ **29.** 0.001 **31.** 20,000.0002

33.
$$h^5 \cdot h^3 = h^8$$
$$h^3 \cdot h^5 = h^8$$
$$h^8 \div h^3 = h^5$$
$$h^8 \div h^5 = h^3$$

35.
$$\frac{1}{v} \cdot v^5 = v^4$$
$$v^5 \cdot \frac{1}{v} = v^4$$
$$v^4 \div v^5 = \frac{1}{v}$$
$$v^4 \div \frac{1}{v} = v^5$$

37.
$$z^2 \cdot z^4 = z^6$$
$$z^4 \cdot z^2 = z^6$$
$$z^6 \div z^2 = z^4$$
$$z^6 \div z^4 = z^2$$

39. $-\frac{6}{m^2}$ **41.** $4V^2$ **43.** $3M^6$ **45.** xy^2 **47.** $\frac{3y^2}{4xm^3}$ **49.** True **51.** True **53.** False **55.** False **57.** $\frac{17}{16}$ **59.** 11 **61.** -2 **63.** c **65.** 0.0000623 **67.** 0.00078306

1.8 Pages 27–29

1. The square root of a number a is a number x such that $x^2 = a$. **3.** $\frac{7}{2}$ **5.** $\sqrt{10}$ or $-\sqrt{10}$ **7.** Product **9.** ab **11.** ab **13.** 7 **15.** $\frac{a}{3}$ **17.** False **19.** False **21.** True **23.** True **25.** False **27.** False **29.** True **31.** False **33.** True **35.** $15\sqrt{2} \doteq 21.2$ **37.** $1000\sqrt{10} \doteq 3162.3$ **39.** $11\sqrt{6} \doteq 26.9$ **41.** $30\sqrt{7} \doteq 79.4$ **43.** 56 **45.** $\sqrt{61} \doteq 7.8$ **47.** $\frac{1}{3}\sqrt{3} \doteq 0.6$ **49.** $\frac{2}{5}\sqrt{5} \doteq 0.9$ **51.** 120 **53.** -1.6 **55.** $(20.78)^2 = 431.8084 \doteq 432$

1.9 Page 31

1. An assumption **3.** A proved statement **5.** It is impossible to define all terms. **7.** TA: real numbers, addition **9.** $1 + 1 = 2$ by the definition of 2, so 2 is a real number by closure of add. **11.** Since 2 is real, $\frac{1}{2}$ is real because every nonzero real has a real reciprocal.

13.

$5 = 4 + 1$	Def. of 5
$= (2 + 2) + 1$	Theorem, p. 31
$= 2 + (2 + 1)$	Assoc. of add.
$= 2 + 3$	Def. of 3

2.1 Pages 36–37

1. Transitive property of $<$ **3.** Trichotomy property **5.** $>$ **7.** $>$ **9.** $<$ **11.** $<$ **13.** True only if $a > 0$

15. $c < b < a$ **17.** $z \geq 7$ **19.** $x < 0$ **21.** $m > -8$
23. $x \geq -2.2$ **25.** $m \geq -1$ **27.** $-\frac{10}{3}$ and $-\frac{20}{3}$

2.2 Pages 39–40

1. TA: $2x + 3$ **3.** TA: $x^2 = 9$ **5.** False **7.** True **9.** -2 **11.** -2
13. $(-9, -11)$ or $(-11, -9)$ **15.** $10x + 3y$ **17.** $3x + 100$ **19.** $100 - 8x$ **21.** 10,000
23. 14 **25.** $\emptyset$ **27.** TA: $(0, -1)$ **29.** TA: $(1, -1)$

2.3 Pages 42–43

1. Adding any number or multiplying by a positive
3. Added $10y$ **5.** Multiplied by $\frac{1}{19}$ **7.** $0 \leq 2M$
9. $6y + 27 < 7y - 2$ **11.** Add -10, $4t = -12$ **13.** Add $-v$, $-3 = 10$
15. Apply distributivity, $2x + 2 \geq 3 - 12x$ **17.** Apply distributivity, $9z - 18 + 3z < 400$ **19.** Multiply by 10, $15t + 4t = 170$
21. Multiply by 9, $d \leq 27(d - 5) + 54$ **23.** Add $-A^2$, $3A - \pi \leq 0$ **25.** Multiply by 10, $5(3c - 3) = 2(c + 4)$
27. Multiply by 3, $3 - (2F - 1) > 3F$ **29.** Multiply by 6, $2(v + 2) < 2 - 4v$ **31.** $t = -3$
33. $\emptyset$ **35.** $x \geq \frac{1}{14}$ **37.** $z < \frac{209}{6}$ **39.** $t = \frac{170}{19}$ **41.** $d \geq \frac{81}{26}$
43. $A \leq \frac{\pi}{3}$ **45.** $c = \frac{23}{13}$ **47.** $F < \frac{4}{5}$ **49.** $v < -\frac{1}{3}$ **51.** $H \geq 0$
53. All reals **55.** $w = 750$ **57.** $K \geq \frac{1}{3}$ **59.** $x = -12$ **61.** 1640

2.4 Pages 46–47

1. for $x - 5$ **3.** for $3m + 8$ **5.** A, s **7.** $d = \frac{c}{\pi}$
9. $4x - 8 = 6x$ **11.** $y \leq 3x - 2$ **13.** $f = 2g - e$ **15.** $A = 11$
17. $x = -\frac{11}{3}$ or $x = -\frac{5}{3}$ **19.** $t = -\frac{13}{4}$ **21.** $x \leq \frac{13}{3}$ **23.** $m = -2$ or $m = -\frac{10}{3}$
25. $F = \frac{9}{5}C + 32$ **27.** TA: 95°F = 35°C **29.** $n = \frac{S + 360}{180}$ **31.** $r = \frac{3600}{t}$
33. 72 sec, 80 sec, $55\frac{5}{13}$ sec **35.** $65\frac{5}{11}$ mph **37.** $y \leq x + 3m$

2.5 Pages 49–50

1. TA: $2x + 3$ **3.** TA: $2x + 3y + 4z + 5$
5. The FOIL theorem shows how to multiply two binomials. It takes its name from the first letters of the four terms.
7. $9a^2 + 9a + 2$ **9.** $8 - 6y + y^2$ **11.** $4x^2 - 1$
13. $3a^2 - 6a + 4ab - 8b$ **15.** $x^2 + 2xy + y^2$ **17.** $a^2 - 2ab + b^2$
19. $100t^2 + 20tu + u^2$ **21.** $(50 + 8)(60 + 7) = 3000 + 350 + 480 + 56 = 3886 = 58 \cdot 67$
23. $3x^2 + xy - 2y^2$ **25.** $3x^3 - 2x^2y - 3xy^2 + 2y^3$ **27.** $6x^2 - 4xy$
29. Substitute for the variables **33.** Any value but zero **35.** True

2.6 Pages 53–54

1. The real numbers **3.** d **5.**
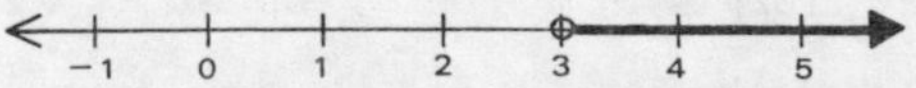

7.
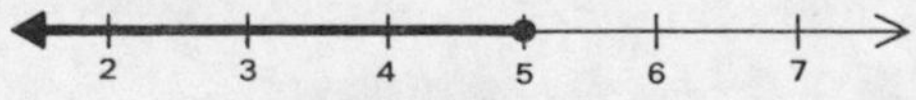

9.
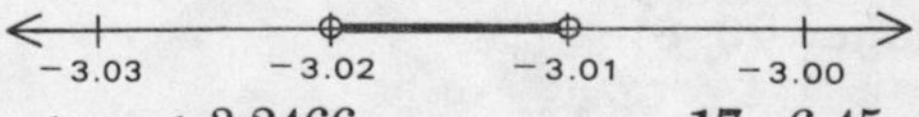

11. b **13.** Yes **15.** $3.2456 < w < 3.2466$ **17.** 6.45 million

19. TA: $x \to 109 - x$ **21.** TA: $x \to 5x$ **23.** $y \geq -4.8$

25. $A \geq -\frac{1}{2}$  **27.** All reals **29.** $m \leq 31$ 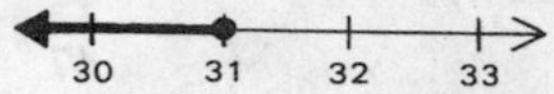 **31.** $\emptyset$ **33.** $\emptyset$

2.7 Pages 57–58

1. Existence of multiplicative identity, closure of addition
3. Existence of reciprocals, closure of multiplication
5. The set of numbers between two given numbers, possibly inclusive
7. No **9.** Yes **11.** An ordered list of intervals, each a subset of the last
13–19. *Answers will vary.* **23.** TA: $\{y: 2.0013 < y < 2.0017\}$ **25.** $99.75 < t < 99.85$

3.1 Pages 62–64

1–7. *Answers will vary.*
9. TA: What is the total stopping time? $x + y$, addition—joining
11. TA: How many are there altogether? $x + y$, addition—counting
13. TA: How far did I drive? $x \cdot y$, multiplication—repeated addition
15. Subtraction **17.** Division **19.** 3920 km **21.** rt miles
23. $0.20x$ grams **25.** $0.20x + y$ grams **27.** $3x$ dollars **29.** $0.13x + 0.17y$ dollars
31. $0.08P$, $1.08P$ dollars **33.** $n - 4$ **35.** $n - 1$
37. $n + 3$ or $n + 4$, depending on when his birthday is
39. $t - 16$ **41.** $t + 32$ **43.** $r + t$ **45.** $T - g$

3.2 Pages 67–68

1. A mathematical representation of a situation **3–11.** *Answers will vary.*
18. Geometric abstractionist whose work is influenced by her interest in the fourth dimension of modern physics and mathematics

3.3 Pages 71–72

1. 10 **3.** 0 **5.** x **7.** $-z$ **9.** $|x|$ **11.** 97
13. 828 **15.** 46 **17.** 1 **19.** 16 **21.** False **23.** True
25. True **27.** True **29.** False **31.** 244 **33.** 781 **35.** $\frac{7}{1100}$
37. False, for example, $\{x: a < x < b\}$ and $\{x: a \leq x \leq b\}$ **39.** When $x < 0$ **41.** $\emptyset$

3.4 Pages 75–76

1. 7 and -7 **3.** $-1.5, -6.5$ **5.** $9, -5$ **7.** $-1.5, -6.5$ **9.** L to 26
11. Interval **13.** b **15.** 15 **17.** 0 **19.** 3.015
21. 17 **23.** $\{x: |x - 17| \geq 10\}$ or $\{x: x \leq 7$ or $x \geq 27\}$
25. **27.** **29.**
31. $|W - 132| \leq 3$ **33.** $|L - \sqrt{2}| \leq 0.0001$ **35.** $|P - 30{,}000| \leq 300$

3.5 Pages 79–81

1. All on a vertical line through (2, 0) **3.** All on y-axis

Ex. 5–9: Typical answers: **5.** (2, 3) **7.** (−3, −5) **9.** (0, 5) **11.** Points of the plane
13. 10 **15.** 5 **17.** 50 **19.** $\sqrt{2}$ **21.** 8 **23.** 5
25. $\sqrt{41}$ **27.** $5\sqrt{2}$ **29.** $17\sqrt{2}$ **31.** $\sqrt{a^2 + (b - 1)^2}$ **33.** 1 to 2
35. 13.9″ **37.** $\sqrt{13}$ **39.** $\sqrt{404} \doteq 20$ miles **41.** a, b, and c are all true
43. Yes **45.** Yes **47.** Yes **49.** 500 m **51.** $400 - 200\sqrt{2} \doteq 118$ m

3.6 Pages 82–83

1. xy **3.** $n - 3$ **5.** $2a$ **7.** $\frac{x}{30}$
9. $a > b$ **11.** $n - 68$ **13.** $2x - 6\frac{1}{5}$
15. $3 - \frac{2}{3}n$ **17.** $\frac{6}{x} = \frac{1}{3}y$ **19.** $15(n - 6) > n$
21. $\frac{b}{17} = \frac{5}{3}$ **23.** $|n - 212| \le 0.01$ **25.** $x + y + z$
27. $7x + 3y + \frac{1}{2}z$ hr **29.** $400x + 150y + 75z$ dollars **31.** $3(x - 30) + 1.5y$ lb
33. $0.011b$ **35.** $\frac{p}{100}(10{,}000) = 100p$ **37.** $0.048w + 0.10n$

4.1 Pages 89–91

1. Images in a mirror **3.** F' is located so that m is the ⊥ bisector of $\overline{FF'}$.
5. Property 2 **7.** Def. of reflection **9.** Property 3 **11.** Property 4
13. Property 1 **15.** Clockwise **17.** Clockwise **19.** Counterclockwise
21. Orientation

23.

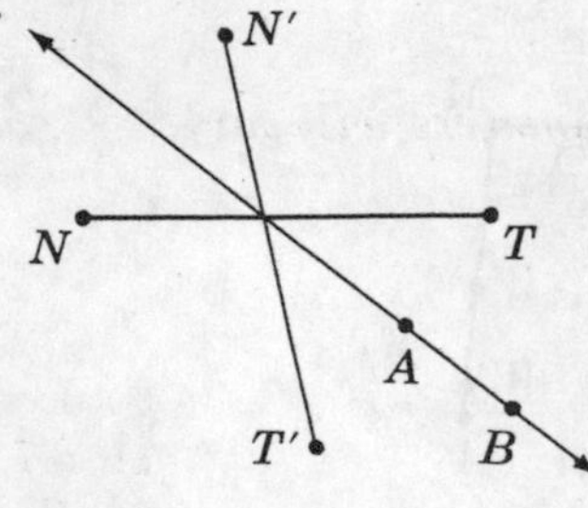

25.

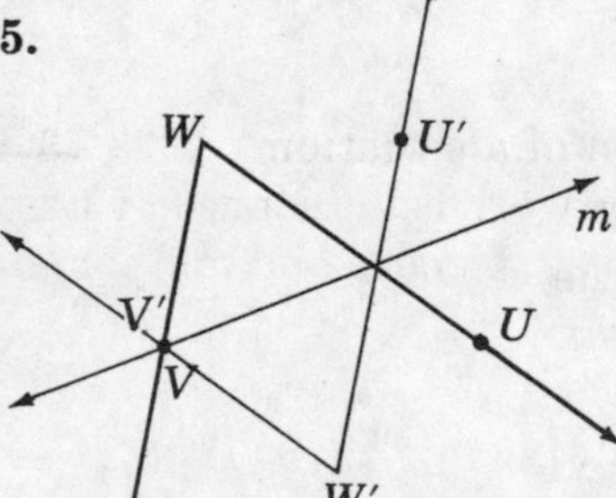

27.

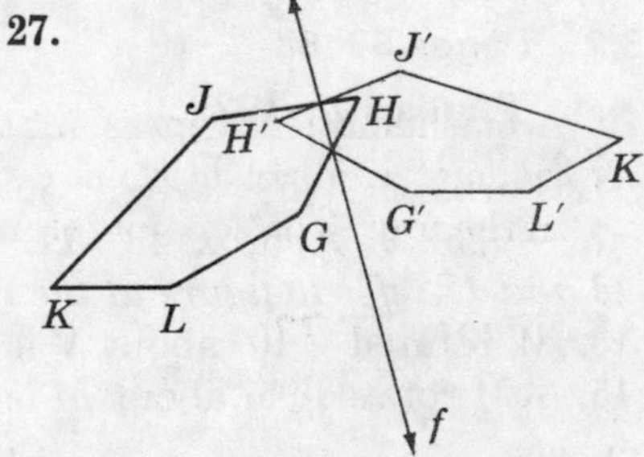

29.

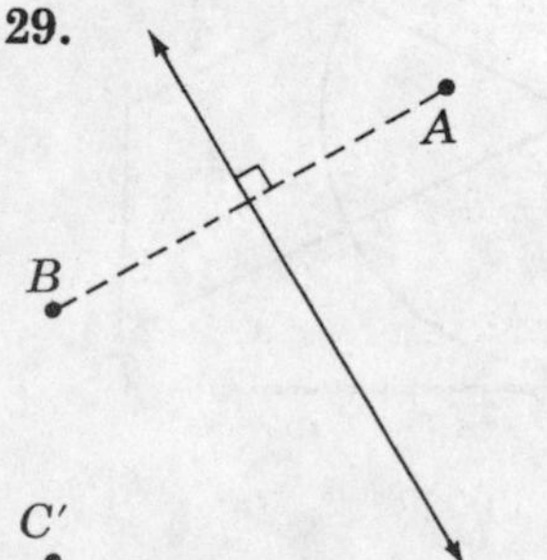

31.

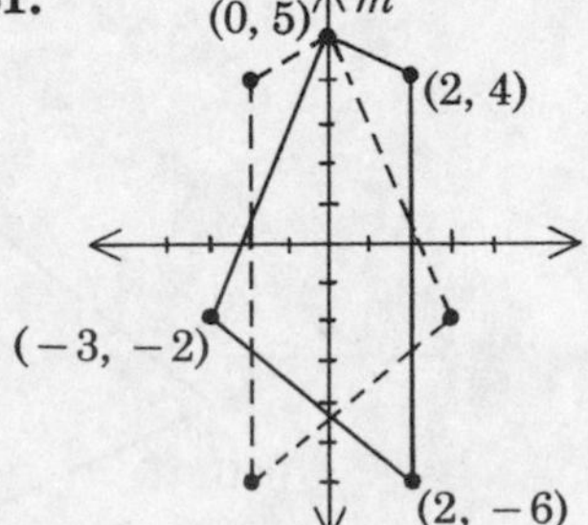

Images are (−2, 4), (0, 5), (3, −2), and (−2, −6). The corresponding sides and angles have the same measure.

4.2 Pages 94–95

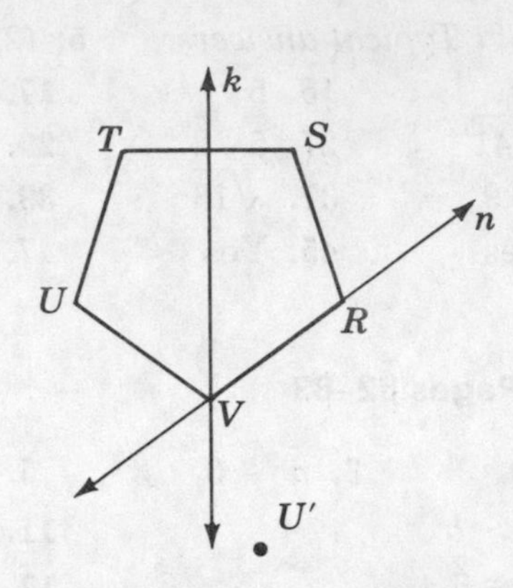

1. Reflection image of P over line m
3. Reflection image of $\overline{PQ}$ over line t
5. $\triangle HEG$ 7. $\overline{FH}$
9. A 1-1 correspondence between sets of points
11. $(-5, 4)$ 13. $(-8, 0)$ 15. Mapped
17. Reflections preserve angle measure.
19. Def. of reflection 21. Refls. switch orientation

23 and 25 refer to figure at right.

23. $r_n(U) = U'$ 25. $r_k(\angle VUT) = \angle VRS$

4.3 Pages 97–98

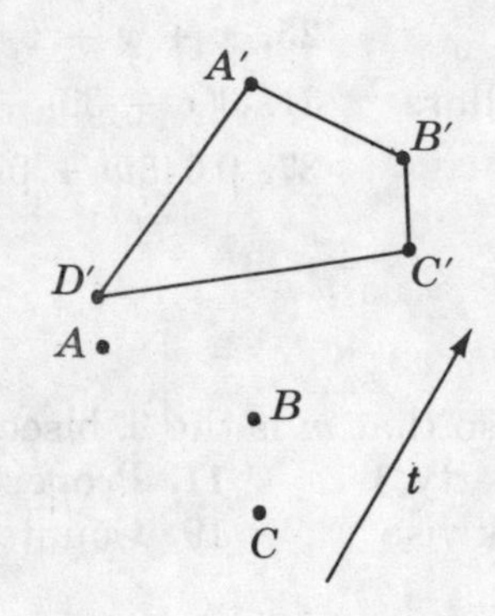

1. AM or BP or CQ or the distance between any point of $\triangle ABC$ and its image
3. $t(Q)$ is a point on $\overleftrightarrow{CQ}$ the same distance from Q as C, but in the opposite direction.
5. Slides 7. $(-4, 2\frac{1}{2})$ 9. $(0, 0)$

11 and 13 refer to figure at left.

11. $t(A) = A'$ 13. $t(ABCD) = A'B'C'D'$
15. $(x + 2, y + 9)$
17. Image has vertices $(4, 2)$, $(5, -5)$ and $(0, 7)$.
19. d

4.4 Pages 101–102

1. Turns 3. 135° 5. 135°
7. −135° 9. Approx. 43° 11. True

13 and 15 refer to figure at the right.

13. W rotated −10° about V is W'
15. $\overline{AM}$ rotated 95° about M is $\overline{A'M}$

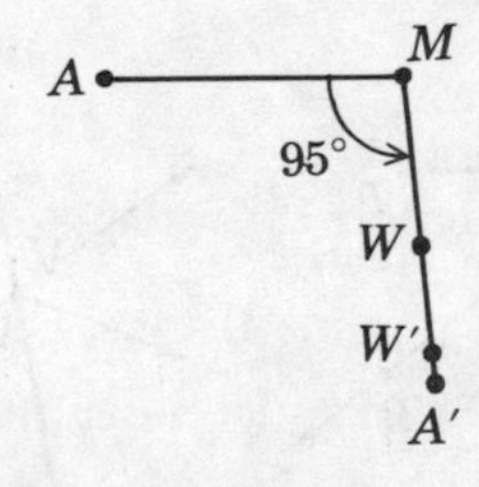

17.

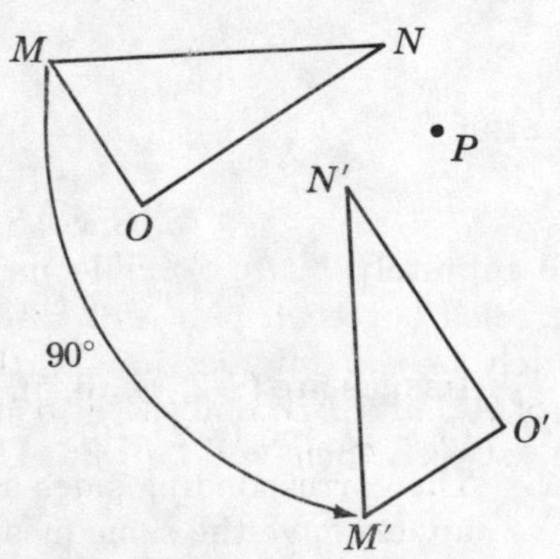

19.

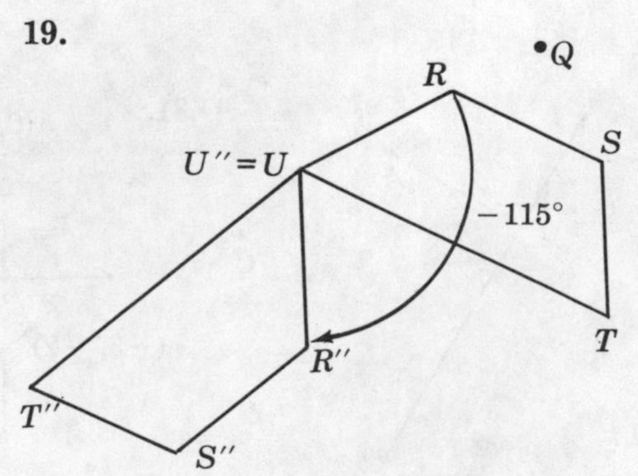

$\overleftrightarrow{MN}$ and $\overleftrightarrow{M'N'}$ seem to be perpendicular.

21. Close to the point $(2, -6)$ which would be the image under a rotation of −90°

4.5 Pages 105–106

1. Composite 3. $T_2 \circ T_1$
5. Rotation of 150° with the same center
7. Rotation of $-30°$ with the same center
9. Translation 11. (12, 27)
13. $(-3, 15)$ 15. $h \circ t(x, y) = (x, y + 7)$
17. L 19. $\triangle AOP$ 21. N
23. L 25. $EOAM$

For 27, 29, and 31, the image of $\triangle ABC$ under the given composite is shown at right.

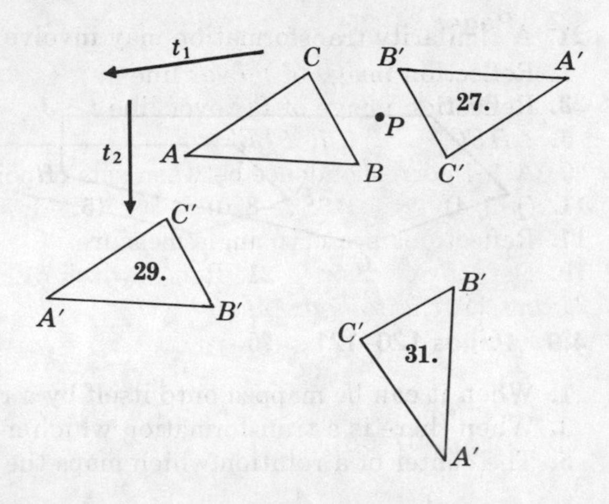

4.6 Pages 109–110

1. Translation 3. Translation 5. Perpendicular to m and n
7. Center P and magnitude 140° 9. A given center and magnitude, a composite of reflections over intersecting lines

11.

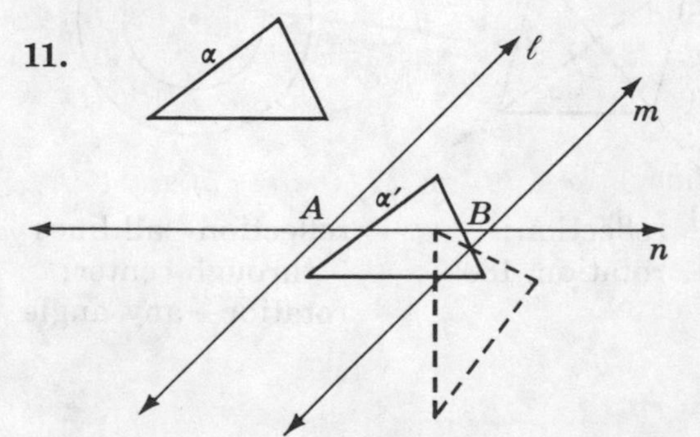

$r_m \circ r_\ell$ is a translation of 20 units perpendicular to line ℓ.

13.

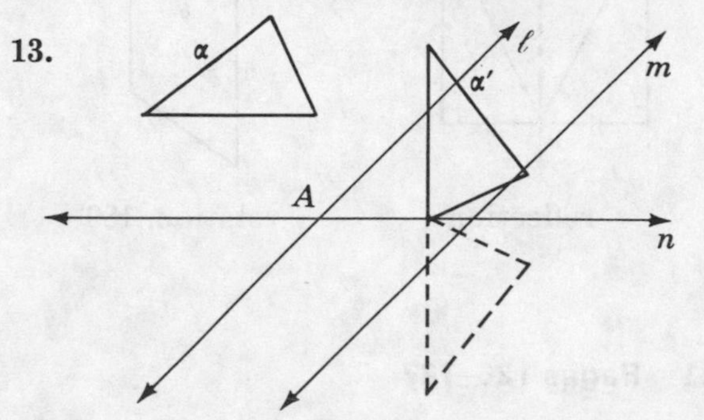

$r_m \circ r_\ell$ is a rotation of $-90°$ about A.

15. $r_k \circ r_m$ is a rotation of 180° about the point of intersection.
17. The composite of two reflections over parallel lines is a translation.

4.7 Pages 113–114

1. When there is an isometry which maps one onto the other
3. Collinearity, segments, distance, angle measure
5. Same radii 7. Same measure 9. *SSS, SAS, ASA*
11. Three reflections reverse orientation but $\triangle ABC$ and $\triangle XYZ$ have the same orientation.
13. There are infinitely many possible pairs of reflecting lines but each pair will intersect at P, which is the intersection of the $\perp$ bisectors of $\overline{AC}$ and $\overline{BD}$, and the measure of the angle between them will be $\frac{1}{2}m\angle APC$.

4.8 Pages 117–118

1. Center, magnitude 3. They multiply distance by the magnitude.
5. 12 7. 21 9. I 11. 2 13. $\frac{24}{5}$ 15. $(\frac{1}{2}, -\frac{5}{2})$
17. $(2, -\frac{9}{2})$ 19. A composite of isometries and/or size transformations

21. A similarity transformation may involve isometries.

23.

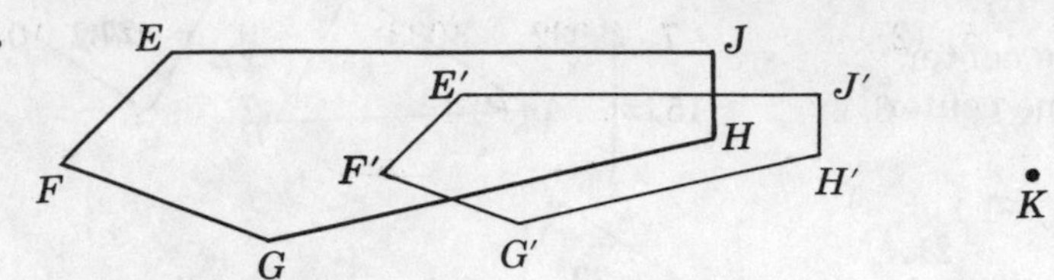

25. Is
27. Is not

4.9 Pages 120–121

1. When it can be mapped onto itself by a reflection
3. When there is a transformation which maps the figure onto itself
5. The center of a rotation which maps the figure onto itself

7.

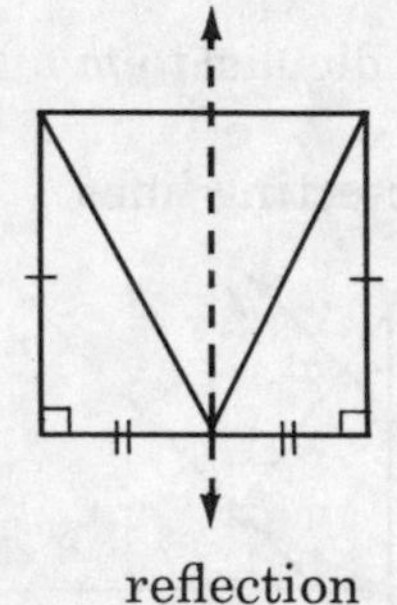

reflection

9.

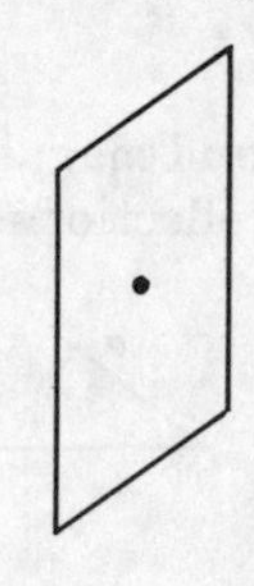

rotation, 180°

11.

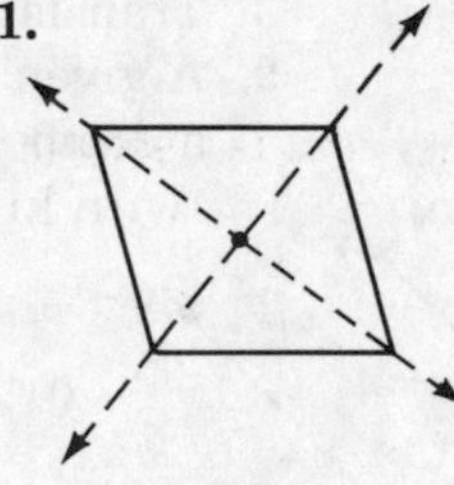

reflection; rotation, 180°

13.

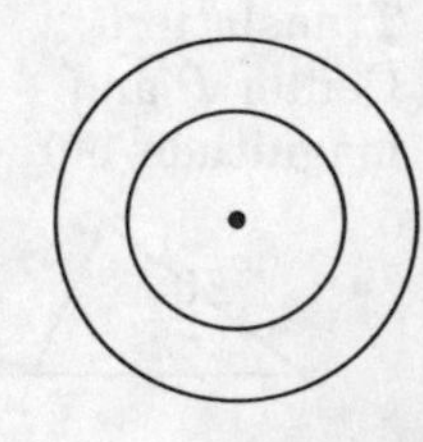

reflection—all lines through center; rotation—any angle

5.1 Pages 126–127

1. 4×6 **3.** c **5.** $\begin{bmatrix} 5 \\ 2 \end{bmatrix}$ **7.** mn **9.** Cayley, 1858
11. -7 **13.** 15 **15.** 2×6 **17.** $\sqrt{10}, 7\sqrt{2}, 2\sqrt{13}$

5.2 Pages 130–131

1. [23] **3.** [8] **5.** [0] **7.** 2×3 **9.** 45
11. 3×4 **13.** 8×9 **15.** Any of the form $a \times b$ and $c \times d$, where $b \neq c$
17. $\begin{bmatrix} 6 & 11 \\ 12 & 18 \end{bmatrix}$ **19.** Not possible **21.** $\begin{bmatrix} 0 & 1 \\ -1 & 0 \end{bmatrix}$ **23.** $\begin{bmatrix} 0 & \sqrt{2} & 8\sqrt{2} \\ 0 & \sqrt{2} & 0 \end{bmatrix}$
25. [26 58 3.9] **27.** $a = -\frac{1}{2}, b = -\frac{7}{6}$

5.3 Pages 133–134

1. $\begin{bmatrix} -4 \\ -9 \end{bmatrix}$ **3.** $\begin{bmatrix} 0 \\ 0 \end{bmatrix}$ **5.** $\begin{bmatrix} 1 & 0 \\ 0 & -1 \end{bmatrix}$ **7.** (100, −70) **9.** (6, 0) **11.** $A \cdot P$

13. $\begin{bmatrix} -2 & -3 & 4 & -2 \\ 4 & 2 & -6 & 5 \end{bmatrix}$; reflection over y-axis.

15. $\begin{bmatrix} 10 & 7 & -16 & 12 \\ 4 & 2 & -6 & 5 \end{bmatrix}$; this type has not been discussed.

17. a. $\begin{bmatrix} 30 \\ -17 \end{bmatrix}, \begin{bmatrix} 14 \\ -8 \end{bmatrix}, \begin{bmatrix} -18 \\ 10 \end{bmatrix}$ **b.** No **c.** Yes **19.** b

5.4 Page 137

1. $\begin{bmatrix}1 & 0\\0 & -1\end{bmatrix}$ **3.** $\begin{bmatrix}-1 & 0\\0 & 1\end{bmatrix}$ **5.** (2, −7) **7.** (1032, −1033) **9.** (−1032, 1033)
11. ⊥ bisector **13.** (−1, 0), (−1, 1), (−6, 2) **15.** $r_{x=-y}(P) = P'$ **17.** $(-y, -x)$

5.5 Pages 141–142

1. h **3.** g **5.** f **7.** j **9.** True
11. *See p. 140.* **13.** $B \cdot A$ **15.** $C \cdot C$ **17.** $u \circ v$ **19.** $v \circ t$
21. $CD = \begin{bmatrix}7 & -8\\10 & -8\end{bmatrix}$, $DP = \begin{bmatrix}27\\65\end{bmatrix}$, $C(DP) = \begin{bmatrix}103\\130\end{bmatrix}$, $(CD)P = \begin{bmatrix}103\\130\end{bmatrix}$
$C(DP) = (CD)P$ because matrix multiplication is associative.
23. *Answers will vary.* **25.** $\begin{bmatrix}112 & 75 & -170\\-8 & -3 & -2\end{bmatrix}$ **27.** $\begin{bmatrix}1 & 0\\0 & -1\end{bmatrix}$

5.6 Page 144

1. R_{90} **3.** The theorem is used to find the matrix for the composite of two transformations with known matrices.
5. $\begin{bmatrix}-1 & 0\\0 & -1\end{bmatrix}$ **7.** (−8, −10) **9.** $(-a, -b)$ **11.** $r_{x=y}$ or R_{180}
13. $\begin{bmatrix}0 & 1\\-1 & 0\end{bmatrix}$ **15.** $\begin{bmatrix}-1 & 0\\0 & -1\end{bmatrix} \cdot \begin{bmatrix}-1 & 0\\0 & -1\end{bmatrix} = \begin{bmatrix}1 & 0\\0 & 1\end{bmatrix}$ **17.** $\begin{bmatrix}0 & -1\\-1 & 0\end{bmatrix}$ which is the matrix for $r_{x=-y}$

5.7 Pages 147–148

1. In general, translations do not map (0, 0) onto itself.
3. $\begin{bmatrix}2 & 0\\0 & 2\end{bmatrix}$ **5.** *See p. 146.* **7. a.** (0, 1) **b.** (1, 0) **c.** $\begin{bmatrix}0 & 1\\1 & 0\end{bmatrix}$
9. a. (−1, 0) **b.** (0, −1) **c.** $\begin{bmatrix}-1 & 0\\0 & -1\end{bmatrix}$ **11.** Yes **13.** $\begin{bmatrix}3 & -1\\1 & 1\end{bmatrix}$
15. The first image has vertices (−4, −6), (4, 6), (4, −2) and (−4, −8), and the second has vertices (−2, −3), (2, 3), (2, −1) and (−2, −4), so $S_{\frac{1}{2}} \circ S_{-2}$ is R_{180}. **17.** 63%
19. The matrix for R_{180} is $\begin{bmatrix}-1 & 0\\0 & -1\end{bmatrix}$, which is the matrix for S_{-1} by Theorem 5.7.2.

6.1 Pages 152–153

1. A variable is a symbol which may stand for any object from a given set of objects. **3.** The dimension of a sentence is the number of variables in the sentence.
5. Ordered pair **7.** TA: (200, 1) **9.** TA: (2, −1)
11. TA: (0, 9), (1, 9), (2, 9), (5, 9), (−2, 9), (−3, 9) **13.** 2
15. 2 **17.** 2 **19.** 2 **21.** 17, 19 **23.** 2
25. It may be a simplification of $0 \cdot x + y = 4$. **27.** 2 **29.** 0
31. TA: (0, −5), (2, 0), (4, 5), (−2, −10) **33.** TA: (2, 0), (3, 1), (3, 2), (4, 4)
35. TA: (2, 2), (3, 1), (4, 0), (5, −1) **37.** (39, 31) **39.** $(\frac{49}{2}, \frac{31}{10})$

6.2 Pages 156–157

1. A line which is neither horizontal nor vertical

3. Any equation of the form $x = a$, for any real number a

5. True
7. $x = 2$
9. $y = 4$
11. $\frac{x}{-1} = \frac{y}{4}$
13. $x = a$

Ex. 15–25: Graphs are described.

15. Vertical line through $(-4, 0)$
17. Horizontal line through $(0, 14)$
19. The y-axis
21. Line through $(0, 0)$ and $(1, 4)$
23. Line through $(0, 0)$ and $(3, 2)$
25. Line through $(0, 0)$ and $(5, 6)$
27. Lines approach x-axis
29. Lines approach y-axis
31. $(1, 1.75)$, $(2, 3.50)$, etc., $c = 1.75n$
33. $(1, 1.1)$, $(2, 2.2)$, etc., $y = 1.1m$
35. $(2, 1)$, $(4, 2)$, etc., $h = \frac{1}{2}n$

6.3 Pages 159–160

1. The set of points a given distance from a given point
3. Yes
5. No
7. $x^2 + y^2 = \frac{1}{4}$
9. $x^2 + y^2 = 143.5$
11. $(x - h)^2 + (y - k)^2 = r^2$
13. $(x - 6)^2 + y^2 = 81$
15. $(-2, -3)$, 2
17. $(-7, 0)$, 5
19. TA: $(8, 9)$, $(8, -9)$, $(12, 1)$, $(12, -1)$, $(0, \sqrt{145})$, circle, center $(0, 0)$, $r = \sqrt{145}$
21. TA: $(\sqrt{11}, 0)$, $(0\sqrt{11})$, $(3, \sqrt{2})$, $(\sqrt{2}, -3)$, $(\sqrt{7}, 2)$, circle, center $(0, 0)$, $r = \sqrt{11}$
23. Graph is a circle, center $(0, 0)$, $r = \sqrt{10}$
25. Graph is a circle, center $(0, 5)$, $r = 4$
27. TA: $(-3, 2)$, $(-13, 2)$, $(-8, -3)$, $(-4, 5)$, $(-11, 6)$
29. TA: $(x + 3)^2 + (y - 3)^2 = 9$
31. $(x - 3)^2 + (y + 1)^2 = 148$
33. 0.8 or -0.8
35. $\frac{\sqrt{2}}{2}$ or $\frac{-\sqrt{2}}{2}$
37. c

6.4 Pages 162–163

1. $a = 1$, $b = 0$
3. $a = -1$, $b = -14$
5. TA: $(6, 0)$, $(0, 6)$, $(-6, 0)$, $(0, -6)$
7. $(x, y) \rightarrow (x + 2, y)$
9. TA: $(3, 3)$, $(-2, 8)$, $(2, 6)$, $(1, 7)$, $(-7, 3)$, $(-5, -1)$
11. *See page 162.*
13. $x + 2, y$
15. $x - \pi, y$
17. $x + 2, y + 6$
19. $(8, -2)$, $2\sqrt{2}$
21. $(x, y) \rightarrow (x + 3, y - 2)$
23. $(-67, 14)$
25. The first points are on the line through $(1, 1)$ and $(3, 4)$; second points are on the parallel line $(1, 0)$ and $(3, 3)$.

6.5 Pages 167–168

1. They are parallel, and the first is 4 units above the second.
3. $\frac{3}{2}$
5. -3
7. $\frac{2}{3}$
9. $-\frac{1}{2}$
11. The second coordinate of the point where the line intersects the y-axis
13. $\frac{5}{2}$
15. 4
17. Horizontal
19. $y = -\frac{1}{4}x + 6$
21. $x = -3$
23. No
25. Yes
27. $\frac{5}{8}$
29. No slope
31. -2

Ex. 33–37: Graph is the line containing the given points.

33. $(1, -1)$, $(5, 2)$
35. $(0, 5)$, $(-1, 0)$
37. $(8, 0)$, $(9, 3)$
39. TA: $(2, -65)$
41. 1.75, cost per gallon
43. 1.1, yards per metre
45. $\frac{1}{2}$, heads per toss
47. $\frac{y_2 - y_1}{x_2 - x_1} = \frac{y_1 - y_2}{x_1 - x_2}$ Slopes are equal, not opposite. It *is* the same line.
49. $5x - 4y = 0$

6.6 Pages 172–173

1. Two points, a point and a parallel line, a point and a perpendicular line

3. $(y + 7) = \frac{1}{2}(x - 4)$ **5.** $-\frac{1}{10}$ **7.** -4 **9.** $\frac{1}{2}$
11. $-\frac{3}{14}, \frac{14}{3}$, Theorem 6.6.2 **13.** $y - 180 = 180(x - 3)$ **15.** $y - 7 = -\frac{3}{4}(x - 4)$
17. $y - 8 = -\frac{8}{9}(x - 6)$ **19.** $y = -\frac{2}{3}x - 2$ **21.** $y - 65 = \frac{81}{281}(x + 281)$
23. It gives relation between Fahrenheit and Celsius temperatures. **25.** $A = 40t + 500$
27. $\frac{70}{9}$ **29.** 30.82 **31.** $y - 4 = -\frac{3}{4}(x - 3)$ **33.** Yes

6.7 Page 175

1. The point of a segment equidistant from its endpoints
3. (3, 15) **5.** $(-\frac{7}{2}, -5)$ **7.** $\left(\frac{x_1 + x_2}{2}, \frac{y_1 + y_2}{2}\right)$ **9.** True
11. $(x - \frac{3}{2})^2 + (y - 2)^2 = \frac{229}{4}$ **13.** $y - 50 = \frac{1}{15}(x + 5)$
15. $\frac{1}{2}(c - a) + a = \frac{1}{2}c - \frac{1}{2}a + a = \frac{1}{2}c + \frac{1}{2}a = \frac{a + c}{2}$

$\frac{1}{2}(d - b) + b = \frac{1}{2}d - \frac{1}{2}b + b = \frac{1}{2}d + \frac{1}{2}b = \frac{b + d}{2}$

6.8 Page 178

1. Half-plane, left **3.** The union of the line $Ax + By = C$ and one of its half-planes
5. The exterior of the circle with center $(-4, 3)$ and radius 4
Ex. 7–15: Graphs are described.
7. The half-plane above the line through (1, 1) and $(-1, 4)$
9. The circle with center $(3, -4)$ and radius $\sqrt{6}$ and its interior
11. The whole plane except (0, 0)
13. The half-plane above the horizontal line through $(0, \frac{11}{3})$
15. The line through (0, 11) and $(-2, 3)$

7.1 Pages 184–185

1. Two or more sentences connected by the word *and* or the word *or*
3. $a > -2.02$ and $a < -2.01$ **5.** Union **7.** $3 - t \leq 5$ and $3 - t \geq -5$
9. $a = 0$ and $b - 3 = 0$ **11.** d **13.** 96 97 98 99 100 101
15. $\emptyset$ **17.** Because no number can be both more than 5 and less than -1
19. Any number between 2 and 3 **21.** Any number between -3.1 and -2.9
23. $y(y + 6) = 0$ **25.** $(w - 5)^2 + (x - 2)^2 = 0$ **27.** $(x - 5)^2 + (y + 2)^2 + (z - 1)^2 = 0$
29. 0 **31.** $\emptyset$ **33.** $y \leq 0$ **35.** $|S - 0.25(\frac{1900}{4})| < 0.05(\frac{1900}{4})$
37. $x - 3 \geq -4$ and $x - 3 \leq 4$, $-1 \leq x \leq 7$ **39.** $x - 3 = -4$ or $x - 3 = 4$, $\{7, -1\}$

7.2 Pages 188–189

1. Finding the solutions which satisfy every sentence **3.** $-\sqrt{17}$ **5.** $(9, -17)$
7. TA: (6, 0) **9.** TA: $(-1, 0)$, (2, 1), (5, 2), (8, 3)
11. TA: (9, 0), (9, 1), (9, 2), $(9, -6)$ **13.** TA: (0, 1), (0, 2), (0, 5), (0, 8)
15. True **17.** TA: $(1, \frac{1}{2})$ **19.** Infinite, $\{u: u \geq 4\}$
21. Infinite, $\{z: -2 < z < 2\}$ **23.** One, $\{3\}$ **25.** $\emptyset$ **27.** One, $\{(22, -\frac{19}{2}, \frac{25}{2})\}$
29. Near $(-4, -14)$ **31.** $(-6, -3)$ **33.** Near $(6, -19)$ **35.** $\emptyset$

7.3 Pages 192–193

1. $(1, \frac{1}{4})$ **3.** $(3, \frac{1}{5})$ **5.** $-2b = 5$ **7.** Yes
9. $15x + 10y = 50$ **11.** $17x = 52$ **13.** $17y = 7$ **15.** 11 and 13

17. TA: $-5x - 25y = 85$
$5x + 2y = 3$

19. TA: $6a = b - 2$
$-6a = -12b - 6$

21. $(\frac{6}{19}, \frac{8}{19})$ **23.** $(\frac{1}{6}, \frac{13}{2})$

25. (0, 6) **27.** (0, 0) **29.** (90, 30) **31.** $\left(\frac{2\sqrt{2} - 3\sqrt{3}}{13}, \frac{-\sqrt{3} - 8\sqrt{2}}{13}\right)$ **33.** $(\frac{2}{7}, -\frac{20}{7})$

7.4 Pages 195–196

1. Solve the system of the first two equations, and test the solutions in the third.

3. $\begin{bmatrix} 1 & 4 & -3 \\ 0 & 2 & 1 \\ 0 & 0 & 1 \end{bmatrix}$ dimensions 3×3, one solution likely

5. $\left(m, \frac{4m - 5}{11}, \frac{7m - 6}{11}\right)$, m any number **7.** $(\frac{2}{3}, 3, \frac{1}{2})$ **9.** No solution **11.** $(\frac{20}{13}, -\frac{2}{13})$

7.5 Pages 201–202

1. Russian, 20th, showed large systems have applications in production planning

3. American, 20th, developed diet problem solution by linear programming

5. As large as $5{,}000 \times 10{,}000$

7. The way to make maximum profit

9. *See p. 199.* **11.** (100, 0) **13.** (100, 0)

15. t = no. of tables, d = no. of desks, c = no. of chairs, r = no. of dressers

17. $t + d + 3c + 20r \leq 4000$ **19.** TA: $t = 1500$, $d = c = r = 0$

8.1 Pages 207–208

1. On the unit circle **3.** $\sin t$ **5.** R_{330} **7.** c **9.** g

11. i **13.** a **15.** i **17.** $\frac{1}{2}$ **19.** $\frac{\sqrt{3}}{2}$ **21.** $\frac{\sqrt{2}}{2}$

23. 1.414 **25.** 1.732 **27.** (−0.50, 0.87) **29.** 0 **31.** 1

33. 0.707 **35.** 0.5 **37.** 0 **39.** −1 **41.** −0.5 **43.** 0.866

45. cos 63° **47.** sin 94° **49.** True **51.** $90° < t < 270°$ **53.** 0 or 180°

8.2 Pages 210–211

1. 0.208 **3.** 0.875 **5.** 0.342 **7.** 0.707

9. If the sum of two degree measures is 90, then the sine of one is the cosine of the other. **11.** 82° **13.** 1

15. $(\frac{12}{13}, -\frac{5}{13})$, $(-\frac{12}{13}, -\frac{5}{13})$

17. 24° **19.** 42° **21.** No, rounded to 3 decimal places they are the same.

23. $\frac{\sqrt{2}}{2}$ **25.** 1 **27.** $\frac{\sqrt{3}}{2}$ **29.** $\frac{1}{2}$

8.3 Page 213

1. (cos t, sin t) **3.** 270° **5.** 0.940 **7.** 0.342 **9.** 0.342 **11.** −0.342

13. −0.342 **15.** −0.342 **17.** −0.988 **19.** −0.616 **21.** 0.559 **23.** −0.292

8.4 Pages 215–216

1. Those with the center (0, 0)

3. $\begin{bmatrix} 0.819 & -0.574 \\ 0.574 & 0.819 \end{bmatrix}$ **5.** $\begin{bmatrix} 0 & -1 \\ 1 & 0 \end{bmatrix}$ **7.** $\begin{bmatrix} 0 & 1 \\ -1 & 0 \end{bmatrix}$

9. $\begin{bmatrix} 1.036 & 4.116 & -1.752 \\ 3.452 & 0.212 & 5.736 \end{bmatrix}$

11. (−1159, 811) whose distance is $\sqrt{2{,}001{,}002} \doteq \sqrt{2{,}000{,}000}$

13. $\begin{bmatrix} -0.017 & -1 \\ 1 & -0.017 \end{bmatrix}$

8.5 Pages 218–219

1. False **3.** 1 **5.** First, $x + y$ **7.** y **9.** $\cos x \cdot \cos y - \sin x \cdot \sin y$

11. $\frac{\sqrt{6}+\sqrt{2}}{4}$ **13.** $\frac{\sqrt{2}+\sqrt{6}}{4}$ **15.** $\frac{\sqrt{6}+\sqrt{2}}{4}$ **17.** $\frac{\sqrt{2}-\sqrt{6}}{4}$ **19.** True

8.6 Pages 221–222

1. The magnitudes of a size transformation and rotation, each with center (0, 0), which map (1, 0) onto the point
3. $[\frac{3}{2}, 90°]$
5. [4.4, 30°]
7. $[\frac{3}{2}, 225°]$
9. $[\frac{3}{2}, 270°]$
11. [3, 180°]

13–27. *Pictured below.*

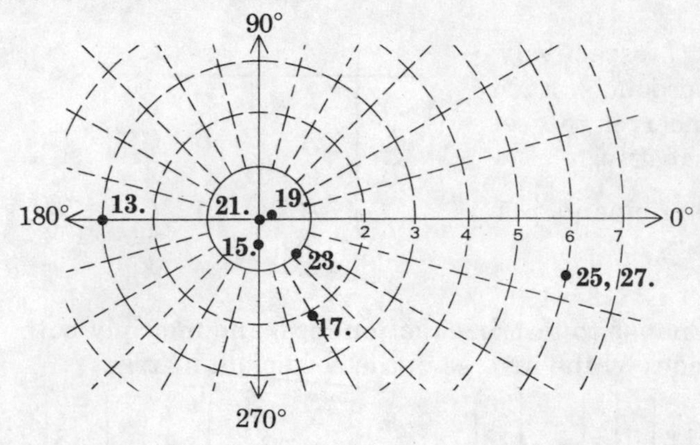

29. (0, 4.1)
31. (0, −0.001)
33. TA: [1, 460°]
35. On the circle with center (0, 0) and radius 5
37. On the line through (0, 0) making 100° angle with the positive x-axis
39. TA: [2, 377°], [2, 737°], [2, 1097°], [−2, 197°], [−2, 557°]
41. 270°
43. $292\frac{1}{2}°$

8.7 Pages 224–225

1. $(\cos\theta, \sin\theta)$ **3.** $(r\cos\theta, r\sin\theta)$ **5.** $(-2\cos 45°, -2\sin 45°)$
7. (2.0, 2.2) **9.** (34.2, −94.0) **11.** a **13.** b **15.** [1, 100°]
17. [3, 12°] **19.** [−1, 142°] **21.** [5, 180°] **23.** [1, 90°]

9.1 Pages 230–231

1. Closure, associativity, identity, inverses
3. A group in which the operation is multiplication
5. TA: The multiplicative group of positive rational numbers
7. Lacks closure **9.** 0 has no inverse. **11.** *Z*, *E* **13.** *Z*, *E*
15. A group in which the set is finite, $\langle\{1, -1\}, \cdot\rangle$
17. **a.** 1 **b.** TA: 3, $\frac{1}{3}$
19. **a.** 0 **b.** TA: 10, −10
21. No **23.** No **25.** Yes **27.** Yes

9.2 · Page 233

1. Yes **3.** No **5.** True **7.** TA: $-1 + x = 1$ **9.** TA: $-2 \cdot x = 1$
11. No **13.** No **15.** Yes **17.** No

9.3 Pages 236–238

1. Additive group of integral multiples of 10
3. By repeatedly adding 2 to itself and including 0 and inverses
5. TA: 6, 36, $\frac{1}{6}$ **7.** x^3 and x^{-3} are reciprocals. **9.** $(y^{13})^{17} = y^{221}$
11. 125 **13.** 2 **15.** 10^5 **17.** 10^{-6} **19.** 1 **21.** $\frac{1}{25}$
23. 3 **25.** 4^6 **27.** 3^{-8} **29.** 11^{34} **31.** 0.01 **33.** y^{15}
35. 2^{a+b} **37.** $\frac{1}{9m^2}$
39. TA: Additive group of integral multiples of a and multiplicative group of integral powers of a
41. Multiplication of powers **43.** $3(ma) = (3m)a$ **45.** $4(7) + 4(3) = 4(10)$

47. $x^6 + x^{20}$ **49.** $\frac{9v^6}{4t^2}$ **51.** $\frac{m^7}{3^7}$ **53.** 648 **55.** 6

9.4 Page 241

1. See if the product is the identity matrix. **3.** -17 **5.** -34
7. It determines if the matrix has an inverse. **9.** The inverse of A
11. $\begin{bmatrix} \frac{3}{17} & \frac{1}{17} \\ \frac{2}{17} & -\frac{5}{17} \end{bmatrix}$ **13.** $\begin{bmatrix} 0 & -1 \\ 1 & 0 \end{bmatrix}$ **15.** $\begin{bmatrix} \frac{1}{2} & \frac{1}{2} \\ -\frac{1}{2} & \frac{1}{2} \end{bmatrix}$ **17.** $\begin{bmatrix} \frac{1}{22} & \frac{2}{11} \\ \frac{3}{11} & \frac{1}{11} \end{bmatrix}$ **19.** False

21. If the matrices are named $A, I, B,$ and C respectively, then the table at the right gives the products. Each of the 16 possible products is a member of the set (closure) and each element is its own inverse.

$\cdot$	A	I	B	C
A	I	A	C	B
I	A	I	B	C
B	C	B	I	A
C	B	C	A	I

23. The absolute value of each of their determinants is 1.

9.5 Pages 245–246

1. The group of all invertiple marices with matrix multiplication **3.** Change to matrix equation form and multiply both sides by the inverse of the coefficient matrix.

5. $\begin{bmatrix} -8 & -3 \\ 4 & 6 \end{bmatrix} \cdot \begin{bmatrix} A \\ B \end{bmatrix} = \begin{bmatrix} 10 \\ 5 \end{bmatrix}$; one solution **7.** $\begin{bmatrix} 10 & 15 \\ 4 & 6 \end{bmatrix} \cdot \begin{bmatrix} x \\ y \end{bmatrix} = \begin{bmatrix} 30 \\ 12 \end{bmatrix}$; many solutions **9.** $\begin{bmatrix} 2 & -4 \\ 1 & -2 \end{bmatrix} \cdot \begin{bmatrix} w \\ z \end{bmatrix} = \begin{bmatrix} -9 \\ 18 \end{bmatrix}$; no solutions

11. Intersecting lines **13.** $(\frac{8}{17}, \frac{2}{17})$ **15.** $(-\frac{25}{12}, \frac{20}{9})$ **17.** $y = -\frac{2}{3}x + 2$ **19.** $\emptyset$

21. $Y = \begin{bmatrix} \frac{12}{5} & -\frac{3}{5} \\ 2 & \frac{3}{2} \end{bmatrix}$ **23.** If $\begin{bmatrix} 0 & 0 \\ 0 & 0 \end{bmatrix} \cdot \begin{bmatrix} w & x \\ y & z \end{bmatrix} = \begin{bmatrix} a & b \\ c & d \end{bmatrix}$, then $\begin{bmatrix} a & b \\ c & d \end{bmatrix} = \begin{bmatrix} 0 & 0 \\ 0 & 0 \end{bmatrix}$.

25. The sentence $\begin{bmatrix} 0 & 0 \\ 0 & 0 \end{bmatrix} \cdot \begin{bmatrix} a & b \\ c & d \end{bmatrix} = \begin{bmatrix} 0 & 0 \\ 0 & 0 \end{bmatrix}$ has infinitely many solutions. **27.** $(\frac{7}{5}, -\frac{1}{5})$ **29.** $z = -\frac{4}{3}w$

9.6 Pages 248–250

1. The transformation mapping each point onto itself **3.** No **5.** Yes **7.** No
9. A transformation $T_2 \circ T_1$ such that for any point P, $T_2 \circ T_1(P) = T_2(T_1(P))$ **11.** T^{-1}
13. Translation mapping (3, 4) to (0, 0) **15.** Rotation of 180° about M
17. The composite of two translations is a translation. **19.** Closure, associativity, identity, inverses
21. No **23.** No **25.** Yes **27.** $\left(\frac{x}{3}, \frac{y}{3}\right)$ **29.** S_{18}
31. R_6 **33.** I **35.** All 4 **37.** Closure, associativity, identity
39. TA: If ℓ and m are two different nonperpendicular lines, then $r_\ell \circ r_m \neq r_m \circ r_\ell$.

9.7 Pages 251–252

1. If t and u have matrices M and N, then $t \circ u$ has matrix MN. **3.** They are inverses.
5. $\cos x$ **7.** $\sin x \cos y + \cos x \sin y$ **9.** $-\frac{3}{5}$ **11.** $-\frac{\sqrt{3}}{2}$

13. $\begin{bmatrix} \cos x & \sin x \\ -\sin x & \cos x \end{bmatrix}$ and $\begin{bmatrix} \cos(-x) & -\sin(-x) \\ \sin(-x) & \cos(-x) \end{bmatrix}$ **15.** The matrix for T^{-1} is $\begin{bmatrix} \frac{1}{3} & 0 \\ 0 & \frac{1}{2} \end{bmatrix}$.

17. $\begin{bmatrix} 0 & -1 \\ 1 & 0 \end{bmatrix} \cdot \begin{bmatrix} 0 & 1 \\ -1 & 0 \end{bmatrix} = \begin{bmatrix} 1 & 0 \\ 0 & 1 \end{bmatrix}$ **19.** -0.857

21. Vertices are $A' = (0, 0)$, $B' = (2, 0)$, and $C' = (17, 3)$. Matrix is $\begin{bmatrix} 1 & -5 \\ 0 & 1 \end{bmatrix}$.

9.8 Page 255

1. TA: Flexibility
3. a. Geo. **b.** $\{(x, y): Ax + By = C\}$
5. a. Geo. **b.** $\frac{y_2 - y_1}{x_2 - x_1}$
7. a. Alg. **b.** Perpendicularity
9. a. Geo. **b.** (x, y)
11. a. Geo. **b.** $\{(x, y): (x - h)^2 + (y - k)^2 < r^2\}$
13. a. Geo. **b.** $\sqrt{(x_1 - x_2)^2 + (y_1 - y_2)^2}$
15. a. Alg. **b.** Reflection over x-axis
17. a. Alg. **b.** $r_{x=y}$
19. a. Alg. **b.** Translation
21. Yes. The interior of the circle has been corresponded to 100% of the readers, and $\frac{3}{4}$ of the interior has been corresponded to 75% of the readers (those under 30).
23. The half-plane above the line through $(0, -3)$ and $(4, 0)$
25. The interior of the circle with center $(0, 0)$ and radius $\sqrt{11}$

9.9 Page 258

1. *See p. 256.*
3. TA: How cold is it? How much is that worth?
5. The process of approximating past or future events from present data
7. About 117 seconds
9. About 115.5 seconds

10.1 Pages 267–268

1. One **3.** Distance from the origin **5.** 2 **7.** 17 **9.** 12
11. 0 **13.** Infinitely many **15.** Any point 5 units from $(0, 0)$
17. a **19.** a **21.** Polar **23.** $13\frac{1}{4}$

10.2 Page 271

1. $(0, 6)$ **3.** $(-10.8, -8)$ **5.** $(4, 4)$ **7.** $(5, 12)$ **9.** $(-2, 13)$
11. $(4, -3)$ **13.** $(-5, 1)$ **15.** $\langle\{\text{translations}\}, \circ\rangle$ **17.** $(0, 0)$
19. $(-\frac{1}{2}, -1)$ **21.** (a, b) **23.** $(8, 12)$ **25.** $(-7, 6)$ **27.** $(-10, -9)$
29. $3\sqrt{10}$ **31.** $2\sqrt{689}$ **33.** $(48, -20)$
35. Image is a circle with center $(6, -1)$ and radius 1. The transformation is $(x, y) \rightarrow (x + 6, y - 1)$.
37. $|v - w|$
39. $[-r, \theta]$

10.3 Pages 274–275

1. $S_r \circ R_\theta$ **3.** $[10, 40°]$ **5.** $[1, 3°]$ **7.** $[2, 0°]$ **9.** $[1, 0°]$
11. $[3, 60°]$ **13.** $[\sqrt{2}, -70°]$ **15.** $[\frac{1}{2}, -50°]$ **17.** $[\frac{1}{17}, 0°]$ **19.** $[4, 144°]$
21. $[27, 0°]$ **23.** $[1, 90°]$ **25.** $[7, 135°]$, $[5, 180°]$, $[2, 270°]$; R_{90}

10.4 Pages 277–278

1. True because of distributivity and commutativity of multiplication
3. True because fractions can be dealt with in the same way as the reals
5. $[rs, \theta + \phi]$ **7.** $(11, 3)$ **9.** $(0, 0)$ **11.** $(ab, 0)$ **13.** $(\frac{7}{120}, \frac{11}{60})$
15. $(-7, 0)$
17. Use distributivity. $(4, 13) \cdot (1, 0) = (4, 13)$
19. $[-7, 270°] = (0, 7)$
$(-7, 0) \cdot (0, -1) = (0, 7)$
21. True

10.5 Pages 280–281

1. x-axis of the complex plane **3.** $(0, 1)$ or $[1, 90°]$ **5.** 10 **7.** $[1, 90°]$
9. $(7, 0)$, $(-7, 0)$, $(0, 7)$, $(0, -7)$
11. It might lead someone to wrongly think that imaginary numbers are fictitious.
13. $(-6, 0)$ **15.** $(0, 7)$
17. $(0, -2.5)$ **19.** $(-3, 0)$ **21.** -4 **23.** 1 **25.** $2i$ or $-2i$ **27.** 2 or -2

29. (0, 1), (−1, 0), (0, −1), (1, 0)

31. $(0, \sqrt{2}), (0, -\sqrt{2})$

10.6 Pages 282–283

1. $6 + 4i$

3. $-2 + 4i$

5. $-1.5 - 2i$

	7.	9.	11.	13.	15.	17.
$a =$	5	−2	0	$\frac{1}{2}$	0	−3
$b =$	9	1	7	$\frac{1}{2}$	0	0

19. (1, 1), (1, 2), (1, 3), (1, 4)

21. (2, −2), (3, −2), (−4, −2), (0, −2)

23. −29

25. $31 + 50i$

27. $\doteq (309, 951) = 309 + 951i$

29. $(0, -4) = -4i$

10.7 Pages 285–286

1. $5 + 4i$ **3.** -9 **5.** $5 + 3i$ **7.** $8 - 2i$ **9.** $4 + i$

11. $-1 + 2i$ **13.** $-9 - 2i$ **15.** $21 - 7i$ **17.** $10 + 2i$ **19.** $4 + i$

21. $3 + 11i$ **23.** $1 - 9i$ **25.** $-94 + 81i$ **27.** 36 **29.** $29 - 2i$

31. −5 **33.** 0 **35.** $7 + i$

37. $(2 + 3i) + (4 - 5i) = 6 - 2i$
$(4 - 5i) + (2 + 3i) = 6 - 2i$
$(6 - 2i) - (2 + 3i) = 4 - 5i$
$(6 - 2i) - (4 - 5i) = 2 + 3i$

39. $(1 + 4i)(3 - 2i) = 11 + 10i$
$(3 - 2i)(1 + 4i) = 11 + 10i$
$(11 + 10i) \div (1 + 4i) = 3 - 2i$
$(11 + 10i) \div (3 - 2i) = 1 + 4i$

41. $\frac{9}{10} + \frac{7}{10}i$ **43.** $-1 + 9i$ **45.** $-\frac{114}{89} - \frac{49}{89}i$ **47.** $\frac{14}{37} - \frac{27}{37}i$ **49.** $b - ai$

51. 5 **53.** $\sqrt{2}$ **55.** $\frac{2}{5} - \frac{1}{5}i$ **57.** $\frac{1}{7}$ **59.** $4 - i$

61. $-7 - 24i$ **63.** $22 + 7i$ **65.** 12 **67.** 4 **69.** $10 + 10i$

10.8 Page 288

1. TA: i

3. Assuming i is positive leads to $-1 > 0$, which is not true.

For 5 and 7 let $x = a + bi$ and $y = c + di$.

5. Choose $b > 0$, $d > 0$, a, and c so that $ad + bc < 0$.

7. Choose $a > 0$, $b > 0$, $c > 0$, and $d > 0$ so that $ac < bd$.

10.9 Pages 290–291

1. A **3.** E **5.** Add the endpoints of the vectors. **7.** c

9. $t + u \doteq (212.1, 412.1)$ **11.** $|t + u| \doteq 767$ km **13.** $Q = -R$

10.10 Pages 293–294

1. 0 **3.** TA: $\sqrt{2}$ **5.** TA: 0.5 **7.** Impossible **9.** TA: $2 + i$ **11.** *See p. 293.*

13. $\frac{47}{230}$ **15.** TA: $\frac{1}{4}$ **17.** $\frac{26}{1}$ **19.** $\frac{1}{9}$ **21.** −0.015625 **23.** 0.008

11.1 Pages 299–301

1. 1, −1 **3.** Positive **5.** Positive, y **7.** 2, −2 **9.** $\sqrt{7}, -\sqrt{7}$

11. 8, −8 **13.** 3 **15.** i **17.** $\frac{1}{4}i$ **19.** $10i$

21. $2i$ **23.** $5 - 2i$ **25.** −1 **27.** −25 **29.** −8

31. True **33.** True **35.** True **37.** False **39.** $2i, -2i$

41. $3i, -3i$ **43.** $7i, -7i$ **45.** e

11.2 Pages 302–303

1. No **3.** No **5.** Multiply by $\frac{2\sqrt{8} - 6}{2\sqrt{8} - 6}$ **7.** $3 + 2\sqrt{5}$
9. False **11.** True **13.** $\frac{\sqrt{7}}{7}$ **15.** $8\sqrt{5}$ **17.** $\frac{6}{5}$
19. $3 + 2\sqrt{2}$ **21.** 11 **23.** $56 + 2\sqrt{14} + 14\sqrt{2} + 8\sqrt{7}$ **25.** $\frac{4 - \sqrt{5}}{11}$
27. $\frac{16 + 4\sqrt{10}}{3}$ **29.** $\frac{39 + 3i}{20}$ **31.** $\frac{1}{3\sqrt{6} - 8}$ **33.** $\frac{a\sqrt{b} + b\sqrt{a}}{ab}$

11.3 Pages 305–306

1. $x = \pm\frac{3}{2}$ **3.** $\frac{7}{2}, \frac{1}{2}$ **5.** $a = \pm\sqrt{10}$ **7.** $c = 3 \pm \sqrt{10}$ **9.** $e = -6 \pm \sqrt{10}$
11. True **13.** 9 **15.** -4 **17.** $\pm\sqrt{461}$ and $8 \pm \sqrt{461}$
19. $\frac{2\sqrt{3}}{15}$ **21.** 35 **23.** $\frac{169}{9}$ **25.** $\frac{3}{4} \pm \sqrt{2}$ **27.** $\frac{3 \pm 5i\sqrt{6}}{15}$
29. $\frac{-9 \pm 2i\sqrt{11}}{6}$ **31.** $4 \pm 2\sqrt{2}$ **33.** $\frac{-2 \pm 6\sqrt{3}}{3}$ **35.** $\frac{9}{2}$ or 3

11.4 Page 308

1. TA: $x^2 + 2x - 4$ **3.** $x^2 + 12x + 36$ **5.** $z^2 + z + \frac{1}{4}$ **7.** $y^2 + 2y + 1$
9. TA: Solving equations **11.** $(z - 4)^2 - 16$ **13.** $(t + \frac{1}{2})^2 - \frac{1}{4}$
15. $(d - 35)^2 - 1225$ **17.** $(y + 3)^2$ **19.** $(c - \frac{5}{2})^2 - \frac{21}{4}$ **21.** $(c - \frac{1}{7})^2 - \frac{36}{49}$
23. $-v^2 + 4v + 4$ **25.** $-4m^2 + 12m - 5 = 0$

11.5 Pages 311–312

1. Every solution to any quadratic equation **3.** $-4x^2 + 3x + 9 = 0$; $-4, 3, 9$; $D = 153$
5. $8z^2 + 9z + 6 = 0$; $8, 9, 6$; $D = -111$ **7.** $c^2 - c - 14 = 0$; $1, -1, -14$; $D = 57$
9. A solution of the equation **11.** Two real solutions
13. Two imaginary solutions **15.** Two real solutions
17. 1 **19.** $-3 \pm i$ **21.** $\frac{1 \pm \sqrt{5}}{2}$ **23.** $\frac{-5 \pm \sqrt{73}}{4}$
25. $\frac{1}{10}$ **27.** $\frac{-b \pm \sqrt{b^2 - 4ac}}{2c}$ **29.** $\frac{-1 \pm \sqrt{65}}{2}$ **31.** $5, -4$
33. $\frac{3 \pm 3\sqrt{17}}{8}$ **35.** $\frac{-9 \pm i\sqrt{111}}{16}$ **37.** $\frac{1 \pm \sqrt{57}}{2}$

11.6 Pages 315–316

1. Height above or below the point from which an object is tossed **3.** Time after throwing **5.** 8 **7.** 8
9. Parabola **11.** 1.2 seconds
13. After 0.6 seconds, the object is 8.68 feet above its starting point. **15.** Solve: $24t - 16t^2 = -2$
17. Solve: $24t - 16t^2 > 6$
19. $\frac{3 + \sqrt{11}}{4} \doteq 1.6$ seconds

11.7 Pages 319–320

1. The set of points equidistant from a given point and a given line **3.** The given line of Exercise 1
5. Focus $(0, \frac{1}{4})$, directrix $y = -\frac{1}{4}$, vertex $(0, 0)$

7. (2, 6) **9.** (0, −3) **11.** *See drawing p. 317.*

In 13–19 the graph is a translation image of $y = x^2$. The vertex is given.

13. (−5, 0) **15.** (4, 11) **17.** (−4, −18) **19.** (0, 0)

21. (2, 4) and (−3, 4) **23.** (0, −2)

11.8 Pages 322–323

1. $1 \pm \sqrt{2}$ **3.** $1 - \sqrt{2} \le x \le 1 + \sqrt{2}$ **5.** c

Ex. 7–25: Graphs omitted. **7.** $\frac{1}{4} < a < 3$ **9.** $\frac{1}{4} \le a \le 3$

11. All real numbers **13.** All real numbers but 3 **15.** $1 - \frac{\sqrt{2}}{2} < x < 1 + \frac{\sqrt{2}}{2}$

17. $2 < x < 6$ **19.** $y \le -\frac{4}{3}$ or $y \ge \frac{2}{5}$ **21.** $w < 1$ or $w > 5$

23. $y \le \frac{1}{3}$ or $y \ge \frac{5}{7}$ **25.** $x \le 0$ or $x \ge \frac{11}{2}$

12.1 Pages 327–328

1–8. *See drawings pp. 326–327.* **9.** Conic section **11.** Circle

13. Part of a hyperbola **15.** Parabola **17.** Circle

12.2 Pages 331–332

1. Given points F_1 and F_2 and a constant $2a > 0$, the set of points P such that $PF_1 + PF_2 = 2a$

3. The set of points equidistant from a given point and a given line

4–6. *See figure p. 329.* **7–12.** *See figure p. 330.* **13.** TA: It has two branches; it has asymptotes.

15. Draw the segment $\overline{F_1F_2}$ 8 units long. Then any point P such that $PF_1 + PF_2 = 18$ is on the ellipse.

Ex. 17–19: Graphs omitted.

17. (−10, 0), (0, −5), (−8, 3), (8, −3), (−8, −3), (−6, 4), (6, −4), (−6, −4); ellipse; symmetry lines are x and y axes.

19. (13, 5), (13, −5), (−13, 5), (−13, −5), (15, 9), (15, −9), (−15, 9), (−15, −9), (12, 0), (−12, 0), (20, 16), (20, −16), (−20, 16), (−20, −16); $y = x$ and $y = -x$

21. Because of the triangle inequality

12.3 Pages 335–336

1. *Same as Ex. 1 of 12.2* **3.** 4 **5.** $x = 0, y = 0$ **7.** $2a$ **9.** $2b$

11. (0, 0); on an axis **13.** 2, $\sqrt{5}$ *Ex. 15–19: Graphs omitted.*

15. (2, 0), (−2, 0), (0, 3), (0, −3) **17.** (3, 0), (−3, 0), (0, 1), (0, −1)

19. (3, 0), (−3, 0), (0, 4), (0, −4) **21.** $(\sqrt{5}, 0)$ and $(-\sqrt{5}, 0)$

23. $\frac{x^2}{4} + \frac{y^2}{9} < 1$ **25.** $\sqrt{(x-3)^2 + (y-11)^2} + \sqrt{(x-7)^2 + (y-14)^2} = 50$

12.4 Pages 339–340

1. Given points F_1 and F_2 and a constant $2a > 0$, the set of points P with $|PF_1 - PF_2| = 2a$

3. x-axis and y-axis

5. $(\sqrt{2}, \sqrt{2}), (-\sqrt{2}, -\sqrt{2})$ **7.** (0, 0)

9. TA: (5, 1), (−5, −1), (1, 5), (−1, −5), $(10, \frac{1}{2})$, $(-10, -\frac{1}{2})$, $(\frac{1}{2}, 10)$, $(-\frac{1}{2}, -10)$, $(\sqrt{5}, \sqrt{5})$, $(-\sqrt{5}, -\sqrt{5})$

11. $y = x, y = -x$

Ex. 13–19: Graphs omitted.

13. *Similar to graph on p. 338.*

15. TA: (1, 1), (−1, −1), $(2, \frac{1}{2})$, $(\frac{1}{2}, 2)$, $(-2, -\frac{1}{2})$, $(-\frac{1}{2}, -2)$, $(3, \frac{1}{3})$, $(4, \frac{1}{4})$, $(5, \frac{1}{5})$, $(6, \frac{1}{6})$

17. TA: (2, 6), (−2, −6), (6, 2), (−6, −2), (3, 4), (−3, −4), (4, 3), (−4, −3), (12, 1), (1, 12)

19. The first quadrant branch of $rt = 2.5$

12.5 Pages 343–345

1. (ax, by) **3.** $(-3, 2)$ **5.** $(0, 0)$ **7.** e **9.** e

11. b **13.** $\begin{bmatrix} 2 & 0 \\ 0 & 1 \end{bmatrix}$ **15.** $\begin{bmatrix} \frac{1}{4} & 0 \\ 0 & 1 \end{bmatrix}$ **17.** $\frac{x}{5}, \frac{y}{6}$ **19.** Ellipse

21. $(3x)^2 + y^2 = 1$ **23.** The image under the scale transformation $(x, y) \to (15x, 6y)$

25. b **27.** Replace x with $5x$ and y with $10y$.

29. Since $T(0, 0) = (0, 0)$ and $T(1, 0) = (4, 0)$, distance is not preserved so T is not an isometry. The matrix for T $\begin{bmatrix} 4 & 0 \\ 0 & 2 \end{bmatrix}$ is not of the form $\begin{bmatrix} k & 0 \\ 0 & k \end{bmatrix}$ so T is also not a size transformation and therefore not a similarity transformation.

Ex. 31–35: Graphs omitted.

31. Image is $\begin{bmatrix} -3 & 2 & 2 & -3 \\ 2 & 2 & 0 & -\frac{1}{2} \end{bmatrix}$

33. Image is $\left(\frac{x}{2}\right)^2 + y^2 = 36$

35. Image is $\left(\frac{x}{2}\right)^2 + \left(\frac{y}{-5}\right)^2 = 36$

37. $x \to \frac{x}{1000}$ **39.** True

12.6 Pages 348–349

1. $\frac{x^2}{a^2} - \frac{y^2}{b^2} = 1$ **3.** $(2, 0), (-2, 0)$ **5.** $(1, 0), (-1, 0)$ **7.** $(\sqrt{5}, 0), (-\sqrt{5}, 0)$

9. $\frac{y}{b} = \frac{x}{a}, \frac{y}{b} = -\frac{x}{a}$ **11.** No *Ex. 13–15: Graphs omitted.*

13. Vertices $(2, 0), (-2, 0)$; asymptotes $y = x, y = -x$ **15.** Vertices $(3, 0), (-3, 0)$; asymptotes $2u = 3v, 2u = -3v$ **17.** True **19.** $(2\sqrt{2}, 0), (-2\sqrt{2}, 0)$

12.7 Pages 352–353

1. The set of points equidistant from a given point and a given line **3.** False **5.** False **7.** $y = 2x^2$ **9.** $xy = 360$ **11.** $y < \frac{x^2}{3}$

13. By showing that for any two parabolas there is a similarity transformation mapping the directrix and focus of one onto the directrix and focus of the other

In 15–19 graphs are parabolas.

15. Vertex $(0, 0)$ through $(3, \frac{9}{10}), (4, \frac{8}{5})$

17. Vertex $(0, 0)$ through $(1, 5), (2, 20)$

19. Vertex $(0, 0)$ through $(1, -3), (2, -12)$

12.8 Pages 356–357

1. $(-4, -17)$ **3.** $(17, -4)$ **5.** $(-100, 1)$ **7.** Replace y by $-y$.

9. Switch x and y. **11.** If replacing x by $-x$ gives an equivalent sentence

13. $x = 3(-y)^2$, yes **15.** $x^2 + (-y + 1)^2 = 20$, no **17.** $x - y = 12$, no

19. $y = 3x^2$, no **21.** $y^2 + (x + 1)^2 = 20$, no **23.** $y + x = 12$, yes

25. $-x = 3y^2$, no **27.** $(-x)^2 + (y + 1)^2 = 20$, yes **29.** $-x + y = 12$, no

31. Parabola with vertex $(0, 0)$ containing $(4, 2)$ and $(4, -2)$

33. Parabola with vertex $(0, 0)$ containing $(-2, 1)$ and $(-2, -1)$

35. Hyperbola with vertices $(0, 5), (0, -5)$; asymptotes $4y = 5x, 4y = -5x$

37. Hyperbola with vertices $(\sqrt{6}, -\sqrt{6}), (-\sqrt{6}, \sqrt{6})$; asymptotes $x = 0, y = 0$

39. *Graph at right*

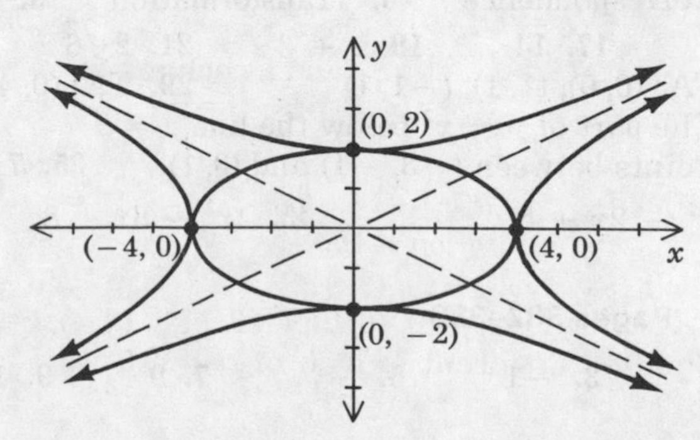

12.9 Pages 359–360

1. If x is replaced by $x - h$ and y by $y - k$ in a sentence for a relation, then the result is a sentence for the image under the translation $(x, y) \rightarrow (x + h, y + k)$.
3. $x = 5$
5. $4(y + 3)^2 - (x - 4)^2 = 3$
7. True
9. Parabola with vertex $(-1, -4)$; translation image of $y = 3x^2$
11. Hyperbola with vertices $(1, -3)$, $(-1, -3)$; asymptotes $x = y + 3$, $x = -y - 3$
13. Parabola with vertex $(-7, 0)$; translation image of $y = \frac{1}{2}x^2$
15. Two parabolas congruent to $y = 2x^2$ with vertices $(-1, 3)$ and $(1, 3)$
17. Parabola **19.** Hyperbola **21.** Hyperbola **23.** Hyperbola **25.** Ellipse

12.10 Pages 363–364

1. A number or ordered set of numbers which work in each sentence of the system
3. Graphing, substitution, addition and multiplication
5. $(2\sqrt{2}, \sqrt{5})$, $(2\sqrt{2}, -\sqrt{5})$, $(-2\sqrt{2}, \sqrt{5})$, $(-2\sqrt{2}, -\sqrt{5})$ **7.** None **9.** Two **11.** None
13. $(-3, -5)$, $(2, 10)$ **15.** $(4, 2)$, $(4, -2)$, $(-4, 2)$, $(-4, -2)$ **17.** $\emptyset$ **19.** $(3, 0)$
21. $(1, 0)$, $(0, 1)$ **23.** $(\frac{9}{4}, \frac{1}{2})$ **25.** $(\pm\frac{10}{73}\sqrt{730}, \pm\frac{12}{73}\sqrt{219})$

13.1 Pages 369–370

1. A set of ordered pairs **3.** Use vertical-line test (p. 368).
5. Not **7.** Is **9.** Is **11.** Not **13.** A quadratic relation which is a function
15. Not **17.** Is **19.** Not **21.** Not **23.** Is **25.** Is **27.** Not **29.** Is **31.** Is
33. TA: $x = 3$ **35.** TA: $(0, 1)$, $(0, 2)$ **37.** TA: $(2\sqrt{2}, \sqrt{2})$, $(2\sqrt{2}, -\sqrt{2})$
39. TA: $(-1, 1)$, $(-1, 2)$

13.2 Pages 374–375

1. $(2, 4)$, $(2, 5)$, $(3, 5)$, $(4, 2)$ **3.** $\{2, 3, 4\}$ **5.** TA: Set of integers
7. A set of ordered pairs, no two of which have the same first component
9. Set of real numbers **11.** $y = x^2$ **13.** Domain: $\{0, 1, 2\}$, range: $\{-3, 0, 3\}$
15. Domain: all reals except 0; range: all reals except 0 **17.** Yes
19. TA: Word $\rightarrow$ number of letters **21.** $\{2, 3, 4, 5\}$ **23.** Set of odd integers
25. Set of reals **27.** Negative numbers **29.** 0 **31.** None
33. True—a 1-1 correspondence satisfies the alternate definition of a function.

13.3 Pages 378–379

1. Correspondence **3.** Transformation **5.** -6 **7.** -3 **9.** -10 **11.** 1 **13.** 0
15. 6 **17.** 14 **19.** $t + 3$ **21.** $2\sqrt{6}$ **23.** 20 **25.** TA: $(0, 0)$, $(1, -1)$, $(-1, 1)$
27. TA: $(0, 0)$, $(1, 1)$, $(-1, 1)$ **29.** TA: $(0, 4\frac{1}{2})$, $(1, 4\frac{1}{2})$, $(-1, 4\frac{1}{2})$
31. The part of $y = x^2$ below the line $y = 9$
33. Points between $(-3, -1)$ and $(3, 1)$ **35.** $7 - 4i$ **37.** 8 **39.** $x^2 - 4x + 8$
41. $x^2 - 2x + 5$ **43.** $4x^2 - 8x + 8$ **45.** $x^2 - 1$ **47.** $\frac{-1 \pm \sqrt{5}}{2}$

13.4 Pages 382–383

1. 0 **3.** -1 **5.** $-\frac{3}{4}$ **7.** 9 **9.** 10,005 **11.** g **13.** 255 **15.** 15

17. It maps -3 onto 12.
19. If no horizontal line intersects the graph more than once
21. The inverse of f
23. $3y + 5x = -12$
25. $x = y^3 + 413.2$
27. $-14x + 17$
29. $x^4 - 5x^2 + 4$
31. TA: $(0, 1), (1, 2), (2, 4), (-1, \frac{1}{2}), (-2, \frac{1}{4})$; inverse: $(1, 0), (2, 1), (4, 2), (\frac{1}{2}, -1), (\frac{1}{4}, -2)$
33. $n \to 6n$
35. c

13.5 Pages 385–386

1. z 3. Yes 5. 2, 1 7. 1, 1 9. The largest number in the range
11. Look at the second coordinate of the highest point. 13. Maximum, 9; minimum, 0
15. Maximum, 5; minimum, 2 17. Maximum, 0; no minimum
19. No maximum; minimum, -7 21. Vertex 23. Maximum, 13

13.6 Pages 389–391

1. Doubled 3. Direct 5. Inverse 7. Multiplied by 12 9. $y = kx$ 11. 5
13. Lines through the origin 15. Inversely 17. $\frac{42}{5}$ 19. 49 21. π 23. $431\frac{11}{27}$
25. a. Divided by 4 b. Divided by 9 c. Divided by 36 d. Multiplied by 4 e. Multiplied by 25
27. a. Divided by 8 b. Divided by 27 c. Divided by 216 d. Multiplied by 8 e. Multiplied by 125
29. c 31. Stress $= k \cdot$ strain 33. $d = \frac{h}{T}$, d = density, T = absolute temperature

13.7 Pages 394–395

1. $y = |x|$ 3. 18 5. 4 7. 12 9. 1 11. 10 13. \$6.45 15. \$10.48
17. \$18.60 19. Angle DEF, where $D = (0, 2)$, $E = (2, 0)$, $F = (4, 2)$; minimum, 0
21. Angle ABC and its interior, where $A = (-1, 1)$, $B = (0, 0)$, $C = (1, 1)$
23. Angle MNO, where $M = (3, -6)$, $N = (1, -5)$, $O = (3, -4)$
25. Angle ABC, where $A = (0, 0)$, $B = (5, 5)$, $C = (10, 5)$
27. Graph resembles:
29. Graph includes points on the path from (0, 7.10) to (80, 7.10) to (200, 14.60) through (240, 16.90)

13.8 Pages 397–399

1. The greatest integer less than or equal to t 3. 7 5. -3
7. 0 9. -3 11. 11 13. The set of nonnegative integers
15. Translation image of graph at top of p. 396 with $(0, 0)$ mapped onto $(-2, -3)$
17. Image of graph at top of p. 396 under horizontal stretch $(x, y) \to (3x, y)$
19. $-y = [x]$ 21. $y + 2 = [x]$

13.9 Pages 402–404

1. Approximation of specific values by interpolation; approximation of graphs by segments
3. Points on curves can be approximated by points on segments.
5. 1 7. 7 9. a 11. b 13. $(-0.8, 3)$ 15. $\frac{4}{15}$
17. 1.446 19. 0.926 21. 0.834 23. No 25. 162,524,749

14.1 Pages 408–409

1. $x^2 = t$ 3. b, a, a, b 5. 9 is the cube root of 729. 7. -2 is the 7th root of -128.
9. $\frac{1}{3}$ 11. -2 13. 10 or -10 15. 2 or -2 17. Largest real nth root of x
19. $\sqrt[3]{\frac{1}{27}}$ 21. $\sqrt[5]{-32}$ 23. $\pm\sqrt[6]{1{,}000{,}000}$ 25. $\pm\sqrt[4]{16}$ 27. -5 29. -2 31. x^4

33. 7 **35.** 10 **37.** 25 **39.** > **41.** = **43.** > **45.** <
47. 1, 8, 27, 64, 125, 216, 343, 512, 729, 1000 **49.** $n = 10$ **51.** $n = 4$

14.2 Pages 411–412

1. A function in which the independent variable is in the exponent
3. 18 billion **5.** 3 **7.** 1890 **9.** \$105 **11.** \$115.76 **13.** \$116.64
15. TA: (0, 100), (1, 108), (2, 116.64), (3, 125.97), (4, 136.05) **17.** 12.5%
19. TA: $(0, 3)$, $(5600, \frac{3}{2})$, $(11{,}200, \frac{3}{4})$, $(16{,}800, \frac{3}{8})$, $(22{,}400, \frac{3}{16})$, $(28{,}000, \frac{3}{32})$

14.3 Pages 415–416

1. Positive square root **3.** x **5.** x
7. A number which when raised to the nth power gives the original number **9.** 10 **11.** For $x > 0$, $x^{\frac{m}{n}} = (\sqrt[n]{x})^m = \sqrt[n]{x^m}$.
13. $14^{\frac{1}{3}}$ **15.** $x^{\frac{3}{4}}$ **17.** Z^5
19. $\sqrt[4]{m}$ **21.** TA: $\sqrt[4]{12^3}$ **23.** Imp. **25.** Imp. **27.** $\frac{1}{4}$ **29.** $\frac{1}{16}$
31. $\frac{1}{64}$ **33.** $\frac{3}{2}$ **35.** 7 **37.** 128 **39.** $\frac{1}{8}$ **41.** $\frac{1}{16}$
43. 0.5 **45.** $\frac{2187}{78125}$ **47.** $(x^m)^{\frac{1}{n}} = x^{\frac{m}{n}}$ **49.** $x^{\frac{22}{5}}$ and $x^{-\frac{22}{5}}$ are reciprocals.
51. $(x^{\frac{1}{4}})^2 = x^{\frac{1}{2}}$ **53.** $\frac{1}{2}$ **55.** $\sqrt[12]{20}$ **57.** y^2 **59.** $2x^5 + 3x^4$ **61.** 64, 729

14.4 Pages 418–419

1. 4, 8 **3.** An ordered list of intervals, each a subset of the last
5. Exponential function with base 2 **7.** $x = 6$ **9.** $z = -1$ **11.** $\frac{1}{2}$
13. 6, 7 **15.** $-1, -2$ **17.** 5, 6 **19.** 0, 1 **21.** 2, 3 **23.** $-3, -2$
25. 3^4 **27.** $3^{\frac{1}{2}}$ **29.** 10^4 **31.** 10^{-2} **33.** -3 **35.** -1
37. $\frac{5}{2}$ **39.** -4 **41.** $-\frac{1}{2}$ **43.** $\frac{1}{2}$ **45.** True

14.5 Pages 423–424

1. Addition **3.** $a - b$ **5.** nth part of b **7.** Opposite **9.** $0 \cdot a$
11. If $x \to a$, then $x^m \to ma$. **13.** Theorem 14.5.3 **15.** $(xy)^{\frac{1}{n}} = x^{\frac{1}{n}} \cdot y^{\frac{1}{n}}$
17. $2\sqrt[3]{2}$ **19.** $15^{\frac{1}{10}}$ **21.** 3 **23.** 2 **25.** Not possible
27. $10\sqrt[4]{3}$ **29.** $\sqrt{6}$ **31.** $a - b = c$ **33.** $a + b + c = d$
35. $m(a + b) = ma + mb$ **37.** $\frac{1}{n}(a - b) = \frac{1}{n}a - \frac{1}{n}b$
39. For any a there is exactly one real number b with $nb = a$.
41. If m is negative and $a > b$, then $ma < mb$. **43.** False

14.6 Pages 427–428

1. 2 **3.** 3 **5.** -6 **7.** 0.322 **9.** 3
11. -6 **13.** 0.322 **15.** 5.611 **17.** 1 **19.** $3.456 \cdot 10^3$
21. $6.53 \cdot 10^{-4}$ **23.** -0.6179 **25.** $0.6857 - 1$ **27.** 7.6857 **29.** Of 1 to 10
31. Characteristic **33.** 2.4440 **35.** 0.9350 **37.** 6.9350 **39.** $0.9542 - 3$
41. 0.6031 **43.** $0.6031 - 1$ **45.** 9.8904 **47.** 3.7324 **49.** 0.1492
51. 3.3979 **53.** 0.0043 **55.** Between 0.2380 and 0.2405
57. The characteristic is 1. **59.** e **61.** 0.6990 **63.** -0.1761
65. 0.1505 **67.** 1.5562 **69.** 0.0602 **71.** -0.5283 **73.** $0.9084 - 3$

14.7 Pages 430–431

1. $x \to \log x$, $10^a \to a$ **3.** Preimage **5.** 0.01 **7.** 10^6
9. 74.0 **11.** 0.5432 **13.** 9.34 **15.** 2.58 **17.** 3.49
19. 5.55 **21.** 1 **23.** 1990 **25.** 87,900 **27.** 0.0000114
29. 0.489 **31.** 0.000565 **33.** 6.31 **35.** 2.70 **37.** 84.8
39. $0.54 + (-3)$ **41.** $0.0849 + 1$ **43.** $0.2078 + 6$

14.8 Pages 433–434*

1. $a + b = c$ **3.** True **5.** $\log d = \log e + \log f$
7. $2 \log m = -\log p$ **9.** $\log y = 2 \log x$ **11.** $\log N = \frac{1}{3} \log 106$
13. $\log P = \log 49.6 + \log 215$ **15.** 4.73 **17.** 10,700 **19.** 84,300,000
21. 11,100 **23.** 1.15 **25.** 46.7 **27.** $5.10 \cdot 10^{14}$ **29.** 0.0889
31. $1.26 \cdot 10^9$ **33.** 1,600,000 **35.** $3^{\sqrt{2}}$ **37.** 3 and 4, 10 digits

14.9 Pages 436–437*

1. $T = 100(1 + 0.08)^6$ **3.** $5000 = P(1 + 0.005)^{120}$ **5.** $0.75 = (1 - 0.03)^n$
7. $x \log 8 = \log 3$ **9.** $\log \frac{1}{2} + \log P = \log P + t \log 3.5$
11. -3 and -4 **13.** -3 and -4 **15.** $\doteq -3.341$ **17.** $\doteq -3.81$
19. $\doteq 2.15$ **21.** $\doteq$ \$159 **23.** $\doteq$ \$2720 **25.** $\doteq 9.5$

14.10 Pages 442–443*

1. 5 **3.** $\log_{64} \frac{1}{4} = -\frac{1}{3}$ **5.** $\log_{0.7} 0.343 = 3$
7. TA: $e = 1 + \frac{1}{1} + \frac{1}{1 \cdot 2} + \frac{1}{1 \cdot 2 \cdot 3} + \frac{1}{1 \cdot 2 \cdot 3 \cdot 4} + \cdots$ **9.** Log of x to the base e
11. $\frac{1}{2}$ **13.** $\frac{1}{3}$ **15.** -4 **17.** 3 **19.** 50 **21.** 0
23. 2 **25.** 0 **27.** 0 **29.** d **31.** $e^{0.04}$ **33.** 2.485
35. -1.386 **37.** -0.406 **39.** 1.17 **41.** 2.3 **43.** -2.3 **45.** 7
47. $\frac{1}{3}$ **49.** 10 **51.** 2 **53.** 1

14.11 Pages 445–446

1. $\log x$ **3.** TA: $(\frac{1}{2}, \sqrt{10})$, (0, 1), (1, 10), (2, 100), (3, 1000) **5.** $\log_3 x$
7. Graph $y = 4^x$ and reflect over $y = x$. **9.** Graph rises less quickly than that of $\log_2 x$, p. 445. **11.** Very similar to that of $\log_2 x$, p. 445
13. If $B > 1$, the graph continually rises. **15.** (1, 0) is on the graph regardless of B. **17.** Around (1, 0) where graph is most curved

15.1 Page 451

1. π rad = 180 degrees **3.** 0 **5.** 1 **7.** $\frac{\pi}{2}$ **9.** $\frac{\pi}{4}$
11. 720° **13.** 150° **15.** $\frac{\pi}{2}$ **17.** -1 **19.** $\frac{\sqrt{3}}{2}$ **21.** $-\frac{\sqrt{2}}{2}$
23. $-\frac{1}{2}$ **25.** 0 **27.** $\frac{\sqrt{3}}{2}$ **29.** $\left(\frac{1}{2}, -\frac{\sqrt{3}}{2}\right)$
31. $\frac{\pi}{4}$ **33.** $\frac{5\pi}{8}$ **35.** $\frac{7\pi}{8}$ **37.** $\begin{bmatrix} -0.500 & 0.866 \\ -0.866 & -0.500 \end{bmatrix}$

*Interpolation not used

15.2 Pages 455–456

1. $\sin x$
3. TA: $(0, 1)$, $\left(\frac{\pi}{4}, \frac{\sqrt{2}}{2}\right)$, $\left(\frac{\pi}{3}, \frac{1}{2}\right)$, $\left(\frac{\pi}{2}, 0\right)$, $(\pi, -1)$
5. Pos., pos.
7. Neg., neg.
9. Increases; 0, 1
11. Decreases; 0, -1
13. Increases; -1, 0
15. Every 2π
17. *See page 455.*

19.

x	0	$\frac{\pi}{6}$	$\frac{\pi}{4}$	$\frac{\pi}{3}$	$\frac{\pi}{2}$	$\frac{2\pi}{3}$	$\frac{3\pi}{4}$	$\frac{5\pi}{6}$	π	$\frac{7\pi}{6}$	$\frac{5\pi}{4}$	$\frac{4\pi}{3}$	$\frac{3\pi}{2}$	$\frac{5\pi}{3}$	$\frac{7\pi}{4}$	$\frac{11\pi}{6}$	2π
$\cos x$	1	$\frac{\sqrt{3}}{2}$	$\frac{\sqrt{2}}{2}$	$\frac{1}{2}$	0	$-\frac{1}{2}$	$-\frac{\sqrt{2}}{2}$	$-\frac{\sqrt{3}}{2}$	-1	$-\frac{\sqrt{3}}{2}$	$-\frac{\sqrt{2}}{2}$	$-\frac{1}{2}$	0	$\frac{1}{2}$	$\frac{\sqrt{2}}{2}$	$\frac{\sqrt{3}}{2}$	1

21. TA: $x = \frac{\pi}{2}$, $x = \frac{3\pi}{2}$, infinitely many
23. A translation can map it onto itself.
25. $\sin(x + y) = \sin x \cos y + \cos x \sin y$

15.3 Pages 460–461

1. When it can be mapped onto itself by a rotation
3. Infinitely many
5. The magnitude of a translation which maps the function onto itself
7. 2π
9. Equal
11. Cosines
13. -0.755
15. TA: 2, 4, 6, 8, 10; 2
17. TA: $(\frac{1}{2}, \frac{1}{2})$, $(\frac{3}{4}, \frac{3}{4})$, $(\frac{3}{2}, \frac{1}{2})$, $(\frac{8}{3}, \frac{2}{3})$, $(5, 0)$
19. 1
21. 104°
23. 152°
25. $\cos x = \sin(90° - x)$, $\sin x = \cos(90° - x)$

15.4 Pages 464–465

1. The study of the application of sines and cosines to triangles and other polygons
3. $c^2 = a^2 + b^2 - 2ab \cos C$
5. $\cos Q$
7. Given the three sides of a triangle, the measures of the angles are determined.
9. 25.5
11. $m\angle B \doteq 22°$
13. $m\angle x \doteq 32°$
15. $m\angle z \doteq 95°$
17. $AC \doteq 55.0$
19. $\cos C = \frac{a^2 + b^2 - c^2}{2ab}$

15.5 Pages 468–470

1. $(0, 0)$
3. $(b \cos C, b \sin C)$
5. $(0, 0)$
7. $(x, y) \to (x - a, y)$
9. z
11. $m\angle X = 180 - (m\angle V + m\angle W)$
13. $\frac{AC}{\sin 30°} = \frac{15}{\sin 100°}$
15. $\frac{\sin T}{13} = \frac{\sin 12°}{8}$
17. Use the law of sines to find $m\angle T$, then use the triangle-check theorem.
19. Yes
21. Yes
23. $\doteq 7.6$
25. $\doteq 20°$
27. $\doteq 20.2$
29. $m\angle F = 75°$, $DE \doteq 6.7$, $DF \doteq 6.6$
31. $\doteq 12°$
33. $\doteq 1273$ feet
35. TA: $\frac{\sin 35°}{2.25} \doteq \frac{\sin 15°}{1} \doteq \frac{\sin 130°}{3}$; $0.255 \doteq 0.259 \doteq 0.255$

15.6 Pages 472–473

1. $\cos x$
3. Secant
5. When $\cos x = 0$
7. TA: $\frac{\pi}{2}$
9. 2
11. $\sqrt{2}$
13. $\frac{2\sqrt{3}}{3}$
15. $\sqrt{2}$
17. -1.662
19. -1.079
21. 1.252
23. -2.669
25. $-\sqrt{2}$
27. $\frac{2\sqrt{3}}{2}$
29. $\sqrt{2}$
31. 2
33. Image of $y = \sec x$ under the translation $(x, y) \to \left(x + \frac{\pi}{2}, y\right)$
35. All real numbers except those of the form $(n + \frac{1}{2})\pi$, n an integer

37. $x = n\pi$, n an integer
39. TA: $2\pi, 4\pi, 6\pi, 8\pi, 10\pi; 2\pi$
41. $\{x: |x| \geq 1\}$
43. $(n\pi, 0)$, n an integer

15.7 Pages 475–476

1. $\sin x, \cos x$ **3.** 1 **5.** When $\cos x = 0$ **7.** $\frac{\pi}{2}, \frac{3\pi}{2}$
9. $\sqrt{3}$ **11.** 1 **13.** $\frac{\sqrt{3}}{3}$ **15.** 1 **17.** -1.327 **19.** 0.404
21. -0.754 **23.** 2.475 **25.** -1 **27.** $-\frac{\sqrt{3}}{3}$ **29.** -1 **31.** $-\sqrt{3}$
33. TA: $(0, 0), \left(\frac{\pi}{6}, \frac{\sqrt{3}}{3}\right), \left(\frac{\pi}{4}, 1\right), \left(\frac{\pi}{3}, \sqrt{3}\right), \left(\frac{3\pi}{4}, -1\right)$
35. All real numbers except those of the form $(n + \frac{1}{2})\pi$, n an integer
37. None **39.** π **41.** All real numbers **43.** $((n + \frac{1}{2})\pi, 0)$, n an integer

15.8 Pages 479–480

1. d **3.** c **5.** b **7.** $\frac{13}{85}$ **9.** $\frac{84}{85}$ **11.** $\frac{13}{84}$
13. $\frac{84}{13}$ **15.** $\frac{85}{84}$ **17.** $\frac{85}{13}$ **19.** Law of sines
21. Complement's sine **23.** 71° **25.** 28° **27.** 1.022 **29.** 1.036
31. 1.804 **33.** 1.556 **35.** $\frac{12}{13}, \frac{5}{12}, \frac{12}{5}, \frac{13}{12}, \frac{13}{5}$ **37.** 37°, 53°, 90°
39. 34°, 56°, 90° **41.** Near 0.64, 0.77, 0.84 **43.** b **45.** a

15.9 Pages 481–482

1. $\frac{a}{23} = \tan 28°$
3. Area of parallelogram with sides a and b and $\angle\theta$ is $ab \sin\theta$.
5. $10\sqrt{3}$ **7.** $\doteq 32.6$ **9.** $\doteq 19°$ **11.** $\doteq 12.24$
13. $\doteq 265m$ **15.** $[\sqrt{26}, 101°]$ **17.** $[\sqrt{10.10}, 294°]$

16.1 Pages 488–490

1. When, by the order of operations, the last operation performed is multiplication
3. $3x(1 + 3x)$ **5.** $4y(2x - 3y + 4y^2)$
7. $-\frac{1}{3}, 2$ **9.** c
11. $(a - b)^2$ **13.** False **15.** False **17.** False **19.** $-2, \frac{1}{3}$ **21.** $\sqrt{2}, -\sqrt{2}$
23. $\frac{7}{5}, \frac{1}{2}$ **25.** $\frac{5}{7}, 2$ **27.** $-1, -0.5$ **29.** $\frac{1}{4}, \frac{1}{2}$ **31.** 0, 2 **33.** $0, \frac{7}{2}$
35. $(4 - y)(4 + y)$ **37.** $(3 - 2a)(3 + 2a)$ **39.** $(2 + a)(k - 3m)$
41. $(2c - 1)(c - 3)$ **43.** $y(x - 11)(x - 13)$ **45.** $(m + 3p)^2$
47. $(2u - 3v)^2$ **49.** $(10 + x)(z - 3)$ **51.** $(4a^2 - 3b)^2$

16.2 Pages 493–494

1. *See page 491.* **3.** $1, -1, \frac{1}{2}, -\frac{1}{2}$ **5.** $1, -1, 2, -2, 4, -4, 8, -8$
7. One equivalent to $a_n x^n + a_{n-1}x^{n-1} + \cdots + a_1 x + a_0 = 0$
9. TA: $x^4 + 2x^3 + 3x^2 + 4x + 5 = 0$ **11.** TA: $x^3 + 2x^2 + 3x + 4 = 0$
13. $1, -\frac{1}{2}$ **15.** None **17.** $-\frac{1}{2}$ **19.** 1 **21.** -2.3 **23.** TA: 1.8

16.3 Pages 497–498

1. Yes **3.** Multiply quotient by divisor and add the remainder.

5. $x^2 + ax + a^2$ **7.** 2 is a solution. **9.** *See page 496.*
11. d **13.** $4y^2 - 14y - 1$ **15.** $8B^2 - 22B + 61$, *Rem.* -189
17. $y - 2$ **19.** $z^2 + 2z + 1$ **21.** $-2, -5$ **23.** $3, \frac{-3 \pm \sqrt{5}}{2}$
25. $(3 - 4m)(9 + 12m + 16m^2)$ **27.** $(A^2 + 10B)(A^4 - 10A^2B + 100B^2)$

16.4 Pages 500–502

1. If $k \neq 0, \frac{a}{b} = \frac{ka}{kb}$ **3.** m^{14} **5.** a^2b^2 **7.** True
9. False **11.** True **13.** $\frac{35}{4}$ **15.** $\frac{3}{2}$ **17.** $\frac{x^4}{2}$
19. Not possible **21.** $\frac{a-2}{a}$ **23.** $\frac{m^4}{2}$ **25.** $\frac{b^2 + a^2}{ab(b+a)}$ **27.** $\frac{z+1}{2}$
29. -1 **31.** Not possible **33.** $\frac{7\sqrt{6}}{6}$ **35.** $\frac{-11}{5 + 3\sqrt{15}}$ **37.** $\frac{-96}{47 + 5\sqrt{41}}$
39. $\frac{1}{\frac{1}{6} + \frac{1}{8}} = \frac{24}{7}$ Together the two take $3\frac{3}{7}$ hours to do the job. **41.** $\frac{3}{2}$ **43.** $\frac{2x^2 - x}{4x^2 + 2}$ **45.** $\frac{(x-4)(x+3)}{(x-2)^2}$

16.5 Page 505

1. $-a$ **3.** $\frac{8b - 8a}{c^2}$ **5.** $x(x - 3)$ **7.** $(a - 1)(a + 2)$ **9.** x^3
11. $\frac{7a + 7}{12}$ **13.** 0 **15.** $\frac{7x + 6}{x(x - 3)}$ **17.** $\frac{6a^2 + 4a + 2}{(a-1)(a+2)}$ **19.** $\frac{x^2 + 2x + 3}{x^3}$
21. $\frac{15 - 3x}{2(x + 3)}$ **23.** $\frac{-3}{a(a + 3)}$ **25.** $\frac{-w^2 - 1}{w + 1}$ **27.** $\frac{3}{20(x + 1)}$ **29.** $\frac{23x^2 - 52x + 41}{30}$

16.6 Pages 507–508

1. $(4x - 2)(2x + 5)$ **3.** $y + 2$ **5.** z^3 **7.** Whether the multiplier is positive or negative
9. $\frac{7}{3}, -\frac{7}{3}$ **11.** $\frac{37}{38}$ **13.** $y < -2$ or $0 < y < 1$
15. $\frac{1}{4}, -\frac{1}{6}$ **17.** $x < 0$ or $x > \frac{1}{3}$ **19.** $\frac{81 \pm \sqrt{161}}{2}$ **21.** 5, 1

16.7 Pages 512–516

1. What is asked for? **3.** $30 + x$ **5.** $0.97(30) + x$ **7.** $\frac{88}{60}$
9. 150 **11.** $0.25Q$ **13.**

	d	r	t
at 4 mph	y	4	x
at 6 mph	$5600 - y$	6	$1200 - x$

15. 118 km/h **17.** 500 seconds
19. 72 km **21.** $\doteq$ 71 mph or faster
23. 75 miles **25.** \$7.80, 12% **27.** \$3.00 by A, \$1.10 by B **29.** 42
31. \$16,000 **33.** 125 kg **35.** 9 ℓ **37.** \$40 **39.** $\frac{2}{47}$ ℓ

16.8 Pages 519–521

1. $x - 3$ **3.** $x - h$ **5.** They might help or hinder each other.
7. 38 and 16 **9.** This year $(c, c - 12)$ and last year $(49 - c, 54 - c)$ **11.** 60 km
13. 41 **15.** Rowing, 4.5 km/h; current 1.5 km/h; rates are constant
17. June, 112; Jean, 102; Joan, 115; Jane, 128; John, 168
19. $1\frac{3}{14}$ yr **21.** $85\frac{5}{7}$ min **23.** Town X; TA: distance traveled

16.9 Pages 523–525

1. $abcde$
3. $10{,}000a + 1000b + 100c + 10d + e$
5. $10{,}000e + 1000d + 100c + 10b + a$
7. When the sum of their measures is 90
9. 180
11. $n - 1, n, n + 1$
13. $2n - 4, 2n - 2$
15. $18\frac{3}{4}°, 71\frac{1}{4}°$
17. Impossible
19. 2 and 4 or -2 and -4
21. Never, $n + (n + 1) + (n + 2) + (n + 3) = 4n + 6 = 4(n + \frac{3}{2})$
23. 72°, 54°, 54°

25. Let $X = 10a + b, Y = 10b + a$

$$X + Y = 10a + b + 10b + a = 11a + 11b = 11(a + b)$$

So $X + Y$ is divisible by 11.

27. Let $X = 1000a + 100b + 10c + d$

$$Y = a + 10b + 100c + 1000d$$

$$X + Y = 1001a + 110b + 110c + 1001d = 11(91a + 10b + 10c + 91d)$$

So $X + Y$ is divisible by 11.

29. 45
31. 12

33. Given $a + b + c + d$ is divisible by 9

$X = 1000a + 100b + 10c + d,$

so $X = a + b + c + d + 999a + 99b + 9c$

$= 9(k) + 9(111a + 11b + c)$ k an integer

$= 9(k + 111a + 11b + c)$

So X is also divisible by 9.

35. $\begin{cases} x + y = -15 \\ x - y = -4 \end{cases}$ or

$x - (-15 - x) = -4$

Numbers are $-\frac{19}{2}$ and $-\frac{11}{2}$.

37. Let $10a + b$ be the number;
then $a + b = \frac{1}{2}(10a + b)$ so $b = 8a$.
There can be only one choice for a which makes b a digit, 1, so $b = 8$.

17.1 Pages 532–533

1. 0
3. 4
5. 1
7. 100
9. v_{14}
11. 6
13. 120
15. 2
17. 4
19. 5
21. 35
23. TA: $a_1 = 2$, $a_{n+1} = 3a_n + 2$
25. $S_1 = 2, S_{n+1} = S_n + 2;$ $S_n = 2n$
27. *See p. 529.*
29. *B, C*
31. 1, 2, 6, 24, 120, 720, 5040, 40,320, 362,880, 3,628,800
33. $-1, 1, -1, 1, -1, 1$
35. $\frac{1}{2}, \frac{2}{3}, \frac{3}{4}, \frac{4}{5}, \frac{5}{6}, \frac{6}{7}$
37. $i, -1, -i, 1, i, -1$
39. 0.2, 0.02, 0.002, 0.0002, 0.00002, 0.000002
41. TA: $S_n = 2n - 1, S_n = 2n^2 - 6n + 6 + (-1)^n$
43. $S_1 = 10, S_{n+1} = S_n + 3$
45. $S_1 = 5, S_{n+1} = 3S_n$
47. $S_1 = 1.1, S_{n+1} = S_n + 0.1$
49. 1, 1, 2, 3, 5, 8, 13, 21, 34, 55, 89, 144, 233, 377, 610

17.2 Pages 536–537

1. c
3. $10, \frac{19}{2}, 9, \frac{17}{2}, 8$
5. 1, 2, 3, 4, 5
7. Arithmetic sequence, arithmetic progression
9. $A_1 + 2d$
11. $A_n = 3n - 2$; 298
13. $a_n = 5n + 1$; 71
15. $c_n = 14n - 7$; 217
17. $a_n = 21n - 226$; -205
19. $500 + 5n$
21. 54 months
23. 1101.5, 1.5
25. Graph of (1, 12), (2, 11.5), (3, 11), etc.
27. It is the slope.

17.3 Pages 540–541

1. Multiplying
3. 1, 5, 25, 125, 625
5. 2, -6, 18, -54, 162
7. Geometric sequence, geometric progression
9. ar^4
11. $a_n = 6561 \cdot (\frac{1}{3})^{n-1}$; $\frac{1}{81}$
13. $a_n = \sqrt{2} \cdot (\sqrt{3})^{n-1}$; $27\sqrt{2}$
15. $c_n = \frac{64}{27} \cdot (\frac{3}{2})^{n-1}$; $\frac{64}{27}$
17. $c_n = 1 \cdot (a + b)^{n-1}$; $(a + b)^9$
19. 1050, 1102.50, 1157.63 1215.51, 1276.28; 1.05

21. $a_n = 7 \cdot (-1)^{n-1}$
23. Graph of (1, 6561), (2, 2187), (3, 729), (4, 243), etc.
25. Graph of (1, −2), (2, −6), (3, −18), (4, −54), etc.

17.4 Pages 544–545

1. $\frac{1}{2}n(n+1)$
3. $\frac{1}{2}n(L_1 + L_n)$ or $\frac{1}{2}n(2L_1 + d(n-1))$
5. 55
7. 145
9. $\frac{81}{4}(1 - (-\frac{1}{3})^n)$
11. 2475
13. 1650
15. $15\sqrt{3} + 15\sqrt{6}$
17. $\frac{5^{10} - 1}{6}$
19. $\frac{18}{5}(1 - (-\frac{2}{3})^6)$
21. $n(n+1)$

17.5 Pages 547–548

1. c
3. b
5. Index variable
7. $\sum_{i=1}^{50} (2 - 8i)$
9. 120
11. 55
13. 0
15. 10,200
17. −4520
19. $\frac{16}{3}(4^9 - 1)$
21. 840
23. 11,500
25. 13
27. 64
29. $\sum_{i=1}^{n} i^3 = \left(\sum_{i=1}^{n} i\right)^2$; for $n = 3$, $36 = 6^2$

17.6 Pages 551–552

1. 0.7, 0.07, 0.007, ⋯
3. 0.0198, 0.0000198, 0.0000000198, ⋯
5. 9
7. $\frac{2}{3}$
9. No
11. $\frac{1}{9}$
13. $\frac{29}{111}$
15. $\frac{1}{22}$
17. $\frac{1}{1}$ can be represented by 1.0 or 0.999 ⋯.
19. $\frac{2}{3}$
21. 81
23. 70 m
25. TA: It does not consider friction or air resistance.

17.7 Pages 555–556

1. 4.5
3. 7
5. 21.5
7. $\sqrt{\dfrac{\sum_{i=1}^{n} (S_i - m)^2}{n}}$
9. $40, 10\sqrt{2}$
11. A number used to describe a set of numbers
13. Standard deviation
15. It is less affected by one wealthy person or one poor person.
17. **a.** 14 **b.** 13 **c.** 12 **d.** $\sqrt{\frac{37}{4}} \doteq 3$
19. **a.** $\frac{256}{3}$ **b.** 89 **c.** Any **d.** $\sqrt{130} \doteq 11.4$
21. **a.** 102.3 **b.** 24 **c.** Any **d.** $\sqrt{24{,}489.21} \doteq 156.5$

17.8 Pages 559–560

1. *See page 557.*
3. Row 8: 1 8 28 56 70 56 28 8 1
   Row 9: 1 9 36 84 126 126 84 36 9 1
   Row 10: 1 10 45 120 210 252 210 120 45 10 1
5. $\frac{n!}{r!(n-r)!}$
7. 35
9. 252
11. 1
13. 15
15. TA: 11, 6
17. True
19. 10
21. Reflection

17.9 Page 563

1. The coefficients of the terms in the expansion of a power of $a + b$
3. $a^2 + 2ab + b^2$
5. $a^4 + 4a^3b + 6a^2b^2 + 4ab^3 + b^4$
7. 7
9. 7
11. $(a+b)^n = \sum_{r=0}^{n} \binom{n}{r} a^{n-r}b^r$
13. $x^5 + 5x^4 + 10x^3 + 10x^2 + 5x + 1$
15. $x^6 + 6x^5y + 15x^4y^2 + 20x^3y^3 + 15x^2y^4 + 6xy^5 + y^6$
17. $a^4 - 8a^3b + 24a^2b^2 - 32ab^3 + 16b^4$

19. $p^{10} + 10p^9q + 45p^8q^2 + 120p^7q^3 + 210p^6q^4 + 252p^5q^5 + 210p^4q^6 + 120p^3q^7 + 45p^2q^8 + 10pq^9 + q^{10}$

17.10 Page 565

1. 1 **3.** 15 **5.** 0 **7.** 70 **9.** 32 **11.** 2

13. $\binom{n}{r}$ **15.** $\emptyset$, {1}, {2}, {3}, {4}, {1, 2}, {1, 3}, {1, 4}, {2, 3}, {2, 4}, {3, 4} {1, 2, 3}, {1, 2, 4}, {1, 3, 4}, {2, 3, 4}, {1, 2, 3, 4}

17. 2^{n-1}

17.11 Pages 567–568

1. 16 **3.** 32 **5.** 1 **7.** 6 **9.** 1 **11.** 10

13. The number of possibilities satisfying conditions for the event divided by the total number of possibilities

15. $\frac{1}{2}$ **17.** $\frac{1}{32}$ **19.** $\frac{11}{32}$

21. a. $\frac{1}{8}$ **b.** $\frac{3}{8}$ **c.** $\frac{3}{8}$ **d.** $\frac{1}{8}$

23. $\frac{1}{256}, \frac{8}{256}, \frac{28}{256}, \frac{56}{256}, \frac{70}{256}, \frac{56}{256}, \frac{28}{256}, \frac{8}{256}, \frac{1}{256}$

25. $\frac{1}{6}$ **27.** $\frac{7}{8}$ **29.** $\frac{4}{13}$ **31.** $\frac{7}{13}$ **33.** $\frac{11}{32}$

17.12 Page 572

1. By mapping an event onto the probability of that event **3.** TA: Standardized scores

5. $\frac{63}{256}$ **7.** $\frac{1}{1024}$ **9.** 97.7% **11.** 2.3%

13. They are scaled so the distribution is a normal curve.

15.

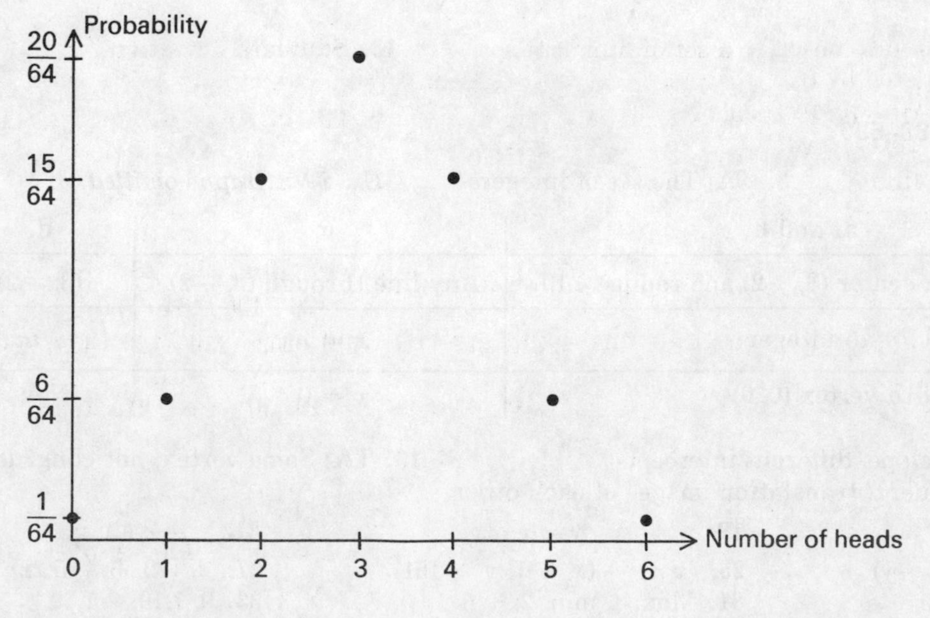

17. $y = \frac{1}{\sqrt{200\pi}} e^{-\frac{(x-500)^2}{20{,}000}}$ **19.** 34.1% **21.** 50%

18.1 Pages 581–583

1–35. *See text for definitions.* **37.** If $m\angle A + m\angle B = 180$, then $\sin A = \sin B$.
39. $xy = 6, y = x - 6$ **41–48.** *See text for theorem, property, etc.*
49. 1 **51.** 8 **53.** $i\sqrt{5}$ **55.** 0.982 **57.** $\doteq 11.314$ **59.** $\doteq 1.63$
61. $\doteq 1.656$ **63.** $\frac{7}{13} - \frac{22}{13}i$ **65.** $\doteq 122.5$ **67.** 1 **69.** 9 **71.** $8 - 6i$
73. $-\frac{1}{12}$ **75.** $\doteq (-2.820, 1.026)$ **77.** $\frac{104}{33}$ **79.** d

18.2 Pages 584–586

1. Finding all the numbers or objects which make the sentence true
3. $\frac{-1 \pm \sqrt{5}}{2}$ **5.** $m \geq 0$ **7.** $\frac{-b \pm \sqrt{b^2 + 4ac}}{2a}$
9. $E \geq \frac{2}{3}$ or $E \leq -\frac{2}{3}$ **11.** $t = \frac{2\pi}{P^2}$ **13.** $y = \frac{3x - 6}{8}$
15. $\doteq 0.6021$ **17.** $u = 256$ *Ex. 19–23: Graphs omitted.*
19. $\{t: t > \frac{1}{2}\}$ **21.** $\{n\pi: n \text{ an integer}\}$ **23.** $\left\{\frac{\pi}{4} + n\pi: n \text{ an integer}\right\}$
25. $(\frac{47}{8}, -\frac{25}{8})$ **27.** (7, 26) **29.** $\left(\frac{5\sqrt{26}}{26}, \frac{25\sqrt{26}}{26}\right), \left(-\frac{5\sqrt{26}}{26}, -\frac{25\sqrt{26}}{26}\right)$
31. $4, \frac{4}{3}, -5$ **33.** Not possible **35.** $b(2b + 3)(a - 2)$
37. $\frac{6}{(x-1)(x+2)(x+3)}$ **39.** $\frac{1}{x^4}$ **41.** $2x^2 + 4$
43. $\frac{1}{ab}$ **45.** $a = 3, h = \frac{2}{3}, k = \frac{2}{3}$ **47.** Not possible
49. $x^4 + 8x^3y + 24x^2y^2 + 32xy^3 + 16y^4$ **51.** $2x^3 - 11x + 37 - \frac{114}{x + 3}$

18.3 Pages 588–590

1. Points of a line **3.** TA: The set of integers *Ex. 5–9: Graphs omitted.*

a. and b.	c.	d.
5. Circle with center (3, −2) and radius $\sqrt{10}$	Any line through (3, −2)	(3, −2)
7. $\left(\frac{\pi}{2} + n\pi, 0\right)$, n an integer	$x = n\pi$	$\left(\frac{\pi}{2} + n\pi, 0\right)$
9. Parabola with vertex (0, 0)	$x = 0$	None

11. TA: Same slope, different intercepts **13.** TA: Same vertex, not congruent
15. TA: Congruent, translation images of each other
17. $y = \frac{8}{7}x + \frac{24}{7}$ **19.** $y = 3x^2, y = -3x^2$ **21.** $y = 3 \sin \frac{x}{3}$
23. $(x, y) \to (x, -y)$ **25.** $(x, y) \to (x - 1, y + 151)$ **27.** $\doteq (29.55, -5.22)$
29. Minimum 0 **31.** Max. 4, min. 2 **33.** 0, 1.19, −1.19
35. 14 **37.** 1223 **39.** Rotation **41.** Size transformation
43. TA: $y = 2^x$ **45.** False, true **47.** False, false
49. True, true **51.** $\sin x \cos y + \cos x \sin y$ **53.** $\left(\frac{x_1 + x_2}{2}, \frac{y_1 + y_2}{2}\right)$

18.4 Pages 591–594

1. If $a + x = b$, then $x = b - a$.

3. $0 \cdot a = 0$

5. $a^{\frac{1}{3}} \cdot b^{\frac{1}{3}} = (ab)^{\frac{1}{3}}$

7. The nth term of the geometric sequence G with ratio r is $G_1 \cdot r^{n-1}$.

9. $Q = \frac{p}{3}$, $\log N = \frac{1}{3} \log m$

11. $x \log 150 = \log 300$, $x \doteq 1.14$

13. $\begin{bmatrix} 3 & 4 \\ -8 & -2 \end{bmatrix} \cdot \begin{bmatrix} x \\ y \end{bmatrix} = \begin{bmatrix} 2 \\ 0 \end{bmatrix}$

15. $R_{180} = R_{-90} \circ R_{-90}$

17. $y + 3 = 3(x - 4)^2$

19. $y = e^{-x}$

21. $\langle \{I, r_{x=y}, R_{180}, r_{x=-y}\}, \circ \rangle$

23. **a.** Closed **b.** $\begin{bmatrix} 1 & 0 \\ 0 & 1 \end{bmatrix}$ **c.** Yes **d.** TA: $\begin{bmatrix} 2 & 5 \\ 1 & 3 \end{bmatrix}$ and $\begin{bmatrix} 3 & -5 \\ -1 & 2 \end{bmatrix}$ **e.** Yes

25. **a.** Closed **b.** $\begin{bmatrix} 1 & 0 \\ 0 & 1 \end{bmatrix}$ **c.** Yes **d.** TA: $\begin{bmatrix} 2 & 0 \\ 0 & 2 \end{bmatrix}$ and $\begin{bmatrix} \frac{1}{2} & 0 \\ 0 & \frac{1}{2} \end{bmatrix}$ **e.** Yes

27. **a.** Closed **b.** $(\frac{1}{4})^0 = 1$ **c.** Yes **d.** TA: $(\frac{1}{4})^2$ and $(\frac{1}{4})^{-2}$ **e.** Yes

29. **a.** Closed **b.** 1 **c.** No **d.** TA: $2 + 3i$ and $\frac{2}{13} - \frac{3}{13}i$ **e.** No

31. **a.** Closed **b.** i^4 **c.** Yes **d.** TA: i and i^3 **e.** Yes

33. $(x, y) \to (x + 2, y - 3)$

35. Reflection-symmetric to the line through the foci and the ⊥ bisector of the segment joining the foci; rotation-symmetric about the midpoint of the segment joining the foci

37. Reflection-symmetric to the lines $y = n\pi$, n an integer; rotation-symmetric about the points $\left(\frac{\pi}{2} + n\pi, 0\right)$, n an integer; translation-symmetric for translations $(x, y) \to (x + 2n\pi, y)$, n an integer

39. Reflection-symmetric to the lines $y = \frac{a}{2}$, $x = \frac{a}{2}$, $y = x$, and $x + y = a$; rotation-symmetric for rotations of 90°, 180°, and 270° about the point $\left(\frac{a}{2}, \frac{a}{2}\right)$

41. a

43. When the slopes are equal; when the product of the slopes is -1

45. $\begin{cases} xy = 42 \\ x + y = 13 \end{cases}$, 6 and 7

47. The number of subsets containing r elements in a set of n elements

49. TA: Fields and ideals

18.5 Pages 594–597

1. $3 < x < 4$, $3.4 < x < 3.5$, $3.46 < x < 3.47$, $\cdots$; these could be successive decimal approximations to $\sqrt{12}$.

5. $3217.5 < w < 3282.5$
$|w - 3250| < 32.5$

7. $t = 2\pi \sqrt{\frac{L}{g}}$

9. $2\frac{1}{7}$ grams

11. $\doteq$ 58 km/h, $\doteq$ 63 km/h

13. $c = 15[w + 1]$

15. About 13.5 years

17. 0.389, 0.398, 0.3979

19. The mean income is the average income. The median is the figure such that 50% of the incomes are more than it and 50% less than it. The median is considered the better statistic.

21. State actual situation, simplify, translate into mathematics, solve mathematical model, translate back into real terms, interpret.

23. 0.4 metres

25. 32 feet per second, 36 feet

27. About 15.9%

29. About 5.83 m

31. $3a + 4.50b + 8c$

33. $t \doteq (5.6, 5.6)$, $u \doteq (5.7, -13.9)$, $t + u \doteq (11.3, -8.3)$; the actual path of the bird's flight

1 2 3 4 5 6 7 8 9 10 11 12 13 14 15 4 3 2 1 0 9 8 7 6 5